AMERICAN COUNCIL OF LEARNED SOCIETIES

Dictionary
of Scientific
Biography
cSs

DICTIONARY
OF
SCIENTIFIC BIOGRAPHY

PUBLISHED UNDER THE AUSPICES OF
THE AMERICAN COUNCIL OF LEARNED SOCIETIES

The American Council of Learned Societies, organized in 1919 for the purpose of advancing the study of the humanities and of the humanistic aspects of the social sciences, is a nonprofit federation comprising thirty-three national scholarly groups. The Council represents the humanities in the United States in the International Union of Academies, provides fellowships and grants-in-aid, supports research-and-planning conferences and symposia, and sponsors special projects and scholarly publications.

Member Organizations

AMERICAN PHILOSOPHICAL SOCIETY, 1743

AMERICAN ACADEMY OF ARTS AND SCIENCES, 1780

AMERICAN ANTIQUARIAN SOCIETY, 1812

AMERICAN ORIENTAL SOCIETY, 1842

AMERICAN NUMISMATIC SOCIETY, 1858

AMERICAN PHILOLOGICAL ASSOCIATION, 1869

ARCHAEOLOGICAL INSTITUTE OF AMERICA, 1879

SOCIETY OF BIBLICAL LITERATURE, 1880

MODERN LANGUAGE ASSOCIATION OF AMERICA, 1883

AMERICAN HISTORICAL ASSOCIATION, 1884

AMERICAN ECONOMIC ASSOCIATION, 1885

AMERICAN FOLKLORE SOCIETY, 1888

AMERICAN DIALECT SOCIETY, 1889

ASSOCIATION OF AMERICAN LAW SCHOOLS, 1900

AMERICAN PHILOSOPHICAL ASSOCIATION, 1901

AMERICAN ANTHROPOLOGICAL ASSOCIATION, 1902

AMERICAN POLITICAL SCIENCE ASSOCIATION, 1903

BIBLIOGRAPHICAL SOCIETY OF AMERICA, 1904

ASSOCIATION OF AMERICAN GEOGRAPHERS, 1904

AMERICAN SOCIOLOGICAL ASSOCIATION, 1905

COLLEGE ART ASSOCIATION OF AMERICA, 1912

HISTORY OF SCIENCE SOCIETY, 1924

LINGUISTIC SOCIETY OF AMERICA, 1924

MEDIAEVAL ACADEMY OF AMERICA, 1925

AMERICAN MUSICOLOGICAL SOCIETY, 1934

SOCIETY OF ARCHITECTURAL HISTORIANS, 1940

ECONOMIC HISTORY ASSOCIATION, 1940

ASSOCIATION FOR ASIAN STUDIES, 1941

AMERICAN SOCIETY FOR AESTHETICS, 1942

METAPHYSICAL SOCIETY OF AMERICA, 1950

AMERICAN STUDIES ASSOCIATION, 1950

RENAISSANCE SOCIETY OF AMERICA, 1954

SOCIETY FOR ETHNOMUSICOLOGY, 1955

DICTIONARY
OF
SCIENTIFIC BIOGRAPHY

CHARLES COULSTON GILLISPIE

EDITOR IN CHIEF

Volume I

PIERRE ABAILARD—L. S. BERG

CHARLES SCRIBNER'S SONS · NEW YORK

Editorial Staff

MARSHALL DE BRUHL, *MANAGING EDITOR*

SARAH FERRELL, *Assistant Managing Editor*

LELAND S. LOWTHER, *Associate Editor*

JOYCE D. PORTNOY, *Associate Editor*

ROSE MOSELLE, *Editorial Assistant*

ELIZABETH I. WILSON, *Copy Editor*

DORIS ANNE SULLIVAN, *Proofreader*

JOEL HONIG, *Copy Editor*

LINDA FISHER, *Secretary-Typist*

Panel of Consultants

Preface

The *Dictionary of Scientific Biography* is designed to make available reliable information on the history of science through the medium of articles on the professional lives of scientists. All periods of science from classical antiquity to modern times are represented, with the exception that there are no articles on the careers of living persons. In many instances the articles are either the first or the most considerable study yet made of an individual body of work, for the purpose of the *Dictionary* is not only to draw upon existing scholarship but to constitute scholarship where none exists.

The work is published under the sponsorship of the American Council of Learned Societies with the endorsement of the History of Science Society. The undertaking has been made possible by a generous grant from the National Science Foundation.

In planning the work, the Editorial Board has intended it to perform for the historiography of science services like those that the *Dictionary of National Biography* and the *Dictionary of American Biography* have long rendered in British and American historiography. During the compilation of those indispensable instruments of study and research, their editors enlisted the efforts of virtually all members of the historical profession concerned with national history in the respective countries. So it has been in the creation of this *Dictionary,* which has depended throughout upon large participation by professional historians of science all over the world. Theirs is a discipline which has now become a well-defined field of historical scholarship in recognition of the importance that science has held in the evolution of modern civilization. At the same time the Board has been equally fortunate to be able to rely (as, indeed, does the historiography of science generally) upon the contributions of many professional scientists who, in consequence of their commitment to science itself, take a lively and scholarly interest in its past.

Authors of articles were asked to place emphasis upon the scientific accomplishments and careers of their subjects. In some instances it has seemed wise to divide among several authors the account of figures whose work was manifold. Personal biography has intentionally been kept to the minimum consistent with explaining the subject's place in the development of science. Each article concludes with a bibliography that will guide the reader to the original scientific work and also to the main biographical items concerning personal and public life. Authors of articles on prolific scientists have included in the bibliographies the most important papers and indicated in what publications others may be found. In many cases, the citation of a systematic and authoritative bibliography makes it unnecessary to duplicate readily available information.

The aim has been to include articles on those figures whose contributions to science were sufficiently distinctive to make an identifiable difference to the profession or community of knowledge. The Board has felt reasonable confidence in the information available to it in selecting the more important figures and doubts that notable bodies of scientific work have been excluded. For the subjects of marginal significance, however, an important and often decisive limiting factor in reaching decisions about their inclusion or omission has been the availability of scholarship. The Board has not wished to commission any articles unless satisfied that they could be based on first-hand study of the sources. Given the way in which the selection of the lesser subjects had to be made, it does not appear that either the configuration of the list as a whole, or that of various distributions that might be discerned within it, could properly serve for statistical analysis of the population of science in various times, places, or disciplines. One exception to that caveat may be admitted. The high proportion of persons who worked in the biological sciences, amounting to almost a third of the total, does not appear to be an accident of the selection procedure. Their number reflects the historical situation. Until the nineteenth century only the sciences now pertaining to biology formed any part of the responsibility of a well-defined and populous profession, that of medicine. Perhaps for that reason, among others, the manner of growth of the biological and descriptive sciences requires taking account of a larger number of discrete investigations than does that of the physical and mathematical sciences.

Areas of science covered by the *Dictionary* are those that in modern times fall within the purview of mathematics, astronomy, physics, chemistry, biology, and the sciences of the earth. There are a few articles on historians of science. Technology, medicine, the behaviorial and social sciences, and philosophy are included only in the instances of persons whose work was intrinsically related to the sciences of nature or to mathematics. Thus physiologists who were also physicians appear in virtue of their biological contributions. Authors of articles in these ancillary fields were asked to treat mainly the matters relevant to science, and if they have not always been as restrictive as the policy contemplated, there is a limit to the rigidity with which such distinctions can usefully be applied.

Several other disproportions in the selection of subjects must be noted. In the twentieth century, the choice has been held to relatively important figures. The justification might well be that historical perspective on the recent past is notoriously deceptive in science as elsewhere, but a more practical reason is the shortage of technically qualified scholars in the contemporary history of science. The same consideration has governed in certain decisions about whether to publish articles on the careers of notable scientists who have died while the *Dictionary* was in preparation. In a number of cases it has not been possible to obtain a worthy article.

The limited availability of scholarship is also the factor that has determined policy in respect to the treatment afforded the scientific knowledge and natural philosophy of early India, China, and Japan. In modern times the scientific culture of Asia has merged with that of the West, the continuous history of which goes back from Europe in large part through Islam to its origins in classical antiquity and the ancient Near East. Although this latter tradition was the one that developed the type of science that has become world-wide since the seventeenth century, we should not want to assert that it alone was scientific. Ancient Indian, Chinese, and Japanese sciences are vast and fascinating subjects. The difficulty is that they have been very little studied in the West. In this situation, we have decided that the most practical course is to publish a few articles that could be written to illustrate the kinds of work done in the ancient East and to leave any attempt at adequate representation of these subjects to the development of scholarship in the future.

In the case of Indian science, a biographical format is not well suited to the matter since many of the names associated with its schools of astronomy and natural philosophy are mythical or legendary. Professor David Pingree has undertaken to write brief articles identifying the Indian names at the appropriate places in the alphabetical sequence and further to write a series of essays giving accounts of the several schools and traditions to which they belonged. Those essays appear in the Supplement. Similar treatment is accorded the main topics of ancient Babylonian and Egyptian science, the identity of the scribes who founded it being largely unknown to history. Also published in the Supplement are certain articles that for one reason or another could not be printed in their proper places in the alphabetical sequence, where references to them will be found. The Supplement forms part of the final volume, containing also the Index.

The Index itself is organized to permit tracing the evolution of problems, concepts, and subjects through the articles about the persons who contributed to their development. During the initial planning discussions for the *Dictionary* some took the view that a basic work of reference in the history of science would better be organized by subject matter and topic, i.e., *Gravity, Natural Selection, Atomism,* etc., rather than by individual careers. The Board decided against it, however, on the grounds that history of science like other aspects of history is made by men and not by themes or abstractions, that in any case the specification of topics would prove difficult, arbitrary, and liable to obsolescence and that the purpose might be served by a suitably detailed analytical Index.

In producing this work, the Board of Editors has incurred immense obligations, which are a pleasure to acknowledge with the greatest of gratitude. The first and foremost is to the authors of the articles, who have taken time and energy from their own writing, research, and teaching in order to serve the interest of the subject as a whole. In establishing the list of subjects to be treated, we have enjoyed invaluable assistance from the Panel of Consultants, who advised us from the outset and who kindly put us in touch with many of the authors represented. The members both of that Panel and of the Advisory Committee established by the American Council of Learned Societies have answered innumerable inquiries and responded to all requests for advice. From the beginning, Mr. Charles Scribner's relation to the work has been that of colleague as much as publisher.

Finally, certain colleagues as well as certain members of the staff rendered services in the organization of the work at the outset that required a high degree of imagination and attention. The Board would like to record its particular gratitude to Professor H. G. Georgiadis and Professor Derek J. de Solla Price, and to Miss Jeanne Armel, Mr. Joseph G. E. Hopkins, Mr. Steven Pappayliou, and Miss Arlene Witt.

THE EDITORIAL BOARD

Contributors to Volume I

Hans Aarsleff

Giorgio Abetti

Dean C. Allard

Torsten Althin

Peter Amacher

D. M. Balme

Hans Baumgärtel

Whitfield J. Bell, Jr.

Enrique Beltrán

John A. Benjamin

Arthur Birembaut

Maria Luisa Righini-Bonelli

Franck Bourdier

Marjorie Nice Boyer

J. Morton Briggs

W. H. Brock

Theodore M. Brown

K. E. Bullen

Vern L. Bullough

G. V. Bykov

Albert V. Carozzi

Ettore Carruccio

Carlo Castellani

Seymour L. Chapin

F. B. Churchill

Marshall Clagett

Thomas H. Clark

Edwin Clarke

Eric M. Cole

William Coleman

Albert B. Costa

Pierre Costabel

Ruth Schwartz Cowan

A. C. Crombie

M. P. Crosland

Charles A. Culotta

J. al-Dabbagh

F. Dagognet

Eugenio Dall'Osso

Glyn Daniel

Allen G. Debus

R. G. C. Desmond

Bern Dibner

Sally H. Dieke

J. G. Dorfman

Stillman Drake

Louis Dulieu

A. Hunter Dupree

J. M. Edmonds

Olin J. Eggen

H. Engel

Gunnar Eriksson

V. A. Esakov

Charles L. Evans

Joseph Ewan

V. A. Eyles

Eduard Farber

Ivan A. Fedoseyev

Lucienne Félix

Konradin Ferrari D'Occieppo

Bernard S. Finn

C. S. Fisher

Marcel Florkin

Menso Folkerts

George A. Foote

Paul Forman

Pietro Franceschini

Eugene Frankel

Hans Freudenthal

B. v. Freyberg

Kurt von Fritz

Justo Garate

Gerald L. Geison

Ruth Anne Gienapp

Bertrand Gille

Jean Gillis

Charles C. Gillispie

Owen Gingerich

Harry Godwin

Stanley Goldberg

J. B. Gough

Joseph T. Gregory

Norman T. Gridgeman

N. Grigorian

M. D. Grmek

Morton Grosser

Francisco Guerra

Norbert Günther

Douglas Guthrie

Ian Hacking

Roger Hahn

A. Rupert Hall

Owen Hannaway

Bert Hansen

Robert H. Hardie

Willy Hartner

Jagdish N. Hattiangadi

John L. Heilbron

Mary Hesse

Frederic L. Holmes

William T. Holser

R. Hooykaas

Michael A. Hoskin

Pierre Huard

G. L. Huxley

Aaron J. Ihde

Jean Itard

Charles W. Jones

Phillip S. Jones

Miroslav Katětov

Alan S. Kay

Martha B. Kendall

G. B. Kerferd

Daniel J. Kevles

Pearl Kibre

John S. Kieffer

George Kish

Marc Klein

Friedrich Klemm

David M. Knight

Huldrych M. Koelbing

Zdeněk Kopal

Edna E. Kramer

Claudia Kren

Fridolf Kudlien

P. G. Kulikovsky

V. I. Kuznetzov

Yves Laissus

L. L. Laudan

Martin Levey

James Longrigg

Edward Lurie

CONTRIBUTORS TO VOLUME I

ERIC MCDONALD

A. G. MACGREGOR

ROBERT M. MCKEON

H. LEWIS MCKINNEY

ERNAN MCMULLIN

MICHAEL MCVAUGH

M. S. MAHONEY

C. L. MAIER

DANIEL MASSIGNON

SEYMOUR H. MAUSKOPF

KENNETH O. MAY

ROBERT M. MENGEL

PHILIP MERLAN

WYNDHAM DAVIES MILES

LORENZO MINIO-PALUELLO

ERNEST A. MOODY

J. E. MORÈRE

SHIGERU NAKAYAMA

HENRY NATHAN

J. P. NICOLAS

J. D. NORTH

HERBERT OETTEL

ROBERT OLBY

C. D. O'MALLEY

JANE OPPENHEIMER

OYSTEIN ORE

G. E. L. OWEN

SHIN'ICHI OYA

A. PABST

JACQUES PAYEN

GIORGIO PEDROCCO

GEORGES PETIT

SHLOMO PINES

DAVID PINGREE

MARTIN PLESSNER

LORIS PREMUDA

P. M. RATTANSI

NATHAN REINGOLD

GLORIA ROBINSON

ANDREW DENNY RODGERS III

FRANCESCO RODOLICO

ALFRED ROMER

VASCO RONCHI

CONRAD E. RONNEBERG

P. G. ROOFE

EDWARD ROSEN

GEORGE ROSEN

CHARLES E. ROSENBERG

FRANZ ROSENTHAL

JOSEF SAJNER

WILLIAM SCHAAF

H. SCHADEWALDT

RUD. SCHMITZ

BRUNO SCHOENEBERG

DOROTHY V. SCHRADER

DOROTHY M. SCHULLIAN

E. L. SCOTT

PAUL SENTEIN

ALEKSEI NIKOLAEVICH SHAMIN

HAROLD I. SHARLIN

KAZUO SHIMODAIRA

O. B. SHEYNIN

C. S. SMITH

H. A. M. SNELDERS

E. SNORRASON

WILLIAM H. STAHL

JERRY STANNARD

JOHANNES STEUDEL

LLOYD G. STEVENSON

BERNHARD STICKER

DIRK J. STRUIK

CHARLES SÜSSKIND

L. TARÁN

JULIETTE TATON

RENÉ TATON

GEORGE TAYLOR

ARNOLD THACKRAY

JEAN THÉODORIDÈS

PHILLIP DRENNON THOMAS

V. V. TIKHOMIROV

G. J. TOOMER

G. L'E. TURNER

JUAN VERNET

KURT VOGEL

WILLIAM A. WALLACE, O.P.

CHARLES WEBSTER

C. E. WEGMANN

D. T. WHITESIDE

GWENETH WHITTERIDGE

L. PEARCE WILLIAMS

HELMUT M. WILSDORF

LEONARD G. WILSON

R. P. WINNINGTON-INGRAM

F. R. WINTON

J. WITKOWSKI

M. WONG

HELEN WRIGHT

A. P. YOUSCHKEVITCH

DICTIONARY
OF
SCIENTIFIC BIOGRAPHY

DICTIONARY OF
SCIENTIFIC BIOGRAPHY

ABAILARD—BERG

ABAILARD, PIERRE, also known as **Peter Abelard** (*b.* Le Pallet, or Palais, Brittany, France, 1079; *d.* near Chalon-sur-Saône, France, 21 April 1142), *logic, theology, philosophy.*

Abailard was the son of Berengar, lord of Le Pallet, but he abandoned the militaristic and governmental traditions of the nobility. He did preserve, however, a determination to impose his personality on the studies and intellectual polemics of his time, and often he dominated the entire field. Intolerant of what was not the best, he moved from school to school, fighting against his masters and colleagues and founding his own schools and a religious community. When he was forced as a punishment to reside in a monastery and when he accepted the leadership of another, he applied his exacting moral principles, his scholarship, and his energy to correcting and reforming mistakes and practices; if defeated, he prepared for further battle.

Of the subjects forming the basic curriculum for scholars, Abailard was interested only in those concerning language, especially grammar and dialectic. He confesses not to have mastered mathematics, although he shows himself competent to deal with the question of continuity. In astrology he follows the accepted views. At this time in France doctrinal conflicts centered largely on dialectic, both within its proper field and in its applications to the problems of human life, then usually presented in theological terms. As a discipline in its own right, it was expanding into the province of metaphysics. Combined with deeper inquiries into grammatical concepts, it was developing new distinctions, refining its procedures, and purifying itself from the sources of easy sophistry. In its applications, it would claim to be the method of clarifying ideas, organizing statements, even extending the province of knowledge, and producing statements normally accepted as having a supernatural origin as valid conclusions derived from non-revealed truths.

Such was the background of Abailard's career. He was an uneasy pupil at the school of Roscelin in

Loches (*ca.* 1094–1096). Roscelin's doctrines on significant words being merely words had appeared to endanger traditional views on knowledge and the dogma of the Trinity. Abailard soon passed on to William of Champeaux's school in Paris; but impatient of this master's opinions concerning the existence in our world (and possibly also in a Platonic world of ideas) of things referred to by general words, he began teaching in Melun and Corbeil. Perhaps, too, he was impatient of being just a pupil. About 1106 illness forced him to return to Brittany. Again in Paris (*ca.* 1110) he fought it out, victoriously, with William. The latter abandoned his chair, which soon after was given to Abailard. But intrigue had the better of learning; Abailard was dismissed. Undaunted, he opened a new school on the outskirts of the city, on the Montagne Ste. Geneviève.

So far, language, logic, and their metaphysical implications had dominated Abailard's mind; after a business sojourn in Brittany he was attracted to Anselme and Ralph of Laon's theological school (*ca.* 1114). Instead of clear words he found verbosity, instead of a scientific approach the smoke of traditional apologetics. The cathedral school of Paris now opened its doors to him as to an honored master of dialectic and theology. The disturbing love affair with Héloïse, physically concluded with Abailard's emasculation, turned into a friendship of a religious and intellectual character. He withdrew to the abbey of St. Denis outside Paris, and became a monk (*ca.* 1118): a bad choice for the abbey and for Abailard. He attacked the laxity of the monks; they attacked the dangers of his dialectical theology. The monks promoted the Council of Soissons (1121), where his doctrine of the Trinity was condemned. An attempt at demolishing, with the tools of historical criticism, the legend concerning the foundation of St. Denis by a pupil of St. Paul involved the *enfant terrible* in further trouble. He escaped, and finally obtained permission to settle at a place of his choice: a new convent was thus born under the symbolic name of Paraclete (the consoling Holy Spirit).

Peace was short-lived: too many people were attracted to the rebel. He accepted the position of abbot of St. Gildas in Brittany, leaving the Paraclete to Héloïse and her nuns, only to fight once more in vain against irreligiosity and immorality. By 1136 he was again on his Montagne Ste. Geneviève, again provoking hostility by his methods and doctrines. The unflinching St. Bernard was among the attackers. The Council of Sens (1140) dramatically—or theatrically—condemned, with the pope's support, the man for whom reason was a good companion of faith and intention rather than action the touchstone of sin. Abailard set out toward Rome for an appeal, but was persuaded by Peter the Venerable of Cluny to accept the verdict. From Cluny he moved to the priory of St. Marcel, where he died soon after.

Abailard's more strictly logico-philosophical works are partly documents of the elaborate development and preparation for his activity as a teacher and partly the systematic organization of his knowledge and critical evaluation of others' views concerning the whole of logico-philosophical studies. The *Introductiones parvulorum* is an elementary commentary on the three basic texts studied by every boy aiming at a career that required learning: Porphyry's *Isagoge* and Aristotle's *Categories* and *De interpretatione*. The more extensive commentaries on these same works and on Boethius' *De differentiis topicis* embody, both in the form of a penetrating analysis and in the form of constructive and destructive argument, much of Abailard's most original philosophical production. The *Dialectica* is the first full-scale attempt, in the Latin West, at producing a system of logic covering all the recognized sections of that discipline, until then dispersed in disconnected works composed by authors of different periods and treated without a uniform pattern and often without a clear plan. Abailard's own plan, however, depended too much on a traditional set of texts and on an old division of the parts of logic: his contribution is to be found more in details than in the general scheme.

Most of Abailard's philosophico-theological works, including sections of two biblical commentaries (on the beginning of Genesis and on St. Paul's Letter to the Romans) contain elaborations of the main themes of Christian doctrine from the point of view of the man of faith. But the elaborations are aimed at showing how much of this doctrine is accessible to the man without faith who uses his reason (itself, after all, of divine origin) both for directly establishing truth and for critically accepting non-Christian reasonable authorities, such as Plato and Aristotle. This is most evident in the successive editions of his *Theologia*. His *Scito te ipsum* (*Know Yourself*), the study

of the psychology of intention, volition, and action, as related to the concept of guilt, appeared to revolutionize the dogma of original sin. The *Sic et non* (*Yes and No*) is an analysis of texts chosen from works of the Fathers of the Church; in it, critical rules of interpretation of the written word are applied to show to what extent apparently contradictory statements can be seen to agree in their basic meaning.

Abailard's contributions that are of interest to science are more of a methodological character than discoveries of facts and laws of nature. From the introduction to the *Yes and No* the following principles or rules can be elicited: (1) methodical doubt (doubting is necessary [Aristotle]); search and you will find (the Gospels); (2) distinguish statements that compel assent from those on which free judgment must be exercised; (3) distinguish between the levels of language used (technical [proper] or common [vulgar, improper], explicit or metaphorical or rhetorical, stating the writer's views or quoting the opinions of others); (4) meanings of words change with time; (5) fallibility of human writers, however authoritative (mistakes even in Scripture); (6) fallibility of written tradition (textual criticism); (7) context affects meanings.

Abailard's discussion of "universals" in his longer commentary on Porphyry's *Isagoge* exemplifies his procedure. It can be schematized in this way: (*a*) be clear about the meaning that is ascribed to "universal," starting, as one normally does, from Aristotle's statement "universals are those that are predicated of many"; (*b*) properly used, the key term "predicated" applies only to words; (*c*) consequently "this kind of universals" can only be words, i.e., universal (or common) words; (*d*) these words have, in a proposition, the special function of "being predicated," not of "signifying"; (*e*) a more serious problem is this: What makes us invent and use universal words, i.e., what is the cause (common cause) of common words; is it a community in things or a community in our concept; (*f*) there is a common state of affairs ("status") for A and B such that each can be said to be man; this "status" is not a thing (*res*); (*g*) our mind "melts together" (*confundit*) into one image that which it elicits, abstracts, from things according to their "common status"; (*h*) the "common cause" of universal words is primarily to be found in the common "status" of things, secondarily in the *imago confusa,* i.e., in our concept; (*i*) extrapolating from the common status to the knowledge of it possessed by the maker of things (not by us, men), it is possible to conceive a knowledge of the common cause as *forma* (a Platonic idea in God's mind). In this way, Abailard surveys the linguistic, logical, naturalistic, gnoseological, metaphysical, and theological aspects of the problems of universals.

In the *Dialectica* as well as in the several commentaries there are many statements of importance to philosophy, theory of language, logic, methods of expression, and possibly of research in science, which were either first put forward clearly or strongly endorsed by Abailard. Some are to the effect that (*a*) "is," "are," etc., in sentences like *John is a man* and *John is,* have no existential import (the second sentence being elliptical = *John is an existing being*) but are connectives (*copulae*); (*b*) propositions in the future or past must be resolved into propositions in the present; (*c*) a self-referring word, e.g., "Man" (= "the word *Man*"), does not alter the nature of "is" qua *copula*; (*d*) "not every . . ." and "some . . . not" are not equivalent; (*e*) "all" implies both collectivity and exclusivity; (*f*) modal words ("possible," "necessary" . . . , "true," "false" . . . , etc.) have two different functions according to whether they affect the relationship between subject and predicate or the status of a proposition. In the study of conditional propositions, often called by Abailard *consequentiae* (possibly a new, systematically technical use of this term), a number of rules are made explicit in forms easily translatable into modern symbolism, e.g., the rules of transitivity of entailment, of incompatibility between a true affirmation and a true negation, and of entailments between modalities.

With his inquiries into the logic of language Abailard contributed possibly more than anyone else to the developments of the new logico-linguistic theories, especially those concerning *suppositio, copulatio,* and *appellatio.*

BIBLIOGRAPHY

I. ORIGINAL WORKS. All the known works of Abailard have been published at least once, but no single edition contains more than about half the extant texts. The largest collection is in J. P. Migne, ed., *Patrologia Latina,* 178 (Paris, 1855). This volume includes all the works ed. before, with the exception of the logical texts published by Victor Cousin as part of *Ouvrages inédits d'Abélard* (Paris, 1836). Migne gives, for each work, the necessary information on the eds. reproduced in his volume. We mention here only the two complementary collections older than Migne's. The first was ed. by F. d'Amboise and A. Duchesne, *Petri Abaelardi filosofi* [sic] *et theologi . . . et Heloissae coniugis . . . opera* (Paris, 1616); the second, ed. by Cousin, Ch. Jourdain, and E. Despois, *Abaelardi opera hactenus seorsim edita* (Paris, 1849–1859), includes little of what Cousin had published in 1836.

The following eds. contain, with minor exceptions, all the works that had not been published by 1855, or had

been published in an incomplete form: (*a*) the longer commentaries on Porphyry's *Isagoge* and Aristotle's *Categories* and *De interpretatione* (the latter incomplete and with an apocryphal last section), which came to be known as *Logica "Ingredientibus,"* together with an incomplete commentary on the *Isagoge,* now known as *Logica "Nostrorum petitioni,"* were ed. by B. Geyer, *Peter Abaelards philosophische Schriften* (Münster, 1919–1935), Vol. XXI of *Beiträge zur Geschichte der Philosophie und Theologie des Mittelalters*; (*b*) the shorter commentaries on Porphyry and Aristotle (*Introductiones parvulorum*) and the commentaries on Boethius' *De divisione* and *De differentiis topicis,* all published—incompletely—by Cousin in 1836, were published in full by M. Dal Pra, *Abelardo, Scritti filosofici* (Rome–Milan, 1954); (*c*) the *Dialectica,* also incompletely published by Cousin, was published in full by L. M. De Rijk (Assen, 1956); (*d*) the last section of the longer commentary on Aristotle's *De interpretatione,* missing from the Geyer ed., was published, together with two shorter texts, by L. Minio-Paluello, *Abaelardiana inedita* (Rome, 1958), Vol. II of *Twelfth Century Logic*; (*e*) *De unitate et trinitate,* R. Stölzle, ed. (Freiburg, 1891); (*f*) "Ein neuaufgefundenes Bruchstück der Apologia Abaelards," P. Ruf and M. Grabmann, eds., in *Sitzungsberichte der Bayerischen Akademie der Wissenschaften,* Philos.-hist. Abt., **5** (1930); (*g*) *Theologia "Summi boni,"* H. Ostlender, ed. (Münster, 1939), Vol. XXXV. 2–3 of *Beiträge zur Geschichte der Philosophie und Theologie des Mittelalters.*

Mention should also be made of the new critical ed. of the first letter of Abailard, the autobiographical *Historia calamitatum,* prepared by J. Monfrin (Paris, 1959), and of the new ed. by J. T. Muckle of "The Personal Letters Between Abelard and Heloise," in *Mediaeval Studies,* **15** (1953), 47–94.

There are English trans. of the following: (*a*) the section on universals from the *Logica "Ingredientibus,"* in R. McKeon, ed., *Selections From Medieval Philosophers,* I (New York, 1929, 1957), 208–258; (*b*) C. K. Scott Moncrieff, *Letters to Heloise* (London, 1925–1926); (*c*) J. R. McCallum, *Scito te ipsum* (*Ethics*) (Oxford, 1935); (*d*) J. T. Muckle, *Historia calamitatum* (*The Story of Abelard's Adversities*) (Toronto, 1954).

II. SECONDARY LITERATURE. A quite extensive bibliography on Abailard down to 1928 is in B. Geyer, pp. 213–214 and 702–703 of the vol. mentioned below. More detailed bibliographical material for special fields will be found in several of the works listed here.

The following general histories contain important sections on Abailard: *Histoire littéraire de France,* XII (Paris, 1763), 86–152 (repr. in Migne, *Patrologia Latina,* CLXXVIII, 10–54); G. Robert, *Les écoles et l'enseignement de la théologie . . .* (Paris, 1909), pp. 149–211, reelaborated by G. Paré, A. Brunet, and P. Tremblay, *La Renaissance du XIIᵉ siècle* (Paris–Ottawa, 1933), pp. 275–312; M. Grabmann, *Geschichte der scholastischen Methode,* II (Freiburg, 1911), 177–221; M. De Wulf, *History of Mediaeval Philosophy,* English trans. by E. C. Messenger of the 6th French ed. (London, 1935, 1952), pp. 194–205; L. Thorndike, *A History of Magic and Experimental Science,* II (New York,

1923), 3–8; B. Geyer, *Die patristische und scholastische Philosophie*, Vol. II of F. Ueberweg, *Grundriss der Geschichte der Philosophie*, 11th ed. (Berlin, 1928), 213–226; I. M. Bocheński, *Formale Logik* (Freiburg-Munich, 1956), English trans. by I. Thomas (South Bend, Ind., 1961); W. and M. Kneale, *The Development of Logic* (Oxford, 1962), pp. 202–224.

Comprehensive works on Abailard's life and doctrines include P. de Rémusat, *Abélard, sa vie, sa philosophie et sa théologie* (Paris, 1845, 1855); C. Ottaviano, *Pietro Abelardo, la vita, le opere, il pensiero* (Rome, 1931); J. G. Sikes, *Peter Abailard* (Cambridge, 1932); and H. Waddell, *Peter Abelard* (London, 1933).

Among the many books and articles on particular fields or problems, the following call for special attention: E. Kaiser, *Pierre Abélard critique* (Fribourg, 1901); J. Cottiaux, "La conception de la théologie chez Abélard," in *Revue d'histoire ecclésiastique*, **28** (1932), 247–295, 533–551, 788–828; H. Ostlender, "Die Theologia 'Scholarium' des Peter Abailard," in *Beiträge zur Geschichte der Philosophie und Theologie des Mittelalters*, Supp. III (Münster, 1935), 263–281; T. Reiners, *Der Nominalismus in der Frühscholastik*, ibid., VIII.3 (1910), 41–59; B. Geyer, "Die Stellung Abaelards in der Universalienfrage," *ibid.*, Supp. I (1913), 101–127; E. A. Moody, *Truth and Consequence in Mediaeval Logic* (Amsterdam, 1953); J. R. McCallum, *Abelard's Christian Theology* (Oxford, 1949); G. Engelhardt, *Die Entwicklung der dogmatischen Psychologie in der mittelalterlichen Scholastik* in *Beiträge zur Geschichte der Philosophie und Theologie des Mittelalters*, Vol. XXX.4–6 (Münster, 1933); O. Lottin, "Le problème de la morale intrinsèque d'Abélard à S. Thomas," in *Revue Thomiste*, **39** (1934), 477–515; E. Gilson, *Héloïse et Abélard* (Paris, 1938, 1955, 1958), English trans. by L. K. Shook (Chicago, 1951).

The intros. to several of the eds. listed in Section I of this bibliography are of particular importance. The following deserve special mention: V. Cousin, *Ouvrages inédits*; L. M. De Rijk, *Dialectica*; L. Minio-Paluello, *Abaelardiana inedita*; P. Ruf and M. Grabmann, "Ein neuaufgefundenes Bruchstück"; H. Ostlender, *Theologia "Summi boni"*; J. Monfrin, *Historia calamitatum*; and the section "Untersuchungen" at the end of B. Geyer's ed. of *Peter Abaelards philosophische Schriften*.

L. MINIO-PALUELLO

ABANO, PIETRO D' (*b.* Abano, Italy, 1257; *d.* Padua, Italy, *ca.* 1315), *medicine, natural history, alchemy, philosophy.*

D'Abano completed his early studies in Padua and later took many voyages which focused his attention upon nature studies and ethics. He lived in Constantinople and then, about 1300, went to Paris, where he attended the university and perhaps taught and composed his *Conciliator differentiarum philosophorum et praecipue medicorum.* In 1307 d'Abano returned to Padua, where for several years he taught philosophy and medicine, arousing the apprehension and the perplexity of the academic and ecclesiastical authorities. Although he was acquitted during his lifetime of the charge of heresy—of which he had been accused because of his attempt to interpret the birth and ministry of Christ as other than miraculous—his reputation as a sorcerer persisted. Some forty years after his death his writings were again put on trial; they were found to be heretical, and his bodily remains were disinterred and burned.

In his *Conciliator,* d'Abano undertook a superb synthetic program: the reconciliation of medicine with philosophy. In this he states 120 questions that give rise to as many controversies between physicians and philosophers. For their solution he adopts the method of didactic demonstration that is characteristic of the period, yet on the whole there are signs of a new intention and a new uncertainty.

The practice of medicine implies the necessity of resolving every problem in a natural manner. D'Abano maintained more or less that "the art of medicine must not consider only things that can be seen and felt." Hence he possessed a good knowledge of anatomy; he affirmed, in opposition to the authority of Aristotle (who thought the nerves originated in the heart) that the center of all sensation and motion resides in the brain. His notions of the central nervous system are probably derived from direct visualization. According to d'Abano, the doctor is the symbol of the zealous servant and the collaborator of nature. Considerable importance is attached to the relationship of trust that exists between the doctor and the patient. A good reputation is more useful to the doctor than rare drugs.

These concepts, as d'Abano developed them in his work, have considerable importance. The doctor must be free in his reasoning and must have no ties with scholastic authorities. Such ideas imply a revolt against established and wearisome tradition: they prepare for a rupture with the past and indicate a new path for scientific progress. D'Abano's voice was one of those that, at the dawn of humanism, announced the beginning of a scientific revival.

The Paduan master acknowledged the dependence of every living being and of earthly events on planetary influences. The *Conciliator* gives an outline of astrology as a two-part science comprising one that deals with the laws of celestial movements (astronomy) and another, more important, that draws from these laws the judgments and predictions concerning the effects of those motions on our world—on all human events, on human conception, and even on religion.

D'Abano has been considered by such scholars as Ferrari and Troilo as the initiator of Latin Averroism in Italy. Others—Thorndike, Nardi, and Giacon—have maintained that d'Abano's thought bears no trace of Averroistic theses—above all, that dealing with the unity of the intellect, either as an agent or as a possibility.

BIBLIOGRAPHY

I. ORIGINAL WORKS. The most important works of d'Abano are *Additio in librum Joh. Mesue* (Venice, 1471); *Conciliator differentiarum philosophorum et praecipue medicorum* (Mantua, 1472); *De venenis* (Mantua, 1473); *Liber compilationis physiognomiae* (Padua, 1474); *Expositio problematum Aristotelis* (Mantua, 1475); *Expositiones in Dioscoridem* (Colle [Tuscany], 1478); *Quaestiones de febribus* (Padua, 1482); *Hippocratis libellus de medicorum astrologia* (Venice, 1485); and *Geomantia* (Venice, 1549).

II. SECONDARY LITERATURE. The most important works on d'Abano are M. T. d'Alverny, "Pietro d'Abano et les 'naturalistes' à l'époque de Dante," in Leo S. Olschki, Vittore Branca, Giorgio Pedoan, eds., *Dante e la cultura veneta* (Florence, 1966), pp. 207–219; G. Della Vedova, *Biografia degli scrittori padovani,* I (Padua, 1832), 25–33; P. Duhem, *Le système du monde. Histoires des doctrines cosmologiques de Platon à Copernic,* IV (Paris, 1916), 229–263; S. Ferrari, *I tempi, la vita, le dottrine di Pietro d'Abano* (Genoa, 1900), which contains considerable information on d'Abano, and "Per la biografia e per gli scritti di Pietro d'Abano," in *Atti Regale Accademia Lincei, Memorie Classe Scienzi Morali, Storiche e Filologiche,* 5th ser., **15** (1915), 629–725; C. Giacon, "Pietro d'Abano e l'averroismo padovano," in *Atti XXVI riunione S.I.P.S.* (Rome, 1938), pp. 334–339; B. Nardi, "La teoria dell'anima e la generazione delle forme secondo Pietro d'Abano," in *Rivista filosofica neoscolastica,* **4** (1912), 723–737; "Intorno alle dottrine filosofiche di Pietro d'Abano," in *Nuova rivista storica,* **4** (1920), 81–97, and **5** (1921), 300–313; and *Dante e Pietro d'Abano, saggi di filosofia dantesca* (Milan, 1930), pp. 43–65; L. Norpoth, "Zur Bio-Bibliographie und Wissenschaftslehre des Pietro d'Abano, Mediziners, Philosophen und Astronomen in Padua," in *Kyklos,* **3** (1930), 292–353, which contains considerable information on d'Abano; J. H. Randall, Jr., *The School of Padua and the Emergence of Modern Science* (Padua, 1961); G. Saitta, *Il pensiero italiano nell'umanesimo* (Bologna, 1949), pp. 32–39; L. Thorndike, *A History of Magic and Experimental Science,* II (New York, 1947), 874–947; and E. Troilo, "Averroismo o aristotelismo 'alessandrista' padovano," in *Rendiconti classe scienze morali, storiche e filologiche, Accademia Nazionale Lincei,* 8th ser., **9,** nos. 5–6 (1954), 188–244.

LORIS PREMUDA

'ABBĀS IBN FIRNĀS (*b.* Ronda, Spain; *d.* 274/A.D. 887), *humanities, technology.*

'Abbās ibn Firnās, who was of Berber origin, is sometimes confused with the poet 'Abbās ibn Nāṣiḥ (*d.* 240/A.D. 844). He was the court poet and astrologer of the emirs 'Abd al-Raḥmān II and Muḥammad I, but he attracted the attention of his compatriots because of his inventions and his dissemination of oriental science in the West. Ibn Firnās was the first Andalusian to understand the prosodic rules first laid down by al-Khalīl ibn Aḥmad in the eighth century, and he made known the tables of the *Sind Hind,* which later had great influence on the development of astronomy in Europe. He also attempted to fly—and actually managed to glide for a distance—but the landing was rough because, according to his critics, he did not devote enough study to the way birds use their tails when they land. This flight was often mentioned in Spanish and Arabic writings.

Ibn Firnās constructed a planetarium, a clock, and an armillary sphere; and he is often credited with the discovery of rock crystal. The texts now available are not explicit, however, and one cannot judge on the basis of the statements of E. Lévi-Provençal, for he had access to the *Muqtabis* manuscript, which has been lost. In any case, the historians Ibn Sa'id and Maqqarī state that "he was the first in al-Andalus [Andalusia] to invent (discover) stone crystal." The statement can be interpreted in various ways, but it seems clear that rather than inventing or discovering "stone crystal," Ibn Firnās introduced the cutting of rock crystal, an industry already known in other regions, into the Islamic West. This would have brought about a reduction in the export of quartz to the east, especially to Egypt, for it could now be worked where it was mined. The technique of making glass, known at least since the third millennium before Christ, does not seem to have undergone any change at this time.

BIBLIOGRAPHY

None of Ibn Firnās' original works is extant. His biography can be reconstructed only from a few verses and from the information given by the chroniclers, which can be found in the monograph by Elias Terés, in *Al-Andalus,* **25** (1960), 239–249. Also of value is that of E. Lévi-Provençal, in *Encyclopaedia of Islam,* I, 11. For a discussion of crystal, see P. Kahle, "Bergkristall, Glas und Glasflüsse nach dem Steinbuch von al-Beruni," in *Zeitschrift der Deutschen morgenländischen Gesellschaft,* **90** (1936), 322–356; and *Libri Eraclii de coloribus et artibus Romanorum,* in *Quellenschriften für Kunstgeschichte,* IV (1873).

JUAN VERNET

AL-'ABBĀS IBN SA'ĪD AL-JAWHARĪ. See al-Jawharī.

ABBE, CLEVELAND (*b.* New York, N.Y., 3 December 1838; *d.* Washington, D.C., 28 October 1916), *meteorology.*

As the first regular official weather forecaster of the U.S. government and a promoter of research in atmospheric physics, Abbe served as a symbol of what a meteorologist should be. Unlike many of his colleagues, he was well trained. After studying under Oliver Wolcott Gibbs at the City College of New York, Abbe worked with the German astronomer F. F. E. Brünnow, then at the University of Michigan (1859–1860), and later (1860–1864) with B. A. Gould, who was on detached duty with the Coast Survey, at Cambridge, Massachusetts. In Cambridge he came in contact with the group of astronomers and mathematicians in the *Nautical Almanac* office, notably William Ferrel. Desiring better preparation in astronomy, Abbe spent two years (1864–1866) at Pulkovo, Russia, working under Otto Struve.

Abbe's Russian stay had two consequences. First, Pulkovo provided a model of the symbiotic relationship between theory and practice, ironically like the one that had obtained in Cambridge with the Coast Survey. Second, through his translations and personal connections Abbe provided a point of contact between the American and Russian scientific communities.

Today we would characterize Abbe as a geophysicist, for he sought to apply the methods of astronomy to the development of a physics of the earth. Outlets for this ambition were scarce in nineteenth-century America, and after failing to establish in New York an observatory modeled on Pulkovo, Abbe served from 1868 to 1870 as director of the Cincinnati Observatory before joining the Weather Service of the Signal Corps, the predecessor of the present Weather Bureau, in 1871. Under his aegis the Corps established a laboratory and a "study room," a center for basic research. Although not a notable discoverer, Abbe insisted on mathematical rigor and a close following of new developments in the physical sciences.

BIBLIOGRAPHY

I. PRIMARY SOURCES. Abbe's personal papers are in the Library of Congress. They are described in Nathan Reingold, "A Good Place to Study Astronomy," in Library of Congress, *Quarterly Journal of Current Acquisitions,* **20** (Sept. 1963), 211–217. Other documents bearing on Abbe's career are in the U.S. Weather Bureau records in the National Archives, Washington, D.C., and in the papers of his son, Cleveland Abbe, Jr., in the library of the City University of New York. His reprint collection is in the library of the Johns Hopkins University, Baltimore, Md.

A good bibliography of Abbe's writings is in W. J. Humphreys, "Biographical Memoir of Cleveland Abbe, 1838–1916," in U.S. National Academy of Sciences, *Biographical Memoirs,* **8** (1919), 469–508.

II. SECONDARY WORKS. The Humphreys memoir is still the best single account of Abbe's career. The only full biography was written by Abbe's son Truman: *Prof. Abbe and the Isobars* (New York, 1965). Although a work of filiopietism, it is quite charming and still useful because of the son's liberal use of his father's papers, then in his possession. Nathan Reingold interprets one aspect of Abbe's career in "Cleveland Abbe at Pulkowa: Theory and Practice in the Nineteenth Century Physical Sciences," in *Archives internationales d'histoire des sciences,* **17** (April–June 1964), 133–147. Useful background information is in D. R. Whitnah, *A History of the United States Weather Bureau* (Urbana, Ill., 1961).

NATHAN REINGOLD

ABBE, ERNST (*b.* Eisenach, Germany, 23 January 1840; *d.* Jena, Germany, 14 January 1905), *physics.*

Abbe's importance for the development of scientific and practical optics can be comprehended only in connection with the founding and rise of the Zeiss Works.

In 1846 Carl Zeiss, a thirty-year-old mechanic, established his shop in Jena; in 1866, he began a technical and scientific collaboration with Abbe, who was then a lecturer at the university there. Abbe's fortunes grew with those of the Zeiss company; he had become a partner in 1876 and held a professorship at the university. Within ten years, the once small Zeiss workshop developed into an internationally famous industrial enterprise. The company's apochromatic lens was the greatest advance in technical optics made to that date. At the same period, Abbe began to manifest that interest in social welfare that soon led to the creation of the Carl Zeiss Foundation.

Abbe, according to Jena University curator M. Seebeck, "was born of lowly station, but with predestined claim to scientific fame." His father, Adam Abbe, a spinning-mill worker, would never have been able to send his son through high school and university if his employers had not provided a scholarship for the intelligent and industrious youth.

Upon graduating from the Eisenach Gymnasium in 1857, Abbe studied physics in Jena and subsequently in Göttingen, where he received the doctorate on 23 March 1861. Among the Göttingen professors who exerted a lasting influence on him were the mathematician Riemann, the famous exponent of the theory of functions, and the physicist Wilhelm Weber, former assistant to Gauss and one of the "Göttingen Seven," who had been temporarily suspended because of their protest against the king of Hannover's violation of the constitution.

Abbe's decision to apply for the position of lecturer at Jena University must not have been an easy one to make, since there would be a two-year interval, with its inevitable economic hardships, between his doctorate and his inauguration. He managed to make ends meet by accepting a poorly paid teaching position with the Physikalischer Verein in Frankfurt am Main, a group founded by local citizens for the propagation of the natural sciences. He also did some private tutoring. On 8 August 1863, at the age of twenty-three, Abbe finally achieved his ambition and was admitted to the faculty of Jena University as lecturer in mathematics, physics, and astronomy.

Abbe's straitened circumstances did not improve until he was made associate professor in 1870. On 24 September 1871 he married Elise Snell, the daughter of Karl Snell, head of the physics department at the University of Jena. The marriage was an extremely happy one from the start. The couple had two daughters. In 1876 Abbe's economic difficulties were resolved when Zeiss offered him a partnership. During the preceding ten years Abbe had contributed eminently to the phenomenal rise of Zeiss's company; he now shared in the quite considerable profits.

Zeiss had early begun experiments to convert the production of his microscope, consisting of an objective and an ocular lens, into a scientific process; whereas formerly he had relied on trial and error to find the best lenses, he now wished to use scientific methods. In this effort, Zeiss had met with as little success as his teacher Friedrich Körner; he had also attempted to use the knowledge of the mathematician Friedrich Barfuss. After the latter's death, Zeiss remained unable to solve this problem because of his limited scientific training. He therefore turned to Abbe in 1866 and succeeded in interesting the young physicist in the systematic production of microscopes. During the following decade they constructed the machinery required for industrial production and turned out many commercially marketed instruments (illuminating apparatus for the microscope, known in England as "the Abbe," the Abbe refractometer, and others). Abbe also solved their main problem so completely and ingeniously that his theoretical findings became the basis for the further development of practical optics for decades to come. For example, in 1934 Frits Zernike derived from these findings the

phase-contrast process, for which he was awarded the Nobel Prize in physics (1953). Somewhat earlier, Hans Busch, on the basis of Abbe's theory, had seen the possibility of developing electron microscopes.

Abbe's two most important scientific achievements were in radiation optics (the "sine condition") and undulatory optics ("Beiträge zur Theorie des Mikroskops und der mikroskopischen Wahrnehmung," 1873). The latter led Helmholtz to offer Abbe a professorship at the University of Berlin, but Abbe declined, mainly because of his ties to Zeiss.

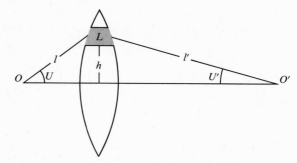

Figure 1. For the Determination of the Sine Condition.

The sine condition is easily derived with the aid of Figure 1. By imaging object point O in the image point O' through the decentered lens L, we obtain the image scale

$$(1) \qquad M = l'/l,$$

which, in accordance with the known image formula, equals the quotient of the image distance l' divided by the real distance l. The relation

$$(2) \qquad h = l \cdot \sin u = l' \cdot \sin u'$$

can also be derived from Figure 1. If the decentered lens L is regarded as the zone of a microscope objective at distance h from the optical axis, then it follows from the above equations that in the case of

$$(3) \qquad \sin u/\sin u' = M = \text{constant},$$

the image scale M is constant for any zone of the lens, that is, over the entire aperture of the objective. Abbe applied the term "aplanatic" to optical systems where the spherical aberration has been corrected, i.e., the axis point O is accurately refracted in the axis point O' and the sine condition (3) has been fulfilled, so that the surface element around O is imaged by all lens zones on the surface element at the image point O' at the same scale. These two corrective conditions can be simultaneously fulfilled only for a single object and image distance; therefore, in the case of the microscope we are limited to a tube of a certain length.

In examining a number of hit-or-miss microscope objectives, Abbe found that in operational position they all fulfilled the sine condition, thus solving the mystery of the success of the hit-or-miss method.

Now Abbe was in a position—through application of the sine condition—to undertake accurate corrections of the aberrations of image systems that did not have too large a divergence. His pupil, Siegfried Czapski, remarked that despite the vastly superior ray union, the images of fine microscopic objects produced by these objectives were duller, showed fewer details, and had less resolving power than the old, poorly corrected systems with larger divergence. After many strenuous and often vain attempts—at tremendous expense to Zeiss—Abbe finally came upon the solution to the problem, as follows.

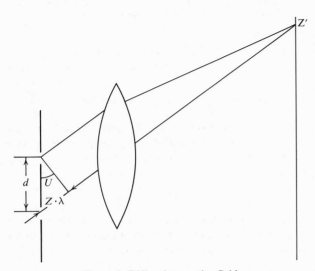

Figure 2. Diffraction on the Grid.

If—as shown in Figure 2—a graticule (heavy vertical lines in figure) is illuminated with, say, red filtered sunlight, then the light rays passing the edges of the graticule gap are deflected. Thus the lower ray in the figure, when it meets the upper ray in point Z' of the rear focal plane of the objective, has covered a distance longer by a fraction or multiple z of the wavelength λ than the upper ray has. Consequently, the two rays are out of phase by

$$(4) \qquad z \cdot \lambda = d \cdot \sin u.$$

The rays are optimally intensified when z is an integer, i.e., the wave crests coincide. The resulting images of the light source are designated as diffraction images of the order of $z = 0, 1, 2, \cdots$. According to Abbe, the accuracy of the image reproduction is a function of the number of diffraction patterns received by the microscope. For the resolution of a

graticule the diffraction image of the first order suffices.

If the space between object and objective is filled with a substance (immersion fluid) having the refractive index n, the wavelength λ is reduced to λ/n. Accordingly, the diffraction equation is

$$(5) \qquad d = \lambda/(n \cdot \sin u)$$

limited to the diffraction maximum of the first order $(z = 1)$. This renders possible calculation of the grating constants d, that is, the smallest still separable structures of the sample, provided the first-order diffraction maxima of the light source are recognizable in the microscope without the eyepiece. Abbe called the denominator of equation (5) "numerical aperture":

$$(6) \qquad A = n \cdot \sin u.$$

Thus it is possible to separate microscopically such structures as

$$(7) \qquad d = \lambda/A$$

which become finer as the wavelength of the rays used for illumination diminishes and the numerical aperture of the objective used increases. But even if the aperture of the microscope is too small to accommodate diffraction images of the first order, the grating constant can be calculated if, in addition to the diffraction image of 0 order of magnitude of the light source, at least one of the two diffraction images of the first order is accommodated in the microscope. In the extreme case, given oblique illumination, grating structures of the order

$$(8) \qquad d = \lambda/2A$$

can still be calculated and thus resolved.

With the setting up of equations (3) and (7) or (8) the last difficulty was cleared and the reason found for the previously puzzling observation that a poorly corrected objective with large aperture revealed more details in the sample than did a well-corrected objective with small divergence. This peculiarity, derived from Abbe's theory of image resolution, had a powerful effect upon electron microscopy, which developed half a century later. According to (7), the extraordinarily short equivalent wavelength of the electrons should have made the resolution in the electron microscope 100,000 times greater than that in the light microscope. The numerical apertures (6) achieved to date, however, amount to only a fraction of a percent of those of the light microscope, resulting in a much smaller superiority—hardly 100 times—of the electron microscope in the resolution of the smallest objects.

Today it is difficult to realize the magnitude of the effect that the above theoretical considerations exerted on the optical production of the Jena workshop.

The effort to discover a better chromatic correction of the microobjective is also noteworthy. In his report on his visit to the South Kensington Exposition in London (1876), which had an excellent optical section, Abbe points out the causes for this shortcoming: the refusal of the glassworks to consider not only economic but also scientific interests in the application of glass smelting. Nevertheless, his report led one glass chemist, Otto Schott, to undertake this task. Joining forces with Zeiss and Abbe, Schott perfected production methods in the Jena glassworks of Schott & Associates by refining a great number of new optical glasses to high perfection. Ten years after the London Exposition, the Zeiss Works celebrated its greatest triumph to that date with the development of an apochromatic system in which not only the primary but also the secondary color spectrum had been eliminated.

Of no lesser importance is the change in Ernst Abbe's personal outlook that occurred at this time and turned the physicist into a social reformer of equal stature. Having become sole owner of the optical plant and its share in the glassworks, after the death of Carl Zeiss in 1888 and the departure from the firm of the latter's son Roderich, in 1891 he created the Carl Zeiss Foundation, to which he bequeathed his personal fortune, with his wife's approval. In the foundation's charter—which in some respects later served the Prussian state as the model for its progressive social legislation (then generally admired) and turned over the larger part of the profits to the University of Jena—Abbe originated an economic system that unites socialism and capitalism. The economist Alfred Weber, in Volume I of *Schriften der Heidelberger Aktionsgruppe zur Demokratie und zum freien Sozialismus* (1947), proposed a voluntary socialization of German industry modeled after the Carl Zeiss Foundation.

BIBLIOGRAPHY

Abbe's work is collected in the *Gesammelte Abhandlungen von Ernst Abbe,* 5 vols. (Jena, 1904–1940). Further bibliographical information may be obtained from Firma Carl Zeiss, Oberkochen, or Volkseigener Betrieb, Jena.

N. GÜNTHER

'ABD AL-, 'ABDALLAH. See last element of name.

ABEL, JOHN JACOB (*b.* near Cleveland, Ohio, 19 May 1857; *d.* Baltimore, Maryland, 26 May 1938), *pharmacology, biochemistry.*

Abel, the son of George M. and Mary Becker Abel, was born on a farm. His parents were moderately prosperous, and their Rhenish origin may have helped in shaping his receptivity to German academic values. Abel attended high school in Cleveland and entered the University of Michigan in 1876, graduating with a Ph.B. in 1883. He overcame the obstacle of a financially dictated three-year interruption, during which he served first as principal in and then as superintendent of the La Porte, Indiana, public schools. During that period he met Mary Hinman, who was also teaching in La Porte and whom he married in 1883. After graduation Abel went to the Johns Hopkins University, and spent part of a year in Newell Martin's laboratory.

In 1884 Abel sailed for Germany, where he remained until late 1890—the longest German apprenticeship served by any prominent American scientist of his generation. The first two years were spent in Leipzig, studying the basic medical sciences—physiology, histology, pharmacology, and chemistry; like many other Americans he worked with Carl Ludwig. Not surprisingly, Abel undertook an electrophysiological problem. Finally titled "Wie verhalt sich die negative Schwankung des Nervenstroms bei Reizung der sensiblen und motorischen Spinal-surzeln des Frosches?," it was presented as a doctoral thesis at Strasbourg in 1888.

The next two years were spent in Strasbourg, with short periods of clinical study at Würzburg and Heidelberg. Abel received his M.D. from Strasbourg in 1888, then spent the winter semester of 1888–1889 in Vienna, taking postgraduate clinical courses. His interests had already turned to biochemistry and experimental pharmacology; in 1889–1890 he worked in M. von Nencki's laboratory in Berne and in the fall of 1890 returned to Leipzig to work with Drechsel, the physiological chemist at Ludwig's institute. He completed his first essentially biochemical studies in Berne, one on the composition of melanin and another on the determination of the molecular weights of cholic acid, cholesterol, and hydrobilirubin.

While studying in Europe, Abel was aware that when he returned to the United States, he would in all probability have to depend upon clinical work for a livelihood, although he hoped to find a position in which he would have the opportunity to conduct research. He was fortunate to be offered a full-time teaching position at the University of Michigan school of medicine just as his funds were running low. This offer came through the good offices of Victor Vaughan, who had taught Abel as an undergraduate and shared his conviction that chemistry was to play an increasingly central role in the future of medical research.

Abel was appointed lecturer in materia medica and therapeutics in January 1891. Classroom teaching, of course, and not research or laboratory instruction, at first made up the bulk of Abel's duties. By his third year, however, he was able to offer a graduate course on "the influence of certain drugs in the metabolism of tissue" and another on "the methods of modern pharmacology." In 1893 the Johns Hopkins University offered Abel its first professorship of pharmacology, a position that he accepted and occupied continuously until his retirement in 1932. Until 1908 he was also nominally in charge of instruction in physiological chemistry. Abel's research was his life: in his mature years he evinced little concern for the formal routine of teaching. From his retirement until his death, Abel remained steadfastly and constructively at work in his laboratory.

Through this ascetic dedication to research, Abel made one of his most significant contributions to the development of biochemistry and pharmacology in the United States. It was his way of life, his students and colleagues agreed, that influenced them—not his teaching of particular techniques. Almost all his memorialists, for example, mention the intellectual stimulation they received at the austere lunch the laboratory staff shared each day at a plain table, the legs of which were immersed in cans of kerosene to discourage Baltimore's predatory cockroaches. Photographs show Abel's never-changing laboratory attire— white operating-room cap, gray laboratory coat, and long white apron. In values and style of life, Abel seemed to embody the idealized figure of the German professor.

The character of Abel's work played a significant and distinct influence in the reshaping of his discipline. The key to this influence lay in his complete and farsighted commitment to the importance of chemistry in medicine and physiology. Few other biological scientists of his generation had had the prescience to undertake the high-level chemical training necessary in a world of medical and biological research that was increasingly dependent upon chemical and physical sophistication. In the analysis of vital phenomena, Abel warned in 1915, "the investigator must associate himself with those who have labored in fields where *molecules and atoms rather than multi-cellular tissues or even unicellular organisms are the units of study.*" In his own work, Abel was consistently motivated by the chemist's concern

with determining the composition and structure of the substances with which he worked; such concerns were, of course, highly atypical in the medical world of the 1890's. At Johns Hopkins, Abel sought, for example, to introduce microanalytic techniques and even the formal teaching of biophysics. His correspondence and programmatic statements indicate his assumption of what might, if formally articulated, be called a biochemical and biophysical reductionism.

Despite an occasional disdain for mere matters of administration, Abel also played a significant role in the institutional development of American science. He was instrumental in the founding of the *Journal of Experimental Medicine* in 1896 and, in conjunction with Christian Herter, the *Journal of Biological Chemistry* in 1905. Abel was one of the principal organizers of the American Society of Biological Chemists in 1906 and the American Society for Pharmacology and Experimental Therapeutics in 1908. A year later he led in establishing the *Journal of Pharmacology and Experimental Therapeutics,* a publication that he edited until his retirement. Abel's statements and actions indicate a rare mixture of insight and practicality in his understanding of the conditions favoring institutional growth. He of course also figured prominently in shaping the evolution of the traditionally didactic and empirical field of materia medica into modern, laboratory-oriented pharmacology.

After his physiological interlude with Ludwig, Abel's work was, for the half century of his active scientific life, essentially biochemical. His first significant work related to the metabolism of sulfur, a problem he had begun in Leipzig with Drechsel and had continued in Ann Arbor. Abel succeeded in demonstrating the presence of ethyl sulfide in dog urine and, in a related project, in explaining the presence of ammonia in the urine of children who had been given large quantities of limewater. He suggested that it was a product of the breakdown of carbamic acid, a substance Abel had previously studied in alkaline horse urine.

Soon after coming to Johns Hopkins, Abel turned to work with the physiologically active substance found in extracts from the adrenal medulla; this became his all-consuming interest from 1895 to 1905. He published his first article on the substance he had isolated in 1897 (with A. C. Crawford), and in 1899 he christened this blood-pressure-raising hormone "epinephrine." The substance he described, however, was not the free hormone, but a monobenzoyl derivative. This work was the first to give Abel international prominence, although in 1900 Jokichi Takamine was able to isolate the hormone without the benzoyl radical. Both assumed, of course, that they were dealing with a unitary substance. In the years after 1905, Abel completed less elaborate studies of the physiological effects of alcoholic beverages, isolated epinephrine from the parotid secretions of the South American toad *Bufo agua,* studied the poisons of the mushroom *Amanita phalloides*—and even published on the pharmacology of several new chemotherapeutic agents. Work on the pharmaceutical action of phthalein derivatives led to the elaboration of a test for kidney function.

In 1912 and the years immediately following, Abel became deeply interested in work with the protein constituents of the blood. He suggested in 1912 that an "artificial kidney" might be utilized in the removal and study of diffusible substances of the blood. An apparatus of coiled collodion tubes surrounded by a saline solution was soon devised and used for this purpose; arterial blood was shunted through these tubes and then returned to the experimental animal's vein. Using this technique, Abel succeeded in demonstrating the existence of free amino acids in the blood. Even at this time (1913), Abel seems to have been aware of the clinical potential of what he called his "vividiffusion" apparatus; it might, he suggested, prove useful in managing renal failure. A second and related aspect was Abel's demonstration that large quantities of blood could be removed from the circulation if the washed and centrifuged corpuscles were returned. Abel also showed remarkable foresight in his suggestion that "plasmaphaeresis"—his term for this procedure—might ultimately be used to create "blood banks" for use in traumatic and surgical emergencies.

A natural extension of this work led Abel's laboratory to a concern with amino acids and protein degradation products in the blood. A related study of histamines, however, soon revived his earlier interest in hormones. (A resemblance between histamine and the active principle of the posterior pituitary seemed at first to exist.) From the publication of his first paper on the pituitary in 1917 until 1924, when he turned abruptly to work with insulin, Abel labored single-mindedly, although fruitlessly, to isolate a unitary hormone with the protean physiological characteristics associated with pituitary extracts.

Abel's interest in insulin resulted from the explicit invitation of his personal friend A. A. Noyes of the California Institute of Technology. Noyes had acquired funds to subsidize an attempt to isolate pure insulin from the expensive, although readily available, commercial preparation. Abel accepted Noyes' invitation, arrived in Pasadena in October 1924, and was soon able to report encouraging findings. A key step forward lay in his insight that amounts of labile sulfur in his fractions of commercial insulin were directly correlated with physiological activity. Not only did this have ultimate structural implications but—more immediately—it allowed Abel to save a great deal of time; he could now separate out the more active fractions by the use of this criterion without resorting to as yet unstandardized bioassay procedures, in which his laboratory had never excelled and which were far more time-consuming.

Late in 1925, Abel succeeded in forming crystals that, according to the chemical criteria he instinctively employed—crystallization, optical rotation, melting point, and elementary analysis—seemed to be the pure hormone. Despite early scientific enthusiasm at the announcement of this finding in 1926, Abel spent much of the next four years in defending his discovery. The reasons for skepticism were several. One was an initial difficulty in reproducing his crystals. Perhaps more important were certain theoretical implications. It seemed apparent that the substance isolated was a protein, and it was difficult for Abel's contemporaries to believe that the immense protein molecule, of which the regularity of structure was still very much in doubt, could be capable of performing the precise physiological functions of a hormone. The protein, many biochemists believed, must necessarily be an inert carrier, the active principle an adsorbent on its surface. (Similar objections greeted the parallel findings of J. B. Sumner and of J. H. Northrop and M. Kunitz when they announced the protein nature of enzymes they had crystallized.)

By the mid-1930's, however, it was becoming generally assumed that proteins could act as enzymes. The isolation of insulin and its attendant publicity had, of course, helped to sharpen the debate. Abel's insulin work and that of his students played an important part in the line of research culminating in Frederick Sanger's identification in 1955 of the complete primary structure of insulin, the first protein structure to be thus elucidated. After his crystallization of insulin, Abel turned back to his earlier work on the pituitary. When he retired in 1932, he was placed at the head of a laboratory of endocrinology created especially for him at Johns Hopkins. With a touch of characteristic individuality, he then abandoned his hormone work and devoted the remaining years of his life to a study of tetanus toxin and the pathological mechanism through which it acts.

BIBLIOGRAPHY

I. ORIGINAL WORKS. A complete bibliography of Abel's work is available in William deB. MacNider, "Biographical

Memoir of John Jacob Abel 1857–1938," in National Academy of Sciences, U.S.A., *Biographical Memoirs,* **24** (1946), 231–257. Several of Abel's own papers provide valuable synthetic and expository accounts of his work. See *Experimental and Chemical Studies of the Blood With an Appeal for More Extended Chemical Training for the Biological and Medical Investigator,* the first Mellon lecture, given at the University of Pittsburgh under the auspices of the Society for Biological Research (Pittsburgh, 1915), also in *Science,* **42** (1915), 135–147, 165–178; "Some Recent Advances in Our Knowledge of the Ductless Glands," in *Bulletin of the Johns Hopkins Hospital,* **38** (January 1926), 1–32; and "Chemistry in Relation to Biology and Medicine With Especial Reference to Insulin and Other Hormones," in *Science,* **66** (1927), 307–319, 337–346.

The most important source for Abel's life and scientific career is his papers, deposited at the Welch Medical Library, the Johns Hopkins University. This extensive collection, including correspondence, notebooks, and other memoranda, constitutes an important source of information on the development of American biochemistry and pharmacology as well as for the history of the specific research areas that concerned Abel.

II. SECONDARY LITERATURE. There is no full-length biography of Abel available, but among the most useful of numerous biographical sketches are Carl Voegtlin, "John Jacob Abel. 1857–1938," in *Journal of Pharmacology and Experimental Therapeutics,* **67** (1939), 373–406, a detailed account of Abel's scientific work; H. H. Swain, E. M. K. Geiling, and A. Heingartner, "John Jacob Abel at Michigan. The Introduction of Pharmacology Into the Medical Curriculum," in *University of Michigan Medical Bulletin,* **29** (1963), 1–14; E. K. Marshall, Jr., "Abel the Prophet," in *The Johns Hopkins Magazine,* **1** (1950), 11–14; Paul D. Lamson, "John Jacob Abel—A Portrait," in *Bulletin of the Johns Hopkins Hospital,* **68** (1941), 119–157, an engagingly detailed personal portrait; McNider's "Biographical Memoir," cited above; H. H. Dale, "John Jacob Abel. 1857–1938," in *Obituary Notices of Fellows of the Royal Society,* **2** (1939), 577–581; and E. M. K. Geiling, "John Jacob Abel," in *Dictionary of American Biography,* XXII, Supp. 2 (New York, 1958), 4–5. *John Jacob Abel, M.D., Investigator, Teacher, Prophet. 1857–1938* (Baltimore, 1957) is a useful commemorative volume that includes the Lamson and Marshall sketches cited above, as well as a number of Abel's most important papers. In 1957 the Johns Hopkins University celebrated the centenary of Abel's birth with a symposium to which contributions were made by Torald Sollman, Samuel Amberg, Carl Voegtlin, L. G. Rowntree, E. K. Marshall, Jr., E. M. K. Geiling, and Warfield M. Firor; the proceedings appeared in the *Bulletin of the Johns Hopkins Hospital,* **101** (1957), 297–328. An excellent recent study of Abel's insulin work by Jane Murnaghan and Paul Talalay that succeeds in placing this research in the broader context of twentieth-century biochemistry is "John Jacob Abel and the Crystallization of Insulin," in *Perspectives in Biology and Medicine,* **10** (1967), 334–380.

CHARLES E. ROSENBERG

ABEL, NIELS HENRIK (*b.* Finnöy, an island near Stavanger, Norway, 5 August 1802; *d.* Froland, Norway, 6 April 1829), *mathematics.*

Abel's father, Sören Georg Abel, was a Lutheran minister and himself the son of a minister. He was a gifted and highly ambitious theologian, educated at the University of Copenhagen, which was at that time the only such institution in the united kingdom of Denmark-Norway. He had married Ane Marie Simonson, the daughter of a wealthy merchant and shipowner in the town of Risör, on the southern coast. Finnöy was the first parish for pastor Abel; it was small and toilsome, comprising several islands. The couple had seven children, six sons and a daughter; Niels Henrik was their second child.

In 1804 Sören Georg Abel was appointed successor to his father in the parish of Gjerstad, near Risör. The political situation in Norway was tense. Because of its alliance with Denmark the country had been thrown into the Napoleonic Wars on the side of France, and a British blockade of the coast created widespread famine. Pastor Abel was prominent in the nationalistic movement, working for the creation of separate Norwegian institutions—particularly a university and a national bank—if not for outright independence. At the conclusion of the peace treaty of Kiel, Denmark ceded Norway to Sweden. The Norwegians revolted and wrote their own constitution, but after a brief and futile war against the Swedes under Bernadotte, they were compelled to seek an armistice. A union with Sweden was accepted, and Abel's father became one of the members of the extraordinary Storting called in the fall of 1814 to write the necessary revision of the new constitution.

Niels Henrik Abel and his brothers received their first instruction from their father, but in 1815 Abel and his older brother were sent to the Cathedral School in Christiania (Oslo). This was an old school to which many public officials in the province sent their children; some fellowships were available. The Cathedral School had been excellent, but was then at a low ebb, because most of its good teachers had accepted positions at the new university, which began instruction in 1813.

Abel was only thirteen years old when he left home, and it seems probable that deteriorating family life expedited his departure. During the first couple of years his marks were only satisfactory; then the quality of his work declined. His brother fared even worse; he began to show signs of mental illness and finally had to be sent home.

In 1817 an event took place at the school that was destined to change Abel's life. The mathematics teacher mistreated one of the pupils, who died shortly afterward, possibly as a consequence of the punishment. The teacher was summarily dismissed and his place was taken by Bernt Michael Holmboe, who was only seven years older than Abel. Holmboe also served as an assistant to Christoffer Hansteen, professor of astronomy and the leading scientist at the university.

It did not take Holmboe long to discover young Abel's extraordinary ability in mathematics. He began by giving him special problems and recommending books outside the school curriculum. The two then started to study together the calculus texts of Euler, and later the works of the French mathematicians, particularly Lagrange and Laplace. So rapid was Abel's progress that he soon became the real teacher. From notebooks preserved in the library of the University of Oslo one sees that even in these early days he was already particularly interested in algebraic equation theory. By the time he finished school, he was familiar with most of the important mathematical literature. Holmboe was so delighted by the mathematical genius he had discovered that the rector of the school made him moderate his statements about Abel in the record book. But the professors at the university were well informed by Holmboe about the promising young man and made his personal acquaintance. Besides Hansteen, who also taught applied mathematics, there was only one professor of mathematics, Sören Rasmussen, a former teacher at the Cathedral School. Rasmussen, a kindly man, was not a productive scholar; his time was largely taken up by tasks assigned to him by government, particularly in his post as an administrator of the new Bank of Norway.

During his last year at school Abel, with the vigor and immodesty of youth, attacked the problem of the solution of the quintic equation. This problem had been outstanding since the days of del Ferro, Tartaglia, Cardano, and Ferrari in the first half of the sixteenth century. Abel believed that he had succeeded in finding the form of the solution, but in Norway there was no one capable of understanding his arguments, nor was there any scientific journal in which they could be published. Hansteen forwarded the paper to the Danish mathematician Ferdinand Degen, requesting its publication by the Danish Academy.

Degen could not discover any fault in the arguments, but requested that Abel illustrate his method by an example. Degen also found the topic somewhat sterile and suggested that Abel turn his attention to a topic "whose development would have the greatest consequences for analysis and mechanics. I refer to the elliptic transcendentals [elliptic integrals]. A serious investigator with suitable qualifications for research of this kind would by no means be restricted to the many beautiful properties of these most remarkable functions, but could discover a Strait of Magellan leading into wide expanses of a tremendous analytic ocean" (letter to Hansteen).

Abel began constructing his examples for the solution of the fifth-degree equation, but discovered to his dismay that his method was not correct. He also followed Degen's suggestion about the elliptic transcendentals, and it is probable that within a couple of years he had in the main completed his theory of the elliptic functions.

In 1818 pastor Abel was reelected to the Storting, after an unsuccessful bid in 1816. But his political career ended in tragedy. He made violent unfounded charges against other representatives and was threatened with impeachment. This, together with his drunkenness, made him the butt of the press. He returned home in disgrace, a disillusioned man. Both he and his wife suffered from alcoholism, and the conditions at the vicarage and in the parish became scandalous. It was generally considered a relief when he died in 1820. His widow was left in very straitened circumstances, with a small pension barely sufficient to support her and her many children.

The penniless Abel entered the university in the fall of 1821. He was granted a free room at the university dormitory and received permission to share it with his younger brother Peder. But the new institution had no fellowship funds, and some of the professors took the unusual measure of supporting the young mathematician out of their own salaries. He was a guest in their houses and became particularly attracted to the Hansteen home, and to Mrs. Hansteen and her sisters.

Abel's first task at the university was to satisfy the requirements for the preliminary degree, *Candidatus Philosophiae*. Once this was achieved, after a year, Abel was entirely on his own in his studies. There were no advanced courses in mathematics and the physical sciences, but this does not seem to have been a handicap; in a letter from Paris a little later he stated that he had read practically everything in mathematics, important or unimportant.

He devoted his time to advanced research and his efforts received a strong impetus when Hansteen started a scientific periodical, *Magazin for Naturvidenskaben*. In 1823 this journal published Abel's first article, in Norwegian, a study of functional equations. Mathematically it was not important, nor was his second little paper. The subscribers to the magazine had been promised a popular review, however, and Hansteen, probably after criticism, felt obliged to apologize for the character of these papers: "Thus

I believe that the *Magazin* in addition to scientific materials should also further the tools serving for their analysis. It will be reckoned to our credit that we have given the learned public an opportunity to become acquainted with a work from the pen of this talented and skillful author" (*Magazin*, **1**). Abel's next paper, "Opläsning afet Par Opgaver ved bjoelp af bestemte Integraler" ("Solution of Some Problems by Means of Definite Integrals"), is of importance in the history of mathematics, since it contains the first solution of an integral equation. The paper, which went unnoticed at the time, in part because it was in Norwegian, deals with the mechanical problem of the motion of a mass point on a curve under the influence of gravitation. During the winter of 1822–1823 Abel also composed a longer work on the integration of functional expressions. The paper was submitted to the university Collegium in the hope that that body would assist in its publication. The manuscript has disappeared, but it seems likely that some of the results obtained in it are included in some of Abel's later papers.

Early in the summer of 1823 Abel received a gift of 100 daler from Professor Rasmussen to finance a trip to Copenhagen to meet Degen and the other Danish mathematicians. His letters to Holmboe reveal the mathematical inspiration that he received. He stayed in the house of his uncle and here made the acquaintance of his future fiancée, Christine Kemp.

Upon his return to Oslo, Abel again took up the question of the solution of the quintic equation. This time he took the reverse view and succeeded in solving the centuries-old problem by proving the impossibility of a radical expression that represents a solution of the general fifth- or higher-degree equation. Abel fully realized the importance of his result, so he had it published, at his own expense, by a local printer. To reach a larger audience, he wrote it in French: "Mémoire sur les équations algébriques où on démontre l'impossibilité de la résolution de l'équation générale du cinquième degré." To save expense the whole pamphlet was compressed to six pages. The resulting brevity probably made it difficult to understand; at any rate, there was no reaction from any of the foreign mathematicians—including the great C. F. Gauss, to whom a copy was sent.

It had become clear that Abel could no longer live on the support of the professors. His financial problems had been increased by his engagement to Christine Kemp, who had come to Norway as a governess for the children of a family living near Oslo.

Abel applied for a travel grant, and after some delays the government decided that Abel should receive a small stipend to study languages at the university to prepare him for travel abroad. He was then to receive a grant of 600 daler for two years of foreign study.

Abel was disappointed at the delay but dutifully studied languages, particularly French, and used his time to prepare a considerable number of papers to be presented to foreign mathematicians. During the summer of 1825 he departed, together with four friends, all of whom also intended to prepare themselves for future scientific careers; one of them later became professor of medicine, and the three others became geologists. Abel's friends all planned to go to Berlin, while Abel, upon Hansteen's advice, was to spend his time in Paris, then the world's principal center of mathematics. Abel feared being lonely, however, and also decided to go to Berlin, although he well knew that he would incur the displeasure of his protector.

Abel's change of mind turned out to be a most fortunate decision. On passing through Copenhagen, Abel learned that Degen had died, but he secured a letter of recommendation from one of the other Danish mathematicians to Privy Councilor August Leopold Crelle. Crelle was a very influential engineer, intensely interested in mathematics although not himself a strong mathematician.

When Abel first called upon Crelle, he had some difficulty in making himself understood, but after a while Crelle recognized the unusual qualities of his young visitor. The two became lifelong friends. Abel presented him with a copy of his pamphlet on the quintic equation, but Crelle confessed that it was unintelligible to him and recommended that Abel write an expanded version of it. They talked about the poor state of mathematics in Germany. In a letter to Hansteen, dated from Berlin, 5 December 1825, Abel wrote:

> When I expressed surprise over the fact that there existed no mathematical journal, as in France, he said that he had long intended to edit one, and would presently bring his plan to execution. This project is now organized, and that to my great joy, for I shall have a place where I can get some of my articles printed. I have already prepared four of them, which will appear in the first number.

Journal für die reine und angewandte Mathematik, or *Crelle's Journal*, as it is commonly known, was the leading German mathematical periodical during the nineteenth century. The first volume alone contains seven papers by Abel and the following volumes contain many more, most of them of preeminent importance in the history of mathematics. Among the first is the expanded version of the proof of the impossibility of the solution of the general quintic equation by radicals. Here Abel develops the necessary algebraic background, including a discussion of algebraic field extensions. Abel was at this time not aware that he had a precursor, the Italian mathematician Paolo Ruffini. But in a posthumous paper on the equations which are solvable by radicals Abel states: "The only one before me, if I am not mistaken, who has tried to prove the impossibility of the algebraic [radical] solution of the general equations is the mathematician Ruffini, but his paper is so complicated that it is very difficult to judge on the correctness of his arguments. It seems to me that it is not always satisfactory." The result is usually referred to as the Abel-Ruffini theorem.

After Abel's departure from Oslo an event took place that caused him much concern. Rasmussen had found his professorship in mathematics too burdensome when combined with his public duties. He resigned, and shortly afterward the faculty voted to recommend that Holmboe be appointed to fill the vacancy. Abel's Norwegian friends found the action highly unjust, and Abel himself probably felt the same way. Nevertheless, he wrote a warm letter of congratulation to his former teacher, and they remained good friends. But it is evident that from this moment Abel worried about his future and his impending marriage; there was no scientific position in sight for him in his home country.

During the winter in Berlin, Abel contributed to *Crelle's Journal*; among the notable papers are one on the generalization of the binomial formula and another on the integration of square root expressions. But one of his main mathematical concerns was the lack of stringency in contemporary mathematics. He mentioned it repeatedly in letters to Holmboe. In one of these, dated 16 January 1826, he wrote:

> My eyes have been opened in the most surprising manner. If you disregard the very simplest cases, there is in all of mathematics not a single infinite series whose sum has been stringently determined. In other words, the most important parts of mathematics stand without foundation. It is true that most of it is valid, but that is very surprising. I struggle to find the reason for it, an exceedingly interesting problem.

A result of this struggle was his classic paper on power series which contains many general theorems and also, as an application, the stringent determination of the sum of the binomial series for arbitrary real or complex exponents.

During the early spring of 1826, Abel felt obliged to proceed to his original destination, Paris. Crelle had promised to accompany him, and on the way they intended to stop in Göttingen to visit Gauss. Unfortunately, pressure of business prevented Crelle from leaving Berlin. At the same time, Abel's Norwegian friends were planning a geological excursion through central Europe, and, again reluctant to be separated from them, he joined the group. They traveled by coach through Bohemia, Austria, northern Italy, and the Alps. Abel did not reach Paris until July, low on funds after the expensive trip.

The visit to Paris was to prove disappointing. The university vacations had just begun when Abel arrived, and the mathematicians had left town. When they returned, he found that they were aloof and difficult to approach; it was only in passing that he met Legendre, whose main interest in his old age was elliptic integrals, Abel's own specialty. For presentation to the French Academy of Sciences Abel had reserved a paper that he considered his masterpiece. It dealt with the sum of integrals of a given algebraic function. Abel's theorem states that any such sum can be expressed as a fixed number p of these integrals, with integration arguments that are algebraic functions of the original arguments. The minimal number p is the genus of the algebraic function, and this is the first occurrence of this fundamental quantity. Abel's theorem is a vast generalization of Euler's relation for elliptic integrals.

Abel spent his first months in Paris completing his great memoir; it is one of his longest papers and includes a broad theory with applications. It was presented to the Academy of Sciences on 30 October 1826, under the title "Mémoire sur une propriété générale d'une classe très-étendue de fonctions transcendantes." Cauchy and Legendre were appointed referees, Cauchy being chairman. A number of young men had gained quick distinction upon having their works accepted by the Academy, and Abel awaited the referees' report. No report was forthcoming, however; indeed, it was not issued until Abel's death forced its appearance. Cauchy seems to have been to blame; he claimed later that the manuscript was illegible.

Abel's next two months in Paris were gloomy; he had little money and few acquaintances. He met P. G. L. Dirichlet, his junior by three years and already a well-known mathematician, through a paper in the Academy sponsored by Legendre. Another acquaintance was Frédéric Saigey, editor of the scientific revue *Ferrusac's Bulletin*, for whom Abel wrote a few articles, particularly about his own papers in *Crelle's Journal*. After Christmas he spent his last resources to pay his fare to Berlin.

Shortly after his return to Berlin, Abel fell ill; he seems to have then suffered the first attack of the tuberculosis that was later to claim his life. He borrowed some money from Holmboe, and Crelle probably helped him. Abel longed to return to Norway but felt compelled to remain abroad until his fellowship term had expired. Crelle tried to keep him in Berlin until he could find a position for him at a German university; in the meantime he offered him the editorship of his *Journal.*

Abel worked assiduously on a new paper: "Recherches sur les fonctions elliptiques," his most extensive publication (125 pages in the *Oeuvres complètes*). In this work he radically transformed the theory of elliptic integrals to the theory of elliptic functions by using their inverse functions corresponding in the most elementary case to the duality

$$y = \arc \sin x = \int \frac{dx}{\sqrt{1 - x^2}} \quad x = \sin y.$$

The elliptic functions thereby become a vast and natural generalization of the trigonometric functions; in the wake of Abel's work they were to constitute one of the favorite research topics in mathematics during the nineteenth century. Abel had already developed most of the theory as a student in Oslo, so he was able to present the theory of elliptic functions with a great richness of detail, including double periodicity, expansions in infinite series and products, and addition theorems. The theory led to the expressions for functions of a multiple of the argument with the concomitant determination of the equations for fractional arguments and their solution by radicals, much in the way that Gauss had treated the cyclotomic equations; Abel's letters to Holmboe (from Paris in December 1826 and from Berlin on 4 March 1827) indicate that he was particularly fascinated by a determination of the condition for a lemniscate to be divisible into equal parts by means of compass and ruler, analogous to Gauss's construction of regular polygons. The last part deals with the so-called theory of complex multiplication, later so important in algebraic number theory.

Abel returned to Oslo on 20 May 1827, to find that the situation at home was as gloomy as he had feared. He had no position in prospect, no fellowship, and an abundance of debts. His application to have his fellowship prolonged was turned down by the Department of Finance, but the university courageously awarded him a small stipend out of its meager funds. This action was criticized by the department, which reserved the right to have the amount deducted from any future salary he might receive.

Abel's fiancée found a new position with friends of Abel's family, the family of the owner of an iron-works at Froland, near Arendal. During the fall Abel eked out a living in Oslo by tutoring schoolboys and probably with the help of friends. At the new year the situation became brighter. Hansteen, a pioneer in geomagnetic studies, received a large grant for two years to examine the earth's magnetic field in unexplored Siberia. In the meantime Abel became his substitute both at the university and at the Norwegian Military Academy.

The first part of the "Recherches" was published in *Crelle's Journal* in September 1827, and Abel completed the second part during the winter. He lived in isolation at Oslo; there was no package mail during the winter, and he had no inkling of the interest his memoir had created among European mathematicians. Nor did he know that a competitor had appeared in the field of elliptic functions until early in 1828, when Hansteen showed him the September issue of the *Astronomische Nachrichten.* In this journal a young German mathematician, K. G. J. Jacobi, announced without proofs some results concerning the transformation theory of elliptic integrals. Abel hurriedly added a note to the manuscript of the second part of the "Recherches," showing how Jacobi's results were the consequence of his own.

Abel was keenly aware that a race was at hand. He interrupted a large paper on the theory of equations that was to contain the determination of all equations that can be solved by radicals; the part that was published contained the theory of those equations that are now known as Abelian. He then wrote, in rapid succession, a series of papers on elliptic functions. The first was "Solution d'un problème général concernant la transformation des fonctions elliptiques." This, his direct response to Jacobi, was published in *Astronomische Nachrichten;* the others appeared in *Crelle's Journal.* In addition, Abel prepared a book-length memoir, "Précis d'une théorie des fonctions elliptiques," which was published after his death. Jacobi, on the other hand, wrote only brief notices which did not reveal his methods; these were reserved for his book, *Fundamenta nova theoriae functionum ellipticarum* (1829).

Much has been written about the early theory of elliptic functions. There seems to be little doubt that Abel was in possession of the ideas several years before Jacobi. On the other hand, it is also an established fact that Gauss, although publishing nothing, had discovered the principles of elliptic functions long before either Abel or Jacobi.

The European mathematicians watched with fascination the competition between the two young mathematicians. Legendre noticed Jacobi's announcements and also received a letter from him. In a meeting of the French Academy in November 1827, he praised the new mathematical star; the speech was reproduced in the newspapers and Legendre sent the clipping to Jacobi. In his reply Jacobi, after expressing his thanks, pointed out Abel's "Recherches" and its general results. Legendre responded: "Through these works you two will be placed in the class of the foremost analysts of our times." He also expressed his disappointment over Jacobi's method of publication and was irritated when Jacobi confessed that in order to derive some of his results he had had to rely on Abel's paper. About this time also, Abel began a correspondence with Legendre and poured out his ideas to him.

All that the European mathematicians knew about Abel's condition in Norway was that he had only a temporary position and had recently been compelled to tutor schoolboys to make a living. The main source of their information was Crelle, who constantly used his influence to try to obtain an appointment for Abel at a new scientific institute to be created in Berlin. Progress was very slow, however. In September 1828 four prominent members of the French Academy of Sciences took the extraordinary step of addressing a petition directly to Bernadotte, now Charles XIV of Norway-Sweden, calling attention to Abel and urging that a suitable scientific position be created for him. In a meeting of the Academy, on 25 February 1829, Legendre also paid tribute to Abel and his discoveries, particularly to his results in the theory of equations.

In the meantime Abel, in spite of his deteriorating health, wrote new papers frantically. He spent the summer vacation of 1828 on the Froland estate with his fiancée. At Christmas he insisted on visiting her again, notwithstanding that it required several days' travel in intense cold. He was feverish when he arrived, but enjoyed the family Christmas celebration. He may have had a premonition that his days were numbered, however, and he now feared that the great paper submitted to the French Academy had been lost forever. He therefore wrote a brief note, "Demonstration d'une propriété générale d'une certaine classe de fonctions transcendantes," in which he gave a proof of the main theorem. He mailed it to Crelle on 6 January 1829.

While waiting for the sled that was to return him to Oslo, Abel suffered a violent hemorrhage; the doctor diagnosed his illness as tuberculosis and ordered prolonged bed rest. He died in April, at the age of twenty-six, and was buried at the neighboring Froland church during a blizzard. The grave is marked by a monument erected by his friends. One of them, Baltazar Keilhau, wrote to Christine Kemp,

without ever having seen her, and made her an offer of marriage which she accepted. Two days after Abel's death Crelle wrote jubilantly to inform him that his appointment in Berlin had been secured.

On 28 June 1830, the French Academy of Sciences awarded its Grand Prix to Abel and Jacobi for their outstanding mathematical discoveries. After an intensive search in Paris the manuscript of Abel's great memoir was rediscovered. It was published in 1841, fifteen years after it had been submitted. During the printing it again disappeared, not to reappear until 1952 in Florence.

Crelle wrote an extensive eulogy of Abel in his *Journal* (**4** [1829], 402):

All of Abel's works carry the imprint of an ingenuity and force of thought which is unusual and sometimes amazing, even if the youth of the author is not taken into consideration. One may say that he was able to penetrate all obstacles down to the very foundations of the problems, with a force which appeared irresistible; he attacked the problems with an extraordinary energy; he regarded them from above and was able to soar so high over their present state that all the difficulties seemed to vanish under the victorious onslaught of his genius. . . . But it was not only his great talent which created the respect for Abel and made his loss infinitely regrettable. He distinguished himself equally by the purity and nobility of his character and by a rare modesty which made his person cherished to the same unusual degree as was his genius.

BIBLIOGRAPHY

I. ORIGINAL WORKS. Abel's complete works are published in two editions, *Oeuvres complètes de N. H. Abel, mathématicien,* ed. and annotated by B. Holmboe (Oslo, 1839), and *Nouvelle édition,* M. M. L. Sylow and S. Lie, eds., 2 vols. (Oslo, 1881).

II. SECONDARY LITERATURE. Materials on Abel's life include *Niels Henrik Abel: Mémorial publié à l'occasion du centenaire de sa naissance* (Oslo, 1902) which comprises all letters cited in the text; and O. Ore, *Niels Henrik Abel; Mathematician Extraordinary* (Minneapolis, Minn., 1957).

OYSTEIN ORE

ABEL, OTHENIO (*b.* Vienna, Austria, 20 June 1875; *d.* Pichl am Mondsee, Austria, 4 July 1946), *paleontology, paleobiology.*

Abel's greatest scientific achievement, the founding of paleobiology, undoubtedly grew out of his background. For several generations his ancestors on his father's side had been gardeners. His grandfather had taken his examination in botany under Nicolaus Jaquin and had received *summa cum eminentia;* his father was a teacher at the horticulture school and *Dozent* at the Institute of Agriculture in Vienna.

As a sixteen-year-old Gymnasium student Abel eagerly collected fossils. To please his parents, however, he continued his education at the Faculty of Law of the University of Vienna. Soon, though, he devoted more time to the natural sciences, especially botany: his first publications were several papers on orchids.

In 1898, while still a student, Abel became an assistant at the Geological Institute of the University of Vienna under Eduard Suess. He took his major examination in geology and paleontology in 1899 and received the Ph.D. Abel then attended the school of mining in Leoben for a short while, and in 1900 he accepted a position as *Mitarbeiter* at the Imperial–Royal Geological State Institute in Vienna, where he was active until 1907. At the very beginning of this period he published the result of his studies on Cetacea, "Untersuchungen über die fossilen Platanistiden des wiener Beckens," which he had begun while still a student. This paper brought him an invitation to investigate the fossil whales of Belgium. From 1900 on, Abel was *collaborateur étranger* of the Royal Museum of Natural History of Belgium, and several times he traveled to that country. There he met Louis Dollo, who became his teacher of paleontology and his friend. Abel was stimulated by Dollo's teachings, as well as by the writings of Vladimir Kovalevsky and Henry Fairfield Osborn, which were influential in the founding of paleobiology.

In 1901 Abel was appointed *Privatdozent* in paleontology at the University of Vienna; in 1907, associate professor; and in 1912, full professor. He became professor of paleobiology and director of the paleobiology department, later the Paleobiological Institute of the university, in 1917.

Abel's important work *Grundzüge der Paläobiologie der Wirbeltiere* appeared in 1912, *Die vorzeitlichen Säugetiere* in 1914, and *Paläobiologie der Cephalopoden* in 1916. By then he had published over 100 papers. The stream of writings continued. *Die Stämme der Wirbeltiere* (1919) was followed by *Lehrbuch der Paläozoologie* (1920), *Lebensbilder aus der Tierwelt der Vorzeit* (1922), and *Geschichte und Methode der Rekonstruktion vorzeitlicher Wirbeltiere* (1925). Many shorter works were published as well. During this period Abel was in charge of extensive paleozoological excavations in the Drachenhöhle near Mixnitz, Styria; he had previously (1912) undertaken similar excavations at Pikermi, Greece.

In 1911 Abel was awarded the Bigsby Medal of the Geological Society of London; in 1922, the Elliot Medal of the National Academy of Sciences in Washington and the Rainer Medal of the Zoological-Botanical Society of Vienna. He became president of the Paleontological Society in 1921, and was subsequently a member or an honorary member of numerous scientific academies and learned societies, as well as honorary doctor of the universities of Cape Town and Athens. He was also dean (1927/1928) and rector (1932/1933) of the University of Vienna.

Abel had been at the University of Vienna for twenty-eight years and had published more than 250 papers when, in 1935, he accepted a post at the University of Göttingen. He spent five years at Göttingen, amassing new collections and turning his attention to newer subdivisions of paleontology that had not yet been extensively investigated. In 1940 he retired and returned to Austria, where, in Salzburg, he founded a short-lived institute for biological natural history. Despite this failure, he continued his scientific activities until very shortly before his death.

BIBLIOGRAPHY

I. ORIGINAL WORKS. Among the most important of Abel's 275 publications are *Grundzüge der Paläobiologie der Wirbeltiere* (Stuttgart, 1912); *Die vorzeitlichen Säugetiere* (Jena, 1914); *Paläobiologie der Cephalopoden* (Jena, 1916); *Die Stämme der Wirbeltiere* (Berlin–Leipzig, 1919); *Lehrbuch der Paläozoologie* (Jena, 1920); *Lebensbilder aus der Tierwelt der Vorzeit* (Jena, 1922); *Eroberungszüge der Wirbeltiere in die Meere der Vorzeit* (Jena, 1924); *Geschichte und Methode der Rekonstruktion vorzeitlicher Wirbeltiere* (Jena, 1925); *Amerikafahrt* (Jena, 1926); *Paläobiologie und Stammesgeschichte* (Jena, 1929); *Die Drachenhöhle bei Mixnitz in Steiermark,* 3 vols. (Vienna, 1931); *Die Stellung des Menschen im Rahmen der Wirbeltiere* (Jena, 1931); and *Vorzeitliche Lebensspuren* (Jena, 1935).

In 1928 Abel founded the journal *Palaeobiologica,* and most of his shorter papers appeared in it.

II. SECONDARY LITERATURE. Of several obituary notices giving information on Abel's life and works, the most extensive one is written by his son-in-law, Kurt Ehrenberg: "Othenio Abel, sein Werden und Wirken," in *Neues Jahrbuch für Mineralogie, Geologie und Paläontologie,* Mitteilungshefte no. 11/12 (1949), 325–328. See also E. Fischer, "Othenio Abel 1875–1946," in *Die Naturwissenschaften,* **6,** no. 33 (1946); and K. Leuchs, "Othenio Abel," in *Almanach der Österreichischen Akademie der Wissenschaften, 1947* (Vienna, 1948).

An oil portrait of Abel by P. F. Gsur, painted in 1933, is in the possession of the University of Vienna.

HANS BAUMGÄRTEL

ABELARD, PETER. See **Abailard, Pierre.**

ABENARE. See **Ibn Ezra.**

ABENGUEFITH. See **Ibn Wāfid.**

ABETTI, ANTONIO (*b.* S. Pietro di Gorizia, Italy, 19 June 1846; *d.* Arcetri [Florence], Italy, 20 February 1928), *astronomy.*

Although Abetti received a degree in civil engineering from the University of Padua in 1867, he abandoned engineering the following year in order to devote himself to astronomy. He was appointed astronomer of the observatory of the University of Padua in 1868, and he remained there until 1893. In 1894, following a public competitive examination, he was appointed director of the astronomical observatory of Arcetri and professor of astronomy at the University of Florence; he held this post until 1921, when he was obliged to retire because he had reached the compulsory retirement age. Nonetheless, from 1921 to 1928, Abetti continued his researches in astronomy at the observatory. He was a member of the Accademia Nazionale dei Lincei (Rome), associate member of the Royal Astronomical Society (London), and a member of several other Italian academies.

Abetti's scientific activity was devoted essentially to positional astronomy. At Padua, with a modest equatorial telescope, he made many observations on the positions of small planets, comets, occultation of stars, and eclipses. In 1874, as a member of the Italian expedition directed by P. Tacchini, he went to Muddapur in Bengal, to observe the transit of Venus over the disc of the sun; it was the first time that this transit was observed through the spectroscope. Abetti also determined the geographic coordinates of the station.

In addition, Abetti determined the differences in longitude between various Italian localities, a project sponsored by the Italian Geodetic Commission. These studies resulted in the perfection and simplification of determinations of time. When he took over the directorship of the Arcetri observatory, which had been founded by G. B. Donati in 1872 and had been practically abandoned after Donati's death, Abetti set about reconstructing it. He provided the observatory with an equatorial telescope, which he had built in the shops of the observatory of Padua. To it he adapted the well-known objective previously constructed by G. B. Amici, with a diameter of twenty-eight centimeters, and a "Bamberg's small meridian circle." With these instruments he was able to carry out, and to encourage others to carry out, many observations on the positions of small planets, comets, and fixed stars.

All these observations and his scientific studies on the precision of observations, and the solution of equations that are met with in the method of least squares, are published in various issues of *Memoirs and Observations of the Observatory of Arcetri.*

BIBLIOGRAPHY

Obituary notices are G. Armellini, *Rendiconti Accademia dei Lincei,* **9** (1929), 13; L. Carnera, *Vierteljahrschrift der Astronomischen Gesellschaft,* **64** (1929), 2; and G. Silva, *Memorie della Società Astronomica Italiana,* **4** (1928), 193.

GIORGIO ABETTI

ABICH, OTTO HERMANN WILHELM (*b.* Berlin, Germany, 11 December 1806; *d.* Vienna, Austria, 1 July 1886), *geology.*

Abich's interest in natural science and travel was formed under the influence of his father, Wilhelm, an official in the Department of Mines; and two uncles, Martin Klaproth, a chemist, and Julius Klaproth, an ethnographer, orientalist, traveler, and expert on the Caucasian peoples.

He began his higher education at the Faculty of Law of Heidelberg University but later transferred to the department of physics and mathematics at the University of Berlin, from which he graduated in 1831. Having defended a dissertation on the minerals of the spinel group, he received the Ph.D. At Heidelberg, Abich's teachers included Hegel, Humboldt, and Buch. On Buch's advice, Abich traveled to Italy, where he took great interest in the problems of recent volcanicity and published a series of articles that brought him widespread fame.

Shortly thereafter Abich was invited to become extraordinary professor of mineralogy at the University of Dorpat (now Tartu, Estonian S.S.R.), and in 1843 he moved to Russia. As an outstanding expert on volcanic phenomena, he was immediately sent to Transcaucasia in order to determine the causes of the catastrophic earthquake that had destroyed part of the mountain peak Great Ararat in 1840. Abich was captivated by the Caucasus, and for almost thirty-five years he studied this complex, mountainous country. His fundamental papers on the geology of the region, which previously had been totally ignored, made him world famous.

In 1853 the Academy of Sciences in St. Petersburg elected Abich to membership, and in 1866 he was elevated to honorary membership. Since Abich was continuously involved in work far from Dorpat, it became necessary for him to resign his post there. He was then assigned to the headquarters of the Corps of Mining Engineers and was detailed to the command of the viceregent of the Caucasus. Spending the greater part of his time in Armenia, Azerbaijan, and Georgia, Abich went to St. Petersburg or western Europe only to work on the specimens he collected or to publish important monographs. During one such trip in the late 1850's he met and married Adelaide Hess, daughter of the renowned chemist Hermann Heinrich Hess.

Abich was a proponent of the volcanistic theory that assigned the decisive role in geologic processes to hypogene forces and to magma. In the first years of his career Abich's interests were concentrated on mineralogy and petrography. In his paper on spinels he was the first to establish that a characteristic of this group is the constancy of a crystallographic form that is preserved regardless of the wide range of isomorphous replacements. While conducting his petrographic investigations, Abich uncovered the important role of feldspar in the composition of igneous rocks.

In the years that followed, Abich continued his intensive study of various Caucasian magmatic formations, conducting chemical investigations simultaneously with his mineralogic-petrographic analysis. Abich's work in the Caucasus demanded that he answer many stratigraphic questions. The frequent change of facies and the complexity of the tectonics seriously hampered investigation, and Abich therefore paid serious attention to the collecting of fossils, which he determined himself. He studied the fauna of the whole geological sequence exposed in the Caucasus and in Transcaucasia—from the Paleozoic to the Quaternary. Despite the specific features of the Caucasian fauna, Abich successfully established the geological age of the enclosing strata. For some years his stratigraphic conclusions served as the basis of all geological research in the Caucasus, and only in the middle of the twentieth century have his data been subjected to more or less important revision.

Studying the tectonic structure of the areas in which he carried out his investigations, Abich interpreted this structure from the standpoint of ideas then current. He thought that all parallel mountain ranges arose concurrently; thus, in the Caucasus he distinguished four major directions of tectonic lines and, consequently, four stages of tectogenesis. Adhering to Buch's ideas, he considered all mountains to be elevation craters that originated from the intrusion of magmatic masses, and classified canyon-like mountain passes as tectonic fissures.

On the whole, Abich correctly plotted the most important tectonic lines in the Caucasus and established that the highest seismicity is associated with these lines. In the southeastern and northwestern ends of the main Caucasian range Abich discovered a regularity in the location of mud volcanoes according to a definite geometrical grid. He established that the discharge of combustible gases and mineral springs are associated with zones of large faults.

Abich was especially interested in the practical aspects of his geological investigations, and he allotted much time to the study of mineral deposits. He located and described a large number of ore deposits and sources of both ferrous and nonferrous metals, gypsum, rock salt, sulfur, alum, combustible minerals, and mineral waters. He made the important discovery of the Chiatura manganese deposit, one of the largest on earth. Studying the oil shows in the Baku region, Abich established that large accumulations of petroleum are associated with the more elevated parts of tectonic structures, and, from 1847 on, he developed and successfully applied the anticlinal theory in the search for oil fields. He apparently made this discovery independently of American geologists who, in the same period (1840–1860), began prospecting for oil in the arched parts of the uplifts. On the question of the origin of petroleum, Abich adhered to the distillation (inorganic) theory and thought petroleum was the product of sublimation, emanating at a substantial depth from coal beds affected by volcanic heat.

Because he possessed an exceptional capacity for work and the ability to understand the peculiarities of a complex geological structure, Abich had great success in conducting his regional investigations and in mapping the geology of large areas. In addition, he completed a series of papers generalizing data collected by the many Russian geologists then working in the Caucasus; these led to fundamental summaries on the geology of various parts of this mountainous country. The maps published by Abich over a period of many decades have been widely used by geologists.

The range of Abich's scientific interests was wide and varied. Among his printed works, the total number of which exceeds 200, in addition to geological subjects there are papers on geomorphology, glaciology, meteorology, geography, geobotany, meteoritics, and archaeology.

By the time Abich reached the age of seventy, he found it difficult to continue his expeditionary research. Retiring with a pension in 1876, he went to Vienna, where, working intensively, he prepared important summaries on Caucasian geology for publication. He died in his eightieth year from what was tardily diagnosed as acute appendicitis. In accordance with his wishes, Abich's body was cremated and an urn containing his ashes was buried in his mother's grave in Koblenz.

BIBLIOGRAPHY

I. ORIGINAL WORKS. Abich's most important works are *De spinello. Dissertatio inauguralis chemicaquam ad consequendos ab amplissimo Universitatis Berolinensis philosophorum rodine summos in philosophia honores* (Berlin, 1831); "Vergleichende geologische Grundzüge der kaukasischen, armenischen und nordpersischen Gebirge als Prodromus einer Geologie der kaukasischen Länder," in *Mémoires de l'Académie des Sciences de St. Pétersbourg,* 6th ser., **7** (1859), 359–534; "Über eine im Caspischen Meer erschienene Insel nebst Beiträgen zur Kenntniss der Schlammvulkane der caspischen Region," *ibid.,* 7th ser., **6** (1863), i–viii, 1–151, with 4 maps; *Geologische Beobachtungen auf Reisen in der Gebirgsländern zwischen Kur und Araxes* (Tiflis, 1867); "Geologische Beobachtungen auf Reisen im Kaukasus im Jahre 1873," in *Bulletin de la Société des Naturalistes de Moscou,* **48**, pt. 1, no. 2 (1874), 278–342; pt. 2, no. 3 (1874–1875), 63–107, and no. 4, 243–272; *Über krystallinische Hagel im unteren Kaukasus und seine Beziehung zu der Physik des Bodens* (Vienna, 1879); *Geologische Forschungen in den kaukasischen Ländern,* pt. 2, *Geologie des armenischen Hochlands. 1. Westhälfte* (Vienna, 1882); and *Geologische Forschungen in kaukasischen Ländern,* pt. 3, *Geologie des armenischen Hochlands. 2. Östhälfte* (Vienna, 1887).

II. SECONDARY LITERATURE. Works on Abich are E. Suess and A. Abich, "Herman Abich. Biographie und Verzeichnis seiner Werke," in H. Abich's *Geologische Forschungen in den kaukasischen Ländern,* pt. 3, pp. i–xii; and V. V. Tikhomirov and S. P. Volkova, "Zhizn' i trudy Germana Vil'gelmovicha Abikha" ("The Life and Works of Hermann Wilhelm Abich"), in *Ocherki po istorii geologicheskikh znanij* ("Essays on the History of Geological Knowledge"), **8** (Moscow, 1959), pp. 177–238, which includes a portrait of Abich and a bibliography of works by him and about him.

V. V. TIKHOMIROV

ABNEY, WILLIAM DE WIVELESLIE (*b.* Derby, England, 24 July 1843; *d.* Folkestone, England, 2 December 1920), *photography, astronomy.*

Abney was one of the founders of modern photography, combining a scientific approach, ingenuity, and manipulative skill with a talent for popularization. In later life his interest in color photography led him to investigate theories of color vision.

The eldest son of a clergyman, Abney graduated from the Royal Military Academy and served several years with the Royal Engineers in India before being invalided home. In 1869 he was made chemical assistant to the instructor in telegraphy at the Chatham School of Military Engineering, where he was able to pursue a boyhood interest in photography. His first book was *Chemistry for Engineers* (1870); his second, *Instruction in Photography* (1871), rapidly became a standard text.

Abney pioneered in the quantitative sensitometry of photographic images: his studies of how negatives blacken in response to varying amounts of incident light (1874, 1882) preceded the "D-log E" curves of F. Hurter and V. C. Driffield in use today. His early work tended to confirm the photochemical law of Robert Bunsen and Sir Henry Roscoe, which states that intensity of light and the time of exposure to it are reciprocally responsible for the effect produced; but when Julius Scheiner showed, beginning in 1888, that the density of stellar images did not follow this law, Abney was quick to confirm the "failure of reciprocity" in the laboratory, and himself discovered the related intermittency effect (1893).

Abney's first astronomical publications were reports on an expedition he led to Egypt in December 1874, to photograph a transit of Venus across the face of the sun. In preparation for this expedition Abney—by then a captain—invented a dry photographic emulsion (1874): this, his "albumen beer" process, remained in use for general as well as solar photography until superseded by commercial gelatin products. He went on to study the chemistry of latent image developing (1877) and to introduce hydroquinone (1880), still one of the best developing agents known.

Extending his interests to spectroscopy, Abney was the first to suggest (1877) that stars with rapid axial rotation could be detected by broadened lines in their spectra—an idea later to have wide application. He then devised a red-sensitive emulsion and with it made the first spectroscopic analyses of the structure of organic molecules (1882) and the first photographs of the solar spectrum in the infrared (1887). This was followed by comparative studies of how sunlight is altered in passing through our atmosphere, made at sea level and in the Swiss Alps (1888, 1894).

In 1877 Abney began a long supervisory career with the Board of Education for England and Wales. He was already a member of the Royal Photographic Society (which he served as president in 1892–1894, 1896, and 1903–1905), of the Royal Astronomical Society (president 1893–1895), and of the Physical Society of London (president 1895–1897). He had been made a fellow of the Royal Society in 1876 and was awarded its Rumford Medal in 1882, for his spectroscopic work. He was knighted in 1900.

BIBLIOGRAPHY

I. ORIGINAL WORKS. The books and papers by Abney referred to above are *Chemistry for Engineers* (Chatham, 1870); *Instruction in Photography* (Chatham, 1871; 11th ed., London, 1906); "On the Opacity of the Developed Photographic Image," in *Philosophical Magazine,* 4th ser.,

48 (1874), 161–165; "Dry Plate Process for Solar Photography," in *Monthly Notices of the Royal Astronomical Society,* **34** (1874), 275–278; "Photography in the Transit of Venus," *ibid.,* **35** (1875), 309–310, with Abney's report from the scene on 208; "Effect of a Star's Rotation on Its Spectrum," *ibid.,* **37** (1877), 278–279; "On the Alkaline Development of the Photographic Image," in *Philosophical Magazine,* 5th ser., **3** (1877), 46–51; "A New Developer" [hydroquinone], in *Photographic News,* **24** (1880), 345–346; "On the 'Sensitometric' Sensitiveness of Gelatine and Other Plates," in *British Journal of Photography,* **29** (1882), 243–244; "On the Influence of the Molecular Grouping in Organic Bodies on Their Absorption in the Infra-Red Region of the Spectrum," in *Philosophical Transactions of the Royal Society of London,* **172** (1882), 887–918, written with E. R. Festing; "The Solar Spectrum, From λ7150 to λ10,000," *ibid.,* **177** (1887), 457–469; "Transmission of Sunlight Through the Earth's Atmosphere," *ibid.,* **A178** (1888), 251–283 and **A184** (1894), 1–42; and "On a Failure of the Law in Photography That When the Products of the Intensity of the Light Acting and the Time of Exposure Are Equal, Equal Amounts of Chemical Action Will Be Produced," in *Proceedings of the Royal Society* (London), **54** (1893), 143–147.

Other books by Abney include *Thebes, and its Five Greater Temples* (London, 1875); *A Treatise on Photography* (London, 1878; 10th ed., 1916); *The Pioneers of the Alps* (London, 1888), written with C. D. Cunningham; *A Facsimile of Christian Almer's Führerbuch 1856–1894* (London, 1896), edited with C. D. Cunningham; and *Researches in Colour Vision and the Trichromatic Theory* (London, 1913), which summarizes his work in this field.

No complete list of Abney's publications is available: the 117 items in the Royal Society of London's *Catalogue of Scientific Papers,* VII (London, 1877), 5; IX (London, 1891), 7–8; and XIII (Cambridge, 1914), 15–16, do not include anything published after 1900, or any of his numerous short papers in *Photographic News,* and only part of his publications in the *Photographic Journal* (London), of which Abney was editor from 1876 until his death. Many of these additional works are mentioned in Chapman Jones's memorial lecture (see below).

II. SECONDARY LITERATURE. Henry Chapman Jones wrote the article on Abney in *Dictionary of National Biography,* 3rd supp. (London, 1927), pp. 1–2, and also delivered a memorial lecture, printed in *Photographic Journal,* **61** [n.s. **45**] (1921), 296–310. An obituary notice, by Col. Edmund Herbert Grove-Hills, with portrait, appeared in *Proceedings of the Royal Society* (London), **A99** (1921), i–v; and another, by W. B. Ferguson, appeared in *Photographic Journal,* **61** [n.s. **45**] (1921), 44–46.

SALLY H. DIEKE

ABOALY. See **Ibn Sīnā.**

ABRAHAM. See also **Ibrāhīm.**

ABRAHAM BAR ḤIYYA HA-NASI, also known as **Savasorda** (*fl.* in Barcelona before 1136), *mathematics, astronomy.*

In Arabic he was known as Ṣāḥib al-Shurṭa, "Elder of the Royal Suite," denoting some type of official position; this title later gave rise to the commonly used Latin name of Savasorda. He was also known as Abraham Judaeus. Savasorda's most influential work by far is his Hebrew treatise on practical geometry, the *Ḥibbūr ha-meshīḥah we-ha-tishboret.* Translated into Latin as *Liber embadorum* by Plato of Tivoli, the work holds an unusual position in the history of mathematics. It is the earliest exposition of Arab algebra written in Europe, and it contains the first complete solution in Europe of the quadratic equation, $x^2 - ax + b = 0$.

The year the *Ḥibbūr* was translated (1145) also saw the Robert of Chester translation of al-Khwārizmī's algebra and so may well be regarded as the birth year of European algebra. Thus the *Ḥibbūr* was among the earliest works to introduce Arab trigonometry into Europe, and it was also the earliest to treat of Euclid's *Book of Divisions.* Leonardo Fibonacci was influenced by Savasorda and devoted an entire section of his *Practica geometriae* to division of figures. Savasorda made a novel contribution when he included the division of geometric figures in a practical treatise, thus effecting a synthesis of Greek theory with the pragmatic aspects of mathematics.

Savasorda himself recommended Euclid, Theodosius of Bithynia, Menelaus, Autolycus, Apollonius of Perga, Eudemus of Rhodes, and Hero of Alexandria for study in geometry. He knew well al-Khwārizmī and al-Karajī. Following Hero and not Euclid he did not accept the Pythagorean figurate numbers in his explanation of plane and square numbers. In general, Savasorda preferred those definitions and explanations that may be aligned more easily and closely with reality.

To understand this approach, it is necessary to go back to the earliest known Hebrew geometry, the *Mishnat ha-Middot* (*ca.* A.D. 150). This work may be considered as a link in the chain of transmission of mathematics between Palestine and the early medieval Arab civilization. The Arab mathematicians al-Khwārizmī and al-Karajī, and later Savasorda, followed the methodological lines of this old *Mishna.* Savasorda himself provided a new cross-cultural bridge a thousand years after the *Mishna.* In his *Encyclopedia* there is the same teaching of both theory and practice, including not only the art of practical reckoning and business arithmetic but also the theory of numbers and geometric definition. This book is probably the earliest algorismic work written in Western Europe, but knowledge of the work is not apparent in the arithmetical works of either Abraham ibn Ezra or Levi ben Gerson, although they may have had a common origin.

In the history of decimal theory and practice, the two mainstreams of development in the Middle Ages came from the Jewish and Christian cultures. Savasorda, however, did not belong definitely to any one mathematical group. He spent most of his life in Barcelona, an area of both Arab and Christian learning, and was active in translating the masterpieces of Arab science. In an apologetic epistle on astrology to Jehuda ben Barsillae al-Barceloni, he deplored the lack of knowledge of Arab science and language among the people of Provence. He wrote his own works in Hebrew, but he helped translate the following works into Latin: al-'Imrānī's *De horarum electionibus* (1133–1134), al-Khayyāt's *De nativitatibus* (1136), and Almansori's *Judicia seu propositiones* . . . (1136). Savasorda may have worked on translations of the *Quadripartitum* of Ptolemy, the *Spherics* of Theodosius, the *De motu stellarum* of al-Battānī, and others, with Plato of Tivoli. It is also possible that he worked with Rudolf of Bruges on the *De astrolabia*.

BIBLIOGRAPHY

I. ORIGINAL WORKS. Savasorda's *Ḥibbūr*, Michael Guttman, ed., was published in Berlin (1912–1913); a Catalan translation was done by J. Millás-Vallicrosa (Barcelona, 1931). Three treatises of Savasorda constitute a complete astronomical work: *Ẓurat ha-ereẓ* ("Form of the Earth," Bodleian MS 2033) is concerned with astronomical geography and general astronomy; *Ḥeshbon mahlakot hakokhabim* ("Calculation of the Movement of the Stars," Leiden MS 37 Heb.) covers astronomical calculations; and *Luḥot ha-nasi* ("Tables of the Prince," Berlin MS 649; Bodleian MS 443, 437) follows al-Battānī's work. His work on the calendar, *Sefer ha-'ibbur* ("Book on Intercalation," H. Filipowski, ed., London, 1851), written 1122–1123, exerted great influence on Maimonides and Isaac Israeli the Younger. Savasorda's philosophical works include *Megillat ha-megalleh* ("Scroll of the Revealer," A. Poznanski and J. Guttmann, eds., Berlin, 1924) and *Hegyon ha-nefesh* ("Meditation of the Soul," E. Freimann, ed., Leipzig, 1860). See also J. Millás-Vallicrosa, ed., *Llibre de Geometria* (Barcelona, 1931), *Llibre revelador* (Barcelona, 1929), and *La obra enciclopédica yěsodé ha-těbuná u-migdal ha-ěmuná* (Madrid-Barcelona, 1952); and A. Poznanski and J. Guttmann, eds., *Megillat ha-nefesh* (Berlin, 1924).

II. SECONDARY LITERATURE. For other studies of mathematics and Savasorda's contributions, see F. Baer, *Die Juden im Christlichen Spanien*, I (Berlin, 1929), 81, n. 1; M. Curtze, "Der *Liber Embadorum* des Abraham bar Chijja Savasorda in der Übersetzung des Plato von Tivoli," in *Abhandlungen zur Geschichte der mathematischen Wissenschaften,* 12 (1902), 1–183; I. Efros, "Studies in Pre-Tibbonian Philosophical Terminology," in *Jewish Quarterly Review,* 14 (1926–1927), 129–164, 323–368; S. Gandz, "The Invention of Decimal Fractions . . . ," in *Isis,* 25 (1936), 17, and "*Mishnat ha-Middot,*" in *Quellen und Studien zur Geschichte der Mathematik, Astronomie und Physik,* Abt. A, 2 (Berlin, 1932). See also B. Goldberg and L. Rosenkranz, eds., *Yesod Olam* (Berlin, 1846–1848); J. M. Guttmann, *Chibbur ha-Meschicha weha-Tischboreth* (Berlin, 1913); M. Levey, "Abraham Savasorda and His Algorism: A Study in Early European Logistic," in *Osiris,* 11 (1954), 50–63, and "The Encyclopedia of Abraham Savasorda: A Departure in Mathematical Methodology," in *Isis,* 43 (1952), 257–264. Additional studies are by P. A. Sorokin and R. K. Merton, "The Course of Arabian Intellectual Development, 700–1300 A.D., A Study in Method," in *Isis,* 22 (1935), 516–524; M. Steinschneider, *Gesammelte Schriften* (Berlin, 1925), p. 345; H. Suter, "Die Mathematiker und Astronomen der Araber und Ihre Werke," in *Abhandlungen zur Geschichte der mathematischen Wissenschaften,* 10 (1900); J. Tropfke, "Zur Geschichte der quadratischen Gleichungen ueber dreieinhalb Jahrtausend," in *Jahresbericht der Deutschen Mathematiker-vereinigung,* 43 (1933), 98–107; 44 (1934), 95–119.

MARTIN LEVEY

ABRAHAM BEN JACOB. See **Ibrāhīm ibn Ya'qūb.**

ABRAHAM JUDAEUS. See **Ibn Ezra.**

ABRAHAM BEN MEIR IBN EZRA. See **Ibn Ezra.**

ABRAHAM, MAX (*b*. Danzig, Germany, 26 March 1875; *d*. Munich, Germany, 16 November 1922), *physics*.

Abraham was born to a wealthy Jewish merchant family. He studied under Max Planck and completed his doctoral dissertation in 1897. He then assisted Planck at Berlin and in 1900 assumed the position of *Privatdozent* at Göttingen.

Abraham's lifework amounted to the explication of Maxwell's theory. He exhibited a virtuosity in the handling of Maxwell's equations like few others before him. In spite of his many original contributions, however, he was repeatedly passed over for academic appointments. This was due to the fact that he had no patience with what he considered to be silly or illogical argumentation. Abraham had a penchant for being critical and had no hesitation in publicly chastising his colleagues, regardless of their rank or position. His sharp wit was matched by an equally sharp tongue, and as a result he remained a *Privatdozent* at Göttingen for nine years. In 1909, he accepted a professorship at the University of Illinois, but he did not like the atmosphere at a small American university and returned to Göttingen after one semester. He then took the post of professor of rational mechanics at the University of Milan, where he remained until 1914. When World War I broke out, he was forced to return to Germany. He spent the war years investigating theoretical problems in radio transmission for the Telefunkengesellschaft. After the war, unable to return to Milan, he substituted as professor of physics at the Technische Hochschule at Stuttgart. Finally, in 1921, he received the call to a chair of theoretical physics at Aachen. On the trip to Aachen in April 1921, he was stricken with a fatal brain tumor. Abraham died after six painful months in a hospital in Munich. "Just as his life was suffering, his end was full of agony" (Born and von Laue).

Abraham is best remembered for his two-volume textbook, *Theorie der Elektrizität,* which went through five editions during his lifetime. Volume I, first published in 1904, was an adaptation of Föppl's *Einführung in die Maxwellsche Theorie der Elektrizität.* Volume II, subtitled "Der Elektromagnetische Theorie der Strahlung" ("The Electromagnetic Theory of Radiation") contained Abraham's theory of electrons. It appeared in 1905. Subsequent to Abraham's death the book was revised under the authorship of Abraham and Becker. Today the modern counterpart of Abraham's text, R. Becker and F. Sauter's *Electromagnetic Fields and Interactions,* is in use.

The Abraham textbook was the standard work in electrodynamics in Germany for several generations of physicists. His consistent use of vectors was a significant factor in the rapid acceptance of vector notation in Germany. But one of the most noteworthy features of the text was that in each new edition Abraham saw fit to include not only the latest experimental work but also the latest in theoretical contributions, even if these contributions were in dispute. Furthermore, he had no hesitation, after explicating both sides of a question, in using the book to argue his own point of view. This was especially true with regard to theories of the electron as well as with regard to rival views of space and time.

Abraham's theory of the electron was developed in 1902 shortly after a close friend, Wilhelm Kaufmann, had published his first tentative experimental results on the variation of the transverse mass of the electron as a function of its velocity. The basic underlying assumptions of Abraham's theory were, first, that the conception of an ether in which electromagnetic phenomena took place was valid and, second, that the differential equations of the electromagnetic field (Maxwell's equations) are applicable to the dynamics of electrons. In Abraham's view, the central question that had to be answered before any other was to what extent the mass of the electron was electromagnetic. If all the mass of the electron could be ascribed to the interaction of the electron's charge with electromagnetic fields, then one could hope to build a consistent and universal physics based on electrodynamics. Abraham's approach was to calculate the inertia due to the self-induction of the electron as it moved through its own field and the induction due to any external field in which the electron found itself. One could compare the results thus obtained with Kaufmann's results, and if agreement was substantial, then it could be said with some assurance that the mass of the electron was purely electromagnetic. The analysis was difficult, sophisticated, and lengthy. However, making the assumption that the electron was a perfectly rigid sphere and that the charge is distributed uniformly on the surface of the sphere, Abraham calculated the transverse electromagnetic mass of the moving electron to be

$$m = m_0 \cdot \frac{1}{\beta^2}\left(\frac{1 + \beta^2}{2\beta} \ln\left[\frac{1 + \beta}{1 - \beta}\right] - 1\right)$$

where m_0 is the electron's rest mass and $\beta = v/c$, the ratio of the velocity of the electron to the velocity of light. Expressed in terms of powers of β this equation becomes

$$m = m_0(1 + \tfrac{2}{5}\beta^2 + \tfrac{3}{70}\beta^4 + \cdots +).$$

Noting that the data were very difficult to obtain, and that there was a high degree of uncertainty in Kaufmann's results, Abraham was pleased to find agreement between his own predictions and Kaufmann's data.

In 1904 H. A. Lorentz published his second-order theory of the electrodynamics of moving bodies. His expression for the mass of the moving electron, based on the conception of a deformable sphere which contracted in the direction of motion was

$$m = m_0(1 - \beta^2)^{-1/2}$$

which when expressed in terms of powers of β becomes

$$m = m_0(1 + \tfrac{1}{2}\beta^2 + \tfrac{3}{8}\beta^4 + \cdots +).$$

Of course, Einstein obtained the same result as a kinematic consequence of his special theory of relativity.

Finally, in 1906, Kaufmann undertook a new set of measurements in the hopes of distinguishing between Abraham's theory and those of Lorentz and Einstein. He reported that his experiments supported the Abraham theory. Although Kaufmann's work was later criticized on methodological grounds and later experiments vindicated the Lorentz and Einstein predictions, opponents of the theory of relativity often cited Abraham's theory and Kaufmann's data as evidence against Einstein's special theory.

Abraham himself remained unalterably opposed to Einstein's theory throughout his life. Early (*ca.* 1906–1910) he not only was convinced that the data did not support the theory, but he was unwilling to accept the postulates of the theory. By 1912 Abraham admitted that he had no objection to the logic of Einstein's theory; however, he expressed the hope that astronomical observations would contradict it, paving the way for the resurrection of the old absolute ether. "He loved his absolute ether, his field equations, his rigid electron just as a youth loves his first flame, whose memory no later experience can extinguish" (Born and von Laue). But throughout, Abraham's objections were not based on misunderstanding of the theory of relativity. He understood it better than most of his contemporaries. He was simply unwilling to accept postulates he considered contrary to his classical common sense.

BIBLIOGRAPHY

I. ORIGINAL WORKS. *Theorie der Elektrizität,* 1st ed. (Leipzig, 1904–1905), 2nd ed. (1908), 3rd ed. (1912), 4th ed. (1914), 5th ed. (1918); "Energie electrische Drahtwellen," in *Annalen der Physik,* **6** (1901), 217–241; "Prinzipien der Dynamik des Elektrons," *ibid.,* **10** (1903), 105–179; "Die Grundhypothesen der Elektronentheorie," in *Physikalische Zeitschrift,* **5** (1904), 576–579; "Zur Elektrodynamik bewegter Körper," in *Rendiconti del Circolo matimatico di Palermo,* **28** (1909), 1–28; "Zur elektromagnetische Mechanik," in *Physikalische Zeitschrift,* **10** (1909), 731–741; "Relativität und Gravitation; Erwiderung an Herrn A. Einstein," in *Annalen der Physik,* **38** (1912), 1056–1058; "Erhaltung der Energie und die Materie im Schwerkraftfelde," *Physikalische Zeitschrift,* **13** (1912), 311–314; "Theorie der Gravitation," *ibid.,* **13** (1912), 1–4; "Zur Theorie der Drahtwellen in ein leitenden Medium," *ibid.,* **20** (1919), 147–149.

II. SECONDARY LITERATURE. R. Becker and F. Sauter, *Electromagnetic Fields and Their Interactions,* 3 vols. (New York, 1964); Max Born and Max von Laue, "Max Abraham," in *Physikalische Zeitschrift,* **24** (1923), 49–53; Albert Einstein, "Über Relativitätsprinzip und die aus demselben gezogene Folgerungen," in *Jahrbuch der Radioactivität und Elektronik,* **4** (1907), 411–462, esp. 436–439; Stanley Goldberg, "Early Response to Einstein's Special Theory of Relativity," unpublished doctoral thesis (Harvard University, 1969); Gerald Holton, "Influence on and Reception of Einstein's Early Work in Relativity Theory" (mimeo, 1965); Wilhelm Kaufmann, "Die Elektromagnetische Masse des Elektrons," in *Physikalische Zeitschrift,* **3** (1902), 54–57; and "Die Konstitution des Elektrons," in *Annalen der Physik,* **19** (1906), 487–553; Max Planck, "Die Kaufmannschen Messungen der Ablenkbarkeit der Strahlen und ihren Bedeutung für die Dynamik der Elektronen," in *Physikalische Zeitschrift,* **7** (1906), 753–761; Arnold Sommerfeld, "Abraham, Max," *Neue Deutsche Biographie,* I (Berlin, 1953), 23–24; E. T. Whittaker, *A History of the Theories of Aether and Electricity,* 2 vols. (New York, 1960).

STANLEY GOLDBERG

ABREU, ALEIXO DE (*b.* Alcáçovas, Alentejo, Portugal, 1568; *d.* Lisbon, Portugal, 1630), *tropical medicine.*

Abreu was named for his grandfather, captain of an India galleon, who was killed in Malacca in 1500. He entered Évora University in 1577 and graduated as bachelor of arts about 1583. Afterward, against his parents' wishes, he studied medicine at Coimbra University on a royal scholarship, and seven years later graduated as a licentiate of medicine. Abreu practiced medicine in Lisbon with little success until, thanks to his father's friendship with Count Duarte de Castelo Branco, in 1594 he was appointed physician to the governor of Angola, João Furtado de Mendonça, with an annual salary of 24,000 reis. In São Paulo de Loanda he was both physician and colonizer, helping with slaves and horses in the conquest of that territory.

From 1604 to 1606 Abreu was in Brazil with the governor, Diogo Botelho, and served as surgeon during the Dutch attack on Bahía de Todos os Santos. During his tropical sojourn he contracted amoebiasis and yellow fever. In 1606 Abreu returned, ill, to Lisbon, and in 1612 was appointed physician to the treasury officials, a position he had to relinquish in July 1629 because of his poor health. Abreu was of sickly constitution and was very seriously ill in 1605, 1614, and 1621. On this last occasion he began to write a book describing his illness—which lasted five months—and including clinical reports of a case of malaria and of a kidney ailment, a discussion of phlebotomy, and an account of certain tropical diseases he had suffered from or had observed in Angola and Brazil.

Abreu's *Tratado de las siete enfermedades* (1623), the first text on tropical medicine, was written partly in Spanish and partly in Latin, but because of its corrupt language, archaic terminology, and particularly its extraordinary rarity, no full appraisal of its text has ever been made. In it Abreu described his own case of liver involvement in his recurrent amoebiasis (ff. 11–71). His early description of scurvy, which he called *mal de loanda* (ff. 150–192), emphasized gingivitis gum ulcers. He had first observed the disease in slaves, sailors, and travelers arriving in Lisbon after long sea voyages from Brazil and the Orient; his postmortem examinations and his therapeutic preparations made of green vegetables are noteworthy.

The name Abreu gave to yellow fever, *enfermedad del gusano* (ff. 193v.–199v.), or *bicho* in Brazil, has led to confusion because he incorporated in that description the *gusano Trichuris trichiura* (f. 195), a worm found in the rectum in some cases. His account of headache, pain in the lumbar region and the thighs, fever, vomiting, ulcers, and sudden death in otherwise strong young people is clearly recognizable. Abreu also described the *Tunga penetrans* or Brazilian *tungiasis,* the flea that penetrates the skin of the foot, usually around the toenail (f. 199v.), and the Guinea worm, the macrofilaria *Dracunculus medinensis,* which grows to the thickness of a violin string, together with the techniques used by the natives to extract the parasites (ff. 199v.–200).

BIBLIOGRAPHY

Aleixo de Abreu published only one work, the *Tratado de las siete enfermedades, de la inflammación universal del higado, zirbo, pyloron, y riñones, y de la obstrución, de la satiriasi, de la terciana y febre maligna, y passión hipocondriaca. Lleva otros tres tratados, del mal de loanda, del guzano, y de las fuentes y sedales* (Lisbon, 1623). In the preliminary leaves is an autobiography of Abreu that remains the best biographical source.

There are two standard references on Abreu, both published in the nineteenth century: A. Chinchilla, *Anales de la medicina . . . española*, II (Valencia, 1845), 325–328; and A. Hernández Morejón, *Historia bibliográfica de la medicina española*, V (Madrid, 1846), 51–54. More recent is M. Ferreira de Mira, *Historia da medicina portuguesa* (Lisbon, 1947), pp. 132, 178–180. All three are based on Abreu's autobiography. F. M. Sousa Viterbo, "O licenciado Aleixo de Abreu," in *Archivos de historia da medicina portugueza*, n. s. **2** (1911), 121–124, reproduces some documents about Abreu's life; a good discussion of his role in tropical medicine appears in G. Osorio de Andrade and E. Duarte, *Morão, Rosa & Pimenta* (Pernambuco, 1956). See also F. Guerra, "Aleixo de Abreu (1568–1630), Author of the Earliest Book on Tropical Medicine," in *Journal of Tropical Medicine*, **71** (1968), 55–69.

FRANCISCO GUERRA

ABŪ BAKR MUHAMMAD IBN AL-HASAN AL-KARAJĪ, AL-HĀSIB. See al-Karajī.

ABU'L-BARAKĀT AL-BAGHDĀDĪ, HIBAT AL-LAH (*b.* Iraq, *ca.* 1080; *d.* Baghdad, Iraq, after 1164/1165, aged eighty or ninety), *physics, psychology, philosophy.*

Abu'l-Barakāt was physician to the caliph of Baghdad. Of Jewish origin, he was converted to Islam late in life—according to one report, in reaction to a social slight inflicted upon him because of his Judaism; according to another, in order to counter a threat to his life. His writings include *Kitāb al-Mu'tabar,* his main work (the title may be translated as "The Book of What Has Been Established by Personal Reflection"); a philosophical commentary on the Ecclesiastes, written in Arabic in Hebrew characters; and the treatise "On the Reason Why the Stars Are Visible at Night and Hidden in Daytime."

According to Abu'l-Barakāt's own account, which is on the whole quite plausible, *Kitāb al-Mu'tabar* consists in the main of critical remarks jotted down by him over the years while reading philosophical texts and published, at the insistence of his friends, in the form of a philosophical work. From the formal point of view, its composition closely follows that of the *Logic, Naturalia,* and *Metaphysics* of Avicenna's voluminous *Kitab al-Shifā'* (the *Sufficientia* of the Latins), which seems to have been the principal philosophical text studied in Abu'l-Barakāt's time in the Islamic East. The genesis of *Kitāb al-Mu'tabar* as an accumulation of notes may account for various doctrinal inconsistencies in the work; Abu'l-Barakāt's many bold deviations from Avicenna's physics and metaphysics appear to be at variance with his complete acceptance of considerable portions of his predecessor's views.

In his psychology as well as in his physics, Abu'l-Barakāt bases his views on what he regards as immediate certainties rather than on an assessment, made by discursive reasoning, of empirical data. The use of this method clearly renders both the Aristotelian approach and many Aristotelian theories unacceptable to him, and Abu'l-Barakāt is not chary of proclaiming his disagreement with the then dominant philosophical tradition, which he declares to be a corruption of the true doctrines of ancient philosophers. Nonetheless, the starting point of his psychology is identical with that of Avicenna and is obviously taken over from the latter. Like Avicenna, Abu'l-Barakāt considers that immediate self-awareness, the awareness of one's own existence and of one's own actions, constitutes an unchallengeable proof of the existence and activity of the soul (identified with the ego). But unlike Avicenna, he does not try to fit this insight into the categories of Peripatetic psychology.

According to Abu'l-Barakāt, man is aware that his intellectual, imaginative, sensory, and motor activities, and any other psychic activities he may have, are due to one and the same agent: namely the soul. This awareness, accompanied as it is by a sense of certainty, may be relied upon to provide the truth. Abu'l-Barakāt uses this intuition in order to deny the existence of a variety of psychic faculties. He goes even further; he rejects the distinction (fundamental to Aristotelianism) between the intellect and the soul. There is no place in his doctrine for the speculations of the Peripatetics concerning the active, the passive, and the other intellects.

Abu'l-Barakāt regards the soul as an incorporeal entity, linked with the body but not located in it or anywhere else. Not being restricted by position in space, it is able to perceive anything that exists or occurs anywhere in the universe—but only one thing at a time. Thus, according to a conception that is reminiscent of Bergson, it has to choose among the multitudinous external impressions liable to impinge upon it; this choice, the sifting of these potential impressions, is done by the body—more precisely, by the sense organs, which circumscribe the perceptive activities of the soul.

The primordial role played by consciousness and self-awareness in Abu'l-Barakāt's conception of the soul impels him to try to explain the existence of unconscious psychic activities, *inter alia,* the organic ones (for instance, digestion) and latent memories (which, contrary to the Aristotelians, he does not regard as preserved in a part of the brain in the form of corporeal impressions, but as being incorporeal). One of these explanations is centered upon the notion of attention; some of the unconscious activities of the soul are considered as those to which the soul pays no attention.

Abu'l-Barakāt's conception of God seems to be modeled to a considerable extent upon his view of the soul. His God, unlike the Aristotelian one, is not a pure intellect but an entity that, like the human ego but with much greater powers, is engaged in many different activities and has knowledge of particulars (but not of an infinity of particulars at the same time, because the notion is self-contradictory). When His attention is engaged, He may intervene in the course of events. In other cases, this course may be regarded as causally determined, if one envisages only one chain of causes and effects. In fact, however, a large proportion of events is determined by chance, the latter notion being defined by Abu'l-Barakāt as an encounter of two mutually independent chains of causes and effects. He gives as an example the encounter of a scorpion and a man crossing a street; the direction and the speed of both are strictly determined; yet their meeting, which may lead to the man killing the scorpion or to the scorpion stinging the man, is due to chance. A similar theory of chance is set forth by Boethius (see, e.g., *De consolatione philosophiae* V, 1), who could not have influenced Abu'l-Barakāt, and is hinted at by Plotinus (see *Enneads* VI, 8, 10, where coming-about-by-chance appears to be explained as coming-about-through-encounter). These seem to be the only known precursors of Abu'l-Barakāt on this point.

In his physics Abu'l-Barakāt employs a method similar to the one he utilized in his psychology. Like his tenth-century predecessor Abū Bakr al-Rāzī (by whom he may have been influenced, although there is no evidence either way) and in contrast with the Aristotelians, he relies in his physical theories, just as he does in his doctrine of the soul, on what he regards as self-evident, i.e., immediately perceived truths that are not dependent upon empirical data. Applying this method, he rejects the Aristotelian contention that time is the measure of movement. According to him, the notion of time is ontologically prior to the notion of movement. Nor does he regard time as being merely a subjective phenomenon. It is in fact the measure of Being, and as such it should not be regarded as external to Being. Comparisons between the lengths of two or more durations are, however, due to a mental comparison between the two.

The fundamental connection that Abu'l-Barakāt establishes between time and Being leads to his denying the existence of the two other higher modes of temporality postulated in Avicenna's philosophy: according to him there is no eternity (*sarmad*) and no aevum (*dahr*). Time is real even with regard to God.

Abu'l-Barakāt's theory of space, or of place—in the medieval philosophical vocabulary the two notions are designated by one and the same term—resembles his doctrine of time in its rejection of the Aristotelian conception, which was based on empirical data. For the Aristotelian view, according to which place (or space) is the inner surface of the surrounding body (and consequently bidimensional), Abu'l-Barakāt substitutes the conception that there exists a tridimensional space that in itself is empty; in physical reality it is generally (although, according to some passages, which assert in certain cases the existence of vacuums, not always) occupied by bodies. In the mind, however, the conception of a tridimensional empty space is prior to the conception of a plenum. Abu'l-Barakāt also refutes the arguments used by the Aristotelians to prove that infinite space is impossible. According to him, space is infinite because it is impossible for man to conceive a space that has a limit.

In his explanation of the movement of projectiles, Abu'l-Barakāt, like Avicenna, subscribes to the doctrine positing a "violent inclination" (*mayl qasrī;* the notion is similar to, or identical with, the *impetus* of the Schoolmen). "Violent inclination"—opposed to the "natural inclination," in virtue of which bodies removed from their natural place tend to return—is regarded as having been imparted by the mover to a body in a state of violent motion (for instance, to a stone thrown upward or to an arrow shot from a bow). The notion of violent inclination is used to account for the continuation of violent motion after the separation of the projectile from the mover. Contrary to Avicenna, Abu'l-Barakāt regards "violent inclination" as self-expending; it is used up in the very process of violent motion.

The acceleration of the motion of falling bodies is attributed by Abu'l-Barakāt to two causes:

(1) He holds that a violent and a natural inclination can simultaneously coexist in a projectile. Thus, when a body begins to fall, a residue of violent inclination still subsists in it and opposes the natural inclination that causes the body to descend, slowing down its fall. The acceleration of the fall is due to the gradual weakening of the violent inclination.

(2) The second cause of the acceleration of the motion of falling bodies is that the force (i.e., gravity) generating natural inclination resides in the falling body and produces a succession of natural inclinations in such a way that the strength of the inclination increases throughout the fall.

Abu'l-Barakāt's conception of the second cause seems to anticipate in a vague way the fundamental law of classical mechanics, according to which a continually applied force produces acceleration. According to Aristotelian mechanics such a force produces a uniform motion.

While there is no concrete evidence to show that Abu'l-Barakāt exercised a significant influence on Jewish philosophers, Fakhr al-Dīn al-Rāzī (*d.* 1210), a celebrated Muslim author, was his professed disciple. His influence appears to have extended also to other Muslim philosophers.

BIBLIOGRAPHY

The Arabic text of *Kitāb al-Muʿtabar* was published in 3 vols., Serefettin Altkaya, ed. (Hyderabad, 1937–1940). E. Wiedemann, "Über den Grund warum die Sterne bei Nacht sichtbar und bei Tag verborgen sind," in *Jahrbuch für Photographie* (Halle, 1909), pp. 49–54, is a translation of a treatise by Abu'l-Barakāt.

Works on Abu'l-Barakāt or his writings are Shlomo Pines, "Études sur Awḥad al-Zamān Abu'l-Barakāt al-Baghdādī," in *Revue des études juives,* **103** (1938), 4–64, and **104** (1938), 1–34; "La conception de la conscience de soi chez Avicenne et Abu'l-Barakāt al-Baghdādī," in *Archives d'histoire doctrinale et littéraire du moyen âge,* **29** (1954), 21–98; *Nouvelles études sur Awḥad al-Zamān Abu'l-Barakāt al-Baghdādī,* Vol. I of *Mémoires de la Société des études juives* (Paris, 1955); "Studies in Abu'l-Barakāt al-Baghdādī's Poetics and Metaphysics," in *Studies in Philosophy,* Vol. VI of Scripta Hierosalymitana (Jerusalem, 1960), pp. 120–198; and "A Study of Abu'l-Barakāt's Commentary on the Ecclesiastes" (in Hebrew), in *Tarbiz,* **33** (1964), 198–213.

SHLOMO PINES

ABU'L-FIDĀ' ISMĀʿĪL IBN ʿALĪ IBN MAḤMŪD IBN . . . AYYŪB, ʿIMĀD AL-DĪN (*b.* Damascus, Syria, 1273; *d.* Ḥamā, Syria, 1331), *history, geography.*

A prince of the Ayyūbid family, Abu'l-Fidā' participated from the age of twelve in the Muslim campaigns against the Crusaders and the Mongols. During his youth his family lost its estates, which he recovered in 1312 through his fidelity to the Mamelukes, whom he served, as a vassal prince, until his death.

Biographical dictionaries have preserved information on a number of Abu'l-Fidā''s historical-literary and scientific works. Among the most distinguished of the former is the *Mukhtaṣar taʾrīkh al-bashar,* a continuation of the *Kāmil fi ʾl-taʾrīkh* of Ibn al-Athīr. It is a historical treatise that begins with pre-Islamic Arabia and becomes most interesting when it deals with happenings during the author's lifetime. Written in 1315, it was continued by Abu'l-Fidā' himself until 1329 and was the object of attention of a number of fourteenth-century Arabic historians, who kept it up-to-date until 1403 (among them Ibn al-Wardī until 1348, and Ibn al-Shiḥna al-Ḥalabī until the beginning of the fifteenth century). This work was translated into Western languages and became the basis for several historical syntheses by eighteenth-century Orientalists, which explains the strong influence it exerted on nineteenth-century Western historiography.

Abu'l-Fidā''s outstanding scientific work is the *Taqwīm al-buldān* ("A Sketch of the Countries"), written between 1316 and 1321. This is a general geography of twenty-eight chapters of varying lengths, with a prologue containing interesting observations: the gain or loss of a day according to the direction in which one goes around the earth, and the assertion that three-fourths of the earth's surface is covered with water. The descriptions of rivers, lakes, oceans, and mountains are interesting and instructive. The text contains some tables—suggested to Abu'l-Fidā' by his reading of the *Taqwīm al-abdān* ("The Cure of Bodies") of Ibn Jazla—that recapitulate the written variants for each place name, its geographical coordinates, the sources utilized, the climate or zone to which it belongs, and the natural region in which it is located. The order followed in the presentation has often been argued.

The sources of the work are the Arabic translation of Ptolemy and the works of Idrīsī, Ibn Ḥawqal, Isṭakhrī, al-Bīrūnī, and above all the *Geography* or *Kitāb Basṭ al-arḍ fi'l-ṭūl wa'l-ʿard* of Ibn Saʿīd al-Magribī. The latter book is frequently quoted, and Abu'l-Fidā' took from it the information about the trip of one Ibn Fāṭima (very possibly a Berber from the Sahara), who explored in detail the Atlantic and western Mediterranean coasts of Africa. The longitudes recorded in the *Taqwīm al-buldān* often contain obvious errors that are a result of their having been taken from sources that did not adopt the same prime meridian (some used the western coast of Africa, others the Canary Islands); poor conversion of the distance between extreme points on an itinerary into degrees and minutes of latitude and longitude; and faulty reading of the canvas maps in use in the Near East.

The *Taqwīm al-buldān* underwent a number of critical abridgments, among which that in Turkish by Muḥammad ibn ʿAlī Sipāhīzādé (*d*. 1589) should be noted.

BIBLIOGRAPHY

I. ORIGINAL WORKS. For a list of MSS, see C. Brockelmann, *Geschichte der arabischen Litteratur*, II, 44–46, and supp. II, 44. There is a complete edition of the *Mukhtaṣar*, 2 vols. (Istanbul, 1869–1870) and a number of partial translations. The *Taqwīm al-buldān* was edited by Joseph Toussaint Reinaud and Baron de Slane (Paris, 1840). The French translation, Reinaud and Stanislas Guyard, eds., *Géographie d'Aboulféda*, 2 vols. (Paris, 1848–1883), contains a lengthy prologue on Arab geography by Reinaud.

II. SECONDARY LITERATURE. For the Arabic sources and works connected with the book, consult Carra de Vaux, *Les penseurs de l'Islam* (Paris, 1921), I, 139–146, and II, 13–14; H. A. R. Gibb, in *Encyclopaedia of Islam,* 2nd ed., I, 122; Joseph Needham, *Science and Civilization in China*, III (Cambridge, 1959), 561–565; George Sarton, *Introduction to the History of Science*, III (Baltimore, 1947), 793–799; and J. Vernet, "Marruecos en la Geografía de Ibn Saʿīd al-Magribī," in *Tamuda*, 1 (1955), 123–157, and *Kitāb basṭ al-arḍ fi'l-ṭūl wa'l-ʿard* (Tetuán, 1957), a critical edition of the Arabic text.

J. VERNET

ABŪ ḤĀMID AL-GHARNĀṬĪ, also known as **Abū ʿAbdallāh Muḥammad ibn ʿAbd al-Raḥīm . . . al-Māzinī al-Andalusī** (*b*. Granada, Spain, 1080; *d*. Damascus, Syria, 1169), *geography*.

Born of Hispano-Arabic parents, Abū Ḥāmid emigrated to the Orient by sea. In 1117 he was in Alexandria, where he studied with Abū Bakr al-Ṭurṭūshī. He visited Cairo and Baghdad, traveled through Persia, crossed the Caucasus, and went up the Volga as far as Bulgār (55° north). He later visited Bashgird (an area then occupied by Hungarian tribes), and then returned to Baghdad by way of Persia. He later undertook the pilgrimage to Mecca. The latter part of his life was dedicated to the preparation of two works: the *Muʿrib* and the *Tuḥfa*. Both influenced later Arabic cosmographers, such as al-Qazwīnī, and they must have undergone many re-elaborations. Other books that appear in general bibliographies have also been attributed to him. Among these works of secondary importance are *Nukhbat al-adhhān fī ʿajāʾib al-ʿajab* ("Selected Memories Concerning the Greatest Marvels") and *ʿAjāʾib al-makhlūqāt* ("Marvels of Creatures"), both of which appear to be revisions or adaptations of the *Muʿrib* and the *Tuḥfa*.

The work *Muʿrib ʿan baʿḍ ʿajāʾib al-Maghrib* ("Anthology of the Marvels of the Maghrib") has been partially translated into Spanish (folios 96a–114b of the MS of the Royal Academy of History, Madrid). The manuscript contains a description of some of the marvels of Andalucía and, above all, some long dissertations on astronomical, astrological, and chronological matters. The part that has been published contains references to his travels through Eurasia and a series of quite interesting observations about physical geography and ethnography, such as one of the oldest descriptions of the skis used by the so-called Yura peoples of the Arctic, complete with diagram. The first information about this text was provided by Emilio García Gómez in *A.B.C.* (6 January 1947). The description of the flora and fauna of northern Russia is also of great interest.

The *Tuḥfat al-albāb wa-nukhbat al-ʿajāʾib* ("Gift From the Heart and Selection of Marvelous Things") is in some ways similar to the *Muʿrib*, as in the wording of passages dealing with the same material.

But while the *Muʿrib* may be considered authentic (at least the part that has been published), the same cannot be said for the *Tuḥfa,* the last part of which, as it appears in the Ferrand edition, may contain interpolations by other authors. Also, in the *Tuḥfa* the material referring to Abū Ḥāmid's homeland is relatively sparse, and it contains common fables of the period. The work consists of four parts:

(1) A description of the world and the men and spirits who inhabit it. It includes interesting details about the gold and salt trade in the Sudan, as well as information about how the merchants of the time crossed the Sahara, guiding themselves by the stars. (Texts later than Abū Ḥāmid's mention use of the compass.) On the other hand, the description he gives of some quasi-human beings, a description repeated in the Latin cosmographic manuscripts of the early Middle Ages, is completely fanciful.

(2) A description of strange countries and interesting monuments, such as the pyramids of Egypt and the lighthouse at Alexandria.

(3) A description of the seas and the animals that inhabit them, scientifically the most interesting part. He tells us with some degree of realism about flying fish, squid, octopuses, torpedoes, pumice, oil wells, and India paper.

(4) A discussion of caves and tombs. This part contains, in an incidental fashion, a description of fossils, data about the utilization of ivory from the Siberian mammoths, and a mention of fireproof asbestos cloth.

BIBLIOGRAPHY

I. ORIGINAL WORKS. A general bibliography is in George Sarton, *Introduction to the History of Science,* II (Baltimore, 1931), 412. There are lists of MSS in C. Brockelmann, *Geschichte der arabischen Litteratur* (Weimar, 1898; Leiden, 1937), I, 477 and Supp. I, 877; and in F. Pons Boigues, *Ensayo bio-bibliográfico sobre los historiadores y geógrafos arabigoespañoles* (Madrid, 1898), pp. 229–231. A bilingual version of his writings on Eurasia is César E. Dubler, *Abū Ḥāmid el Granadino y su relación de viaje por tierras euroasiáticas. Texto árabe, traducción e interpretación* (Madrid, 1953).

II. SECONDARY LITERATURE. Works dealing with Abū Ḥāmid or his writings are Gabriel Ferrand, "Le Tuḥfat al-albāb de Abū Ḥāmid al-Andalusī al Garnāṭī," in *Journal asiatique,* 2 (1925), 1–148, 193–304; I. Hrbek, in *Archiv Orientální,* 23 (1955), 109–135; and F. Tauer, *ibid.,* 18 (1950), 298–316.

J. VERNET

ABŪ JAʿFAR AL-KHĀZIN. See **al-Khāzin.**

ABŪ KĀMIL SHUJĀʿ IBN ASLAM IBN MUHAM-MAD IBN SHUJĀʿ (*b. ca.* 850, *d. ca.* 930), *mathematics.*

Often called al-Ḥāsib al-Miṣrī ("the reckoner of Egypt"), Abū Kāmil was one of Islam's greatest algebraists in the period following the earliest Muslim algebraist, al-Khwārizmī (*fl. ca.* 825). In the Arab world this was a period of intellectual ferment, particularly in mathematics and the sciences.

There is virtually no biographical material available on Abū Kāmil. He is first mentioned by al-Nadīm in a bibliographical work, *The Fihrist* (987), where he is listed with other mathematicians under "The New Reckoners and Arithmeticians," which refers to those mathematicians who concerned themselves with the practical algorisms, citizens' arithmetic, and practical geometry (see Bibliography). Ibn Khaldūn (1322–1406) stated that Abū Kāmil wrote his algebra after the first such work by al-Khwārizmī, and Ḥajjī Khalīfa (1608–1658) attributed to him a work supposedly concerned with algebraic solutions of inheritance problems.

Among the works of Abū Kāmil extant in manuscripts is the *Kitāb al-ṭarāʾif fiʾl-ḥisāb* ("Book of Rare Things in the Art of Calculation"). According to H. Suter[1] this text is concerned with integral solutions of some indeterminate equations; much earlier, Diophantus (*ca.* first century A.D.) had concerned himself with rational, not exclusively integral, solutions. Abū Kāmil's solutions are found by an ordered and very systematic procedure. Although indeterminate equations with integral solutions had been well known in ancient Mesopotamia, it was not until about 1150 that they appeared well developed in India. Aryabhata (*b.* A.D. 476) had used continued fractions in solutions, but there is uncertain evidence that this knowledge had been passed on in any ordered form to the Arabs by the time of Abū Kāmil.

A work of both geometric and algebraic interest is the *Kitāb . . . al-mukhammas waʾl-muʿashshar . . .* ("On the Pentagon and Decagon"). The text is algebraic in treatment and contains solutions for a fourth-degree equation and for mixed quadratics with irrational coefficients. Much of the text was utilized by Leonardo Fibonacci (1175–*ca.* 1250) in his *Practica geometriae.*[2] Some of the equations solved by Abū Kāmil in this work read as follows:

$$s_{15} = \sqrt{\frac{s}{32}d^2 \sqrt{\frac{s}{1024}d^4} + \sqrt{\frac{3}{64}d^2} - \sqrt{\frac{15}{64}d^2}}$$

$$= \frac{r}{4}\left(\sqrt{10 + 2\sqrt{5}} + \sqrt{3} - \sqrt{15}\right),$$

with s the side of a regular polygon inscribed in a circle. Also

$$S_5 = \sqrt{5d^2 - \sqrt{20d^4}} = 2r\sqrt{5 - 2\sqrt{5}},$$

with S the side of a regular polygon (pentagon here) which has an inscribed circle.[3]

The outstanding advance of Abū Kāmil over al-Khwārizmī, as seen from these equations, is in the use of irrational coefficients.[4] Another manuscript, which is independent of the *Ṭarā'if,* mentioned above, is the most advanced work on indeterminate equations by Abū Kāmil. The solutions are not restricted to integers; in fact, most are in rational form. Four of the more mathematically interesting problems are given below in modern notation. It must be remembered that Abū Kāmil gave all his problems rhetorically; in this text, his only mathematical notation was of integers.

(1) $$x^2 - 8x - 30 = y^2$$

(2) $$x + x^2 = y^2$$
$$x - x^2 = z^2$$

(3) $$20 + x = y^2$$
$$50 - (10 - x) = z^2$$

(4) $$10 + x^2 = y^2$$
$$10 - x^2 = z^2$$

Many of the problems in *Kitāb fi'l-jabr wa'l-muqābala* had been previously solved by al-Khwārizmī. In Abū Kāmil's work, a solution[5] for x^2 was worked out directly instead of first solving for x. Euclid had taken account of the condition x less than $p/2$ in $x^2 + q = px$, whereas Abū Kāmil also solved the case of x greater than $p/2$ in this equation.

Abū Kāmil was the first Muslim to use powers greater than x^2 with ease. He used x^8 (called "square square square square"), x^6 (called "cube cube"), x^5 (called "square square root"), and x^3 (called "cube"), as well as x^2 (called "square"). From this, it appears that Abū Kāmil's nomenclature indicates that he added "exponents." In the Indian nomenclature a "square cube" is x^6, in contradistinction. Diophantus (ca. A.D. 86) also added "powers," but his work was probably unknown to the Arabs until Abu'l Wafā' (940–998) translated his work into Arabic (ca. 998).

Abū Kāmil, following al-Khwārizmī, when using *jadhr* ("root") as the side of a square, multiplied it by the square unit to get the area ($x \cdot 1^2$). This method is older than al-Khwārizmī's method and is to be found in the *Mishnat ha-Middot,* the oldest

Hebrew geometry, which dates back to A.D. 150.[6] This idea of root is related to the Egyptian *khet* ("cubit strip").[7]

The Babylonians stressed the algebraic form of geometry as did al-Khwārizmī. However, Abū Kāmil not only drew heavily on the latter but he also derived much from Heron of Alexandria and Euclid. Thus he was in a position to put together a sophisticated algebra with an elaborated geometry. In actuality, the resulting work was more abstract than al-Khwārizmī's and more practical than Euclid's. Thus Abū Kāmil effected the integration of ancient Mesopotamian practice and Greek theory to yield a wider approach to algebra.

Some of the more interesting problems to be found in the *Algebra,* in modern notation, are:[8]

(No. 57) $$\frac{x \cdot \sqrt{10}}{2 + \sqrt{3}} = x - 10$$

(No. 60) $$x + \sqrt{x} + \sqrt{2x} + \sqrt{5x^2} = 10$$

(No. 61) $$x + y + z = 10; \quad x < y < z$$
$$x^2 + y^2 = z^2$$
$$xz = y^2$$

(No. 63) $$\frac{10}{x} + \frac{10}{10 - x} = 6\frac{1}{4}$$

It is possible that Greek algebra was known to Abū Kāmil through Heron of Alexandria, although a direct connection is difficult to prove. The influence of Heron is, however, definite in Abraham bar Ḥiyya's work.[9] That Abū Kāmil influenced both al-Karajī and Leonardo Fibonacci may be demonstrated from the examples they copied from his work. Thus through Abū Kāmil, mathematical abstraction, elaborated together with a more practical mathematical methodology, impelled the formal development of algebra.

NOTES

1. "Das Buch der Seltenheiten."
2. See also Suter, "Die Abhandlung des Abū Kāmil."
3. *Ibid.,* p. 37. Levey will soon publish the Arabic text of "On the Pentagon and Decagon," discovered by him.
4. At least twenty of these problems from this text may be found in Leonardo Fibonacci, *Scritti,* Vol. I, sect. 15; Vol. II.
5. Tropfke, *Geschichte der Elementar-Mathematik,* pp. 74–76; 80–82; Weinberg, "Die Algebra des abu Kamil."
6. S. Gandz, "On the Origin of the Term 'Root.'"
7. M. Levey, *The Algebra of Abū Kāmil,* pp. 19–20. P. Schub and M. Levey will soon publish Abū Kāmil's advanced work on indeterminate equations, newly discovered in Istanbul.
8. *Ibid.,* pp. 178, 184, 186, 202.
9. M. Levey, "The Encyclopedia of Abraham Savasorda" and "Abraham Savasorda and His Algorism."

BIBLIOGRAPHY

I. ORIGINAL WORKS. The following manuscripts of Abū Kāmil are available: *Kitāb fi'l-jabr wa'l-muqābala* ("Book on Algebra," Paris BN MS Lat. 7377A; Munich Cod. MS Heb. 225; Istanbul-MS Kara Mustafa 379), trans. into Hebrew by Mordecai Finzi *ca.* 1460. See also *Kitāb al-ṭarā'if fi'l ḥisāb* ("Book of Rare Things in the Art of Calculation," Leiden, MS Arabic 1003, ff. 50r–58r; translations are found in Munich Cod. MS Heb. 225 and in Paris BN MS Lat. 7377A); *Kitāb . . . al-mukhammas wa'l-mu'ashshar . . .* ("On the Pentagon and Decagon," Paris BN MS Lat. 7377A; Munich Cod. MS Heb. 225; Istanbul-MS Kara Mustafa 379, ff. 67r–75r); *Al-wāṣāyā bi'l-judhūr* (MS Mosul 294) discusses the ordering of roots. Works of Abū Kāmil listed in *The Fihrist* of al-Nadīm (p. 281) include *Kitāb al-falāḥ* ("Book of Fortune"), *Kitāb miftāḥ al-falāḥ* ("Book of the Key to Fortune"), *Kitāb fi'l-jabr wa'l-muqābala* ("Book on Algebra"), *Kitāb al-misāḥa wa'l-handasa* ("Book on Surveying and Geometry"), *Kitāb al-kifāya* ("Book of the Adequate"), *Kitāb al-ṭayr* ("Book on Omens"), *Kitāb al-'aṣīr* ("Book of the Kernel"), *Kitāb al-khaṭa'ayn* ("Book of the Two Errors"), *Kitāb al-jam' wa'l-tafrīq* ("Book on Augmentation and Diminution").

II. SECONDARY LITERATURE. For works on both Arab mathematics and Abū Kāmil see the following: H. T. Colebrooke, *Algebra with Arithmetic and Mensuration from the Sanskrit* (London, 1817); G. Fluegel, ed. and trans., *Lexicon bibliographicum et encyclopedicum a Haji Khalfa compositum* (Leipzig, 1835–1858); W. Hartner, "Abū Kāmil Shudjā'," in the *Encyclopedia of Islam,* 2nd ed., I (Leiden, 1960), 132–133; II (Leiden, 1962), 360–362; *Ibn Khaldūn The Muqaddimah,* Franz Rosenthal, trans., 3 vols. (New York, 1958); Leonardo Fibonacci, *Scritti di Leonardo Pisano,* 2 vols: Vol. I, *Liber abaci;* Vol. II, *Practica geometriae;* S. Gandz, "On the Origin of the Term 'Root,'" in *American Math. Monthly,* 35 (1928), 67–75; M. Levey, *The Algebra of Abū Kāmil (Kitāb fi'l-jabr wa'l-muqābala) in a Commentary by Mordecai Finzi* (Madison, Wisc., 1966), "The Encyclopedia of Abraham Savasorda: A Departure in Mathematical Methodology," in *Isis* 35 (1952), 257–264; and "Abraham Savasorda and His Algorism: A Study in Early European Logistic," in *Osiris,* 11 (1954), 50–63.

For additional material see G. Libri, *Histoire des sciences mathématiques en Italie* (Paris, 1938), pp. 253–297; 2nd ed. (Paris, 1865), pp. 304–369; al-Nadīm, *Fihrist al-'ulūm,* G. Fluegel, ed. (Leipzig, 1871–1872); M. Steinschneider, *Die Hebraeischen Uebersetzungen des Mittelalters und die Juden als Dolmetscher,* a reprint (Graz, 1956), pp. 584–588; and H. Suter, "Die Abhandlung des Abū Kāmil Šoja' b. Aslam über das Fünfeck und Zehneck," in *Bib. Math.,* 10 (1909–1910), 15–42; "Das Buch der Setenheiten der Rechenkunst von Abū Kāmil el-Misrī," in *Bib. Math.,* Ser. 3, 11 (1910–1911), 100–120; "Die Mathematiker und Astronomen der Araber und ihre Werke," in *Abhandlungen z. Gesch. d. Math. Wissenschaften,* 10 (1900). See also J. Tropfke, *Geschichte der Elementar-Mathematik,* Vol. III (Berlin, 1937); J. Weinberg, "Die Algebra des abū Kāmil Šoǧā' ben Aslam" (doctoral diss., Munich, 1935); A. P. Yousch-

kevitch, *Geschichte der Mathematik im Mittelalter* (Basel, 1964).

MARTIN LEVEY

ABŪ MA'SHAR AL-BALKHĪ, JA'FAR IBN MUḤAMMAD, also known as **Albumasar** (*b.* in or near Balkh in Khurasan, 10 August 787; *d.* al-Wāsiṭ, Iraq, 9 March 886), *astrology.*

The ancient city of Balkh, where Abū Ma'shar grew up, had once been an outpost of Hellenism in central Asia, and then had become a center for the mingling of Indians, Chinese, Scythians, and Greco-Syrians with Iranians during the Sassanian period; when it was conquered by Aḥnaf ibn Qays during the caliphate of 'Uthmān (644–656), its religious communities included Jews, Nestorians, Manichaeans, Buddhists, and Hindus, as well as Zoroastrians. In the revolution of the middle of the eighth century, the people of Khurasan provided the Abbasids with their army, their general, and many of their intellectuals.

These intellectuals, like those from other frontier areas of the former Sassanian empire, were politically inclined toward pro-Iranism and against their Arab masters, and religiously inclined toward heresy, especially the Shī'a sect. They were called upon, despite these tendencies, to play a large role in the activities of the libraries and translation institutes established at Baghdad by the early Abbasids; and they succeeded in making a generous portion of their Sassanian heritage of syncretic science and philosophy an integral part of the Muslim tradition.

Abū Ma'shar was a member of the third generation of this Pahlavi-oriented intellectual elite. He retained a strong commitment to the concept of Iranian intellectual superiority (expressed most vehemently in his *Kitāb ikhtilāf al-zījāt* and *Kitāb al-ulūf*), but he himself relied entirely on translations for his knowledge of Sassanian science. He mingled his already complex cultural inheritance with various intellectual trends current in Baghdad in his time, and became a leading exponent of the theory that all different national systems of thought are ultimately derived from a single revelation (thus, in a sense, paralleling in intellectual history the Neoplatonic doctrine of emanation, which he accepted philosophically in its Harrānian guise). This theory could be used to justify the most astonishing and inconsistent eclecticism; it also permitted an advocate to adopt wildly heretical views while maintaining strict adherence to the tenets of Islam. Abū Ma'shar's great reputation and usefulness as the leading astrologer of the Muslim world also helped to preserve him from persecution; there are reports of only one unfortunate incident, a whipping administered because of his practice of astrology, during the caliphate of al-Mustaʿīn (862–866).

Abū Maʿshar began his career in Baghdad, probably at the beginning of the caliphate of al-Maʾmūn (813–833), as an expert in *ḥadīth,* the sayings traditionally ascribed to Muḥammad and his companions. It was undoubtedly in studying this subject that he developed his proficiency in such subjects as the pre-Islamic Arabic calendar and the chronology of the early caliphs. But, in his forty-seventh year (832–833), according to the biographical tradition, but actually in about 825, an event occurred that completely changed his scholarly career. He became involved in a bitter quarrel with the Arabs' first "philosopher," Abū Yūsuf Yaʿqūb ibn Isḥāq al-Kindī (*ca.* 796–873), who was interested at once in Plato, in Aristotle and his commentators, in various Neoplatonists, in the works that the "Sabaeans" of Ḥarrān attributed to Hermes and Agathodemon, and, in general, in "mathematics" (arithmetic, geometry, music, astronomy, and astrology). It was his urging that made Abū Maʿshar realize the necessity of studying "mathematics" in order to understand philosophical arguments. He henceforth devoted his energies to expounding the philosophical and historical justifications of astrology, and to discoursing on and exemplifying the practical efficacy of this science. In this effort he drew upon elements of all the diverse intellectual traditions to which he was almost uniquely heir: upon the Pahlavi Greco-Indo-Iranian tradition in astrology, astronomy, and theurgy as preserved in Buzurjmihr, Andarzghar, Zaradusht, the *Zīj al-Shāh,* Dorotheus, and Valens; upon a Sanskrit Greco-Indian tradition in astrology and astronomy from Varāhamihira, Kanaka, the *Sindhind,* the *Zīj al-Arkand,* and Āryabhaṭa; upon the Greek tradition in philosophy, astrology, and astronomy through Aristotle, Ptolemy, and Theon; upon the Syriac Neoplatonizing philosophy of astral influences and theurgy from al-Kindī and the books of the Ḥarrānians; and upon the earlier, less complete attempts at such vast syntheses among Persian scholars writing in Arabic as represented by those of Māshāʾallāh, Abū Sahl al-Faḍl ibn Nawbakht, ʿUmar ibn al-Farrukhān al-Ṭabarī, and Abū Yūsuf Yaʿqūb al-Qaṣrānī.

Abū Maʿshar's renown as an astrologer was immense, both among his contemporaries and in later times. He cast the horoscope of an Indian (Rāṣṭrakūṭa?) prince who was born 11 January 826; he advised several rebels against the authority of the caliph; and he accompanied al-Muwaffaq on his expedition against the Zanj in Basra in 880–883. To Ibn al-Qifṭī, as to most students of Islamic astrology,

he was "the teacher of the people of Islam concerning the influences of the stars."

Abū Maʿshar's philosophical proof of the validity of astrology was probably most elaborately presented in his lost *Kitāb ithbāt ʿilm al-nujūm* ("Book of the Establishment of Astrology"), but it is also discussed at length in the first *maqāla* of his *Kitāb al-madkhal al-kabīr* ("Great Introduction"), which was written in 849/850. The argument, as has been pointed out by Lemay, is largely Aristotelian, with some Neoplatonic elements; but Lemay, working only with the Latin translations, failed to realize that the immediate sources of Abū Maʿshar's Aristotelianism were not the Arabic translations of the *De caelo,* the *Physica,* and the *De generatione et corruptione,* but the purported writings of the Ḥarrānian prophets, Hermes and Agathodemon. That the "Sabaeans" of Ḥarrān depended on Aristotle's *Physica, De caelo, De generatione et corruptione,* and *Meteorologica* for their theories regarding the material universe is clearly stated by Aḥmad ibn al-Ṭayyib al-Sarakhsī (*ca.* 835–899), another student of al-Kindī (fr. I B1 in F. Rosenthal). Since the Ḥarrānians were interested in the laws of perceptible nature precisely because they saw the same relationships between the ethereal spheres and the sublunar world of change that Abū Maʿshar seeks to prove (as well as a further relationship between the ethereal spheres and the One which Abū Maʿshar only hints at), it is an easy step to the conclusion that this justification of astrology is, in its main outline, taken by Abū Maʿshar from the books of the Ḥarrānians, and is thus only a part of a much more elaborate universal philosophy of emanation.

That philosophy, closely similar to doctrines common to a number of religious movements of the first half-millennium of the Christian era (they are found, for example, in the *Corpus Hermeticum,* in the *Chaldaean Oracles,* and in the writings of various Neoplatonists), and not unlike the philosophical background of Jābirian alchemy, posits three levels of being analogous to three concentric spheres: the divine (the sphere of light), the ethereal (the eight celestial spheres), and the hylic (the sublunar core, in which matter is involved in a constant process of change due to the motions of the four Empedoclean elements).

This view of the universe gains religious content when there is added to it the idea that man's soul has descended from the sphere of light to the hylic sphere, and now must strive to return to union with the divine. But, according to "Sabaean" doctrine, it cannot leap over the ethereal sphere and attain this union without the assistance of intermediaries, which are the celestial spheres; therefore, man's religion—

his liturgy and his ritual—must be addressed to the deities of the planets and of the constellations rather than to the One. The form of this worship is determined by the attributes, qualities, and conditions of the intermediaries; these are known by the study of astrology and astronomy.

The religious view of the Ḥarrānians, then, assumes an Aristotelian physical universe in which the four Empedoclean elements are confined to the sublunar world, and the celestial spheres consist of a fifth element. The normal astrological view is concerned to some extent with schematic correlations between celestial figures and (*a*) the four Empedoclean elements and (*b*) the various Pythagorean contrasting principles. Primarily, however, it works with somewhat arbitrary associations of planets, zodiacal signs, decans, and so on; with the psychological factors governing man's behavior; with the attributes and characteristics apparent in material objects; and with various selected species of plants, animals, stones, fish, and so on. The Ḥarrānians, followed by Abū Maʿshar, attempted to validate the scientific basis of these arbitrary associations between the celestial and sublunar worlds in astrology by casting over the whole system a peculiar interpretation of Aristotelian physics. According to this interpretation, the nature of the influence of the superior spheres on the inferior is not restricted to the transmission of motion alone; terrestrial bodies each possess the potentiality of being moved by particular celestial bodies, and the celestial bodies similarly each possess the possibility of influencing particular terrestrial bodies. The precise details of the mode of this influence need not detain us here; suffice it to say that the practical effect of this elaborate development of theory in the *Kitāb al-madkhal al-kabīr* was the reassertion of the truth of the astrological doctrines already long current.

For the Ḥarrānians the *Kitāb al-madkhal al-kabīr* also provided the justification for the elaboration of a theory of talismans and planetary theurgy which made them the recognized masters of these esoteric practices (although they had, of course, been popular for centuries in the Roman and Sassanian empires). Abū Maʿshar is among those who helped, in his *Kitāb al-ulūf* and *Kitāb fī buyūt al-ʿibādāt,* to establish their reputation. From time to time he refers to talismans (see especially his *Kitāb ṣuwar al-daraj*), but in general he is interested more in predicting the future than in manipulating it.

For Abū Maʿshar, however, the validity of astrology is determined not only by the Neoplatonizing Aristotelianism of the Ḥarrānians; it also rests on an elaborate world history of the transmission of science which permits one to trace back the fragments of truth about nature scattered among the peoples of the earth to a pristine divine source: it is a sort of prophetology of science.

Man's knowledge of the relationship between the three spheres comes not from his own powers of reasoning, but from revelation. For the Ḥarrānians, the prophet of revelation was Hermes Trismegistus. Abū Maʿshar, however, desired to universalize the personality of the prophet and to demonstrate the essential unity of human thought, and identifies a first Hermes with the Iranian Hūshank and the Semitic Enoch-Idrīs; following this composite figure are a succession of pupils of various nations (including two more named Hermes) who spread the revealed truth among the nations of the *oecumene.* Abū Maʿshar's cultural background helps to explain this universalism, although it must be noted that in certain details his elaborate history of science had been anticipated by Persian scholars of the preceding generation. It was his theory of an original "Sabaeanism" followed by all of mankind, however, which became the basis of much of Muslim historiography of philosophy and religion.

In conformity with this theory as expounded in his *Kitāb al-ulūf,* and on the alleged basis of a manuscript said to have been buried at Isfahan before the Flood, Abū Maʿshar produced his *Zīj al-hazārāt,* which was to restore to mankind the true astronomy of the prophetic age. The mean motions of the planets are computed in this *zīj* by the Indian method of the *yuga* and by using Indian parameters; in this section Abū Maʿshar depended largely on the *Zīj al-Sindhind* of al-Fazārī and the *Zīj al-Arkand* (both of Indian origin), although his *yuga* of 360,000 years, while Indian, was also used by the Ismāʿīlīs. His prime meridian and the parameters for his planetary equations were taken from the Persian *Zīj al-Shāh,* which is greatly indebted to Indian sources. His planetary model, however, was evidently Ptolemaic. Thus this "antediluvian" *zīj* proves by its mixture of Indian, Persian, and Greek elements that the theory of the original unity of the intellectual traditions of mankind is a true one; each has preserved a bit of the revelation.

Accompanying this astronomical work and history of science was an elaborate astrological interpretation of history expounded in the *Kitāb al-qirānāt,* which, being originally of Sassanian (Zoroastrian) origin, reached Abū Maʿshar through the works of Mashāʾallāh, ʿUmar ibn al-Farrukhān al-Ṭabarī, and al-Kindī. This theory, based on periods of varying length under the influence of the several planets and zodiacal signs, on the recurring conjunctions at regular intervals of Saturn and Jupiter and of Saturn and

Mars, on the horoscopes of year transfers, and on transits, postulated the inherent impermanence of all human institutions—including the religion of Islam and the rule of the Arab caliphate. It was particularly popular among the Iranian intellectuals of the eighth, ninth, and tenth centuries, who delighted in predicting the imminent downfall of the Abbasids and restoration of the royal house of Iran to the throne of world empire. And it is one other element in Abū Maʿshar's system that links him with the Ismāʿīlīs.

Parallel to these methods of universal astrological history, Sassanian scientists had developed similar techniques of progressive individual genethlialogy based on periods, the horoscopes of birthdays, and transits. Their sources had been Hellenistic, the primary one being the fourth book of Dorotheus. Abū Maʿshar, like many other Muslim astrologers, has elaborately dealt with this type of astrology (in his *Kitāb tahāwīl sinī al-mawālīd*). He also composed a number of other works on nativities, some mere compilations of the sayings of the wise men of India, Persia, Greece, Egypt, and Islam, intended to demonstrate again their fundamental unity (the *Kitāb al-jamhara* and the *Kitāb aṣl al-uṣūl*), and some more orthodox compositions modeled on the Hellenistic textbooks that had been translated into Arabic (the two versions of the *Kitāb ahkām al-mawālīd*).

In these writings, as in his other works listed in the critical bibliography (see below), Abū Maʿshar did not display any startling powers of innovation. They are practical manuals intended for the instruction and training of astrologers. As such, they exercised a profound influence on Muslim intellectual and social history and, through translations, on the intellectual and social history of western Europe and of Byzantium. Abū Maʿshar's folly as a scientist has been justly pointed out by al-Bīrūnī (*Chronology,* ed. C. E. Sachau, repr. Leipzig, 1923, pp. 25–26; trans. *idem,* London, 1879, pp. 29–31). One gains the strong impression from his pupil Shādhān's *Mudhākarāt* that even as an astrologer he was not intellectually rigorous or honest (no matter what the situation may be now, it certainly was possible to be an intellectually honest astrologer in the ninth century). He is an interesting and instructive phenomenon, but is not to be ranked among the great scientists of Islam.

BIBLIOGRAPHY

I. ORIGINAL WORKS. There are two old lists of Abū Maʿshar's works. The first and most complete is that in the *Fihrist* of Ibn al-Nadīm, who wrote ca. 987, G. Flügel, ed. (Leipzig, 1871–1872), p. 277; this I call N. The second

is a shorter catalog preserved in the *Taʾrīkh al-hukamāʾ* of Ibn al-Qiftī, who wrote before 1248, J. Lippert, ed. (Leipzig, 1903), p. 153; this I call Q I. Ibn al-Qiftī (p. 154) adds a list of those works found in Ibn al-Nadīm's list which he could not identify in Q I; this I call Q II. There are some repetitions of titles in Q I and Q II where Ibn al-Qiftī has been led by differences in wording to believe in the existence of separate works. Note that Ibn al-Nadīm (p. 275; copied by Ibn al-Qiftī, p. 154) claims, on the authority of Ibn al-Jahm (is this Muḥammad ibn al-Jahm al-Barmakī? See *Fihrist,* p. 277) that Abū Maʿshar plagiarized nos. 1, 4, 8, and 16 from Sanad ibn ʿAlī, who flourished under al-Maʾmūn; but this seems to be a mistaken allegation (cf. Ibn Yūnis, *Zīj al-hakimī,* Caussin de Perceval, ed., in *Notices et extraits des manuscrits,* VII [Paris, 1803], 58).

In this catalog, I refer in general only to manuscripts which I have personally examined, and not to all of these. The reader should realize that this list is as exhaustive as it can be made at present, and he should be particularly aware that all of the *genuine* works listed by Brockelmann (*Geschichte der arabischen Literatur,* I²–II² [Leiden, 1943–1949]; and *Supplementum* I–III [Leiden, 1937–1942], henceforth referred to as *GAL*) are included.

(1) *Kitāb al-madkhal al-kabīr ʿalā ʿilm ahkām al-nujūm* ("Great Introduction to the Science of Astrology"). N 1; Q I, 3; Hājjī Khalīfa (*Kashf al-zunūn,* ed. G. Flügel [London, 1835–1858], henceforth referred to as Hājjī Khalīfa), V, 475. I have examined Leiden Or. 47 and NO 2806. This is a work in eight *maqālāt* covering the following: (1) the philosophical and historical justifications of astrology; (2) the numbers and characteristics of the fixed stars and the zodiacal signs; (3) the influence of the seven planets, and particularly of the two luminaries, on the sublunar world; (4) the astrological natures of the planets; (5) the lordships of the planets over the zodiacal signs and their parts; (6) the zodiacal signs in relation to each other and to man; (7) the strengths of the planets, their relations to each other, and their chronocratories; and (8) astrological lots. It was written in 849/850 or shortly thereafter. Only one chapter (6,1—on the decans) has been published of the original Arabic version: see K. Dyroff, in F. Boll, *Sphaera* (Leipzig, 1903), pp. 490–539; cf. D. Pingree, "The Indian Iconography of the Decans and Horās," in *Journal of the Warburg and Courtauld Institutes,* **26** (1963), 223–254.

Lengthy selections from the "Great Introduction" were translated into Greek *ca.* 1000; they form the bulk of the third book of the *Mysteries of Abū Maʿshar,* of which the present writer is preparing an edition. The whole of the "Great Introduction" was translated into Latin by John of Seville in 1133 and (with some abridgments) by Hermann of Carinthia in 1140; the latter translation was printed by Erhard Ratdolt at Augsburg in 1489 and 1495, and by Jacobus Pentius Leucensis (de Leucho) at Venice in 1506. From the Latin versions were derived a Hebrew version by Yakob ben Elia in the late thirteenth century, which is referred to in M. Steinschneider, *Die hebräischen Übersetzungen des Mittelalters* (Berlin, 1893), pp. 567–571 (henceforth referred to as Steinschneider), and the *Liber Albumazarus,* written by Zothorus Zaparus Fendulus in the fourteenth century, as well as German and English translations. The most recent discussion of the Latin translations, in which a strong case has been made for their influence on western European philosophy in the twelfth century, is R. Lemay, *Abū Ma'shar and Latin Aristotelianism in the Twelfth Century* (Beirut, 1962); cf. also J. C. Vadet, "Une défense de l'astrologie dans le madhal d'Abū Ma'sar al Balḥī," in *Annales islamologiques,* **5** (1963), 131–180. The Peripatetic and Neoplatonic background of Abū Ma'shar's theory of tides is discussed by P. Duhem, *Le système du monde,* II (Paris, 1914), 369–386 (henceforth referred to as Duhem). For the date of the "Great Introduction," see H. Hermelink, "Datierung des Liber Introductorius von Albumasar (Kitāb al-mudḫal al-kabīr von Abū Ma'sar)," in *Sudhoffs Archiv,* **46** (1962), 264–265.

(2) *Kitāb al-madkhal al-ṣaghīr,* also called *Kitāb mukhtaṣar al-madkhal* ("Little Introduction"). N 2; Q II, 1. I have consulted British Museum Additional Manuscript 7490, pt. 4 (Yeni Cami 1193, pt. 6, listed by Brockelmann, is the *Kitāb al-madkhal fī 'ilm al-aḥkām al-falakiyya,* in seventy-three chapters, of Abu'l-Qāsim 'Alī ibn Aḥmad al-Balkhī, also known as Abū Ma'shar, but this has nothing to do with the "Little Introduction"). This work was written after the "Great Introduction," which it epitomizes at the expense of all philosophical and historical passages. It consists of seven *fuṣūl:* (1) on the natures, conditions, and indications of the zodiacal signs; (2) on the conditions of the planets alone and with respect to the sun; (3) on the twenty-five conditions of the planets; (4) on the strength and goodness of the planets and their dodecatemoria; (5) on the natures of the planets and their indications; (6) on lots; and (7) on the planetary chronocratories. It was translated into Latin by Adelard of Bath in the early twelfth century.

(3) *Zīj al-Hazārāt* ("Tables of the Thousands"). N 3; Q I, 12; Q II, 2; Ḥājjī Khalīfa, III, 558–559. This work, composed between 840 and 860 in "sixty and some" chapters, is now lost. However, an attempt at recovering its planetary parameters and some of its astronomical theories has been made by the present writer in his *The Thousands of Abū Ma'shar* (London, 1968). Note that the phrase *et ego Albumasar in tabulis nostris maioribus in fine richene elchebir* [*zījinā al-kabīr*] *celestium discursus persecutus sum,* which is found in Hermann of Carinthia's translation of the "Great Introduction" (1,1), does not appear in the Arabic manuscripts I have examined.

(4) *Kitāb al-mawālīd al-kabīr* ("Great Book of Nativities"). N 4; Q II, 3. According to Ibn al-Nadīm, Abū Ma'shar never finished this book. Perhaps it is identical with the "Book of the Multitude"; cf. also the "Book of Judgments About Nativities."

(5) *Kitāb hay'at al-falak wa-ikhtilāf ṭulū'ihi* ("Form of the Sphere and Differences in Rising-times"), N 5; Q I, 7 (?); Q II, 4. Ibn al-Nadīm informs us that this book, of which no copies have survived, was in five *fuṣūl.* Its subject is clear.

(6, 7) *Kitāb al-kadkhudāh* ("Book of the Kadkhudāh")

and *Kitāb al-haylāj* ("Book of the Haylāj"). N 6 and N 7; Q I, 8. Ibn al-Nadīm treats these as two separate books; Ibn al-Qiftī, more naturally, as one. The *Haylāj* ("Prorogator") and *Kadkhudāh* ("Lord of Life") are frequently discussed in Abū Ma'shar's other works (e.g., in the "Book of Judgments About Nativities," chs. 4 and 5), and were often treated by his predecessors—most notably by Dorotheus in his third book. The Persian terminology, of course, indicates a Sassanian background, and we know that the Arabic version of Dorotheus was translated from Pahlavi *ca.* 800. It is at least possible that Abū Ma'shar's work was the source of the *Kitāb al-zā'irjāt fī istikhrāj al-haylāj wa 'l-kadkhudāh,* which forms the fourth part of the *Al-Jāmi' al-Shāhī* of Aḥmad ibn Muḥammad ibn 'Abd al-Jalīl al-Sijzī, which was written in the second half of the tenth century (I have used British Museum Or. 1346, Esad Ef. 1998, and Hamidiye 837). The original of al-Sijzī's work relied on Hermes, Ptolemy, Dorotheus, and "the moderns."

(8) *Kitāb al-qirānāt* ("Book of Conjunctions"), also known as the *Kitāb al-milal wa 'l-duwal*). N 8; Q I, 4; Q I, 5; Ḥājjī Khalīfa, V, 136. I have used British Museum Or. 7716 and Escorial 937. This work, in eight *maqālāt,* as is the "Great Introduction," was written after 869 or perhaps even after 883 (cf. 1,3, which mentions events in Basra predicted for the fifteen years after the sixtieth year following the conjunction of 809; in 2,7 he refers to the murder of al-Mutawakkil, which occurred in December 861). The subjects of the eight *maqālāt* are as follows: (1) the appearance of prophets and their laws; (2) the rise and fall of dynasties and kings; (3) the effects of planetary combinations; (4) the effects of each zodiacal sign's being in the ascendant; (5) the lordships of the planets; (6) transits; (7) each zodiacal sign as *muntahā* and as ascendant of the revolution of the year; and (8) the revolutions of the years and the *intihā'āt.*

Ibn al-Nadīm claims that this work was dedicated to Ibn al-Bāzyār, a pupil of Ḥabash al-Ḥāsib (*fl.* 829–864); this statement is perhaps supported by the fact that one manuscript of the "Book of Conjunctions" ascribes it to Ibn al-Bāzyār (*GAL Suppl.* I, 394; cf. also al-Bīrūnī, *Chronology,* ed. C. E. Sachau, repr. Leipzig, 1923, p. 21; trans. *idem,* London, 1879, p. 25; and *Fihrist,* p. 276). It was translated into Latin by John of Seville; this translation was printed by Erhard Ratdolt at Augsburg in 1489, and reprinted by Jacobus Pentius de Leucho at Venice in 1515 (these are the same two printer-scholars to whom we owe the editions of Hermann's translation of the "Great Introduction"). One chapter of this Latin translation (2, 8), which Abū Ma'shar had plagiarized from al-Kindī, was reprinted by O. Loth in his article "Al-Kindī als Astrolog," in *Morgenländische Forschungen* (Leipzig, 1875), pp. 261–310. For Abū Ma'shar's reference to trepidation in this work, see Duhem, II, 503–504.

(9) *Kitāb taḥāwīl sinī al-'ālam,* or *Kitāb al-nukat* ("Book of Revolutions of the World-years," or "Book of Subtleties"). N 9; Q I, 10; Ḥājjī Khalīfa, I, 171. I have used Bodleian Marsh 618, Escorial 938, and Fatih 3426. This is a relatively short work on the nature of a year (or

month or day) as determined by the horoscope of its beginning. It was translated into Latin by John of Seville under the title *Flores;* cf. J. Vernet, "Cuestiones catalográficas referentes a autores orientales: Problemas bibliográficas en torno a Albumasar," in *Biblioteconomía* (Barcelona, 1952), 12–17. This is undoubtedly identical with the *De revolutionibus annorum mundi seu liber experimentorum,* also translated by John of Seville; for this, see F. J. Carmody, *Arabic Astronomical and Astrological Sciences in Latin Translation* (Berkeley–Los Angeles, 1956), p. 94 (henceforth referred to as Carmody). *Flores* was published by Erhard Ratdolt at Augsburg in 1488, 1489, and 1495, and by the house of Sessa in Venice in 1488 and 1506.

(10) *Kitāb al-ikhtiyārāt* ("Book of Elections"). N 10; Q II, 5; Ḥājjī Khalīfa, I, 198. This may be the fifth text in British Museum Additional Manuscript 7490, which is entitled *Kitāb al-ikhtiyārāt* and which follows Abū Maʿshar's "Little Introduction"; it contains fifty-five chapters quoting from many sources that were favorites of Abū Maʿshar (e.g., Dorotheus). There is also a *Kitāb al-ikhtiyārāt* which is the eighth component of al-Sijzī's *Al-Jāmiʿ al-Shāhī,* but its relation to Abū Maʿshar remains obscure. There are also many chapters on elections in the first book of the Byzantine *Mysteries of Abū Maʿshar* and, in Latin, an *Electiones planetarum* and a *De mode eligendi* (Carmody, p. 96). Cf. also Steinschneider, p. 571.

(11) *Kitāb al-ikhtiyārāt ʿalā manāzil al-qamar* ("Book of Elections According to the Lunar Mansions"). N 11; Q II, 6. This is perhaps different from the preceding work. There is in Latin a *Flores de electionibus* which is based on the moon (Carmody, p. 97) and a *De electionibus lunae* (Carmody, p. 101; cf. Steinschneider, p. 571), both ascribed to Abū Maʿshar. Compare also the *Kitāb masāʾil al-qamar* in Berlin oct. 1617 (not seen by me).

(12) *Kitāb al-ulūf* ("Book of the Thousands"). N 12; Q I, 2; Ḥājjī Khalīfa, V, 50; cf. I, 22. This, one of Abū Maʿshar's most important works, is lost; but we do have summaries of it by al-Sijzī (part 9 of *Al-Jāmiʿ al-Shāhī;* cf. the *Dastūr al-munajjimīn* in Paris Bibliothèque Nationale 5968), al-Tanūkhī (in British Museum Or. 3577), and an anonymous author (in Berlin 5900). Unfortunately, the epitome by Abū Maʿshar's pupil Ibn al-Māzyār (Ibn al-Bāzyār?) is lost. All the available material has been assembled and discussed by the present writer in his *The Thousands of Abū Maʿshar.* The *Kitāb al-ulūf* is not to be confused with the *Kitāb fī buyūt al-ʿibādāt* ("Book of Temples") mentioned by al-Bīrūnī in the *Chronology,* despite what Ḥājjī Khalīfa, who had no copy, says of its nature.

(13) *Kitāb al-ṭabāʾiʿ al-kabīr* ("Great Book of Natures"). N 13; Q I, 1; Q II, 7. According to Ibn al-Nadīm, this apparently lost work was divided into five *ajzāʾ.* According to at least one manuscript, the "Book of the Foundation of Foundations" was called the *Kitāb al-ṭabāʾiʿ,* but this identification is probably not to be taken seriously. If it refers to any part of that work, it could only be to the first section, which precedes the quotations from ancient authorities.

(14) *Kitāb al-sahmayn wa-aʿmār al-mulūk wa ʾl-duwal* ("Book of the Two Lots and the Lives of Kings and Dynasties"). N 14; Q II, 8. The two lots must be the Lot of Fortune and the Lot of the Demon; their relevance to astrological history is not yet clear. The text of this book has not been found.

(15) *Kitāb zāʾirjāt [wa] al-intihāʾāt wa ʾl-mamarrāt* ("Book of Tables of the Intihāʾāt and of the Transits"). N 15. This work, too, must have been on astrological history; cf. books 6 and 8 of the "Book of Conjunctions." No manuscripts of it are known.

(16) *Kitāb iqtirān al-naḥsayn fī burj al-Saraṭān* ("Book of the Conjunction of the Two Malefics in Cancer"). N 16; Q II, 9. The particularly maleficent effects of conjunctions of Saturn and Mars in Cancer are also treated extensively in the "Book of Conjunctions" (2, 8, which is largely copied from al-Kindī). There seem to be no copies of this book extant.

(17, 18) *Kitāb al-ṣuwar wa ʾl-ḥukm ʿalayhā* ("Book of the Images and Their Influences"). N 17; Q II, 10. *Kitāb [al-] ṣuwar [wa] al-daraj wa ʾl-ḥukm ʿalayhā* ("Book of the Images of the Degrees, and Their Influences"). N 18. This is most likely one work, as Ibn al-Qifṭī assumes, and seems to be on talismans ("Zaradusht's" work on talismans, which forms the thirteenth part of *Al-Jāmiʿ al-Shāhī,* is entitled *Kitāb ṣuwar darajāt al-falak*). Again, the Arabic is lost; but there is in Latin a *De ascensionibus imaginum* ascribed to Abū Maʿshar (Carmody, p. 100). Cf. the first part of the "Small Book of Nativities."

(19) *Kitāb taḥāwīl sinī al-mawālīd* ("Book of the Revolutions of the Years of Nativities"). N 19; Q I, 11; Ḥājjī Khalīfa, VI, 242. I have consulted Escorial 917. This work contains nine *maqālāt* rather than just eight, as Ibn al-Nadīm claims: (1) introductory; (2) on the various astrological lords as signifiers; (3) on the direction and the division; (4) on the planetary periods; (5) on the transits of the planets; (6) on various planetary and zodiacal signifiers; (7) on the effects of the planetary motions; (8) on the effects of the planets being in each other's houses and terms; and (9) on casting monthly and daily horoscopes. Al-Sijzī summarized this work in his *Al-Jāmiʿ al-Shāhī* (part five; cf. Ḥājjī Khalīfa, II, 46); he also translated this summary into Persian, cf. C. Storey, *Persian Literature,* II, 1 (London, 1958), 39 (henceforth referred to as Storey). The original Arabic was also translated into Greek; the first five books survive (see the present writer's edition of them [Leipzig, 1968]). These five books were translated from Greek into Latin and were published by H. Wolf at Basel in 1559.

(20) *Kitāb al-mizājāt* ("Book of Mixtures"). N 20; Q II, 11. Ibn al-Nadīm states that this work is rare, and so it is. But perhaps it is identical with the *Kitāb mizājāt al-kawākib* summarized by al-Sijzī (*Al-Jāmiʿ al-Shāhī,* part 6); this deals with combinations of two, three, four, five, six, and seven planets.

(21) *Kitāb al-anwāʾ* ("Star-calendar"). N 21; Q II, 12. This work of Abū Maʿshar I find mentioned nowhere else. The contemporary *Kitāb al-anwāʾ* of Ibn Qutayba (*d.* 879) has been edited by Hamidullah and Pellat (Hyderabad-

Deccan, 1956); a list of twenty-four authors of *Kutub al-anwā'* in the ninth and tenth centuries will be found on p. 14 of their introduction.

(22) *Kitāb al-masā'il* ("Book of Interrogations"). N 22; Q II, 13. Ibn al-Nadīm calls this a compendium; it is probably, then, identical with the "Perfect Book." There is a work entitled *Abwāb al-masā'il wa-mā ba'dahā min al-ikhtiyārāt* in Mingana 922.

(23) *Kitāb ithbāt 'ilm al-nujūm* ("Book of the Proof of Astrology"). N 23; Q II, 14. This work, which presumably expounded in detail the Ḥarrānian theories found in the "Great Introduction," was perhaps written against 'Alī ibn 'Īsā al-Ḥarrāni's *Risāla fī ibṭāl ṣinā'at aḥkām al-nujūm,* which is mentioned by al-Qabīṣī (*d.* 967) in the preface to his *Al-madkhal ilā ṣinā'at aḥkām al-nujūm;* 'Alī ibn 'Īsā participated in the measurement of a terrestrial degree carried out at Sinjar under al-Ma'mūn, and made observations in Baghdad in 843–844.

(24) *Kitāb al-kāmil* or *Kitāb al-masā'il* ("Perfect Book" or "Book of Interrogations"). N 24; Q II, 15. This unfinished compendium is perhaps identical with the "Book of Interrogations."

(25) *Kitāb al-jamhara* ("Book of the Multitude"). N 25; Q I, 9; Q II, 16. Ibn al-Nadīm informs us that this was a collection of sayings of earlier astrologers concerning nativities. It was, then, perhaps the original form of the second part of the "Book of the Foundation of Foundations."

(26) *Kitāb aṣl al-uṣūl* ("Book of the Foundation of Foundations"). N 26; Q II, 17; Ḥājjī Khalīfa, I, 282–283 (?). As Ibn al-Nadīm states, this compendium of sayings about genethlialogy is also attributed to Abu'l-'Anbas al-Ṣaymarī (828–888/889). Most manuscripts (e.g., Hamidiye 829 and British Museum Or. 3540) ascribe the work to al-Ṣaymarī (apparently correctly), but its title in Hamidiye 824 is *Al-aṣl fī 'ilm al-nujūm* and *Sirr al-asrār* by Abū Ma'shar, which is the *Kitāb al-ṭabā'i'* (cf. also Mingana 921); this confusion of three titles does not inspire confidence in the manuscript's accuracy. The "Book of the Foundation of Foundations" is an extremely valuable work, especially its second part, which contains extensive excerpts from such authorities as Antiochus, Teucer, Dorotheus, Valens, Democritus, Zeno, Jina (?) the Indian, Ṛṣi (?) the Indian, Buzurjmihr, and Zaradusht.

(27) *Kitāb tafsīr al-manāmāt min al-nujūm* ("Book of the Explanation of Dreams From the Stars"). N 27; Q II, 18. This work, whose purpose was probably to predict dreams from astrological indications rather than to expound oneiromancy, is not mentioned in the inventory of oneirocritical treatises drawn up by T. Fahd, *La divination arabe* (Leiden, 1966), pp. 329–363. The attribution to Abū Ma'shar of Muḥammad ibn Sīrīn's *Tafsīr al-manāmāt* by J. Leunclavius in his Latin translation of the Greek version (Frankfurt, 1577) is, of course, false.

(28) *Kitāb al-qawāṭi' 'ala 'l-haylājāt* ("Book of Severances [of Life] According to the Haylājāt"). N 28; Q I, 6 (?); Q II, 19. This book on what the Greeks call the ἀφαιρέτης is lost.

(29) *Kitāb al-mawālīd al-ṣaghīr* ("Small Book of Na-

tivities"). N 29; Q II, 20. According to Ibn al-Nadīm this work consists of two *maqālāt* and thirteen *fuṣūl*. It is not, then, identical with the "Book of Judgments About Nativities," but it does coincide with the state of the so-called "Book of the Meticulous Investigator, the Greek Philosopher Known as Abū Ma'shar al-Falakī" (*Kitāb al-muḥaqqiq al-mudaqqiq al-Yūnānī al-faylasūf al-shahīr bi-Abī Ma'shar al-Falakī*). This curious work has several times been published in Cairo, and J.-M. Faddegon has given a brief description of it in "Notice sur un petit traité d'astrologie attribué à Albumasar (Abu-Ma'šar)," in *Journal asiatique,* **213** (1928), 150–158. The first four *fuṣūl* are on magic and astrology related to various times; the next five *fuṣūl* are on the science of prediction from the numerical equivalents of proper names which classical antiquity commonly ascribed to Pythagoras or Petosiris; and the last four *fuṣūl* are concerned with nativities. *Faṣl* 12 is a zodiologion for men, and *faṣl* 13 a zodiologion for women; this last is introduced with a *basmala,* and therefore represents the second *maqāla* mentioned by Ibn al-Nadīm.

(30) *Kitāb zīj al-qirānāt wa 'l-ikhtirāqāt* ("Tables of Conjunctions and Transits"). N 30; Q I, 13; Q II, 21. Ibn al-Qifṭī, who also calls this work *Kitāb zīj al-ṣaghīr* ("Small Tables"), asserts that it gives the mean longitudes of the planets at the times of the (mean) conjunctions of Saturn and Jupiter since the epoch of the Flood (17 February 3102 B.C.). The work, then, is closely related to the "Tables of the Thousands," the "Book of the Conjunctions," and the "Book of the Thousands." The editions' *iḥtirāfāt* I take to be a scribal error for *ikhtirāqāt.* This was not a *zīj* in the normal sense of the term.

(31, 32) *Kitāb al-awqāt* ("Book of Times"). N 31. *Kitāb al-awqāt 'alā ithnā 'ashariyyat al-kawākib* ("Book of Times According to the Dodecatemoria of the Planets"). N 32; Q II, 22. This is clearly one work, as Ibn al-Qifṭī perceived, and was presumably concerned with the proper times for commencing various activities as determined from the ascendant dodecatemorion (a well-known Greek technique of καταρχαί). This may be the *Kitāb al-mas'ala* [*'alā*] *al-ithnā 'ashariyya* in Aya Sofya 2672 (not seen by me).

(33) *Kitāb al-sihām* ("Book of Lots"). N 33; Q II, 23. This work covers the special lots governing the material objects utilized by man; it must, then, to a large extent duplicate the contents of the eighth *maqāla* of the "Great Introduction." It is possible that at least the first tract in the Latin *De partibus et eorum causis* (Carmody, p. 98) is translated from this work. The work entitled *Liber Albumazar de duodecim domibus astrorum* (Carmody, pp. 98–99) also seems to be a translation of the "Book of Lots," and much of this sort of material is found in the first book of the Byzantine *Mysteries.* See also al-Bīrūnī, *Book of Instruction in the Elements of the Art of Astrology,* ed. R. R. Wright (London, 1934), pp. 282–289.

(34) *Kitāb al-amṭār wa 'l-riyāḥ wa-taghayyur al-ahwiya* ("Book of Rains and Winds and of Changes in the Weather"). N 34; Q II, 25; Ḥājjī Khalīfa I, 147, and V, 94. This is probably the *Kitāb al-sirr* ("Book of the Secret") which is found in Escorial 938 (ff. 1v–28) and in Bodleian

Marsh 618 (ff. 162v–173v and 198v et seq.); its first part deals with meteorological astrology, its second with the astrology of prices. This work includes a horoscope cast by Abū Maʿshar in Nīshāpūr on 5 March 832.

(35) *Kitāb ṭabāʾiʿ al-buldān wa-tawallud al-riyāḥ* ("Book of the Natures of Places and the Generation of Winds"). N 35; Q II, 24. This title brings to mind those of two older books: Hippocrates' *Airs, Waters and Places,* and the *Book of the Laws of the Regions* of Bardesanes' pupil Philip. But Abū Maʿshar's work was probably a technical astrological discussion of why the same celestial influences simultaneously cause different meteorological phenomena in the various regions of the world.

(36) *Kitāb al-mayl fī taḥwīl sinī al-mawālīd* ("Book of the Obliquity [of the Ecliptic] in the Revolution of the Years of Nativities"). N 36. In this lost work Abū Maʿshar must have tried to explain the differences between the lives of several individuals born at the same time as due in part to the effect of different terrestrial latitudes on the interpretation of the revolutions of their birth anniversaries.

(37) *Kitāb fī buyūt al-ʿibādāt* ("Book of Temples"). This work, which is mentioned by al-Bīrūnī (*Chronology,* C. E. Sachau, ed. [Leipzig, 1923], p. 205; trans. *idem* [London, 1879], p. 187), described the curious planetary temples of the "Sabaeans"; cf. the "Book of Conjunctions," 1,4. One wonders about the extent to which al-Dimashqī has relied on Abū Maʿshar's work in his description of the temples of Ḥarrān. The "Book of Temples," it should be noted, is different from the "Book of Thousands."

(38) *Kitāb ikhtilāf al-zījāt* ("Book of the Differences Between Tables"). The fragments of this work have been discussed in the present writer's *The Thousands of Abū Maʿshar.*

(39, 40) *Kitāb aḥkām al-mawālīd* ("Book of Judgments About Nativities"). Two versions of this work were written by Abū Maʿshar. The first is found on the last twenty-four ff. of Hamidiye 856, and consists of thirty-one *abwāb;* the second is preserved on ff. 1–64v of Bodleian Huntington 546, and originally contained eighteen *maqālāt* (only 1–15 and the beginning of 16 survive). Both works are traditionally Hellenistic; the second is based on the opinions of Dorotheus, Ptolemy, and Valens, and gives as examples a nativity of 128 of the era of Diocletian (A.D. 412) and the nativity of Paulus of Alexandria in 145 of the same era (A.D. 429). This second work is summarized by al-Sijzī as the third part of *Al-Jāmiʿ al-Shāhī.* The first work has apparently been translated into Persian (Storey, p. 39).

(41) *Kitāb qirānāt al-kawākib fī 'l-burūj al-ithnā ʿashara* ("Book of Conjunctions of the Planets in the Twelve Signs"). Ḥājjī Khalīfa, V, 136. I have used Bodleian Hyde 32. This work—differing from the "Book of Conjunctions"—discusses the effects of combinations of the planets in each of the zodiacal signs. This work has evidently been translated into Persian (Storey, p. 40). It is also apparently the work included in the first book of the Byzantine translation of the *Introduction to Astrology* of Ahmad the Persian, and published in *Catalogus codicum astrologorum Graecorum,* II (Brussels, 1900), 123–130.

(42) *Mudhākarāt Abī Maʿshar fī asrār ʿilm al-nujūm* ("Sayings of Abū Maʿshar on the Secrets of Astrology"). I have used Bodleian Huntington 546 and Cambridge University Gg. 3, 19. (I have not yet seen the manuscript in Ankara.) The *Mudhākarāt* was not written by Abū Maʿshar himself, but by his pupil Abū Saʿīd Shādhān. It contains much valuable information on the practice of astrology in ninth-century Baghdad, and therefore is frequently cited by Muslim historians of the period. It was translated into Greek (it constitutes most of the second book of the *Mysteries*) and into Latin (see L. Thorndike, "Albumasar in Sadan," in *Isis,* **45** [1954], 22–32, which is very inadequate). The present author is preparing an edition of the Arabic to accompany his edition of the Byzantine *Mysteries.*

II. SECONDARY LITERATURE. Besides the evidence of his own writings and the rich anecdotes of his pupil Shādhān, neither of which has yet been adequately explored, biographical information about Abū Maʿshar comes from two Muslim sources. The most important of these is the *Fihrist* of Ibn al-Nadīm (G. Flügel, ed. [Leipzig, 1871–1872], p. 277). Much of this was copied by Ibn al-Qifṭī (*Taʾrīkh al-ḥukamaʾ.* J. Lippert, ed. [Leipzig, 1903], pp. 152–154), but with some important additions taken from Shādhān and other sources, including the allegations that he was a drunkard and an epileptic. Ibn al-Qifṭī's biography was partially copied by Abu'l-Faraj in *Taʾrīkh mukhtaṣar al-duwal* (Beirut, 1958), p. 149.

Modern discussions of Abū Maʿshar are generally unreliable compilations based on secondary sources. The most authoritative of these is that by H. Suter, "Die Mathematiker und Astronomen der Araber und ihre Werke," in *Abhandlungen zur Geschichte der mathematischen Wissenschaften* (Leipzig), **10** (1900), 28–30. His list of Abū Maʿshar's works, however, is extremely unreliable. Most recent is a brief article by J. M. Millás in the *Encyclopaedia of Islam,* I (Leiden, 1960), 139–140.

DAVID PINGREE

ABŪ NAṢR AL-FĀRĀBĪ. See **al-Fārābī.**

ABŪ'L-RAYḤĀN MUḤAMMAD IBN AḤMAD AL-BĪRŪNĪ. See **al-Bīrūnī.**

IBN ABŪ'L-SHUKR. See **Muḥyī al-Dīn al-Maghribī.**

ABŪ ʿUBAYD AL-BAKRĪ. See **al-Bakrī.**

ABŪ'L-WAFĀʾ AL-BŪZJĀNĪ, MUḤAMMAD IBN MUḤAMMAD IBN YAḤYĀ IBN ISMĀʿĪL IBN AL-ʿABBĀS (*b.* Būzjān [now in Iran], 10 June 940; *d.* Baghdad [now in Iraq], 997 or July 998), *mathematics, astronomy.*

Abū'l-Wafāʾ was apparently of Persian descent. In 959 he moved to Baghdad, which was then the capital of the Eastern Caliphate. There he became the last great representative of the mathematics-astronomy school that arose around the beginning of the ninth century, shortly after the founding of Baghdad. With his colleagues, Abū'l-Wafā' conducted astronomical observations at the Baghdad observatory. He continued the tradition of his predecessors, combining original scientific work with commentary on the classics—the works of Euclid and Diophantus. He also wrote a commentary to the algebra of al-Khwārizmī. None of these commentaries has yet been found.

Abū'l-Wafā''s textbook on practical arithmetic, *Kitāb fī mā yaḥtaj ilayh al-kuttāb wa'l-ʿummāl min ʿilm al-ḥisāb* ("Book on What Is Necessary From the Science of Arithmetic for Scribes and Businessmen"), written between 961 and 976, enjoyed widespread fame. It consists of seven sections (*manāzil*), each of which has seven chapters (*abwāb*). The first three sections are purely mathematical (ratio, multiplication and division, estimation of areas); the last four contain the solutions of practical problems concerning payment for work, construction estimates, the exchange and sale of various grains, etc.

Abū'l-Wafā' systematically sets forth the methods of calculation used in the Arabic East by merchants, by clerks in the departments of finance, and by land surveyors in their daily work; he also introduces refinements of commonly used methods, criticizing some for being incorrect. For example, after indicating that surveyors found the area of all sorts of quadrangles by multiplying half the sums of the opposite sides, he remarks, "This is also an obvious mistake and clearly incorrect and rarely corresponds to the truth." Abū'l-Wafā' does not introduce the proofs here "in order not to lengthen the book or to hamper comprehension," but in a series of examples he defines basic concepts and terms, and also defines the operations of multiplication and division of both whole numbers and fractions.

Abū'l Wafā''s book indicates that the Indian decimal positional system of numeration with the use of numerals—which Baghdad scholars, acquainted with it by the eighth century, were quick to appreciate—did not find application in business circles and among the population of the Eastern Caliphate for a long time. Considering the habits of the readers for whom the textbook was written, Abū'l-Wafā' completely avoided the use of numerals. All numbers and computations, often quite complex, he described only with words.

The calculation of fractions is quite distinctive. Operation with common fractions of the type m/n, where m, n are whole numbers and $m > 1$, was uncommon outside the circle of specialists. Merchants and other businessmen had long used as their basic fractions—called *ra's* ("principal fractions") by Abū'l-Wafā'—those parts of a unit from 1/2 to 1/10,

and a small number of *murakkab* ("compound fractions") of the type m/n, with numerators, m, from 2 to 9 and denominators, n, from 3 to 10, with the fraction 2/3 occupying a privileged position. The distinction of principal fractions was connected with peculiarities in the formation of numerical adjectives in the Arabic language of that time. All other fractions m/n were represented as sums and products of basic fractions; businessmen preferred to express the "compound" fractions, other than 2/3, with the help of principal fractions, in the following manner:

$$\frac{2}{5} = \frac{1}{3} + \frac{2}{3} \cdot \frac{1}{10}, \frac{9}{10} = \frac{1}{2} + \frac{1}{3} + \frac{2}{3} \cdot \frac{1}{10}.$$

Any fraction m/n, the denominator of which is a product of the sort $2^P 3^Q 5^R 7^S$, can be expanded into basic fractions in the above form. In the first section of his book, Abū'l-Wafā' explains in detail how to produce such expansions with the aid of special rules and auxiliary tables. Important roles in this operation are played by the expansion of fractions of the type $a/60$ and the preliminary representations of the given fraction m/n in the form $m \cdot 60/n \div 60$ (see below). Since usually for one and the same fraction one can obtain several different expansions into sums and products of basic fractions, Abū'l-Wafā' explains which expansions are more generally used or, as he wrote, more "beautiful."

If the denominator of a fraction (after cancellation of the fraction) contains prime factors that are more than seven, it is impossible to obtain a finite expansion into basic fractions. In this case approximate expansions of the type $^3/_{17} \approx (3 + 1) \div (17 + 1) = ^2/_9$ or $^3/_{17} \approx 3\frac{1}{2} \div 17\frac{1}{2} = ^1/_5$—or still better, $^3/_{17} \approx 3\frac{1}{7} \div 17\frac{1}{7} = ^1/_6 + ^1/_6 \cdot ^1/_{10}$—were used.

Instead of such a method, which required the skillful selection of a number to be added to the numerator and denominator of a given fraction, Abū'l-Wafā' recommended the regular method, which enables one to obtain a good approximation with reasonable speed. This method is clear from the expansion

$$\frac{3}{17} = \frac{180}{17} \div 60 = \frac{10 + \frac{10}{17}}{60} \approx \frac{11}{60} = \frac{1}{6} + \frac{1}{6} \cdot \frac{1}{10}.$$

Analogously, one can obtain

$$\frac{3}{17} \approx \frac{1}{10} + \frac{1}{2} \cdot \frac{1}{9} + \frac{1}{6} \cdot \frac{1}{8}$$

or

$$\frac{3}{17} \approx \frac{1}{10} + \frac{1}{2} \cdot \frac{1}{9} + \frac{1}{6} \cdot \frac{1}{8} + \frac{1}{2} \cdot \frac{1}{6} \cdot \frac{1}{10} \cdot \frac{1}{10} \cdot \frac{1}{10}.$$

The error of this last result, as Abū'l-Wafā' demonstrates, equals

$$\frac{1}{4} \cdot \frac{1}{9} \cdot \frac{1}{10} \cdot \frac{1}{10} \cdot \frac{1}{10} \cdot \frac{1}{17}.$$

The calculation described somewhat resembles the Egyptian method, but, in contrast with that, it (1) is limited to those parts of a unity $1/q$, for which $2 \le q \le 10$; (2) uses products of the fractions $1/q_1 \cdot 1/q_2$ and $2/3 \cdot 1/q$; and (3) does not renounce the use of compound fractions m/n, $1 < m < n \le 10$. Opinions differ regarding the origin of such a calculation; many think that its core derives from ancient Egypt; M. I. Medovoy suggests that it arose independently among the peoples living within the territory of the Eastern Caliphate.

In the second section is a description of operations with whole numbers and fractions, the mechanics of the operations with fractions being closely connected with their expansions into basic fractions. In this section there is the only instance of the use of negative numbers in Arabic literature. Abū'l-Wafā' verbally explains the rule of multiplication of numbers with the same ten's digit:

$$(10a + b)(10a + c) = [10a + b - \{10(a + 1) -$$
$$(10a + c)\}]10(a + 1) + [10(a + 1) -$$
$$(10a + b)] \cdot [10(a + 1) - (10a + c)].$$

He then applies it where the ten's digit is zero and $b = 3$ and $c = 5$. In this case the rule gives

$$3 \cdot 5 = [3 - (10 - 5)] \cdot 10 + [10 - 3] \cdot [10 - 5]$$
$$= (-2) \cdot 10 + 35 = 35 - 20.$$

Abū'l-Wafā' termed the result of the subtraction of the number $10 - 5$ from 3 a "debt [*dayn*] of 2." This probably reflects the influence of Indian mathematics, in which negative numbers were also interpreted as a debt (*kśaya*).

Some historians, such as M. Cantor and H. Zeuthen, explain the lack of positional numeration and "Indian" numerals in Abū'l-Wafā''s textbook, as well as in many other Arabic arithmetic courses, by stating that two opposing schools existed among Arabic mathematicians: one followed Greek models; the other, Indian models. M. I. Medovoy, however, shows that such a hypothesis is not supported by fact. It is more probable that the use of the positional "Indian" arithmetic simply spread very slowly among businessmen and the general population of the Arabic East, who for a long time preferred the customary methods of verbal expression of whole numbers and fractions, and of operations dealing with them. Many authors considered the needs of these people; and, after Abū'l-Wafā', the above computation of fractions,

for example, is found in a book by al-Karajī at the beginning of the eleventh century and in works by other authors.

In the third section Abū'l-Wafā' gives rules for the measurement of more common planar and three-dimensional figures—from triangles, various types of quadrangles, regular polygons, and a circle and its parts, to a sphere and sectors of a sphere, inclusive. There is a table of chords corresponding to the arcs of a semicircle of radius 7, which consists of $m/22$ of the semicircumference ($m = 1, 2, \cdots, 22$), and the expression for the diameter, d, of a circle superscribed around a regular n-sided polygon with side a:

$$d = \sqrt{a^2 \left[(n - 1)\frac{n}{2} + 3\right]\frac{2}{g}}$$

Abū'l-Wafā' thought this rule was obtained from India; it is correct for $n = 3, 4, 6$, and for other values of n gives a good approximation, especially for small n. At the end of the third section, problems involving the determination of the distance to inaccessible objects and their heights are solved on the basis of similar triangles.

Another practical textbook by Abū'l-Wafā' is *Kitāb fī mā yaḥtaj ilayh al-ṣāniᶜ min al-aᶜmāl al-handasiyya* ("Book on What is Necessary From Geometric Construction for the Artisan"), written after 990. Many of the two-dimensional and three-dimensional constructions set forth by Abū'l-Wafā' were borrowed mostly from the writings of Euclid, Archimedes, Hero of Alexandria, Theodosius, and Pappus. Some of the examples, however, are original. The range of problems is very wide, from the simplest planar constructions (the division of a segment into equal parts, the construction of a tangent to a circle from a point on or outside the circle, etc.) to the construction of regular and semiregular polyhedrons inscribed in a given sphere. Most of the constructions can be drawn with a compass and straightedge. In several instances, when these means are insufficient, intercalation is used (for the trisection of an angle or the duplication of a cube) or only an approximate construction is given (for the side of a regular heptagon inscribed in a given circle, using half of one side of an equilateral triangle inscribed in the same circle, the error is very small).

A group of problems that are solved using a straightedge and a compass with an invariable opening deserves mention. Such constructions are found in the writings of the ancient Indians and Greeks, but Abū'l-Wafā' was the first to solve a large number of problems using a compass with an invariable opening. Interest in these constructions was probably aroused by the fact that in practice they give more exact results than can be obtained by changing the compass opening. These constructions were widely circulated in Renaissance Europe; and Lorenzo Mascheroni, Jean Victor Poncelet, and Jakob Steiner developed the general theory of these and analogous constructions.

Also in this work by Abū'l-Wafā' are problems concerning the division of a figure into parts that satisfy certain conditions, and problems on the transformation of squares (for example, the construction of a square whose area is equal to the sum of the areas of three given squares). In proposing his original and elegant constructions, Abū'l-Wafā' simultaneously proved the inaccuracy of some methods used by "artisans."

Abū'l-Wafā''s large astronomical work, *al-majisṭī*, or *Kitāb al-kāmil* ("Complete Book"), closely follows Ptolemy's *Almagest*. It is possible that this work, available only in part, is the same as, or is included in, his *Zīj al-Wāḍiḥ*, based on observations that he and his colleagues conducted. The *Zīj* seems not to be extant. Abū'l-Wafā' apparently did not introduce anything essentially new into theoretical astronomy. In particular, there is no basis for crediting him with the discovery of the so-called variation of the moon (this was proved by Carra de Vaux, in opposition to the opinion expressed by L. A. Sédillot). E. S. Kennedy established that the data from Abū'l-Wafā''s observations were used by many later astronomers.

Abū'l-Wafā''s achievements in the development of trigonometry, specifically in the improvement of tables and in the means of solving problems of spherical trigonometry, are undoubted. For the tabulation of new sine tables he computed sin 30′ more precisely, applying his own method of interpretation. This method, based on one theorem of Theon of Alexandria, gives an approximation that can be stated in modern terms by the inequalities

$$\sin\frac{15°}{32} + \frac{1}{3}\left(\sin\frac{18°}{32} - \sin\frac{15°}{32}\right) < \sin 30'$$

$$< \sin\frac{15°}{32} + \frac{1}{3}\left(\sin\frac{15°}{32} - \sin\frac{12°}{32}\right).$$

The values sin 15°/32 and sin 18°/32 are found by using the known values of sin 60° and sin 72°, respectively, with the aid of rational operations and the extraction of a square root, which is needed for the calculation of the sine of half a given angle; the value sin 12°/32 is found as the sine of the difference 72°/32 − 60°/32. Setting sin 30′ equal to half the sum of the quantities bounding it above and below,

with the radius of the circle equal to 60, Abū'l-Wafā' found, in sexagesimal fractions, sin 30′ = 31^{I} 24^{II} 55^{III} 54^{IV} 55^{V}. This value is correct to the fourth place, the value correct to five places being sin 30′ = 31^{I} 24^{II} 55^{III} 54^{IV} 0^{V}.

In comparison, Ptolemy's method of interpolation, which was used before Abū'l-Wafā', showed error in the third place. If one expresses Abū'l-Wafā''s approximation in decimal fractions and lets $r = 1$ (which he did not do), then sin 30′ = 0.0087265373 is obtained instead of 0.0087265355—that is, the result is correct to 10^{-8}. Abū'l-Wafā' also compiled tables for tangent and cotangent.

In spherical trigonometry before Abū'l-Wafā', the basic means of solving triangles was Menelaus' theorem on complete quadrilaterals, which in Arabic literature is called the "rule of six quantities." The application of this theorem in various cases is quite cumbersome. Abū'l-Wafā' enriched the apparatus of spherical trigonometry, simplifying the solution of its problems. He applied the theorem of tangents to the solution of spherical right triangles, priority in the proof of which was later ascribed to him by al-Bīrūnī. One of the first proofs of the general theorem of sines applied to the solution of oblique triangles also was originated by Abū'l-Wafā'. In Arabic literature this theorem was called "theorem which makes superfluous" the study of complete quadrilaterals and Menelaus' theorem. To honor Abū'l-Wafā', a crater on the moon was named after him.

BIBLIOGRAPHY

I. ORIGINAL WORKS. The text on practical arithmetic has never been published in any modern language; however, discussions of it may be found in Woepcke, Luckey, and Medovoy (see below). Manuscripts of this work are preserved at the library of the University of Leiden (993) and the National Library, Cairo (^{1}V, 185). Besides these, there exist the manuscript of a work containing the fundamental definitions of theoretical arithmetic: "Risāla fī'l-aritmāṭīqī," at the Institute of Oriental Studies of the Academy of Sciences of the Uzbek S.S.R. in Tashkent (4750/8), which is described by G. P. Matvievskaja (see below); an unstudied arithmetical manuscript at the Escorial (Casiri, 933); and an unstudied arithmetical manuscript at the Library Raza, Rampur (I, 414). The text on geometric constructions has been studied in a Persian variant (Paris, Bibliothèque Nationale, pers. anc., 169) by Woepcke; Suter has studied the Milan manuscript (Biblioteca Ambrosiana, arab. 68); and a Russian translation by Krasnova of the Istanbul manuscript (Aya Sofya, 2753) has appeared. Eleven of the thirteen chapters of the latter are extant. The manuscript of the *al-Majisṭī*, only part of which has survived, is in Paris (Bibliothèque Nationale, ar. 2497) and has been studied by Carra de Vaux (see below). MS Istanbul, Carullah, 1479, is unstudied.

II. SECONDARY LITERATURE. General works concerning Abū'l-Wafā' are A. von Braunmühl, *Vorlesungen über Geschichte der Trigonometrie,* I (1900), 45–61; C. Brockelmann, *Geschichte der arabischen Litteratur,* I, 2nd ed. (Leiden, 1943), 255; Supp. I (Leiden, 1937), p. 400; M. Cantor, *Vorlesungen über Geschichte der Mathematik,* 2nd ed., I (Leipzig, 1894), 698–704, Index; Ibn al-Nadīm (Abū'l-Farāj Muḥammad Ibn Isḥāq), *Kitāb al-Fihrist,* G. Flügel, Y. Rödiger, and A. Müller, eds., I (Leipzig, 1871), 266, 283; H. Suter's translation of the *Fihrist,* "Das Mathematikerverzeichnis im Fihrist des Ibn Abī Ya'kūb al-Nadīm," in *Abhandlungen zur Geschichte der mathematischen Wissenschaften,* 6 (1892), 39; A. Youschkevitch, *Geschichte der Mathematik im Mittelalter* (Leipzig, 1964), Index; G. Sarton, *Introduction to the History of Science,* I, 666–667; H. Suter, *The Encyclopaedia of Islam,* new ed., I (Leiden–London, 1954), 159, and *Die Mathematiker und Astronomen der Araber* (Leipzig, 1900–1902), 71–72; Supp., 166–167; and Joh. Tropfke, *Geschichte der Elementar-Mathematik,* 2nd ed., VII (Leipzig, 1921–1924), Index.

The first attention to Abū'l-Wafā''s work was F. Woepcke's "Analyse et extraits d'un recueil de constructions géométriques par Aboûl Wefâ," in *Journal asiatique,* 5th ser., 5 (1855), 218–256, 309–359, which deals with the Paris (Persian) manuscript. For an analysis of Abū'l-Wafā''s practical arithmetic, see P. Luckey, *Die Rechenkunst bei Ğamšīd b. Mas'ūd al-Kāšī mit Rückblicken auf die ältere Geschichte des Rechnens* (Wiesbaden, 1951). There are two detailed investigations of the arithmetic text by M. I. Medovoy: "Ob odnom sluchae primenenija otritsatel'nykh chisel u Abu-l-Vafy" ("On One Case of the Use of Negative Numbers by Abū'l-Wafā'"), in *Istoriko-matematicheskie issledovanija* ("Studies in the History of Mathematics"), 11 (1958), 593–598, and "Ob arifmeticheskom traktate Abu-l-Vafy" ("On the Arithmetic Treatise of Abū'l-Wafā'"), *ibid.,* 13 (1960), 253–324; both articles constitute the first detailed investigation of this work. On the Tashkent manuscript, see G. P. Matvievskaja, *O matematicheskikh mkopissiakh iz sobranija instituta vostokovedenija AN Uz. S.S.R.* ("On the Mathematical Manuscripts in the Collection of the Institute of Oriental Studies of the Academy of Sciences of the Uzbek S.S.R."), Publishing House of the Academy of Sciences of the Uzbek S.S.R. Physical and Mathematical Sciences Series, pt. 9 (1965), no. 3, and *Uchenije o chisle na siednevekovom Vostoke* ("Number Theory in the Orient During the Middle Ages"); (Tashkent, 1967). An exposition of the Milan geometric manuscript is H. Suter, "Das Buch der geometrischen Konstruktionen des Abûl Wefâ," in *Abhandlungen zur Geschichte der Naturwissenschaften und Medizin* (1922), pp. 94–109. A Russian translation of the Istanbul geometric manuscript, with commentary and notes, has been done by S. A. Krasnova: "Abu-l-Vafa al-Buzdzhani, Kniga o tom, chto neobkhodimo remeslenniku iz geometricheskikh postroenij" ("Abū'l-Wafā' al-Būzjānī, 'Geometrical Constructions for the Artisan' "), in *Fiziko-matematicheskie*

nauki v stranakh vostoka ("Physics and Mathematics in the Orient"), I (IV) (Moscow, 1966), 42–140.

The astronomical and trigonometrical works of Abū'l-Wafā' are discussed in Carra de Vaux, "L'*Almageste* d'Abū-l-Wéfā al-Būzjānī," in *Journal asiatique,* 8th ser., 19 (1892), 408–471; E. S. Kennedy, "A Survey of Islamic Astronomical Tables," in *Transactions of the American Philosophical Society,* n.s. 46 (1956), 2; and F. Woepcke, "Sur une mesure de la circonférence du cercle due aux astronomes arabes et fondée sur un calcul d'Aboûl Wefâ," in *Journal asiatique,* 5th ser., 15 (1860), 281–320.

A. P. YOUSCHKEVITCH

ACCUM, FRIEDRICH CHRISTIAN (*b.* Bückeburg, Germany, 29 March 1769; *d.* Berlin, Germany, 28 June 1838), *applied chemistry.*

The son of a converted Jew, Herz Marcus, and a Huguenot, Judith La Motte, Accum was the sixth of seven children and the youngest of the three who lived to maturity. A small family soap-boiling business begun with the aid of his mother's dowry continued to provide income after his father's death in 1772; Friedrich was thus able to follow the usual classical curriculum at the more than usually respected local Gymnasium. It was, however, an interest in chemistry that led to his move to England in 1793, as assistant in the Hannover and London firm of Brande, apothecaries to George III. He married Mary Simpson of London in 1798 and had eight children, of whom one son and one daughter lived to adulthood.

Accum was early indebted to the patronage of Anthony Carlisle and the friendship of William Nicholson. About 1800 he established his own laboratory; he was also "assistant chemical operator" to Humphry Davy, resigning in September 1803. In 1802 he began public lecturing, and the steady stream of laboratory pupils included the Americans Benjamin Silliman (in 1805) and William Peck. Orders for chemical apparatus for Harvard, Yale, even Pondicherry, India, were a natural consequence.

In December 1820 the scandal that followed Accum's arrest for mutilating books in the Royal Institution library led to his flight to Germany. Some of the proceeds from his technological and publishing successes went with him, and he was soon reestablished in Berlin, with two technical professorships. In England he was a subscriber to the Royal Institution, a member of the Royal Irish Academy and the Linnean Society, and a corresponding member of the Royal Academy of Sciences in Berlin. The last connection continued after his move to Germany.

The value of Accum's work lies in the way he saw and exploited the technological possibilities of the rapidly advancing science of chemistry. His activities as lecturer, author, laboratory instructor, merchant, consultant, and technical adviser epitomize the opportunities that the industrial revolution opened to the emerging class of professional chemists. His pioneer work on gas-lighting and food adulteration was of fundamental importance.

Accum was intimately concerned with the application of H. A. Winsor's 1804 patent of a gas-lighting process. He undertook the experimental work necessary to overcome the complaints of Winsor's rival William Murdoch and the scruples of Parliamentary committees. As a result his name appeared as "practical chymist" on the 1812 list of the first Corporation of London's highly successful Gas-Light and Coke Company. Profiting from his experience, Accum advised other fledgling gas companies and wrote the 1815 treatise that became the classic text of gas technology. Equal fame, although not success, surrounded his work on food adulteration. He was long aware of this problem and his deliberately sensational 1820 work (motto "There is death in the pot") did much to awaken that public concern that eventually resulted in the Adulteration Act of 1860. Not surprisingly, Accum's outspoken attacks, and his naming of offending individuals, antagonized powerful interests. This antagonism may well explain the harsh line the Royal Institution took toward his own shortcomings, despite the pleadings of his former patron Carlisle.

BIBLIOGRAPHY

I. ORIGINAL WORKS. In addition to many articles Accum wrote at least fifteen books, from *System of Theoretical and Practical Chemistry*, 2 vols. (London, 1803), to *Physische und chemische Beschaffenheit der Baumaterialien,* 2 vols. (Berlin, 1826). The two most important are his *Practical Treatise on Gas Light; Exhibiting a Summary Description of the Apparatus and Machinery* (London, 1815; 4th ed., 1817), which was trans. into French, German, and Italian, and the *Treatise on the Adulterations of Food, and Culinary Poisons* (London, 1820; 2nd ed., 1820).

II. SECONDARY LITERATURE. C. A. Browne, "The Life and Chemical Services of Fredrick Accum," in *Journal of Chemical Education,* **2** (1925), 829–851, 1008–1034, 1140–1149, and "Recently Acquired Information Concerning Fredrick Accum," in *Chymia,* **1** (1948), 1–9, contain detailed data on Accum's life and work, surviving MSS, and chemical samples; R. J. Cole's largely derivative "Friedrich Accum. A Biographical Study," in *Annals of Science,* **7** (1951), 128–143, contains some information on eds. and trans. of Accum's books.

ARNOLD THACKRAY

ACHARD, FRANZ KARL (*b.* Berlin, Germany, 20 April 1753; *d.* Kunern, Germany, 20 April 1821), *chemistry, experimental physics.*

Achard, baptized François-Charles, was born of French Protestant émigré parents. His father, Guillaume Achard, a minister, died when Franz Karl was only two years old. In 1759 his mother, whose maiden name was Margarette Henriette Roupert, married a Charles Vigne. Of Achard's upbringing and early education, virtually nothing is known. At the age of twenty he began his scientific career in association with the botanist J. G. Gleditsch and with the renowned chemist A. S. Marggraf. It was Marggraf, especially, who trained young Franz Karl, gave him entrée into Berlin scientific circles, and finally obtained, in June 1776, his admission to the Berlin Academy. When Marggraf died in 1782, Achard succeeded him as director of the "Class of Physics" of the Berlin Academy.

In his youth, Achard was a prolific writer. He published articles on the thermal expansion of gases and liquids, the effects of soluble and insoluble fluids on the freezing point of water, cooling by evaporation, and various electrical phenomena, as well as numerous papers on miscellaneous chemical and physical subjects. Most of these articles were published in French in the *Nouveaux mémoires* of the Berlin Academy, in Rozier's journal (*Observations sur la physique. . .*), and in the *Journal littéraire* (Berlin). In addition, Achard published German articles in Crell's *Chemische Annalen* and in two volumes of collected essays (1780, 1784).

None of Achard's early papers was of great importance. In general, he eschewed theoretical discussion and concentrated his efforts on the detailed investigation of facts. Typical of this procedure was his paper on cooling by evaporation, which amounted to little more than a short history of previous investigations of the topic, followed by a description of his experimental method and long lists of various liquids and their relative abilities to cool. The few general remarks that he appended to this discourse had been established years, even decades, before. Achard is known for several minor achievements in applied chemistry, most notably his description of a workable alloy of platinum and arsenic and his process for fabricating lye from common salt and litharge. In addition, he was one of the first to conduct detailed investigations of galvanism.

Achard is best known for his development of a method of extracting sugar from beets in large quantity. In 1747 Marggraf had published a paper in which he showed that crystallizable sugar could be extracted from various plants native to Europe. The most promising of these plants appeared to be the common beetroot. At his estate near Berlin, Achard began experiments in 1786, in an effort to develop a process for extracting sugar from beets in quantities large enough and at cost low enough to be commercially valuable. In 1799, after having tried various methods of cultivation and extraction, he had a loaf of beet sugar, along with a description of the process by which it had been made, presented to Frederick William III. The king appointed a special committee to investigate this new process, and when it issued a favorable report, Achard was given financial aid to build a beet-sugar refinery in Kunern, a Silesian village near Breslau. The factory was completed in 1801, and it began operations the following year.

Achard's new process of obtaining sugar was simple but costly. It consisted of boiling specially cultivated, white Silesian beets and then pressing them to extract a sugary liquid. This liquid, added to that obtained from a second pressing, was boiled to remove excess water and then placed in an oven at moderate temperature to allow crystallization. After a crust had formed, the liquid was cooled and the sugar was separated by filtration. The muscovado, or raw sugar, could be refined to any desired degree of purity by recrystallization. The by-products were beet pulp, which could be used for cattle fodder, and molasses, which could be made into spirits.

News of Achard's accomplishment spread quickly throughout Europe. In France the first details were communicated by Van Mons in an article written for the *Annales de chimie.* The Institut formed a committee of chemists and agriculturalists to examine Achard's process and suggest possible improvements. In June 1800 it issued an encouraging report and made several valuable recommendations, the most important of which was that the beets be pressed without cooking them. Achard afterward adopted this technique in order to reduce the considerable expenditures for fuel.

Under the artificial stimulus of the Continental System, which reduced the supply of West Indian sugar, and with the aid of liberal governmental financing, the beet-sugar industry prospered briefly. In 1813 an investigating commission of the French government reported that there were 334 beet-sugar factories in France, with a combined annual production of 7,700,000 pounds. Although no such specific figures exist for Germany, it seems evident that the beet-sugar industry was also widely established there. However, when the Napoleonic Wars came to an end and normal markets were reestablished, the industry all but disappeared. It revived about the middle of the nineteenth century, and made its greatest strides

with the development of the diffusion process of extraction and with the cultivation of new strains of beets containing over twice as much sugar as those Achard had used.

After a five-week illness, Achard died only a week before his sixty-eighth birthday. He was survived by his second wife and several children. His death passed virtually unnoticed in academic circles, from which he had long since retired.

BIBLIOGRAPHY

I. ORIGINAL WORKS. Achard's writings include *Chymisch-physische Schriften* (Berlin, 1780); *Sammlung physikalischer und chymischer Abhandlungen,* Vol. I only (Berlin, 1784); and *Vorlesungen über die Experimentalphysik,* 4 vols. (Berlin, 1790–1792). Among Achard's many works on the beet-sugar industry, three are especially worthy of mention: *Kurze Geschichte der Beweise welche ich von der Ausführbarkeit im Grossen und den vielen Vortheilen der von mir angegebenen Zuckerfabrication aus Runkelrüben geführt habe* (Berlin, 1800); *Anleitung zum Anbau der zur Zuckerfabrication anwendbaren Runkelrüben und zur vortheilhaften Gewinnung des Zuckers aus denselben* (Breslau, 1809), repr. as Ostwalds Klassiker der exacten Wissenschaften, no. 159 (Leipzig, 1907); and *Die europäische Zuckerfabrication aus Runkelrüben* (Leipzig, 1809).

II. SECONDARY LITERATURE. A detailed and reliable account of Achard's life is found in Wilhelm Stieda, "Franz Karl Achard und die Früzeit der deutschen Zuckerindustrie," in *Abhandlungen der philologisch-historischen Klasse der Sächsischen Akademie der Wissenschaften,* **39,** no. 3 (Leipzig, 1928). See also Adolf von Harnack, *Geschichte der Königlich Preussischen Akademie der Wissenschaften zu Berlin,* IV (Berlin, 1900), 3–7, 389 f.; and Noël Deerr, *The History of Sugar,* II (London, 1950), 471–500.

J. B. GOUGH

ACHARIUS, ERIK (*b.* Gavle, Sweden, 10 October 1757; *d.* Vadstena, Sweden, 14 August 1819), *botany.*

Acharius was the last to defend his thesis (*De planta Aphyteia,* 1776) under Linnaeus, and all his life he pursued the Linnaean tradition of research in his botanical work. Like most of the university-trained botanists of his time, Acharius studied medicine, first at the University of Uppsala and then at Lund, where he received the M.D. in 1782. After that, he practiced medicine and spent the major part of his life in the province of Ostergotland, in the small town of Vadstena. He worked on botany only in his leisure time, but his scientific achievement was nevertheless considerable. He devoted himself almost exclusively to the study of lichens, and his description and classification of them laid the foundation for later scholarship.

Linnaeus had concentrated on the classification of the higher plants, and at the time of his death was the recognized authority on world flora. The generation of botanists who followed him sought to enlarge on his work by defining new areas of the plant kingdom. Some turned to new areas of the world as sources of plants for study, and others devoted themselves to the previously neglected cryptogams, which despite their large numbers and enormous variety were all placed in the twenty-fourth class of the Linnaean sexual system. As for the study of lichens, German botanists, among them J. Hedwig and H. A. Schrader, had considerably extended Linnaeus' findings, but only Acharius laid the rational foundations of their classification.

In his first important publication, *Lichenographiae suecicae prodromus* (1798), Acharius still classified lichens according to the appearance of the thallus, which had been observed earlier, but he soon developed a new system based on structure. His terminology for the morphological description of lichens is still, to a large extent, valid. Using this method, he described a considerable number of new families and species, both Scandinavian and tropical. Some of the tropical specimens were collected from the bark and tissues of tropical plants that came to him in the form of botanical drugs. His advanced views on the taxonomy of lichens were presented in *Methodus* (1803), *Lichenographia universalis* (1810), and *Synopsis methodica lichenum* (1814).

For a long time Acharius thought that lichens were not really plants, but animals, most closely related to polyps. While this shows the vagueness of the conception still held at the beginning of the nineteenth century with regard to the "lower" organisms and their reproduction, it may also serve to illustrate the problems the lichen group posed before it was established that they are composed of an alga and a fungus living symbiotically. Since only inferior microscopes were available, the structure of lichens remained obscure to Acharius. During the decades following his death, Acharius' scientific work was severely criticized, especially by the German botanists H. G. Floerke, G. F. W. Meyer, and K. F. W. Wallroth. Both his terminology and his classification of species were considered defective, and he was thought to have distinguished too many species. In contemporary lichenology, however, Acharius is highly respected, and many of his species are still recognized.

BIBLIOGRAPHY

I. ORIGINAL WORKS. Acharius' complete bibliography is in T. O. B. N. Krok, *Bibliotheca botanica suecana* (Uppsala–Stockholm, 1925), pp. 2–4; and R. Sernander, "Acharius," in *Svenskt biografiskt lexikon,* I (Stockholm, 1917–1918), 39–40. Among his works are *Lichenographiae suecicae prodromus* (Linköping, 1798); *Methodus qua omnes detectos lichenes secundum organa carpomorpha ad genera, species et varietates redigere atque observationibus illustrare tentavit* (Stockholm, 1803); *Lichenographia universalis* (Göttingen, 1810); and *Synopsis methodica lichenum* (Lund, 1814). His lichen herbarium is at the botanical museum of Helsingfors University; his correspondence is in the library of the University of Uppsala.

II. SECONDARY LITERATURE. There is no complete modern biography of Acharius. Information on his life is in *Svenskt biografiskt lexikon* (see above). The best résumé of his work is A. von Krempelhuber, *Geschichte und Literatur der Lichenologie,* I–II (Munich, 1867–1869): I, 96–98, 112–114, 194–196, and *passim;* II, 61–68, 79–88, and *passim.*

GUNNAR ERIKSSON

ACHILLINI, ALESSANDRO (*b.* Bologna, Italy, 29 October 1463; *d.* Bologna, 2 August 1512), *anatomy.*

Alessandro Achillini was the son of Claudio Achillini, of an old family of Bologna. He was graduated doctor of philosophy and of medicine from the University of Bologna in 1484, whereupon he was appointed substitute lecturer of philosophy. After 1495 he taught medicine also. In 1506 he was obliged to leave Bologna, owing to the expulsion of the powerful Bentivoglio family, of whom he was a partisan. He went to Padua, where he was appointed teacher of philosophy. (It is possible that he had taught at Padua before 1506.) In 1508 the regents of the University of Bologna requested Achillini to return. He did so and taught there for three years. He is buried in the Church of Saint Martin, in Bologna. Achillini never married.

During his lifetime, Achillini was known mainly as a philosopher. Today, however, he is remembered for his considerable activity in research on human anatomy. He gave a good description of the veins of the arm, and he described the seven bones of tarsus, the fornix of the brain, the cerebral ventricles, the infundibulum, and the trochlear nerve. He also described, exactly, the ducts of the submaxillary salivary glands—a discovery generally attributed to the Englishman Thomas Wharton (1614–1673)—and the ileocecal valve, described later by Costanzo Varolio and Gaspard Bauhin. Finally, to Achillini is attributed the first description of the two ossicles of the ear, the malleus and incus.

A famous teacher (Magnus Achillinus) and a man of independent critical judgment, Achillini first demonstrated some mistakes of Galen. Among the Italian pre-Vesalian anatomists (Alessandro Benedetti, Gabriele Zerbi, Berengario da Carpi, and Niccolo Massa) the influence of Achillini's work was slight, chiefly because his works were not illustrated and he used an obscure medieval terminology derived largely from Mondino's texts and heavily sprinkled with Arabic terms.

BIBLIOGRAPHY

I. ORIGINAL WORKS. Achillini's major philosophical writings are to be found in *Clarissimi Achillini opera.* I. *Aristotelis, philosophorum maximi, de secretis secretorum ad Alexandrum opusculum;* II. *Eiusdem de regum regimine;* III. *De universalibus et de elementis libri tres;* IV. *De orbibus libri quatuor;* V. *De signis tempestatum;* VI. *De mineralibus;* VII. *Alexandri Aphrodisei de intellectu;* VIII. *Averrois de animae beatitudine;* IX. *Alexandri Macedonis de mirabilibus Indiae ad Aristotilem* (Venice, 1508, 1516, 1545, 1551, 1568). His major anatomical writings include *Alexandri Achillini de humani corporis anatomia* (Venice, 1516; Bologna, 1520); "In Mundini anatomiam adnotationes," in *Fasciculus medicinae* by John of Ketham (Venice, 1522); *Adnotationes anatomicae* (Bologna, 1520).

II. SECONDARY LITERATURE. See also P. Capparoni, *Profili di medici e naturalisti celebri italiani dal secolo XV° al XVIII°,* I (Rome, 1925), 11–14; S. De Renzi, *Storia della medicina in Italia,* II (Naples, 1845), 358–360. The best essay on Achillini's work is L. Münster, "Alessandro Achillini anatomico e filosofo nello Studio di Bologna," in *Rivista di storia delle scienze mediche e naturali,* **24** (1933), 7–22, 54–77. Further material can be found in B. Nardi, *Studi su Pietro Pomponazzi* (Florence, 1965); C. D. O'Malley, "The Discovery of the Auditory Ossicles," in *Bulletin of the History of Medicine,* **35** (1961), 419–441; A. Pazzini, *Storia della medicina,* I (Milan, 1945), 614; V. Putti, *Berengario da Carpi* (Bologna, 1937); G. Rath, "Pre-Vesalian Anatomy in the Light of Modern Research," in *Bulletin of the History of Medicine,* **35** (1961), 142–148.

PIETRO FRANCESCHINI

ACOSTA, CRISTÓBAL (*b.* Bõa Ventura, Santo Antão, Cape Verde Islands, *ca.* 1525; *d.* La Peña de Tharsis [?], Huelva, Spain, *ca.* 1594), *natural history, medicine.*

Born Christovão da Costa—according to Portuguese usage—Acosta moved to Lisbon and lived in Setúbal and Peniche, but his excellent Spanish and broad education indicate that he studied arts and medicine, most probably in Salamanca. He went to the East Indies before 1550 as a soldier and visited Persia, India, Malaya, and perhaps China. There is record of his actions against the Arabs in Hormuz; against the Abexins near Daman, where he lost two horses in battle; and on the Malabar Coast, where he was taken prisoner on the way to Bengal; and of his meetings in Goa with García d'Orta.

Acosta returned to Portugal but soon rejoined his former captain, Luiz de Ataíde, who had been appointed viceroy of India, and landed at Goa in October 1568, a few months after the death of García d'Orta. In 1569 he was appointed physician to the Royal Hospital in Cochin, but by 1571 he was collecting botanical specimens in Tanor, Cranganor, and other parts of India. Luiz de Ataíde ended his term of office in 1572, and Acosta sailed from Cochin back to Lisbon via the Cape of Good Hope. He practiced medicine in Burgos and was that city's physician and surgeon from 1576 to 1587. After his wife died, he retired to the hermitage of La Peña de Tharsis, which was probably where he died.

Like his other books, Acosta's *Tractado de las drogas, y medicinas de las Indias orientales* was written in a fluid and concise style. It offers systematic, firsthand observations of the Oriental drugs and is illustrated by woodcuts made from his own accurate drawings. This book clearly surpasses that of d'Orta, whose contributions Acosta readily acknowledges. His *Tratado in loor de las mujeres* followed Boccaccio's work but was not influenced by Espinosa's *Dialogo en laude de las mugeres* (1580). His other printed work, *Tratado en contra y pro de la vida solitaria,* incorporated two other independent treatises, *Tratado de la religión y religioso* and *Collación á los mohateros, usureros, aparceros, tratantes y seducadores,* both moral works. In all, Acosta wrote thirteen works, but the manuscripts of his *Discurso del viaje á las Indias orientales y lo que se navega en aquellos mares, Tres diálogos teriacales,* and above all his great *Tratado de las yerbas, plantas, frutas y animales, así terrenos como aquatiles que en aquellas partes y en la Persia y en la China hay, no dibujadas al natural hasta agora,* are not extant.

BIBLIOGRAPHY

Acosta's first printed book was the *Tractado de las drogas, y medicinas de las Indias orientales* (Burgos, 1578), trans. into Italian by F. Ziletti (Venice, 1585); into French by A. Colin (Lyons, 1602, 1619); and into Latin by C. L'Ecluse (Antwerp, 1582, 1593, 1605). His two other published books were the *Tratado en loor de las mujeres* (Venice, 1592) and the *Tratado en contra y pro de la vida solitaria* (Venice, 1592).

J. Olmedilla y Puig, *Estudio histórico de . . . Cristóbal*

Acosta (Madrid, 1899), is comprehensive and offers two documents on Acosta's practice in Burgos. Unfortunately, the information that Cristóbal Acosta was born of Jewish parents in Tangier, Ceuta, or Mozambique *ca.* 1515, was a brother of José Acosta, studied at Coimbra or Burgos, returned from India via Jerusalem, was shipwrecked near Italy, and died in Burgos *ca.* 1580 is in conflict with the facts.

FRANCISCO GUERRA

ACOSTA, JOSÉ DE (*b.* Medina del Campo, Spain, 1539; *d.* Salamanca, Spain, 15 February 1600), *geography.*

Acosta was one of the first Europeans to provide a detailed image of the physical and human geography of Latin America; his studies of the Indian civilizations of the New World were a major source of information for several centuries. At the age of fifteen he entered the Jesuit order in his native city and underwent rigorous theological and literary training. He early displayed a strong interest in the New World, and although he was offered a chair of theology in Rome, he asked to be sent to the Americas. He left Spain in 1570 and sailed via Panama to Peru, where he remained for fourteen years. For many years Acosta lived at the Jesuit college on the shore of Lake Titicaca and learned enough of both Aymara and Quechua to produce a trilingual catechism (1583). After acting as historian of the third council of the church at Lima (1582–1583), he embarked for Mexico, where he spent three years. Next he went to Rome, and then to Spain, where he filled several important posts for the Jesuits. He died while serving as rector of the Jesuit college of Salamanca.

Acosta was a prolific writer on both sacred and profane subjects, but his most important scientific work was *Historia natural y moral de las Indias.* It provides firsthand observations on such diverse phenomena as altitude sickness, the nature and uses of coca, and the crops, farm techniques, and domesticated animals of America. Equally important are his descriptions of Inca and Aztec history, religious observances, folk customs, and statecraft. He was the first to describe in detail Mexican ideograms and Peruvian quipu, and the Inca postal system. He may, indeed, be called the first of the true Americanists.

BIBLIOGRAPHY

I. ORIGINAL WORKS. Acosta's most important work on the Americas was *Historia natural y moral de las Indias, en que se tratan las cosas más notables del cielo, y elementos, metales, plantes y animales dellas* (Seville, 1590). The sole English trans., by Edward Grimston, is *The Natural and Moral History of the Indies . . .* (London, 1604), repr. with notes and intro. by C. R. Markham as Vols. LX and LXI of the Hakluyt Society Series (London, 1880).

II. SECONDARY LITERATURE. References to Acosta's writings may be found in Marcelino Menéndez y Pelayo, *La ciencia española,* III (Madrid, 1887); and Carlos Sommervogel, *Bibliothèque de la Compagnie de Jésus,* I (Paris, 1890), cols. 31–38.

GEORGE KISH

ACTEDIUS, PETRUS. See **Artedi, Peter.**

ACYUTA PIṢĀRAṬI (*b.* Tṛkkaṇṭiyūr [Sanskrit, Kuṇḍapura], Kerala, India, *ca.* 1550; *d.* Kerala, 7 July 1621), *astronomy.*

Acyuta was a member of the Piṣāraṭi community, which is a section of the Ampalavāsi community and is traditionally employed in looking after the external affairs of temples. He studied astronomy under Jyeṣṭhadeva (*ca.* 1500–1600), a Nambūtiri Brāhmaṇa of the Paraṅṅoṭṭu family in the village called Ālattūr, who wrote the *Yuktibhāṣā* based on the *Tantrasaṅgraha* of Nīlakaṇṭha Somasutvan. Jyeṣṭhadeva and Nīlakaṇṭha were pupils of Dāmodara, the son and student of Parameśvara, who founded the *Dṛggaṇita* school of astronomy (for an account of this school, see my essay, V A 2). Acyuta's patron was Ravivarman, King of Veṭṭattunād (Sanskrit, Prakāśa; 1595–1607). He was a scholar in grammar (his famous pupil Nārāyaṇa Bhaṭṭatiri [1560–*ca.* 1646] refers to him in his *Prakriyāsarvasva*), poetics, and medicine, as well as in astronomy and astrology. In the field of astrology, there existed in his school a long line of scholars writing in Malayalam.

Acyuta wrote the following works dealing largely with astronomy.

1. *Praveśaka.* This is an introduction to Sanskrit grammar in about six hundred *anuṣṭubh* stanzas. It was edited, with a commentary, by P. S. Anantanarayana Sastri, as Vol. II in Cochin Sanskrit Series (Trippunithura, 1938).

2. *Karaṇottama.* This is a work on astronomy in five chapters and about one hundred verses; it deals with the computation of the mean and true longitudes of the planets, with eclipses, and with the *vyatīpātas* of the sun and moon. Acyuta himself wrote a commentary on it. It was published as Vol. 213 of Trivandrum Sanskrit Series (Trivandrum, 1964).

3. *Uparāgakriyākrama.* This is a treatise in four chapters on lunar and solar eclipses which was completed in 1593. There is a commentary on it in Malayalam.

4. *Sphuṭanirṇaya.* This is a work on astronomy in six chapters, written before the *Rāśigolasphuṭānīti.*

5. *Chāyāṣṭaka.* This is a short astronomical text in eight verses.

6. *Uparāgaviṃśati.* This is a manual in twenty verses on the computation of eclipses. It was published with a Malayalam commentary in Vol. II of the Ravivarma Sanskrit Series (Trippunithura, 1954).

7. *Rāśigolasphuṭānīti.* This work in fifty verses is concerned with the reduction of the moon's true longitude in its own orbit to the ecliptic. Since in this work Acyuta quotes not only the *Sphuṭanirṇaya* but also the *Uparāgakriyākrama,* it is clear that the *Rāśigolasphuṭānīti* was written after 1593. It was edited and translated into English by K. V. Sarma as Adyar Library Series, Paper 29 (Madras, 1955); reprinted from *Brahmavidyā,* **18** (1954), 306–335.

8. *Veṇvārohavyākhyā.* This Malayalam commentary on the *Veṇvāroha* of Mādhava of Saṅgamagrāma (*ca.* 1340–1425) was written at the request of Netranārāyaṇa, a spiritual head of the Nambūtiri Brāhmaṇas. The *Veṇvāroha* deals with the calculation of the *tithis* and *nakṣatras.* The text and its commentary have been edited by K. V. Sarma in Vol. III of the Ravivarma Sanskrit Series (Trippunithura, 1956).

9. *Horāsāroccaya.* This is an adaptation in seven chapters of the *Jātakapaddhati* of Śrīpati. The relationship to it of a Malayalam commentary on the *Jātakapaddhati* entitled *Horātantraṃ Paribhāṣa* remains uncertain.

BIBLIOGRAPHY

Further discussion of Acyuta Piṣārati may be found in S. Venkitasubramonia Iyer, "Acyuta Piṣāroṭi: His Date and Works," in *JOR Madras,* **22** (1952–1953), 40–46; and K. Kunjunni Raja, *The Contribution of Kerala to Sanskrit Literature* (Madras, 1958), pp. 122–125, and "Astronomy and Mathematics in Kerala," in *Brahmavidyā,* **27** (1963), 158–162.

DAVID PINGREE

ADAM OF BODENSTEIN (*b.* 1528; *d.* Basel, Switzerland, 1577), *medicine, alchemy.*

Adam was doctor of arts and medicine at Basel, where he studied and practiced medicine. He was a follower of the doctrines of Paracelsus, who had taught medicine at Basel and had been known especially for his emphasis upon the relationship between medicine and minerals, being noted particularly for his advocacy of the use of metallic compounds in medicine. Adam participated with other scholars of his time, among whom were Michael Toxites, Adam Schröter, George Forberger, Balthasar Flüter, and Gerard Dorn, in the translation, editing and publication of works by Paracelsus still in manuscript. He preceded these editions with prefatory remarks of his own. His chief contemporary rival in the interpretation of Paracelsus was Leo Suavus (Jacques Gohory).

In close association with Paracelsus' special predilection for the use of metallic compounds, Adam developed an interest in minerals, particularly in the traditional alchemical process of transmuting baser metals into gold. In the *Epistola* addressed to the Fuggers, he related the circumstances of the change in his opinion of alchemy from one of scorn and contempt for it as a suspect art and for those who wrote on it as evil men, to a belief in the verity of alchemy and of the philosophers' stone. This change he attributed to his discovery of the famous alchemical tract, the *Rosarium,* of Arnald of Villanova. On reading that work and taking cognizance of the author's orderly procedure and the presentation of the variety of theories, persons, and scientific paraphernalia involved in the art of alchemy, Adam was convinced that the contentions of the alchemists were valid and that the transmutation of baser metals into gold was possible. He strongly affirmed this conviction in the *Isagoge,* or introduction to Arnald of Villanova's *Rosarium,* which he paraphrased or edited. Adam of Bodenstein went on to expound the traditional views set forth by Arnald that mercury (quicksilver) is the primary matter of metallic bodies and that sulfur and mercury, the constituents of gold, are found in the viscera of the earth. Hence, since art follows nature, one may learn to discern the causes of the transmutation of sulfur and mercury into gold by a close observation of the process in nature.

Besides the editions of Paracelsus' works and the introduction to the paraphrase or edition of Arnald of Villanova's *Rosarium,* Adam is credited with the composition of other tracts. His chief biographer, Melchior Adam, ascribed to him further tracts entitled *De podagra* ("On Gout") and *De herbis duodecim zodiaci signis dicatis* ("On the Relation of Herbs to the Twelve Signs of the Zodiac"). Furthermore, the noted Swiss naturalist Conrad Gesner, who was Adam of Bodenstein's contemporary, reported that he had learned about salmon from Adam.

On the whole, Adam of Bodenstein's works contain little that is novel. Rather, as Lynn Thorndike pointed out, they demonstrate the strength of tradition in both medicine and alchemy in the sixteenth century. They do, however, exemplify the proclivity of the scholars of the time to carry on an active correspondence by means of which they exchanged views and the results of their scientific activities and discoveries.

BIBLIOGRAPHY

I. ORIGINAL WORKS. The following printed works are all at the British Museum in London and the Bibliothèque Nationale in Paris. Editions of Paracelsus are: *Libri V de vita longa, cum dedicatoria epistola* ([1562] Basel, 1566); *Drei Bücher von Wunden und Schäden sampt allen iren Zufellen und derselben vollkommener Cur* (Frankfurt, 1563); *Spittal Büch* (Mühlhausen, 1562; Frankfurt, 1566); *Dess erfarnesten Fürsten aller Artzeten Aureoli Theophrasti Paracelsi von ersten dreyen principijs . . .* (Basel, 1563); *Weyssagung Sibylle Tyburtine von . . . Lucas Gauricus . . . ausgelegt für das 1557 Jar,* trans. by Adam of Bodenstein (Nuremberg [?], 1556 [?]); *Baderbüchlin . . . Mit fleyss Adams von Bodenstein publicirt* (Mülhausen, 1562; Frankfurt, 1566, 1576); *Libri quinque de causis, signis et curationibus morborum ex tartaro utilissimi Opera . . .* (Basel, 1563); *De gradibus, de compositionibus et dosibus receptorum ac naturalium . . . libri septem* (Mylau, 1562; Basel, 1568); *Das Buch Paragranum . . . Item, von Aderlassens, Schrepffens und Purgirens rechtem gebrauch* (Frankfurt, 1562); *Das Buch Paramirum* (Mühlhausen, 1562); *Praeparationum libri duo* (Strasbourg, 1569); *Metamorphosis . . . der zerstörten . . . Artzney restauratoris . . .* (Basel, 1572); *Opus chyrurgicum* (Strasbourg, 1566; Basel, 1581); *Operum latine redditorum tomus I (II),* with preface by Adam of Bodenstein (Basel, 1575); *Schreiben von tartarischen Kranckheiten,* trans. into German and ed. by Adam of Bodenstein (n.p., 1563); *Labyrintus und Irrgang der vermeinten Artzet* (Basel, 1574); *Libri duo; I. Defensiones septem adversus aemulos suos; II. De tartaro sive morbis tartareis* (Strasbourg, 1566, 1573); *Drey Schreiben . . . Von tribus principiis aller Generaten, Libro vexationum und thesauro alchimistarum,* in B. G. Penot, *Theophrastisch Vade mecum* (Magdeburg, 1608); *Pyrophilia vexationumque liber* (Basel, 1568); *Schreyben von den Kranckheyten so die Vernunfft berauben als da sein S. Veyts Thantz hinfallender Siechtage; Melancholia und Unsinnigkeit* (n.p., 1567); *De tartaro libri septem . . . nunc vero auctiores et castigatiores denuo excusi* (Basel, 1570); *Schreiben von warmen oder Wildbäden* (Basel, 1576); *Zwey Bücher . . . von der Pestilentz und ihren Zufallen* (Strasbourg, 1559); *Herrlicher philosophischer Rhatschlag zu curirn Pestilentz Brustgeschwer, Carfunckl: Dardurch auch andere Gyfft . . . aussgetriben mögen werden* (Basel, 1577).

Works on Arnald of Villanova and alchemy are: *Isagoge in excellentissimi philosophi Arnaldi de Villanova Rosarium chymicum, paraphrastice et magna diligentia tradita, Epistola operi praefixa ad amplissimos et generosos dominos, dominos Fuggeros in qua argumenta alchymiam infirmantia et confirmantia adducuntur, quibus et eam artem esse certissimam demonstratur* (Basel, 1559); also available in MS: British Museum Sloane 3737, 17th cent., ff. 96r–106r, "Ex Isagoge Adam à Bodenstein in Rosarium Arnaldi."

The two tracts *De podagra* and *De herbis duodecim zodiaci signis dicatis,* noted by Melchior Adam (see below), have not been otherwise identified or located.

II. SECONDARY LITERATURE. The principal modern account is Lynn Thorndike, *History of Magic and Experimental Science,* V (New York, 1959), 619, 636; VI, 267. Dr. Thorndike utilized for the biographical information Melchior Adam, *Vitae medicorum Germanorum,* 3rd ed. (Frankfurt, 1706), pt. 4, p. 104, the sole extended source of information on Adam of Bodenstein; also Conrad Gesner, *Historia animalium* (Frankfurt, 1604), p. 829, "lib. IV, qui est de piscium et aquatilium animalium natura."

PEARL KIBRE

ADAMS, FRANK DAWSON

ADAMS, FRANK DAWSON (*b.* Montreal, Canada, 17 September 1859; *d.* Montreal, 26 December 1942), *geology.*

Adams' father, Noah Adams, belonged to the distinguished Adams family of New England; his mother, Frances Tait Dawson, was a United Empire Loyalist from Northern Ireland. At nineteen he graduated with first rank honors in natural science from McGill University, where he came under the influence of the scholarly principal, J. W. Dawson (no relation), and the versatile and magnetic B. J. Harrington of the department of chemistry and mineralogy. Comfortable family financial circumstances allowed Adams to study chemistry and mineralogy at Yale University (1878–1879), and later to attend several sessions at Heidelberg University.

After spending 1880 to 1889 in government service, Adams joined the staff at McGill as lecturer (1890–1893); he followed Dawson as holder of the Logan chair of geology in 1893. Adams became dean of the Faculty of Applied Science in 1908 and dean of the Faculty of Graduate Studies in 1922. He retired in 1924, after thirty-five years of arduous service. He was deeply but quietly religious. His *History of Christ Church Cathedral* (1941) was a tribute to the church to which he was devoted and to his wife, Mary Stuart Finley, to whom the book was dedicated. Adams also found time to devote to many philanthropic and social benevolences.

Adams belonged to numerous scientific societies, including the Royal Society of London, the Geological Society of America (of which he was president in 1918), the Royal Society of Canada (president in 1913; Flavelle Gold Medal in 1937), and the Geological Society of London (Lyell Medal in 1906; Wollaston Medal in 1939). He was also president of the Twelfth International Geological Congress (Montreal, 1913). He received honorary degrees from McGill, Toronto, Queen's, and Mount Allison universities, and Bishop's College.

In 1880 Adams joined the Geological Survey of Canada as assistant chemist and lithologist. One of the first tasks given him by the director, A. R. C. Selwyn, was to determine the nature and origin of certain rocks from southern Quebec. In order to work out these derivations and associations, Adams requested, and was granted, leave of absence to master the new petrographic technique being developed by H. Rosenbusch at Heidelberg. He completed this work to Selwyn's satisfaction and was next assigned to study areas of partly foliated anorthosites in southwestern Quebec that William Logan had considered to be the upper and stratified portion of the Laurentian series. To this difficult task he applied his newly won skill in the use of the petrographic microscope, an instrument with which he had become familiar in Heidelberg and which he was probably the first in Canada to use. He was able to demonstrate conclusively not only the igneous origin of the anorthosites but also the sedimentary origin of some of the Grenville crystalline rocks upon which Logan had supposed the anorthosites rested. The presentation of the results of this study gained him the Ph.D. *summa cum laude* at Heidelberg. The publication of his thesis (1893) established Adams as one of the North American experts in the use of the petrographic microscope. Several publications resulted from his work with the Geological Survey, among the more important being descriptions of Precambrian rocks north of Montreal and St. Jerome (1896), based on field work carried out from 1885 to 1891.

The Laurentian system had been considered by Logan to consist of two divisions, the lower a complex of metamorphosed sedimentary rocks, which he named Grenville and Ottawa, and an upper, or Norian, division, made up largely of anorthosite, which was considered to be an altered and crystallized sediment. This anorthosite, well exposed around Morin, Quebec, was very carefully inspected by Adams, who showed that it was composed largely of plagioclase feldspar, with few accessories. He established its igneous nature both by his petrographic determinations in the laboratory and by the intrusive contacts with the Grenville rocks that he was able to demonstrate in the field. He attributed the marked differences in grain size to crystal fracturing, which in places was carried to granulation. He also recognized that the Laurentian granites, then supposed to be the oldest rocks of the Canadian shield and possibly part of the original crust, were intrusive into metamorphic rocks, which therefore must have preceded them in time and space. These conclusions were among the foundations upon which the modern classification of the Precambrian series rests.

After leaving the Geological Survey and joining the staff of McGill, Adams devoted the summers of 1902 to 1908 to the mapping and description of the forbiddingly difficult Haliburton and Bancroft areas of southern Ontario. In his report (1910), written with A. E. Barlow, who had collaborated with him during the later years of the project, he showed that the oldest rocks were highly metamorphosed sediments, now gneisses, schists, quartzites, and marbles, and assigned them to the Grenville series. He found widespread intrusions of granite, diorite, and gabbro penetrating the Grenville rocks, and correctly attributed most of the metamorphism to the thermal effects of the abundant granite bodies. Adams noted that the metamorphism of the stratified rocks became more intense and the sedimentary rocks were "fretted away and [ultimately] represented only by occasional shreds and patches of amphibolite," as the intrusive granites were approached. His discovery of nepheline syenite adjacent to granite and marble bodies was of great scientific importance, and paved the way for their later industrial exploitation. Because of the clarity of the writing, the painstaking carefulness of the descriptions, and the logical deductions, Adams' report has become one of the classics of Canadian geology.

At McGill, Adams could not fail to be impressed by the peculiar rocks of Mount Royal. He found that the same general rock types prevailed in the half-dozen prominent hills dotted across the Paleozoic plain between Montreal and the Appalachian front. He announced the occurrence of these remarkable rock types in his paper "The Monteregian Hills: A Canadian Petrographical Province" (1903).

Close study of the deformed foliated gneisses and schists of the Grenville area had stimulated Adams' curiosity concerning the causes of such structures and the possibility of their being duplicated in laboratory experiments. Aided by colleagues in the engineering laboratories at McGill, he started a sequence of experiments, spread over the first decade of the present century, utilizing a gigantic (for that time) press in which he could subject rocks to enormous pressures. High pressures had long been used to test the strength of cubes of rock to determine architectural suitability; but to duplicate the conditions within the earth's crust, Adams subjected cylinders of rock encased in metallic tubes to compression under high confining pressures—for the most part less than 20,000 pounds per square inch but on one occasion 296,725 pounds per square inch. Manipulation of the apparatus allowed Adams to develop differential stresses and presumably to imitate the conditions under which some of the foliated rocks may have originated; he was also able to correlate some of the experimentally developed structures with natural ones observed in the field. The influence of this work upon our understanding of metamorphic processes is profound, and it has contributed in no small measure to the development of modern ideas of mountain building.

Adams' first paper in this field, written with J. T. Nicholson, concerned a thumb-size cylinder of Carrara marble that he exposed to a confining pressure of 18,000 pounds per square inch; after 124 days the column had shortened by 11.4 percent of its original height. Examined microscopically, it showed many of the characteristics peculiar to the Grenville marbles. Never before had properties of metamorphic rocks been imitated in controlled experiments. Adams returned to this topic several times, and by using the highest available pressure, 296,725 pounds per square inch, he developed in his samples a schistose structure essentially similar to that of some highly metamorphic calcareous rocks. One interesting result was his discovery that quick-loading techniques caused calcite to yield to stress along intergranular slip planes, giving a cataclastic structure, whereas slow increase in loading produced intracrystalline polysynthetic twinning.

Other experiments were designed to record the plasticity of rocks under high pressures, up to 200,000 pounds per square inch. Most soft materials were easily deformed, but the harder rocks, such as granite, failed along fracture lines, yielding zones of granulation; this corroborated Adams' own early ideas of the granulation of anorthosite by crystal fracturing. Other studies were directed to the determination of the depth at which pressure would close cavities in rocks. In granite, one of the least plastic rocks, Adams determined that cavities could exist as deep as eleven miles below the surface. One of his last papers on experimentation (1917), written with J. A. Bancroft, showed that the strength of rocks increases with pressure, and hence with depth in the crust, the conclusion being that rocks at great depth have great strength. To Adams must go the credit for establishing this phase of geological investigation upon a sure engineering foundation. His reputation as a pioneer in the field is secure.

In the decade following his retirement from active participation in university affairs, he and Mrs. Adams traveled widely, and following their third visit to Ceylon, he published the first complete geological report and map of that island (1929). Adams had always been intrigued by the beginnings of geological thinking, and during his travels he visited most of the Old World universities whose libraries held a wealth of early geological treatises. Wherever he could, he acquired early writings and amassed what was certainly the greatest such collection in private hands (now kept, intact, at McGill). This formed the basis for his scholarly work *Birth and Development of the Geological Sciences* (1938), a text that will long remain a standard treatment of the subject.

BIBLIOGRAPHY

I. ORIGINAL WORKS. Complete listings of Adams' geological papers relating to North America are in United States Geological Survey Bulletins 746, 823, 937, 1049, and 1195. His most important works are "Notes on the Microscopic Structures of Some Rocks of the Quebec Group," in *Geological Survey of Canada, Report of Progress for 1880–1882,* Part A (1883), 8–23; "Ueber das Norian oder Oberlaurentian von Canada," in *Neues Jahrbuch,* **8** (1893), 419–498; trans. in *Canadian Record of Science* (1895–1896), 169–198, 277–305, 416–443; "Report on the Geology of a Portion of the Laurentian Area Lying to the North of the Island of Montreal," in *Geological Survey of Canada, Annual Report* (*New Series*), **8,** Part J (1896); "The Monteregian Hills: A Canadian Petrographical Province," in *Journal of Geology,* **11** (1903), 239–282; "An Experimental Investigation Into the Flow of Marble," in *Royal Society of London, Philosophical Transactions* (Section A), **195** (1901), 363–401, with J. J. Nicholson; *An Investigation Into The Elastic Constants of Rocks, More Especially With Reference to Cubic Compressibility,* Carnegie Institute Publication 46 (Washington, 1905), with E. G. Coker; "An Experimental Investigation Into the Action of Differential Pressure of Certain Minerals and Rocks," in *Journal of Geology,* **18** (1910), 489–525; "An Experimental Investigation Into the Flow of Rocks—the Flow of Marble," in *American Journal of Science,* ser. 4, **29** (1910), 465–487; "An Experimental Investigation Into the Flow of Rocks" [with discussion], in Eleventh International Geological Congress, *Comptes rendus,* **14** (1912), 911–945; "On the Amount of Internal Friction Developed in Rocks During Deformation and on the Relative Plasticity of Different Types of Rocks," in *Journal of Geology,* **25** (1917), 597–637, with J. A. Bancroft; "Earliest Use of the Term Geology," in *Geological Society of America Bulletin,* **43** (1932), 121–123; "Geology of Ceylon," in *Canadian Journal of Research,* **1** (1929), 425–511; "Origin and Nature of Ore Deposits, an Historical Study," in *Geological Society of America Bulletin,* **45** (1934), 375–424; *The Birth and Development of the Geological Sciences* (Baltimore, 1938); and *History of Christ Church Cathedral* (Montreal, 1941).

II. SECONDARY LITERATURE. Of the many biographies the following are selected: H. M. Tory, "Frank Dawson Adams (1859–1942)," in *Royal Society of Canada Proceedings,* ser. 3, **37** (1943), 69–71; J. A. Dresser, "Memorial to Frank Dawson Adams," in *Geological Society of America Proceedings 1944* (1945), 143–150; and J. W. Flett, "Frank

Dawson Adams 1859–1942," in *Royal Society of London, Obituary Notices of Fellows,* **4**, no. 12 (1943), 381–393.

THOMAS H. CLARK

ADAMS, JOHN COUCH (*b.* Laneast, Cornwall, England, 5 June 1819; *d.* Cambridge, England, 21 January 1892), *astronomy, mathematics.*

John Couch Adams was born at Lidcot farm, seven miles from Launceston. He was the eldest son of Thomas Adams, a tenant farmer and a devout Wesleyan, and Tabitha Knill Grylls. The family circumstances were modest but respectable: Tabitha Adams' cousin was the headmaster of a private school in Devonport, and in 1836 her adoptive mother left her some property and a small income which helped support John's education.

Adams had his first schooling in a Laneast farmhouse. In 1827 he was tutored in calligraphy, Greek, and mathematics, but quickly outpaced his teacher. He developed an early interest in astronomy, inscribing a sundial on his window sill and observing solar altitudes with an instrument he built himself. In 1831 he was sent to his cousin's academy, where he distinguished himself in classics, spending his spare time on astronomy and mathematics. Teaching himself, he finished the standard texts on conic sections, differential calculus, theory of numbers, theory of equations, and mechanics. Adams' precocity convinced his parents that he should be sent to a university, and in October 1839 he sat for examinations at St. John's College, Cambridge University, and won a sizarship. He went on to win the highest mathematical prizes in his college and took first prize in Greek testament every year that he was at Cambridge.

In July 1841, Adams, having read about the irregularities in the motion of the planet Uranus, decided to investigate them as soon as he had taken his degree. He graduated from Cambridge in 1843 as senior wrangler in the mathematical tripos and first Smith's prizeman; shortly afterward he became a fellow and tutor of his college. At the beginning of the next long vacation he returned to Lidcot and began the long-deferred investigation of Uranus.

By October 1843 Adams had arrived at a solution of the inverse perturbation problem: given the mass of a body and its deviations from the path predicted for it by Newtonian mechanics, find the orbit and position of another body perturbing it through gravitational attraction. This problem required, among other procedures, the solution of ten simultaneous equations of condition for as many unknowns. Although Adams' first result was approximate, it convinced him that the disturbances of Uranus were due to an undiscovered planet.

In February 1844, Adams applied through James Challis to the astronomer royal, Sir George Biddell Airy, for more exact data on Uranus. Using figures supplied by Airy, Adams computed values for the elliptic elements, mass, and heliocentric longitude of the hypothetical planet. He gave his results to Challis in September 1845, and after two unsuccessful attempts to present his work to Airy in person, he left a copy of it at the Royal Observatory on 21 October 1845. Although Airy wrote to Adams a few weeks later criticizing his paper, he did not institute a search for the planet until July 1846.

In the meantime a French astronomer, Urbain Jean Joseph Leverrier, independently published several papers on the theory of Uranus and reached the same conclusions as Adams had regarding an exterior planet. Although Leverrier began his investigation later, he pressed his case more aggressively, and on 23 September 1846 the perturbing body—Neptune—was discovered as a result of his efforts. Johann Gottfried Galle, an astronomer at the Berlin Observatory, found the planet less than one degree distant from the point where Leverrier predicted it would lie.

Leverrier was immediately showered with honors and congratulations. Adams' earlier prediction, which agreed closely with Leverrier's, was thus far unpublished. It was first publicized in a letter from Sir John Herschel to the London *Athenaeum* on 3 October 1846 and provoked a long and bitter controversy over priority of discovery. The two principals took little part in the feud, but the issue became a public sensation. It still seems remarkable that Airy suppressed Adams' work for so long and that Adams was so reticent about pressing his claims. This behavior was, however, characteristic of Adams. The modesty that temporarily cost him some glory endeared him to colleagues and friends throughout his life.

The disparity between the credit accorded to Leverrier and that accorded to Adams was not made up for some years, but the two men met at Oxford in 1847 and became good friends. Adams was offered a knighthood by Queen Victoria in 1847 but declined it; the following year the Adams Prize, awarded biennially for the best essay in physics, mathematics, or astronomy, was instituted at Cambridge. The Royal Society gave Adams its highest award, the Copley Medal, in 1848.

In 1851 Adams was elected president of the Royal Astronomical Society and shortly afterward began to work on lunar theory. After much laborious calculation he finished new tables of the moon's parallax which corrected several errors in lunar theory and gave more accurate positions. In the meantime, since he had not taken holy orders, his fellowship at St. John's expired in 1852. He was elected a fellow of Pembroke College in 1853, and shortly afterward he presented to the Royal Society a remarkable paper on the secular acceleration of the moon's mean motion. This quantity was thought to have been definitively investigated by Pierre Simon de Laplace in 1788, but Adams showed that Laplace's solution was incorrect. In particular, Laplace had ignored a variation in solar eccentricity that introduces into the differential equations for the moon's motion a series of additional terms. Adams calculated the second term of the series, on which the secular acceleration depends, as $3771/64\,m^4$; the value computed from Laplace's work was $2187/128\,m^4$. The effect of the correction was to reduce the figure for the moon's secular acceleration by about half, from $10''.58$ to $5''.70$.

This paper caused a sharp scientific controversy, marked by angry chauvinism on the part of several French astronomers. Their attacks stimulated a number of independent investigations of the subject, all of which confirmed Adams' result. The matter was definitely settled in his favor by 1861, but not without hard feelings.

In 1858 Adams occupied the chair of mathematics at the University of St. Andrews, vacating it the following year to accept the appointment as Lowndean professor of astronomy and geometry at Cambridge. In 1861 he succeeded James Challis as director of the Cambridge Observatory, and in 1863, when he was forty-four, he married Eliza Bruce of Dublin. In 1866 the Royal Astronomical Society awarded Adams a gold medal for his work on lunar theory.

The brilliant Leonid meteor shower of November 1866 stimulated Adams to investigate the elements of the Leonid system. By dividing the orbit into small segments, he calculated an analysis of perturbations for the meteor group, resulting in improved values for its period and elements. This work provided another demonstration of Adams' extraordinary ability to manipulate equations of great length and complexity without error.

In 1870 the Cambridge Observatory acquired a Simms transit circle. In order to exploit it fully, Adams undertook—a rarity for him—the direction of a program of observational astronomy. The circle was used to map a zone lying between 25° and 30° of north declination for the *Astronomische Gesellschaft* program. This work was first published in 1897.

In 1874 Adams was elected to a second term as president of the Royal Astronomical Society. His scientific interest at this time turned to mathematics.

Like Euler and Gauss, Adams enjoyed the calculation of exact values for mathematical constants. In 1877 he published thirty-one Bernoullian numbers, thus doubling the known number. With sixty-two Bernoullian numbers available, he decided to compute a definitive value of Euler's constant; this required the calculation of certain logarithms to 273 decimal places. Using these terms, Adams extended Euler's constant to 263 decimal places. This result was published in the *Proceedings* of the Royal Society in 1878; in the same year Adams published expressions for the products of two Legendrian coefficients and for the integral of the product of three.

Adams was a fervent admirer of Isaac Newton. In 1872, when Lord Portsmouth presented Newton's scientific papers to Cambridge University, Adams willingly undertook to arrange and catalog those dealing with mathematics. He was also an omnivorous reader in other fields, especially botany, history, and fiction. He usually kept a novel at hand when working on long mathematical problems.

In retrospect Adams' many mathematical and astronomical achievements pale in comparison to his analysis of the orbit of Uranus and his prediction of the existence and position of Neptune at the age of twenty-four. Much of his later work has been superseded, but as the co-discoverer of Neptune he occupies a special, undiminished place in the history of science.

BIBLIOGRAPHY

I. Original Works. Works by Adams include MSS on the perturbations of Uranus, 1841–1846, St. John's College Library, Cambridge, England; *Lectures on the Lunar Theory* (Cambridge, England, 1900); and William Grylls Adams, ed., *The Scientific Papers of John Couch Adams,* 2 vols. (Cambridge, England, 1896–1900).

II. Secondary Literature. See Morton Grosser, *The Discovery of Neptune* (Cambridge, Mass., 1962); Urbain Jean Joseph Leverrier, MS of the memoir "Recherches sur le mouvement de la planète Herschel (dite Uranus)," in the library of the Paris Observatory; W. M. Smart, "John Couch Adams and the Discovery of Neptune," in *Occasional Notes of the Royal Astronomical Society* (London), **2** (1947), 33–88.

Morton Grosser

ADAMS, WALTER SYDNEY (*b.* Kessab, near Antioch, Syria, 20 December 1876; *d.* Pasadena, California, 11 May 1956), *astrophysics.*

The son of Lucien Harper Adams and Nancy Dorrance Francis, missionaries in Syria, Adams was brought up in a strict, though broad-minded, environment. He received his early schooling from his mother and from his father's classical and historical library. His childhood was spent near Antioch, crossroads of the Crusades, and at the age of six he knew more of the history of Athens and Rome and the campaigns of Alexander the Great and Hannibal than of the United States. Here, too, his interest in astronomy was aroused when his father pointed out the constellations in the clear Syrian skies.

In 1885 the family returned to Derry, New Hampshire. Adams graduated with the A.B. from Dartmouth College in 1898 and, on the advice of Edwin B. Frost, his teacher of astronomy, entered the University of Chicago. There he earned a reputation as a skillful mathematician. He gained his first practical observing experience under George Ellery Hale, founder and director of the Yerkes Observatory, which, with its forty-inch refracting telescope, was then the largest in the world. After receiving his M.A. in 1900, he went to the University of Munich; the following year he returned to Yerkes as computer and general assistant.

Adams was married twice, first to Lillian Wickham, who died in 1920, and in 1922 to Adeline L. Miller, by whom he had two sons, Edmund and John.

Inspired by Hale's vision of the future of astrophysics and by his belief in the importance of an observatory as a physical laboratory, Adams followed his path enthusiastically. In 1947, fifty years after the dedication of the Yerkes Observatory, he described the revolution in astronomy:

> It opened at a time when visual observations were still a major factor in observatory activities, photographic methods were in their infancy, the spectrum was studied empirically and cosmogony was almost a completely sealed book. The period ends with visual observations greatly reduced in amount, although still holding an important place, with photographic methods applied almost universally and enormously improved and extended, with the spectrum analyzed and used as an extraordinarily powerful tool to seek out physical processes in the sun and stars, and with a clear and logical picture of a physical universe beyond the imagination of the astronomer of fifty years ago.[1]

In this transformation Adams played a leading role, first at the Yerkes, then at the Mount Wilson Observatory. As acting director of Mount Wilson at various periods, then as director from 1923 to 1946, he contributed significantly to the design of instruments, especially of the 100-inch and of the 200-inch Hale telescopes on Palomar Mountain. Through his leadership he helped to make the Mount Wilson and Palomar observatories preeminent, so that astrono-

mers the world over came to use these, the most powerful astronomical instruments on earth, to push back the frontiers of the universe.

Adams' observations ranged from planetary atmospheres to interstellar gases, from sunspot spectra to his greatest achievement—the discovery of a method for determining stellar distances. His research was characterized by notable skill in observation and precision in measurement.

His influence on astronomical development, both nationally and internationally, was reflected in his positions in the American Astronomical Society (president, 1931–1934), the Astronomical Society of the Pacific (president, 1923), and the International Astronomical Union (vice-president, 1935–1948, acting secretary, 1940–1945). His broader interests in science were reflected in his membership in the American Philosophical Society (elected 1915) and the National Academy of Sciences (1917) and by his election as foreign associate to many academies of science, including those of France, Sweden, and the Soviet Union, and the Royal Society of London (foreign member).

His earliest work, on the polar compression of Jupiter, was followed by research with Frost on radial velocities in B-type, or helium, stars. By 1903, despite the difficulty of observing the diffuse spectral lines, measurement of the velocities in twenty such stars showed the average motion to be exceptionally small. This result would prove important in discussions of stellar motions, especially in the recognition by W. W. Campbell of the so-called K-term. In April 1904, Adams joined Hale on the Yerkes expedition to Pasadena, California; this led to the establishment by the Carnegie Institution of Washington of the Mount Wilson Solar Observatory on 20 December 1904. In his vivid "Early Days at Mount Wilson," he described the wild and primitive conditions, the joys and difficulties of a pioneer time when transportation of equipment was wholly by pack train and the only means of reaching the peak was by mule or burro, or on foot. He had a wiry, athletic build and an indefatigable spirit, and often climbed the steep, twisting, eight-mile trail; prepared the telescope for observing; worked the night through; then walked down the mountain the following morning.

At Mount Wilson he joined Hale in an intensive study of that "typical star," our sun, first with the horizontal Snow reflector, then with the sixty-foot and 150-foot tower solar telescopes. Visually it had been observed that the spectrum of a sunspot differs from that of the solar disk, but little was known of the nature of the spot spectrum, and nothing of its cause. Now, for the first time, it became possible to study spot spectra photographically with adequate apparatus. In 1906 Adams and Hale took the first photograph of a spot spectrum at Mount Wilson and undertook a detailed comparison of spot spectra with those of the solar disk. Simultaneously experiments were begun in the primitive laboratory on the mountain to imitate the conditions observed in the sun. Working with Henry Gale on arc spectra, Adams and Hale were able to show that temperature must be the cause of the differences observed between spots and disk, and thus to prove that sunspots are cooler than the surrounding solar surfaces. From further laboratory studies of pressure and density, they also showed that "enhanced lines" (those lines identified and named by Norman Lockyer to denote lines that are much stronger in the electric spark spectrum than in that of the arc) are the result of a lower density of the gases, while in sunspots the density proved to be higher. These and other results found a rational explanation when, in 1920, M. N. Saha published his theory of ionization.

In the course of this investigation Adams became interested in the problem of solar rotation. From a study of the minute Doppler displacements at various solar levels, he found that higher levels in the sun showed a higher rate of rotation and a smaller equatorial acceleration than the lower levels. In 1909, with Hale, he succeeded in photographing the flash spectrum without eclipse.

Gradually Adams turned from studies of the sun to other, larger stars. Yet, as he was often to show, the early sunspot studies played an important role in the understanding of other stars, and especially in the determination of their distances. In "Sunspots and Stellar Distances" he described the fascinating chain of events that led from the classification of groups of spectral lines according to temperature, to show how unexpected the ramifications of scientific investigation can be. "The study attained its primary objectives, but in addition it provided in the field of physics the first clues to the analysis of complex spectra according to energy levels in the atom, in solar physics the discovery of magnetism in the sun, and in astrophysics a new and fundamental method for determining the distances of the stars."[2]

In 1906, using the Snow telescope, Adams had succeeded in taking a twenty-three-hour exposure, on five successive nights, of the line spectrum of the cool star Arcturus. When he compared this spectrum with that of a sunspot, he found them to be similar. In 1908, after the sixty-inch reflecting telescope was set up on Mount Wilson, he extended his comparative studies to other stars—their motions, spectral classifications, magnitudes, and the distances of those too

far away to be measured trigonometrically. These studies included the first thorough investigation of the differences in the spectra of the large and massive stars of high luminosity called giants and the comparatively dense bodies of very low luminosity known as dwarfs.

In 1914, working at first with Arnold Kohlschütter, Adams compared pairs of stars of nearly the same spectral type, and therefore of nearly the same temperature, but of very different luminosity.

> It soon appeared that a few lines were stronger in the spectrum of the highly luminous star, and others in that of the intrinsically faint star. With the use of all the available material for well-determined luminosities it then became possible to establish numerical correlations between luminosity and the intensities of these sensitive lines. The process could then be reversed and in the case of a star of unknown luminosity its value could be derived from the intensities of the lines; the distance of the star is then readily calculated from the simple relationship connecting apparent brightness, luminosity and distance.[3]

This ingenious method of obtaining "spectroscopic parallaxes," applied to thousands of stars, has become a fundamental astronomical tool of immense value in gaining knowledge of giant and dwarf stars and of galactic structure. Otto Struve commented, "It is not an exaggeration to say that almost all our knowledge of the structure of the Milky Way which has developed during the past quarter of a century has come from the Mount Wilson discovery of spectroscopic luminosity criteria."[4]

In 1917 the 100-inch telescope went into operation. Adams had made the Hartmann tests of the mirror which were vital to its successful figuring. For it he built the powerful Coudé spectrograph that would provide higher dispersion and make the penetration of hitherto unknown regions possible. The following year, in studies that stemmed from his investigation of giants and dwarfs, he became interested in Sirius B, the companion of Sirius that he had first identified as a tiny white-hot star, or white dwarf, in 1915. He found that while the companion is small, it has a mass not much less than that of the sun (actually four-fifths of that mass). It proved, almost incredibly, to be about 50,000 times as dense as water. A ton of such material could be squeezed into a matchbox. Sir Arthur Eddington predicted that, since the Einstein effect is proportional to the mass divided by the radius of the star and the radius of the companion of Sirius is very small, the relativity effect should be large. In 1925 Adams performed the difficult feat of taking a spectrogram of the faint companion, which is 10,000 times fainter than its neighbor, yet only twelve arc seconds away. He confirmed Eddington's prediction when he found a displacement to the red of 21 km./sec., a result he later modified to 19 km./sec. Eddington wrote: "Prof. Adams has thus killed two birds with one stone. He has carried out a new test of Einstein's general theory of relativity, and he has shown that matter at least 2,000 times denser than platinum is not only possible, but actually exists in the stellar universe."[5]

In the 1920's and 1930's Adams also applied the spectrograph to studies of the atmospheres of Venus and Mars—these observations were difficult because of the problem of identifying such substances as oxygen, carbon dioxide, and water vapor, which are also contained in the earth's atmosphere. In 1932, with Theodore Dunham, Jr., he identified carbon dioxide in the infrared spectrum of Venus. In 1934 similar observations of Mars indicated that the amount of free oxygen above a given area of the surface of Mars cannot exceed one-tenth of one percent.

Over the years other investigations included Cepheids, spectroscopic binaries, and, from 1901 to 1936, the spectra of novae that he felt might be explained by an expanding shell or succession of shells. In his last extensive research on the clouds of interstellar gas he had the arduous task of sorting out the lines in a star's own spectrum from those belonging to the tenuous interstellar gases. He found double or multiple interstellar lines in 80 percent of the stars examined, identified two classes of clouds, and observed four clouds moving with radial velocities up to 100 km./sec. The highly accurate velocities provided good values for the relative motions caused by the rotation of the galaxy.

These, then, were the far-ranging programs through which Adams contributed to our knowledge of the nature of the universe and profoundly influenced the development of cosmogony.

NOTES

1. "Some Reminiscences of the Yerkes Observatory," p. 196.
2. *Cooperation in Solar Research,* pp. 135–137.
3. "Biographical Notes—Walter S. Adams," written for the National Academy of Sciences (Jan. 1954), p. 9 (unpublished).
4. "Fifty Years of Progress in Astronomy," p. 6.
5. *Stars and Atoms,* p. 52.

BIBLIOGRAPHY

I. ORIGINAL WORKS. Adams' bibliography in Joy's biographical article (see below) includes 270 papers, in addition to his annual Mount Wilson reports. Among these papers are "The Polar Compression of Jupiter," in *Astronomical Journal,* **20** (1899), 133, written while he was still a graduate student; "Radial Velocities of Twenty Stars Having Spectra of the Orion Type," in *Publications of the Yerkes Observatory,* **2** (1904), 143–250, written with E. B. Frost; "Photographic Observations of the Spectra of Sunspots," in *Astrophysical Journal,* **23** (1906), 11–44, written with G. E. Hale; "Preliminary Paper on the Cause of the Characteristic Phenomena of Sunspot Spectra," *ibid.,* **24** (1906), 185–213, written with G. E. Hale and H. G. Gale; "Sunspot Lines in the Spectrum of Arcturus," *ibid.,* 69–77; "Spectroscopic Observations of the Rotation of the Sun," *ibid.,* **26** (1907), 203–224; "Photography of the Flash Spectrum Without an Eclipse," *ibid.,* **30** (1909), 222–230, written with G. E. Hale; "The Radial Velocities of 100 Stars With Measured Parallaxes," *ibid.,* **39** (1914), 341–349, written with A. Kohlschütter; "The Spectrum of the Companion of Sirius," in *Publications of the Astronomical Society of the Pacific,* **27** (1915), 236–237; "A Spectroscopic Method of Determining Parallaxes," in *Proceedings of the National Academy of Sciences,* **2** (1916), 147–152; "Address of the Retiring President . . .," in *Publications of the Astronomical Society of the Pacific,* **36** (1924), 2–9; "The Relativity Displacement of the Spectral Lines in the Companion of Sirius," in *Proceedings of the National Academy of Sciences,* **11** (1925), 382–387; "The Past Twenty Years of Physical Astronomy," in *Publications of the Astronomical Society of the Pacific,* **40** (1928), 213–228; "The Astronomer's Measuring Rods," *ibid.,* **41** (1929), 195–211; "Absorption Bands in the Spectrum of Venus," *ibid.,* **44** (1932), 243–245, written with Theodore Dunham, Jr.; "The B-Band of Oxygen in the Spectrum of Mars," in *Astrophysical Journal,* **79** (1934), 308–316, written with Theodore Dunham, Jr.; "The Planets and Their Atmospheres," in *Scientific Monthly,* **39** (1934), 5–19; "The Sun's Place Among the Stars," in *Annual Report of the Smithsonian Institution for 1935,* pp. 139–151; "Sunspots and Stellar Distances," in *Cooperation in Solar Research,* Carnegie Institution of Washington pub. no. 506 (1938), pp. 135–147; "George Ellery Hale," in *Biographical Memoirs of the National Academy of Sciences,* **21** (1940), 181–241; "Newton's Contributions to Observational Astronomy," in *The Royal Society Newton Tercentenary Celebrations* (Cambridge, 1946), pp. 73–81; "Early Days at Mount Wilson," in *Publications of the Astronomical Society of the Pacific,* **59** (1947), 213–231, 285–304; the Henry Norris lecture of the American Astronomical Society (29 Dec. 1947), *ibid.,* **60** (1948), 174–189; "Some Reminiscences of the Yerkes Observatory," in *Science,* **106,** no. 2749 (5 Sept. 1947), 196–200; "The History of the International Astronomical Union," in *Publications of the Astronomical Society of the Pacific,* **61** (1949), 5–12; "The Founding of the Mount Wilson Observatory," *ibid.,* **66** (1954), 267–303; and "Early Solar Research at Mount Wilson," in Arthur Beer, ed., *Vistas in Astronomy,* I (London, 1955), 619–623. See also the *Annual Report* of the Mount Wilson Observatory (1923–1945).

The bulk of Adams' correspondence, original manuscripts, and other source materials are (as of 1968) in the

Hale Solar Laboratory and in the director's files of the Mount Wilson and Palomar observatories.

II. SECONDARY LITERATURE. Biographical articles on Adams include Alfred H. Joy, "Walter S. Adams, a Biographical Memoir," in *Biographical Memoirs of the National Academy of Sciences,* **31** (1958); Paul W. Merrill, "Walter S. Adams, Observer of Sun and Stars," in *Science,* **124** (13 July 1956), 67; Harlow Shapley, "A Master of Stellar Spectra," in *Sky and Telescope,* **15** (1956), 401; and F. J. M. Stratton, "Walter Sydney Adams (1876–1956)," in *Biographical Memoirs of the Royal Society,* **2** (Nov. 1956), 1–18.

Additional works that contribute to a picture of the development of astronomy in this period, and of Adams' role in that development, are Charles G. Abbot, *Adventures in the World of Science* (Washington, D.C., 1958), esp. ch. 6; Giorgio Abetti, "Solar Physics," in *Handbuch der Astrophysik,* IV (Berlin, 1929), 161–168, and VII (Berlin, 1936), 184; *The History of Astronomy,* Betty B. Abetti, trans. (New York, 1952), pp. 255, 258, 259, 274, 291–292, 298, 306, 327; and *The Sun,* J. B. Sidgwick, trans. (New York, 1957), pp. 103, 142, 143, 144, 145, 147, 148, 164–165, 206, 231, 232; Herbert Dingle, "The Message of Starlight," in T. E. R. Phillips and W. H. Steavenson, eds., *Splendour of the Heavens,* II (London, 1924), 479–499; Sir Arthur Eddington, *Stars and Atoms* (Oxford, 1927), pp. 48–53; Edwin B. Frost, *An Astronomer's Life* (Boston, 1933); George Ellery Hale, *The Study of Stellar Evolution* (Chicago, 1908); Caryl Haskins, *The Search for Understanding* (Washington, D.C., 1967), which includes a large part of "Early Days at Mount Wilson" (pp. 301–326) and other material relating to the observatory (pp. 234–277); Gerard P. Kuiper, ed., *The Sun* (Chicago, 1953), especially the excellent introduction by Leo Goldberg, pp. 7–22; Knut Lundmark, "Luminosities, Colours, Diameters, Densities, Masses of the Stars," in *Handbuch der Astrophysik,* V (Berlin, 1932), ch. 4; A. Pannekoek, *A History of Astronomy* (New York, 1961); M. N. Saha, "Ionization in the Solar Chromosphere," in *Philosophical Magazine,* **40** (1920), 479; Harlow Shapley, "Brief Historical Analysis on the Spectra of Stars and Nebulae," in *Source Book in Astronomy, 1900–1950* (Cambridge, Mass., 1960), pp. 159–161, 162–164, in which Shapley discusses Adams' work on star distances and reprints two of his papers; Otto Struve, "The Story of an Observatory (The Fiftieth Anniversary of the Yerkes Observatory)," in *Popular Astronomy,* **55,** nos. 5–6 (May–June 1947); and "Fifty Years of Progress in Astrophysics," in *The Science Counselor* (Mar. 1948), 4–6, esp. 6, 26–27; Otto Struve and Velta Zebergs, *Astronomy of the 20th Century* (New York, 1962); and Helen Wright, *Palomar, the World's Largest Telescope* (New York, 1952), and *Explorer of the Universe, a Biography of George Ellery Hale* (New York, 1966).

HELEN WRIGHT

ADANSON, MICHEL (*b.* Aix-en-Provence, France, 7 April 1727; *d.* Paris, France, 3 August 1806), *natural history, philosophy.*

Adanson belonged to an Auvergne family that moved to Provence at the beginning of the eighteenth century and to Paris about 1730. He was educated at the Plessis Sorbon, the Collège Royal, and the Jardin du Roi. Among his *maîtres* were Pierre Le Monnier, Réaumur, G.-F. Rouelle, and Antoine and Bernard de Jussieu. He made his first four-year scientific expedition to Senegal on behalf of the Compagnie des Indes and brought back a large group of natural history specimens; a few of these later became part of the royal collection, then under the care of Buffon. While traveling in Africa, Adanson was elected (24 July 1750) a corresponding member of the Académie des Sciences. His travel journal (1757) was accompanied by a general survey of the living mollusks he had found in Senegal. His classification of mollusks was an original one; based on the anatomical structure of the living animals inside the shells, it appeared the same year as the work of Argenville, who claimed to have originated such a scheme.

In 1761 Adanson was elected a foreign member of the Royal Society of London, and in 1763–1764 he published *Familles des plantes.* In this book he proclaimed his contempt for "systems" and proposed a natural classification based upon all characters rather than upon a few arbitrarily selected ones, an attempt that brought him into conflict with Linnaeus. Recent historical studies have shown that Adanson's views were shared by many Parisian botanists and that he was responsible for the maintenance of Joseph Tournefort's system at the Jardin du Roi until 1774, when A. L. de Jussieu's system was adopted. Adanson owed much to Bernard de Jussieu's plant families as they were developed in his manuscript plan for the Trianon garden in which he arranged the plants in beds in an order corresponding to his system of classification. He soon recognized that his *Familles des plantes* was only an outline of his general conception, and in 1769 he prepared a new edition that was never published.

Adanson knew Diderot but did not collaborate on the *Encyclopédie,* although he played an important role in the publication of the supplement (1776) by Panckoucke, to whom he sent more than 400 articles. He had his own views about encyclopedias, and in 1775 he presented a plan for one to the Académie des Sciences. By that time he had amassed a collection of documents, observations of his own, and natural history specimens. Nothing came of this plan, however, and he spent the rest of his life in futile attempts to publish his own encyclopedia. On 23 July 1759 Adanson had been elected *adjoint botaniste;* on 25 February 1773, *associé botaniste;* and on 6 December 1782, *académicien pensionnaire.* Upon the creation of the Institut de France, he was immediately selected a member of the first college. Later Napoleon made him a member of the Legion of Honor.

In many respects Adanson played a hidden role in the development of science, for he was in touch with most of the learned people of Europe. He studied static electricity in the torpedo fish, the tourmaline, and various plants; agricultural problems concerning corn, wheat, barley, and fruits; microscopic animalcules; and the circulation of sap in lower plants. He also experimented on regeneration of the limbs and head of frogs and snails. Although he kept most of his materials for his own use, we know that he was an important contributor to Buffon's *Histoire naturelle générale,* where he is quoted more than a hundred times. He had sent several hundred new plant species from Senegal to Bernard de Jussieu, and before his controversy with Linnaeus, he had sent to Sweden a number of African plants that Linnaeus said he included with those of Hasselquist. His general herbarium, now in the Muséum National d'Histoire Naturelle, contains about 30,000 specimens, many of which have been studied; the plants he sent to Jussieu were used by A. L. de Jussieu for his *Genera plantarum* and by later botanists. Lamarck used Adanson's articles in the *Encyclopédie* supplement for his *Dictionnaire de botanique.*

Adanson survived the Revolution without political difficulties, but suffered much from the financial crash. His whole life, however, was one of periodic financial insecurity, alleviated by the patronage obtained for him by his friends and by the life annuity granted in the 1760's when his natural history collection became part of the Cabinet du Roi. Intellectually, he was perhaps equally insecure, admired by many of his contemporaries and disliked by others for both scientific and personal reasons. It is only recently that his historical influence and his role in introducing modern statistical methods into systematic botany have received proper recognition.

BIBLIOGRAPHY

I. ORIGINAL WORKS. Adanson's first book was *Histoire naturelle du Sénégal. Coquillages. Avec la relation abrégée d'un voyage fait en ce pays pendant les années 1749 . . . 1753* (Paris, 1757); the travel portion was translated by "an English gentleman" as *A Voyage to Senegal, the Isle of Goree and the River Gambia* (London-Dublin, 1759), and into German by Martini as *Reise nach Senegall* (Brandenburg, 1772) and by Schreber as *Nachricht von seiner Reise nach Senegall* (Leipzig, 1773); a review of the *Histoire naturelle* is in G. R. Boehmer, *Bibliotheca scriptorum historiae naturalis oeconomiae, aliarum que artium ac scientiarum,* Vol. I (Leipzig, 1785). His other book is *Familles des plantes,* 2 vols. (Paris, 1763–1764), reviewed in G. R. Boehmer, *op. cit.*

See also "Marées de l'Ile de Gorée," in *Mémoires de mathématiques et de physique, présentés à l'Académie royale des sciences, par divers sçavans,* **2** (1755), 605–606; "Plan de botanique," in *Collection académique (Savants français),* **8** (n.d. [after 1759]), appendix p. 59; "Description . . . du baobab," in *Mémoires de l'Académie des sciences* (1761 [1763]), pp. 218–243; "Description d'une nouvelle espèce de vers . . . ," *ibid.* (1759 [1765]), pp. 249–279; "Remarques sur les bleds appelés de miracle," *ibid.* (1765 [1768]), pp. 613–619; "Mémoire sur un mouvement particulier . . . de la tremelle," *ibid.* (1767 [1770]), pp. 564–572; "Examen de la question: si les espèces changent parmi les plantes . . . ," *ibid.* (1769 [1772]), pp. 31–48; "Premier mémoire sur l'acacia des anciens," *ibid.* (1773 [1777]), pp. 1–17; "Deuxième mémoire sur le gommier blanc . . . ," *ibid.* (1778 [1781]), pp. 20–35; and "Observations météorologiques . . . ," *ibid.,* p. 425.

Published after Adanson's death were *Cours d'histoire naturelle fait en 1772,* 2 vols. (Paris, 1845), and *Histoire de la botanique et plan des familles naturelles des plantes* (Paris, 1864), A. Adanson and J. B. Payer, eds.

Manuscripts on botanical subjects and a large part of Adanson's library, with many annotated books, are in the Hunt Botanical Library of Carnegie Institute of Technology, Pittsburgh, Pa. Letters are in the Royal Society of London; Wellcome Library, London; Académie des Sciences, Paris; Institut de France, Paris; Bibliothèque Nationale, Département des Manuscrits, Paris; Bibliothèque Centrale du Muséum National d'Histoire Naturelle, Paris; Bibliothèque Publique et Universitaire de Genève; and Bibliothèque de la Bourgeoisie, Berne.

II. SECONDARY LITERATURE. Although rather superficial in its judgments, Cuvier's *éloge* of Adanson, in *Recueil des éloges historiques,* new ed. (Paris, 1861), I, 173–204, was the basic source used by nineteenth-century biographers. More recent is *Adanson,* 2 vols., Hunt Monograph Series, G. H. M. Lawrence, ed. (Pittsburgh, 1963–1964), containing several original papers, a biography, a bibliography, and notes. A general review of J. P. Nicolas's studies of Adanson is the pamphlet "Adanson et les Encyclopédistes," Lecture D.104, Palais de la Découverte, Paris (3 April 1965).

J. P. NICOLAS

ADDISON, THOMAS (*b.* Long Benton, England, *ca.* April 1793; *d.* Brighton, England, 29 June 1860), *medicine.*

Although the birth date generally assigned to Thomas Addison is April 1793, the tablet in Guy's Hospital Chapel in London and that in Lanercost Abbey in Cumberland, where he is buried, state that he died on 29 June 1860, at the age of sixty-eight. The Long Benton church baptismal register has the following entry: "1795, Oct. 11. Thomas s. of Joseph and Sarah Addison, Lg. Benton." The same register gives 13 April 1794 as the baptismal date of John, the second son of Joseph and Sarah Addison. Since it is unlikely that if Thomas had been born in 1793 his baptism would have been deferred until after that of his younger brother, it is reasonable to believe that in the course of transcription a five has become a three, as Hale-White suggested.

Addison married Elizabeth Catherine Hauxwell at Lanercost Church in September 1847. They were childless, although she had two children by her first marriage.

Addison was first sent to school near Long Benton, and then went to a grammar school at Newcastle-on-Tyne. He learned Latin so well that he made notes in that language and spoke it fluently. His father had wished him to become a lawyer, but in 1812 he entered the University of Edinburgh as a medical student. He graduated in 1815, at the age of twenty-two, as a Doctor of Medicine. The title of his thesis was "De syphilide et hydrargyro" ("Concerning Syphilis and Mercury"). Guy's Medical School book records his entrance: "Dec. 13, 1817, from Edinburgh, T. Addison, M.D., paid £22-ls. to be a perpetual Physician's Pupil."

Addison became house surgeon at Lock Hospital in London in 1815 and was appointed assistant physician to Guy's Hospital on 14 January 1824. He became lecturer on materia medica three years later. He was joint lecturer on medicine with Richard Bright in 1835, and in 1837 he became physician to Guy's Hospital. In 1840 Bright retired from the lectureship, and Addison became sole lecturer. He held this position until either 1854 or 1855. He obtained his licentiateship in the Royal College of Physicians on 22 December 1819 and was elected a fellow on 4 July 1838.

Addison's numerous clinical studies include works on the clinical signs of a fatty liver (1836), appendicitis (1839), pneumonia (1843), phthisis (1845), and xanthoma (1851). In 1849 he described Addison's anemia before a meeting of the South London Medical Society: "For a long period I had from time to time met with a remarkable form of general anemia. . . ." His clinical findings fit with both Vitamin B_{12} and folic acid deficiency states. One feature peculiar to Vitamin B_{12} deficiency is: ". . . the bulkiness of the general frame and the obesity often present, a most striking contrast."

In the absence of a separate formal report, it is not surprising that the world overlooked this excellent description of pernicious anemia. That description, good as it was, was quite overshadowed by Addison's spectacular discovery of the disturbance of the suprarenal capsules. In 1855, in a paper entitled "On the Constitutional and Local Effects of Disease of the Suprarenal Capsules," he described what is now known as Addison's disease, a condition characterized by progressive anemia, bronze skin pigmentation, severe weakness, and low blood pressure. It is now known that in Addison's disease the blood sodium and chloride are lowered, potassium and nitrogen are increased, and there is a diminution in the blood volume. The intravenous administration of a physiologic solution of sodium chloride helps the patient to recover from these conditions. This work laid the foundation for modern endocrinology.

At Guy's Hospital both conditions became increasingly familiar and were recorded separately from time to time in Guy's Hospital Reports, but elsewhere Addison's description of anemia was forgotten until his pupils Samuel Wilks and Thomas Daldy published his collected work and made it clear that Addison had described the disease in 1849, although A. Biermer reported it as a new disease in 1872.

In 1839 Bright and Addison published Elements of Practical Medicine. Only Volume I (two volumes were planned) appeared, and the work is incomplete and very rare.

Probably the best evaluation of Addison comes from Wilks, who said: "The personal power which he possessed was the secret of his position, much superior to what Bright could ever claim, and equal, if not greater, than that of Sir Astley Cooper."

On 7 July 1860 the Medical Times and Gazette published a notice of Addison's death on 29 June 1860, but neither Lancet nor the British Medical Journal recorded it.

BIBLIOGRAPHY

I. ORIGINAL WORKS. Addison's writings include "Observations on Fatty Degeneration of the Liver," in Guy's Hospital Reports, 1st Series, 1 (1836), 476–485; Elements of the Practice of Medicine (London, 1839), written with Richard Bright; "Observations on the Anatomy of the Lungs" (1840), in his Collected Writings (London, 1868), pp. 1–6; "Observations on Pneumonia and Its Consequences," in Guy's Hospital Reports, 2nd Series, 1 (1843), 365–402; "On the Pathology of Phthisis," ibid., 3 (1845), 1–38; "Disease: Chronic Suprarenal Insufficiency, Usually due to Tuberculosis of Suprarenal Capsule. 1st Announcement," in London Medical Gazette, n.s. 43 (1849), 517–518, reprinted in his Collected Writings (London, 1868), pp. 209–239, and in Medical Classics, 2 (1937), 239–244; "On a Certain Affection of the Skin, Vitiligoidea—a. plana, b. tuberosa, With Remarks," in Guy's Hospital Reports, 2nd Series, 7 (1851), 265–276, written with William Gull; On the Constitutional and Local Effects of Disease of the Suprarenal Capsules (London, 1855), also in Medical Classics,

2 (1937), 244–280; and *A Collection of the Published Writings of the Late Thomas Addison,* Samuel Wilks and Thomas M. Daldy, eds. (London, 1868).

II. SECONDARY LITERATURE. More on Addison and his work may be found in Thomas Bateman, in *The Roll of the Royal College of Physicians of London,* 2nd ed. (London, 1878), III, 19–22; A. Biermer, "Form von progressiver perniciöser Anämie," in *Korresp.-Bl. schweizer Ärtze,* **2** (1872), 15; Herbert French, "Pernicious Anemia," in Clifford Allbutt and Humphrey Davy Rolleston, eds., *System of Medicine* (London, 1909), V, 728–757; William Hale-White, "Biography by Sir William Hale-White," in *Guy's Hospital Reports,* **76** (July 1926), 253–279; Victor Herbert, "The Megaloblastic Anemias," in *Modern Medical Monographs* (New York and London, 1959), p. 63; and E. R. Long, "Addison and His Discovery of Idiopathic Anemia," in *Annals of Medical History,* **7** (1935), 130–132.

See also "Obituary," in *Medical Times and Gazette,* **2** (1860), 20; and "Biography," in *The Roll of the Royal College of Physicians of London,* 2nd ed. (London, 1878), III, 205.

JOHN A. BENJAMIN

ADELARD OF BATH (*b.* Bath, England; *fl.* 1116–1142), *mathematics, astronomy.*

Among the foremost of medieval English translators and natural philosophers, Adelard of Bath was one of the translators who made the first wholesale conversion of Arabo-Greek learning from Arabic into Latin. He traveled widely, first journeying to France, where he studied at Tours and taught at Laon. After leaving Laon, he journeyed about for seven years, visiting Salerno, Sicily (before 1116, perhaps before 1109), Cilicia, Syria, and possibly Palestine. It seems probable that he spent time also in Spain, on the evidence of his manifold translations from the Arabic (particularly his translation of the astronomical tables of al-Khwārizmī, from the revised form of the Spanish astronomer Maslama al-Majrīṭī).

It may be, however, that he learned his Arabic in Sicily and received Spanish-Arabic texts from other Arabists who had lived in or visited Spain, for example, Petrus Alphonsus and Johannes Ocreatus. He is found in Bath once more in 1130 when his name is mentioned in the Pipe Roll for 31 Henry I as receiving 4*s.* 6*d.* from the sheriff of Wiltshire. There are several indications in his writings of some association with the royal court. The dedication of his *Astrolabe* to a young Henry (*regis nepos*) seems to indicate a date of composition for that work between 1142 and 1146, and no later date for his activity has been established. F. Bliemetzrieder[1] has attempted to show that Adelard made a later trip to Salerno and Sicily, where he undertook the translation from the Greek of the

Almagest of Ptolemy (completed about 1160), but a lack of any positive evidence and an improbable chronology militate against acceptance of this theory.

Adelard's modest contributions to medieval philosophy are found in two of his works: *De eodem et diverso* (1), written prior to 1116 and dedicated to William, bishop of Syracuse, and *Quaestiones naturales* (6), certainly written before 1137 and probably much earlier. [The numbers assigned here to the works of Adelard are those used by Haskins.[2] The author of this article has divided no. (5) into three parts, (5*a*), (5*b*), and (5*c*), and also has added a no. (15), which may reflect a further possible work.]

In the first work no trace of Arabic influence is evident, and he speaks as a quasi Platonist. From the *Timaeus,* he drew the major theme of *Philosophia* as representing "the same" and *Philocosmia* "the diverse." To the problem of universals, Adelard proposed as a kind of harmonizing of Plato and Aristotle his theory of *respectus,* that is, that the names of individuals, species, and genus are imposed on the same essence but under different aspects. ("Nam si res consideres, eidem essentiae et generis et speciei et individui nomina imposita sunt, sed respectu diverso."[3])

Both in *De eodem et diverso* and *Quaestiones naturales,* Adelard exhibits eclectic tendencies rather than strictly Platonic views. The *Natural Questions,* a dialogue with his unnamed nephew, comprises seventy-six chapters covering such manifold subjects as the nature and growth of plants (with attention to the doctrine of the four elements and four qualities); the nature of animals (including the question of whether animals have souls, which is answered in the affirmative); the nature of man (including his psychology and physiology); and meteorology, physics, and astrology.

Although professedly written to reveal something of his recent Arabic studies, no Arabic author is mentioned by name or quoted directly. Still the work shows traces of Arabic influence. The nephew describes a pipette-like vessel with holes in both ends. Water is prevented from flowing out of the holes in the lower end by covering the holes in the upper end with the thumb; "but with the thumb removed from the upper perforations the water [is] wont to flow immediately through the lower holes."[4] This is not unlike the vessel described in Hero's *Pneumatica* or in Philo of Byzantium's *Pneumatica,* which was translated from the Arabic in the twelfth century. Adelard explains this phenomenon by using a theory of the continuity of elements; no element will leave its place unless another element succeeds it; but with the upper holes covered and a vacuum formed, no air can enter the tube to replace the water. Hence the water cannot fall from the open holes below until the upper holes are uncovered and air can enter and replace it.

While there is some tendency to exaggerate Adelard's use of observation and experiment, it is clear that the *Natural Questions* exhibits a naturalistic trend, a tendency to discuss immediate natural causation rather than explain natural phenomena in terms of the supernatural.[5] This was also to become the practice of later writers such as William of Auvergne and Nicole Oresme. Adelard expressly prefers reason to authority, calling authority a *capistrum* ("halter") like that used on brutes.[6] He claims in the final chapter of the *Natural Questions* that he will write (7) on pure elements, simple forms, and the like, which lie behind the composite things treated in the *Natural Questions;* but no such work has been found.

There is extant, however, the tract *On Falcons* (8), which harkens back to the *Natural Questions.* According to Haskins, it is the "earliest Latin treatise on falconry so far known."[7] Perhaps also indicative of his interest in natural phenomena is the enlarged edition of the work on chemical recipes, *Mappae clavicula* (12), which is attributed to him.[8] However, the pristine version of that work is far earlier than Adelard. It is possible that some miscellaneous notes (14) that appear in a manuscript at the British Museum are by Adelard.[9] These are philosophical, astronomical, cosmological, and medical notes that seem to conform to Adelard's wide naturalistic interests, and the lunar cycle therein is that of 1136–1154.

Adelard's chief role in the development of medieval science lay, as has been noted, not so much in his contributions to natural philosophy as in the various translations he made from the Arabic. His translations were of a crucial and seminal nature in several areas.

Adelard gave the Latin Schoolmen their first example of the work of one of the most important Arabic astrologers with his *Ysagoga minor Iapharis matematici in astronomicam per Adhelardum bathoniensem ex arabico sumpta* (10), a translation of Abū Maʿshar's *Shorter Introduction to Astronomy.*[10] Consisting of some astrological rules and axioms, it was abridged by Abū Maʿshar from his longer *Introductorium maius.* Adelard's translation may well have served to whet the appetite of the Schoolmen for the longer work, which was twice translated into Latin: by John of Seville in 1135 and five years later by Hermann of Carinthia. Adelard also translated an astrological work of Thābit ibn Qurra on images and horoscopes, *Liber prestigiorum Thebidis* (*Elbidis*) *secundum Ptolomeum et Hermetem per Adelardum bathoniensem translatus* (11).[11]

In astronomy Adelard's most significant achievement was his translation of the *Astronomical Tables* of al-Khwārizmī, *Ezich Elkauresmi per Athelardum bathoniensem ex arabico sumptus* (3). At the end of chapter 4, the Arabic date A.H. 520 Muḥarram 1 is said to be 26 January 1126,[12] and this has usually been taken as the approximate date of translation. However, a manuscript at Cambridge gives examples for 1133 and 1134 and mentions a solar eclipse in 1133, throwing some doubt on the date.[13] These additional examples may, of course, be accretions not present in the original translation. How dependent this translation was on a possible earlier translation of the *Tables* by Petrus Alphonsus cannot definitely be determined from the available evidence. Millás-Vallicrosa has proposed that Petrus composed an earlier translation or adaptation of al-Khwārizmī's work, which Adelard then retranslated in 1126 with the assistance or collaboration of Petrus himself.[14]

At any rate, the *Tables* (comprising some 37 introductory chapters and 116 tables in the edition published by Suter) provided the Latin West with its initial introduction (in a considerably confused form) to the complex of Hellenistic-Indian-Arabic tabular material, including, among others, calendric tables; tables for the determination of the mean and true motions of the sun, moon, and planets; and trigonometric tables. (Tables 58 and 58*a* were very probably the first sine tables to appear in Latin.) In addition to this basic translation, Adelard also composed a tract on the *Astrolabe* (9),[15] continuing a line of work that began with translations from the Arabic as early as the middle of the tenth century. It is in this work that he cites his *De eodem et diverso,* his translation of the *Tables* of al-Khwārizmī, and his rendering of the *Elements* of Euclid.

Adelard's earliest efforts in arithmetic appear in a work entitled *Regule abaci* (2), which was apparently a work composed prior to his study of Arabic mathematics, for it is quite traditional and has Boethius and Gerbert for its authorities. But another work, the *Liber ysagogarum Alchorismi in artem astronomicam a magistro A. compositus* (4), based in part on Arabic sources, might well have been composed by him. Manuscript dates and internal evidence point to a time of composition compatible with the period in which Adelard worked. Hence the "magister A." is usually thought to be Adelard. The first three books of this work are concerned with arithmetic; the remaining two consider geometry, music, and astronomy. The subject of Indian numerals and the fundamental operations performed with them is introduced as follows: ". . . since no knowledge (*scientia*) goes forth if the doctrine of all the numbers is neglected, our tract begins with them, following the reasoning of the Indians." [16] (The section on geometry is, however, based on the Roman-Latin tradition rather than the Arabic-Indian tradition. The astronomical section returns to Arabic and Hebrew sources.) It has been suggested that the first three books on Indian reckoning have been drawn from an early Latin translation of al-Khwārizmī's *De numero Indorum* (not extant in its pristine state) or from a version of that translation revised sometime before 1143, which is preserved in an incomplete state at Cambridge and which has the incipit "Dixit algorizmi laudes deo rectori. . . ." [17] This work has been published three times: in transcription by B. Boncompagni,[18] in transcription and facsimile by K. Vogel,[19] and in facsimile only by A. P. Youschkevitch.[20] It has been suggested by Vogel[21] and Youschkevitch,[22] without any decisive evidence, that the original Latin translation of the *De numero Indorum* was executed by Adelard.

Adelard of Bath in all likelihood was the first to present a full version, or versions, of the *Elements* of Euclid in Latin and thus to initiate the process that led to Euclid's domination of high and late medieval mathematics. Prior to Adelard's translation (5a–5c) from the Arabic, the evidence exists that there were only grossly incomplete translations from the Greek, such as that of Boethius. Adelard's name is associated in twelfth-century manuscripts with three quite distinct versions. Version 1 (5a) is a close translation of the whole work (including the non-Euclidean Books XIV and XV) from the Arabic text, probably that of al-Hajjāj. No single codex contains the whole version, but on the basis of translating techniques and characteristic Arabicisms the text has been pieced together.[23] Only Book IX, the first thirty-five propositions of Book X, and the last three propositions of Book XV are missing.

The second treatment of the *Elements* bearing Adelard's name, Version II (5b), is of an entirely different character. Not only are the enunciations differently expressed but the proofs are very often replaced by instructions for proofs or outlines of proofs. It is clear, however, that this version was not merely a paraphrase of Version I but derives at least in part from an Arabic original since it contains a number of Arabicisms not present in Version I. It may be that Version II was the joint work of Adelard and his student Johannes Ocreatus or that Ocreatus revised it in some fashion since some manuscripts of Version II include a statement specifically attributed to "Joh. Ocrea," i.e., Ocreatus.[24] (In another work, addressed "to his master Adelard of Bath," Ocreatus' name is given as "N. Ocreatus.") It was Version II that became the most popular of the various translations of the *Elements* produced in the twelfth century. Apparently this version was the one most commonly studied in the schools. Certainly its enunciations provided a skeleton for many different commentaries, the most celebrated of which was that of Campanus of Novara, composed in the third quarter of the thirteenth century. Version II also provided the enunciations for Adelard's Version III (5c).

Version III does not appear to be a distinct translation but a commentary. Whether or not it is by Adelard, it is attributed to him and distinguished from his translation in a manuscript at the Bibliothèque National in Paris;[25] and judging from a twelfth-century copy at Oxford,[26] it was written prior to 1200. This version enjoyed some popularity and was quoted by Roger Bacon, who spoke of it as Adelard's *editio specialis*. Still another quasi commentary, consisting of a hodgepodge of geometrical problems, is found in a Florence manuscript, *Bachon Alardus in 10 Euclidis* (15).[27] It may be based in some way on a work of Adelard. Incidentally, the set of proofs for the *Elementa de ponderibus*, which were almost certainly composed by Jordanus de Nemore, is assigned in one manuscript to "Alardus."[28] Finally, in the area of geometry, note should be made of a thirteenth-century reference to a commentary on the *Spherica* of Theodosius, *Dicti Theodosii liber de speris, ex commentario Adelardi* (13), in the *Biblionomia* of Richard de Fournival.[29] No such work has been found, and the fact that the *Spherica* was translated only later by Gerard of Cremona makes it quite unlikely that Adelard did a commentary. The foregoing is an impressive list of geometrical translations and compositions; and, if by any chance, Bliemetzrieder should be proven correct concerning Adelard's role as the translator of the *Almagest* of Ptolemy, then the recently discovered translation from the Greek of the *Elements*[30] would also have to be assigned to Adelard since both translations exhibit identical translating techniques and styles.

The conclusion that must be drawn from the widespread translating activity described above is that Adelard should be considered, along with Gerard of Cremona and William of Moerbeke, as one of the pivotal figures in the conversion of Greek and Arabic learning into Latin.

NOTES

1. Bliemetzrieder, *Adelhard von Bath*, pp. 149–274.
2. Haskins, *Studies in Medieval Science*, ch. 2.
3. *De eodem*, edit. of Willner, p. 11, ll. 20–21.
4. *Quaestiones naturales*, edit. of Müller, ch. 58, p. 53.
5. *Ibid.*, ch. 4, p. 8.
6. *Ibid.*, ch. 6, p. 11.
7. Haskins, p. 28.

8. Brit. Mus., Royal MS 15.C.iv., Table of Contents.
9. Brit. Mus., Old Royal and King's Collections, MS 7.D.xxv.
10. Oxford, Bodleian Lib. MS Digby 68, 116r. The opening paragraphs are published in Richard Lemay, *Abu Ma'shar*, p. 355.
11. MS Lyons 328, 70r–74r, is among the extant MSS.
12. Edit. of Suter in Björnbo et al., ch. 4, p. 5.
13. Oxford, Corpus Christi Coll. MS 283, f. 142r.
14. Millás-Vallicrosa, *Nuevos estudios*, p. 107.
15. Cf. Cambridge, Fitzwilliam Mus., McClean MS 165, ff. 81r–88r, and Brit. Mus. Arundel MS 377, ff. 69r–74r.
16. *Liber ysagogarum*, edit. of Curtze, p. 18.
17. Cambridge Univ. Lib. MS Ii.6.5.
18. *Trattati d'aritmetica*, pp. 1–23.
19. *Mohammed ibn Musa Alchwarizmi's Algorismus.*
20. "Über ein Werk," pp. 1–63; cf. his earlier paper, in Russian, cited on p. 22, n. 2.
21. *Op. cit.*, p. 43.
22. *Op. cit.*, p. 22.
23. Clagett, "The Medieval Latin Translations," p. 18.
24. *Ibid.*, p. 21.
25. Paris, BN MS Lat. 16648, f. 58r.
26. Oxford, Balliol Coll. MS 257.
27. Biblioteca Nazionale Centrale Conv. Soppr. J.IX.26, 46r–55r.
28. Oxford, Corpus Christi Coll., MS 251, 10r–12v.
29. Haskins, p. 31.
30. Cf. Paris, BN MS Lat. 7377 and Florence, Biblioteca Nazionale Centrale Conv. Soppr. C.I.448.

BIBLIOGRAPHY

Among the works of Adelard of Bath available in modern editions and in manuscript form are the following: *De eodem et diverso,* edit. of H. Willner, in *Beiträge zur Geschichte der Philosophie des Mittelalters,* **4,** Heft 1 (1903); (?) *Liber ysagogarum Alchorismi in artem astronomicam a magistro A. compositus,* MSS Paris, BN Lat. 16208, ff. 67r–71r; Milan, Ambrosian Lib., A. 3 sup., ff. 1r–20r; Munich, Staatsbibliothek, Cod. 13021, ff. 27r–68v, Cod. 18927, ff. 31r *seq.;* Vienna, Nationalbibliothek, Cod. 275, f. 27r; first three books, edit. of M. Curtze, in *Abhandlungen zur Geschichte der Mathematik,* Heft 8 (1898), 1–27; *Quaestiones naturales,* edit. of M. Müller, in *Beiträge zur Geschichte der Philosophie und Theologie des Mittelalters,* **31,** Heft 2 (1934); *Regule abaci,* edit. of B. Boncompagni, in *Bullettino di bibliografia e di storia delle scienze matematiche e fisiche,* **14** (1881), 1–134.

For the texts of Adelard's translations and studies on his activities, see A. Björnbo, R. Besthorn, and H. Suter, *Die astronomischen Tafeln des Muḥammed ibn Mūsā al-Khwārizmī in der Bearbeitung des Maslama ibn Aḥmed al-Madjrītī* (Copenhagen, 1914); F. Bliemetzrieder, *Adelhard von Bath* (Munich, 1935); B. Boncompagni, *Trattati d'aritmetica, I. Algoritmi de numero Indorum* (Rome, 1857), pp. 1–23; M. Clagett, "The Medieval Latin Translations from the Arabic of the *Elements* of Euclid, with Special Emphasis on the Versions of Adelard of Bath," in *Isis,* **44** (1953), 16–42; C. H. Haskins, *Studies in the History of Mediaeval Science,* 2nd ed. (Cambridge, Mass., 1927), pp. 20–42; R. Lemay, *Abu Ma'shar and Latin Aristotelianism in the Twelfth Century* (Beirut, 1962), p. 355; and J. M. Millás-Vallicrosa, "La aportación astronómica de Pedro Alfonso," in *Sefarad,* **3** (1943), 65–105, and *Nuevos estudios sobre historia de la ciencia española* (Barcelona, 1960), pp. 105–108; O. Neugebauer, *The Astronomical Tables of al-Khwārizmī. Translation with Commentaries of the Latin Versions edited by H. Suter supplemented by Corpus Christi College MS 283* (Copenhagen, 1962); T. Phillipps, "The *Mappae Clavicula*; a Treatise on the Preparation of Pigments During the Middle Ages," in *Archaeologia,* **32** (1847), 183–244; G. Sarton, *Introduction to the History of Science,* II (Baltimore, 1931), 167–169; L. Thorndike, *A History of Magic and Experimental Science,* II (New York, 1923), 19–49; K. Vogel, *Mohammed ibn Musa Alchwarizmi's Algorismus* (Aalen, 1963); A. P. Youschkevitch, "Über ein Werk des 'Abdallah Muḥammad ibn Mūsā al-Ḥuwārizmī al-Maǧusī zur Arithmetik der Inder," in *Beiheft 1964 zur Schriftenreihe Geschichte der Naturwissenschaften, Technik und Medizin,* pp. 1–63.

MARSHALL CLAGETT

ADET, PIERRE-AUGUSTE (*b.* Nevers, France, 17 May 1763; *d.* Paris, France, 19 March 1834), *chemistry.*

Although Adet was *docteur-régent* of the Faculty of Medicine in Paris, his life was devoted to politics rather than to science. He was deeply interested in chemistry but it was, nevertheless, only a spare-time pursuit, and he made no important contributions to it. In 1789, however, he did participate in the founding of the *Annales de chimie,* which was designed to permit easy publication of papers on antiphlogistic chemistry since, at that time, the *Journal de physique* was opposed to the new doctrines. Adet was one of the editors for several years and in this capacity published a number of translations of English papers in the journal and a few original works. He was, then, a keen supporter of the "new chemistry" from his early years; further evidence of this may be found in the appendix that he added to his translation of Priestley's *Considerations on the Doctrine of Phlogiston and the Decomposition of Water,* in which he replied to a number of Priestley's arguments (1797).

Adet was also interested in other reforms in chemistry and, to supplement the new system of chemical nomenclature that was being developed, he and Hassenfratz, Lavoisier's assistant, proposed a new system of chemical symbols. In it, a symbol indicated not merely the identity of the substance but its physical state, the proportion of oxygen it contained (as in sulfurous and sulfuric acids) and, if it was a salt, the extent to which the acid had been neutralized by the base. The system was never generally adopted, however, perhaps because of its complexity.

Adet's last published work before the Revolution, when he became much more involved in politics, was on stannic chloride (1789). He then became a colonial administrator and, while in Santo Domingo in 1791, investigated pineapple juice, in which he believed he had found both citric and malic acids. He could not confirm the presence of citric acid, however, because someone threw away his liquids.

In 1798 Adet investigated "acetous" and acetic acids. When verdigris is heated strongly, one of the products is a very concentrated acetic acid, which was known as "radical vinegar." No acid as concentrated as this could be obtained from vinegar, so it was thought that two acids existed—acetous acid (vinegar) and acetic acid (radical vinegar), which contained a higher proportion of oxygen. Adet was unable to oxidize "acetous acid" to acetic acid, but obtained acetic acid when he distilled "acetites" with concentrated sulfuric acid. He therefore concluded that the acids differed only in the proportion of water they contained. Although this conclusion was not widely accepted, it was confirmed by Proust in 1802.

After 1803, when he became prefect of the Nièvre, Adet seems to have published nothing of consequence apart from his textbook, *Leçons élémentaires de chimie* (1804). This had the distinction of being translated into modern Greek, but nonetheless was not a work of outstanding merit.

BIBLIOGRAPHY

All the articles translated from English by Adet are omitted from the following selection of his works, except those written by Priestley and Kirwan, to which Adet appended notes which show his attitude to the new doctrines of chemistry. The new system of chemical symbols devised by Adet and Hassenfratz is in De Morveau, Lavoisier, Berthollet, and Fourcroy, *Méthode de nomenclature chimique* (Paris, 1787), pp. 253–287 (N.B., some of the pages within this range are incorrectly numbered), immediately followed by a report by the Academy on this work, pp. 288–312. The English translation, *A Translation of the Table of Chemical Nomenclature* (London, 1799), contains as an appendix "Explanation of the Table of Symbols of Messrs. Hassenfratz and Adet; With the Additions and Alterations of the Editor." His text is *Leçons élémentaires de chimie* (Paris, 1804).

Adet's articles are "Lettre à M. Ingenhouz sur la décomposition de l'eau," in *Observations sur la physique,* **28** (1786), 436–439; "Lettre à M. de La Métherie," *ibid.,* **30** (1787), 215–218, written with Hassenfratz, and a reply by La Métherie, pp. 218–226; "Sur le muriate d'étain fumant ou liqueur de Libavius," in *Annals de chimie,* **1** (1789), 5–18; "'An Essai on Phlogiston and the Constitution of Acids,' Kirwan. Extrait de l'anglois avec des notes par P. A. Adet," *ibid.,* **7** (1790), 194–237; "Essai sur l'analyse du suc acide de l'ananas," *ibid.,* **25** (1798), 32–36; "Mémoire sur l'acide acétique," *ibid.,* **27** (1798), 299–319; and

"Réflexions sur la doctrine du phlogistique et la décomposition de l'eau par J. Priestley etc., traduit de l'anglais et suivi d'une réponse, par P. Adet," *ibid.,* **26** (1798), 302–309; according to Partington (III, 244), this French translation was also published in Philadelphia in 1797.

Nothing in any detail exists on Adet as a chemist, but J. Balteau's article in *Dictionnaire de biographie française,* I (1933), 574–575, gives the background of his life as a politician.

E. McDonald

ADRAIN, ROBERT (*b.* Carrickfergus, Ireland, 30 September 1775; *d.* New Brunswick, New Jersey, 10 August 1843), *mathematics.*

Adrain was a teacher in Ireland and took part in the rebellion of 1798. With his wife, Ann Pollock, he escaped to America, where he first served as a master at Princeton Academy, then moved to York, Pennsylvania, as principal of the York County Academy. In 1805 he became principal of the academy in Reading, Pennsylvania. From 1809 to 1813 Adrain was professor of mathematics at Queen's College (now Rutgers), New Brunswick, New Jersey, and from 1813 to 1826 at Columbia College, New York. He then returned to Queen's College for a short while. He taught from 1827 to 1834 at the University of Pennsylvania in Philadelphia, where in 1828 he became vice-provost. From 1836 to 1840 he taught at the grammar school of Columbia College, after which he returned to New Brunswick. It is reported that in the classroom he often showed impatience with ill-prepared students. He had seven children, one of whom, Garnett Bowditch Adrain (1815–1878), was a Democratic member of Congress from New Brunswick between 1857 and 1861.

Adrain's first mathematical contributions were in George Baron's *Mathematical Correspondent* (1804), in which he solved problems and wrote on the steering of a ship and on Diophantine algebra. He continued the latter subject in *The Analyst* (1808), a short-lived periodical that he published himself. Here we find Adrain's most interesting mathematical paper, a study of errors in observations with the first two published demonstrations of the normal (exponential) law of errors. Gauss's work was not published until 1809. This volume also contains Adrain's paper on what he calls isotomous curves, inspired by Rittenhouse's hygrometer. If a family of curves (e.g., circles or parabolas) are all tangent at a point A, then an isotomous curve cuts these curves at equal arcs measured from A. Another article deals with the *catenaria volvens,* the form taken by a homogeneous, flexible, nonelastic string uniformly revolving about two points, without gravity.

Adrain shares with his contemporary Nathaniel Bowditch the honor of being the first creative mathematician in America. Like Bowditch, he was an ardent student of Laplace, and his paper on errors is in the spirit of Laplace.

Adrain became a member of the American Philosophical Society in 1812, and six years later he published in its *Transactions* a paper on the figure of the earth, in which he found 1/319 as its ellipticity (Laplace had 1/336; the modern value is 1/297). In the same issue of the *Transactions* he also published a paper on the mean diameter of the earth. Both papers were inspired by Laplace.

BIBLIOGRAPHY

I. ORIGINAL WORKS. Adrain's papers include "A Disquisition Concerning the Motion of a Ship Which Is Steered in a Given Point of the Compass," in *Mathematical Correspondent,* **1** (1804), 103–114; "Research Concerning the Probabilities of the Errors Which Happen in Making Observations," in *The Analyst,* **1** (1808), 93–109; "Researches Concerning Isotomous Curves," *ibid.,* 58–68; "Investigation of the Figure of the Earth and of the Gravity in Different Latitudes," in *Transactions of the American Philosophical Society,* n.s. **1** (1818), 119–135; and "Research Concerning the Mean Diameter of the Earth," *ibid.,* 352–366. He also contributed to *Portico,* **3** (1817); *Scientific Journal and Philosophical Magazine* (1818–1819); *Ladies and Gentleman's Diary* (1819–1822); and *The Mathematical Diary* (1825–1833), of which he edited the first six issues. In addition, Adrain prepared American editions of T. Keith, *A New Treatise on the Use of Globes* (New York, 1811); and C. Hutton, *Course in Mathematics* (New York, 1812).

II. SECONDARY LITERATURE. The most easily available source of information on Adrain is J. L. Coolidge, "Robert Adrain and the Beginnings of American Mathematics," in *American Mathematical Monthly,* **33** (1926), 61–76, with an analysis of Adrain's mathematical work. On his theory of errors, see also O. R. Seinin, "R. Adrain's Works in the Theory of Errors and Its Applications," in *Istoriko-matematicheskie issledovaniya,* **16** (1965), 325–336 (in Russian). An early source is an article in *United States Magazine and Democratic Review,* **14** (1844), 646–652, supposedly written by Adrain's son Garnett. See also G. E. Pettengill, in *Historical Review of Berks County* (Penna.), **8** (1943), 111–114; and D. E. Smith, in *Dictionary of American Biography,* I (1928), 109–110.

Coolidge mentions the existence of manuscript material of Adrain's on which M. J. Babb of Princeton was working. These papers seem to have been lost after Babb's death in 1945. The library of the American Philosophical Society has some letters by and concerning Adrain to John Vaughan in Philadelphia, and a letter written to Adrain by M. Roche in 1831.

D. J. STRUIK

ADRIAANSON, ADRIAAN. See **Metius, Adriaan.**

AEGIDIUS. See **Giles of Rome.**

AEPINUS, FRANZ ULRICH THEODOSIUS (*b*. Rostock, Germany, 13 December 1724; *d*. Dorpat, Russia [now Tartu, Estonian Soviet Socialist Republic], 10 August 1802), *mathematics, electricity, magnetism.*

Aepinus came from a family long distinguished for its learning. His great-grandfather, who had translated the family name, Hoeck, into Greek, had been an important evangelical theologian. His father held the chair of theology and his elder brother that of oratory at the University of Rostock. Aepinus studied medicine and mathematics at Jena, particularly under the guidance of G. E. Hamberger, and at Rostock, where he took his M.A. in 1747 with a dissertation on the paths of falling bodies. Until 1755 he taught mathematics at Rostock, as a junior lecturer, and published only on mathematical subjects: the properties of algebraic equations, the integration of partial differential equations, the concept of negative numbers. In 1751–1752 one of his auditors was J. C. Wilcke, who had come to Rostock to study under Franz's brother. With Franz's encouragement and instruction, Wilcke concentrated on physics and mathematics, and soon decided against the clerical career for which his father had intended him. A few years later Wilcke played an equally important role in reorienting his mentor's professional career.

In the spring of 1755 Aepinus became director of the observatory in Berlin and a member of the Academy of Sciences there. These appointments were apparently merely a device for establishing Aepinus, who had begun to acquire a reputation, in Frederick's capital: he was neither especially interested nor experienced in astronomy, and his closest published approach to the subject during his Berlin sojourn was a mathematical analysis of a micrometer adapted to a quadrant circle. His main preoccupation at the time was the study of the tourmaline, to which he was introduced by Wilcke, who had followed him to Berlin. Aepinus' first researches on the thermoelectric properties of this stone, which was then of extreme rarity, were fundamental. He recognized the electrical nature of the attractive power of a warmed tourmaline and attempted, not altogether successfully, to reduce its apparent capriciousness to rule. He was particularly struck by the formal similarity between the tourmaline and the magnet in regard to polarity, which inspired him to reconsider the possibility, then occasionally discussed, that electricity and magnetism were basically analogous. This thought became the theme for his masterwork, *Tentamen theoriae electricitatis et magnetismi* (1759).

In experimenting on the tourmaline Aepinus was often assisted by Wilcke, who was then preparing a dissertation on electricity. Their closeness made it natural for Wilcke to bring to Aepinus' attention certain phenomena he had discovered that apparently conflicted with Franklin's principles. In seeking an explanation, Aepinus came to the anti-Franklinian idea of a Leyden jar without the glass. The success of this air condenser eventually helped to persuade many to abandon Franklin's special assumptions about electrical atmospheres and the electricity of glass, and to prepare the ground for more general views of the kind Aepinus urged in his *Tentamen.*

In October 1756 Aepinus asked to be relieved of his positions in Berlin in order to accept the directorship of the observatory and the professorship of physics, vacant since the death of Richmann, at the Imperial Academy of St. Petersburg. Euler, with whom he boarded in Berlin, warmly recommended him for the job and interceded with Frederick to procure his release, which occurred in the spring of 1757. The Petersburg academicians expected that Aepinus, as befitted Richmann's successor, would continue to work on electricity. They were not disappointed. Late in 1758 Aepinus completed the lengthy *Tentamen,* which the Academy rushed into print before its author could finish his polishing.

The *Tentamen* is one of the most original and important books in the history of electricity. It is the first reasoned, fruitful exposition of electrical phenomena based on action-at-a-distance. Aepinus emphatically rejects the current notion of electrical atmospheres. Not that he believes that bodies act where they are not: he merely takes literally Newton's precepts about natural philosophy, and deduces the phenomena from certain assumed forces, without inquiring into the manner in which the forces themselves might be effected. Three such forces, according to him, create all the appearances of electricity: a repulsion between the particles of the electric fluid, an attraction between them and the corpuscles of common matter, and a repulsion between the corpuscles. This last is necessary to prevent unelectrified bodies—bodies with their normal complement of electrical fluid—from attracting one another. Aepinus observes that although such a repulsion might appear to conflict with universal gravitation there is no reason not to suppose several types of forces between matter corpuscles, and in fact the phenomena require it. As for the law of force, it is proportional to the excess or deficiency of fluid, and the same for all pairs of particles and corpuscles. Aepinus does not pretend

to know its precise form. Analogy, he thinks, favors the inverse square, which he uses in one numerical application; but generally he leaves the matter open, the great unanswered question in electrical theory.

Aepinus does not need the precise law, however, to explain the phenomena qualitatively. He is particularly successful with induction effects, which had puzzled philosophers since Canton's experiments of 1752; his explanations, with appropriate terminological changes, are essentially those used in elementary electrostatics today. Although his exposition is not quantitative, it is mathematical, with symbols used to indicate the excess or deficiency of fluid and the associated forces. Assuming that the forces decrease with distance, he is able to anticipate the direction of electrical interactions. In this way he predicts apparently paradoxical phenomena, e.g., that if two bodies with like charges of greatly different strengths are pushed together, their repulsion will at some point change to attraction. The magnetic theory of the *Tentamen* operates on the same principles, except that the magnetic fluid can freely penetrate all substances but iron, in which it is so tightly held that it can neither increase nor decrease. A piece of iron is thus to the magnetic fluid what a perfect insulator would be to the electric. All magnetic phenomena depend on the displacement of the magnetic fluid within iron. Aepinus' analysis of magnetization is exactly analogous to his treatment of electrical induction; it is adequate to all problems he considers except the formation of two magnets by the halving of one. Most notably it leads him to improve on Canton's and Michell's method of preparing artificial magnets, and on the usual disposition of armatures.

In 1760 or 1761 Aepinus became instructor to the Corps of Imperial Cadets, a position that left him too little time to fulfill his duties at the academy. The observatory was seldom used, and the equipment in the physics laboratory deteriorated. These circumstances gave Lomonosov the opportunity for a furious attack on Aepinus, whose haughtiness toward Russian scientists and quick preferment at court had already irritated him. Despite such unfavorable conditions, Aepinus continued for a few years to produce papers on various mathematical and physical subjects. He published the most important and coherent of these, several dissertations on the tourmaline, along with some criticism and corrections of his earlier work, as *Recueil des différents mémoires sur la tourmaline* (1762). Among the more occasional pieces, perhaps the most interesting are a masterful discussion of the mercurial phosphorus and a critical examination of Mayer's theory of magnetism, both of which appeared in the *Novi commentarii* of the Petersburg Academy for 1766–1767. About that time Aepinus' scientific activity ceased almost entirely. He became preceptor to the crown prince, a member of the prestigious Order of St. Anne, an educational reformer, a diplomat, a courtier, and finally a privy councillor. In 1798, after forty years in Russia, he resigned his offices and retired to Dorpat.

Except for his work on the tourmaline, which established a new subject, it is difficult to assess Aepinus' immediate influence. He had no distinguished students besides Wilcke. His contributions to mathematics, astronomy, and optics were competent but not outstanding. The *Tentamen* was at first not widely read. It was not easy to find (Beccaria had not seen a copy as late as 1772), and it was not easy to read (it demanded greater mathematical facility than most physicists then possessed). Although it was known and praised by Volta, Cavendish, and Coulomb, those physicists appear largely to have developed their own views before they came across it. But, less directly, the *Tentamen* was of great importance. Most of its content became easily available in 1780 in the excellent nonmathematical epitome composed by R. J. Haüy, who managed to preserve the spirit and clarity of the original. A much less adequate notice appeared in Priestley's *History*. Through such means the message of the *Tentamen* became widely diffused. Those who returned to the original then discovered in it a model for the application of mathematics to electricity and magnetism, and a store of apposite experiments. As one can see from P. T. Riess's *Die Lehre von der Reibungselektricität* (1853), the *Tentamen* remained an important source until the middle of the nineteenth century.

BIBLIOGRAPHY

I. ORIGINAL WORKS. Aepinus' most important works are "Mémoire concernant quelques nouvelles expériences électriques remarquables," in *Histoire de l'Académie Royale des Sciences de Berlin* (1756), 105–121; *Tentamen theoriae electricitatis et magnetismi* (St. Petersburg, 1759); *Recueil des différents mémoires sur la tourmaline* (1762); and the discussions of phosphorus and Mayer's theory of magnetism in *Novi commentarii* of the Imperial Academy (1766–1767). The best bibliography is in Poggendorff, to which should be added *Commentatio de notatione quantitatis negativae* (Rostock, 1754); and "Two Letters on Electrical and Other Phenomena," in *Transactions of the Royal Society of Edinburgh*, **2** (1790), 234–244. In addition, there are a few essays, in Russian, listed in Ia. G. Dorfman, ed., *Teoriia elektrichestva i magnetizma* (Moscow, 1951), a modern translation of the *Tentamen* and of Aepinus' contributions to the *Recueil*. Notes on Aepinus' lectures in Rostock, taken by Wilcke, are preserved in the library of the Swedish Academy of Sciences; other manuscripts may exist in the Soviet Union.

II. SECONDARY LITERATURE. Biographical information about Aepinus is sparse and scattered. The older, standard biographical entries are summarized and slightly expanded in W. Lorey's notice in *Allgemeine deutsche Biographie* and in H. Pupke, "Franz Ulrich Theodosius Aepinus," in *Naturwissenschaften,* **37** (1950), 49–52. For other data, see Euler's correspondence, particularly A. P. Youschkevitch and E. Winter, eds., *Die Berliner und die Petersburger Akademie der Wissenschaften im Briefwechsel Leonhard Eulers. I. Der Briefwechsel L. Eulers mit G. F. Müller* (Berlin, 1959); A. A. Morosow, *Michail Wassilyewitsch Lomonossow 1711–1765* (Berlin, 1954); and E. Winter, ed., *Die Registres der Berliner Akademie der Wissenschaften 1746–1766* (Berlin, 1957).

For Aepinus' work, see Dorfman's essay in *Teoriia* (above); Haüy's abridgment, *Exposition raisonée de la théorie de l'électricité et du magnetisme d'après les principes de M. Aepinus* (Paris, 1787); C. W. Oseen, *Johan Carl Wilcke. Experimental-fysiker* (Uppsala, 1939); Joseph Priestley, *The History and Present State of Electricity,* 2 vols., 3rd ed. (London, 1775); and P. T. Riess, *Die Lehre von der Reibungselektricität,* 2 vols. (Berlin, 1853).

JOHN L. HEILBRON

AËTIUS OF AMIDA (*b*. Amida, Mesopotamia [now Diyarbakir, Turkey], *fl. ca.* A.D. 540), *medicine.*

Aëtius had the title *comes obsequii,* which indicates that he had a relatively high rank, possibly of a military nature, at court. Since this title seems not to have been introduced until the reign of Justinian I, Aëtius cannot have lived before the sixth century. It is sometimes supposed that he was physician in ordinary at the Byzantine court, and this is occasionally stated as a fact both in books dealing with antiquity and in books on medical history. In any case, Aëtius lived after Oribasius, for the latter's medical encyclopedia is one of his main sources. Several times in his work Aëtius speaks of a sojourn in Alexandria. It cannot be proved that he was a Christian, for he does no more than mention Christian institutions and customs several times. In any event, he ought not to be confused with the physician and Arian Christian Aëtius who lived in the fourth century and is mentioned in Philostorgios' church history, as well as in Gregory of Nyssa's *Contra Eunomium.*

Aëtius wrote a large medical encyclopedia that is called either *Sixteen Medical Books* or *Tetrabibloi* (i.e., four volumes, each containing four parts or books). This form of medical encyclopedia, typical of late antiquity and the Byzantine period, corresponds to that of the known encyclopedias of Oribasius and Paul of Aegina. They are all collections of more or less verbatim excerpts from the works of previous medical authors, primarily Galen.

Aëtius' originality has often been questioned, but since there exists only an incomplete critical edition of his work (with proof of sources), the question cannot be answered conclusively. The Byzantine Photius stated that Aëtius had "added nothing and left out much" from his original sources, but this must be viewed skeptically, for there are indications that Aëtius evaluated his sources, using his own experiences and his own thoughts.

BIBLIOGRAPHY

The first eight books of Aëtius' encyclopedia have been critically edited by Alexander Olivieri in *Corpus medicorum Graecorum,* VIII, Part 1 (Berlin-Leipzig, 1935), and VIII, Part 2 (Berlin, 1950). The few notices on Aëtius' biography are in Olivieri, VIII, 1, p. 8, 11.14–15; his sojourn in Alexandria, *ibid.,* p. 65, 1.4, and p. 67, 1.1. Photius' statement on Aëtius' originality, *ibid.,* p. 8, 11.12 ff. For Aëtius' criticism of his predecessors see, e.g., *ibid.,* VIII, 1, p. 153, 11.16 ff. The most usable appreciation of Aëtius is by Ivan Bloch, in Max Neuburger and Julius Pagel, *Handbuch der Geschichte der Medizin,* I (Jena, 1902), 529 ff.

FRIDOLF KUDLIEN

IBN AFLAḤ. See **Jābir ibn Aflaḥ.**

AGARDH, CARL ADOLPH (*b.* Bastad, Sweden, 23 January 1785; *d.* Karlstad, Sweden, 28 January 1859), *botany.*

Agardh's fame is based on his contributions to the taxonomy of algae, but his scientific interests covered a far wider area. In many ways he reflects the philosophic romanticism that flourished when he was a professor at the University of Lund (1812–1835).

In Sweden, where Linnaeus had been active until 1778, as well as abroad, knowledge of algae and their classification was still rudimentary at the beginning of the nineteenth century. Linnaeus had divided the algae known to him into three families (*Fucus, Ulva, Conferva*), and after his death botanists continued to incorporate new forms into the same groups. In 1812 the French botanist Lamouroux took an important step toward a more comprehensive and natural differentiation, especially among the red algae, but a new understanding of the relationships existing within the larger groups of algae was first presented in Agardh's *Synopsis algarum Scandinaviae* (1817). Although it dealt basically with only one limited regional flora, the introduction presented an entirely new systematic survey of everything then considered

algae. Agardh's broad outline became the *Species algarum* (1821–1828), which was never finished, and the more concentrated *Systema algarum* (1824), which summarized the state of algology at that time with precise groupings and clearly defined descriptions. In these works, with a collection of illustrations, he presented theories that are still considered nodal points in the development of algology. He achieved eminence partly through fieldwork, but he acquired a thorough knowledge of the literature and an extensive knowledge of various collections (among others, the herbaria of algae in Paris, which he examined in 1820–1821). It was not until 1827 that he undertook an extensive field trip to the north shore of the Adriatic Sea, where he became familiar with the little-known algal flora.

Although Agardh is remembered mainly as an algologist, he represents several of the main trends in botany at that time. He took an active part in contemporary discussions of the natural system of plant classification. Agardh presented his outline of the plant kingdom in his *Aphorismi botanici,* in the form of sixteen academic dissertations (1817–1826), and *Classes plantarum* (1825), in which he characterized several new plant families, some of which are still considered valid. His opinions reflect the views of nature developed by German Romantic *Naturphilosophen:* Schelling, Oken, and Nees von Esenbeck. Agardh, however, opposed the deductive, speculative method of the Romantics. He insisted that all study of nature had to be approached inductively, that it is not possible to establish a few groups within which all species can be classified. He believed that attention must be focused on the individual species and genera, which step by step, and with great care, might be arranged in larger groupings whose mutual relationships could be established only by further research. But in his plea for caution he expounded the Romantic *Naturphilosophie.* Nature is freedom; therefore it does not obey human logic, but its own logic, which cannot be penetrated by reason. Thus, no deductive, logically functioning system of classification can conform to the laws of nature.

Agardh's romanticism was even more pronounced in his writings on plant anatomy and plant physiology. On his way home from the Adriatic he stopped at the mineral springs of Karlsbad, where he met the Romantic philosopher Schelling. Together they studied algal forms in the hot springs, and Agardh demonstrated their life cycle. He later called his visit to Karlsbad "the most interesting days of my life"; it is evident that his interests here shifted from taxonomy to the problems of plant life. He first published his views on this subject in several articles in French, and then in a more extensive form in *Lärobok i botanik* (1830–1832), which was translated into German and dedicated to Schelling. The general tenor of the manual, and in particular the importance that Agardh attributes to chemistry, led to a violent disagreement with his friend Berzelius. Their animated correspondence on this subject reveals a strong contrast between a romantic, speculative temperament and an empirical one.

Agardh had divided personal aims and was often quite disturbed. He found himself increasingly at odds with his academic surroundings. He was, however, politically active, made important contributions to economics, and participated in pedagogical and theological debates.

In 1835 Agardh was offered the bishopric of the Karlstad diocese in western Sweden, which he accepted, and thereupon gave up writing on botany.

BIBLIOGRAPHY

I. ORIGINAL WORKS. A complete bibliography of Agardh's writings can be found in both J. E. Areschoug and A. B. Carlsson (see below). His works include *Synopsis algarum Scandinaviae* (Lund, 1817); *Aphorismi botanici* (Lund, 1817–1826); *Species algarum*, I, pt. 1 (Greifswald, 1821); I, pt. 2 (Lund, 1822); II, pt. 1 (Greifswald, 1828); *Systema algarum* (Lund, 1824); *Classes plantarum* (Lund, 1825); and *Lärobok i botanik* (Malmö, 1830–1832). His correspondence with Berzelius is in H. G. Soderbaum's ed. of Berzelius' letters, *Jac. Berzelius' brev*, X (Uppsala, 1925). His unpublished correspondence is mainly in the library of the University of Lund.

II. SECONDARY LITERATURE. Two articles on Agardh, both in Swedish, are J. E. Areschoug, "Carl Adolph Agardh," in *Levnadsteckningar över Kungliga Svenska Vetenskapsakademiens ledamöter*, I (Stockholm, 1869–1873); and A. B. Carlsson, *Svenskt biografiskt lexikon*, I (Stockholm, 1917–1918).

GUNNAR ERIKSSON

AGARDH, JACOB GEORG (*b.* Lund, Sweden, 8 December 1813; *d.* Lund, 17 January 1901), *botany*.

As the son of the prominent botanist Carl Adolph Agardh, Jacob had exceptional opportunities to acquire scientific experience at an early age. He was only fourteen when he accompanied his father on an important algological expedition to the Adriatic, and he showed both keen powers of observation and a marked aptitude for collecting. He also began to do research on phanerogams and cryptogams. Agardh followed in his father's footsteps and soon gained international renown as an algologist, specializing in sea algae. Agardh was basically a taxonomist, but his scientific approach was different. When Agardh began his scientific career, the conditions for research were better (through the improvement of microscopy) than in his father's time.

Agardh's first research on algae dealt with the germination process in some species. He studied their development and explained the nature of the swarm spores, which had previously been unclear. At the same time he began to observe how such external conditions as depth of water and currents influenced the appearance of the various species. This was of primary importance for the understanding of the taxonomic characteristics.

Agardh soon acquired firsthand knowledge of numerous types of algae by undertaking an extensive field trip to the Mediterranean and through herbarium studies in the large collections at the Muséum d'Histoire Naturelle in Paris, among others, which had also been studied by his father. His important *Algae maris Mediterranei et Adriatici* (1842) dealt with his new findings and contained his first work on the taxonomy of the *Florideae*, which was to become his most important field of research. The point of departure for his research on the differentiation of the classes of the *Florideae* was the structure of the reproductive organ and the structure of the cystocarp. Although his criteria are no longer considered definitive, many of the groups he differentiated are still valid. His *magnum opus* as an algae taxonomist was *Species, genera et ordines algarum,* in six volumes, published during the course of more than half a century (1848–1901). It contains all the then known species of the *Florideae* and all the known species of *Fucaceae* (brown algae) as well as their description and a general morphological survey, all in accordance with the Swedish Linnaean tradition. When the plant physiologist Julius Sachs published a critical appraisal of Linnaeus' contribution in his history of botany, Agardh was one of Linnaeus' most ardent defenders. Agardh's interest in taxonomy encompassed the entire plant kingdom, and he developed his ideas in *Theoria systematis plantarum* (1858). Here he reveals himself as an idealist, as were many leading scientists during the pre-Darwinian era. He interprets the natural relationship between various genera, as well as between other taxa, not as a phylogenetic one but as one dependent on the premise that all genera within a family reflect the same prototype, that is, a pattern according to which the Creator worked when He created the various species.

Following the trend of his contemporaries, Agardh combined idealism with certain evolutionary beliefs. Hence, he considered that each species had evolved from a lower to a higher state and had developed through the ages into different and progressively more perfect forms. He definitely dismissed the thought that one species could develop into another, and thereby denied the theory of the origin of species that has constituted the nucleus of the philosophy of evolution that originated with Darwin. Still less did he concur with the materialistic approach to life that was often expressed by Darwin's followers, for nature, to him, was a harmonious whole, the development of which had been planned from the beginning and had been directed by an omnipotent and omniscient Creator.

As have those of most other taxonomists, many of Agardh's concepts have become obsolete, especially the more general ones. For his descriptions of species, he had only pressed and dried material in herbaria; thus, his ideas about species have often had to be revised. He introduced many new ideas to algology, however, and was active in developing an increasingly keener systematic and morphological approach. His algae collection, which had been started by his father, was given to the University of Lund, where Agardh had been active as a teacher since 1834 and professor of botany from 1854 to 1879. The collection is one of the most varied in the world and contains many type specimens—an indication of the importance of his work.

BIBLIOGRAPHY

I. ORIGINAL WORKS. Complete bibliographies of Agardh's writings are in J. Ericksson, "Jacob Georg Agardh," in *Levnadsteckningar över Kungliga Svenska Vetenskapsakademiens ledamöter,* V, pt. 2 (Stockholm, 1915–1920); and N. Svedelius, in *Svenskt biografiskt lexikon,* I (Stockholm, 1917–1918), 268–274. Among his works are *Algae maris Mediterranei et Adriatici* (Paris, 1842); *Species, genera et ordines algarum,* 6 vols. (Lund, 1848–1901); and *Theoria systematis plantarum* (Lund, 1858). Most of his letters and MSS are in the library of the University of Lund.

II. SECONDARY LITERATURE. Writings on Agardh are the articles of Ericksson and Svedelius cited above and G. B. de Toni, "G. G. Agardh e la sua opera scientifica," in *La nuova notarisia,* **17** (1902), 1–28.

GUNNAR ERIKSSON

AGASSIZ, ALEXANDER (*b.* Neuchâtel, Switzerland, 17 December 1835; *d.* mid-Atlantic, 27 March 1910), *zoology, oceanography, engineering.*

Alexander Agassiz was the son of Louis Agassiz and Cécile Braun Agassiz, the sister of the botanist Alexander Braun. From 1847, after his father departed for America, until 1849, when he went to Cambridge, Massachusetts, following the death of his mother, he lived at Freiburg im Breisgau, where he came under the influence of his uncle. In America he soon formed a lasting bond with his stepmother, Elizabeth Cary Agassiz, and moved naturally into a scientific career. Agassiz graduated from Harvard College in 1855, from the Lawrence Scientific School with a degree in engineering in 1857, and again from the Lawrence Scientific School with a degree in zoology in 1862. After a short career in the U.S. Coast Survey in 1859, he became his father's assistant at the Museum of Comparative Zoology, which he continued to serve for the rest of his life, chiefly as its director.

In 1866 Agassiz undertook, on behalf of himself and a brother-in-law, the management of the Calumet and Hecla copper mines in the Upper Peninsula of Michigan. By 1869, although he had impaired his health, he had laid the basis for a fortune that he plowed into scientific research, both by gifts to Harvard and the museum and by freeing himself from a conventional career in either teaching or business. After 1873 (when his wife, Anna Russell, whom he had married in 1860, died within a few days of his father) his life consisted of a regular round of research in the tropics in the winter, summers at his laboratory near Newport, Rhode Island, and stays in Cambridge and Michigan each fall and spring. Although his fortune and his benefactions place him first among those late nineteenth-century captains of industry who supported science in the United States, he was distinguished as both a zoologist and an oceanographer. He died while crossing the Atlantic from England to America.

Although usually reticent about large theoretical schemes, in 1860 Agassiz spoke in private letters in terms that were closer to the theories of his father about the geographical distribution of animals than to the ideas of Charles Darwin which were sweeping through the American scientific community (including among their adherents most of Louis Agassiz's own students). By 1872, when Agassiz visited the British exploring ship *Challenger* at Halifax, Nova Scotia, he impressed its naturalists, including Sir John Murray, as holding views quite different from his father's. His work from 1860 to the late 1870's was largely concerned with the study of zoology, beginning with the animals of the New England shore, especially the echinoderms, and culminating in his *Revision of the Echini* (1872–1874). Using the embryological and paleontological approach of his father, he produced a masterly work that belonged to the era of Darwin, writing that it "is astonishing that so little use has been made of the positive data furnished by embryology in support of the evolution hypothesis." He also worked up the echinoderms from the *Challenger* expedition.

In 1877 Agassiz's interest began to shift to deep-sea dredging for abyssal fauna. Using his engineering background to good advantage and his wealth to support both operations and publications, he began with three cruises of the Coast Survey steamer *Blake* in the Caribbean. In 1891 he explored the deep water of the Pacific from the Galápagos Islands to the Gulf of California in the Fish Commission steamer *Albatross*. His aim in this period was to make a comparative study of marine fauna on both sides of the Isthmus of Panama. His interest from 1892 onward shifted strongly to the problem of the formation of coral atolls. Questioning the universality of Darwin's theory of atoll formation by subsidence, he used his knowledge of the Caribbean and Hawaiian islands as a basis of comparison. In 1893 and 1894 he explored the Bahama and Bermuda islands, in 1896 the Great Barrier Reef, in 1897 the Fijis, in 1898–1900 the central Pacific, and in 1900–1902 the Maldives. The publications of his later years were usually reports of the various voyages; a general work on coral reefs was never finished. Agassiz's later work is as close to modern oceanography and marine zoology as his earlier work was to that of his father.

BIBLIOGRAPHY

A list of Alexander Agassiz's published writings appears in George Lincoln Goodale, "Biographical Memoir of Alexander Agassiz 1835–1910," in National Academy of Sciences, *Biographical Memoirs*, VII (Washington, D. C., 1912), 291–305. Manuscripts, letter books, incoming letters, and many photographs are preserved at the Museum of Comparative Zoology, Harvard University.

The preeminent biographical source is George R. Agassiz, ed., *Letters and Recollections of Alexander Agassiz With a Sketch of His Life and Work* (Boston-New York, 1913).

A. HUNTER DUPREE

AGASSIZ, JEAN LOUIS RODOLPHE (*b.* Motier-en-Vuly, Switzerland, 28 May 1807; *d.* Cambridge, Massachusetts, 14 December 1873), *ichthyology, geology, paleontology.*

Louis Agassiz, the son of Rodolphe and Rose Mayor Agassiz, grew to manhood enjoying the prosperity and status of his family and the natural beauty of the Swiss cantons of Fribourg, Vaud, and Neuchâtel. He never identified with a sectarian religious persuasion. He did embrace the Protestant pietism of his

minister father, but was more fundamentally devoted to an idealistic romanticism that saw the power of the Creator exemplified in all flora and fauna. The Agassiz and Mayor families were anxious to see Louis succeed in the world of commerce or medicine, but he triumphed over their opposition and entered the larger world of European scholarship and cosmopolitanism by attending the universities of Zurich, Heidelberg, and Munich. In 1829 he earned his doctorate in philosophy at the universities of Munich and Erlangen and published a monograph on the fishes of Brazil that brought him to the attention of Baron Georges Cuvier. In 1830 he earned the doctor of medicine degree at Munich. After studying under Cuvier's tutelage in Paris, Agassiz accepted a professorship at the newly established College of Neuchâtel in 1832. In the same year he married Cécile Braun, the sister of his Heidelberg classmate Alexander Braun. In 1846 he accepted an invitation to lecture at the Lowell Institute in Boston. On the death of his wife in 1847, he accepted a professorship at the Lawrence Scientific School of Harvard University, where he continued to teach until his death. Agassiz's decision to make the United States his permanent home—despite attractive offers to return to Europe—was influenced by his love for and marriage to Elizabeth Cabot Cary. From 1850 until 1873 she raised Agassiz's three children by his first wife and acted as a constant companion in the writing, exploration, and interpretation of natural history.

Agassiz's career had two distinct geographic and intellectual aspects. As a European, he published monographs on ichthyology, paleontology, and geology whose promise earned him the admiration of such established savants as Cuvier, Alexander von Humboldt, and Sir Charles Lyell. As an American, Agassiz made nature study popular and appealing, explored the American environment with great enthusiasm, and established lasting institutions of research and education. His robust attitude toward life and nature study was a perpetual passion that tolerated no opposition to plans he deemed vital. Agassiz demanded unquestioning loyalty, and repaid such dedication by deep love and devotion. His dedication to science and culture won him the admiration of statesman and commoner alike, although his reputation among fellow scientists diminished with the passing of time. His exceptionally strong constitution sustained him on journeys of exploration through central Europe, the Swiss Alps, the eastern United States and the trans-Mississippi West, and South America. In 1873, shortly after an expedition through the Strait of Magellan, Agassiz died of a cerebral hemorrhage. Among his numerous awards and honors were the Wollaston Medal of the Geological Society of London and the Copley Medal of the Royal Society of London.

Agassiz thought of himself primarily as a naturalist, generalizing about the entire range of organic creation. Nevertheless, it is the modern sciences of ichthyology, geology, and paleontology that bear the stamp of his contributions. In the middle decades of the nineteenth century, when the natural sciences were in transition from classical to evolutionary biology, Agassiz's work and career were typical. He had an insatiable desire to record data; he described and analyzed material significant for the study of marine biology, freshwater fishes, embryology, and fossil fishes. In this last realm, his *Poissons fossiles,* written directly in the tradition of his mentor Cuvier, contained precise descriptions of more than 1,700 ancient species, together with illustrated reconstructions based on principles of comparative anatomy. This pioneer effort was a model of exactitude, providing future students with primary data relating zoology to geology and paleontology.

Agassiz never viewed his work in paleoichthyology as providing a framework for conceptions of natural history related to the development of lower forms into higher ones. He insisted that ancient and modern species were permanent representations of a divine idea, and bore no genetic relationship to each other. While employing techniques of close empirical study learned from such teachers as Cuvier and Ignaz Döllinger, Agassiz affirmed a view of the world above and beyond experience. In this sense, he reflected the teaching of Lorenz Oken and Friedrich Schelling. These diverse influences in Agassiz's intellectual history make it impossible to separate his contributions to exact science from his philosophy of nature. He worked in two divergent traditions, and his efforts reflected the virtues and deficiencies of each. This is why evolutionists found Agassiz so mystifying an opponent and why the Swiss naturalist found their views to be mere restatements of ideas absorbed and partly rejected in his youth.

These divergent qualities were reflected in Agassiz's geological investigations. From 1835 to 1845, while still serving as a professor at Neuchâtel, Agassiz studied the glacial formations of Switzerland and compared them with the geology of England and central Europe. The resulting concept of the "Ice Age" was remarkable for its breadth of generalization and for the exacting field study represented. Agassiz held that in the immediately recent past there had been an era during which large land masses over much of northern Europe were covered with ice. With the onset of warming periods, the recession of the ice was

responsible for upheaval and subsistence. The marks of glaciers could be discerned in the scratched and polished rocks as well as in the configurations of the earth in glaciated regions. Glacial movement was responsible for modern geological configurations, and could be traced in such areas as Switzerland. Agassiz was not the first to observe the phenomena of glaciation, but he was innovative in the wide-ranging character of his research, his measurement of ice formations, and his elaboration of local geology into a theory explaining Continental natural history. Such events, now known to have been of greater cyclical duration than Agassiz asserted, were still sufficient to convince such naturalists as Darwin and Lyell that Pleistocene glaciation was a primary mechanism in causing the geographical distribution and consequent genetic relationship of flora and fauna otherwise inexplicably separated by land and water masses. But Agassiz could never accept such a conclusion. He interpreted glaciation in metaphysical terms. To him, the Deity had been responsible for the Ice Age, a catastrophe that provided a permanent physical barrier separating the species of the past from those of the present era. There were as many as twenty separate creations in the history of the earth, each distinguished by animal and plant forms bearing no relationship to present types. At best, paleontology could only provide a glimpse of those "prophetic types" that suggested the course of future development, while those forms that remained unchanged over time were evidence of the wisdom of the Creator in inspiring perfect creatures from the beginning. Agassiz extended his conception of natural history to include mankind, asserting that men, like other animals, were of distinct types or species and were marked by different physical and intellectual traits. In the United States of the pre-Civil War years, such ideas provided convenient rationalizations for defenders of the slave system.

Agassiz's visit to the United States in 1846 was a notable success, for the brilliant young naturalist described his adventures and communicated his love of nature to lecture hall audiences in Boston and other eastern cities. He had also come to compare the natural history of the Old World with that of America, but this temporary purpose soon vanished in the adulation he received from all classes of Americans. Agassiz found the natural environment fascinating, and after accepting the Harvard professorship, he determined to explore it and interpret it to his new countrymen. In 1855 he announced a grand plan for the publication of a monumental ten-volume study, *Contributions to the Natural History of the United States,* that would depict the full scope of the

American natural environment. Only four volumes appeared; and these, although magnificently illustrated, were valuable only for their descriptions of North American turtles. The work was at once too complicated for the general public and too descriptive for those naturalists increasingly interested in new theoretical conceptions identifiable with the work of Charles Darwin.

Agassiz was philosophically and scientifically unprepared to meet the challenge of the theory of evolution as it was propounded in 1859. During his early years in the United States he extended his glacial theory to North America, he explored large portions of the country, and conducted some potentially valuable research in marine biology. More than all these efforts, it was the collection of the raw data of nature that drove Agassiz ever onward, so that Harvard University became a center for natural history instruction and research. The capstone of such efforts was the establishment at Harvard College in 1859 of the Museum of Comparative Zoology, an institution made possible by private gifts and funds supplied by the state of Massachusetts. The museum always bore the impress of Agassiz's conception of the relationship between graduate instruction, research, fieldwork, and publication, centered in an institution of higher learning and supported by private philanthropy and public funds.

It was inevitable that Agassiz became the leading American opponent of Darwin, but regrettable that his public activity left little time for reflection on the data he had collected or on alternate interpretations of its significance. Agassiz had become a public man in the fullest sense, but even had he devoted more time to intellectual labor, it is doubtful that he could have accepted an interpretation of nature that seemed to deny permanence and immaterialism. Some of his critiques of evolution were trenchant ones, but in the main his attacks were inconclusive efforts that failed to convince his scientific colleagues. Many of these appeared in popular journals, reflecting Agassiz's conviction that this "error" had to be opposed with the full power of his public position. While Agassiz's opposition to evolution was inconsequential, the years from 1859 to his death were nevertheless a period of notable public accomplishment. He was able to obtain more than $600,000 in public and private support for the Harvard museum, and to convince fellow scientists to establish the National Academy of Sciences in 1863. This achievement, coupled with his earlier efforts to advise the federal government on the operations of the U.S. Coast Survey and the Smithsonian Institution, revealed Agassiz in the prime of his American influence and international prestige.

By 1873, despite Darwin, Agassiz's name was synonymous with the study of natural history. It was fitting that in that last year of his life he established the Anderson School of Natural History on Penikese Island, off the Massachusetts coast, as a combined summer school and marine biological station. In testimony to Agassiz's American influence, the faculty of the school was entirely composed of his former students. The *Poissons fossiles* and *Études sur les glaciers* were high points of Agassiz's career in Europe; in America, the life and work of such students as William James, David Starr Jordan, Alexander Agassiz, Frederick Ward Putnam, and Nathaniel Southgate Shaler exemplify his role and cultural significance.

BIBLIOGRAPHY

I. ORIGINAL WORKS. Bibliographies of Agassiz's writings are in his *Bibliographia zoologiae et geologiae*, 4 vols. (London, 1848–1854), I, 98–103; Jules Marcou, *Life, Letters, and Works of Louis Agassiz* (see below), II, 258–303; and Max Meisel, *A Bibliography of American Natural History*, 3 vols. (New York, 1924–1929), *passim.* Among his significant works are *Selecta genera et species piscium quas in itinere per Brasiliam 1817–1820 . . .* (Munich, 1829); *Recherches sur les poissons fossiles,* 5 vols. (Neuchâtel, 1833–1844); *Monographies d'échinodermes vivans et fossiles . . .,* 4 vols. (Neuchâtel, 1838–1842); *Études sur les glaciers* (Neuchâtel, 1840); *Twelve Lectures on Comparative Embryology* (Boston, 1849); *Lake Superior* (Boston, 1850); *Contributions to the Natural History of the United States,* 4 vols. (Boston, 1857–1862); *Essay on Classification* (London, 1859), also ed., with intro., by Edward Lurie (Cambridge, Mass., 1962); *Geological Sketches* (Boston, 1866); "Evolution and Permanence of Type," in *Atlantic Monthly,* **33** (Jan. 1874), 94–101; and *Geological Sketches, Second Series* (Boston, 1876).

II. SECONDARY LITERATURE. Works on Agassiz are Elizabeth Cary Agassiz, ed., *Louis Agassiz, His Life and Correspondence,* 2 vols. (Boston, 1885); Lane Cooper, *Louis Agassiz as a Teacher,* rev. ed. (Ithaca, N.Y., 1945); Edward Lurie, *Louis Agassiz: A Life in Science* (Chicago, 1960); Jules Marcou, *Life, Letters, and Works of Louis Agassiz,* 2 vols. (New York, 1896); and Ernst Mayr, "Agassiz, Darwin and Evolution," in *Harvard Library Bulletin,* **13** (Spring 1959), 165–194.

EDWARD LURIE

AGATHINUS, CLAUDIUS (*fl. ca.* A.D. 50), *medicine.*

Agathinus was a Spartan physician who lived in Rome, where he was connected with the family of the Stoic philosopher L. Annaeus Cornutus. His association with known Stoics was certainly not fortuitous, since he is known to have been a practitioner of the Pneumatic school of medicine founded by Athenaeus of Attalia under the influence of Poseidonius, another Stoic philosopher. Although the identity of Agathinus' medical teacher is not known, it was certainly not Athenaeus of Attalia (*fl.* 50 B.C.) himself. Agathinus founded his own school, which he called episynthetic (i.e., eclectic). In direct opposition to the schismatic spirit of Imperial Roman medicine, the episynthetic school championed the intellectual unity of medicine as interpreted by Galen.

Agathinus had many medical disciples, of whom the best known was the celebrated Archigenes, who described his teacher's scientific attitude: "Therefore Agathinus—who was particular about everything and never relied on mere eclecticism, but for safety's sake always required empirical verification—administered hellebore (elleborus) to a dog, which therewith vomited" (see Oribasius in *Corpus medicorum Graecorum,* VI, part 1, 1 [Leipzig–Berlin, 1928], 252).

None of Agathinus' original writings survive intact, but antique sources mention a work on the pulse, dedicated to his pupil Herodot; a work on fever, especially the kind he called "semitertian fever"; and, finally, a work on hellebore. All of these show, therefore, that Agathinus was neither a narrow specialist nor a dubious charlatan, as were so many of his colleagues in Imperial Rome. On the contrary, although only scant information about Agathinus' life and a few fragments of his writings remain, it is apparent that he was among the really important and influential physicians of the intellectually rich first century A.D.

BIBLIOGRAPHY

Information on Agathinus' personality and the episynthetic school can be found in G. Kaibel, ed., *Epigrammata Graeca* (Berlin, 1878), no. 558; and in Galen's *Works,* ed. C. G. Kühn, XIX (Leipzig, 1830), 353. His associations in Rome are discussed in Suetonius; see *Suetonii Reliquiae,* ed. A. Reifferscheid (Leipzig, 1860), p. 74, with textual correction by Osann. Agathinus' disciples are discussed in Galen; see *Corpus medicorum Graecorum,* V, part 10, 2, 2 (Berlin, 1956), 86. His writing on the pulse is mentioned in Kühn's edition of Galen's *Works,* VIII (Leipzig, 1824), 749 ff.; on fever, in *Corpus medicorum Graecorum,* V, part 10, 1 (Leipzig, 1934), 62; and on the hellebore, in Caelius Aurelianus, *Celeres vel acutae passiones,* Bk. 3, sec. 135. Agathinus' influence is assessed in Galen, *Über die medizinischen Namen,* M. Meyerhof and J. Schacht, eds. (Berlin, 1931), p. 10. To be used, with some reservations, is

M. Wellmann, *Die pneumatische Schule bis auf Archigenes* (Berlin, 1895), pp. 9 ff.

FRIDOLF KUDLIEN

AGNESI, MARIA GAETANA (*b.* Milan, Italy, 16 May 1718; *d.* Milan, 9 January 1799), *mathematics.*

Maria Gaetana Agnesi, the first woman in the Western world who can accurately be called a mathematician, was the eldest child of Pietro Agnesi and Anna Fortunato Brivio. Her father, a wealthy Milanese who was professor of mathematics at the University of Bologna, encouraged his daughter's interest in scientific matters by securing a series of distinguished professors as her tutors and by establishing in his home a cultural salon where she could present theses on a variety of subjects and then defend them in academic disputations with leading scholars. Agnesi invited both local celebrities and foreign noblemen to his soirées. During the intermissions between Maria Gaetana's defenses, her sister, Maria Teresa, a composer and noted harpsichordist, entertained the guests by playing her own compositions.

In all her discourses at these gatherings, Maria Gaetana demonstrated her genius as a linguist. At age five she spoke French fluently. At age nine, she translated into Latin, recited from memory, and released for publication a lengthy speech advocating higher education for women. By age eleven, she was thoroughly familiar with Greek, German, Spanish, and Hebrew. The disputations were conducted in Latin, but during the subsequent discussions a foreigner would usually address Maria in his native tongue and would be answered in that language. The topics on which she presented theses covered a wide range—logic, ontology, mechanics, hydromechanics, elasticity, celestial mechanics and universal gravitation, chemistry, botany, zoology, and mineralogy, among others. Some 190 of the theses she defended appear in the *Propositiones philosophicae* (1738), her second published work.

Although the 1738 compilation does not contain any of Agnesi's purely mathematical ideas, various other documents indicate her early interest in mathematics and her original approach to that subject. At fourteen she was solving difficult problems in analytic geometry and ballistics. Her correspondence with some of her former tutors indicates that, as early as age seventeen, she was beginning to shape her critical commentary on the *Traité analytique des sections coniques* of Guillaume de L'Hospital, a leading mathematician of the Newtonian era. The manuscript material that she prepared, although judged excellent by all the professors who examined it, was never published.

In 1738, after the publication of the *Propositiones philosophicae*, Agnesi indicated that the constant public display of her talents at her father's gatherings was becoming distasteful to her, and she expressed a strong desire to enter a convent. Persuaded by her father not to take that step, she nevertheless withdrew from all social life and devoted herself completely to the study of mathematics. In the advanced phases of the subject she was guided by Father Ramiro Rampinelli, a member of the Olivetan order of the Benedictines, who later became professor of mathematics at the University of Pavia. A decade of concentrated thought bore fruit in 1748 with the publication of her *Istituzioni analitiche ad uso della gioventù italiana,* which she dedicated to Empress Maria Theresa of Austria. This book won immediate acclaim in academic circles all over Europe and brought recognition as a mathematician to Agnesi.

The *Istituzioni analitiche* consisted of two huge quarto volumes containing more than a thousand pages. Its author's objective was to give a complete, integrated, comprehensible treatment of algebra and analysis, with emphasis on concepts that were new (or relatively so) in the mid-eighteenth century. In this connection one must realize that Newton was still alive when Agnesi was born, so that the development of the differential and integral calculus was in progress during her lifetime. With the *gioventù* (youth) in mind, she wrote in Italian rather than in Latin and covered the range from elementary algebra to the classical theory of equations, to coordinate geometry, and then on to differential calculus, integral calculus, infinite series (to the extent that these were known in her day), and finally to the solution of elementary differential equations. She treated finite processes in the first volume and infinitesimal analysis in the second.

In the introduction to the *Istituzioni analitiche,* Agnesi—modest as she was, with too great a tendency to give credit to others—had to admit that some of the methods, material, and generalizations were entirely original with her. Since there were many genuinely new things in her masterpiece, it is strange that her name is most frequently associated with one small discovery which she shared with others: the formulation of the *versiera*, the cubic curve whose equation is $x^2 y = a^2 (a - y)$ and which, by a process of literal translation from colloquial Italian, has come to be known as the "witch of Agnesi." She was apparently unaware (and so were historians until recently) that

Fermat had given the equation of the curve in 1665 and that Guido Grandi had used the name *versiera* for it in 1703.

Agnesi's definition of the curve may be stated as follows: If C is a circle of diameter a with center at $(O, 1/2\, a)$, and if the variable line OA through the origin O intersects the line $y = a$ at point A and the circle at point B, then the *versiera* is the locus of point P, which is the intersection of lines through A and B parallel to the Y axis and X axis, respectively. The curve, generated as the line OA turns (Latin *vertere,* hence the name *versiera*), is bell-shaped with the X axis as asymptote. There are interesting special properties and some applications in modern physics, but these do not completely explain why mathematicians are so intrigued by the curve. They have formulated a *pseudo-versiera* by means of a change in the scale of ordinates (a similarity transformation). Even Giuseppe Peano, one of the most formidable figures in modern axiomatics and mathematical logic, could not resist the temptation to create the "*visiera* of Agnesi," as he called it, a curve generated in a fashion resembling that for the *versiera*.

The tributes to the excellence of Agnesi's treatise were so numerous that it is impossible to list them all, but those related to translations of the work will be noted. The French translation (of the second volume only) was authorized by the French Academy of Sciences. In 1749 an academy committee recorded its opinion: "This work is characterized by its careful organization, its clarity, and its precision. There is no other book, in any language, which would enable a reader to penetrate as deeply, or as rapidly, into the fundamental concepts of analysis. We consider this treatise the most complete and best written work of its kind."

An English translation of the *Istituzioni analitiche* was made by John Colson, Lucasian professor of mathematics at Cambridge, and was published in 1801 at the expense of the baron de Masères. In introducing the translation, John Hellins, its editor, wrote: "He [Colson] found her [Agnesi's] work to be so excellent that he was at the pains of learning the Italian language at an advanced age for the sole purpose of translating her book into English, that the British Youth might have the benefit of it as well as the Youth of Italy."

The recognition of greatest significance to Agnesi was provided in two letters from Pope Benedict XIV. The first, dated June 1749, a congratulatory note on the occasion of the publication of her book, was accompanied by a gold medal and a gold wreath adorned with precious stones. In his second letter, dated September 1750, the pope appointed her to the chair of mathematics and natural philosophy at Bologna.

But Agnesi, always retiring, never actually taught at the University of Bologna. She accepted her position as an honorary one from 1750 to 1752, when her father was ill. After his death in 1752 she gradually withdrew from all scientific activity. By 1762 she was so far removed from the world of mathematics that she declined a request of the University of Turin to act as referee for the young Lagrange's papers on the calculus of variations.

The years after 1752 were devoted to religious studies and social work. Agnesi made great material sacrifices to help the poor of her parish. She had always mothered her numerous younger brothers (there were twenty-one children from Pietro Agnesi's three marriages), and after her father's death she took his place in directing their education. In 1771 Agnesi became directress of the Pio Albergo Trivulzio, a Milanese home for the aged ill and indigent, a position she held until her death.

BIBLIOGRAPHY

I. ORIGINAL WORKS. Agnesi's main works are *Propositiones philosophicae* (Milan, 1738) and *Analytical Institutions,* an English translation of the *Istituzioni analitiche* by the Rev. J. Colson (London, 1801).

II. SECONDARY LITERATURE. Further information about Agnesi and her work may be found in L. Anzoletti, *Maria Gaetana Agnesi* (Milan, 1900); A. F. Frisi, *Elogio storico di Domina Maria Gaetana Agnesi milanese* (Milan, 1799); and A. Masotti, "Maria Gaetana Agnesi," in *Rendiconti del seminario matematico e fisico di Milano,* **14** (1940), 1–39.

EDNA E. KRAMER

AGRICOLA, GEORGIUS, also known as **Georg Bauer** (*b.* Glauchau, Germany, 24 March 1494; *d.* Chemnitz, Germany [now Karl-Marx-Stadt, German Democratic Republic], 21 November 1555), *mining, metallurgy.*

Agricola's father was probably Gregor Bauer, a dyer and woolen draper. His youngest son, Hans, Georg's favorite brother, who joined Georg at Chemnitz in 1540, followed the same profession. The eldest son, Franciscus, became a priest at Zwickau and later at Glauchau. Georg attended various schools in Glauchau, Zwickau, and Magdeburg (1511), and in 1514—rather late, since the average age at matriculation was between twelve and fifteen—he entered Leipzig University. In 1515 he received the B.A. and remained at the university as lecturer in elementary Greek until he was chosen *ludi moderator* at Zwickau in 1517. In 1519, as *rector extraordinarius,* he organized the new Schola Graeca and wrote his first work, *De prima ac simplici institutione grammatica* (1520). This short booklet is an excellent specimen of the new humanistic pedagogy, with interesting examples taken from a schoolboy's experiences.

Zwickau was a center of the Reformation, and although Agricola believed a reformation was necessary, he did not approve of its revolutionary aspects. He therefore returned to Leipzig in 1523 to study medicine under Heinrich Stromer von Auerbach; to support himself, he had been endowed with the prebend of the St. Erasmus altar for three years by the council of Zwickau. This enabled him to visit Italy, and on his way he stopped in Basel to pay his respects to Erasmus. Agricola spent three years at Bologna and Venice as a member of the editorial staff for the Aldina editions of Galen and Hippocrates. He also joined the English group headed by Edward Wotton and John Clement, son-in-law of Sir Thomas More. This group may have aroused Agricola's interest in politics and economics.

Following the route through the mining districts in Carinthia, Styria, and the Tyrol, Agricola returned to Germany in the fall of 1526 with the M.D. and a wife, the widow of Thomas Meiner, director of the Schneeberg mining district. The following spring he was elected town physician and apothecary of St. Joachimsthal (now Jáchymov), Czechoslovakia. Here he continued his studies on the pharmaceutical use of minerals and smelting products, with a view to compiling comments on Galen and Hippocrates.

In those days St. Joachimsthal was the most important mining center in Europe besides Schwaz in the Tyrol. Miners and smelters, some of whom suffered from occupational diseases, were crowded together. Agricola studied not only their ailments but also their life, labor, and equipment. Day and night he visited the mines and the smoky smelting houses, and soon he had an excellent knowledge of mining and metallurgy. He recorded his impressions in *Bermannus sive de re metallica dialogus* (1530).

The success of this pioneer delineation of mining and metallurgy was assured by Erasmus, who contributed a letter of recommendation. Agricola was now a well-known author, and he indefatigably sustained his reputation with a flow of important books. The next ones were political and economic: *Oratio de bello adversus Turcam suscipiendo* (1531) and *De mensuris et ponderibus* (1533).

Since there were too many demands on his time in St. Joachimsthal, Agricola decided to return to Chemnitz, to be town physician in this quieter, smaller town on the northern slope of the Erzgebirge. Chemnitz had a copper smelter which was used to extract silver from the ore. Agricola's knowledge of mining enabled him to profit from mining shares. He always seemed to enter into the right partnership and to avoid profitless ventures. By 1542 he was one of the twelve richest inhabitants of Chemnitz. After fifteen years of hard work he succeeded in finishing a complete series of inquiries concerning the principles of geology and mineralogy.

This series must be considered his greatest scientific achievement. It had not yet been published when Agricola became involved in the war of Emperor Charles V against the Protestant Schmalkaldic League: he was elected mayor of Chemnitz, appointed a councillor to the court of Saxony, and sent as an ambassador to the emperor and his younger brother Ferdinand, king of Bohemia. For more than three years Agricola was with the councillors of Moritz, duke of Saxony, as one of the few Roman Catholic representatives at the Protestant court. He never wrote about the diplomatic missions he was charged with, but we may assume that his parleys with the Catholic emperor's commanders and diplomats were effective. He was not able to return to his scientific work until 1548, but new books appeared soon after: *De animantibus subterraneis* (1549) and an enlarged edition of *De mensuris et ponderibus* (1550).

In 1550 Agricola returned to St. Joachimsthal for some weeks. He saw a very changed situation: the prosperity was gone, nearly all of the ruling family had been deposed or expelled, and some of the new royal officials had not the slightest idea of the needs of the town and its inhabitants. Agricola gave a 5,000-thaler credit—worth 2,000 cows in those days—to the counts Schlick to promote prospecting for new deposits, a search that was successful. He went home to Chemnitz conscious of having done a good deed, and with him he took the finished text of his chief work, *De re metallica libri XII,* begun twenty years before in St. Joachimsthal. During his visit to St. Joachimsthal he had met the expert designer Blasius Weffring, who spent the next three years illustrating the text.

When the black plague spread through Saxony in 1552–1553, Agricola worked day and night, going from the pesthouses to his family, always fearing that he would bring the contagion with him; one daughter did die of the plague. His first wife had died in 1541, and the following year he had married Anna Schütz, daughter of the guild master and smelter owner Ulrich

Schütz, who had entrusted his wife and children to Agricola's guardianship when he died in 1534. His studies during the plague led Agricola to publish *De peste libri III* (1554).

Agricola could not retire until another work was finished. In 1534 Georg the Whiskered, duke of Saxony and a patron of the Catholic church, had nominated Agricola as historiographer of the court of Saxony, probably with the hope of discovering genealogical claims on territories by heirs-at-law. For twenty years Agricola studied yellowed parchments and old chronicles. His honesty forbade him to conceal the rulers' mistakes uncovered during his research: he was a scholar, not a courtier. He recorded his findings very frankly—much to the disappointment of Augustus, third duke after Georg the Whiskered. It is no wonder, then, that the *Sippschaft des Hausses zu Sachssen,* an evaluation of all the rulers of Saxony, remained unpublished until 1963.

Augustus ignored the dedication dated 9 August 1555, but more important is that of 18 March 1555, for the second, enlarged edition of the mineralogical works (1558). It contains Agricola's most quoted words on peace and war, written before the Peace of Augsburg (September 1555), when war between the Catholic and Protestant confessions seemed imminent. For Agricola, that decisive agreement was the end of all his hopes for a reunion in faith. He fell ill soon after and died after suffering a relapse in November.

After Agricola's death the religious struggle renewed over his corpse. The Protestant clergy refused to allow his being buried in the parish church at Chemnitz, an honor traditionally accorded to mayors; and it was only through the intervention of his old friend Julius von Pflug, bishop of Zeitz-Naumburg, that he was interred in the cathedral at Zeitz.

Four months after his death, *De re metallica libri XII,* illustrated with 292 woodcuts, appeared. A year later an Old German translation by Philippus Bech was published using the same woodcuts, which were used for 101 years in seven editions.

BIBLIOGRAPHY

I. ORIGINAL WORKS. Agricola's writings include *De prima ac simplici institutione grammatica* (Leipzig, 1520); *Bermannus sive de re metallica dialogus* (Basel, 1530; Paris, 1541); *Oratio de bello adversus Turcam suscipiendo,* original Latin ed. (Basel, 1538), in Old German as *Oration, Anrede und Vermanung . . . widder den Türcken,* Lorenz Bermann, trans. (Dresden–Nuremberg, 1531); *De mensuris et ponderibus* (Basel–Paris, 1533; Venice, 1535), reissued as *De mensuris et ponderibus Romanorum atque Graecorum libri*

V (Basel, 1550), with the following additions: *De externis mensuris et ponderibus, Brevis defensio, De mensuris quibus intervalla metimur, De restituendis mensuris atque ponderibus,* and *De precio metallorum et monetis;* the big foliant, containing *De ortu et causis subterraneorum, De natura eorum quae effluunt e terra, De natura fossilium, De veteribus et novis metallis, Bermannus sive de re metallica dialogus* (revised), and *Interpretatio Germanica vocum rei metallicae addito indice foecundissimo* (Basel, 1546; 2nd ed., rev. and enl., Basel, 1558)—*De natura fossilium* was translated into English by Mark C. Bandy and Jean A. Bandy (New York, 1955); *De animantibus subterraneis* (Basel, 1549); *De peste libri III* (Basel, 1554); *Sippschaft des Hausses zu Sachssen* (1555), in *Ausgewählte Werke,* VII, 77–416; and *De re metallica libri XII* (Basel, 1556, 1561, 1621, 1657), translated into English, with biographical introduction, annotations, and appendixes by Henry Clark Hoover and Lou Henry Hoover (London, 1912; new ed. [unchanged], New York, 1950).

Nearly all of Agricola's works are brought together in *Ausgewählte Werke,* 12 vols., incl. supps., Hans Prescher, ed. (Berlin, 1955–   ).

II. SECONDARY LITERATURE. Works on Agricola are Bern Dibner, *Agricola on Metals,* Burndy Library Publication no. 15 (Norwalk, Conn., 1958); Erwin Herlitzius, *G. A. Seine Weltanschauung und seine Leistung als Wegbereiter einer materialistischen Naturauffassung,* Freiberger Forschungsheft no. D32 (Berlin, 1960); William B. Parsons, *Engineers and Engineering in the Renaissance* (Baltimore, 1939); Georg Spackeler, ed., *Georgius Agricola 1555–1955* (Berlin, 1955); and Helmut M. Wilsdorf, *Präludien zu Agricola,* Freiberger Forschungsheft no. D5 (Berlin, 1954); *Georg Agricola und seine Zeit* (Berlin, 1956); and "Dr. Georgius Agricola und die Begründung des Bergbaumedizin," in *Jahrbuch des Museums für Mineralogie und Geologie Dresden,* **5** (1959), 112–154.

HELMUT M. WILSDORF

AGRIPPA, HEINRICH CORNELIUS, also known as **Agrippa von Nettesheim** (*b.* near Cologne, Germany, 14 September 1486; *d.* Grenoble, France, *ca.* 18 February 1535), *magic, alchemy, philosophy, medicine.*

Agrippa's father, Heinrich von Nettesheim, was a citizen of Cologne; nothing is known of his mother. Agrippa's surname and epithet indicate both his birthplace (Cologne was formerly Colonia Agrippina) and the origin of his family (Nettesheim, a village near Cologne); his given names suggest a Dutch or Flemish influence. Agrippa married three times. His first wife, who came from Pavia and was married to him in 1514, died in 1518 in Metz. They had a son, Theodoricus, who was born in 1515 and died in 1522. Six children were born to his second wife, Jeanne Loyse Tissie, whom he married in Geneva in 1521; she died in 1528. A third union, apparently unhappy, took place the following year.

Agrippa enrolled at the University of Cologne on 22 July 1499. While there he studied law, medicine, magic sciences, and theology—particularly under Peter Ravenna. He also served in the army of Emperor Maximilian I for several years. At the age of twenty he made his first trip to Paris to study; he then went, again in military service, to Catalonia, and finally to Dôle, where he gave lectures on Johann Reuchlin's *De verbo mirifico.* In 1510 he spent a short time in London where he stayed with John Colet, the friend of Erasmus, and then he returned to Cologne, where he held theological disputations. That same year, in Würzburg, he met Johannes Trithemius, the abbot of St. Jacob's monastery. This was probably the most important meeting of Agrippa's life, for Trithemius encouraged him to finish the *De occulta philosophia.* Following this, Agrippa led a restless, roving life throughout Europe, especially in Italy. Among the places he visited were Milan, Pisa, Pavia (where in 1515 he expounded Hermetic writings), and Turin (where he taught theology), sometimes as an independent rhetorician, sometimes in military service.

In 1518 Agrippa was a public advocate in Metz and the defense lawyer in a sorcery trial; the latter service aroused such opposition that he had to leave town. He then went to Geneva via Cologne and became a physician. During 1523 and 1524 he was a salaried town physician in Fribourg, Switzerland. After 1524 he was at the court of Francis I in Lyons, where he was personal physician to the queen mother and court astrologer. He was always in monetary difficulties and constantly being dunned by his creditors.

In 1528 Margaret of Austria, the regent of the Netherlands, summoned Agrippa to become historian and librarian in Antwerp. Two years later he published his polemic *De incertitudine et vanitate scientiarum atque artium declamatio et de excellentia verbi Dei,* which he had begun to draft while still in Lyons. In 1531 he published the first of the three books of the *De occulta philosophia* (the fourth book is apocryphal), which had probably been written around 1510–1515. After the death of Margaret he returned, via Brussels and Cologne, to Lyons, where he was often persecuted because of his writings. He died in great poverty.

Agrippa's personality and *curriculum vitae* are still open to dispute, as is the authorship of his works. He has been described as an "honest, fearless, and generous man, . . . but somewhat vainglorious . . . , whereby he himself several times spoiled his chances at success" and also as a scientific swindler. Today Agrippa's importance is considered to lie in the social criticism that is embodied in his works on magic as well as in his polemic against the vanity and uncertainty of science. He has his *De occulta* and *De incertitudine* to thank not only for his fame but also for the doubt cast upon his having been a scientist. For a long time historians lumped him together with Reuchlin and even with Ramón Lull, for he attempted to combine Neoplatonic mysticism and magic—subject to nature—with Renaissance skepticism. Recent historical investigation does not support this view, however, and assigns him a central place in the history of ideas of the Middle Ages; he is seen as characterizing the main line of intellectual development from Nicholas of Cusa to Sebastian Franck. Modern opinion evaluates him on the basis of his Platonic, Neoplatonic, and Hermetic influences—primarily in the *De occulta philosophia*—without insisting on his skepticism.

The basic idea of Agrippa's *De occulta philosophia* is that from the void God had created several worlds, three of which constitute the All: the domain of the elements, the heavenly world of the stars, and the intelligible cosmos of the angels. These and the things existing in them are endowed with the *spiritus mundi* (the soul, the fifth element, the *quinta essentia* in the sense of the Aristotelian "ether"), which is set above the four classical elements. This spirit of the world represents the all-germinating force (comparable to the "germ-form" of the Stoics). At the center of these three worlds is man, who, because he is a microcosm and thus represents a mirror image of the macrocosm, can obtain knowledge of everything. The effectiveness of magic, according to Agrippa, is based on the connection of the three worlds. Only the human spirit can uncover the hidden forces present in matter, and by the latter's aid man can also call on greater forces to serve him. What Agrippa meant by this becomes evident in his small work *De triplici ratione cognoscendi Deum* (1516), in which the role of the cabala as intermediary step in his system signifies that true knowledge is to be found only in the love of God.

Although Agrippa was an admirer of Luther, he understood the *verbum Dei* as a Catholic; in one letter to Melancthon he called Luther the invincible heretic. Although this aspect of his thought is often neglected, it occupies the key position in his polemic on the arts and sciences, *De incertitudine*. This work gives emphasis to the tension between the *verbum Dei* and human knowledge, without providing any basis for the skepticism of which Agrippa has often been accused. Rather, at the beginning of the era of natural science, it is one of the first testimonials to knowledge of the limits of human understanding. *Incertitudo* here means a real uncertainty of existence, based on the concept of the human being as a created entity.

The question of why the otherwise critical Agrippa published nearly simultaneously two such opposing works as *De occulta philosophia* and *De incertitudine* remains open. In the former he appears to follow the metaphysical and speculative tradition of natural philosophy, while in the latter he attempts to overcome the magic of the *verbum mirificum*. There is no satisfactory explanation for this, a fact of which even Agrippa himself was aware. With a Faustian restlessness (he is considered the historical prototype of Goethe's Faust) he always returns to this theme in his letters; posterity has often considered this a fault in his character. Such a conflict is representative of Agrippa's age, however, and demonstrates a point of view widely held in Germany during the Renaissance.

BIBLIOGRAPHY

I. ORIGINAL WORKS. Agrippa's writings are collected in his *Opera omnia*, 2 vols. (Lyons, n.d.; 2nd ed., Lyons, 1600). During his lifetime thereof was edited: *De occulta philosophia*, 3 vols. (Vol. I, Antwerp, 1531; complete ed., Cologne, 1533); *De incertitudine et vanitate scientiarum atque artium declamatio* (Antwerp, 1530; Cologne, 1531); *Liber de triplici ratione cognoscendi Deum* (1516); *In artem brevem Raymundi Lulli commentaria* (Cologne, 1533). Not in *Opera omnia*: "Contra pestem antidoton," in P. Poitier, *Insignes curationes . . . et observationes centum*, Vol. I (Cologne, 1625).

II. SECONDARY LITERATURE. Works on Agrippa are M. H. Morley, *The Life of Henry Cornelius Agrippa von Nettesheim*, 2 vols. (London, 1856); Auguste Prost, *Les sciences et les arts occultes aux XVIe siècle: Corneille Agrippa, sa vie et ses oeuvres*, 2 vols. (Paris, 1881–1882); J. Orsier, *Henri Cornelis Agrippa, sa vie et son oeuvre d'après sa correspondance* (Paris, 1911); A. Reichl, "Goethes Faust und Agrippa von Nettesheim," in *Euphorion*, 4 (1897) 287–301; G. Ritter, "Ein historisches Urbild zu Goethes Faust (Agrippa von Nettesheim)," in *Preussische Jahrbuecher*, 141, no. 2 (1910), 300–324; J. Meurer, "Zur Logik und Metaphysik des Heinrich Cornelius Agrippa von Nettesheim," in *Renaissance und Philosophie, Beiträge zur Geschichte der Philosophie*, Adolf Dryoff, ed., Vol. XI (Bonn, 1920); E. Hahn, "Die Stellung des H. C. Agrippa von Nettesheim in der Geschichte der Philosophie," diss. (Munich-Leipzig, 1923); R. Stadelmann, "Zweifel und Verzweiflung bei Agrippa von Nettesheim," pp. 80–86 of *Vom Geist des ausgehenden Mittelalters*, Vol. XV of the series *Deutsche Vierteljahrsschrift für Literaturwissenschaft und Geistesgeschichte* (Halle, 1929); E. Cazalas, "Les sceaux planétaires de C. Agrippa," in *Revue de l'histoire des religions* 110 (1934), 66–82; E. Metzke, "Die 'Skepsis' des Agrippa von Nettesheim," in *Deutsche Vierteljahrsschrift für Literaturwissenschaft und Geistesgeschichte*, 13 (1935), 407–420; L. Thorndike, *A History of Magic and Experimental*

Science, V (New York, 1941), 127–138; H. Grimm, *Neue deutsche Biographie,* I (Berlin, 1953), 105–106; Charles G. Nauert, Jr., *Agrippa von Nettesheim, His Life and Thought,* diss. (University of Illinois, 1955), and "Agrippa in Renaissance Italy; the Esoteric Tradition," in *Studies in the Renaissance,* 6 (1959), 195–222; P. Zambelli, "Umanesimo magico-astrologico et raggruppamenti segreti nei platonici della preriforma," in *Umanesimo e esoterismo,* Enrico Castelli, ed. (Padua, 1960), 141–174; R. Schmitz, and K. U. Kuhlmay, "Zum Handschriftenproblem bei Agrippa von Nettesheim," in *Sudhoffs Archiv für Geschichte der Medizin und der Naturwissenschaften,* 46 (1962), 350–354; R. Schmitz, "Agrippa von Nettesheim und seine Bemerkungen ueber die Wirkungen der Magie in Medizin und Pharmazie," in *Pharmazeutische Zeitung,* 110 (1965), 1131–1138; Charles G. Nauert, Jr., "Agrippa and the Crisis of Renaissance Thought," in *Illinois Studies in the Social Sciences,* 55 (Urbana, Ill., 1965); and G. Rudolph, "'De incertitudine et vanitate scientiarum,' Tradition und Wandlung der wissenschaftlichen Skepsis von Agrippa von Nettesheim bis zum Ausgang des 18. Jahrhunderts," in *Gesnerus,* 23, no. 3/4 (1966), 247–265.

R. SCHMITZ

AGUILON, FRANÇOIS D' (*b.* Brussels, Belgium, 1546; *d.* Antwerp, Belgium, 1617), *physics, mathematics.*

The son of the secretary to Philip II, Aguilon became a Jesuit in 1586. After having taught syntax and logic, then theology, he was charged with organizing in Belgium the teaching of the exact sciences, which were useful in commerce, geography, navigation, and architecture, as well as military activities. This project led to the composition of a master treatise on optics that synthesized the works of Euclid, Ibn al-Haytham (Alhazen), Vitellion, Roger Bacon, Pena, Ramus (Pierre de la Ramée), Risner, and Kepler. Its organization into three sections was determined by the manner in which the eye perceives objects (directly, by reflection on polished surfaces, and by refraction through transparent bodies). Aguilon's death prevented the publication of the second and third sections, on catoptrics, dioptrics, and telescopes. Only the first part exists, with six frontispieces drawn by Rubens: *Francisci Aguilonii e Societate Jesu Opticorum libri sex juxta ac mathematicis utiles* (1613).

Aguilon treated, successively, the eye, the object, and the nature of vision; the optic ray and horopter; the general ideas that make possible the knowledge of objects; errors in perception; luminous and opaque bodies; and projections.

The sixth book, on orthographic, stereographic, and scenographic projections, remains important in the history of science. It accounts for a third of the treatise and was meant for the use of astronomers, cosmographers, architects, military leaders, navigators, painters, and engravers. It places particular emphasis on stereographic projection—a type of projection, used by Ptolemy, in which the portion of the sphere to be represented is projected from the pole onto the plane of the equatorial circle.

The balance of the treatise is of interest for the history of optics: description of the eye; controversies on the nature of light and its action; the application of mathematics to optics; the analysis of the concepts of distance, quantity, shape, place, position, continuity, discontinuity, movement, rest, transparency, opacity, shadow, light, resemblance, beauty, and deformity; and explanation of the various errors of perception linked to distance, size, position, shape, place, number, movement, rest, transparency, and opacity.

Book 5, in spite of an Aristotelian concept of light, studies the propagation of light, the limit of its action, the phenomena produced by the combinations of light sources, and the production of shadows. Aguilon proposes an experimental apparatus, drawn by Rubens, that made it possible to study the variations of intensity according to variations in distance and to compare lights of different intensities. This attempt to apply mathematics to the intensity of light was continued by Mersenne, then by Claude Milliet de Chales, and resulted in Bouguer's photometer.

BIBLIOGRAPHY

Aguilon's only work is *Francisci Aguilonii e Societate Jesu Opticorum libri sex juxta ac mathematicis utiles* (Antwerp, 1613; Würzburg, 1685; Nuremberg, 1702).

Writings on Aguilon or his work are P. Alegambe, *Bibliotheca scriptorum Societatis Jesu* (Antwerp, 1643), p. 112; A. de Backer, *Bibliothèque des écrivains de la Compagnie de Jésus* (Liège, 1853); Michel Chasles, *Aperçu historique sur l'origine et le développement des méthodes en géométrie* (Brussels, 1837), pp. 222, 517; F. V. Goethals, *Histoire des lettres, des sciences et des arts en Belgique et dans les pays limitrophes,* I (Brussels, 1840), 149, 153; J. E. Morère, "La photométrie: Les sources de l'Essai d'optique sur la gradation de la lumière de Pierre Bouguer, 1729," in *Revue d'histoire des sciences,* 18, no. 4 (1965), 337–384; L. Moréri, *Dictionnaire historique* (Paris, 1749), I, 231; V. G. Poudra, *Histoire de la perspective ancienne et moderne* (Paris, 1864), pp. 68–70; Adolphe Quetelet, *Histoire des sciences mathématiques chez les Belges* (Brussels, 1864), pp. 192–198; E. Quetelet, "Aíguillon" [*sic*], in *Bibliographie nationale,* I (Brussels, 1866), 141; and C. Sommervogel, *Bibliothèque de la Compagnie de Jésus,* I (Louvain, 1890), 90.

J. E. MORÈRE

AHMAD IBN IBRĀHĪM AL-UQLIDĪSĪ. See **al-Uqlidīsī.**

AHMAD IBN MUHAMMAD IBN ʿABD AL-JALĪL AL-SIZJĪ. See **al-Sizjī.**

AHMAD IBN MUHAMMAD IBN AL-BANNĀʾ. See **Ibn al-Bannāʾ.**

AHMAD IBN MŪSĀ IBN SHĀKIR. See **Banū Mūsā.**

AHMAD IBN YŪSUF (*b.* Baghdad, Iraq [?]; *fl. ca.* 900–905; *d.* Cairo, Egypt, 912/913 [?]), *mathematics.*

Ahmad ibn Yūsuf ibn Ibrāhīm ibn al-Dāya al-Miṣrī was the son of an Arab scholar, Yūsuf ibn Ibrāhīm. Yūsuf's home was in Baghdad, but in 839/840 he moved to Damascus, and later to Cairo; hence his son was known as an Egyptian. Ahmad's birth date is not known, although it seems probable that he was born before the move to Damascus. His death date is likewise in doubt, although the most probable date is 912/913.

Ahmad's father, sometimes referred to as *al-ḥāsib* ("the reckoner"), was one of a group of learned and influential men. A work on the history of medicine, another on the history of astronomy, and a collection of astronomical tables are attributed to him, although no written work of his survives today.

In Egypt, Ahmad ibn Yūsuf was a private secretary to the Ṭūlūn family, which ruled Egypt from 868 to 905. In his writing, Ahmad made several references to one Hudā ibn Ahmad ibn Ṭūlūn. This was probably Abu'l-Baqāʾ Hudā, the thirteenth son of Ahmad ibn Ṭūlūn, and probably Ahmad ibn Yūsuf's employer.

Ahmad ibn Yūsuf wrote a treatise on ratio and proportion, a work on similar arcs, a commentary on Ptolemy's *Centiloquium,* and a work on the astrolabe. All the works survive in Arabic manuscript, and all but the work on the astrolabe exist in Latin translation. While it is impossible to distinguish absolutely the work of the father from that of the son, there seems to be little doubt of Ahmad's authorship of the above four works. A number of other works are attributed to him, but these cannot be authenticated.

Ahmad's most significant work is the treatise on ratio and proportion. This was translated from the Arabic into Latin by Gerard of Cremona and then extensively copied. Manuscript copies of the Latin version exist today in at least eleven libraries in England, Spain, Austria, France, and Italy, thus testifying to the wide interest in the treatise in medieval times. Arabic versions of the work are in manu-

script form in Cairo and Algiers libraries. The work is largely an expansion of and commentary on Book V of Euclid's *Elements.* Ahmad developed and expanded Euclid's definitions of ratio and proportion in a long dialectic argument. Having clarified the meaning of these terms, he went on to show in great detail various methods for finding unknown quantities from given known quantities when the knowns and unknowns existed in certain proportional relationships.

By applying the Euclidean definitions of composition, separation, alternation, equality, and repetition to the given proportional relationships, Ahmad found eighteen different cases: six when there are three different quantities in the proportion, eight when there are four quantities, and four when there are six. The discussion and geometrical interpretation of these eighteen cases form the nucleus of the treatise. Since many of his proofs referred to variations on a single triangular figure, later authors have referred to his work as the eighteen cases of the divided figure.

Besides his obvious dependence on Euclid, Ahmad acknowledged his indebtedness to Ptolemy. The latter part of the treatise on ratio and proportion is actually an extension of two lemmas from Book I, chapter 13, of Ptolemy's *Almagest.* Ahmad also made reference to, and quoted from, Archimedes, Hero, Plato, Empedocles, and Apollonius, indicating that he was acquainted with at least some of their works.

Writing as he did at the beginning of the tenth century, not only was Ahmad ibn Yūsuf profoundly influenced by his Greek predecessors, but also in his turn he exerted an influence on the works of several medieval mathematicians. Leonardo Fibonacci, in his *Liber abacci,* mentioned the work of Ahmad (Ametus in the Latin form) in the eighteen cases of proportion, and he used Ahmad's methods in the solution of tax problems. Some traces of Ahmad's influence have been seen in the work of Jordanus de Nemore, *Arithmetica in decem libris demonstrata.* Ahmad was cited as an authority by Thomas Bradwardine in his differentiating between continuous and discontinuous proportions. Pacioli listed Ahmad (Ametus), along with such well-known scholars as Euclid, Boethius, Jordanus, and Bradwardine, as one of those whose work on proportions was of major significance.

On the somewhat negative side, Ahmad was guilty of a grave logical error. Campanus of Novara, in his commentary on the definitions of Book V of Euclid's *Elements,* devoted considerable attention to Ahmad's method of proof and pointed out a subtle but real bit of circular reasoning. In his eagerness to establish definitions and postulates, Ahmad did, at one point in his treatise, accept as a postulate a principle that he later was to prove as a theorem. This logical error does not detract from the value of his careful classification and solution of the various cases of proportional quantities. In fact, it is for this that he is remembered: his eighteen cases of the divided figure.

BIBLIOGRAPHY

Latin MSS of the *Epistola de proportione et proportionalitate* are in Paris, Bibliothèque Nationale, MS Lat. 9335, ff. 64r–75v; Florence, Biblioteca Medicea-Laurenziana, MS San Marco 184, ff. 90r–112v; and Vienna, Oesterreichische Nationalbibliothek, MS 5292, ff. 158r–179v. Arabic MSS, with the title *Risāla fī ʾl-nisba wa ʾl-tanāsub,* are in Algiers, MS 176 R. 898e + 684, ff. 54r–73r; and Cairo, National Library, MS 39 Riyāḍa mīm, ff. 1–25r.

Works containing information on Aḥmad ibn Yūsuf are Abū Muḥammad ʿAbd Allāh ibn Muḥammad al-Madīnī al-Balawī, *Sīrat Aḥmad ibn Ṭūlūn,* Muḥammad Kurd ʿAlī, ed. (Damascus, 1939); C. Brockelmann, *Geschichte der arabischen Litteratur,* supp. I (1937), 229, and I, 2nd ed. (1943), 155; George Sarton, *Introduction to the History of Science,* I, 598; M. Steinschneider, "Iusuf ben Ibrahim und Ahmed ben Iusuf," in *Bibliotheca mathematica* (1888), 49–117, esp. 52, 111; H. Suter, "Die Mathematiker und Astronomen der Araber und ihre Werke," in *Abhandlungen zur Geschichte der mathematischen Wissenschaften,* **10** (1900), 42–43; and Yāqūt, *Irshād al-arīb ilā maʿrifat al-adīb,* D. S. Margoliouth, ed., II (Leiden, 1909), 157–160.

DOROTHY V. SCHRADER

AḤMAD IBN YŪSUF AL-TĪFĀSHĪ. See **al-Tīfāshī.**

AIDA YASUAKI, also known as **Aida Ammei** (*b.* Yamagata, Japan, 10 February 1747; *d.* Edo [now Tokyo], Japan, 26 October 1817), *mathematics.*

Aida studied mathematics under Yasuyuki Okazaki in Yamagata when he was fifteen. When he was twenty-two, he went to Edo, determined to become the best mathematician in Japan, and worked as a field supervisor of engineering, river improvement, and irrigation under the Edo shogunate. His co-workers in the civil service included Teirei Kamiya, who was one of the ablest disciples of the famous mathematician Sadasuke Fujita. Aida wanted to become Fujita's pupil, and asked Kamiya for an introduction. Fujita did not receive Aida as a pupil, however, perhaps because of a falling-out occasioned by Fujita's pointing out mistakes in the problems inscribed on a tablet donated to a temple by Aida (these tablets, called *sangaku,* were hung on the walls of shrines and temples by recognized mathematicians as votive offerings—they further served as an exhibition of scholarship and as a supplement to textbooks).

Aida then devoted his efforts to composing and publishing his *Kaisei sampo* (1781), in which he criticized and revised Fujita's highly regarded *Seiyo sampo* of 1781. Kamiya accordingly lost face, because he had introduced Aida to Fujita who then was insulted by him; he retaliated by publicly pointing out the faults in Aida's book. Kamiya's criticism of Aida initiated a series of polemics that, conducted in private correspondence and in more than ten published mathematical works, lasted for the next twenty years.

In this dispute Naonobu Ajima, who was a friend of Fujita, sided with Kamiya. Ajima and Fujita had both been pupils of Nushizumi Yamaji, a master of the Seki school, and the private feud was thus transformed into a rivalry between the Seki school of mathematicians and the Saijyo school established by Aida. The Seki school was the most popular of the many schools of mathematics in Japan. Yoriyuki Arima (1714–1783), Lord of Kurume, was one of its leaders and was the first to publish its secret theories of algebra. Arima personifies the anomaly of a member of a hereditary warrior class drawn, in a time of enforced peace, to mathematics of the mostly highly abstract and purely aesthetic sort; he, too, had been a pupil of Yamaji, and he took Fujita under his protection and assisted him in the publication of *Seiyo sampo.* (Arima's own *Shuki sampo* was as popular in its time as Fujita's work, and Aida drew heavily upon both books.)

In 1788 Aida published *Sampo tensei shinan,* a collection of conventional geometry problems which were, however, presented in a new and simplified symbolic notation. The same year saw the coronation of a new shogun, and Aida was released from his post to face the social and cultural dislocation of the masterless samurai. He then decided that it was heaven's will that he concentrate on mathematics; he would live on his savings and devote himself to the perfection of his studies. He also took pupils, including many from the northeastern provinces; these returned to teach in their native regions, where Aida is still revered as a master of mathematics.

In *Sampo tensei shinan,* Aida compiled the geometry problems presented in Arima's *Shuki sampo* and Fujita's *Seiyo sampo* and *Shinpeki sampo.* These were largely the problems of *yo jutsu,* the inscribing in circles or triangles of other circles, a mainstay of traditional Japanese mathematics. In his book, Aida also showed how to develop formulas for ellipses, spheres, circles, regular polygons, and so on, and explained the use of algebraical expressions and the construction of equations.

Aida was well acquainted with the mathematical literature of his time, and edited several other books.

In the course of his research he developed a table of logarithms, transmitted from China, that differed substantially from that of Ajima, being calculated to the base of two.

Aida also worked in number theory and gave an explanation of approximate fractions by developing a continued fraction (a simplification of the methods of Seki and Takebe). And, by expanding $x_1^2 + x_2^2 + x_3^2 + \cdots x_n^2 = y^2$, he obtained the integral solutions of $x_1^2 + k_2 x_2^2 + \cdots + k_n x_n^2 = y^2$.

Aida was hard-working and strong-willed and produced as many as fifty to sixty works a year. Nearly 2,000 works survived him, including many on nonmathematical subjects. He was a distinguished teacher of traditional mathematics and a successful popularizer of that discipline.

                                          KAZUO SHIMODAIRA

AILLY, PIERRE D', also known as **Petrus de Alliaco** (*b.* Compiègne, France, 1350; *d.* Avignon, France, 1420), *theology, cosmography.*

D'Ailly studied at the College of Navarre of the University of Paris, where he received his doctorate of theology in 1381. He was grand master of Navarre from 1384 to 1389, and from 1389 to 1395 he was chancellor of the University of Paris. In 1395 d'Ailly became bishop of LePuy, and in 1397 bishop of Cambrai. He was made a cardinal in 1411. D'Ailly wrote commentaries on Aristotle (the *De anima* and the *Meteorologica*), as well as a number of astronomical and astrological works, including a commentary on the *De sphaera* of Sacrobosco. In his treatises on astrology, he reflects a more lenient attitude than that of either Nicole Oresme or Henry of Hesse. He was also concerned with the problem of calendar reform, and wrote a work on this subject for the Council of Constance (1414).

His most significant scientific work is a collection of cosmographical and astronomical treatises with the collective title *Imago mundi*. The *Imago* includes sixteen treatises on geography and astronomy, and the concordance of astrology, astronomy, and theology with historical events; only the first of these is the *Imago mundi* properly speaking. In the geographical portion of the *Imago* (the first treatise), d'Ailly makes use of the newly translated *Geography* of Ptolemy. It was thought that d'Ailly's work caused Columbus to underestimate his distance from the supposed coast of Asia, but it is now known that Columbus did not read the *Imago* until after his first voyage.

In his philosophical and scientific outlook, d'Ailly is considered a nominalist; however, his scientific writing shows little originality and much unacknowledged borrowing. He has a more significant claim to historical prominence as a leader of the conciliar movement.

BIBLIOGRAPHY

I. ORIGINAL WORKS. There is a modern edition of d'Ailly's *Imago mundi* in Latin-French, edited by Edmond Buron (Paris, 1930). This is only the first of the sixteen treatises in the medieval *Imago mundi.*

II. SECONDARY LITERATURE. Louis Selembier, *Pierre d'Ailly* (Tourcoing, 1931), a French version of a Latin dissertation, *Petrus de Alliaco* (1886). There is a list of secondary material on d'Ailly following the entry on Pierre d'Ailly in the *Lexikon für Theologie und Kirche,* VIII (Freiburg, 1963), 330; also in Francis Oakley, *The Political Thought of Pierre d'Ailly* (New Haven–London, 1964), bibliographical note, pp. 350–356. Other works that discuss d'Ailly are Pierre Duhem, *Le système du monde,* IV (Paris, 1953), 168–183; George H. T. Kimble, *Geography in the Middle Ages* (London, 1938), pp. 92, 208–212, 218, n. 4; Lynn Thorndike, *A History of Magic and Experimental Science,* IV (New York, 1934), 101–113, 322, and *The Sphere of Sacrobosco and Its Commentators* (Chicago, 1949), pp. 38–40, 49–51.

                                          CLAUDIA KREN

AIRY, GEORGE BIDDELL (*b.* Alnwick, Northumberland, England, 27 July 1801; *d.* Greenwich, England, 2 January 1892), *astronomy.*

George Airy was the eldest of four children of William Airy, a farmer who through self-education acquired posts in the Excise, and of Ann Biddell, daughter of a well-to-do farmer. At the age of ten he took first place at Byatt Walker's school at Colchester but, as he himself records, because he had very little animal vitality, he was not a favorite with his schoolmates. In the school he thoroughly learned arithmetic, double-entry bookkeeping, and the use of the slide rule. An introverted but not shy child, Airy was, even for the time and especially for his circumstances, a young snob. Nevertheless, he overcame some of the dislike of his schoolmates by his great skill and inventiveness in the construction of peashooters and other such devices.

At the age of twelve Airy came to know his uncle Arthur Biddell, a well-educated and highly respected farmer near Ipswich. He recognized in his uncle an opportunity to escape what he considered unpromising surroundings, and secretly requested that he be removed from his family. Arthur Biddell almost literally kidnapped him, without any word to his parents, but because of financial difficulties caused by William Airy's loss of his Excise post, the escape was not blocked. From 1814 to 1819 Airy spent nearly half of his time with his uncle. In later life he put great value on this connection, especially because of the resulting acquaintances, including Thomas Clarkson, the abolitionist, who could help his career. It was through Clarkson and Charles Musgrave, fellow of Trinity College, Cambridge, that he was entered as sizar of Trinity College in October 1819.

Airy entered Cambridge with the determination to get on, and he was certainly equipped to do so. Although his own assessment of his abilities was immodestly high, it was nevertheless matched, albeit sometimes reluctantly, by his tutors and college friends. He graduated as a Senior Wrangler in 1823 after far outdistancing all the men of his year, although beginning in his second term he had the burden of supporting himself by taking pupils. He was elected a fellow of Trinity College in 1824.

Three incidents from this period illustrate the care and foresight with which Airy planned his life. The first concerns the habit he adopted, as an undergraduate, of always keeping by him a quire of large-sized scribbling paper, sewn together, upon which everything was entered: translations into Latin and out of Greek, several lines of which he attempted every day, no matter how pressing other business might be; mathematical problems; and nearly every thought he had, complete with date. The sheets, even after the more important items were transferred to exercise books or diaries, were kept, together with nearly every communication received and a copy of those sent throughout his life, and are still extant. He seems not to have destroyed a document of any kind whatever: stubs of old checkbooks, notes for tradesmen, circulars, bills, and correspondence of all sorts were carefully preserved in chronological order from the time that he went to Cambridge. This material provides possibly the best existing documentation of a truly Victorian scientist.

The second illustrative incident involves Airy's courtship of his future wife, Ricarda Smith, the eldest daughter of the Rev. Richard Smith, private chaplain to the duke of Devonshire. He met Miss Smith while he was on a walking tour in Derbyshire, and within two days of first seeing her he made an offer of marriage. Neither his means nor his prospects at the time permitted an immediate marriage, and the Rev. Smith would not permit an engagement. Undaunted, Airy renewed his suit from time to time, and six years after his first proposal they were married.

A similar singleness of purpose is shown in Airy's approach to a prospective position at the Royal Greenwich Observatory. In 1824 an attempt was made to improve the educational level of assistants at the Royal Observatory by hiring one or two Cambridge graduates. Airy was proposed as one of these assistants and traveled to Greenwich to investigate the possibility. However, in his own words, "when I found that succession to the post of Astronomer Royal was not considered as distinctly a consequence of it, I took it cooly [*sic*] and returned to Cambridge the next night."

Airy applied for and won the Lucasian professorship in 1826. In doing this, he exchanged an assistant tutorship worth £150 per annum, and the prospect of succeeding to a tutorship, for the £99 per annum of the professorship, supplemented by a somewhat uncertain £100 per annum as *ex officio* member of the Board of Longitude. Other considerations were that "my prospects in the law or other profession might have been good if I could have waited but marriage would have been out of the question and I much preferred a moderate income in no long time. I had now in some measure taken science as my line (though not irrevocably) and I thought it best to work it well for a time at least and wait for accidents."

The Plumian professorship, which involved the care of the Cambridge Observatory, became vacant in 1828, and Airy "made known that I was a candidate and nobody thought it worthwhile to oppose me. . . . I told everybody that the salary (about £300) was not sufficient and drafted a manifesto to the University for an increase. . . . the University had never before been taken by storm in such a manner and there was some commotion about it. I believe very few people would have taken the same step . . . I had no doubt of success." He was appointed Plumian professor and director of the observatory on 6 February 1828, with a salary of £500 per annum. Although he accepted the post of astronomer royal in 1835, when he moved from Cambridge to Greenwich, Airy's considerable influence on British astronomy stretches without break from his appointment at Cambridge in 1828 to his retirement as astronomer royal in 1881. He was knighted in 1872, after thrice refusing on the basis that he could not afford the fees.

The ruling feature of Airy's character was undoubtedly order, and from the time he went up to Cambridge until the end of his life his system of order was strictly maintained. He wrote his autobiography up to date as soon as he had taken his degree, and made his first will as soon as he had any money to leave. His accounts were personally kept by double entry, and he regarded their keeping as one of his greatest joys. The effect of this sense of order on British observational astronomy is the only reason that Airy is included in this volume, for he was an organizer rather than a scientist. To realize his importance, it is necessary to understand the astronomy of the nineteenth century and the role played by such institutions as the Royal Greenwich Observatory.

The rise of astronomy in the seventeenth and eighteenth centuries took the form of careful observations of stellar positions made to provide a framework within which planetary motions could be measured. The first astronomer royal, John Flamsteed, provided the earliest observations of this kind that are still useful today. Although the emphasis in modern astronomy has shifted beyond the planets to the stars and external galaxies, these early observations provide us with a three-hundred-year base line for measuring the motions of the stars themselves, and knowledge of these motions is vital to the understanding of the origin and evolution of the stars. Observations of this kind are not only necessary in large numbers but they must be extremely exacting if the results are to be of general use. They are therefore best made in a routine way by those more interested in the technological problems of their procurement than in their scientific use. The Royal Greenwich Observatory, following Flamsteed's early lead, became the primary producer of such observations, mainly because the Admiralty was interested in the more immediate need of them for navigational purposes. Partly because the utilitarian purpose was stressed, scientific supervision of the observations eventually decreased and was refocused only in the nineteenth century, when it became obvious that their lack of accuracy was adversely affecting their use in navigation. The situation was ripe for Airy with his scientific training and his sense of order. The reforms he introduced were copied by other countries that, because they were expanding their navies to protect their expanding merchant fleets, needed the navigational aids.

The secret of Airy's long and successful official career was that he was a good servant who thoroughly understood his position. He never set himself in opposition to his masters, the Admiralty. He recognized the task for which he was appointed and transformed the Royal Greenwich Observatory into a highly efficient institution. The cost, however, was high. No independent thought could be tolerated, and as a result no scientists were trained there. The often slipshod methods that lead to scientific discovery were carried on outside, by John Herschel, John Adams, and many others. Airy himself would not understand this criticism. He wrote, in 1832, ". . . in those parts of astronomy which depend principally on the assistance of Governments, requiring only method and judgement, with very little science in the persons

employed, we have done much; while in those which depend exclusively on individual effort we have done little. . . . our principal progress has been made in the lowest branches of astronomy while to the higher branches of science we have not added anything." He needed only to add that he had done *his* job.

In any article on Airy mention must be made of the controversy accompanying the discovery of the planet Neptune. It is ironical that the kind of order Airy restored to the observational work at Greenwich should coincide with the greatest need for the results since Newton had put Flamsteed's observations to such good use in the *Principia*—and then be unfairly blamed in nearly every subsequent article on the discovery of Neptune for withholding these observations. In fact, Airy supplied all the major participants in this discovery with the observational data they requested, and the only basis for the subsequent attacks upon him was that he was not at home when John Adams, then a young Cambridge mathematician, called unannounced to present one of his early predictions that such a planet as Neptune had to exist in order to account for the motions of the other planets. Airy's great efficiency in the observatory was noted by other government services and he rapidly became the prototype of the modern government scientist. This kept him from the observatory a large amount of time.

Always of medium stature and not powerfully built, Airy seemed to shrink as he aged, mainly because of an increasing stoop. His constitution, even at eighty-five, was remarkably sound. He took not the least interest in athletic sports or competition, but he was always a very active walker and could endure a great deal of fatigue. His eyesight was peculiar, and he studied it thoroughly all his life, correcting the astigmatism with a cylindrical lens, a method that he invented and is still used. As his powers failed with age, he was tyrannized by his ruling passion for order, and his efforts went into correctly filing his correspondence rather than understanding its contents. He was by nature eminently practical, and his dislike of mere theoretical problems and investigations put him continually in dissent with some of the resident Cambridge mathematicians. This practical bent led him to undertake, in 1872, the preparation of a numerical lunar theory. This work consisted, essentially, of obtaining from observations numerical values of the 320 periodic terms in Delaunay's equations for the moon's motion. His difficulties are summed up in a note of 29 September 1890:

I had made considerable advance (under official difficulties) in calculations on my favourite Numerical Lunar Theory, when I discovered that, under the heavy pressure of unusual matters (two Transits of Venus and some eclipses) I had committed a grievous error in the first stage of giving numerical value to my Theory. My spirit in the work was broken, and I have never heartily proceeded with it since.

Airy was not a great scientist, but he made great science possible. It is true that he was indirectly responsible for guiding British observational astronomy into a cul-de-sac from which it took many years to retreat, but it was not his fault that the methods he devised to provide a particular service at a particular time were so efficiently contrived and completely implemented that weaker successors continued to apply them, unchanged, to changing conditions.

BIBLIOGRAPHY

Airy's bibliography contains over 500 printed papers and the following books: *Mathematical Tracts on Physical Astronomy, the Figure of the Earth, Precession and Nutation, and the Calculus of Variations* (Cambridge, 1826); 2nd ed. (London, 1831), with the *Undulatory Theory of Optics* added; 4th ed. (London, 1858); *Undulatory Theory of Optics* also published separately (London, 1877); *Gravitation: An Elementary Explanation of the Principal Perturbations in the Solar System* (London, 1834, 1884); *Six Lectures on Astronomy* (London, 1849); *A Treatise in Trigonometry* (London, 1855); *On the Algebraical and Numerical Theory of Errors of Observations and the Combination of Observations* (London, 1861; 3rd ed., 1879); Essays on the invasion of Britain by Julius Caesar, the invasion of Britain by Plautius, and by Claudius Caesar; the early military policy of the Romans in Britain; the Battle of Hastings; and correspondence were published in *Essays* (London, 1865); *An Elementary Treatise on Partial Differential Equations* (London, 1866); *On Sound and Atmospheric Vibrations, With the Mathematical Elements of Music* (London, 1868, 1871); *A Treatise on Magnetism* (London, 1870); *Notes on the Earlier Hebrew Scriptures* (London, 1876); and *Numerical Lunar Theory* (London, 1886).

The complete list of printed papers is given in Wilfred Airy's edition of the *Autobiography of Sir George Airy* (London, 1896). They can be divided into four main categories: optics, both practical and theoretical; practical astronomy, including reports of progress and final publication of results obtained by the observers at Cambridge and Greenwich; government science, concerning the many tasks other than astronomy for which the government claimed his time; and contributions to the many polemics that marked nineteenth-century British science.

The extensive biographical data are housed mainly in the new Royal Greenwich Observatory at Herstmonceux Castle, Sussex. Some of those covering Airy's pre- and post-Greenwich careers are in the hands of the writer, and the remainder are scattered between the archives of the Royal Astronomical Society, the Royal Society, and the Royal Greenwich Observatory. As already noted, Airy apparently never discarded a piece of paper. His son Wilfred (as I have been informed by Airy's granddaughter) had no such inhibitions, and, after including a few extracts in his edition of the *Autobiography,* destroyed the voluminous correspondence between Sir George and Lady Airy.

OLIN J. EGGEN

AITKEN, ROBERT GRANT (*b.* Jackson, California, 31 December 1864; *d.* Berkeley, California, 29 October 1951), *astronomy.*

During forty years at the Lick Observatory, Aitken was an outstanding observer of double stars, and his *New General Catalogue of Double Stars Within 120° of the North Pole* (1932) is still a standard work.

Aitken at first intended to become a minister, but his studies in biology and astronomy at Williams College (1883–1887) diverted his interests to science. In 1891 he became professor of mathematics at the University of the Pacific, where there was a small observatory with a six-inch Clark refractor. In 1894 he visited Mt. Hamilton, and the following year returned there as assistant astronomer at the Lick Observatory. He was successively promoted to astronomer (1907), associate director (1923), and director (1930). He retired in 1935.

Aitken's early work at Lick was routine and varied, but double stars soon came to take up more and more of his time. In 1899 he embarked on a systematic survey of double stars that would provide the basis for statistical investigations. He was soon joined by W. J. Hussey, and together they examined stars given in the *Bonner Durchmusterung* as not fainter than 9.0 (Aitken) or 9.1 (Hussey) down to 22° southern declination. When Hussey left Lick in 1905, Aitken took over his share of the work and completed the survey in 1915. It resulted in the discovery of over 4,400 new pairs with separations mostly below 5″, and over two-thirds of these were found by Aitken; he published statistical investigations of this material in 1918 in *The Binary Stars.* Yet Aitken's real vocation was the observation of doubles; and in 1920, on the death of Eric Doolittle, he took over the compilation of material for a revision of S. W. Burnham's 1906 catalog of double stars, a revision that he published in 1932 as complete to 1927. Meanwhile, he devoted much of his time to the popularization of astronomy, and this became his main interest in retirement.

BIBLIOGRAPHY

I. ORIGINAL WORKS. Aitken's works include *The Binary Stars* (New York, 1918; 2nd ed., rev., 1935) and *A New*

General Catalogue of Double Stars Within 120° of the North Pole, 2 vols., Carnegie Institute of Washington Publication No. 417 (Washington, D.C., 1932). A full bibliography of his articles is in the biographical memoir by Van den Bos (see below).

II. SECONDARY LITERATURE. Works on Aitken are mainly the numerous obituary notices in astronomical and other journals, of which by far the most comprehensive is that by Willem H. Van den Bos, in *National Academy of Sciences, Biographical Memoirs,* **32** (1958), 1–30.

MICHAEL A. HOSKIN

AITON, WILLIAM (*b.* Avondale, Lanarkshire, Scotland, 1731; *d.* Kew, Surrey, England, 2 February 1793), *horticulture.*

According to the parish baptismal roll, Aiton was the eldest of eleven children of William Aiton of Wailsely, whose occupation is not revealed. The son was a trained gardener when he left in 1754 for London, where in the following year he became an assistant to Philip Miller, curator of Chelsea Physic Garden, who was the most eminent gardener of his time and author of the celebrated and immensely important *Gardener's Dictionary.* Miller's influence on young Aiton greatly enlarged the latter's botanical knowledge and to a very large extent determined his future career.

Aiton's aptitude and proficiency led to his engagement in 1759 by Princess Augusta to plant a botanical garden at Kew House, under the supervision of John Haverfield; this was the inauguration of the present-day Royal Botanic Gardens. The princess also engaged Sir William Chambers as landscape architect to lay out the grounds in the fashionable mode; he is responsible for the orangery, the pagoda, and several temples.

At this time the princess depended for scientific direction on John Stuart, third earl of Bute, a most accomplished and knowledgeable botanist, who introduced many new species to Kew. Chambers has recorded Bute's assiduity in the assembling of plants from many parts of the globe to make the collection at Kew the largest in Europe, so Aiton's responsibility for its care was indeed a heavy one. A generous patron of botanical science, Bute encouraged Aiton in every possible way.

Upon the death of Princess Augusta in 1772, the gardens came into the possession of George III, and Bute was replaced by Sir Joseph Banks as the royal adviser on Kew. Banks was undoubtedly the greatest scientific impresario of the day and spared no effort in building up the collection at Kew. He used his connections with naval officers, merchants, doctors, and travelers to obtain plants; these specimens were entrusted to Aiton, who assumed control of the garden in 1783. Like Bute, Banks befriended Aiton; and the two men, together with Daniel Carl Solander and Jonas Dryander, Banks's librarian, enabled Aiton to publish his *Hortus Kewensis* in 1789. This three-volume work is of fundamental importance as a catalog of some 5,500 plants under cultivation at the time, and records their provenance and the date of their introduction. It also contains descriptions of new species. It is unlikely that Aiton, who was a gardener rather than a botanist, had the scholarship required to produce, entirely by himself, a work of this nature. Indeed, in the Preface he acknowledges in general terms the assistance from those more learned than himself, without mentioning them by name. For the strictly botanical content, especially the Latin descriptions, Aiton depended heavily on Solander, but even more on Dryander, who was largely responsible for editing the work and seeing it through the press. The *Hortus* was well received and was sold out in two years.

Aiton is commemorated by the interesting monotypic South African genus *Aitonia,* which was described by Carl Peter Thunberg in 1780. The plant was introduced into cultivation by Aiton's fellow Scot, Francis Masson, whom he had trained as a gardener before Masson went in 1772, on behalf of Kew, to the Cape of Good Hope. The species was featured in *The Botanical Magazine* in 1791 by William Curtis, who remarked:

> The great length of time Mr. Aiton has been engaged in the cultivation of plants, the immense numbers which have been the constant objects of his care through every period of their growth, joined to his superior discernment, give him a decided superiority in the *prima facie* knowledge of living plants over most Botanists of his day; his abilities in the other line of his profession, are displayed in the eulogies of all who have seen the royal collections at Kew, which he has the honour to superintend.

There is little evidence available of his personal affairs. His wife was named Elizabeth, and she lies in the family tomb in Kew churchyard with her husband, four daughters, and two sons. A measure of the high esteem in which Aiton was held is shown by the presence as pallbearers at his funeral of Sir Joseph Banks, Bishop Goodenough, Jonas Dryander, and the famous artist John Zoffany, who lived in nearby Strand-on-the-Green.

BIBLIOGRAPHY

Aiton's only work is *Hortus Kewensis; or, a Catalogue of the Plants Cultivated in the Royal Botanic Garden at Kew,* 3 vols. (London, 1789), with color illustrations.

There is a good deal of minor reference to Aiton in various journals. The most significant sources are under the pseudonym Kewensis in *The Gentleman's Magazine,* **63** (1793), 389–391; James Britten and Edmund G. Baker, *Journal of Botany,* **35** (1897), 481–485; J. Britten, *ibid.,* **50,** supp. 3 (1912), 1–16; and W. Botting Hemsley, *Journal of the Kew Guild,* **2,** no. 10 (1902), 87–90.

GEORGE TAYLOR

AITON, WILLIAM TOWNSEND (*b.* Kew, Surrey, England, 2 February 1766; *d.* Kensington, London, England, 9 October 1849), *horticulture.*

Aiton was the eldest son of William Aiton, who was in charge of the living collections in the Royal Botanic Gardens, Kew, and who described himself as "Gardener to His Majesty." He entered school at Chiswick, and when he was thirteen transferred to one at Camberwell. He remained there until, at the age of sixteen, he entered Kew as assistant to his father. Apart from gaining practical knowledge of horticulture and experience with a wide range of living plants, Aiton became greatly interested in landscaping and acquired a considerable reputation as a landscape gardener. Indeed, he received commissions from many eminent people, including the duke of Kent and a number of noblemen.

In 1793, upon the death of his father, Aiton succeeded to the control of the gardens at Kew and Richmond, and on the accession of George IV he also had charge of other royal gardens, including Kensington, Buckingham Palace, those around the bizarre Royal Pavilion at Brighton, and certain areas at Windsor. He was styled director-general of the royal gardens, but there is evidence that he was more concerned with improvements elsewhere. He left the cultivation of the rich assemblage of plants at Kew to his subordinates (particularly John Smith, the first Kew curator), although he assiduously continued his father's close association with Sir Joseph Banks and sought his advice and support on how best to enrich the Kew collections by sending suitably trained men overseas.

Aiton was one of the seven gentlemen who, on the initiative of John Wedgwood, son of the potter Josiah Wedgwood, assembled "at Mr. Hatchard's House for the purpose of instituting a Society for the improvement of Horticulture" on 7 March 1804. The Royal Horticultural Society was founded at this meeting.

Largely through the encouragement of Banks, a second and much enlarged edition of the senior Aiton's *Hortus Kewensis* was published. Nominally the work of the son, who certainly had considerable knowledge of botany and its literature, it was in fact largely revised by Jonas Dryander, who was mainly responsible for the botanical matter in the original

edition, and by Robert Brown, who became Banks's librarian upon the death of Daniel Carl Solander. An epitome of the *Hortus* was published in 1814, but neither this nor the parent work enjoyed the success of the first edition. Aiton prepared a second edition of the *Epitome* but the manuscript was probably destroyed with his voluminous collection of letters, although James Britten states in the *Journal of Botany* (1912) that two versions appeared in 1814.

Aiton's responsibilities were drastically curtailed when William IV became king and his authority was restricted to the gardens at Kew. After Banks's death in 1820 cut off invaluable patronage, royal funds for Kew's maintenance were severely restricted. In spite of the efforts of Aiton and Smith, the collections and the gardens suffered from so much neglect that in 1838 the Treasury was obliged to appoint a committee of inquiry to investigate the condition of the Royal Gardens at Kew. The report, signed by Professor John Lindley on 28 February 1838, noted "That it is little better than a waste of money to maintain it in its present state, if it fills no intelligible purpose except that of sheltering a large quantity of rare and valuable plants." Lindley suggested that Kew might become a national botanic garden, so the garden was transferred to the nation in 1840 and William Jackson Hooker was appointed the first official director in 1841. For a time Aiton remained in charge of the pleasure grounds at Kew, but he resigned in 1841, taking with him his library, records, and drawings. When he died, apparently unmarried, his enormous and rich correspondence, containing a vast amount of information on Kew affairs over a period of nearly fifty years, was burned by his brother John. His collection of drawings and plant record books were retrieved for Kew after John's death.

BIBLIOGRAPHY

I. ORIGINAL WORKS. Aiton's writings are *Delineations of Exotick Plants Cultivated in the Royal Gardens at Kew* (London, 1796); *Hortus Kewensis; or a Catalogue of the Plants Cultivated in the Royal Botanic Garden at Kew,* 2nd ed., enl., 5 vols. (London, 1810–1813); and *An Epitome of the Second Edition of Hortus Kewensis, for the Use of Practical Gardeners; to Which Is Added a Selection of Esculent Vegetables and Fruits Cultivated in the Royal Gardens at Kew* (London, 1814).

II. SECONDARY LITERATURE. Writings on Aiton are *Proceedings of the Linnean Society,* **2** (1850), 82–83 (anon.); W. T. Thiselton-Dyer, in *Bulletin of Miscellaneous Information, Royal Botanic Gardens, Kew* (1891), pp. 304–305; *ibid.,* (1910), pp. 306–308 (anon.); J. Britten, in *Journal of Botany,* **50,** supp. 3 (1912), 1–16; and E. Nelmes, in *Curtis's Botanical Magazine Dedications* (1931), pp. 7–8, with a portrait. R. G. C. Desmond, "John Smith, Kew's First Curator," in *Kew Guild Journal* (1965), pp. 576–587, has many references to Aiton. See also John L. Gilbert, "The Life and Times of William Townsend Aiton," *ibid.* (1966), pp. 688–693.

GEORGE TAYLOR

AJIMA NAONOBU, also known as **Ajima Chokuyen** (common name, **Manzo**; pen name, **Nanzan**) (*b.* Shiba, Edo [now Tokyo], Japan, *ca.* 1732; *d.* Shiba, 1798), *mathematics.*

Ajima was born at the official residence of the Shinjo family, and was later stationed in Edo as a retainer of that clan. He remained there until his death, and is buried in the Jorin-ji Temple, Mita, Tokyo.

Ajima first studied mathematics under Masatada Irie of the Nakanishi school, and later he studied both mathematics and astronomy under Nushizumi Yamaji, who initiated him into the secret mathematical principles of the Seki school. He was apparently over thirty when he began his studies with Yamaji; his career before then (save for his studies with Masatada) is largely a matter of conjecture. Ajima wrote several works on astronomy soon after becoming Yamaji's pupil; it is presumed that during this time he was also engaged in helping his master to compile an almanac. After Yamaji's death, Ajima began to write on mathematics.

In the traditional succession of the Seki school, Ajima is in the fourth generation of masters. None of his books were published in his lifetime; they existed solely as copies handwritten by his students, perhaps because of the esoteric nature of the discipline. Most of the essential points of his work are summarized in his *Fukyu sampo,* a book that Ajima intended as an emendation of Sadasuke Fujita's *Seiyo sampo,* which was then a popular textbook. His pupil Makoto Kusawa wrote a preface to this book in 1799, a year after Ajima's death: although Kusawa planned to publish the work, he did not do so. Kusawa succeeded Ajima as a master of the Seki school. Masatoda Baba and Hiroyasu Sakabe were also students of Ajima; as did Kusawa, they had their own pupils, many of whom became first-rate mathematicians and continued the tradition of the Seki school until the Meiji restoration (an arithmetic book in the European style was published in Japan in 1856, and marked the end of the native forms of mathematics).

The mathematics originated by Takakazu Seki was refined by his successive pupils and tentatively completed and systematized by Yoshisuke Matsunaga and Yoriyuki Arima, who was the first to publish it. Upon this base Ajima began to develop a new mathematics;

his works reflect an innovative trend toward geometry within a tradition that was basically algebraic and numerical in approach.

This trend is exemplified in the development of *yenri,* a method for determining the area of a circle, of a sphere, or of plane figures composed of curved lines.

Seki's technique for calculating the length of an arc of a circle depended upon giving a fixed number to the diameter of the circle, and was not much more sophisticated a method than that of Archimedes. His pupil Takebe used letters instead of numbers to represent a diameter and found infinite series, expressed exponentially. Matsunaga improved Takebe's method and increased the number of types of infinite series capable of representing the different elements of circles.

The *yenri* process began with the inscription in the circle of a regular polygon to divide the circle or arc into equal parts; this method was, however, by definition limited, and could not be expanded to include curves other than circles and their arcs. Ajima expanded the process by dividing the diameter or chord into equal, small segments, initiating a technique somewhat similar to the definite integration of European mathematics. The earlier Japanese mathematicians had been concerned with subdividing the circle or arc directly; it was Ajima's contribution to proceed from the subdivision of the chord. He introduced his method in his *Kohai jutsu kai,* and used it for the basis of further calculations.

Japanese mathematicians were accustomed to using exponential notation for convenience in dealing with large numbers. Integration was also easier if an exponent were used, and double integrals were thus easily obtained. In the same year that Ajima developed his *yenri* method, he discovered a way to obtain the volume common to two intersecting cylinders by using double integration, which he presented in *Enchu kokuen jutsu.* Ajima's new method was a logical outgrowth of the method he described in *Kohai jutsu kai,* and required the application of the earlier technique.

For his work with logarithms, Ajima drew upon *Suri seiran,* a book published in China in 1723 that almost certainly incorporated some of the Western principles brought to China by the Jesuits. *Suri seiran* introduced the seven-place logarithmic table into Japan, and also showed how to draw up such a table. It is apparent that Ajima knew this book, since he used the same terminology in setting up his own table of logarithms (actually antilogarithms). Ajima's table and its uses are described in *Fukyu sampo,* and there is also a copybook of the table only. The Chinese

90

logarithmic table was useful for multiplication and division; Ajima's was not. Ajima used his table to find the tenth root, and it was also useful in finding the power of a number. Before this table could be used, however, it was necessary to find the logarithm by division. The setting up of Ajima's table, as explained in *Fukyu sampo*, is based upon $\log 10 = 1$, $\log^{10} \sqrt{10} = 0.1$; therefore, the logarithm of $^{10}\sqrt{10} = 1$, while the value of 0.1 is 258925411. Ajima's tables permitted the calculation of a logarithm to twelve places.

Ajima drew upon Japanese mathematical tradition for *yo jutsu*, problems involving transcribing a number of circles in triangles and squares. Ajima wrote a major work on this subject, which included the problem described by Malfatti in 1803: in a given triangle, inscribe three circles, each tangent to the other and to two sides of the triangle. Although this problem became known as "Malfatti's question," it is obvious that Ajima's work preceded Malfatti's, although it is not known when Ajima published his problem. Malfatti approached the problem analytically, while Ajima was concerned with finding the diameters of the circles, but it is apparent that the problems are essentially identical.

BIBLIOGRAPHY

Ajima's works include *Fukyu sampo*; *Kohai jutsu kai*; and *Enchu kokuen jutsu*.

SHIN'ICHI OYA

AL-. See next element of name.

ALAIN DE LILLE, also known as **Alanus de Insulis** (*b.* Lille, France, first half of the twelfth century; *d.* Cîteaux, France, 1203), *theology, philosophy.*

Although he was popular and enjoyed a reputation for wide learning during subsequent centuries, the birthdate of Alain de Lille is a matter of conjecture, the most reasonable surmise being 1128. He taught theology at Paris and Montpellier, and subsequently became a member of the Cistercian order. He is the author of numerous theological works and was among the first to write against the Albigensians (in his *Contra haereticos*). Influenced by the *Quomodo substantiae* (better known as the *De hebdomadibus*) of Boethius, he attempted to construct a deductive theology derived from axioms in the manner of mathematics (in his *Regulae caelestis iuris*). His theological treatises reveal Neoplatonic influences; in addition to Boethius, these works employ such Neoplatonic materials as the *Liber de causis* and the pseudo-Hermetic *Liber XXIV philosophorum.*

Alain's reputation rests largely on two literary works, the *De planctu naturae*, possibly composed between 1160 and 1170, and the very famous *Anticlaudianus,* written around 1182–1184. The *De planctu* is extant in few early manuscripts, and was apparently not the subject of commentary. The work is an exposition of Neoplatonic Christian naturalism. As an allegorical portrayal of Nature and attendant Virtues, it exerted extensive influence on the part of the *Roman de la Rose* written by Jean de Meun.

The popular *Anticlaudianus* survives in countless manuscripts and was a frequent subject of commentary. Consisting of a prose prologue followed by more than 4,000 lines of classic hexameter, the *Anticlaudianus* was intended as a refutation of the *In Rufinum* of Claudian. The Roman poet had portrayed Rufinus as a creation of evil Nature. Alain's theme concerns Nature's wish to atone for previous errors and to create a perfect man. She and the Virtues send Prudence on a celestial journey to the throne of God to seek the soul of the perfect man. Prudence travels in a chariot constructed by the seven liberal arts and drawn by the five senses. Guided by Reason, the chariot ascends through the heavens. As it approaches the throne of God, Reason falters, and Prudence is then guided through these exalted regions by Theology and Faith. Her petition is successful; God grants her request.

The *Anticlaudianus* is a mélange of Neoplatonisms. One can detect the influences of such Chartrain masters and disciples as Bernard and Thierry of Chartres, Bernard Silvester, and Gilbert de la Porrée. There are also traces of the pseudo-Dionysian corpus and its interpreter, John Scotus Erigena. Above all, Alain is indebted to Boethius' *Consolation of Philosophy* and to the *De nuptiis philologiae et Mercurii* of Martianus Capella. In his description of the personification of Astronomy, Alain alludes to the eccentric, and possibly to the equant, and mentions Ptolemy and Abū Maʿshar by name. His treatment of Arithmetic is limited to a few propositions taken possibly from either Boethius or Nicomachus; he mentions the latter by name. Geometry fares even more poorly.

Alain de Lille, although known in the middle ages as "doctor universalis," was not an original thinker. However, he wove together successfully many of the Neoplatonic traditions available to twelfth-century humanism.

BIBLIOGRAPHY

I. ORIGINAL WORKS. Thomas Wright, *The Anglo-Latin Poets and Epigrammatists of the Twelfth Century,* in *Rerum britannicarum medii aevi scriptores,* **59**[2] (London, 1872), 268–428, contains the texts of the *De planctu naturae* and the *Anticlaudianus;* R. Bossuat, *Alain de Lille: Anticlaudianus* (Paris, 1955); J. Huizinga, *Über die Verknüpfung des Poetischen mit dem Theologischen bei Alanus de Insulis* (Amsterdam, 1932), with an edition of the *De virtutibus et vitiis* in an appendix; English versions are D. M. Moffat, *The Complaint of Nature by Alain de Lille* (New York, 1908); W. H. Cornog, *The Anticlaudian of Alain de Lille* (Philadelphia, 1935); M.-T. d'Alverny, *Alain de Lille, Textes inédits* (Paris, 1965) contains two small works by Alain (pp. 185ff).

II. Secondary Literature. Étienne Gilson, *History of Christian Philosophy in the Middle Ages* (New York, 1955), lists many of Alain's theological works and gives their *Patrologia latina* entries, p. 635; P. Duhem, *Le système du monde,* 10 vols. (Paris, 1954–1959), III, 223–230, discusses Alain's scientific importance; R. de Lage, *Alain de Lille, poète du XIIe siècle* (Paris, 1951), has an extensive bibliography on pp. 169–173 and an appendix on pp. 175–186 listing the manuscripts of Alain's works; see also bibliographical material in R. Bossuat, *Anticlaudianus* (see above), and on pp. 322–348 in M.-T. d'Alverny, *Textes inédits* (see above).

Claudia Kren

ALBATEGNI. See al-Battānī.

ALBERT I OF MONACO (HONORÉ CHARLES GRIMALDI) (*b.* Paris, France, 13 November 1848; *d.* Paris, 26 June 1922), *oceanography.*

Albert was the son of Charles III of Monaco (Honoré Grimaldi) and Antoinette Ghislaine, countess of Mérode. He succeeded his father on 10 September 1889. In 1870 he fought against Germany as a lieutenant-commander in the French navy.

His career as a navigator actually began in 1873, when he bought a 200-ton schooner, the *Pleiad,* and renamed it the *Hirondelle.* By 1885 he had decided to devote himself to the study of the sea, and each following year, for nearly forty years, he made voyages in the North Atlantic, taking soundings wherever he went. He made four cruises in the *Hirondelle;* six, between 1892 and 1897, in the *Princesse Alice I;* and twelve, between 1898 and 1910, in the *Princesse Alice II.* He used the *Hirondelle II* until his death, making five cruises between 1911 and 1915. He may truly be considered one of the founders of oceanography.

In physical oceanography, Albert studied currents, especially the Gulf Stream (1885). He set out floating mines to study drift in both the North Atlantic and the Arctic. Using the Richard bottle, he took samples of water at various depths in order to determine the differences in temperature. Albert also established three observation centers in the Azores in order to study the meteorology of the ocean regions. One of his major achievements was a general atlas to the millionth, which had twenty-four plates and illustrated the bathymetry of all the oceans; it represented a synthesis of all previous findings.

Albert conducted valuable physiological research as well. Interested in the venom of *Physalia,* a pelagic coelenterate, he crushed its tentacles, filtered the product, and injected it into experimental animals. The result was a deep state of anesthesia, and the toxin was therefore called hypnotoxin. This was a first step toward the discovery of anaphylaxis.

Plankton was another concern of Albert's—from the surface to depths as great as 5,000 meters. His huge, baited polyhedral nets brought forth abundant evidence of a rich and varied bathypelagic fauna. In the waters off the Cape Verde Islands he broke the previous record of 5,800 meters by dredging at a depth of 6,035 meters. Some of his ideas, accepted today, were far ahead of his time: his protests that the depths were being overfished, the use of airplanes to spot schools of fish, and the creation of underwater preserves.

In order to display his collections, Albert founded the Musée Océanographique de Monaco in 1910 and the Institut Océanographique, Paris, in 1911. He also established publications for these institutions: *Bulletin du Musée Océanographique* in 1904, which became *Bulletin de l'Institut Océanographique* in 1906, and *Annales de l'Institut Océanographique* in 1910. Since he was also interested in man's origin and evolution, Albert founded the Musée Anthropologique de Monaco and the Institut de Paléontologie Humaine in Paris.

Albert was a corresponding member of the Académie des Sciences, Paris, and later a foreign associate member (1909), succeeding Lord Kelvin; a foreign associate member of the Académie de Médecine; and a member of the Académie d'Agriculture (for the model farming practices on his property at Marchais, Aisne).

BIBLIOGRAPHY

I. Original Works. Between 1885 and 1915 Albert published numerous reports in the *Comptes rendus de l'Académie des sciences* (Paris), *Comptes rendus des séances de la Société de Biologie* (Paris), *Bulletin de la Société de Géographie* (Paris), *Bulletin du Musée Océanographique,* and *Revue scientifique* (*Revue rose*), among others. His works include *Sur le Gulf-Stream. . . .* (Paris, 1886); "La pêche de la Sardine sur les côtes d'Espagne," in *Revue scientifique,* 3rd ser., **13,** no. 17 (1887), 513–519—a very similar work with the title *L'industrie de la Sardine sur les côtes de la Galice* was published separately with the notation "taken from the *Revue scientifique*" (Paris, 1887); "Sur les filets fins de profondeur employés à bord de l'*Hirondelle*," in *Comptes rendus des séances de la Société de Biologie*, 8th ser., **4**, no. 37 (1887), 661–664; "Sur l'alimentation des naufragés en pleine mer," in *Comptes rendus de l'Académie des sciences*, **107** (Dec. 1888), 980–982; "Recherche des animaux marins. . . ," in *Congrès International de Zoologie*, **1** (1889), 133–159; "Sur le développement des tortues (*T. caretta*)," in *Comptes rendus des séances de la Société de Biologie*, 10th ser., **5**, no. 1 (1898), 10–11; *La carrière d'un navigateur* (Monaco, 1901, 1951, 1966), the 1966 ed. with intro. by J. Y. Cousteau and preface by J. Rouch; "Les progrès de l'océanographie," in *Bulletin du Musée Océanographique*, no. 6 (1904), 1–13; "Progrès de la biologie marine," *ibid.*, no. 14 (1904), 1–7; "Sur le lancement de ballons pilotes au-dessus des océans," in *Comptes rendus de l'Académie des sciences*, **141** (1905), 492–493; "L'outillage moderne de l'océanographie," in *Bulletin du Musée Océanographique*, no. 25 (1905), 1–12; "Vingt-cinquième campagne scientifique (*Hirondelle II*)," in *Bulletin de l'Institut Océanographique de Monaco*, **10**, no. 268 (1913), 1–4; "Marche des mines flottantes dans l'Atlantique nord et l'océan Glacial pendant et après la guerre," *ibid.*, **16**, no. 357 (1919), 1–8; *Sur les résultats partiels des deux premières expériences pour déterminer la direction des courants de l'Atlantique nord* (Paris, n.d.); and "Discours sur l'océan" (delivered 25 Apr. 1921 to National Academy of Sciences, Washington), in *Bulletin du Musée Océanographique*, no. 392 (1921), 1–16.

II. SECONDARY LITERATURE. Works on Albert are C. Carpine, "Les navirés océanographiques dont les noms ont été choisis par S.A.S. le Prince Albert 1er pour figurer sur la façade du Musée Océanographique de Monaco . . .," in *Bulletin de l'Institut Océanographique*, spec. no. 2 (1966), 627–638; R. Damien, *Albert 1er Prince Souverain de Monaco, précédé de l'historique des origines de Monaco et de la dynastie des Grimaldi* (Villemomble, 1964); M. Fontaine, "La découverte de l'anaphylaxie," in *Bulletin de l'Institut Océanographique*, no. 997 (1951), 3–9; "Liste des campagnes scientifiques de S.A.S. Prince Albert 1er de Monaco," in *Bulletin des amis du Musée Océanographique*, no. 5 (1948), 9–14; L. Mayer, "S.A.S. Albert 1er, Prince de Monaco. L'homme et l'oeuvre," in *Bulletin de l'Institut Océanographique*, no. 421 (1922), 1–8; P. Portier, "La carrière scientifique du Prince de Monaco," in *Revue générale des sciences pures et appliquées*, **33**, no. 19 (1922), 542–544, and in *Bulletin des amis du Musée Océanographique*, no. 6 (1948), 2–7; J. Richard, *Les campagnes scientifiques de S.A.S. le Prince Albert 1er de Monaco* (Monaco, 1900), and many articles on Albert's cruises and the apparatus used on board his vessels in *Bulletin du Musée Océanographique* and *Bulletin de l'Institut Océanographique* between 1904 and 1941; J. Rouch, "Le Prince Albert 1er et Jean Charcot . . .," in *Bulletin de l'Institut Océanographique*, spec. no. 2 (1967); and J. Thoulet, "S.A.S. le Prince Albert 1er de Monaco," in *Bulletin des amis du Musée Océanographique*, no. 5 (1948), 1–6.

GEORGES PETIT

ALBERT OF BOLLSTÄDT. See **Albertus Magnus.**

ALBERT OF SAXONY (*b.* Helmstedt, Lower Saxony, *ca.* 1316; *d.* Halberstadt, Saxony, 8 July 1390), *physics, logic, mathematics.*

The family name of Albert of Saxony was de Ricmestorp; his father, Bernard de Ricmestorp, was a well-to-do burgher of Helmstedt. A brother, John, was a master of arts at the University of Paris in 1362, while Albert himself was still there. Of Albert's youth and early schooling nothing is known, although there is some evidence to indicate that he studied at Prague before going to Paris, where he obtained the degree of master of arts in 1351.

He quickly achieved renown as a teacher on the faculty of arts at Paris and was made rector of the university in 1353. During most of the period of Albert's study and teaching at Paris, the most influential figure on the faculty of arts was Jean Buridan, and Albert's own lectures on natural philosophy, represented by his books of questions on Aristotle's *Physics* and *De caelo et mundo*, were modeled closely on those of Buridan. Nicole Oresme, another pupil of Buridan, also taught at Paris at this time, and there is evidence that he influenced Albert in the direction of mathematical studies. Albert apparently studied theology also but never received a theological degree.

It is believed that he left Paris by the end of 1362, going to Avignon and spending the next two years carrying out various commissions for Pope Urban V. The pope obtained for him a benefice at Mainz, later made him parochial priest at Laa, and shortly afterward canon of Hildesheim. Albert played a major role in obtaining the authorization of the pope for the establishment of a university at Vienna and in drawing up its statutes. When the university was established in June 1365, Albert was its first rector. But he held this position for only a year; at the end of 1366 he was appointed bishop of Halberstadt and his academic career came to an end. His twenty-four years as bishop were marred by political and financial difficulties, and at one point he was even accused of heresy by some inimical clergy of his own region who intimated that he was "more learned in human science than in divine wisdom," and that he had openly taught an astrological determinism with denial of human freedom of choice. Surviving these vicissitudes, he held the bishopric until he died at the age of seventy-six. He was buried in the cathedral of Halberstadt.

Albert's writings, which were probably composed during the years when he was teaching at Paris, consist mostly of books of questions on Aristotle's treatises and of some treatises of his own on logic and mathematical subjects. Extant in early printed editions are questions on Aristotle's *Physics, De caelo et mundo, De generatione et corruptione, Posterior Analytics,* and on the "old logic" (Porphyry's *Predicables* and Aristotle's *Categories* and *De interpretatione*); a complete textbook of logic published in 1522, under the title *Logica Albertutii;* an extensive collection of logical puzzles, entitled *Sophismata;* and a treatise on the mathematical analysis of motion, entitled *Tractatus proportionum.* In unpublished manuscripts there are sets of questions on Aristotle's *Meteora, Ethics, De sensu et sensato,* and *Oeconomica;* a book of questions on John of Sacrobosco's *De sphaera;* and two short treatises on the mathematical problems of "squaring the circle" and of determining the ratio of the diameter of a square to its side. Suter's ascription of the second of these mathematical treatises to Albert has been questioned by Zoubov (see Bibliography), who attributes it to Oresme. It does in fact echo passages found in one of Oresme's known works, but since Albert often paraphrased the content of works whose ideas he borrowed, this does not prove that the work was not written by Albert. There is much uncertainty concerning the attribution of a number of these manuscript works to Albert. It has been shown that his *Questions on the Ethics,* although written by Albert as his own work, is an almost literal plagiarism of the corresponding work of Walter Burley.

Albert's significance in the history of science is primarily that of a transmitter and an intelligent compiler of scientific ideas directly drawn from the works of Buridan, Thomas Bradwardine, William of Ockham, Burley, Oresme, and other writers in the medieval scientific tradition. His works in physics are heavily dependent on the corresponding works of Buridan, to the extent that all but a few of the questions devoted to the *Physics* and the *De caelo et mundo* correspond directly to those of Buridan's works of similar title, both in form and in content. Most of the questions that Albert adds, and which are not found in Buridan's works, draw their materials from the Oxford tradition of Bradwardine and his Mertonian pupils, or, in a few cases, from the early thirteenth-century works on statics and hydrostatics associated with Jordanus de Nemore. Albert's *Tractatus proportionum* is modeled directly on Bradwardine's treatise *De proportionibus velocitatum in motibus,* although it adds some refinements in terminology and in the analysis of curvilinear motions that reflected the later Mertonian developments and probably also the influence of Oresme.

Despite his lack of originality Albert contributed many intelligent discussions of aspects of the problems dealt with, and he had the particular merit of seeing the importance of bringing together the mathematical treatments of motion in its kinematic aspect, stemming from the Oxford tradition of Bradwardine, with the dynamical theories that Buridan had developed without sufficient concern for their mathematical formulation. As a transmitter of Buridan's work, Albert played an important part in making known the explanations of projectile motion and of gravitational acceleration provided by Buridan's theory of impetus, although he tended to blur the distinction between Buridan's quasi-inertial concept of impetus and the older doctrine of the self-expending "impressed virtue." Unlike Buridan, he introduced an error into the analysis of projectile motion, by supposing that there is a short period of rest between the ascent of a projectile hurled directly upward and its descent. Yet this led him to initiate a fruitful discussion by raising the question of the trajectory that would be followed by a projectile shot horizontally from a cannon. He supposed that it would follow a straight horizontal path until its *impetus* ceased to exceed the force of its gravity, but that it would then follow a curved path for a short period in which its lateral impetus would be compounded with a downward impetus caused by its gravity, after which it would fall straight down. Leonardo da Vinci took up the problem, but it remained for Nicolò Tartaglia to show that the entire trajectory would be a curve determined by a composition of the two forces.

Albert's textbook of logic is one of the best organized of the late medieval works in the field. In its first three sections it presents the analysis of the signification and supposition of terms, and the internal analysis and classification of propositional forms, provided by the work of Ockham and Buridan. The fourth section, on "consequence," shows influence by Burley and Buridan, developing the theory of inference on the foundation of the logic of unanalyzed propositions, exhibiting the syllogism as a special type of consequence, and ending with a very full treatment of modal syllogisms and a shorter formulation of the rules of topical argumentation. The last two sections deal with logical fallacies, with the "insoluble" (or paradox of self-reference), and with the rules of disputation known as *Obligationes.* There is little that is not directly traceable to the sources Albert used, but these materials are skillfully integrated, reduced to a uniform terminology, and presented with systematic elegance.

Despite its excellence as a textbook, this work did not achieve the popularity or influence attained by Albert's *Tractatus proportionum* and by his questions on the physical treatises of Aristotle. These, printed in many editions at Venice, Padua, and Pavia, became the principal means by which the contributions of the northern Scholastics of the fourteenth century to the science of mechanics were made known to the physicists and mathematicians of Italy, from Leonardo da Vinci to Galileo himself.

BIBLIOGRAPHY

I. ORIGINAL WORKS. *Expositio aurea et admodum utilis super artem veterem . . . cum quaestionibus Alberti parvi de Saxonia* (Bologna, 1496); *Quaestiones subtilissimae Alberti de Saxonia super libros Posteriorum* (Venice, 1497); *Logica Albertutii* (Venice, 1522); *Sophismata Alberti de Saxonia* (Paris, 1490, 1495); *Tractatus obligationum* (Lyons, 1498; with Albert's *Insolubilia,* Paris, 1490, 1495); *Subtilissimae quaestiones super octo libros Physicorum* (Venice, 1504, 1516); *Quaestiones in libros de caelo et mundo* (Pavia, 1481; Venice, 1492, 1497, 1520); *Quaestiones in libros de generatione et corruptione* (Venice, 1504, 1505, 1518); *Quaestiones et decisiones physicales insignium virorum . . .,* Georgius Lockert, ed. (Paris, 1516, 1518), contains Albert's questions on the *Physics* and the *De caelo et mundo; Tractatus proportionum* (Bologna, 1502, 1506; Padua, 1482, 1484, 1487; Venice, 1477, 1494, 1496; Paris, *s.a.*).

II. SECONDARY LITERATURE. Philotheus Boehner, *Medieval Logic* (Chicago, 1952); B. Boncompagni, "Intorno al Tractatus proportionum di Alberto de Sassonia," in *Bolletino di bibliografia e di storia delle scienze matematiche e fisiche,* **4** (1871), 498 ff.; Maximilian Cantor, *Vorlesungen über die Geschichte der Mathematik,* II, 2nd. ed. (1900), 137–154; Marshall Clagett, *The Science of Mechanics in the Middle Ages* (Madison, Wis., 1959); Pierre Duhem, *Études sur Léonard de Vinci,* Vols. I–III (Paris, 1906–1913); A. Dyroff, "Ueber Albertus von Sachsen," in *Baeumker-Festgabe* (Münster, 1913), pp. 330–342; G. Heidingsfelder, "Albert von Sachsen: Sein Lebensgang und sein Kommentar zur Nikomachischen Ethik des Aristoteles," in *Beiträge zur Geschichte der Philosophie und Theologie des Mittelalters,* **22,** 2nd ed. (Münster, 1926); M. Jullien, "Un scolastique de la décadence: Albert de Saxe," in *Revue Augustinienne,* **16** (1910), 26–40; Anneliese Maier, *Zwei Grundprobleme der scholastischen Naturphilosophie* (Rome, 1951), pp. 259–274; C. Prantl, *Geschichte der Logik im Abendlande,* **4** (Leipzig, 1870), 60–88; H. Suter, "Der Tractatus 'De quadratura circuli' des Albertus de Saxonia," in *Zeitschrift für Mathematik und Physik,* **29** (1884), 81–102 (reedited and translated in M. Clagett, *Archimedes in the Middle Ages* [Madison, Wis., 1964], pp. 398–432); H. Suter, "Die Quaestio 'De proportione dyametri quadrati ad costam eiusdem' des Albertus de Saxonia," in *Zeitschrift für Mathematik und Physik,* **32** (1887), 41–56; V. P. Zoubov, "Quelques Observations sur l'Auteur du Traité Anonyme 'Utrum dyameter alicuius quadrati sit commensurabilis costae ejusdem,'" in *Isis,* **50** (1959), 130–134.

ERNEST A. MOODY

ALBERTI, FRIEDRICH AUGUST VON (*b.* Stuttgart, Germany, 4 September 1795; *d.* Heilbronn, Germany, 12 September 1878), *geology, mining.*

Alberti's father, Karl Franz, was a colonel in Württemberg and a teacher at the well-known Karlsschule in Stuttgart; a member of the middle class, he was ennobled in 1807. His mother, Christiane Friederike, also came from the middle class; she had family connections with the princely court and was the aunt of the novelist and short-story writer Wilhelm Hauff.

In 1809 Alberti entered the Bergkadettenkorps in Stuttgart, in which he received instruction in general scientific subjects as well as special training in mineralogy, geology, and mining. In 1815 he went to the saltworks at Sulz; in 1818 he supervised drilling experiments near Jagstfeld; and in 1820 he was appointed inspector of the saltworks at Friedrichshall. The first proof of his abilities came in 1823, when he drilled a rock salt deposit near Schwenningen and established the saltworks at Wilhelmshall; he became manager in 1828. In his book *Über die Gebürge des Königreiches Württemberg, in besonderer Beziehung auf Halurgie* (1825) he also demonstrated his scientific abilities.

Alberti was appointed mining counselor in 1836. From 1852 to 1870 he was again manager of the saltworks at Friedrichshall. There, under his direction, between 1854 and 1859 the Friedrichshall shaft was bored, and the center of Württemberg's salt production was shifted from Wilhelmshall to Friedrichshall. His most important technical improvement was the introduction of steam heating into salt processing. Alberti was considered one of the foremost saltmining engineers, but like other German mining officials of his era, he was not only a good manager with technical capabilities but also a scientist of significant achievement.

After Quenstedt, Alberti must be reckoned one of the founders of the geology of southwest Germany. His investigations of the Triassic period and its fossils were of fundamental significance. He coined the name Triassic for the oldest formations of the Mesozoic era and thoroughly investigated the three divisions—variegated sandstone, shell limestone, and Keuper sandstone—dividing them into groups characterized by petrographic and paleontologic features. In 1834 he published his most important results in *Beiträge zu einer Monographie des Bunten Sandsteins, Muschelkalks und Keupers und der Verbindung dieser Gebilde zu einer Formation.* He also investigated and described crystalline slate and the eruptive rocks, as well as their superimposed formations in the Black Forest.

BIBLIOGRAPHY

I. ORIGINAL WORKS. Alberti's main writings are *Über die Gebürge des Königreiches Württemberg, in besonderer Beziehung auf Halurgie* (Stuttgart–Tübingen, 1825); *Beiträge zu einer Monographie des Bunten Sandsteins, Muschelkalks und Keupers und der Verbindung dieser Gebilde zu einer Formation* (Stuttgart–Tübingen, 1834); *Halurgische Geologie,* 2 vols. (Stuttgart–Tübingen, 1852); and *Überblick über die Trias* (Stuttgart, 1864).

II. SECONDARY LITERATURE. Biographical notices are in *Schwäbische Kronik* (1878), 2165; and in W. Serlo, *Männer des Bergbaues* (1937). The best recent summary is Erich Krenkel, in *Neue deutsche Biographie,* I (1953), 140–141.

HANS BAUMGÄRTEL

ALBERTI, LEONE BATTISTA (*b.* Genoa, Italy, 18 February 1404; *d.* Rome, Italy, April 1472), *mathematics, physics, natural history, technology.*

In the twelfth century Alberti's ancestors were feudal lords of Valdarno who settled in Florence, where they became judges and notaries and were members of the wealthy bourgeoisie. In the fourteenth century they engaged in commercial and banking enterprises, organizing a firm with branches scattered all over Europe; their wealth enriched Florence. At the same time, the Albertis became involved in politics. Toward the end of the fourteenth and the beginning of the fifteenth centuries, this led to the family's exile; they sought refuge in the foreign branches of their firm. Thus Leone Battista Alberti, the son of Lorenzo Alberti, came to be born in Genoa. It is possible that he was illegitimate.

From his early childhood Alberti is said to have been precocious; little else is known about his youth. Fleeing the plague, his father went to Venice, the site of perhaps the most important branch of the house of Alberti. The father died suddenly, leaving his children in the care of their uncle, who disappeared soon thereafter. It is possible that unscrupulous relatives liquidated the Venice branch in order to make themselves rich at the orphans' expense.

Alberti seems to have started his advanced education at Padua. At any rate, after 1421 he continued it at Bologna, where he began the study of law. Overwork caused him to fall ill, and he had to interrupt his studies; nevertheless, he received a doctorate in canon law. For relaxation he took up the study of mathematics, natural sciences, and physics, subjects that he pursued to a rather advanced level. Subsequently, the decrees of exile against his family having been revoked, Alberti undoubtedly returned to Florence, or at least to Tuscany. In Florence he met Brunelleschi, who became a good friend. Between 1430 and 1432 he was in the service of a cardinal, who took him with his entourage to France, Belgium, and Germany.

In 1432 Alberti arrived in Rome, where he became a functionary at the papal court. In Rome he discovered antiquity and became the artist we know today—painter, sculptor, and then architect. His paintings and sculptures, however, have never been found or identified. As part of the papal court, he necessarily shared all its tribulations. In 1437 he was in Bologna and Ferrara with Pope Eugene IV, who was roaming all over northern Italy. He was often in Rome, yet he also served those humanistic families who ruled small, more or less independent principalities. Thus he certainly spent some time at the court of Rimini, with the Malatesta family. Here Alberti conceived and partially executed his most important architectural work, the Malatesta Temple, a chapel designed to shelter their tombs.

Alberti was, we are told, amiable, very handsome, and witty. He was adept at directing discussions and took pleasure in organizing small conversational groups. Alberti represented, perhaps even better than Brunelleschi, the first scholar-artists of the Renaissance, more inquisitive than given to realization, more collectors of facts and ideas than imaginative and creative. Still close to the expiring Middle Ages, Alberti had trouble freeing himself of its shackles on the scientific level. He was possessed of a perpetual need to know—and a perpetual need to expound his ideas—as well as a desire to mingle with intellectual equals. It is certain that from these encounters at the courts of rulers like the Malatestas, a new scientific spirit arose. In this sense Alberti occupies a place of particular importance in the history of thought. At the end of his life, aside from architectural works or such engineering projects as the attempt to refloat the Roman galleys in Lake Nemi in 1447 (on which he wrote a short treatise, now lost), he was occupied with these meetings and with the editing of his written works, which were numerous.

Unfortunately, a large part of Alberti's scientific work has been lost. It is not impossible, however, that some of his works may be submerged in the scientific literature of the age without being known. Like all of his contemporaries, Alberti inherited a fragmentary science. He seems to have been interested in isolated problems which furnished subjects for discussion but which individually could not result in anything important. It was difficult to give them a personal emphasis, for these questions had already been debated, discussed, and restated many times.

Alberti's mathematics is exactly that of his times.

He wrote, at least on an advanced level, only a small treatise, the *Ludi matematici,* dedicated to his friend Meliadus d'Este, himself an accomplished mathematician. Only twenty problems were involved, some of which had to do with mathematics only remotely. Only one of them touched on an abstract question— lunules in "De lunularum quadratura," in which he furnished an elegant solution to the problem but lost his way in the squaring of the circle. On all other points he shared the preoccupation of a great number of fifteenth-century scholars, considering mathematics as a tool rather than an independent science. Often he merely applied formulas. Thus, geometry was used to calculate the height of a tower, the depth of a well, the area of a field. In this work we find notions of the hygrometer which is simply the hygrometer of Nicholas of Cusa. Alberti wrote a book of mathematical commentaries that may have contained more precise ideas, but unfortunately the manuscript has never been found.

Not much is known about Alberti's physics. He wrote *De motibus ponderis,* which has been lost also. In some of his works we can find some references to physics, but they are rather elusive ones. Some years ago the *Trattati dei pondi, lieve e tirari,* long attributed to Leonardo da Vinci, was reattributed to Alberti. It concerns gravity, density (harking back to the works of Archimedes), hydrostatics, and heat. There are only vague, undoubtedly traditional ideas on the preservation of labor. His optics is more pragmatic than theoretical, although he sets forth a theory of vision. In his opinion bodies, even dark ones, emit in all directions rays that move in a straight line. They converge toward the eye and together form a visual pyramid. This theory is also completely traditional. The camera obscura, which may be his greatest discovery, deeply impressed his contemporaries, although he perhaps borrowed this device from Brunelleschi, to whom he was greatly indebted for his studies on perspective. In his *Elementa picturae,* however, he contributed nothing more than applied geometry. He worked from the idea that the construction of similar figures was the basis for all figure representation.

Alberti displayed the same attitude in his writings on the natural sciences, in which he speculated on nature rather than on scientific data. Like many others, he admitted the roundness of the earth, and also wrote briefly on the development of its crust. He seemingly spoke knowledgeably of earthquakes, atmospheric erosion, water circulation, the action of plants on soil, plant decomposition and formation of humus, sedimentary layers, and the formation of deltas. He considered fossils merely a freak of nature.

Alberti's best-known work, containing many of his scientific ideas, is his *De re aedificatoria,* which was presented to Pope Nicolas V about 1452. The work was printed in 1485 and exerted a certain influence. It was to be a treatise on the art of engineering, but this aim was not completely achieved. Alberti dealt with lifting devices, grain bins and "other conveniences that albeit of little esteem nevertheless bring profit," water supply, ways of quarrying rock and cutting through mountains, the damming of the sea or of rivers, the drying up of swamps, machines of war, and fortresses. In this work he was concerned less with architecture per se and architectural techniques than with an actual attempt at town planning. His ideas of a city were still largely inspired by the Middle Ages, but they also contained elements clearly belonging to the Renaissance, such as the respect for urban aesthetics, perspective, and orderly arrangement. Something that certainly seems new—but we hardly know his predecessors—is the application of the entire range of scientific knowledge to town planning and architectural practice. Alberti applied his knowledge of the natural sciences to building materials; his knowledge of physics was applied to equilibrium of buildings, the flexibility of beams, and the construction of engines; and that of mathematics (still very simple mathematics) was shown in the very Pythagorean layout of cities and the arrangement of fortresses.

As was typical of his time, Alberti was preoccupied with various machines and apparatuses, some in current use and some the subject of scattered and almost confused observation which made it impossible to draw the parallels and comparisons necessary to develop a technology. He spoke of balances, clocks, sundials, pulleys, water mills and windmills, and canal locks. He developed topographical instruments and envisaged the odometer and the "sulcometer," which measured distances traveled by ships. He studied the methods of sounding in deep waters. In all of this work he manifested more interest in manual crafts than in true science.

Alberti is difficult to place in both the history of science and the history of technology. Contemporary works in these fields almost invariably cite him in their lists of scholars, but he is not credited with anything really new. He contributed no new principles, but he seems to have had a very profound knowledge. In short, he seems to have regarded science as a means for action rather than as a system of organized knowledge. On many occasions he admitted his interest in knowledge, but more for reasons of efficiency than as an abstract science, as power rather than as intellectuality. He knew only the perspective and natural science that serve the artist or the architect, and only the mathematics and physics of use to the engineer and the technician. Nevertheless, he perceived certain directions for research. He was well aware of the difference between sensation (common observation) and scientific ideas: "Points and lines are not the same for the painter as for the mathematician." Observation was a point of departure for scientific hypothesis, which must be verified by systematic observation. In the last analysis, although Alberti contributed nothing but a supplementary collection of special cases to scientific progress, he nevertheless outlined some promising avenues for future work.

BIBLIOGRAPHY

I. Original Works. In most cases only very old editions of Alberti's works are extant. *De re aedificatoria* was first published in Florence in 1485; there were many subsequent editions in Italian, and a French version appeared in Paris in 1553. *Opere volgari dei L. B. Alberti,* IV (Florence, 1847), contains *Ludi matematici. Opera inedita et pauca separatim impressa* (Florence, 1890) includes *Elementa picturae;* it also contains a treatise on perspective incorrectly attributed to Alberti. *Trattati dei pondi, lieve e tirari* was published as an appendix to Vasari (Florence, 1917).

II. Secondary Literature. There are few works on Alberti. The essential work is P. H. Michel, *La pensée de L. B. Alberti* (Paris, 1930), with an exhaustive bibliography of works published until then. There is a good chapter on Alberti in L. Olschki, *Geschichte der neuspralichen Literatur* (Leipzig, 1919). The technological aspects of Alberti's work are discussed by B. Gille in *Les ingénieurs de la Renaissance* (Paris, 1967), pp. 80–84.

Bertrand Gille

ALBERTI, SALOMON (*b.* Naumburg, Germany, October 1540; *d.* Dresden, Germany, 29 March 1600), *medicine.*

Although he is usually associated with Nuremberg, where his family moved in 1541 and where he received his elementary education, Alberti studied medicine at Wittenberg (M.D., 1574) and taught in the medical faculty there for many years. He was chiefly interested in anatomy. As early as 1579, he began public demonstrations of the venous valves; his study of these valves was his most noteworthy achievement. A knowledge of the venous valves was essential to the formation of Harvey's concept of a systemic circulation of the blood, fifty years later. First referred to in 1546, they were apparently forgotten after about 1560; they were rediscovered in 1574 by Girolamo Fabrizio (Fabrizio d'Acquapendente) at Padua. Although Alberti acknowledged his indebtedness to Fabrizio for rediscovery of these valves, he deserves recognition as being the first to provide illustrations of venous valves in his *Tres orationes* (Nuremberg, 1585), which also included the first extensive printed account devoted solely to their structure.

Alberti also studied and described the lacrimal apparatus (*De lacrimis,* Wittenberg, 1581), as well as such then curious but rational problems as why boys ought not to be forbidden to cry, why sobbing usually accompanies weeping, and whether asthma might be ameliorated by breathing the fumes of various minerals burned on coals (*Orationes quatuor,* Wittenberg, 1590). In addition, he provided an extended account of the ileocecal valve, or Bauhin's valve (mentioned by Mondino in 1316 and described briefly by Laguna in 1535), the cochlea (described in detail by Fallopio in 1561), and, as an original contribution, the renal papillae. (See *Orationes duae,* Wittenberg, 1575–1576; and *Historia plerarunque partium humani corporis,* a textbook for medical students, Wittenberg, 1583, and later editions.) Alberti discussed the problem of deafness and muteness in *Oratio de surditate et mutitate* (Nuremberg, 1591). He emphasized the difference between hardness of hearing and deafness, which latter condition he considered as possibly being caused by a defect in the development of the fetus.

In 1592 Alberti became physician to Duke Friedrich Wilhelm of Saxony. A year earlier, his interest in the problem of scurvy had led to the treatise *De schorbuto* (Wittenberg, 1591). Alberti made a survey of the incidence of the deficiency disease in the ducal territory, and the result was his *Schorbuti historia* (Wittenberg, 1594), which for the most part is of no great significance except for its demonstration of the prevalence of the complaint and the recommendation of citrus fruit as part of a preventive diet. The book was known by James Lind and referred to by him in his celebrated treatise of 1753.

BIBLIOGRAPHY

For bibliographies of Alberti's writings see Georg Andreas Will, *Nürnbergisches Gelehrten-Lexicon,* 1 (Nuremberg, 1755); and Claudius F. Mayer, "Bio-bibliography of XVI. Century Medical Authors. Fasciculus 1, Abarbanel-Alberti, S.," in *Index Catalogue of the Library of the Surgeon General's Library,* ser. 4, 3rd supp. (Washington, D. C., 1941), which contains an exhaustive list but without indication of imprint. See also Lynn Thorndike, *A History of Magic and Experimental Science, The Sixteenth Century,* VI (New York, 1941), 229–230.

C. D. O'Malley

ALBERTUS MAGNUS, SAINT, also known as **Albert the Great** and **Universal Doctor** (*b.* Lauingen, Bavaria, *ca.* 1200; *d.* Cologne, Prussia, 15 November 1280). *Proficient in all branches of science, he was one of the most famous precursors of modern science in the High Middle Ages.*

Albert was born in the family castle and probably spent his childhood at the family manor in nearby Bollstädt—whence he is variously referred to as Albert of Lauingen and Albert of Bollstädt. His birth date could have been as early as 1193 or as late as 1206 or 1207. His family was wealthy and powerful, of the military nobility, and he received a good education.

He studied liberal arts at Padua, where, over strong opposition from his family, he was recruited into the Dominican Order by its master general, Jordan of Saxony—identified by some (but probably falsely) as Jordanus de Nemore, the mechanician. He likely studied theology and was ordained a priest in Germany, where he also taught in various priories before being sent to the University of Paris *ca.* 1241. In Paris he was the first German Dominican to become a master of theology and to lecture in the chair "for foreigners" (1245–1248). In the summer of 1248 he went to Cologne to establish a *studium generale*: among his students were Thomas Aquinas, Ulrich of Strassburg, and Giles (Aegidius) of Lessines.

He began the administrative phase of his career as provincial of the German Dominicans (1253–1256). Subsequently he became bishop of Regensburg (1260), a post he resigned in 1262. The latter part of his life was spent in preaching and teaching, mainly at Cologne. He took part in the Council of Lyons (1274) and journeyed to Paris in an unsuccessful attempt to block the famous condemnation of 1277, where some of Aquinas' teachings were called into question. His health was good and he had great powers of physical endurance, even to old age, although his eyesight failed during the last decade of his life. Albert was canonized by Pope Pius XI on 16 December 1931 and was declared the patron of all who cultivate the natural sciences by Pope Pius XII on 16 December 1941.

Albert's principal importance for the history of modern science derives from the role he played in rediscovering Aristotle and introducing Greek and Arab science into the universities of the Middle Ages. Before his time, what was to become the subject matter of modern science was usually treated in encyclopedias, which assembled a curious mélange of fact and fable about nature, or in theological treatises, which described the cosmos in terms of the six days of creation, as recounted in Genesis and variously analyzed by the church fathers. Aristotle, of course, had already made his entry into the Latin West through the translations of Gerard of Cremona and James of Venice, among others; but Christendom was generally hostile to the teachings of this pagan philosopher, particularly as contained in his *libri naturales* ("books on natural science"). In 1210, the ecclesiastical authorities at Paris had condemned Aristotle's works on natural philosophy and had prohibited their being taught publicly or privately under pain of excommunication. Although this condemnation was revoked by 1234, it had a general inhibiting effect on the diffusion of Greek science in the schools of the Middle Ages.

Albert seems to have become acquainted with the Aristotelian corpus while at the Paris priory of St. Jacques in the 1240's. Here too he probably began his monumental paraphrase of all the known works of Aristotle and Pseudo-Aristotle, to which are allotted seventeen of the forty volumes in the Cologne critical edition of Albert's works (see Bibliography). The project was undertaken by Albert, then studying and teaching theology, at the insistence of his Dominican brethren, who wished him to explain, in Latin, the principal physical doctrines of the Stagirite so that they could read his works intelligently. Albert went far beyond their demands, explaining not only the natural sciences but also logic, mathematics, ethics, politics, and metaphysics, and adding to Aristotle's exposition the discoveries of the Arabs and of whole sciences that were not available to him. The gigantic literary production that this entailed was recognized as one of the marvels of his age and contributed in no small measure to Albert's outstanding reputation. Roger Bacon, a contemporary who was not particularly enamored of the German Dominican, complained of Master Albert's being accepted as an authority in the schools on an equal footing with Aristotle, Avicenna, and Averroës—an honor, he protested, "never accorded to any man in his own lifetime."

Like all medieval Aristotelians, Albert incorporated considerable Platonic thought into his synthesis, and even commented on a number of Neoplatonic treatises. In several places he represents himself as merely reporting the teachings of the Peripatetics and not as proposing anything new; some historians charge him, on this basis, with being a compiler who was not too judicious in his selection of source materials. Those who have studied his works, however, detect there a consistent fidelity to Aristotle's basic theses, a clear indication of his own views when he thought Aristotle in error, a repudiation of erroneous interpretations of Aristotle's teaching, and an explicit rejection of Platonic and Pythagorean physical doctrines—all of which would seem to confirm his Aristotelianism. J. A. Weisheipl, in particular, has stressed the differences between thirteenth-century Oxford masters such as Robert Grosseteste, Robert Kilwardby, and Roger Bacon (all of whom were more pronouncedly Platonist in their scientific views) and Paris masters such as Albert and Aquinas (who were more purely Aristotelian). Whereas the former held that there is a successive subalternation between physics, mathematics, and metaphysics (so that the principles of natural science are essentially mathematical, and the principle of mathematics is the unity that is identical with Being), the latter held for the autonomy of these sciences, maintaining that each has its own proper principles, underived from any other discipline.

Albert's early identification as a precursor of modern science undoubtedly stemmed from his empiricist methodology, which he learned from Aristotle but which he practiced with a skill unsurpassed by any other Schoolman. From boyhood he was an assiduous observer of nature, and his works abound in descriptions of the phenomena he noted, usually in great detail. Considering that his observations were made without instruments, they were remarkably accurate. Some of the "facts" he reported were obviously based on hearsay evidence, although he was usually at pains to distinguish what he had himself seen from what he had read or been told by others. *Fui et vidi experiri* ("I was there and saw it happen") was his frequent certification for observations. Sometimes, as Lynn Thorndike has well illustrated in his *A History of Magic and Experimental Science,* even these certifications test the reader's credulity; what is significant in them, however, is Albert's commitment to an empiricist program. He stated that evidence based on sense perception is the most secure and is superior to reasoning without experimentation. Similarly, he noted that a conclusion that is inconsistent with the evidence cannot be believed and that a principle that does not agree with sense experience is really no principle at all. He was aware, however, that the observation of nature could be difficult: much time, he remarked, is required to conduct an experiment that will yield foolproof results, and he suggested that it be repeated under a variety of circumstances so as to assure its general validity.

On the subject of authority, he pointed out that science consists not in simply believing what one is told but in inquiring into the causes of natural things. He had great respect for Aristotle, but disagreed with the Averroists of his day on the Stagirite's infallibility. "Whoever believes that Aristotle was a god, must also believe that he never erred. But if one believes that he was a man, then doubtless he was liable to error just as we are." His *Summa theologica,* for example, contains a section listing the errors of Aristotle, and

in his *Meteorology* he observes that "Aristotle must have spoken from the opinions of his predecessors and not from the truth of demonstration or experiment."

Albert recognized the importance of mathematics for the physical sciences and composed treatises (unfortunately lost) on its pure and applied branches. Yet he would not insist that the book of nature is written in the language of mathematics, as Galileo was later to do, and as Roger Bacon intimated in his own lifetime. Rather, for Albert, mathematics had only a subsidiary role to play in scientific activity, insofar as it assisted in the discovery of physical causes. Mathematics is itself an abstract science, prescinding from motion and sensible matter, and thus its applications must be evaluated by the science that studies nature as it really exists, *in motu et inabstracta* ("in motion and in concrete detail").

The mechanics of Albert was basically that of Aristotle, with little innovation in either its kinematical or its dynamical aspects. One part of Albert's teaching on motion, however, did assume prominence in the late medieval period and influenced the emerging new science of mechanics. This was his use of the expressions *fluxus formae* and *forma fluens* to characterize the scholastic dispute over the entitative status of local motion. Arab thinkers such as Avicenna and Averroës had pursued the question whether this motion, or any other, could be located in the Aristotelian categories; the question quickly led to an argument whether motion is something really distinct from the terminus it attains. Local motion, in this perspective, could be seen in one of two ways: either it was a *fluxus formae* (the "flowing" of successive forms, or locations) or a *forma fluens* (a form, or absolute entity, that is itself a process). Although Albert made no clear dichotomy between these two views and allowed that each described a different aspect of motion, later writers came to be sharply divided over them. Nominalists, such as William of Ockham, defended the first view: this equivalently denied the reality of local motion, equating it simply with the distance traversed and rejecting any special causality in its production or continuance—a view that stimulated purely kinematical analyses of motion. Realists, such as Walter Burley and Paul of Venice, on the other hand, defended the second view: for them, local motion was an entity really distinct from the object moved and from its position, and thus had its own proper causes and effects—a view that stimulated studies of its more dynamical aspects.

Albert mentioned the term *impetus* when discussing projectile motion, but spoke of it as being in the medium rather than in the projectile, thus defending the original Aristotelian teaching; certainly he had no treatment of the concept to match that found in the work of fourteenth-century thinkers. His analysis of gravitational motion was also Aristotelian: he regarded the basic mover as the generator of the heavy object, giving it not only its substantial form but also its gravity and the motion consequent on this. He knew that bodies accelerate as they fall, and attributed this to their increasing propinquity to their natural place.

The cause of sound, for Albert, is the impact of two hard bodies, and the resulting vibration is propagated in the form of a sphere whose center is the point of percussion. He speculated also on the cause of heat, studying in detail how light from the sun produces thermal effects; here his use of simple experiments revealed a knowledge of the method of agreement and difference later to be formulated by J. S. Mill. He knew of the refraction of solar rays and also of the laws of refraction of light, although he employed the term *reflexio* for both refraction and reflection, as, for example, when discussing the burning lens and the burning mirror. His analysis of the rainbow was diffuse in its historical introduction, but it made an advance over the theory of Robert Grosseteste in assigning individual raindrops a role in the bow's formation, and undoubtedly prepared for the first correct theory of the rainbow proposed by another German Dominican, Dietrich von Freiberg, who was possibly Albert's student. In passing, he corrected Aristotle's assertion that the lunar rainbow occurs only twice in fifty years: "I myself have observed two in a single year."

Although he had no telescope, he speculated that the Milky Way is composed of stars and attributed the dark spots on the moon to configurations on its surface, not to the earth's shadow. His treatise on comets is notable for its use of simple observation to verify or falsify theories that had been proposed to explain them. He followed Grosseteste in correlating the occurrence of tides with the motion of the moon around its deferent. He favored the mathematical aspects of the Ptolemaic theory of the structure of the solar system, contrasting it with that of al-Biṭrūjī, although he acknowledged the superiority of the latter's theory in its physical aspects. Albert accepted the order of the celestial spheres commonly taught by Arabian astronomers; he knew of the precession of the equinoxes, attributing knowledge of this (falsely) to Aristotle also. Like most medieval thinkers, Albert held that heavenly bodies are moved by separated substances, but he denied that such substances are to be identified with the angels of Christian revelation, disagreeing on this point with his celebrated disciple Thomas Aquinas.

On the structure of matter, when discussing the presence of elements in compounds, Albert attempted to steer a middle course between the opposed positions of Avicenna and Averroës, thereby preparing for Aquinas' more acceptable theory of "virtual" presence. In a similar vein, he benignly viewed Democritus' atoms as equivalent to the *minima naturalia* of the Aristotelians. He seems to have experimented with alchemy and is said to have been the first to isolate the element arsenic. He compiled a list of some hundred minerals, giving the properties of each. During his many travels, he made frequent sidetrips to mines and excavations in search of specimens. He was acquainted with fossils, and made accurate observations of "animal impressions" and improved on Avicenna's account of their formation. Albert suggested the possibility of the transmutation of metals, but he did not feel that alchemists had yet found the method to bring this about.

Extensive as was Albert's work in the physical sciences, it did not compare with his contributions to the biological sciences, where his powers of observation and his skill at classification earned for him an unparalleled reputation. Some aspects of his work have been singled out by A. C. Crombie as "unsurpassed from Aristotle and Theophrastus to Cesalpino and Jung." His *De vegetabilibus et plantis,* in particular, is a masterpiece for its independence of treatment, its accuracy and range of detailed description, its freedom from myth, and its innovation in systematic classification. His comparative study of plants extended to all their parts, and his digressions show a remarkable sense of morphology and ecology. He drew a distinction between thorns and prickles on the basis of their formation and structure, classified flowers into the celebrated three types (bird-form, bell-form, and star-form), and made an extensive comparative study of fruits. His general classification of the vegetable kingdom followed that proposed by Theophrastus: he ranged plants on a scale reaching from the fungi to the flowering types, although, among the latter, he did not explicitly distinguish the monocotyledons from the dicotyledons. He seems to have been the first to mention spinach in Western literature, the first to note the influence of light and heat on the growth of trees, and the first to establish that sap (which he knew was carried in veins—like blood vessels, he said, but without a pulse) is tasteless in the root and becomes flavored as it ascends.

On plant evolution, Albert proposed that existing types were sometimes mutable and described five ways of transforming one plant into another; he believed, for example, that new species could be produced by grafting. Here he registered an advance over most medieval thinkers, who accounted for the succession of new species not by modification but by generation from a common source such as earth.

Albert's *De animalibus* includes descriptions of some fabulous creatures, but it also rejects many popular medieval myths (e.g., the pelican opening its breast to feed its young) and is especially noteworthy for its sections on reproduction and embryology. Following Aristotle, Albert distinguished four types of reproduction; in sexual reproduction among the higher animals he taught that the material produced by the female was like a seed (a *humor seminalis*), differentiating it from the catamenia (*menstruum*) in mammals and the yolk of the egg in birds, but incorrectly identifying it with the white of the egg. The cause of the differentiation of the sexes, in his view, was that the male "vital heat" could "concoct" semen out of surplus blood, whereas the female was too cold to effect the change.

He studied embryology by such simple methods as opening eggs at various intervals of time and tracing the development of the embryo from the appearance of the pulsating red speck of the heart to hatching. He was acquainted, too, with the development of fish and mammals, and understood some aspects of fetal nutrition. His studies on insects were especially good for their descriptions of insect mating, and he correctly identified the insect egg. He showed that ants lose their sense of direction when their antennae are removed, but concluded (wrongly) that the antennae carry eyes.

Among the larger animals, he described many northern types unknown to Aristotle, noting changes of coloration in the colder climates, and speculating that if any animals inhabited the poles they would have thick skins and be of a white color. His knowledge of internal anatomy was meager, but he did dissect crickets and observed the ovarian follicles and tracheae. His system of classification for the animal kingdom was basically Aristotelian; occasionally he repeated or aggravated the Stagirite's mistakes, but usually he modified and advanced Aristotle's taxonomy, as in his treatment of the ten genera of water animals. His anthropology was more philosophical than empirical in intent, but some have detected in it the adumbration of methods used in experimental psychology.

Apart from these more speculative concerns, Albert made significant contributions also to veterinary and medical science, dentistry included. In anatomy, for example, he took the vertebral column as the basis for structure, whereas in his day and for long afterward most anatomists began with the skull. He was reported to have cures for all manner of disease, and despite his own repudiation of magic and astrology came to be regarded as something of a magician. Many spurious works, some utterly fantastic, were attributed to him or published under his name to assure a wide diffusion—among these are to be included the very popular *De secretis mulierum* ("On the Secrets of Women") and other occult treatises.

Albert's productivity in science was matched by a similar output in philosophy and theology. In these areas his teachings have been overshadowed by those of his most illustrious disciple, Thomas Aquinas. The latter's debt to Albert is, of course, considerable, for Aquinas could well attribute the extent of his own vision to the fact that he stood on the shoulders of a giant.

BIBLIOGRAPHY

I. Major Works and Writings. Standard editions include *Omnia opera*, B. Geyer, ed. (Cologne, 1951–   ), a critical edition, in progress, 40 vols.; Vol. XII (1955) is the only work of direct scientific interest to appear thus far; it contains the *Quaestiones super de animalibus* and other treatises related to Albert's work in zoology; *Omnia opera*, A. Borgnet, ed. (Paris, 1890–1899), 38 quarto vols.; *Omnia opera*, P. Jammy, ed. (Lyons, 1651), 21 folio vols., available on microfilm positives from the Vatican Library; his *Book of Minerals* is translated from the Latin by Dorothy Wychoff (Oxford, 1967). Special texts include H. Stadler, ed., "Albertus Magnus De animalibus libri XXVI," in *Beiträge zur Geschichte der Philosophie des Mittelalters,* **15–16** (Münster, 1916; 1921); L. Thorndike, *Latin Treatises on Comets Between 1238 and 1368 A.D.* (Chicago, 1950), pp. 62–76; J. A. Weisheipl, "The Problema Determinata XLIII ascribed to Albertus Magnus (1271)," in *Mediaeval Studies,* **22** (1960), 303–354.

II. Secondary Literature. For a compact summary of Albert's life and works, with bibliography, see J. A. Weisheipl, "Albert the Great (Albertus Magnus), St.," in the *New Catholic Encyclopedia* (New York, 1967). Biographies include S. M. Albert, *Albert the Great* (Oxford, 1948) and T. M. Schwertner, *St. Albert the Great* (Milwaukee, 1932), a fuller biography with indication of sources. Works concerned with scientific teachings include H. Balss, *Albertus Magnus als Biologe* (Stuttgart, 1947); M. Barbado, *Introduction à la psychologie expérimentale*, P. Mazoyer, trans. (Paris, 1931), pp. 114–189; C. B. Boyer, *The Rainbow: From Myth to Mathematics* (New York, 1959), esp. pp. 94–99; A. C. Crombie, *Medieval and Early Modern Science*, I (New York, 1959), esp. 147–157; A. C. Crombie, *Robert Grosseteste and the Origins of Experimental Science* (Oxford, 1953), esp. pp. 189–200; E. J. Dijksterhuis, *The Mechanization of the World Picture*, C. Dikshoorn, trans. (Oxford, 1961); P. Duhem, *Le système du monde*, III (Paris, 1914; reprinted, 1958), 327–345; A. Maier, *Die Vorläufer Galileis im 14. Jahrhundert*, Edizioni di Storia e Letteratura, **22** (Rome, 1949), 11–16, 183–184; L. Thorndike, *A History of Magic* *and Experimental Science,* II (New York, 1923), esp. pp. 517–592; J. A. Weisheipl, *The Development of Physical Theory in the Middle Ages* (London, 1959); J. A. Weisheipl, "Celestial Movers in Medieval Physics," in *The Thomist,* **24** (1961), 286–326. See also *Serta Albertina,* a special issue of the Roman periodical *Angelicum,* **21** (1944), 1–336, devoted to all branches of Albert's science; includes a bibliography classified by fields.

WILLIAM A. WALLACE, O. P.

ALBRECHT, CARL THEODOR (*b.* Dresden, Germany, 30 August 1843; *d.* Potsdam, Germany, 31 August 1915), *surveying, astronomy.*

Albrecht's father, Friedrich Wilhelm Albrecht, and both grandfathers were soap boilers. Indeed, his maternal grandfather, Christian Friedrich Pohle, was a senior official of the soap boilers' guild of Dresden. Carl, however, did not continue the family tradition. His parents recognized the boy's intelligence, and set him on quite another path in that era when technology and the exact sciences flowered. As a student his major fields were mathematics and the natural sciences, but he occupied himself independently with astronomy and meteorology. About 1865, after passing his examinations at the Polytechnicum in Dresden, which at that time was an engineering school, Albrecht studied astronomy at the University of Leipzig in order to follow his special inclinations and to enlarge his theoretical knowledge.

From 1866 on, Albrecht was an assistant in the central European degree measurement project while continuing his studies. In 1869 he graduated from Leipzig and was immediately accepted at the newly founded Geodetic Institute in Potsdam, an indication that he already had a good scientific reputation. In 1873 he was appointed director of the astronomy department of the Geodetic Institute, a post he held until his death. In 1875 he became professor; in the same year he married Marie Stiemer.

The Geodetic Institute quickly became one of the leading research institutes in astronomy and geodesy. From 1895 on, Albrecht also directed the International Latitude Service, a cooperative group of various research institutes in many countries that sought the precise determination of the geographic degree of latitude.

BIBLIOGRAPHY

I. ORIGINAL WORKS. Albrecht published a large number of scientific writings, most of which appeared in various astronomical and geodetic journals. The most notable are "Über die Bestimmung von Längendifferenzen mit Hilfe des elektrischen Telegraphen" (Leipzig, 1869), his dissertation; "Genauigkeit der telegraphischen Ortsbestimmung," in *Astronomische Nachrichten,* **89** (1877); "Ausgleichungen des deutschen Längenbestimmungsnetzes," *ibid.,* **95** (1879); "Provisorische Resultate der Beobachtungsreihen Berlin, Potsdam und Prag betr. der Veränderlichkeit der Polhöhe," in *Internationale Erdmessung, Publikationen* (Berlin, 1890); "Stand der Erforschung der Breitenvariation," in *Internationale Erdmessung, Verhandlungen* (Berlin, 1894–1896); "Bestimmung der Längendifferenz Potsdam–Pulkovo im Jahre 1901," *ibid.* (Berlin, 1901); "Bestimmung der Längendifferenz Potsdam–Greenwich im Jahre 1903," *ibid.* (Berlin, 1904); "Bestimmung der Polhöhe und des Azimutes in Memel im Jahre 1907. Telegraphische Längenbestimmung Potsdam–Jena, Jena–Gotha und Gotha–Göttingen im Jahre 1909," *ibid.* (Berlin, 1910); and "Ergebnisse der Breitenbeobachtungen auf dem Observatorium in Johannesburg von März 1910 bis März 1913. Bearbeitet von Theodor Albrecht," *ibid.* (Berlin, 1915). For the *Astronomisch-geodätische Arbeiten für die Gradmessung im Königreich Sachsen* he wrote the third section, "Die astronomischen Arbeiten" (Berlin, 1883–1885). He also wrote *Formeln und Hilfstafeln für geographische Ortsbestimmungen* (Leipzig, 1869; 1873; 5th ed., Berlin, 1967).

II. SECONDARY LITERATURE. Obituary notices with *curriculum vitae* are A. Galle, in *Vierteljahrsschrift der Astronomischen Gesellschaft,* **50** (1915), 170–175; and F. R. Helmert, in *Astronomische Nachrichten,* **201** (1915), 269. A short biography is Hans-Ulrich Sandig, in *Neue deutsche Biographie,* I (1953), 183.

HANS BAUMGÄRTEL

ALBUMASAR. See **Abū Ma'shar.**

ALCABITIUS. See **al-Qabīṣī.**

ALCMAEON OF CROTONA (*b.* Crotona, Magna Graecia, *ca.* 535 B.C.), *medicine, natural philosophy.*

Alcmaeon, the son of Peirithoos and a pupil of Pythagoras, is often reported to have been a physician. There is no support for this in ancient sources, however, although Diogenes Laertius stated that Alcmaeon "wrote mostly about medical affairs." As far as we can judge, he also wrote about meteorological and astrological problems and about such philosophical questions as the immortality of the soul. It may therefore be best to call him a natural philosopher, deeply versed in medicine, who was in close contact with both the Pythagoreans and the physicians in Crotona (in this connection we may also think of his contemporary, the physician Democedes of Crotona). One must also keep in mind that at that time the "physiological" side of medicine was treated predominantly by philosophers, Hippocrates being the first to "separate medicine from philosophy," as Celsus states in the preface to *De re medicina.* Aristotle's lost writing *Against Alcmaeon* apparently concerned Alcmaeon as a philosopher.

In the history of science Alcmaeon is especially important for two reasons: he may have written the very first Greek prose book, a *physikos logos;* and he furnished medicine with the first material for a fundamental intellectual mastery of the nontraumatic internal diseases. He defined health as "the isonomy [balance] of forces" (that is, a balance of the opposite bodily qualities of cold and warm, bitter and sweet, and so forth) and internal disease as the "monarchy" of one of these "forces." He further divided the causes of disease into disorders of environment (climatic factors and the like), of nutrition, and of physical mode of living (exertion and such). From these definitions he formulated the bases of a general pathophysiology of internal diseases; similar hypotheses were made by the Hippocrateans. Apparently Alcmaeon clearly recognized the conjectural character of his formulae; they constituted, for him, an "opinion about the invisible."

Alcmaeon also seems to have engaged in dissection, especially ocular dissection for the investigation of the visual process. Obviously, the word *exsectio* in Chalcidius' report is to be taken in this sense; it could hardly refer to a surgical operation on a man since human dissection in a systematic form was, for religious reasons, neither then nor until much later possible in Greece. Among the pre-Socratic philosophers of around 500 B.C., Alcmaeon is the one most closely connected with medicine and therefore had the greatest significance for medicine *per se,* although he himself did not practice as a physician.

BIBLIOGRAPHY

Information on Alcmaeon and fragments of his writings are most accessible in H. Diels and W. Kranz, eds., *Die Fragmente der Vorsokratiker,* I (Berlin, 1951), 210 ff., which covers his statement on nontraumatic internal diseases; his description of his mode of thought as "an opinion about the invisible"; and his references to dissection and Chalcidius' report. Another work of value is Johannes Wachtler, *De Alcmaeone Crotoniata* (Leipzig, 1896). Also of value is Diogenes Laërtius, *Lives of Eminent Philosophers,* V, §25, and VIII, §83, which deal, respectively, with Aristotle's *Contra Alkmaion* and with Alcmaeon's early life.

FRIDOLF KUDLIEN

ALCUIN OF YORK (*b.* York, England, *ca.* 735; *d.* Tours, France, 19 May 804), *education.*

Alcuin is not famous for contributing to a specific scientific discipline; rather, his reputation and renown are based upon more general accomplishments. As Charlemagne's educational advisor, he brought Anglo-Saxon learning and teaching methods to the Franks.

Alcuin was born of a noble Northumbrian family. His English name was Ealhwine (Alchvine), but he preferred the Latin form, Albinus; at the court of Charlemagne he acquired the surname Flaccus. Educated at the cathedral school of York under the supervision of the archbishops Egbert and Aelbert, he was exposed to the best traditions of the early English schools. The school of York was heir to the rich pedagogical legacy of the Venerable Bede, and by the beginning of the eighth century its library was the finest in England. The methods and curriculum developed at York brought vitality to early medieval learning.

Alcuin's abilities attracted the attention of his teachers, and he became the protégé of Aelbert. At the death of Egbert in 766, Aelbert became archbishop and Alcuin assumed a major role in the leadership of the school; in 778 he became head of the school and library. When Eanbald became archbishop in 780, Alcuin was sent to Rome to receive the *pallium.* On his return journey the following year, he met Charlemagne at Parma. By this time Alcuin's fame as an educator and scholar had spread to the Continent. The Frankish king needed a competent educational advisor, for education in his kingdom was in a state of decline; he therefore invited Alcuin to become his minister of education. Upon accepting the offer in 782, Alcuin initiated a reform of the Frankish schools. He now became the guiding force behind Charlemagne's educational policies and the leading spirit of the palace school. Charlemagne rewarded Alcuin well for his services: he was granted the abbeys of Ferrières, Troyes, and St. Martin at Tours.

Alcuin popularized the study of the seven liberal arts in France and wrote elementary textbooks on these subjects. While these works do not demonstrate brillant philosophical insight, they do reflect the mind of a creative teacher. His dialogue method of instruction brought needed vitality to teaching; there was now more give and take between teacher and pupil. The emphasis on the elementary subjects of the *trivium* and *quadrivium* encouraged both secular and sacred learning—indeed, the schools themselves were opened to both clerics and laymen, for both church and state needed educated servants.

The knowledge of science imparted by the schools was restricted, and Alcuin's works show only a limited awareness of the physical world. In his *Disputation of the Royal and Most Noble Youth Pepin with Albinus, the Scholastic,* there is a very general discussion of man, the universe, and the natural world. This work is presented in the form of 101 questions, problems, and riddles, with symbolic answers. There are almost no natural or scientific answers; the explanations are in terms of effects rather than causes:

> Pepin: What is the sun?
> Albinus: The splendor of the universe, the beauty of the sky, the glory of the day, the divider of the hours.

Alcuin expressed some interest in astronomy, but it was an interest based on the need for an understanding of calendrical calculations. He helped to develop the Continental interest in the *computus,* and to aid the development of the skills needed to establish the date of Easter, he encouraged the study of mathematics.

In a work ascribed to him, *Propositions for Sharpening the Minds of Youth,* Alcuin presents fifty-three mathematical puzzles. While some can be solved through elaborate and ingenious calculations, many of them require geometrical and algebraic solutions. His encouragement of education was a valuable stimulant to the culture of Charlemagne's realm, and thus he left a lasting legacy to both the culture and the science of Europe.

BIBLIOGRAPHY

I. ORIGINAL WORKS. Alcuin's writings, both in verse and in prose, cover a wide range of subjects. They can be topically classified as educational texts, philosophical and theological treatises, historical works, and letters. Collected editions of his writings have been made by A. Quercetanus (Paris, 1617) and Frobenius Forster, *Alcuini opera* (Regensburg, 1777). The latter edition is reprinted in J. P. Migne, *Patrologia Latina,* C and CI; the letters are in W. Wattenbach and E. L. Duemmler, eds., *Monumenta Alcuiniana,* Vol. VI of Bibliotheca Rerum Germanicarum, P. Jaffe, ed. (Berlin, 1873).

II. SECONDARY LITERATURE. General surveys of Alcuin's life and accomplishments are in E. S. Duckett, *Alcuin, Friend of Charlemagne* (New York, 1951); C. J. B. Gaskoin, *Alcuin: His Life and Work* (London, 1904); A. Kleinclausz, *Alcuin* (Lyons, 1948); J. B. Laforet, *Alcuin restaurateur des sciences en Occident* (Louvain, 1851); Luitpold Wallach, *Alcuin and Charlemagne* (Ithaca, N.Y., 1959); and K. Werner, *Alcuin und sein Jahrhundert* (Paderborn, 1876).

PHILLIP DRENNON THOMAS

ALDER, KURT (*b.* Königshütte, Germany [now Chorzów, Poland], 10 July 1902; *d.* Cologne, Germany, 20 June 1958), *organic chemistry.*

Alder, the son of a schoolteacher in the heavily industrialized area around Kattowitz (now Katowice) in Upper Silesia, received his early education in the German schools of Königshütte. When the region became a part of the new Polish nation after the end of World War I, his family left in order to remain in Germany. After completing the Oberrealschule in Berlin, Alder studied chemistry at the University of Berlin and later at the University of Kiel, where he received the doctorate in 1926. His dissertation, "On the Causes of the Azoester Reaction," was carried out under the direction of Otto Diels. Alder continued his work at Kiel, being made a reader in organic chemistry in 1930 and extraordinary professor of chemistry in 1934. He became a research director at the Bayer Werke in Leverkusen, a branch of I. G. Farbenindustrie, in 1936. In 1940 he returned to academic life as ordinary professor of chemistry and director of the chemical institute at the University of Cologne, where he served until his death. In 1949–1950 he was dean of the Faculty of Philosophy. With Diels, he received the Nobel Prize for chemistry in 1950.

Alder's principal contributions to organic chemistry are associated with the diene synthesis, which grew out of his studies in Diels's laboratory and was first reported in 1928. The synthetic method, frequently referred to as the Diels-Alder reaction, involves the addition of dienes (compounds with conjugated unsaturation, i.e., double bonds on adjacent carbon atoms) to dienophiles (compounds having a double bond activated by nearby carbonyl or carboxyl groups). A simple example is the addition of butadiene to maleic anhydride:

Diene   Dienophile   Diels–Alder adduct

Although a few reactions of this type had been reported over a period of more than 30 years, Diels and Alder recognized the widespread and general nature of the reaction and subsequently spent much of their lives in developing the consequences. They called particular attention to the ease with which such reactions take place and the high yield of adduct.

Their earliest work involved the addition of cyclopentadiene (I) to *p*-quinone (II). The nature of the product (III) of this reaction was the subject of controversy from the time of its preparation by Walter Albrecht in 1893. Diels and Alder, utilizing the corresponding addition of cyclopentadiene to azoester

105

(IV), were able to identify the structure of Albrecht's compound correctly.

(It will be recalled that azoester had been the subject of Alder's doctoral dissertation.) The two investigators were able to show that, besides azoester and *p*-quinone, they could obtain a reaction of cyclopentadiene with the double bonds in maleic, citraconic, and itaconic acids. They also demonstrated that the adduct is always a six-membered ring, with the addition taking place between the double bond of the dienophile and the carbon atoms at the 1 and 4 positions in the diene.

At first in association with Diels, and then independently with his own students, Alder studied the general experimental conditions of the diene synthesis and the overall scope of the method for synthetic purposes. He was a particularly able stereochemist and showed that diene addition took place at double bonds with a *cis* configuration. In his Nobel Prize address he listed more than a dozen diene types of widely differing structures that had been shown to participate in the reaction. Similarly, he showed that the reaction was equally general with respect to dienophiles, provided the double bond was properly activated by nearby carbonyl, carboxyl, cyano, or nitro groups. Unsaturated compounds without such properly placed activating groups failed to participate in an addition reaction. Many of the compounds studied were prepared in Alder's laboratory for the first time. The Diels-Alder reaction also became useful in structural studies because it provided an analytical means for the detection of conjugated double bonds.

The bridged-ring compounds formed by the use of cyclic dienes were closely related to such naturally occurring terpenes as camphor and norcamphor. The diene synthesis stimulated the understanding of ter-

pene chemistry by providing a synthetic method for preparing such compounds. The ease with which such reactions took place suggested that the diene synthesis might occur in biosynthetic reactions in nature. This role in biosynthesis was also found relevant in connection with anthraquinone-type dyes and a compound that could substitute for vitamin K in stimulating blood coagulation.

The diene synthesis proved to have broad applicability, not only in laboratory syntheses but in commercial operations as well. Commercial products prepared by Diels-Alder reactions include dyes, drugs, insecticides (e.g., dieldrin, aldrin, chlordane), lubricating oils, drying oils, synthetic rubber, and plastics.

During his period of industrial research Alder was involved in the study of polymerization processes connected with the production of Buna-type synthetic rubbers by polymerization of butadiene with such suitable compounds as styrene.

In 1955 he joined seventeen other Nobel laureates in issuing a declaration requesting the nations of the world to renounce war.

BIBLIOGRAPHY

I. ORIGINAL WORKS. Most of Alder's papers were published in *Berichte der Deutschen chemischen Gesellschaft, Liebig's Annalen der Chemie,* and *Angewandte Chemie.* For a full bibliography, see Poggendorff. The original paper on the diene synthesis is in *Liebig's Annalen der Chemie,* **460** (1928), 98–122. Alder's Nobel Prize address, "Diensynthese und verwandte Reaktionstypen," appears in *Les Prix Nobel in 1950* (Stockholm, 1951), pp. 157–194. An English translation is available in the Nobel Foundation's *Nobel Lectures Including Presentation Speeches and Laureates' Biographies, Chemistry, 1942–1962* (Amsterdam, 1964), pp. 266–303. His two main works are "Die Methoden der Diensynthese," in *Handbuch der biologischen Arbeitsmethoden,* sec. 1, II, pt. 2 (1933); and *Neuere Methoden der präparativen organischen Chemie* (Berlin, 1944).

II. SECONDARY LITERATURE. There is no lengthy biography of Alder. Short sketches are Eduard Farber, *Nobel Prize Winners in Chemistry* (New York, 1953), pp. 205–207; M. Günzl-Schumacher, in *Chemikerzeitung,* **82** (1958), 489–490; H. Hauptman, in *Boletim da Associação química do Brasil,* **9** (1951), 1–6; M. Lora-Tamayo, in *Revista de ciencia aplicada* (Madrid), **14** (1960), 193–205; *McGraw-Hill Encyclopedia of Science and Technology* (New York, 1966), I, 6–7; *Les Prix Nobel in 1950* (Stockholm, 1951), pp. 117–118; and *Nobel Lectures Including Presentation Speeches and Laureates' Biographies, Chemistry, 1942–1962* (Amsterdam, 1964), pp. 304–305.

AARON J. IHDE

ALDEROTTI

ALDEROTTI, TADDEO, also known as **Thaddaeus Florentinus** (*b.* Florence, Italy, 1223; *d.* Bologna, Italy, *ca.* 1295), *medicine.*

Biographical information about Alderotti is for the most part based on references to himself in his writings. From these it is known that he was born and brought up in extreme poverty and was an adult before he began his education. Once started on his studies at Bologna, however, he made rapid progress, and within a few years (*ca.* 1260) he was teaching at the university. Indeed, he was one of the founders of medical study at Bologna and was held in such esteem in the city that he was accorded citizenship in 1289.

Alderotti's commentaries on various classical and Islamic writers established the dialectical method of teaching in the medical school, a method that was used until the sixteenth century. He also developed a new form of medical literature, the *Consilia,* a collection of clinical cases with advice on how to treat them. Besides being a teacher of medicine, Alderotti was a well-known and successful practitioner; Pope Honorius IV was one of his patients. The extent of his reputation is attested to by the fact that he is mentioned by Dante in *Paradiso,* XII, 83. He also had a reputation for charging very high fees. His pupils included such persons as Bartolomeo da Varignana, Henri de Mondeville, and Mondino dei Luzzi.

In his commentaries on the works of Hippocrates, Galen, Hunayn ibn Isḥāq, Avicenna, and others, Alderotti utilized the translations of Burgundio of Pisa in preference to those of Constantine the African. He is unique in that he urged his readers to read the original as well as his commentary. At the same time he encouraged more and better translations of classical and Arabic works.

BIBLIOGRAPHY

I. ORIGINAL WORKS. In spite of Alderotti's influence, his *Consilia* was not published until the twentieth century (Turin, 1937, G. M. Nardil, ed.). Other works include *In Claudii Galeni artem parvam commentarii* (Naples, 1522); *Expositiones in arduum aphorismorum Hippocratis volumen, in divinum prognosticorum Hippocratis volumen, in praeclarum regiminis acutorum Hippocratis opus, in subtilissimum Joanniti Isagogarum libellum* (Venice, 1527). His treatise *Sulla conservazione della salute* is one of the oldest medical texts in Italian, although it was not published until the nineteenth century, G. Manuzzi and L. Razzolini, eds. (Florence, 1863). A Latin version, *De conservatione sanitatis,* was published much earlier (Bologna, 1477).

II. SECONDARY LITERATURE. Much of the information about Alderotti was brought together by George Sarton, *Introduction to the History of Science,* II (Baltimore, 1927–1948), 1086–1087. There have been additions and corrections, however, and these have been incorporated in this article. See also Lynn Thorndike, *A History of Magic and Experimental Science,* III (New York, 1923–1958), 14; and "Further Incipits," in *Speculum,* **26** (1951), 675. For a bibliography that gives some of the most recent Italian scholarship, see L. Belloni and L. Vergnano, "Alderotti," in *Enciclopedia Italiana,* II (Rome, 1960), 85. Further information can be found in H. Adelmann, *Marcello Malpighi and the Evolution of Embryology,* I (Ithaca, N. Y., 1966), 76–78.

VERN L. BULLOUGH

ALDINI

ALDINI, GIOVANNI (*b.* Bologna, Italy, 10 April 1762; *d.* Milan, Italy, 17 January 1834), *physics.*

The most significant single event in the history of the development of electricity was the discovery by Alessandro Volta in 1797 of the continuous-flow electric current from a voltaic pile. Next in importance to Volta stood Luigi Galvani, the uncle of Giovanni Aldini.

In the controversy over Galvani's "animal electricity" and Volta's "galvanic current," it was not the modest Galvani but his lusty nephew who wrote, lectured, and published in Italian, French, and English on the theories and experiments of both his uncle and himself. Aldini added notes and a commentary to the second edition of Galvani's important *De viribus electricitatis in motu musculari* (1792). An ardent partisan of his uncle's cause, he followed this supplement with *De animale electricitate, dissertatione duae* (1794) and his best-known work, *Essai théorique et expérimentale sur le galvanisme* (1804). This appeared in two volumes and also, in the same year, as a single quarto volume dedicated to Napoleon. The *Dissertatione duae* resulted from Aldini's galvanic experiments, including those on warm-blooded animals, and generally followed suggestions made by Galvani. A paper on the results of these experiments was read before the Accademia delle Scienze di Bologna; an English translation appeared in 1803 and a French one in 1804.

While Galvani (with one exception) remained silent during the growing controversy over the true nature of his animal electricity, the effervescent Aldini became his uncle's champion—so much so that Volta addressed his arguments to Aldini instead of Galvani. Aldini also probably joined Galvani in the preparation of the anonymous *Dell'uso e dell'attività dell'arco conduttore* (1794). This contained an important experiment, intended to demonstrate the contraction of a dissected frog's leg without the use of any metal, that established the existence of electrical forces within living tissue. Early in 1803 he attempted to determine the velocity of an electric current across the harbor of Calais.

Aldini became professor of physics at the University of Bologna in 1794 and earnestly investigated galvanism. He helped organize a society at Bologna to foster the practices of galvanism in opposition to a Volta society established at the University of Pavia. In 1802 Aldini lectured before the Société Galvanique of Paris and in the following year demonstrated galvanic action in England. Some of his more dramatic experiments involved motion in the anatomical members of a just-executed murderer and induced muscular contraction in dissected parts of sheep, oxen, and chickens. His final writings concerned lighthouses, fire fighting, and quarrying. For his work he was knighted by the emperor of Austria and made councillor of state in Milan.

BIBLIOGRAPHY

Aldini's first known writing is his contribution of notes and a commentary to the second edition of Galvani's *De viribus electricitatis in motu musculari* (Modena, 1792). He and Galvani probably prepared the anonymous *Dell'uso e dell'attività dell'arco conduttore* (Bologna, 1794). Other works by Aldini are *De animale electricitate, dissertatione duae* (Bologna, 1794) and *Essai théorique et expérimentale sur le galvanisme* (Paris, 1804).

BERN DIBNER

ALDROVANDI, ULISSE (*b.* Bologna, Italy, 11 September 1522; *d.* Bologna, May 1605), *natural sciences.*

Aldrovandi is a typical representative of those "universal" and multifaceted minds which seem to have been characteristic of the Renaissance. He was the son of a nobleman, Teseo Aldrovandi, a notary who served as secretary of the Senate of Bologna, and of Veronica Marescalchi, also of a noble family. His mother was a first cousin of Pope Gregory XIII, a circumstance that was helpful to Aldrovandi later in his life, for Bologna was then a papal state.

As a young man, Aldrovandi first studied mathematics under Annibale della Nave, a famous mathematician of the period. Restless by nature and eager to see new things, new countries, and new people, he ran away from home on several occasions. During one of these escapades he went as far as Spain.

After the voyage to Spain, which had been replete with adventures and perils, Aldrovandi returned to Bologna, where he enthusiastically studied Latin under Giovanni Gandolfo, one of the most distinguished humanists of the period.

Aldrovandi's mother, now a widow, wanted him to become a jurist, and he readily applied himself to studying law. Within seven years he was on the verge of receiving his degree, which would have qualified him to practice law, but instead of completing the work he dedicated himself to philosophy. After having studied under the best philosophers of Bologna, he decided, about 1545, to go to Padua to complete his preparation there. This decision had a major influence on his life, for at Padua he began to study medicine and, with the aid of Pietro Catena, again took up mathematics.

On his return to Bologna, Aldrovandi and some of his friends were charged with heresy, probably because at that time the University of Padua was reputed to be one of the main centers for the teaching of Averroës' doctrines. He was obliged to go to Rome to exonerate himself, and there, after proving his innocence, he became interested in the archaeological discoveries in which the city abounded. Later he collected his observations in a book, but perhaps more important, at Rome he met Guillaume Rondelet, who was there as the personal physician of Cardinal Tournon.

Rondelet was then gathering material for his work on fishes. Aldrovandi, who accompanied the French physician to fish markets in order to study the various species, finally decided to study natural history, and began collecting specimens for his own museum.

Upon his return to Bologna, Aldrovandi met Luca Ghini, who then held the professorship of pharmaceutical botany at the university. When Ghini moved to Pisa, Aldrovandi followed him in order to attend his lectures.

The need to earn his living obliged Aldrovandi to take his medical degree, which he received on 23 November 1553. On 14 December, at a solemn ceremony, he was admitted to the Collegio dei Dottori of Bologna, a membership that entitled him not only to practice medicine but also to teach in the university. Thanks to the support given him by an uncle who was a senator, he was also appointed a teacher of "logic" in the University of Bologna. Teaching, however, was merely an easy way of earning an income that would enable him to devote himself entirely to the study of the natural sciences. During vacation periods, Aldrovandi went on long trips, to study nature firsthand and to enrich his knowledge and collections. In 1551 he went as far as Monte Baldo, which he climbed with Luigi dell'Anguillara and Luigi Alpago, who were well-known botanists of the period. In later years he was frequently accompanied on these expeditions by his pupils, who went with him to study botany and to collect samples of fossils and minerals to enrich his "museum" with specimens from every part of Italy.

As a direct result of his intense scientific activity, the Senate appointed Aldrovandi professor of the history of "simples" (which study Aldrovandi had extended to embrace what would now be called natural sciences, including animals and minerals, as well as plants, whether they were of medicinal value or not). His appointment to this professorship was important for the development of natural history, for until then, lectures had been confined to the concise illustration of some single specimen of medicinal value. He was so successful in arousing a lively interest in the more systematic study of natural science, however, that his lectures were attended by an increasing number of students. At the request of the students themselves, the chair was finally declared a full professorship on 11 February 1561.

In the wake of his first success, Aldrovandi, after long and bitter battles, also established at Bologna a botanical garden, of which he was named curator. This new appointment aroused further opposition and envy, and shortly afterward new quarrels arose when he was assigned the task of preparing an *Antidotario,* an official pharmacopoeia. It was to be authoritative in the state of Bologna and would fix the exact characteristics of the drugs and medicinal substances that druggists would be required to use in filling prescriptions.

The variety of tasks, the public and semipublic positions he held, and the conflicts and disputes (which his somewhat obstinate character served only to embitter) were responsible for Aldrovandi's recurrent disagreements with his colleagues on the medical faculty of Bologna. They did not, however, seriously interfere with his truly prodigious studies in natural history. Aldrovandi also had the support of Pope Gregory XIII, who granted him, as a token of his benevolence and esteem, a large sum of money to aid him in the publication of his works.

At his death, Aldrovandi bequeathed to the city of Bologna his museum, his library, and the manuscripts of his unpublished works. During his life he had been able to publish only four folio volumes, illustrated with beautiful copperplates; other volumes were published after his death. His manuscripts are preserved in the libraries of Bologna.

Aldrovandi carried out studies in several fields of natural history: botany, teratology, embryology, icthyology, and ornithology. He has been criticized for having included in his works information and legends devoid of any scientific basis—material that he derived largely from the works of Pliny and that would have been better confined to a medieval bestiary than included in scholarly works.

The period in which Aldrovandi lived and studied was one of transition, however. Science was then being born through the labors of men who, like Aldrovandi, wrote of distant lands but were still obliged to base their accounts almost entirely on secondhand information, gleaned from texts and accounts of travelers. Very often the authors of these accounts were not men of science, but merchants and adventurers whose chief interests had nothing in common with science.

On the other hand, science assumes the existence of a critical, experimental mind, which the men of the Renaissance (Aldrovandi among them) were striving to achieve; it also assumes the inheritance of knowledge, already critically evaluated and classified, with which to compare and test new knowledge as it is acquired. It would therefore be mistaken to ridicule the minute descriptions that Aldrovandi gives us of the sirens, or of other fabulous animals and things.

In embryology, Aldrovandi was able to carry out, within certain limitations, studies in which he excelled and which influenced the work of Volcher Coiter, the Flemish scientist considered one of the founders of embryology. He and Coiter were the first to examine, as Aristotle had suggested, the development of the chick in the egg day by day, opening the eggs successively on each day of the incubation period, in order to describe minutely the changes that take place in the embryo. By this method it became possible for him to show that the heart of the embryo is formed in the "sacco vitellino" and not in the albumen, as other writers had maintained. He also showed that, just as Aristotle had correctly stated, the formation of the heart in the embryo precedes that of the liver, which Galen had incorrectly stated as taking place at the start of the embryonic development.

Aldrovandi also deserves credit for having carried out, in this area of studies, keen observations of a teratological nature, tracing the cause of the morphological changes of the chick to corresponding chemicophysical changes in the substance of the egg yolk.

Even if, from a practical viewpoint, his work and his observations did not contribute greatly to the progress of embryology, they unquestionably had the merit of recalling to the attention of scholars the method of direct observation of natural phenomena. Aldrovandi's studies in this field paved the way for work along the same lines by Fabrizio (Fabricius ab Aquapendente), Malpighi, and Harvey.

Although he did not practice medicine, Aldrovandi's efforts to place botany and pharmacology on a scientific plane and the lucidness and modernity of the legislation he suggested for public health and the civic sanitation of Bologna (found in his unpublished works) suggest that he was a pioneer in hygiene and pharmacology.

Although Aldrovandi is not identified with any revolutionary discoveries, his work as a teacher and as the author of volumes that constitute an irreplaceable cultural patrimony earns him a place among the fathers of modern science. Perhaps most importantly, he was among the first to attempt to free the natural sciences from the stifling influence of the authority of textbooks, for which he substituted, as far as possible, direct study and observation of the animal, vegetable, and mineral worlds.

BIBLIOGRAPHY

I. ORIGINAL WORKS. Works by Aldrovandi, all published at Bologna and all in folio, are *Ornithologiae, hoc est, de avibus historiae libri XII. Agunt de avibus rapacibus* (1600); *Ornithologiae tomus alter de avibus terrestribus, mensae inservientibus et canoris* (1600); *De animalibus insectis libri VII* (1602); *Ornithologiae tomus tertius et ultimus de avibus aquaticis et circa quas degentibus* (1603); *De reliquis animalibus exanguibus, utpote de mollibus, crustaceis, testaceis et zoophytis, libri IV* (1606); *Quadrupedum omnium bisulcorum historia* (1613); *De piscibus libri V et de cetis liber unus* (1613); *De quadrupedibus digitatis viviparis libri III, et de quadrupedibus oviparis libri II* (1637); *Historiae serpentum et draconum libri duo* (1640); *Monstruorum historia* (1642); *Museum metallicum* (1648); and *Dendrologiae naturalis, scilicet arborum historiae libri duo* (1668).

II. SECONDARY LITERATURE. Works on Aldrovandi are H. B. Adelmann, *Marcello Malpighi and the Evolution of Embryology* (Ithaca, N.Y., 1966), for Aldrovandi's contributions to the advancement of embryology; G. Fantuzzi, *Memorie sulla vita e sulle opere di U. Aldrovandi* (Bologna, 1774); L. Frati, *Catalogo dei manoscritti di Ulisse Aldrovandi* (Bologna, 1907); "La vita di U. Aldrovandi," in *Intorno alla vita e alle opere di U. Aldrovandi* (Bologna, 1907); and *La vita di U. Aldrovandi scritta da lui medesimo* (Imola, 1907); L. Samoggia, *Ulisse Aldrovandi medico e igienista* (Bologna, 1962), containing an extensive and up-to-date bibliography of Aldrovandi's manuscripts; and A. Sorbelli, "Contributi alla bibliografia delle opere di Ulisse Aldrovandi," in *Intorno alla vita e alle opere di Ulisse Aldrovandi* (Bologna, 1907), which lists the published works of Aldrovandi and gives information on the various editions.

CARLO CASTELLANI

ALEMBERT, JEAN LE ROND D' (*b.* Paris, France, 17 November 1717; *d.* Paris, 29 October 1783), *physics, mathematics.*

Jean Le Rond d'Alembert was the illegitimate child of Madame de Tencin, a famous salon hostess of the eighteenth century, and the Chevalier Destouches-Canon, a cavalry officer. His mother, who had renounced her nun's vows, abandoned him, for she feared being returned to a convent. His father, however, located the baby and found him a home with a humble artisan named Rousseau and his wife. D'Alembert lived with them until he was forty-seven years old. Destouches-Canon also saw to the education of the child. D'Alembert attended the Collège de Quatre-Nations (sometimes called after Mazarin, its founder), a Jansenist school offering a curriculum in the classics and rhetoric—and also offering more than the average amount of mathematics. In spite of the efforts of his teachers, he turned against a religious career and began studies of law and medicine before he finally embarked on a career as a mathematician. In the 1740's he became part of the *philosophes,* thus joining in the rising tide of criticism of the social and intellectual standards of the day. D'Alembert published many works on mathematics and mathematical physics, and was the scientific editor of the *Encyclopédie.*

D'Alembert never married, although he lived for a number of years with Julie de Lespinasse, the one love of his life. A slight man with an expressive face, a high-pitched voice, and a talent for mimicry, he was known for his wit, gaiety, and gift for conversation, although later in life he became bitter and morose. D'Alembert spent his time much as the other *philosophes* did: working during the morning and afternoon and spending the evening in the salons, particularly those of Mme. du Deffand and Mlle. de Lespinasse. He seldom traveled, leaving the country only once, for a visit to the court of Frederick the Great. D'Alembert was a member of the Académie des Sciences, the Académie Française, and most of the other scientific academies of Europe. He is best known for his work in mathematics and rational mechanics, and for his association with the *Encyclopédie.*

D'Alembert appeared on the scientific scene in July 1739, when he sent his first communication to the Académie des Sciences. It was a critique of a mathematical text by Father Charles Reyneau. During the next two years he sent the academy five more *mémoires* dealing with methods of integrating differential equations and with the motion of bodies in resisting media. Although d'Alembert had received almost no formal scientific training (at school he had studied Varignon's work), it is clear that on his own he had become familiar not only with Newton's work, but also with that of L'Hospital, the Bernoullis, and the other mathematicians of his day. His communications to the academy were answered by Clairaut, who although only four years older than d'Alembert was already a member.

After several attempts to join the academy, d'Alembert was finally successful. He was made *adjoint* in astronomy in May 1741, and received the title of *associé géometre* in 1746. From 1741 through 1743 he worked on various problems in rational mechanics and in the latter year published his famous *Traité de dynamique.* He published rather hastily (a pattern he was to follow all of his life) in order to forestall the loss of priority; Clairaut was working along similar lines. His rivalry with Clairaut, which continued until Clairaut's death, was only one of several in which he was involved over the years.

The *Traité de dynamique,* which has become the most famous of his scientific works, is significant in many ways. First, it is clear that d'Alembert recognized that a scientific revolution had occurred, and he thought that he was doing the job of formalizing the new science of mechanics. That accomplishment is often attributed to Newton, but in fact it was done over a long period of time by a number of men. If d'Alembert was overly proud of his share, he was at least clearly aware of what was happening in science. The *Traité* also contained the first statement of what is now known as d'Alembert's principle. D'Alembert was, furthermore, in the tradition that attempted to develop mechanics without using the notion of force. Finally, it was long afterward said (rather simplistically) that in this work he resolved the famous *vis viva* controversy, a statement with just enough truth in it to be plausible. In terms of his own development, it can be said that he set the style he was to follow for the rest of his life.

As was customary at the time, d'Alembert opened his book with a lengthy philosophical preface. It is true that he was not always faithful to the principles he set down in the preface, but it is astonishing that he could carry his arguments as far as he did and remain faithful to them. D'Alembert fully accepted the prevailing epistemology of sensationalism. Taken from John Locke and expanded by such men as Condillac, sensationalism was to be d'Alembert's metaphysical basis of science. The main tenet of this epistemology was that all knowledge was derived, not from innate ideas, but from sense perception. In many ways, however, d'Alembert remained Cartesian. The criterion of the truth, for example, was still the clear and simple idea, although that idea now had a

different origin. In science, therefore, the basic concepts had to conform to this ideal.

In developing his philosophy of mechanics, d'Alembert analyzed the ideas available to him until he came to those that could be analyzed no further; these were to be his starting points. Space and time were such. So simple and clear that they could not even be defined, they were the only fundamental ideas he could locate. Motion was a combination of the ideas of space and time, and so a definition of it was necessary. The word "force" was so unclear and confusing that it was rejected as a conceptual building block of mechanics and was used merely as a convenient shorthand when it was properly and arbitrarily defined. D'Alembert defined matter as impenetrable extension, which took account of the fact that two objects could not pass through one another. The concept of mass, which he defined, as Newton had done, as quantity of matter, had to be smuggled into the treatise in a mathematical sense later on.

In the first part of the *Traité,* d'Alembert developed his own three laws of motion. It should be remembered that Newton had stated his laws verbally in the *Principia,* and that expressing them in algebraic form was a task taken up by the mathematicians of the eighteenth century. D'Alembert's first law was, as Newton's had been, the law of inertia. D'Alembert, however, tried to give an a priori proof for the law, indicating that however sensationalistic his thought might be he still clung to the notion that the mind could arrive at truth by its own processes. His proof was based on the simple ideas of space and time; and the reasoning was geometric, not physical, in nature. His second law, also proved as a problem in geometry, was that of the parallelogram of motion. It was not until he arrived at the third law that physical assumptions were involved.

The third law dealt with equilibrium, and amounted to the principle of the conservation of momentum in impact situations. In fact, d'Alembert was inclined to reduce every mechanical situation to one of impact rather than resort to the effects of continual forces; this again showed an inheritance from Descartes. D'Alembert's proof rested on the clear and simple case of two equal masses approaching each other with equal but opposite speeds. They will clearly balance one another, he declared, for there is no reason why one should overcome the other. Other impact situations were reduced to this one; in cases where the masses or velocities were unequal, the object with the greater quantity of motion (defined as mv) would prevail. In fact, d'Alembert's mathematical definition of mass was introduced implicitly here; he actually assumed the conservation of momentum and defined mass accordingly. This fact was what made his work a mathematical physics rather than simply mathematics.

The principle that bears d'Alembert's name was introduced in the next part of the *Traité*. It was not so much a principle as it was a rule for using the previously stated laws of motion. It can be summarized as follows: In any situation where an object is constrained from following its normal inertial motion, the resulting motion can be analyzed into two components. One of these is the motion the object actually takes, and the other is the motion "destroyed" by the constraints. The lost motion is balanced against either a fictional force or a motion lost by the constraining object. The latter case is the case of impact, and the result is the conservation of momentum (in some cases, the conservation of *vis viva* as well). In the former case, an infinite force must be assumed. Such, for example, would be the case of an object on an inclined plane. The normal motion would be vertically downward; this motion can be resolved into two others. One would be a component down the plane (the motion actually taken) and the other would be normal to the surface of the plane (the motion destroyed by the infinite resisting force of the plane). Then one can easily describe the situation (in this case, a trivial problem).

It is clear that the use of d'Alembert's principle requires some knowledge beyond that of his laws. One must have the conditions of constraint, or the law of falling bodies, or some information derived either empirically or hypothetically about the particular situation. It was for this reason that Ernst Mach could refer to d'Alembert's principle as a routine form for the solution of problems, and not a principle at all. D'Alembert's principle actually rests on his assumptions of what constitutes equilibrium, and it is in his third law of motion that those assumptions appear. Indeed, in discussing his third law (in the second edition of his book, published in 1758) d'Alembert arrived at the equation $\phi = dv/dt$, which is similar to the standard expression for Newton's second law, but which lacks the crucial parameter of mass. The function ϕ was to contain the parameters for specific problems. For example (and this is d'Alembert's example), should the assumption be made that a given deceleration is proportional to the square of the velocity of an object, then the equation becomes $-gv^2 = dv/dt$. The minus sign indicates deceleration, and the constant g packs in the other factors involved, such as mass. In this fashion d'Alembert was able to avoid dealing with forces.

It has often been said that d'Alembert settled the *vis viva* controversy in this treatise, but such a view must be qualified. In the preface d'Alembert did discuss the issue, pointing out that in a given deceleration the change in velocity was proportional to the time. One could therefore define force in terms of the velocity of an object. On the other hand, if one were concerned with the number of "obstacles" that had to be overcome to stop a moving body (here he probably had in mind Gravesande's experiments with objects stopped by springs), then it was clear that such a definition of force depended on the square of the velocity and that the related metric was distance, not time. D'Alembert pointed out that these were two different ways of looking at the same problem, that both methods worked and were used with success by different scientists. To use the word "force" to describe either mv or mv^2 was therefore a quarrel of words; the metaphysical notion of force as a universal causal agent was not clarified by such an argument. In this way d'Alembert solved the controversy by declaring it a false one. It involved convention, not reality, for universal causes (the metaphysical meaning of the idea of force) were not known, and possibly not even knowable. It was for this reason that d'Alembert refused to entertain the possibility of talking of forces in mechanics. He did not throw the word away, but used it only when he could give it what today would be called an operational definition. He simply refused to give the notion of force any metaphysical validity and, thus, any ontological reality.

In this way d'Alembert was clearly a precursor of positivistic science. He employed mathematical abstractions and hypothetical or idealized models of physical phenomena and was careful to indicate the shortcomings of his results when they did not closely match the actual events of the world. The metaphysician, he warned in a later treatise, too often built systems that might or might not reflect reality, while the mathematician too often trusted his calculations, thinking they represented the whole truth. But just as metaphysics was suspect because of its unjustified claim to knowledge, so mathematics was suspect in its similar claim. Not everything could be reduced to calculation.

> Geometry owes its certainty to the simplicity of the things it deals with; as the phenomena become more complicated, the results become less certain. It is necessary to know when to stop, when one is ignorant of the thing being studied, and one must not believe that the words *theorem* and *corollary* have some secret virtue so that by writing QED at the end of a proposition one proves something that is not true   [*Essai d'une nouvelle théorie de la résistance des fluides,* pp. xlii–xliii].

D'Alembert's instincts were good. Unfortunately, in this case they diverted him from the path that was eventually to produce the principle of the conservation of energy.

A major question that beset all philosophers of the Enlightenment was that of the nature of matter. While d'Alembert's primary concern was mathematical physics, his epistemology of sensationalism led him to speculate on matter theory. Here again, he was frustrated, repeating time after time that we simply do not know what matter is like in its essence. He tended to accept the corpuscular theory of matter, and in Newton's style; that is, he conceived of the ideal atom as perfectly hard. Since this kind of atom could not show the characteristic of elasticity, much less of other chemical or physical phenomena, he was sorely perplexed. In his *Traité de dynamique,* however, he evolved a model of the atom as a hard particle connected to its neighbors by springs. In this way, he could explain elasticity, but he never confused the model with reality. Possibly he sensed that his model actually begged the question, for the springs became more important that the atom itself, and resembled nothing more than a clumsy ether, the carrier of an active principle. Instead of belaboring the point, however, d'Alembert soon returned to mathematical abstraction, where one dealt with functional relations and did not have to agonize over ontology.

In 1744 d'Alembert published a companion volume to his first work, the *Traité de l'équilibre et du mouvement des fluides.* In this work d'Alembert used his principle to describe fluid motion, treating the major problems of fluid mechanics that were current. The sources of his interest in fluids were many. First, Newton had attempted a treatment of fluid motion in his *Principia,* primarily to refute Descartes's *tourbillon* theory of planetary motion. Second, there was a lively interest in fluids by the experimental physicists in the eighteenth century, for fluids were most frequently invoked to give physical explanations for a variety of phenomena, such as electricity, magnetism, and heat. There was also the problem of the shape of the earth: What shape would it be expected to take if it were thought of as a rotating fluid body? Clairaut published a work in 1744 which treated the earth as such, a treatise that was a landmark in fluid mechanics. Furthermore, the *vis viva* controversy was often centered on fluid flow, since the quantity of *vis viva* was used almost exclusively by the Bernoullis in their work on such problems. Finally, of course, there was the inherent interest in fluids themselves. D'Alembert's first treatise had been devoted to the study of rigid bodies; now he was giving attention to the other class of matter, the fluids. He was actually giving an alternative treatment to one already published by Daniel Bernoulli, and he commented that both he and Bernoulli usually arrived at the same conclusions. He felt that his own method was superior. Bernoulli did not agree.

In 1747 d'Alembert published two more important works, one of which, the *Réflexions sur la cause générale des vents,* won a prize from the Prussian Academy. In it appeared the first general use of partial differential equations in mathematical physics. Euler later perfected the techniques of using these equations. The pattern was to become a familiar one: d'Alembert, Daniel Bernoulli, or Clairaut would pioneer a technique, and Euler would take it far beyond their capacity to develop it. D'Alembert's treatise on winds was the only one of his works honored by a prize and, ironically, was later shown to be based on insufficient assumptions. D'Alembert assumed that wind patterns were the result of tidal effects on the atmosphere, and he relegated the influence of heat to a minor role, one that caused only local variations from the general circulation. Still, as a work on atmospheric tides it was successful, and Lagrange continued to praise d'Alembert's efforts many years later.

D'Alembert's other important publication of 1747 was an article in the *Mémoirs* of the Prussian Academy dealing with the motion of vibrating strings, another problem that taxed the minds of the major mathematicians of the day. Here the wave equation made its first appearance in physics. D'Alembert's mathematical instincts led him to simplify the boundary conditions, however, to the point where his solution, while correct, did not match well the observed phenomenon. Euler subsequently treated the same problem more generally; and although he was no more correct than d'Alembert, his work was more useful.

During the late 1740's, d'Alembert, Clairaut, and Euler were all working on the famous three-body problem, with varying success. D'Alembert's interest in celestial mechanics thus led him, in 1749, to publish a masterly work, the *Recherches sur la précession des équinoxes et sur la nutation de la terre.* The precession of the equinoxes, a problem previously attacked by Clairaut, was very difficult. D'Alembert's method was similar to Clairaut's, but he employed more terms in his integration of the equation of motion and arrived at a solution more in accord with the observed motion of the earth. He was rightly proud of his book.

D'Alembert then applied himself to further studies in fluid mechanics, entering a competition announced by the Prussian Academy. He was not awarded the prize; indeed, it was not given to anybody. The

Prussian Academy took this action on the ground that nobody had submitted experimental proof of the theoretical work. There has been considerable dispute over this action. The claim has been made that d'Alembert's work, although the best entered, was marred by many errors. D'Alembert himself viewed his denial as the result of Euler's influence, and the relations between the two men deteriorated further. Whatever the case, the disgruntled d'Alembert published his work in 1752 as the *Essai d'une nouvelle théorie de la résistance des fluides.* It was in this essay that the differential hydrodynamic equations were first expressed in terms of a field and the hydrodynamic paradox was put forth.

In studying the flow lines of a fluid around an object (in this case, an elliptical object), d'Alembert could find no reason for assuming that the flow pattern was any different behind the object than in front of it. This implied that whatever the forces exerted on the front of the object might be, they would be counteracted by similar forces on the back, and the result would be no resistance to the flow whatever. The paradox was left for his readers to solve. D'Alembert had other difficulties as well. He found himself forced to assume, in order to avoid the necessity of allowing an instantaneous change in the velocity of parts of the fluid moving around the object, that a small portion of the fluid remained stagnant in front of the object, an assumption required to prevent breaking the law of continuity.

In spite of these problems, the essay was an important contribution. Hunter Rouse and Simon Ince have said that d'Alembert was the first "to introduce such concepts as the components of fluid velocity and acceleration, the differential requirements of continuity, and even the complex numbers essential to modern analysis of the same problem." Clifford Truesdell, on the other hand, thinks that most of the credit for the development of fluid mechanics must be granted to Euler; thus historians have continued the disputes that originated among the scientists themselves. But it is often difficult to tell where the original idea came from and who should receive primary recognition. It is certain, however, that d'Alembert, Clairaut, Bernoulli, and Euler were all active in pursuing these problems, all influenced one another, and all deserve to be remembered, although Euler was no doubt the most able of the group. But they all sought claims to priority, and they guarded their claims with passion.

D'Alembert wrote one other scientific work in the 1750's, the *Recherches sur différens points importants du systême du monde.* It appeared in three volumes, two of them published in 1754 and the third in 1756.

Devoted primarily to the motion of the moon (Volume III included a new set of lunar tables), it was written at least partially to guard d'Alembert's claims to originality against those of Clairaut. As was so often the case, d'Alembert's method was mathematically more sound, but Clairaut's method was more easily used by astronomers.

The 1750's were more noteworthy in d'Alembert's life for the development of interests outside the realm of mathematics and physics. Those interests came as a result of his involvement with the *Encyclopédie.* Denis Diderot was the principal editor of the enterprise, and d'Alembert was chosen as the science editor. His efforts did not remain limited to purely scientific concerns, however. His first literary task was that of writing the *Discours préliminaire* of the *Encyclopédie,* a task that he accomplished with such success that its publication was largely the reason for his acceptance into the Académie Française in 1754.

The *Discours préliminaire,* written in two parts, has rightly been recognized as a cardinal document of the Enlightenment. The first part is devoted to the work as an *encyclopédie,* that is, as a collection of the knowledge of mankind. The second part is devoted to the work as a *dictionnaire raisonnée,* or critical dictionary. Actually, the first part is an exposition of the epistemology of sensationalism, and owes a great deal to both John Locke and Condillac. All kinds of human knowledge are discussed, from scientific to moral. The sciences are to be based on physical perception, and morality is to be based on the perception of those emotions, feelings, and inclinations that men can sense within themselves. Although d'Alembert gives lip service to the truths of religion, they are clearly irrelevant and are acknowledged only for the sake of the censors. For this reason, the *Discours préliminaire* came under frequent attack; nevertheless, it was generally well received and applauded. It formed, so to say, the manifesto of the now coalescing party of *philosophes;* the body of the *Encyclopédie* was to be the expression of their program.

The second part of the *Discours préliminaire* is in fact a history of science and philosophy, and clearly shows the penchant of the *philosophes* for the notion of progress through the increased use of reason. As a history, it has often quite properly been attacked for its extreme bias against the medieval period and any form of thought developed within the framework of theology, but this bias was, of course, intentional. At the end of this history, the *philosophes*' debt to Francis Bacon is clearly acknowledged in the outline of the organization of knowledge. A modified version of Bacon's tree of knowledge is included and briefly explained. All knowledge is related to three functions of the mind: memory, reason, and imagination. Reason is clearly the most important of the three. Bacon's emphasis on utility was also reflected in the *Encyclopédie,* although more by Diderot than by d'Alembert. D'Alembert's concept of utility was far wider than that of most people. To him, the things used by philosophers—even mathematical equations—were very useful, even though the bulk of the public might find them mysterious and esoteric.

In the midst of this activity, d'Alembert found time to write a book on what must be called a psychophysical subject, that of music. In 1752 he published his *Élémens de musique théorique et pratique suivant les principes de M. Rameau.* This work has often been neglected by historians, save those of music, for it was not particularly mathematical and acted as a popularization of Rameau's new scheme of musical structure. Yet it was more than simply a popularization. Music was still emerging from the mixture of Pythagorean numerical mysticism and theological principles that had marked its rationale during the late medieval period. D'Alembert understood Rameau's innovations as a liberation; music could finally be given a secular rationale, and his work was important in spreading Rameau's ideas throughout Europe.

As time went on, d'Alembert's pen was increasingly devoted to nonscientific subjects. His articles in the *Encyclopédie* reached far beyond mathematics. He wrote and read many essays before the Académie Française; these began to appear in print as early as 1753. In that year he published two volumes of his *Mélanges de littérature et de philosophie.* The first two were reprinted along with two more in 1759; a fifth and last volume was published in 1767. The word *mélanges* was apt, for in these volumes were essays on music, law, and religion, his treatise on the *Élémens de philosophie,* translations of portions of Tacitus, and other assorted literary efforts. They make an odd mixture, for some are important in their exposition of Enlightenment ideals, while others are mere polemics or even trivial essays.

In 1757 d'Alembert visited Voltaire at Ferney, and an important result of the visit was the article on Geneva, which appeared in the seventh volume of the *Encyclopédie.* It was clearly an article meant to be propaganda, for the space devoted to the city was quite out of keeping with the general editorial policy. In essence, d'Alembert damned the city by praising it. The furor that resulted was the immediate cause of the suspension of the license for the *Encyclopédie.* D'Alembert resigned as an editor, convinced that the enterprise must founder, and left Diderot to finish the task by himself. Diderot thought that d'Alembert had deserted him, and the relations between the men became strained. Rousseau also attacked d'Alembert for his view that Geneva should allow a theater, thus touching off another of the famous controversies that showed that the *philosophes* were by no means a totally unified group of thinkers.

D'Alembert's chief scientific output after 1760 was his *Opuscules mathématiques,* eight volumes of which appeared from 1761 to 1780. These collections of mathematical essays were a mixed bag, ranging from theories of achromatic lenses to purely mathematical manipulations and theorems. Included were many new solutions to problems he had previously attacked—including a new proof of the law of inertia. Although the mathematical articles in the *Encyclopédie* had aired many of his notions, these volumes provide the closest thing to a collection of them that exists.

As Carl Boyer has pointed out, d'Alembert was almost alone in his day in regarding the differential as the limit of a function, the key concept around which the calculus was eventually rationalized. Unfortunately, d'Alembert could never escape the tradition that had made geometry preeminent among the sciences, and he was therefore unable to put the idea of the limit into purely algorithmic form. His concept of the limit did not seem to be any more clear to his contemporaries than other schemes invented to explain the nature of the differential.

It has often been said that d'Alembert was always primarily a mathematician and secondarily a physicist. This evaluation must be qualified. No doubt he sensed the power of mathematics. But, as he once said, "Mathematics owes its certainty to the simplicity of the things with which it deals." In other words, d'Alembert was never able to remove himself to a world of pure mathematics. He was rather in the tradition of Descartes. Space was the realization of geometry (although, unlike Descartes, d'Alembert drew his evidence from sense perception). It was for this reason that he could never reduce mathematics to pure algorithms, and it is also the reason for his concern about the law of continuity. In mathematics as well as physics, discontinuities seemed improper to d'Alembert; equations that had discontinuities in them gave solutions that he called "impossible," and he wasted no time on them. It was for this reason that the notion of perfectly hard matter was so difficult for him to comprehend, for two such particles colliding would necessarily undergo sudden changes in velocity, something he could not allow as possible.

It was probably the requirement of continuity that led d'Alembert to his idea of the limit, and it also led him to consider the techniques of handling series. In Volume V of the *Opuscules* he published a test for convergence that is still called d'Alembert's theorem. The mathematical statement is:

If $\lim\limits_{n\to\infty} |S_{n+1}/S_n| = r$, and $r < 1$, the series $\sum\limits_{n=1}^{\infty} S_n$ converges. If $r > 1$, the series diverges; if $r = 1$, the test fails.

But in spite of such original contributions to mathematical manipulation, d'Alembert's chief concern was in making this language not merely descriptive of the world, but congruent to it. The application of mathematics was a matter of considering physical situations, developing differential equations to express them, and then integrating those equations. Mathematical physicists had to invent much of their procedure as they went along. Thus, in the course of his work, d'Alembert was able to give the first formulation of the wave equation, to express the first partial differential equation, and to be the first to solve a partial differential equation by the technique of the separation of variables. But probably the assignment of "firsts" in this way is not the best manner of evaluating the development of mathematics or of mathematical physics. For every such first, one can find other men who had alternative suggestions or different ways of expressing themselves, and who often wrote down similar but less satisfactory expressions.

More important, possibly, is the way in which these ideas reflect the mathematicians' view of nature, a view that was changing and was then very different from that of a mathematical physicist today. D'Alembert's very language gives a clue. He used, for example, the word *fausse* to describe a divergent series. The word to him was not a bare descriptive term. There was no match, or no useful match, for divergence in the physical world. Convergence leads to the notion of the limit; divergence leads nowhere—or everywhere.

D'Alembert has often been cited as being oddly ineffective when he considered probability theory. Here again his view of nature, not his mathematical capabilities, blocked him. He considered, for example, a game of chance in which Pierre and Jacques take part. Pierre is to flip a coin. If heads turns up on the first toss, he is to pay Jacques one *écu*. If it does not turn up until the second toss, he is to pay two *écus*. If it does not turn up until the third toss, he is to pay four *écus,* and so on, the payments mounting in geometric progression. The problem is to determine how many *écus* Jacques should give to Pierre before the game begins in order that the two men have equal chances at breaking even. The solution seemed to be that since the probability on each toss was one-half,

and since the number of tosses was unlimited, then Jacques would have to give an infinite number of *écus* to Pierre before the game began, clearly a paradoxical situation.

D'Alembert rebelled against this solution, but had no satisfactory alternative. He considered the possibility of tossing tails one hundred times in a row. Metaphysically, he declared, one could imagine that such a thing could happen; but one could not realistically imagine it happening. He went further: heads, he declared, must *necessarily* arise after a finite number of tosses. In other words, any given toss is influenced by previous tosses, an assumption firmly denied by modern probability theory. D'Alembert also said that if the probability of an event were very small, it could be treated as nothing, and therefore would have no relevance to physical events. Jacques and Pierre could forget the mathematics; it was not applicable to their game.

It is no wonder that such theorizing caused d'Alembert to have quarrels and arguments with others. Moreover, there were reasons for interest in probability outside games of chance. It had been known for some time that if a person were inoculated with a fluid taken from a person having smallpox, the result would usually be a mild case of the disease, followed by immunity afterward. Unfortunately, a person so inoculated occasionally would develop a more serious case and die. The question was posed: Is one more likely to live longer with or without inoculation? There were many variables, of course. For example, should a forty-year-old, who was already past the average life expectancy, be inoculated? What, in fact, was a life expectancy? How many years could one hope to live, from any given age, both with and without inoculation? D'Alembert and Daniel Bernoulli carried on extensive arguments about this problem. What is significant about d'Alembert's way of thinking is that he expressed the feeling that the laws of probability were faint comfort to the man who had his child inoculated and lost the gamble. To d'Alembert, that factor was as important as any mathematical ratio. It was not, as far as he was concerned, irrelevant to the problem.

Most of these humanitarian concerns crept into d'Alembert's work in his later years. Aside from the *Opuscules,* there was only one other scientific publication after 1760 that carried his name: the *Nouvelles expériences sur la résistance des fluides* (published in 1777). Listed as coauthors were the Abbé Bossut and Condorcet. The last two actually did all of the work; d'Alembert merely lent his name.

In 1764 d'Alembert spent three months at the court of Frederick the Great. Although frequently asked by Frederick, d'Alembert refused to move to Potsdam as president of the Prussian Academy. Indeed, he urged Frederick to appoint Euler, and the rift that had grown between d'Alembert and Euler was at last repaired. Unfortunately, Euler was never trusted by Frederick, and he left soon afterward for St. Petersburg, where he spent the rest of his life.

In 1765 d'Alembert published his *Histoire de la destruction des Jésuites.* The work was seen through the press by Voltaire in Geneva, and although it was published anonymously, everyone knew who wrote it. A part of Voltaire's plan *écraser l'infâme,* this work is not one of d'Alembert's best.

In the same year, d'Alembert fell gravely ill, and moved to the house of Mlle. de Lespinasse, who nursed him back to health. He continued to live with her until her death in 1776. In 1772 he was elected perpetual secretary of the Académie Française, and undertook the task of writing the eulogies for the deceased members of the academy. He became the academy's most influential member, but, in spite of his efforts, that body failed to produce anything noteworthy in the way of literature during his pre-eminence. D'Alembert sensed his failure. His later life was filled with frustration and despair, particularly after the death of Mlle. de Lespinasse.

Possibly d'Alembert lived too long. Many of the *philosophes* passed away before he did, and those who remained alive in the 1780's were old and clearly not the vibrant young revolutionaries they had once been. What political success they had tasted they had not been able to develop. But, to a large degree, they had, in Diderot's phrase, "changed the general way of thinking."

BIBLIOGRAPHY

I. Original Works. There have been no collections made of d'Alembert's scientific works, although reprints of the original editions of his scientific books (except the *Opuscules mathématiques*) have recently been issued by Éditions Culture et Civilisation, Brussels. There are two collections of d'Alembert's *Oeuvres* which contain his literary pieces: the Bélin ed., 18 vols. (Paris, 1805); and the Bastien ed., 5 vols. (Paris, 1821). The most recent and complete bibliographies are in Grimsley and Hankins (see below).

II. Secondary Literature. The following works are devoted primarily to d'Alembert or accord him a prominent role: Joseph Bertrand, *D'Alembert* (Paris, 1889); Carl Boyer, *The History of the Calculus and Its Conceptual Development* (New York, 1949), ch. 4; René Dugas, *A History of Mechanics* (Neuchâtel, 1955), pp. 244–251, 290–299; Ronald Grimsley, *Jean d'Alembert* (Oxford,

1963); Maurice Müller, *Essai sur la philosophie de Jean d'Alembert* (Paris, 1926); Hunter Rouse and Simon Ince, *A History of Hydraulics* (New York, 1963), pp. 100–107; Clifford Truesdell, *Continuum Mechanics*, 4 vols. (New York, 1963–1964); and Arthur Wilson, *Diderot: The Testing Years* (New York, 1957). Of the above, Boyer, Dugas, Rouse and Ince, and particularly Truesdell, deal specifically and in detail with d'Alembert's science.

Three recent doctoral dissertations on d'Alembert are J. Morton Briggs, *D'Alembert: Mechanics, Matter, and Morals* (New York, 1962): Thomas Hankins, *Jean d'Alembert, Scientist and Philosopher* (Cornell University, 1964); and Harold Jarrett, *D'Alembert and the Encyclopédie* (Durham, N. C., 1962).

J. Morton Briggs

ALEXANDER OF APHRODISIAS (*fl.* second–third century A.D.), *philosophy.*

Alexander was a Peripatetic philosopher of the second–third century among whose masters were Herminus, Sosigenes, and Aristocles. His fame rests mainly on his interpretation of Aristotle's doctrines, the scholarly qualities of which earned him the sobriquet of "the interpreter" ($\delta \grave{\epsilon} \xi \eta \gamma \eta \tau \acute{\eta} \varsigma$). Of his works other than commentaries, four have survived in Greek manuscripts: *On the Soul; On Fate;* a writing going under the title *On Mixture;* and another, in four books, going under the title *Natural Questions,* of which the fourth book, however, deals mainly with ethical problems. Additional material is likely to be found in Arabic and Armenian.

Of these, the second part of *On the Soul* and the *Natural Questions* are collections of short pieces (some twenty-five in *On the Soul,* sixty-nine in the *Questions*) dealing with a great variety of topics and representing different literary forms. It is rather certain that these collections were not arranged or edited by Alexander, and that some pieces are inauthentic. But few of the problems thus posed have yet been sufficiently explored; the following presentation of Alexander's doctrines will be based indiscriminately on texts handed down to us under his name.

Of his commentaries on Aristotle, those on *Analytica priora I, Topics, Meteorologica,* and *On Sense and Sensibilia* survive in their entirety. Of the commentary on *Metaphysics* under his name, only the part dealing with *Metaphysics A–Λ* is genuine; the rest, usually referred to as a work by Pseudo-Alexander (his identity is not known), is not his, although it does contain some genuine passages. Of other commentaries, only fragments in the form of quotations in other commentators on Aristotle survive. Of his interpretations of Aristotle (either in formal commentaries or in other writings), two are particularly famous. Whereas Aristotle made Plato's ideas immanent in the sensible individuals but insisted that only this "ideal" (i.e., universal) aspect of sensibles can be known, so that with regard to us the individual (object of sensation) is prior to the universal—although the universal is actually prior to the individual—Alexander went one step further and declared that only individuals actually exist, the universals existing only as products of our mental (noetic) activity (νοεῖν), which abstracts them from the individuals (or the individual existing only in one exemplar, e.g., the phoenix). Therefore, the universals exist only as long as they are perceived. Alexander calls them νοητά (usually translated "intelligibles," in which case νοεῖν would best be translated "to intelligize"; we could then translate the noun νοῦς, the agent of intelligizing, as "intelligence"; one of the Latin translations of νοῦς is mens, to which, unfortunately, only the adjective "mental" corresponds in English).

But in addition to these intelligibles (corresponding to Plato's transcendent ideas made immanent by Aristotle) existing only as the results of our mental acts, Alexander admits the existence of intelligibles existing outside the realm of the sensible. Roughly, they correspond to Aristotle's "pure" forms, of which the best-known example is his supreme deity, the Unmoved Mover. These "higher" intelligibles (κυρίως νοητά) have one thing in common with the lower ones: they exist only as objects of mental (noetic) acts, but the νοῦς (intelligence) that intelligizes ("perceives") them is not our human intelligence. Rather, it is a (or the) divine intellect, one of whose marks is that its activity is eternal and incessant, so that these "higher" intelligibles also exist eternally and incessantly. They are "caused" by the highest intelligible, in the description of whose causality Alexander anticipates some Neoplatonic categories. The mental act perceiving them does not "abstract" them from matter, for they are not embodied.

Connected with this piece of noetics is another, with the help of which Alexander interprets a most difficult aspect of Aristotle's psychology in his *On the Soul,* Book III, chapters 4 and 5. According to Alexander, Aristotle teaches the existence of human intelligence (Alexander calls it passive, or potential, or material intelligence), which is different for different individuals and is part of everybody's soul, and of another intelligence, which is identical with the Supreme Deity, called active intelligence (it is this intelligence that incessantly and eternally perceives itself by perceiving the "higher" intelligibles). This intelligence–Deity is unique; it "enters" man from without (i.e., it is not connected in any way with his body); it is active also in the sense of activating the human

intelligence, thus enabling this intelligence to perceive intelligibles of both the lower and the higher order. Human intelligence thus activated (we could also say "transformed," and Alexander almost says "divinized") in different aspects of its activity is called by Alexander intelligence "in action," or "acquired as habit," or "acquired as disponible skill" (ἐνεργείαι, ἐπίκτητος, καθ' ἕξιν). The most conspicuous result of this theory is the denial of any kind of personal immortality. Man's soul perishes with his body; his intelligence, qua transformed by the active intelligence, survives by being reabsorbed into that unique, impersonal, divine intelligence. It is remarkable that Pseudo-Alexander describes the experience of "transformation," after which human intelligence becomes capable of perceiving the "higher" intelligibles, as a mystical (ineffable) experience. The assertion or the denial of the correctness of Alexander's interpretation of Aristotle and, even more, the correctness of the doctrine (denial of personal immortality) became one of the great controversies of the Middle Ages and early modern times.

Only a few other doctrines of Alexander can be mentioned here.

(1) In Aristotle's writings all change is ultimately reduced to locomotion, and prime locomotion is attributed to the celestial bodies (fixed stars and planets, and their spheres). Three explanations are given of the cause of this locomotion. One is that all celestial bodies are moved by being attracted to their Unmoved Mover as lovers are attracted by the objects of their love; the second is that they consist of an element, the ether, which by nature moves eternally, incessantly, and circularly; the third is that they are animated and moved by their souls. Alexander tried to reconcile these three explanations. Ether is animated and the soul is its nature. This soul desires to imitate the Unmoved Mover, which it does by eternally circling him.

(2) Alexander undertakes to prove that man's will is free (or, as the Greek has it, that there are things in our power, ἐφ' ἡμῖν). One of his main arguments is that nature distinguished man from other animals by endowing him with the faculty of deliberation, which mediates between stimuli (φαντασίαι) and actions, whereas animals simply react to stimuli. And since nature does nothing in vain, the exercise of this deliberative faculty results in reasonable assent to (or dissent from) stimuli, which proves that we are free to choose.

(3) Another theory explaining the freedom of will is based on the assertion that whereas the realm of the eternal and immutable is, if we may say so, full of being, the realm of the changeable (of becoming

and perishing) is permeated by nonbeing. In fact, this nonbeing is responsible for such things as chance and freedom of the will; there is no cause of these phenomena.

(4) Connected with the free-will theory is Alexander's treatment of the problem of fate or destiny ($\epsilon i\mu\alpha\rho\mu\acute{\epsilon}\nu\eta$), i.e., the doctrine of an unbroken causal chain. The fact of human freedom proves this doctrine wrong. The meaning of the word "fate" should be taken to indicate that everything acts according to its own, individual, nongeneric nature ($\phi\acute{\upsilon}\sigma\iota\varsigma$); in fact, "fate" and "nature" coincide without abridgment of man's freedom.

(5) Alexander discusses the problem of providence. He denies that the divine provides in a direct way ($\pi\rho o\eta\gamma o\upsilon\mu\acute{\epsilon}\nu\omega\varsigma$), i.e., the way a shepherd provides for his flock; such providence, says Alexander, would amount to saying that the divine (superior) exists for the sake of or profits from the inferior. He also denies that the effects of divine providence are merely accidental ($\kappa\alpha\tau\grave{\alpha}\ \sigma\upsilon\mu\beta\epsilon\beta\eta\kappa\acute{o}\varsigma$), but he does insist that there are other manners of divine providence, and promises to prove that contrary to what others have asserted, Aristotle recognizes providence. Alexander himself at least tentatively identifies the sum total of effects emanating from the everlasting circular movement of the celestial bodies with providence, its main effect being the *generic* immortality of perishable individuals of which the world of becoming consists.

(6) Alexander asserts the existence of natural justice. His main proof is that nature created man to live in community; that there can be no community without justice; that therefore justice is natural ($\phi\acute{\upsilon}\sigma\epsilon\iota$).

(7) The object of man's fundamental desire ($\tau\grave{o}$ $\pi\rho\tilde{\omega}\tau o\nu\ o i\kappa\epsilon\tilde{\iota}o\nu$) is pleasure (the apparent good) rather than, e.g., self-preservation.

(8) Moral perfection ($\grave{\alpha}\rho\epsilon\tau\acute{\eta}$) does not guarantee a happy life, as can be seen from the fact that a morally perfect man is justified in committing suicide for good reasons ($\epsilon\check{\upsilon}\lambda o\gamma o\varsigma\ \grave{\epsilon}\xi\alpha\gamma\omega\gamma\acute{\eta}$), which he would never do if his life were a happy one.

(9) Nobody can possess one moral perfection ($\grave{\alpha}\rho\epsilon\tau\acute{\eta}$), such as courage, without possessing all others.

(10) Alexander devotes a comparatively large amount of space to the problem of vision and related problems.

(11) Alexander refutes in great detail the Stoic doctrine of total interpenetration of bodies ($\kappa\rho\tilde{\alpha}\sigma\iota\varsigma\ \delta\iota'$ $\acute{o}\lambda o\upsilon$), which he feels is the foundation of the main tenets of the whole Stoic system.

(12) The magnet attracts because iron desires it, just as other things, although inanimate, desire that which nature has destined for them.

In any history of the problem of squaring the circle, Alexander is likely to be mentioned as he commented on all passages in which Aristotle criticized the methods used for this purpose by Hippocrates of Chios, Bryson, and Antiphon, always briefly to the point of obscurity. It seems that Alexander, probably misled by Aristotle, falsely assumed that Hippocrates did not distinguish lunules formed on quadrants (sides of a square inscribed in a circle) from sextants (sides of a hexagon inscribed in a circle), and also assumed that Antiphon violated the principle that a curve and a straight line can have only a point in common, which probably implies that Antiphon asserted the existence of atomic lengths of which both curves and straight lines would consist. On this basis Alexander rejected Hippocrates' and Antiphon's methods of squaring the circle.

BIBLIOGRAPHY

I. ORIGINAL WORKS. All commentaries mentioned in the text are available in the collection *Commentaria in Aristotelem Graeca,* 23 vols. (Berlin, 1882–1909), Vols. II and III in 2 parts each. All his other writings preserved in Greek are in *Supplementum Aristotelicum,* II, pts. 1 and 2 (Berlin, 1887–1892). The content of a writing on providence, translated from Greek into Arabic, has been translated into French in P. Thillet, "Un traité inconnu d'Alexandre d'Aphrodise sur la Providence dans une version arabe inédite," in *Actes du Premier Congrès International de Philosophie Médiévale* (Louvain–Paris, 1960), pp. 313–324. See also A. Dietrich, "Die arabische Version einer unbekannten Schrift des Alexander von Aphrodisias über die differentia specifica," in *Nachrichten der Akademie der Wissenschaften in Göttingen,* 1 (1964), 90–148; E. G. Schmidt, "Alexander von Aphrodisias in einem altarmenischen Kategorien-Kommentar," in *Philologus,* 110 (1966), 277–286; J. van Ess, "Über einige neue Fragmente des Alexander von Aphrodisias und des Proklos in arabischer Übersetzung," in *Der Islam,* 42 (1966), 148–168. Translations of Alexander's works include *On Destiny,* A. FitzGerald, ed. and trans. (London, 1931); and *Commentary on Book IV of Aristotle's Meteorologica,* V. C. B. Coutant, trans. (New York, 1936).

II. SECONDARY LITERATURE. A brief but comprehensive presentation is E. Zeller, *Die Philosophie der Griechen,* 5th ed., III, pt. 1 (Leipzig, 1923; repr. 1963), 817–830. Still briefer are A. Tognolo, "Alessandro di Aphrodisia" and "Alessandrismo," in *Enciclopedia filosofica,* I (Venice–Rome, 1957), 136–139; and F. Ueberweg and K. Praechter, *Die Philosophie des Altertums,* 12th ed. (Berlin, 1926; repr. Basel, 1953). Special problems are discussed in I. Bruns, "Studien zu Alexander von Aphrodisias," in *Rheinisches Museum,* 44 (1889), 613–630; 45 (1890), 138–145, 223–235; and Preface to his ed. of the *Natural Questions* in *Supplementum Aristotelicum* (see above), pp. v–xiv; E. Freudenthal, "Die durch Averroes erhaltenen Fragmente Alexanders zur Metaphysik des Aristoteles," in *Abhandlungen der Berliner Akademie vom Jahre 1884* (Berlin, 1885); P. Merlan, "Ein Simplikios-Zitat bei Ps. Alexandros und ein Plotinos-Zitat bei Simplikios," in *Rheinisches Museum,* **84** (1935), 154–160; *Philologische Wochenschrift,* **58** (1938), 65–69; and *Monopsychism, Mysticism, Metaconsciousness* (The Hague, 1963), Index, under "Alexander" and "Pseudo-Alexander"; P. Moraux, *Alexandre d'Aphrodise, exégète de la noétique d'Aristote* (Paris, 1942); and J. Zahlfleisch, "Die Polemik Alexanders von Aphrodisias gegen die verschiedenen Theorien des Sehens," in *Archiv für Geschichte der Philosophie,* **8** (1895), 373–386, 498–509; **9** (1896), 149–162. Additional literature is listed in Ueberweg and Praechter (see above).

Virtually all presentations of Aristotle's noetics deal with Alexander; a recent example is L. Barbotin, *La théorie aristotelicienne de l'intellect d'après Théophraste* (Louvain, 1954). Other recent literature includes O. Becker, "Formallogisches und Mathematisches in griechischen philosophischen Texten," in *Philologus,* **100** (1956), 108–112; R. Hackforth, "Notes on Some Passages of Alexander Aphrodisiensis *De fato,*" in *Classical Quarterly,* **40** (1946), 37–44; F. P. Hager, "Die Aristotelesinterpretation des Alexander von Aphrodisias und die Aristoteleskritik Plotins bezüglich der Lehre vom Geist," in *Archiv für Geschichte der Philosophie,* **46** (1964), 174–187; P. Henry, "Une comparaison chez Aristote, Alexandre et Plotin," in *Les sources de Plotin* (Geneva, 1960), pp. 429–444; H. Langerbeck, "Zu Alexander von Aphrodisias' *De fato,*" in *Hermes,* **64** (1936), 473–474; S. Luria, "Die Infinitesimaltheorie der antiken Atomisten," in *Quellen und Studien zur Geschichte der Mathematik, Astronomie und Physik, Abteilung B: Studien,* **2** (1932), 106–185; P. Moraux, "Alexander von Aphrodisias *Quaestiones* 2, 3," in *Hermes,* **95** (1967), 159–169; R. A. Pack, "A Passage in Alexander of Aphrodisias Relating to the Theory of Tragedy," in *American Journal of Philology,* **58** (1937), 418–436; S. Pines, "Omne quod movetur necesse est ab aliquo moveri: A Refutation of Galen by Alexander of Aphrodisias and the Theory of Motion," in *Isis,* **52** (1961), 21–54; J. M. Rist, "On Tracking Alexander of Aphrodisias," in *Archiv für Geschichte der Philosophie,* **48** (1966), 82–90.

PHILIP MERLAN

ALEXANDER OF MYNDOS (*b.* Myndos, Caria; *fl. ca.* A.D. 25–50), *biology.*

Nothing certain is known of Alexander's life and his dates are conjectural, but internal evidence indicates that he flourished in the first half of the first century. None of his writings has survived intact, although he seems to have been widely read in antiquity and is cited by Aelian, Athenaeus, Diogenes Laertius, and Photius. He was essentially a compiler, but with wide interests ranging from animal lore and medicine to dream analysis and mythology.

Alexander's principal work in natural history was entitled Περὶ ζῴων (*On Animals*). A second work,

Περὶ τῆς τῶν πτηνῶν ἱστορίας (*Inquiry on Birds*) may have been an alternate title of Book II of his *On Animals.* The extant fragments from his zoological writings are a mixture of fact and fancy, in which the strange, unusual, or fabulous behavior of land animals and birds is emphasized. Unable to explain certain observed and authenticated data, such as the annual migration of birds, Alexander resorted to analogies with human behavior or to religious and mythological symbolism. Despite his apparent lack of originality, he wisely followed Aristotle in reporting on zoological matters and provided, in turn, one of the principal sources for the account of birds in Book IX of Athenaeus' *Deipnosophistae.* There the size, behavior, and feeding habits of about a dozen identifiable species of birds are recounted, although most of the passages derive ultimately from one of Aristotle's lost writings. Additional remarks deal with the color of the plumage and the external differences between males and females of the same species. The description of the internal organs of a female quail (*Coturnix* sp.) probably derives from Aristotle as well. The only evidence of independent research concerns Alexander's inability to hear the legendary song of a dying swan. Another zoological fragment describes an unusual animal that has been tentatively identified as a gnu. His interest in animal behavior tends to merge with the fabulous in his moralizing tales about the transformations of storks after death and the semihuman intelligence of chameleons and goats.

Only one identifiable fragment exists from Alexander's Περὶ θηριακῶν (*On Theriac*), which may have been an account of the miraculous curative properties of theriac as a drug and as a universal protection against poisons. He may have written a separate book on plants, but the title is not known.

The combination of natural history and an interest in miracles is further evidenced in Alexander's "Dream Book," whose exact title is not recorded. In the few surviving fragments, predictions are based upon the behavior and properties of plants and birds.

No certain opinion can be formed of Alexander's study of early myths. His Τὰ μυθικά (*Mythical Stories*), originally in nine books, is represented by only two fragments. He may also be the author of Περίπλους τῆς Ἐρυθρᾶς θαλάττης (*Voyage Around the Red Sea*), of which a fragment that deals with monstrous snakes and their symbolic associations with Poseidon is preserved by Aelian.

BIBLIOGRAPHY

For further information on Alexander, see Eugen Oder, "Das Traumbuch des Alexander von Myndos," in *Rhein-*

isches Museum für Philologie, **45** (1890), 637–639; Max Wellmann, "Alexander von Myndos," in Hermes, **26** (1891), 481–566, a fundamental study containing an edition of the thirty-four identifiable fragments, and "Alexandros von Myndos" [Alexandros 100], in Pauly-Wissowa, Real-Encyclopädie der classischen Altertumswissenschaft.

JERRY STANNARD

ALEXANDER OF TRALLES (b. Tralles, in Lydia, first half of the sixth century A.D.; fl. in the time of Justinian), medicine.

Alexander of Tralles was the son of Stephanus, a physician. He had four brothers: Anthemius, a famous mechanician who was involved in rebuilding Hagia Sophia; Metrodorus, a grammarian; Olympius, a jurist; and Dioscorus, another physician. As we know by his own dedicatory preface, Alexander was the protégé of the father of a certain Cosmas; to this Cosmas he dedicated his work, which he says that he wrote, at the behest of Cosmas, at an advanced age, when he was no longer able to practice medicine. It is unlikely, however, that this Cosmas was the famous geographer Cosmas Indicopleustes, as his modern biographer Theodor Puschmann hypothesizes. The historian Agathias, a contemporary of Alexander, indicates that Alexander's life was beset with hardships. Agathias also records that Alexander practiced in Rome for some time, while Alexander's own writings mention his travels in Gaul and Spain.

The writings of Alexander that have survived have been subjected to a thorough and critical examination by Puschmann, whose findings may well be accepted. According to him, the dedicatory preface to the works as a whole and the book Concerning Fever were written during Alexander's last years; the other eleven books are either hastily sketched or more elaborate notes for a handbook on internal medicine, in accordance with a plan set forth at the beginning of the work. A letter about intestinal worms, directed to an unknown Theodorus, is extant, and Puschmann has collected a few additional fragments; all of Alexander's other writings are apparently lost. The entirety of Alexander's work is known to have been available in Greek in numerous codices and in equally numerous Latin translations; his work was also much read and translated by the Arabs.

Puschmann is perhaps biased in favor of his subject. One must remember that Alexander's importance lies within the framework of Byzantine medicine—a rather sterile, literary tradition. Alexander is praised for his self-reliance; this independence should, however, be more precisely formulated as deriving from the consideration that Alexander did not simply edit a medical anthology composed of other people's texts, as did Oribasius or Aetios of Amida, but wrote a work of his own. He was not the only Byzantine author to do so, however—compare especially the work of Johannes Actuarios. Alexander indeed had an extensive practice, made many original observations, and knew the value of empiricism; but this may also be said of other Byzantine physicians (again, especially Johannes Actuarios). While Alexander sometimes dared to criticize even Galen, Johannes Actuarios, too, had a self-confident sense of the value of his own work as compared to the work of his predecessors, as is especially apparent in his book About the Urine. Alexander's style is justly praised for its comprehensibility and clarity; not all other Byzantine physicians wrote pompously, however. Moreover, Alexander—like all other Byzantine physicians, and like all those of late antiquity—was uncritical of a great deal of the older medical literature that he cited, and was by no means entirely free from superstition. Finally, very few remnants of Byzantine medical texts and practice are available to us to provide a measure by which Alexander may be objectively evaluated. In summary, one may state that Alexander was, as a representative of Byzantine medicine, rather refreshing, not uninteresting, and not, perhaps, altogether unimportant.

BIBLIOGRAPHY

Text, German translation, and an extensive introduction may be found in Theodor Puschmann, Alexander von Tralleis, 2 vols. (Vienna, 1878–1879). It includes Alexander's mention of his father (II, 139), Alexander's preface to his work on medicine (I, 289), mention of Cosmas Indicopleustes (I, 83), Alexander's accounts of his travels (I, 565), and descriptions of his works (I, 101 ff.). Also by Puschmann is "Nachträge zu Alexander von Tralleis," in Berliner Studien für classische Philologie und Archaeologie, **5,** part 2 (1887).

For a French translation with an extensive introduction, see F. Brunet, Oeuvres medicales d'Alexandre de Tralles, 4 vols. (Paris, 1933–1937); this does not go far beyond Puschmann, however.

A good source of material on Alexander is Agathias; see "Agathias Histor.," in Historici Graeci Minores, W. Dindorf, ed., II (Leipzig, 1871), 357. Reference to Greek codices and Latin translations may be found in H. Diels, Die Handschriften der griechischen Ärzte, II (Berlin, 1906), 11–13; the Arabic versions are mentioned by I. Bloch in Theodor Puschmann, Handbuch der Geschichte der Medizin, I (Jena, 1902), 537–538. This work also covers Alexander's criticism of Galen (p. 539).

FRIDOLF KUDLIEN

ALEXIS OF PIEDMONT. See Ruscelli, Girolamo.

ALFONSO EL SABIO (*b*. Toledo, Spain, 23 November 1221; *d*. Seville, Spain, 24 April 1284), *astronomy, dissemination of science and learning.*

Alfonso el Sabio, "the learned," was the son of Ferdinand III of Castile and León, and Beatrice of Swabia, granddaughter of Frederick Barbarossa. Upon the death of his father in 1252, he became Alfonso X. Descended from the Hohenstaufens through his mother, he sought between 1256 and 1272 to become Holy Roman Emperor by pressing the Swabian claims to that position. This continued pre-occupation alienated the Castilian nobility and depleted his treasury. Upon the death of his eldest son, Ferdinand, in 1275, his second son, Sancho, sought to dethrone him and gain power. Seville remained loyal to Alfonso, but the majority of his subjects opposed him and the Cortes declared him deposed in 1282.

Although Alfonso's domestic policies threatened the stability of the state, his patronage of science and learning sowed the seeds of later Castilian greatness. In the tradition of his predecessors, he supported the translation of Arabic works into Latin and Castilian. Alfonso gave Spain a great legal code, *Las siete partidas,* a compilation of the legal knowledge of his time, and sponsored important scientific translations. These translations of Arabic astronomical, astrological, and magical treatises reveal Alfonso's active interest in science. He gained his most lasting scientific fame by supporting a new edition of the Toledan Tables of the Cordoban astronomer al-Zarqālī (Arzachel, *ca.* 1029–*ca.* 1087). This new edition, the *Tablas alfonsinas,* was not an original work. Although new observations were made from 1262 to 1272, it still followed the general format of al-Zarqālī's earlier compilation and, with only minor qualifications, retained the Ptolemaic system for explaining celestial motion. It utilized mean solar, lunar, and planetary orbits and equations; declination of stars; ascension, opposition, and conjunction of the sun and moon; visibility of the moon and of eclipses; and a trigonometrical theory of sines and chords to predict the motion of celestial bodies. The original Spanish edition of the *Tablas* has been lost. Its popularity in the medieval period was based on the Latin versions.

Alfonso also supported the translation of a series of Arabic astronomical studies known collectively as the *Libros del saber de astronomia.* The fifteen treatises in this collection are either based on or translated from Arabic astronomical works written in the ninth through the twelfth centuries. The collection, which includes a catalog of stars and a study of the celestial globe, spherical astrolabe, quadrants, clocks, and other assorted astronomical instruments, was pre-pared while observations were being made for the Alfonsine Tables. Never as popular as the latter, it was not published until 1863–1867. Alfonso may have also encouraged Rabi Zag of Toledo to prepare a treatise on the quadrant. Entitled *Tratado del cuadrante "sennero,"* it exists today in an incomplete manuscript; only eight of its thirteen chapters are extant. Alfonso is said also to have sponsored a vernacular translation of an Arabic work on magic, the Latin *Liber picatrix.* His reputation is based not on his occult endeavors but on the royal patronage he gave so willingly to astronomy.

BIBLIOGRAPHY

The Alfonsine Tables may be found in numerous Latin editions, none of which is, in any sense, a critical edition. The 1st ed. of the Latin version is *Alfonti . . . celestium motuum tabule: nec non stellarum fixarum longitudines ac latitudines Alfontii tempore ad motus veritatem mira diligentia reducte* (Venice, 1483; 2nd ed., with *canones* of Joannes Lucilius Santritter, 1492). The *Libros del saber de astronomia* was ed. by Manuel Rico y Sinobas, 5 vols. (Madrid, 1863–1867). A beautiful color facsimile of Alfonso's famous study on lapidaries has been reproduced by José Fernandez Montaña in *Lapidario, reproducción fotolitográfica* (Madrid, 1881). The fragmented *Tratado del cuadrante "sennero"* was ed. by José M.ª Millás Vallicrosa in his *Nuevos estudios sobre historia de la ciencia española* (Barcelona, 1960). The work on magic was trans. by H. Ritter and H. Plessner in their *Picatrix: Das Ziel des Weisen* (London, 1962).

The definitive portrait of Alfonso's political activities is Antonio Ballesteros y Baretta, *Alfonso el Sabio* (Barcelona, 1963). Excellent brief biographies are John Esten Keller, *Alfonso X, El Sabio* (New York, 1967), and Evelyn S. Proctor, *Alfonso X of Castile, Patron of Literature and Learning* (Oxford, 1951). For his scientific works and translations see Evelyn S. Proctor, "The Scientific Works of the Court of Alfonso X of Castile," in *Modern Language Review,* **40** (1945), 12–29; and Moritz Steinschneider, "Die europäischen Uebersetzungen aus dem Arabischen," in *Sitzungsberichte der Akademie der Wissenschaften in Wien,* **4, 9, 40, 55, 60, 61, 69, 87, 93, 97,** and **108** (1904–1905). For his astronomy and its influence see J. L. E. Dreyer, "The Original Form of the Alfonsine Tables," in *Monthly Notices of the Royal Astronomical Society,* **80** (1920), 243–267; Jose Soriano Viguera, *La astronomia de Alfonso X* (Madrid, 1926); Pierre Duhem, *Le système du monde,* II, (Paris, 1914), 259–266; and Alfred Wegener, *Die Alfonsinischen Tafeln für den Gebrauch eines modernen Rechners* (Berlin, 1905), and "Die astronomischen Werke Alfons X," in *Bibliotheca mathematica,* **6** (1905), 129–185.

PHILLIP DRENNON THOMAS

ALFRAGANUS. See **al-Farghānī.**

ALHAZEN. See **Ibn al-Haytham.**

ʿALI. See last element of name.

ALKINDUS. See **al-Kindī.**

ALLEN, EDGAR (*b.* Canyon City, Colorado, 2 May 1892; *d.* New Haven, Connecticut, 3 February 1943), *endocrinology.*

Edgar Allen discovered estrogen and investigated the hormonal mechanisms that control the female reproductive cycle. In so doing he helped to create the science of endocrinology, one of the most significant branches of modern biology.

Allen, the son of a physician, received his early education in the public schools of Pawtucket and Cranston, Rhode Island. He attended Brown University and earned all of his higher degrees at that institution: Ph.B. (1915), M.A. (biology, 1916), Ph.D. (biology, 1921). During World War I his studies were interrupted for a short time by military service. In 1918 he married Marion Pfieffer of Providence; the couple had two daughters.

Allen's distinguished academic career began in 1919 when he was appointed instructor in anatomy at Washington University, St. Louis, Missouri. In 1923 he moved to the University of Missouri, where he served initially as professor of anatomy and subsequently as dean of the medical school and director of university hospitals. In 1933 he returned to the east coast as professor of anatomy and chairman of the department at the Yale School of Medicine, a position he held until his death.

Allen's Ph.D. thesis on the estrous cycle of the mouse (published in 1922) is a thorough description of the histological changes that occur in primary and secondary sex organs during the reproductive cycle. During the early 1920's several investigators had suggested that the ovary might be the control center for this cycle; it was thought that the fluid content of the *corpus luteum* might be the active agent of control. Allen's Ph.D. thesis cast doubt on this latter hypothesis. He noticed that at any given time during the cycle *corpora lutea* can be found in many different stages of degeneration, making it highly unlikely that they could be controlling a continuous series of progressive histological changes.

In 1923 Allen undertook a study of ovogenesis during sexual maturity and discovered that females are not born with a complete complement of ova; ova are continually formed in the germinal epithelium and the follicles that develop around them have a cycle of growth and decay not unlike that of the *corpus luteum.* This fact led Allen to suspect that the ovarian follicle, not the *corpus luteum,* might be the focus of control. In collaboration with a biochemist, E. A. Doisy, Allen proceeded to test this hypothesis by extracting a fluid from the follicle and determining its effects. He found that repeated injections of the follicular fluid produced histological changes that were identical to the early stages of normal estrus; when the injections were halted, the later phases ensued.

Allen and Doisy had discovered the existence and the effects of estrogen. Within fifteen years the other hormones that influence estrus were also discovered (see the work of Zondek, Aschheim, H. M. Evans and J. A. Long on pituitrin and Hartmann, Corner, Hisaw and Zuckerman on progesterone) and the relations between them were becoming clear. All of Allen's subsequent investigations were concerned, in some way, with these sex hormones. He proved, for example, that estrogen causes the onset of puberty in immature female animals and demonstrated that the hormonal mechanisms of primates (including man) are very similar to those of rodents, on which the original studies had been done. Allen also studied the relation between estrogen and malignancy, in order to determine whether there is any similarity between rapid cell growth caused by estrogenic stimulation and rapid cell growth that is characteristic of cancerous tissue. In addition, Allen's publications contain a wealth of methodological information that was of great value to subsequent researches in endocrinology.

Allen was a member, and president, of two scientific societies, the American Association of Anatomists and the Association for the Study of Internal Secretions. Brown, Yale, and Washington universities awarded him honorary degrees. The French government made him a member of the Legion of Honor (1937), and the Royal College of Physicians awarded him its Baly Medal (1941). He was also an advisory trustee (1939–1943) and member of the Scientific Advisory Committee of the International Cancer Research Foundation.

A devoted sailor, Allen joined the Coast Guard Auxiliary at the onset of World War II and died of a heart attack while commanding a patrol boat on Long Island Sound.

BIBLIOGRAPHY

Allen's total bibliography contains more than 140 items; it can be found in the *Yale Journal of Biology and Medicine,* **17**, part 1 (1944–1945), 2–12, along with his *curriculum vitae.* The *Yale Journal,* **15** (1943), 641–644, contains an excellent biographical sketch of Allen.

For an understanding of the development of follicular control, see, in the following order, "The Estrous Cycle in the Mouse," in *American Journal of Anatomy,* **30** (1922), 297 (Allen's doctoral dissertation); "Ovogenesis During Sexual Maturity," in *American Journal of Anatomy,* **31** (1923), 439; and "The Hormone of the Ovarian Follicle; Its Localization and Action in Test Animals, and Additional Points Bearing Upon the Internal Secretion of the Ovary," in *American Journal of Anatomy,* **34** (1924), 133. The last study was written in collaboration with E. A. Doisy.

Some of the extensions of his original idea can be found in "The Induction of a Sexually Mature Condition in Immature Females by Injection of the Ovarian Follicular Hormone," in *American Journal of Physiology,* **69** (1924), 577; "The Menstrual Cycle of the Monkey, *Macacus Rhesus* . . .," in *Contributions to Embryology,* Carnegie Institute of Washington, No. 380 (1927), p. 98; and "The Estrous Cycle of Mice During Growth of Spontaneous Mammary Tumors and the Effects of Ovarian Follicular and Anterior Pituitary Hormones," in *American Journal of Cancer,* **25** (1935), 291.

RUTH SCHWARTZ COWAN

ALLIACO, PETRUS DE. See **Ailly, Pierre D'.**

ALLONVILLE, J. E. D'. See **Louville, J. E. d'A., Chevalier de.**

ALPETRAGIUS. See **al-Biṭrūjī.**

ALPHARABIUS. See **al-Fārābī.**

ALPINI, PROSPERO (*b.* Marostica, Italy, 23 November 1553; *d.* Padua, Italy, 23 November 1616), *botany.*

Alpini was among the first of the Italian physician-botanists of the sixteenth century to examine plants outside the context of their therapeutic uses. Although he shared his contemporaries' reverence for the past, he helped to advance the frontiers of botanical science by taking advantage of knowledge gained through his travels.

The oldest of the four children of Francesco Alpini, a physician, and Bartolomea Tarsia, Alpini studied medicine at the University of Padua, from which he received his degree on 28 August 1578. His master was Melchiore Guilandino (originally Melchior Wieland of Königsberg), the second director of the botanical garden at Padua, who acted as respondent in Alpini's dialogue *De plantis Aegypti.* For a short time Alpini practiced medicine in Camposampiero, near Padua. In 1580 he became physician to Giorgio Emo, the Venetian consul to Cairo, and in September of that year he accompanied Emo to Egypt. En route, he botanized on the island of Crete. After three years in Egypt, he returned to Venice. In 1594 the Venetian

Senate elected him *lettore dei semplici* ("reader in simples") at the University of Padua. He succeeded to the directorship of the botanical garden at Padua in 1603, assuming both the title and the duties of *prefetto ed ostensore dei semplici* ("prefect and demonstrator of simples"). Alpino, a son by his first wife, Guadagnina Guadagnini, later became the seventh prefect of the botanical garden. Alpini is said to have died of a kidney infection contracted during his stay in Egypt. He is buried in the Church of St. Anthony, Padua.

Alpini's major contributions are the outgrowth of his travels. From a scientific point of view, the *De plantis Aegypti* (1592) is his most important work. The pioneer study of Egyptian flora, it introduced exotic plants to the still-parochial European botanical circles. Obviously incomplete, this small book later was used by such systematists as F. Hasselquist and P. Forskål as a basis for their more complete studies. Moreover, some of Alpini's original descriptions were included in the writings of Linnaeus, who regarded him with sufficient esteem to name the genus *Alpinia* (*Zingiberaceae*) in his honor.

Fifty-seven plants and trees are described in the *De plantis Aegypti,* and forty-nine are illustrated. Alpini's medical training led him to approach the new flora in the traditional manner of attempting to correlate these plants with the names and descriptions found in classical sources. When this proved impossible, he described the plant under its local name. The descriptions are based upon specimens that Alpini personally examined, either cultivated in gardens or growing wild. This in itself provided a much-needed corrective to the fables and vague reports associated with Eastern plants. Among the plants previously undescribed in a European botanical text were the coffee bush (*Coffea arabica* L.), banana (*Musa* sp.), and baobab (*Adansonia digitata* L.). Perhaps because of the dialogue form of the book, there is no discernible system. There is, however, a wide range of miscellaneous information based upon observation. Alpini observed that the fertilization of the date palm was a sexual process, described the phototropic movements of the leaves of the tamarind (*Tamarindus indica* L.), speculated that the tree cotton (*Gossypium arboreum* L.) was the *byssos* of the ancients, and noted the edibility of plants unknown in Europe, such as bammia or okra (*Hibiscus esculentus* L.). Evidently puzzled by the treelike banana plant, he accepted the story that it was the result of a sugar cane grafted onto the root of colocasia (*Colocasia esculenta* Schott.) and supplied a good description of the latter.

Another product of Alpini's study of Egyptian plants is the *De balsamo dialogus* (1591). In the form of a dialogue involving the author, an Egyptian physician, and a Jew, the source of balsam (*Commiphora* spp.) is discussed and questions are raised concerning its identity, ancient names, and medical uses, and the possibility that the true balsam has become extinct. Closely related in form and method is the *De rhapontico* (1612). The source and therapeutic properties of rhubarb (*Rheum* sp.) are discussed with a show of classical scholarship controlled by a personal examination of specimens grown in the botanical garden under Alpini's supervision.

The material for the *De plantis exoticis,* which was published posthumously, also derived from Alpini's travels. With Onorio Belli he carefully studied the flora of Crete. Information on plants from other areas was later incorporated into the manuscript, which was edited by his son Alpino and completed in 1614. Data concerning some of these plants were obtained by examining specimens grown from seeds sent to Alpini. A total of 145 plants, each illustrated by a woodcut, formed a notable contribution to Mediterranean floristics. This is especially true of the flora of Crete, many of whose plants were described for the first time. The accuracy of Alpini's descriptions was demonstrated by A. Baldacci and P. A. Saccardo, who identified seventy-one of the eighty-five Cretan plants on which he reported.

Alpini's interest in medicine was expressed in several books, of which the most important were *De medicina Aegyptiorum* (1591) and *De praesagienda vita* (1601). The former, like his study of Egyptian plants, was based upon personal experience. Primarily an examination of contemporary Egyptian (i.e., Turkish) medicine, it ranks as one of the earliest studies of non-European medicine. Although he took a dim view of local customs, Alpini was sufficiently impressed by novel therapeutic practices to introduce the technique of *moxa* into European medicine. The *De praesagienda vita* is a detailed study of prognostics in which attention is devoted to the patient's mental state and its bearing on health, as well as to the usual physical and diagnostic signs.

Mention should be made of the *Rerum Aegyptiarum* (Volume I of *Historiae Aegypti naturalis*), a pioneer and undeservedly neglected contribution to Egyptology. Edited after Alpini's death by Bartolomeo Cellari, it contains a wealth of information on the natural history (including zoology and mineralogy), customs, and ancient monuments of Egypt.

BIBLIOGRAPHY

I. ORIGINAL WORKS. Principal editions of Alpini's works include *De balsamo dialogus* (Venice, 1591; Padua, 1639), also in *Medicina Aegyptiorum* (Leiden, 1719) and in Blasius Ugolino, *Thesauro antiquitatum sacrarum* (Venice, 1750),

also translated by Antoine Colin as "Histoire du baulme . . ., version françoise . . .," in Garcia d'Orta, *Histoire des drogues, espisceries, et de certains medicamens simples* (Lyons, 1619); *De medicina Aegyptiorum libri quatuor* (Venice, 1591; Paris, 1646), also published as *Medicina Aegyptiorum. Accedunt huic editioni ejusdem auctoris libri de balsamo et rhapontico* (Leiden, 1719; 1745); *De plantis Aegypti liber . . . Accessit etiam liber de balsamo, alias editus* (Venice, 1592), later edited by Johannes Vesling (Padua, 1638; 1640); *De praesagienda vita et morte aegrotantium libri septem* (Venice-Frankfurt, 1601; Leiden, 1733; Hamburg, 1734), later edited by H. Boerhaave (Leiden, 1710; Venice, 1735; 1751; Bassano, 1774) and by J. B. Friedrich, 2 vols. (Nördlingen, 1828), and translated by R. James as *The Presages of Life and Death in Disease,* 2 vols. (London, 1746); *De medicina methodica libri tredecim* (Padua, 1611; Leiden, 1719); *De rhapontico—disputatio in gymnasio Patavino habita* (Padua, 1612), also in *De plantis Aegypti liber* (Padua, 1640) and *Medicina Aegyptiorum* (Leiden, 1719); "Trattato della teriaca egittia," in Ippolito Ceccarelli, *Antidotario romano latino e volgare tradotto . . .,* A. Manni, ed. (Rome, 1619); *De plantis exoticis libri duo* (Venice, 1627; 1629); *Historiae Aegypti naturalis,* 2 vols. (Leiden, 1735), Vol. I, *Rerum Aegyptiarum libri quattuor . . .*; Vol. II, *De plantis Aegypti liber auctus et emendatus, cum observationibus et notis Johannis Veslingii*; and *De longitudine et brevitate morborum, libri duo,* introduction, translation, and notes by Giuseppe Ongaro (Marostica, 1966).

II. SECONDARY LITERATURE. Works dealing with Alpini and his contributions to botany are A. Baldacci and P. A. Saccardo, "Onorio Belli e Prospero Alpino e la flora dell'isola di Creta," in *Malpighia,* **14** (1900), 140–163; Augusto Béguinot, "Prospero Alpini," in Aldo Mieli, ed., *Gli scienziati italiani dall'inizio del medio evo ai nostri giorni,* I, pt. 1 (Rome, 1921), 84–90; Pietro Capparoni, "Prosper Alpini (1553–1616)," in *Bulletin de la Société Française d'Histoire de la Médecine,* **23** (1929), 108–115, and *Profili bio-bibliografici di medici e naturalisti celebri italiani dal sec. XV al sec. XVIII* (Rome, 1932), pp. 20–23; G. Fasoli and C. Cappelletti, "Prospero Alpino (1553–1616)," in *Rassegna trimestrale di odontoiatria,* **41** (1960), 597–613; Ludwig Keimer, "Quelques détails oubliés ou inconnus sur la vie et les publications de certains voyageurs européens venus en Égypte pendant les derniers siècles," in *Bulletin de l'Institut d'Égypte,* **31** (1949), 121–175; Giuseppe Ongaro, "Contributi alla biografia di Prospero Alpini," in *Acta medicae historiae Patavina,* **8–9** (1961–1963), 79–168— the most complete study to date, based on Alpini's unpublished manuscripts at Padua; John Ray, *A Collection of Curious Travels and Voyages,* 2 vols. (London, 1693), II, 92–98; P. A. Saccardo, "Contribuzioni alla storia della botanica italiana," in *Malpighia,* **8** (1894), 476–539; and Kurt Sprengel, *Geschichte der Botanik,* 2 vols. (Altenburg-Leipzig, 1817–1818), I, 356–359.

JERRY STANNARD

ALSTED, JOHANN HEINRICH (*b.* Ballersbach, Germany, 1588; *d.* Stuhlweissenburg [Székesfehérvár], Hungary, 9 November 1638), *natural philosophy.*

Alsted was the second son of Jacob Alsted (d. 1622), a Reformed Church minister, and Rebecca Pincier, the daughter of a Reformed Church minister and sister of Johannes Pincier, humanist scholar and professor of medicine and philosophy at the Herborn Academy. After an elementary education at Ballersbach, Alsted entered the lower school of the Herborn Academy in 1602. This academy, founded in 1584, had achieved considerable prominence as a center of Calvinist and Ramist influence.

After completing his studies at Herborn, Alsted undertook the customary *peregrinatio academicae,* visiting Frankfurt am Main, Heidelberg, Strasbourg, and Basel, where he met Amandus Polanus von Polandsdorf. In 1608 he returned to Herborn and was appointed teacher and examiner at the high school of the academy. Two years later he became professor of philosophy, and in 1619 rector and professor of theology. He made brief visits to other parts of Europe, attending the Synod of Dordrecht in 1618.

Alsted married Anna Katherine Rab (1593–1648), daughter of the Herborn printer Christoph Rab (Corvinus), who was to print the majority of Alsted's works. They had four children.

Alsted attracted students from numerous German and Slavic states; the most famous was Jan Amos Komenský (Comenius), who taught for a short time at Herborn before embarking upon his pansophic missions. The Thirty Years' War upset the continuity of Alsted's work, and he reluctantly decided to leave Herborn in 1629, to become the first rector of the new high school at Stuhlweissenburg, which had been established by the Protestant prince Gabriel Bethlen von Siebenbürgen.

The majority of Alsted's writings were on theology, and in them he displayed the same logical and encyclopedic approach found in the philosophical writings. Throughout the areas of Calvinist influence, from Transylvania to New England, Alsted's systematic treatises on educational theory, theology, and philosophy exerted great influence in the universities during most of the seventeenth century. His writings covered the whole spectrum of natural philosophy: commentaries on the cabala, the *Ars magna* of Lull, mnemonics, traditional and Ramist logic, physics, mathematics, and astronomy.

Alsted's major monographs—compendia or harmonia of logic, physics, the Scriptures, and education—display a strikingly uniform organization, at the cost of oversimplification. This was an inherent danger of the Ramist approach. The *Systema physicae harmonicae* (1612) is typical. It analyzes the principles of "physics" derived according to four conflicting systems: *physicum Mosaicum; rabbinica et cabbalistica; peripateticam;* and *chemicam.* These systems are based, respectively, on the Old Testament, Jewish mystical writings, Aristotle, and Paracelsus. The principles of each system are discussed in a clear logical sequence that draws upon a wide range of sources, from the humanist editors of the cabala to the late sixteenth-century neo-scholastic commentators Magirus and Scaliger, and the Paracelsian or mystical authors John Dee and Oswald Croll. Throughout, Alsted gives his own judgments on the physical principles, favoring a "Christianized" Peripatetic philosophy, the description of which occupies more than half the book.

The *Methodus admirandorum* contains information about improved techniques of surveying and physical astronomy, and discusses the merits of the Copernican hypothesis. Copernicus is admired, but his system is deemed unacceptable, for it is refuted by the Scriptures and common sense.

Alsted's ultimate fame rests upon his conception of the encyclopedia as a universal system of knowledge. He believed in the fundamental unity of divine and secular knowledge, the nature of which unity could be displayed by the use of *logica-mnemonica,* the art of directing the mind and perfecting the memory. Also prominent was his logical analysis of the nature and divisions of the parts of knowledge, or *technologia,* which provided the basis for the organization of his encyclopedia.

These systematic writings had an immediate but ephemeral appeal in institutions of higher education, his *Encyclopaedia* being to such students as Cotton Mather the "North-West Passage to all the sciences." More important, they influenced the educational theories of Comenius, as well as his pansophia, and the encyclopedic philosophies of Leibniz and Morhof.

BIBLIOGRAPHY

I. ORIGINAL WORKS. Alsted's writings most directly related to natural philosophy are *Clavis artis Lullianae et verae logices* (Strasbourg, 1609); *Methodus formandorum studiorum, continens commonfactiones concilia, regulas . . . de ratione bene discendi et ordine studiorum recte instituendo* (Strasbourg, 1610); *Panacea philosophica, id est . . . Methodus docendi et discendi universam encyclopaediam* (Herborn, 1610), to which was appended *Harmonico philosophiae Aristotelicae, Lullianae et Rameae; Systema mnemonicum duplex* (Frankfurt, 1610); *Theatrum scholasticum . . . I Systema et gymnasium mnemonicum . . . II Gymnasium logicum . . . III Systema et gymnasium oratorium* (Herborn, 1610); *Compendium I Systematis logici . . . II Gymnasii logici* (Herborn, 1611); *Elementale mathematicum in quo mathesis methodice traditur* (Frankfurt, 1611); *Philosophia digne restituta: libros quatuor* (Herborn, 1612); *Systema physicae harmonicae* (Herborn, 1612), entitled *Physica harmonica* in later editions; *Compendium logicae harmonicae . . . accedit nucleus logicae* (Herborn, 1613), which appeared in a slightly different form in 1614; *Methodus admirandorum mathematicorum* (Herborn, 1613), an expanded version of the *Elementale mathematicum* that was often reprinted; *Theologia naturalis exhibens augustissimam naturae scholam* (Frankfurt, 1615); *Cursus philosophici encyclopaedia libris XXVII* (Herborn, 1620), also in an expanded edition with a new section entitled *Compendium lexici philosophici* (Herborn, 1626); and *Encyclopaedia septem tomis distincta* (Herborn, 1630; Leiden, 1649; Stuttgart, 1663, abridged).

II. SECONDARY LITERATURE. Works on Alsted are *Allgemeine deutsche Biographie,* I, 354–355; C. G. Jöcher, *Allgemeines Gelehrten-Lexicon* (Leipzig, 1750), I, 302–303; Johann Kvacsala, "Johann Heinrich Alsted," in Ungarische *Revue,* **9** (1889), 628–642, and *J. A. Comenius* (Leipzig, 1892), pp. 98–104; Max Lippert, *J. H. Alsted pädagogisch-didactische Reform Bestrebungen* (Meissen, 1899); L. E. Loemker, "Leibniz and the Herborn Encyclopaedists," in *Journal of the History of Ideas,* **22** (1961), 323–338; *Neue deutsche Biographie,* I, 206; Walter J. Ong, *Ramus, Method, and the Decay of Dialogue* (Cambridge, Mass., 1958); Wilhelm Risse, *Die Logik der Neuzeit,* I (Stuttgart–Bad Canstatt, 1964), 477–485, and *Bibliographia logica,* I (Hildesheim, 1965); E. W. E. Roth, "Johann Heinrich Alsted (1588–1638), sein Leben und sein Schriften," in *Monatshefte der Comenius-Gesellschaft,* **4** (1895), 29–44, the most complete bibliography of Alsted's works; and Max Wundt, *Die deutsche Schulmetaphysik des 17 Jahrhunderts* (Tübingen, 1939), pp. 80–83, 236–237.

CHARLES WEBSTER

ALZATE Y RAMÍREZ, JOSÉ ANTONIO (*b.* Ozumba, Mexico, 1738; *d.* Mexico City, Mexico, 1799), *natural history, mathematics, geography, astronomy.*

Born into a wealthy country family, Alzate attended San Ildefonso College and graduated in 1753 with a bachelor of arts degree. In 1756, he received a bachelor of divinity degree from the University of Mexico, and was subsequently ordained as a Roman Catholic priest.

An enthusiastic naturalist and man of letters, Alzate was a member of the Sociedad Económica Vascongada, the Real Jardín Botánico de Madrid, and the Académie Royale des Sciences de Paris. He embraced the ideas of the Enlightenment and devoted his life to the study of all branches of natural science. On various occasions, he was commissioned by the colonial government to solve problems affecting the public interest. His principal aim was to transcend the Aristotelian philosophy of his day and to promote the development of technology in New Spain. The value of his scientific production was not consistent,

however, for his work covered a great many fields and was often conducted in an unfavorable atmosphere.

Aggressive by nature, Alzate was continually involved in scientific polemics, and his sarcasm aroused the animosity of his colleagues. He struggled to contradict the European opinions regarding the inferiority of American scientific knowledge. When Charles III of Spain sent a botanical expedition to New Spain, Alzate touched off a lengthy controversy by defending the advanced botanical knowledge of the ancient Mexicans and criticizing the Spaniards' application of Linnaean methods and principles.

Using his own limited economic resources, Alzate founded several scientific periodicals: *Diario literario de México* (1768); *Asuntos varios sobre ciencias y artes* (1772); *Observaciones sobre la física, historia natural y artes utiles* (1787); and *Gazeta de literatura* (1788–1795). On the basis of these journals, all of which were designed to improve the country's welfare through technology, Alzate is considered to be one of the pioneers of scientific journalism in the western hemisphere.

As a result of his continuous efforts to promote the scientific advancement of his countrymen and his successful fight to abolish the scholastic systems used in the colonial institutions, Alzate is regarded as one of the forerunners of Mexican independence. In 1884, the Sociedad Científica Antonio Alzate (now known as the Academia Nacional de Ciencias) was founded in Mexico City. Many Mexican intellectuals consider Alzate to be the father of modern natural science in Mexico.

BIBLIOGRAPHY

For information on Alzate's life and work, see F. Fernández del Castillo, "Apuntes para la biografía del Presbítero Bachiller J. A. F. de Alzate y Ramírez," in *Memorias de la Sociedad científica "Antonio Alzate,"* **48** (1927), 347–375; J. Galindo y Villa, "El Pbro. J. A. Alzate y Ramírez. Apuntes biográficos y bibliográficos," *ibid.,* **3** (1889–1890), 125–183, and "El enciclopedista Antonio Alzate," in *Memorias de la Academia nacional de ciencias "Antonio Alzate,"* **54** (1934), 9–14; A. Gómez Orozco, "Don Antonio Alzate y Ramírez," in *Humanidades,* **1** (1943), 169–177. See also R. Moreno Montes de Oca, "Alzate y la conciencia nacional," in *Memorias de la Academia nacional de ciencias "Antonio Alzate,"* **57** (1955), 561–572, and "Alzate y su concepción de la ciencia," in *Memorias del primer coloquio mexicano de historia de la ciencia,* **2** (1965), 185–200; B. Navarro, "Alzate, símbolo de la cultura ilustrada mexicana," in *Memorias de la Academia nacional de ciencias "Antonio Alzate,"* **57** (1952), 176–183.

ENRIQUE BELTRÁN

AMAGAT, ÉMILE (*b.* Saint-Satur, Cher, France, 2 January 1841; *d.* Saint-Satur, 15 February 1915), *physics.*

Amagat became *docteur-es-sciences* at Paris in February 1872 and was then, successively, *agrégé*, professor of physics at the Faculté Libre des Sciences of Lyons, and examiner at the École Polytechnique. He was elected a corresponding member of the Académie des Sciences on 5 May 1890, received from the Institut the Prix Lacaze pour la Physique in 1893, and became a full member of the Académie on 9 June 1902.

Amagat's work dealt with fluid statics. At the time he began his work, Andrews had just announced the structure of a few isotherms of carbon dioxide at between 10° and 50°C. and up to 110 atmospheres, the region in which the product of pressure times volume is at a minimum for this compound. Andrews' report was published in France in 1870, and his research was the only one, at the time, to use varying temperatures. From 1869 to 1872 Amagat studied the effect of temperatures up to 320° on the compressibility and expansion of gases. These studies led to his doctoral thesis.

Knowledge of liquids was even more limited. It was known that, except for water, the coefficient of compressibility increases with the temperature. Amagat published an extensive report on this subject in 1877, showing that this coefficient clearly decreases when pressure increases, which was contrary to the results reached by other experimenters.

There remained the search for the laws of the coefficients of compressibility, the coefficients of expansion under constant pressure and constant volume, the coefficients of pressure when both pressure and temperature are varied, and the limits toward which these laws tend when matter is more and more condensed by pressure. It was to this research that Amagat devoted the active phase of his career.

His first works were published between 1879 and 1882. They display the isotherms of a number of gases for temperatures between 0° and 100° and for pressures up to slightly more than 400 atmospheres (the limit that could be borne by the sturdiest glass tubes available).

The experimental data used as a base for this research were furnished by measurements taken in 1879 in a mine shaft at Verpilleux, near Saint-Étienne. Amagat determined by means of a column of mercury 327 meters high the compressibility of nitrogen up to 430 atmospheres. His results were universally adopted for the calculation of gas manometers. Until then only Regnault's results had been available, and they went only to thirty atmospheres. As for Andrews, he had

been content to apply Mariotte's (Boyle's) law up to 110 atmospheres, using a compressed-air manometer.

At the end of this first stage of his research Amagat realized that certain questions vital to the theory of fluids could be elucidated only by greatly increasing the limit of pressures. But having already gone beyond the possible resistance of glass tubes, he had to invent new experimental methods. At this point Amagat created his most ingenious apparatus, the manometer with free-moving pistons in viscous liquids; thus he was able to measure with certainty and regularity pressures above 3,000 atmospheres. Using an idea that originated with Gally-Cazolat, Amagat constructed an apparatus that was a back-acting hydraulic press made gas-tight by means of a viscous liquid such as molasses or castor oil.

Amagat's manometer served his own research and was also adopted in many military and firearms laboratories. The same apparatus, put in reverse, made it possible to create considerable pressures while measuring them. A remarkable application of this device is credited to Vieille in the adjustment of crushing cylinders for the creation of pressure in firearms.

Amagat's own work, which had to do with gases and a fairly large number of liquids, was published between 1886 and 1893. After having constructed his network of isotherms (1887–1891), he spent the next two years extracting the experimental laws of fluid statics as they emerged from these results. Without the experimental data contributed by Amagat, many important theoretical works would have been impossible: research on liquids, Tait's kinetic theory of gases, the works of Van Der Waals, the computation of coefficients in Sarrau's formula (pressure and temperature in the detonation of explosives), and Sarrau's application of his formula to oxygen, which made it possible to determine the critical temperature of this gas before it was liquefied by Wroblewski.

Having been forced to study the elasticity of glass in order to gauge the variations in volume of the containers holding the fluids studied, in 1889–1890 Amagat broadened his study until it embraced the elasticity of solids in general, starting with a verification of the general formulas of elasticity. As a correlative study he had to determine the compressibility of mercury. As early as 1876 and 1882 he had done research on the elasticity of rarefied gases. Amagat found that air, hydrogen, and carbon dioxide follow Mariotte's law at pressures as low as 1/10,000 atmosphere.

Amagat then turned to various special studies related to his general research: interior pressure of fluids; negative interior pressure; laws regulating the specific heats of fluids at different temperatures and pressures, and their relationship; verification of Van Der Waals' law of corresponding states, according to which the equation of the state of all gases can be represented by a single function in which critical temperature, pressure, and volume appear as parameters; solidification of liquids by pressure; determination of the density of liquefied gases and of their saturated vapor; the atomic volume of oxygen and of hydrogen; the interaction of oxygen and mercury; the differential equation of the speed of sound in gases; and the relations between the coefficients of the formulas of Coulomb (magnetism), Laplace, and Ampère: "The Laplace formula connects those of Coulomb and of Ampère but only by employing an almost constant factor that experience alone can determine."

BIBLIOGRAPHY

Amagat presented all accounts of his work to the Académie des Sciences; his papers are listed in the following indexes to the *Comptes rendus* of the Académie: for Vols. **62–91** (12 papers); **92–121** (48 papers); **122–151** (18 papers); and **152–181** (4 papers). Individual papers are "Compressibilité de l'air et de l'hydrogène à des températures élevées," in *Annales de chimie et de physique,* 4th series, **28** (1873), 274–279; "Dilatation et compressibilité des gaz à diverses températures," *ibid.,* **29** (1873), 246–285; "Recherches sur l'élasticité de l'air sous de faibles pressions," *ibid.,* 5th series, **8** (1876), 270–278; "Recherches sur la compressibilité des liquides," *ibid.,* **11** (1877), 520–549; "Sur l'équation différentielle de la vitesse du son," in *Journal de physique,* 1st series, **9** (1880), 56–59; "Mémoire sur la compressibilité des gaz aux fortes pressions. Influence de la température," in *Annales de chimie et de physique,* 5th series, **22** (1881), 353–398; "Mémoire sur la compressibilité de l'air et de l'acide carbonique de 1 atm. à 8 atm. et de 10° à 300°," *ibid.,* **28** (1883), 456–464; "Mémoire sur la compressibilité de l'air, de l'hydrogène et de l'acide carbonique raréfiés," *ibid.,* 464–480; "Sur une forme nouvelle de la fonction φ (pvt) = 0," *ibid.,* 480–507; "Sur la détermination du rapport $\frac{C}{c}$," in *Journal de physique,* 2nd series, **4** (1885), 174–177; "Mémoires sur l'élasticité des solides et la compressibilité du mercure," in *Annales de chimie et de physique,* 6th series, **22** (1891); "Sur la détermination de la densité des gaz et de leur vapeur saturée, éléments du point critique de l'acide carbonique," in *Journal de physique,* 3rd series, **1** (1892), 288–298; "Sur le déplacement de la température du maximum de densité de l'eau par la pression et le retour aux lois ordinaires sous l'influence de la pression et de la température," *ibid.,* 3rd series, **2** (1893), 449–459; "Mémoires sur l'élasticité et la dilatation des fluides jusqu'aux très hautes pressions," in *Annales de chimie et de physique,* 6th series, **29** (1893), 68–137 and 505–574, 2 articles; "Pressions intérieures dans les fluides et forme de la fonction φ (pvt) = 0," in *Journal de physique,* 3rd series, **3** (1894), 307–316; and "Sur les chaleurs spécifiques des gaz et les propriétés des isothermes," *ibid.,* 3rd series, **5** (1896), 114–123.

No general study has been made of Amagat's life or his work. See, however, *Notice sur les travaux scientifiques de M. E. H. Amagat . . .*(Paris, 1896), which, although published anonymously, was written by Amagat himself to be presented to the Académie des Sciences at the time of his candidature, in accordance with traditional practice.

JACQUES PAYEN

AMATUS LUSITANUS. See **Lusitanus, Amatus.**

AMEGHINO, FLORENTINO (*b.* Luján, Buenos Aires province, Argentina, or somewhere on the Atlantic, or in Liguria, Italy, *ca.* 28 September 1854; *d.* La Plata, Argentina, 6 August 1911), *paleontology, prehistory, anthropology, geology.*

The son of Antonio Ameghino, a mason and a warehouse keeper, and Maria Dina Armanino, both of whom had come to Argentina from Italy, Florentino received only a scanty formal education. One of his teachers, Carlos D'Aste, awed by Ameghino's intelligence, took him to his home in Buenos Aires in 1868 so that he could attend the Escuela Normal de Preceptores. He was thus able to teach school in Mercedes in the early 1870's.

At fourteen Ameghino read Lyell in French and was imbued with the spirit of evolutionism. The geology and geography of the Luján area, particularly the exposed strata and the fauna fossils in the ravines of the Luján River, had aroused his interest in natural science. In 1869 he explored the area around Luján, collecting fossil bones of extinct fauna and Indian relics. His studies at this time included anthropology, Argentine geology, and paleontology. He also frequented the German naturalist Karl Burmeister's natural history museum and library. Ironically, in later life Ameghino and Burmeister became bitter enemies through the combination of Burmeister's professional jealousy and Ameghino's bold advocacy of his doctrines.

In 1873 Ameghino contracted an unidentified illness and was directed to take long walks as part of the cure. His interest in and love of nature were thus increased, as was his endurance; in 1882, short of funds, he walked from the capital to Luján. His health was again threatened when he was poisoned by a mushroom of the type identified by R. Singer as *Amanita ameghinoi.* From 1890 on, Ameghino suffered from diabetes and other disabilities, especially in the four years after 1898. He died of gangrene of the foot.

Soon after he turned twenty, Ameghino published his first important geological work, "El Tajamar y sus futuras consecuencias y el origen de la Tosca." On 31 October 1875 he announced to Paul Gervais, director of the *Journal de zoologie,* that he had made a discovery in the Frías brook near Mercedes, which had been verified by Ramorino, and another in the Luján River. Gervais also helped him to publish a summary of his years in Mercedes. In it Ameghino claimed that the Argentine Amerindian was contemporary with the extinct fauna of the Pampas, a position that encountered stiff opposition. Ameghino sent a work on fossil man, espousing Darwin's transformist view, to the Scientific Society of Argentina. It was not published, but it put him in touch with Francisco Moreno and Estanislao Zeballos. Articles on the Pampean formation, written in 1875, were incorporated into "Los terrenos de transporte cuaternario de la provincia de Buenos Aires," which was presented to the Scientific Society of Argentina in 1876 but was never published. In this work he defended his Pliocene chronology (now accepted as Pleistocene) and Lyell's uniformitarianism against catastrophism.

Nogaro and Salomones, two friends from Mercedes, provided Ameghino with the means to go to Paris. "El hombre de la formación pampeana," presented at the French Exposition early in 1878, was published in *The American Naturalist.* During his three years in Europe, Ameghino did much to increase his knowledge: he traveled to Copenhagen, where he examined the Brazilian fossils collected by Lund; he attended the Zoological Congress in Bologna; he visited museums in Belgium and England; and he took courses at the Museum of Natural Sciences and the School of Anthropology in Paris. Ameghino supported himself at this time mainly through selling fossils he had brought with him. He became a friend of Paul Gervais, who helped him classify many specimens, and of Henri Gervais, with whom he collaborated on the publication of a work detailing seventy new species of fossil mammals. With the help of Adolph and Oskar Doering he published his principal work, *Contribución al conocimiento de los mamíferos fósiles de la República Argentina* (1880). The two-volume work was so expensive to produce that he suffered financially, but it brought him gold medals at the Paris Exposition of 1889 and the Chicago Exposition of 1892. In 1880–1881 he published *La antigüedad del hombre en el río de La Plata,* the first work on Argentine prehistory in both Spanish and French. He acquired direct knowledge of the first European fossil discoveries and, with Mortillet, he visited the Chelles site near Paris.

While he was in Paris, Ameghino lost his teaching position in Mercedes. When he returned to Buenos Aires he started a bleaching business, which soon failed. He then opened a secondhand bookshop in 1882 and brought his brother Juan into the business. Later Ameghino gave the shop to his mother, who ran it until 1908, and then to his brother, who kept it going until his death in 1932.

In 1884 Ameghino published *Filogenia,* in which he proposed to find irrefutable proof of transformism. This gave rise to a great quarrel with the Linnaean-Cuvierist wing of the clergy. In the same year, with the help of Juárez Celman, he obtained the chair of zoology at the University of Córdoba. Through the intercession of Adolph Doering, he was also offered the directorship of the Anthropological Museum, but he remained there for only a year. Two years later Francisco Moreno nominated him for secretary of the La Plata Museum, and he was appointed to the post in July 1886. Ameghino sold to the museum at least part of his collection of fossils and archaeological finds for $16,500. The collection was thought to number about 15,000 items, although Ameghino later said that there were only 8,000, of which half would go to the museum. He was named professor of geology and mineralogy at the University of La Plata in 1887. Unfortunately, his friend Moreno had an exaggerated concept of his authority, and they quarreled. Ameghino resigned as secretary of the museum in 1890.

The saddest period of Ameghino's life began in 1890, when he lost his professorship and was barred from entering the museum housing his collection. He attempted to support himself by opening a bookstore in La Plata and by founding the *Revista argentina de historia natural,* which lasted for only six issues. What little money he did accumulate was lost in the depression of 1893. Ameghino therefore sent a collection to Zittel in Munich, and was too poor to refuse the pittance offered for it. The American paleontologist William B. Scott, who benefited from Ameghino's hospitality and scholarly materials during this period, wrote: "I do not know of a finer example of courage and abnegation under the most distressing circumstances in the history of science. . . . He has made a vow of humility and poverty in the name of science and he is one of the greatest civil heroes in Argentina."

Despite the hardships, the period from 1895 to 1902 was Ameghino's most fruitful; the *Proceedings of the Zoological Society of London* published his account of the plexodontal molars of mammals in 1899. His fortunes improved considerably in 1902, when, thanks to the minister of education, Joaquín González, he was made director of the Museum of Natural Sciences in Buenos Aires. During his nine years as director he added 71,000 objects to its collections and published fifteen issues of its *Anales*. In 1906 he assumed the added duties of professor of geology at the University of La Plata.

Ameghino's brothers were of great help to him. Carlos assisted him on sixteen classification explorations, and his accurate observations resulted in Florentino's modification of his identification of a number of orders and genera. Juan, although an accomplished botanist, was too timid to publish any of his work; he preferred to help in the family bookstore, thereby freeing Florentino for science.

Ameghino was one of the most eminent geologists and paleontologists of his day and discovered many fossil fauna. On the other hand, his anthropological works are of doubtful value today. For instance, it is now known that his Pampas finds were more recent than he and his disciples thought. His errors were unavoidable, however, because of his early isolation and because the sciences themselves were so new. As so often happens, his fame was greater outside his own country.

In geology, Ameghino placed the Guaraní and Chubut formations in the Cretaceous period of the Secondary; six Argentine formations in the Tertiary period; the post-Pampean in the Pleistocene period of the Quaternary; and upper alluvial deposits in the Holocene. He then divided each of these formations into subaerial and freshwater stages with marine parallels, detailing and dividing them further in 1908. This paleontological geochronology has been disputed by geologists relying upon tectonic and mineralogical characteristics. Ingenieros, however, believes that Ameghino's stratigraphy itself is correct, very valuable, and based upon a great deal of material.

In paleontology, his first specialty, Ameghino achieved the same results that Haeckel had achieved in embryology by utilizing mathematical zoology with the seriation procedure. In 1889 he determined 450 species of fossil mammals, an astounding year's work. By 1906 he had classified thirty-five suborders; in all, he discovered over 6,000 species. His most controversial theory was that these fossils were older than those of other countries and that Argentina was the center from which those creatures had spread.

It is very possible that Ameghino had no knowledge of the work in prehistory that occurred during his early life, and therefore, according to Schobinger, he re-created and rediscovered human prehistory in Argentina. This brought him into conflict with Euro-

peans over the characteristics he attributed to Pampean man, although his contacts with Gervais lead one to suppose that he soon came to know the work of his French contemporaries. In Luján and Mercedes he found worked stones (chips), arrowheads, boleadora stones, and other more modern items, as well as ceramics and objects made of bone. Near the Córdoba observatory he found an authentic Pleistocene site with a fire site, some stone chips, and animal bones. He was not infallible, however: he attributed two rough artifacts from the Buenos Aires seashore to the Tertiary period, when they actually belonged to the beginning of the Holocene.

In his later years Ameghino had four theories on the evolution of the higher primates: (1) He excluded *Homo heidelbergensis* (Mauer's mandible) and *Pithecanthropus erectus* from the direct line of human phylogeny, considering them extinct lateral branches. (2) The primitive hominids of the early Miocene were derived from the anthropoid apes. (3) *Homo simius*, or *Homo australopithecus*, of Africa, was derived from the *Tetraprothomo*. (4) The Neanderthal man (*Homo primigenus*) was derived laterally from *Homo sapiens*.

All was not success, however, for Ameghino's construction of Eocene ancestors and his stubborn identification of remains he found with various stages of protohumanity (his *prothomo*) have since been repudiated. His anthropological knowledge of the *Tetraprothomo* was based only on an atlas and a femur he found in Monte Hermoso in 1907, and the latter was accepted as human by only a few scholars. Ameghino provided no physical evidence for the *Triprothomo*, and the *Diprothomo* of 1909 was also very weak, for it was based only on a piece of cranial cap. Ever since Father Blanco there has been criticism of the circumstances of the latter discovery, which took place in terrain of doubtful antiquity in the port of Buenos Aires, and was based upon an erroneous bone orientation.

This was not the only criticism of Ameghino's work. Márquez considered his four phylogenetic links irritatingly simple, but he accepted the contemporaneity of the extinct large mammals of the loess and Pampean man. He also felt Ameghino's philosophical elucidations were colored by a markedly candid materialism. Frenguelli criticized his geological stratigraphy because the Pampas were more modern than Ameghino claimed, but nevertheless recognized Ameghino's great perceptivity, his profound powers of observation, and his great talent. His theory that man originated during the Tertiary period on the Pampas has been rejected, and the bones and archaeological items he uncovered have proved, upon investigation, to be the weakest part of his work in prehistory.

BIBLIOGRAPHY

I. ORIGINAL WORKS. Ameghino's writings were collected as *Obras completas y correspondencia científica,* Alfredo Torcelli, ed., 24 vols. (La Plata, 1913–1936). Individual works are "El Tajamar y sus futuras consecuencias y el origen de la Tosca," in *El pueblo* of Mercedes (2 June 1875) and in *Obras completas,* I, 11; "Nouveaux débris de l'homme et de son industrie melés à des ossements quaternaires recueillis auprès (près) de Mercedes," in *Journal de zoologie,* 4 (1875), 527; 5 (1875), 27; "The Man of the Pampean Formation," in *The American Naturalist,* 12 (1880), 828; *Contribución al conocimiento de los mamíferos fósiles de la República Argentina,* 2 vols. (1880); *Los maníferos fósiles de la América Meridional* (Paris–Buenos Aires, 1880), text in both Spanish and French, written with H. Gervais; "Un recuerdo a la memoria de Darwin. El transformismo considerado como ciéncia exacta," in *Boletín del Instituto geográfico argentino,* 3, no. 12 (1882), 205–213; *Filogenia* (Buenos Aires, 1884, 1915); "New Discoveries of Fossil Mammalians of Southern Patagonia," in *The American Naturalist,* 27 (1893), 445 ff.; the account of the primitive types of plexodontal molars of mammals, in *Proceedings of the Zoological Society of London* (1899), 555–571 (or 575), also trans. into French in *Anales del Museo nacional de historia natural de Buenos Aires* (16 Dec. 1902); and *La antigüedad del hombre en el río de La Plata,* Vol. III of Ameghino's *Obras completas* (La Plata, 1915), also published separately in 2 vols. (Buenos Aires, 1918).

II. SECONDARY LITERATURE. Among the works on Ameghino or his contributions are Juan B. Ambrosetti, "Florentino Ameghino," in *Anales del Museo nacional de historia natural de Buenos Aires* (1912); José María Blanco, *La evolución antropológica y Ameghino* (Buenos Aires, 1916); Ángel Cabrera, *El pensamiento vivo de Ameghino* (Buenos Aires, 1944); Arturo Capdevila, "Ameghino el vidente," in *La prensa* of Buenos Aires (25 May 1932); Alfredo Castellanos, *Homenaje a Florentino Ameghino* (Rosario, 1937); Pedro Daniels, "Presencia y actualidad de Ameghino," in *La hora médica argentina* (Sept. 1954), pp. 167–169; Joaquín Frenguelli, *La personalidad y la obra de Florentino Ameghino* (La Plata, 1934); Max Friedmann, "Vorlage eines Gipsabgusses des Schädeldaches von *Diprothomo Platensis* Ameghino," in *Zeitschrift für Ethnologie* (1910); Bernardo González Arrili, *Vida de Ameghino* (Santa Fe, 1954); Mario Graci Larravide, *Florentino Ameghino* (Mendoza, 1944); Alex Hrdlicka, *Early Man in South America* (Washington, D.C., 1912), see index; José Ingenieros, *Las doctrinas de Ameghino,* Vol. XVIII of his *Obras completas* (Buenos Aires, 1939); Arthur Keith, *The Antiquity of Man* (London, 1916), ch. 17; Robert Lehmann-Nitsche, "Ameghino como antropólogo," in *Renacimiento,* 3 (31 Aug. 1911); P. G. Mahoudeau, "Les primates et les prosimiens fossiles de la Patagonie d'après les travaux de M. Florentino Ameghino," in *Revue de l'École d'anthropologie de Paris,* 11 (1907), 354–361; Osvaldo Menghin, *Origen y desarrollo racial de la especie humana* (Buenos Aires, 1957), p. 70; Fernando Márquez Miranda, *Ameghino. Una vida heróica* (Buenos Aires, 1951); Victor Mercante, "Dr. Florentino Ameghino. Su vida y sus obras," in Ameghino's *Obras completas,* I, 148–170; Aldobrandino Mocchi, "Nota preventiva sul *Diprothomo platensis,*" in *Revista del Museo de La Plata,* 17 (1910–1911), 70; Ricardo Rojas, *Historia de la literatura argentina,* VII (Buenos Aires, 1960), 53–60; Alberto Rovero and Victor Delfino, "La obra antropológica de Florentino Ameghino," in *La semana médica,* no. 18 (1914); V. G. Ruggeri, "Die Entdeckungen Florentino Ameghino's und der Ursprung des Menschen," in *Globus,* 94, no. 11 (1908), 21–26; Carlos Rusconi, *Florentino Ameghino. Rasgos de su vida y su obra* (Mendoza, 1965); and *Animales extinguidos de Mendoza y de la Argentina* (Mendoza, 1967), see index; Antonio Santiana, *La personalidad creadora de Ameghino* (Quito, 1954); Domingo Sarmiento, "El señor Ameghino," in *El nacional* (10 July 1883) and in his *Obras completas,* XLII (Buenos Aires, 1900), 140; Juan Schobinger, *Cincuentenario de la muerte de Ameghino* (Mendoza, 1961); G. Schwalbe, "Studien zur Morphologie der südamerikanischen Primatenformen," in *Zeitschrift für Morphologie und Anthropologie,* 13 (1910); William B. Scott, *A History of Land Mammals in the Western Hemisphere* (New York, 1937), pp. 114, 500, 504, 544; Rodolfo Senet, *Ameghino. Su vida y su obra* (Buenos Aires, 1934); George Simpson, "The Beginning of Mammals in South America," in *Bulletin of the American Museum of Natural History,* 91 (1948), which lists 19 works by Ameghino; Miguel Soria, "Intoxicación accidental por *Chlorophyllum molybdites,*" in *Prensa universitaria* of Buenos Aires (28 Nov. 1966), pp. 2427–2428; Kasimiers Stolihwo, "Contribución al estudio del hombre fósil sudamericano y su pretendido precursor el *Diprothomo platensis,*" trans. from the Polish by Victor Delfino, in *Semana médica* (15 Aug. 1912); Herbert Wenk, *Tras las huellas de Adán* (Barcelona, 1958), pp. 545, 547, 548; and Karl von Zittel, *Grundzüge der Paläontologie. Vertebrata* (Munich–Berlin. 1911), see index.

JUSTO GARATE

AMES, JOSEPH SWEETMAN (*b.* Manchester, Vermont, 3 July 1864; *d.* Baltimore, Maryland, 24 June 1943), *physics.*

Ames's father, George L. Ames, a physician, died in 1869; in 1874 his mother, Elizabeth Bacon Ames, married Dr. James Dobbin, rector of the Shattuck School in Fairbault, Minnesota, where Ames was a student. At home, Ames, who was raised an Episcopalian, acquired a lasting taste for classical education, books, and good society. At Johns Hopkins University, where he went after the Shattuck School, he developed an enthusiasm for physics. After graduating in 1886, he spent two years in Helmholtz' laboratory in Berlin. He returned to Johns Hopkins to take his Ph.D. in 1890 under Henry A. Rowland, the inventor of the curved spectral grating, and then joined the Johns Hopkins faculty. He was director of the physical laboratory from 1901 to 1926, provost of the university from 1926 to 1929, and president from 1929 to 1935. In 1899 he married Mary B. Harrison, a widow from Maryland.

Ames's research was limited in quantity and largely confined to the field of spectroscopy. Working closely with Rowland in the 1890's, he struggled with the problem of finding relationships among the lines of particular spectra. Johann Balmer had already advanced his formula for the hydrogen lines; Ames, measuring with great exactitude the spectra of more complex atoms, tried empirically to find relationships among the wave numbers (the reciprocals of the wave lengths in vacuo). He concluded that the answer could come only from theoretical considerations. But by 1913, when Bohr's theory was published, Ames had given up research and had turned to administration.

Ames, a man of courtly manner and executive talent, was an able administrator. He kept the physics department at Johns Hopkins alive despite persistent budgetary problems by cooperating with the National Bureau of Standards. He encouraged the faculty to offer courses there and graduate students to do their research at the Bureau's well-equipped laboratories.

In World War I Ames, a member of the National Academy of Sciences, was drawn into the affairs of government research. He served on the Academy's National Research Council and on the National Advisory Committee for Aeronautics. The NACA, created by Congress in 1915 to promote the scientific study of flight, was deeply enmeshed in policy matters. Ames got into trouble for writing publicly that the government's ambitious aircraft program was far behind schedule; Secretary of Commerce William C. Redfield considered the statement a treasonous act. But Ames, as it turned out, was right. His judgment won increasing respect, and he became chairman of the NACA's Executive Committee in 1919, the year that he was elected president of the American Physical Society.

Ames held the chairmanship of the Executive Committee until 1936 and served as chairman of the entire NACA from 1927 to 1939. During his administration the agency's technical publications won the respect of aeronautical experts all over the world. In 1935 the Smithsonian Institution awarded Ames the Langley Gold Medal for his leadership of the NACA. In 1939 the Committee decided to name its new Moffet Field, California, research facility the Ames Aeronautical Laboratory.

BIBLIOGRAPHY

Aside from a scattering of Ames's papers in the Archives of the Johns Hopkins University, Baltimore, Maryland, the principal body of his extant correspondence is in the records of the National Advisory Committee for Aeronautics in the National Archives, Washington, D. C. In the *Annual Reports* of the NACA during his administration, Ames discussed the work of the Committee and provided a running commentary on the development of aeronautics.

Henry Crew, "Joseph Sweetman Ames," in *National Academy of Sciences Biographical Memoirs,* **23** (1945), 181–201, is a shallow, sentimental essay but contains a complete bibliography of Ames's scientific work.

DANIEL J. KEVLES

AMES, WILLIAM (*b.* Ipswich, Suffolk, England, 1576; *d.* Rotterdam, Netherlands, 1 November 1633), *theology, natural philosophy.*

Ames was the son of a prosperous Ipswich merchant, William Ames, and his wife, Joan Snelling. His parents died during his childhood, and he was brought up by an uncle, Robert Ames, at Oxford. He proceeded to Cambridge, where he matriculated as a pensioner at Christ's College in 1593/1594, obtaining his B.A. in 1597/1598 and his M.A. in 1601. As a fellow of Christ's College from 1601 until 1610, Ames took up the controversial theological position of his tutor, the celebrated Puritan William Perkins (1558–1602). Ames became a central figure in Puritan agitation at Cambridge, with the result that, in 1609, he was suspended from his degrees and expelled from his college and the university.

For a short time Ames preached at Colchester, but the opposition of George Abbot, bishop of London, caused him to emigrate to the Netherlands in 1610. There he occupied minor clerical positions at Leiden and The Hague, and became chaplain to Sir Horace Vere, English governor at Brill, succeeding another well-known Puritan, John Burgess, whose daughter became Ames's first wife. She died childless shortly after the marriage.

Ames achieved prominence at the Synod of Dordrecht (1618), where he advised the Calvinist faction. As a result of his success in the theological debates emanating from the synod, he was appointed to the chair of divinity at the University of Franeker in Friesland, in 1622. There, his erudition and abilities as a teacher attracted students from many parts of Europe, one of them the future first head of Harvard College, Nathaniel Eaton. Ames was rector of the university from 1626 to 1632. During this Franeker period he wrote most of his philosophical and theological works. He was not entirely settled in Holland, however, for the climate did not favor his health.

Plans were made for emigration to New England (1629), but instead he became minister and lecturer to the English congregation at Rotterdam (1633). Among his colleagues there were Hugh Peter and Thomas Hooke, both of whom eventually settled in America. Soon after his arrival at Rotterdam, Ames died of a fever contracted after his house was flooded. His second wife, Joan Fletcher Ames, a relation of Governor John Winthrop, and their three children went to New England in 1637. Two sons were educated at Harvard College.

As the numerous editions of Ames's works indicate, he occupied a prominent role in the Protestant theology of the first half of the seventeenth century, systematizing and developing certain aspects of the Calvinist theology of Perkins. Two particular points—practical divinity and Ramist philosophy—make Ames significant, not only for theology but also for the general intellectual history of the seventeenth century.

First, he stressed the role of "practical divinity," in reaction against the tendency of contemporary Dutch philosophers to divorce ethics from theology. By analyzing the nature of conscience, it could be shown that the tenets of theology and ethics had the same origin. The unity of theology and ethics was also proved by their mutual reliance on the Scriptures. Ames's resultant system of divinity paid the greatest attention to the rules of personal behavior and organization of the community. Like Bacon, Ames directed all Christians to the practical reform of society. This practical divinity certainly influenced the scientific outlooks of such figures as John Winthrop, Jr., Samuel Hartlib, and Robert Boyle, directing them to problems of social usefulness.

One of the reasons for the enormous popularity of Ames's writings was their strict logical organization. Through Alexander Richardson, George Downham, and Perkins, Ames had become an enthusiastic exponent of Ramist philosophy: his *Demonstratio logicae verae* and *Theses logicae* were commentaries on Ramus' *Dialecticae libri duo*. His theological works were organized according to the Ramist dichotomies, and the Ramist logic was applied to the interpretation of the dictates of conscience and the Scriptures. In this system, the scholastic boundaries of knowledge were broken down. Theology impinged on natural philosophy, and mathematics and physics were seen as having inherent moral and spiritual value. These three subjects, the *artes speciales,* took their place alongside the three *artes generales*—dialectic, grammar, and rhetoric. All were subject to logical analysis, and all amalgamated into an encyclopedic system, the *Technometria.*

The apprehension of the principles of the arts was seen as an important moral duty. Ames adopted an empirical approach to this problem, believing that these principles were derived from a knowledge of the objects of nature, by a process of observation and experiment that he recognized as akin to the philosophy of induction announced in Bacon's *Novum organum* (*Technometria,* §§ 69, 70). This encyclopedic and empirical view of nature appealed greatly to the Puritan educationalists of New England, and Ames's works became the dominant forces in the curriculum of the newly founded college of Harvard, as well as in Cambridge, the Low Countries, and Transylvania. Because of the influence of such authors as Ames, there was constant interaction between theology, ethics, and natural philosophy in the areas of Calvinist influence during the seventeenth century.

BIBLIOGRAPHY

I. ORIGINAL WORKS. *Philosophemata* (Leiden, 1643; Cambridge, 1646; Amsterdam, 1651) is the collected edition of Ames's philosophical writings. Certain theological works are included in *The Works of the Reverend and Faithfull Minister of Christ William Ames* (London, 1643). Ames's collected works are *Opera, quae Latine scripsit omnia,* Matthias Nethemus, ed., 5 vols. (Amsterdam, 1658), with a biographical account in the Preface; the philosophical writings are in Vol. V.

Some of Ames's individual works are *Medulla theologia* (Franeker, 1623; Amsterdam, 1627, 1659), translated into English as *The Marrow of Sacred Divinity, Drawne Out of the Holy Scriptures, and the Interpreters Thereof* (London, ca. 1638, 1642, 1643); *De Conscientia et eius iure vel casibus libri quinque* (Amsterdam, 1631, 1670), translated into English as *Conscience With the Power and Cases Thereof* (London [?], 1639 [?], 1643); *Demonstratio logicae verae* (Leiden, 1632; Cambridge, 1646); *Disputatio theologica adversus metaphysicam* (Leiden, 1632; Hanau, 1640; Cambridge, 1646); *Technometria, omnium & singularum artium fines adaequate circumscribens* (Amsterdam–Leiden, 1632, 1633); and *Theses logicae* (Cambridge, 1646).

II. SECONDARY LITERATURE. See "William Ames," in *Biographia Britannica,* A. Kippis, ed., I (London, 1747), 135–137; J. Bass Mullinger, "William Ames," in *Dictionary of National Biography,* I (London, 1885), 355–357; Paul Dibon, *La philosophie néerlandaise au siècle d'or,* I (Amsterdam, 1954), 151–154; G. L. Kittredge, "A Note on Dr. William Ames," in *Transactions of the Colonial Society of Massachusetts,* 13 (1910/1911), 60–69; Perry Miller, *The New England Mind* (New York, 1939); S. E. Morison, *The Founding of Harvard College* (Cambridge, Mass., 1935), and *Harvard College in the Seventeenth Century,* 2 vols. (Cambridge, Mass., 1936), I, 164–165; George L. Mosse, *The Holy Pretence* (Oxford, 1957), ch. 5; *Nieuw Nederlandsch biographisch Woordenboek* (Amsterdam, 1911–

1937), VI, 36; J. Piele, *Biographical Register of Christ's College,* 2 vols. (Cambridge, 1910), I, 211–212; Karl Reuter, *Wilhelm Amesius der führende Theologe des erwachenden reformierten Pietismus* (Neukirchen, 1940); Keith L. Sprunger, "Technometria: A Prologue to Puritan Theology," in *Journal of the History of Ideas,* **29** (1968), 115–122; and Hugo Visscher, *Gulielmus Amesius. Zijn Leven en Werken* (Haarlem, 1894), theology thesis, Leiden University.

CHARLES WEBSTER

AMICI, GIOVAN BATTISTA (*b.* Modena, Italy, 23 March 1786; *d.* Florence, Italy, 10 April 1868), *optics, microscopy, natural sciences.*

Amici was the son of Giuseppe Amici, a ministerial official, and Maria Dalloca, a member of a well-to-do family. In 1806 he married Teresa Tamanini, the daughter of a wealthy Tyrolean bookseller. The following year he graduated as an engineer-architect from the University of Bologna and immediately became a mathematics teacher at the Modena *liceo.* In 1831 Amici was invited to Florence by the grand duke of Tuscany to head the astronomical observatory and the Royal Museum of Physics and Natural History. He held this office until 1859, when, because of his advanced age of seventy-three, he accepted the less demanding office of director of microscopic research at the museum.

From early youth, Amici was interested in optical instruments, particularly microscopes, and it was in this field that he achieved his fame. In spite of the efforts of many pioneers during the previous two centuries to refine the microscope, in the early nineteenth century scientific microscopy was carried out exclusively with the simple microscope because it performed better than the compound microscope, particularly in resolving power. A comparative study of the microscopes of the past centuries has been made by P. Harting and the Van Citterts, who have thoroughly examined the microscopes in the collection of the Museum of the History of Science at Utrecht. Their study clearly indicates Amici's decisive contribution to the use of the compound microscope.

In the early nineteenth century, compound microscopes were much less accurate than the simple microscopes, not only because their objectives caused strong aberrations, especially chromatic ones, but above all because the numerical aperture was not yet known to be the determining factor of the resolving power; therefore construction was governed by the erroneous conviction that enlargement was the most important factor. In 1791 the first achromatic lens for compound microscopes was built as the result of the work of an Amsterdam amateur, F. Beeldsnijder; the images were quite good, but the resolution was only 0.01

mm., while the resolution of simple microscopes reached 0.0015 mm. Only around 1806 did microscopes with achromatic objectives appear on the market, through the efforts of Harmanus Van Deyl, also of Amsterdam; these were instruments that could magnify 150 times and could resolve to 0.005 mm.

This lead was immediately followed by scientists all over the world, especially Chevalier and Nachet; Oberhäuser and Plössl; Tulley, Pritchard, and Ross; and Amici, who was just embarking on his career. Within thirty years, the efforts of these and many other scientists succeeded in making the resolving power of the compound microscope equal to that of the simple microscope. For example, as early as 1818 Amici, after having built a type of catadioptric microscope that was free of chromatic aberrations, succeeded in appreciably improving the knowledge of the circulation of protoplasm in *Chara* cells, thereby becoming immediately famous not only as an optician but also as a microscopic biologist.

His most sensational innovation was achieved in 1837, when Amici arrived at a resolving power of 0.001 mm. with a new type of microscope that had a numerical aperture of 0.4 and was capable of magnifying up to 6,000 times. This device consisted of a hemispheric frontal lens applied to the objective; only through this contrivance was it possible to increase the numerical aperture to an appreciable extent. It was the hemispheric lens that permitted maximum use of the compound microscope. All opticians, with the exception of the French, immediately adopted this new design.

The improvement introduced by Amici also led to a significant theoretical clarification. The moderate influence of the magnification in the operation of the microscope was soon recognized and values ranging around 1,000X were generally achieved. It was emphasized, however, that resolution was due mainly to the numerical aperture and to the optical correction by the objective. Amici clearly stated his discovery in a letter of 25 October 1855 to his friend Ottaviano Mossotti, professor at the University of Pisa and a famous optical mathematician; the following passage is particularly interesting:

The objectives of my microscopes consisting of six lenses, three crown lenses and three flint lenses, happen to be achromatic. I found out, however, that the sets consisting of three pairs of lenses, as I mentioned, were not the best suitable for achieving greater magnification, particularly due to the fact that the lower pair closer to the object are too large and make it impossible to obtain a very short focal distance of the system and its very large aperture. I then had the idea of replacing the lower pair with a simple lens, i.e., a half-sphere of any transparent substance, either crown, flint, low-grade ruby, diamond, molten rock crystal, etc., and thus eliminating its aberrations by means of the two suitably processed upper pairs. In order to accomplish this, I needed a flint with very high dispersion, which I was able to obtain from Faraday thanks to Airy. The English opticians laughed at this request but, when I showed them the superiority of the new construction in London in 1844, they soon tried to imitate it, and the Americans followed suit. The French, who were not interested and who were unable to understand the improvement, were outdistanced by the others.

Amici was so convinced that the numerical aperture was the theoretical factor determining a microscope's power that he continued to do everything possible to increase it, not only by manufacturing objectives with ever greater numerical aperture (Harting states that in 1856 he purchased from Amici a microscope objective with a numerical aperture of 0.985) but also by inventing the technique of immersion microscopy; he first used water, then olive oil, and finally sassafras oil. He even became aware of the influence that the thickness of the cover glass has on the quality of the image in the microscope.

Amici moved to Florence, where he devoted his attention to other optical processes, although his interest in microscopy never flagged. He invented widely used prisms that still bear his name, and reconsidered the direct-vision prism, which had been forgotten. He also built concave mirrors and astronomical lenses. His masterpiece was a lens with a diameter of 285 mm.: this was so far in advance of his time that it was presented as a rarity to the Third Congress of Italian Scientists, held in Florence in 1841. Only one lens larger than this existed at that time. Amici's lens was so successful that it is still in use at the Arcetri Astronomical Observatory. Amici also invented new micrometers to improve the accuracy of astronomical measurements, and new types of distance-measuring telescopes.

While Amici kept increasing the power of his instruments, through his theoretical know-how and his skill in optical processing, he also used them in astronomical and microscopical observations. His findings in microscopy attracted the attention of the entire biological world of his time. Besides studying the circulation of protoplasm, Amici made remarkable observations in anatomy, physiology, histology, and plant pathology, as well as in leaf morphology (discovering palisade parenchyma) and animal biology. The discovery that made him famous, however, was that of the fertilization of phanerogams, particularly the travel of the pollen tube through the pistil of the flower (1821). His early observations were followed by a heated controversy with the best-known botanists of the world, who for thirty years disputed Amici's ideas. However, by making ever finer microscopic observations, he finally won over his rivals.

The splendid wax models by which Amici illustrated the results of his microscopic observations can still be seen in many museums of natural history.

BIBLIOGRAPHY

I. ORIGINAL WORKS. Amici's main works in optics and astronomy are "Descrizione di un nuovo micrometro," in *Memorie di matematica e fisica della Società Italiana delle Scienze,* **17** (1816), 344–349; "Dei microscopii catadiottrici," *ibid.,* **18,** no. 1 (1818), 107–118; "Memoria sopra un cannocchiale iconantidiptico," in *Memorie della Società Italiana delle Scienze,* **1** (1821), 113–125; *Description d'une nouvelle lunette micrométrique* (Genoa, 1823), IX, 517–521; *Osservazioni sopra i satelliti di Giove* (Genoa, 1825), XII, 539–560; "Descrizione di un nuovo strumento per livellare," in *Atti della R. e I. Accademia dei Georgofili,* **15** (1837), 129–137; "Lettura relativa a due macchine ottiche da lui inventate," in *Atti della Prima Riunione degli Scienziati Italiani* (Pisa, 1839), pp. 49–50; and "Di alcuni perfezionamenti recentemente ottenuti in fotografia," in *Atti della Sesta Riunione degli Scienziati Italiani* (Milan, 1844), pp. 87–97.

Amici's principal publications in biology are "Osservazioni sulla circolazione del succhio nella Chara," in *Memorie della Società Italiana delle Scienze,* **18** (1818), 183–198; "Osservazioni microscopiche sopra varie piante," *ibid.,* **19** (1823), 234–255; "Descrizione di alcune specie nuove di Chara," in *Memorie della R. Accademia di Scienze, Lettere ed Arti di Modena,* **1** (1833), 199–207; "Opinione relativa all'ascensione della linfa nelle piante," in *Atti della Prima Riunione degli Scienziati Italiani* (Pisa, 1839), pp. 165–167; "Sulla presenza dei pori nei casi delle conifere e sulla loro struttura," *ibid.,* pp. 162–164; "Sul processo col quale gli ovuli vegetabili ricivono l'azione fecondante del polline," *ibid.,* pp. 134–139; "Sull'uredo rosae," *ibid.,* p. 157; "Sulla fecondazione delle piante (cucurbita pepo)," in *Atti della Quarta Riunione degli Scienziati Italiani* (Padua, 1842), pp. 279–283; "Nuove osservazioni sugli stomi del *Cereus Peruvianus," ibid.,* pp. 327–333; "Sulla struttura degli stomi," in *Atti della Sesta Riunione degli Scienziati Italiani* (Milan, 1844), pp. 513–518; "Sulla fecondazione delle orchidee," in *Atti della Ottava Riunione degli Scienziati Italiani* (Genoa, 1846), pp. 542–550; "Nota in risposta al primo articolo dello Schleiden," *ibid.,* pp. 89–90; "Sulla malattia dell'uva," in *Atti della I. e R. Accademia dei Georgofili,* **30** (1852), 454–460; "Sulla malattia della foglia del gelso, detta fersa o seccume," *ibid.,* n.s. **1** (1853), 72–79; "Sulla malattia del frumento detta rachitide," *ibid.,* 570–577; and "Sulla fibra muscolare," in *Il tempo,* **1** (1858), 2–4.

Amici's correspondence, which consists of more than 6,000 letters and has not yet been published, is in the Biblioteca Estense of Modena.

II. Secondary Literature. The principal publications on Amici are *Celebrazione del centenario della morte di G. B. Amici* (Modena, 1963); G. B. Donati, "Elogio del Prof. G. B. Amici," in *Reale Accademia dei Georgofili,* **1** (1864), 1–23; H. von Mohl, "Giovambattista Amici," in *Botanische Zeitung,* **15** (1863), 21–32; P. Pagini, "L'ottica geometrica in Italia nella prima metà del secolo XIX e l'opera di G. B. Amici," in *Rassegna nazionale* (1917), 1–35; F. Palermo, "Sulla vita e le opere di G. B. Amici," in *Bollettino di bibliografia e storia delle scienze matematiche e fisiche,* **28** (1870), 3–18; V. Ronchi, "Sopra gli obbiettivi astronomici dell'Amici," in *Rivista d'ottica e meccanica di precisione,* **2** (1922), 3–21; and "Giovan Battista Amici, Optician," in *Atti della Fondazione Giorgio Ronchi,* **18** (1963), 481–504; and P. H. Van Cittert and J. G. Van Cittert-Eymers, "The Amici Microscopes About 1850 in Possession of the University of Utrecht," in *Proceedings of the Koninklijke Nederlandsche Akademie van Wetenschappen,* **50** (1947), 5–10.

Also of value for an understanding of the microscope and its development are P. Harting, *Das Mikroskop,* 2nd German ed. (Brunswick, 1866); Maria Roseboom, *Microscopium* (Leiden, 1956); and P. H. Van Cittert and J. G. Van Cittert-Eymers, "Some Remarks on the Development of the Compound Microscope in the 19th Century," in *Proceedings of the Koninklijke Nederlandsche Akademie van Wetenschappen,* **54** (1951), 1.

Vasco Ronchi

AMMONIUS, SON OF HERMIAS (*d.* Alexandria, Egypt, *ca.* A.D. 517–526), *philosophy.*

Ammonius, surnamed "son of Hermias" to distinguish him from namesakes, was head of the Platonic school in Alexandria from 485. He is one of the characters in Zacharias Scholasticus' dialogue *Ammonius* (probably historical in essence), in which Zacharias refutes Ammonius' assertion that the cosmos is coeternal with God and explains to him the doctrine of Trinity. A sober and scholarly interpreter of Plato and Aristotle, Ammonius "harmonized" them. His works and lecture courses were frequently edited and fully utilized by three generations of his students, including Johannes Philoponus, Simplicius, Olympiodorus, David, Elias, and perhaps Boethius. He and his school managed to come to terms with Christian authorities; he himself perhaps became a Christian, albeit in name only: the faculty and students of the school were partly pagan, partly Christian. The school survived until the Arab conquest of Alexandria (*ca.* 641/642), whereas Plato's Academy was closed in 529. Its Platonism was in many respects pre-Plotinian, as has been shown especially by Praechter (*pace* Lloyd's doubts).

Damascius praised Ammonius as an accomplished mathematician and astronomer. Having witnessed his astronomical observations, Simplicius (and probably Ammonius himself) deduced the existence of a starless sphere (the *primum mobile*) enveloping the sphere of fixed stars and imparting its own motion to that sphere. Ammonius agreed with Aristotle that mathematical objects do not subsist, although they can be abstracted from physical objects. He divided theoretical philosophy into theology, mathematics, and physics (and mathematics into arithmetic, geometry, music, and astronomy), thereby again combining Aristotelian and Platonic points of view, as did Boethius later.

BIBLIOGRAPHY

I. Original Works. Ammonius' works include *In Porphyrii Isagogen,* in *Commentaria in Aristotelem Graeca,* 23 vols., Vol. IV, pt. 3 (Berlin, 1891); *In Aristotelis De interpretatione, ibid.,* Vol. IV, pt. 5 (1897) (the part defending both free will and providence in J. C. von Orelli, ed., *Alexandri Aphrodisiensis, Ammonii Hermiae filii, Plotini, Bardesanis Syri, et Georgii Gemisti Plethonis de fato quae supersunt Graece* [Zurich, 1824]); *In Aristotelis Anal. pr. 1, I,* in *Commentaria in Aristotelem Graeca,* Vol. IV, pt. 6 (1890); and lectures on Aristotle's *Metaphysics,* edited with additions by Asclepius, *ibid.,* Vol. VI, pt. 2 (1888).

See also Damascius, *Vita Isidori,* C. Zintzen, ed. (Hildesheim, 1967); Simplicius, *In De caelo,* in *Commentaria in Aristotelem Graeca,* Vol. VII (1894); and Zacharias Scholasticus, *Ammonius,* in J. P. Migne, ed., *Patrologiae cursus completus, Series graeca,* 162 vols. (Paris, 1857–1866), Vol. LXXXV.

II. Secondary Literature. Writings on Ammonius or his work are J. Freudenthal, "Ammonios 15," in Pauly-Wissowa, *Real-Encyclopädie;* P. Duhem, *Le système du monde,* II (Paris, 1914); E. Zeller and R. Mondolfo, *La filosofia dei Greci,* Vol. VI, pt. 3, G. Martano, ed. (Florence, 1961); P. Courcelle, *Les lettres grecques en Occident* (Paris, 1948); P. Merlan, *From Platonism to Neoplatonism,* 2nd ed. (Berlin, 1960), pp. 75 f.; K. Kremer, *Der Metaphysik-Begriff in den Kommentaren der Ammonius-Schule* (Berlin, 1961); L. G. Westerink, *Anonymous Prolegomena to Platonic Philosophy* (Amsterdam, 1962); A. H. Armstrong, ed., *The Cambridge History of Late Greek and Early Medieval Philosophy* (1967), the contributions by A. C. Lloyd, J. P. Sheldon-Williams, and H. Liebeschütz; and P. Merlan, "Ammonius Hermiae, Zacharias Scholasticus and Boethius," in *Greek-Roman-Byzantine Studies,* **9** (1968).

For the character of the school of Alexandria in general, see K. Praechter, "Richtungen und Schulen im Neuplatonismus," in *Genethliakon für C. Robert* (Berlin, 1910), pp. 147–156; "Christlich-neuplatonische Beziehungen," in *Byzantinische Zeitschrift,* **21** (1912), 1–27; and "Simplicius 10," in Pauly-Wissowa, *Real-Encyclopädie,* III (1927), 1.

Philip Merlan

AMONTONS

AMONTONS, GUILLAUME (*b.* Paris, France, 31 August 1663; *d.* Paris, 11 October 1705), *physics.*

Amontons's father was a lawyer from Normandy who settled in Paris. The boy became almost deaf during adolescence, and his interest then turned toward mechanics. After vain efforts to develop a perpetual motion machine, he decided, despite his family's opposition, to study physical sciences and mathematics. After studying drawing, surveying, and architecture, he was employed on various public works projects that gave him practical knowledge of applied mechanics. Later he studied celestial mechanics and applied himself to the improvement of hygrometers, barometers, and thermometers.

His first scientific production was a hygrometer in 1687. The apparatus consisted of a ball of beechwood, horn, or leather filled with mercury; it varied in size according to the humidity of the atmosphere. In 1688 he developed his shortened barometer, composed of several parallel tubes connected alternately at the top and bottom, with only alternate tubes containing mercury.

Sometime between 1688 and 1695, Amontons tried out his optical telegraph in the presence of the royal family. He published no data on this experiment, but the device is known to have consisted of a series of stations, each equipped with a spyglass, for the rapid transmission of signals. The nature of the signals to be transmitted is not known, however.

In 1695 Amontons sought to renew the use of the clepsydra as a timing apparatus on ships in order to solve the problem of determining longitude at sea. In his paper on this, he described two apparatuses that became well known by his name in the eighteenth century, although their use was never common. One was a cisternless barometer consisting of a tube narrow enough for the column of mercury to remain suspended. In his experiments with this, Amontons gradually broadened the tube into the shape of an inverted funnel. The mercury column then became shortened as atmospheric pressure decreased and lengthened as it increased.

The other was an air thermometer independent of the atmospheric pressure. Air occupied the top of one of the branches of a U-shaped tube, and by its dilation it pushed down one of the mercury columns so that the other end of the branch formed a barometric chamber.

As early as 1699 Amontons proposed a thermic motor: a machine using hot air and external combustion with direct rotation. The experiments carried on in connection with this machine led him to note that ordinary air going from the temperature of ice to that of boiling water increases its volume by about one third.

In the same year Amontons produced the first known study on the question of losses caused by friction in machines. He then established the laws of proportionality between the friction and the mutual pressure of the bodies in contact.

In 1702 Amontons returned to thermometry. Having noted that water ceases to increase its temperature from the boiling point, he proposed that the latter be the fixed thermometric point. He also observed that for an equal elevation of temperature, the increase of pressure of a gas always exists in the same proportion, no matter what the initial pressure.

The following year Amontons indicated practical ways of graduating ordinary alcohol thermometers. Also, returning to his observations of 1702, he proposed an explanation for certain natural catastrophes, such as earthquakes: If there is air very deep within the earth, it is extremely compressed and could reach an irresistible pressure as the result of a relatively small increase in temperature.

Among Amonton's last works was a barometer with a U-tube, without an open surface of mercury, to be used on shipboard. Using the same receptacle and liquids whose coefficients of expansion differed, Amontons was able to establish as false the theory that liquids "condense and cool first, before expanding with approaching heat." The observed results were due only to the expansion of the containers. Also, using a barometer as an altimeter, he tried to verify the exactitude of Mariotte's (Boyle's) law at low pressures.

One really cannot understand what has led certain authors to attribute to Amontons the creation of an air thermometer of unvarying volume. As for the idea of absolute zero, he barely implies it in his memoir of 1703 ("Le thermomètre réduit à une mesure fixe," pp. 52–54); this brief notice nevertheless presented Johann Heinrich Lambert with a point of departure for his explication of this idea (1779).

BIBLIOGRAPHY

I. Original Works. Excerpts from letters are in *Journal des savants* (8 March 1688), 245–247, and (10 May 1688), 394–396. His only book is *Remarques et expériences physiques sur la construction d'une nouvelle clepsydre . . .* (Paris, 1695). Amontons's papers, all in *Mémoires de l'Académie des Sciences,* are "De la résistance causée dans les machines . . ." (1699), 206–227, and *Histoire . . .,* 104, 109; "Moyen de substituer commodément l'action du feu . . .," *ibid.,* 112–126, and *Histoire . . .,* 101; "Discours sur quelques propriétes de l'air . . ." (1702), 155–174, and *Histoire* . . ., 1; "Que les nouvelles expériences que nous avons du poids et du ressort de l'air . . ." (1703), 101–108, and *Histoire* . . ., 6; "Remarques sur la table des degrés de chaleur . . .," *ibid.*, 200–212, and *Histoire* . . ., 9; "Le thermomètre réduit à une mesure fixe et certaine . . .," *ibid.*, 50–56 and *Histoire* . . ., 9; "Discours sur les baromètres" (1704), 271–278, and *Histoire* . . ., 1; "Que tous les baromètres tant doubles que simples . . .," *ibid.*, 164–172, and *Histoire* . . ., 1; "Baromètres sans mercure à l'usage de la mer" (1705), 49–54, and *Histoire* . . ., 1; "De la hauteur du mercure dans les baromètres" (four articles), *ibid.*, 229–231, 232–234, 234–236, 267–272, and *Histoire* . . ., 10; "Expériences sur la raréfaction de l'air," *ibid.*, 119–124 and *Histoire* . . ., 10; "Expériences sur les solutions et sur les fermentations froides . . .," *ibid.*, 83–84, and *Histoire* . . ., 68; and "Que les expériences sur lesquelles on se fonde pour prouver que les liquides se condensent et se refroidissent . . .," *ibid.*, 75–80, and *Histoire* . . ., 4.

II. SECONDARY LITERATURE. Works that discuss Amontons and his instruments are Maurice Daumas, *Les instruments scientifiques aux XVIIe et XVIIIe siècles* (Paris, 1953); [Bernard le Bovier de Fontenelle] "Éloge de M. Amontons," in *Histoire de l'Académie Royale des Sciences* (1705), 150–154; René Taton, *Histoire générale des sciences*, II, *La science moderne (de 1450 à 1800)* (Paris, 1958), pp. 258, 472, 516; and W. E. Knowles Middleton, *The History of the Barometer* (Baltimore, 1964).

JACQUES PAYEN

AMPÈRE, ANDRÉ-MARIE (*b.* Lyons, France, 22 January 1775; *d.* Marseilles, France, 10 June 1836), *mathematics, chemistry, physics.*

Ampère's father, Jean-Jacques, was a merchant of independent means who, soon after his son's birth, moved the family to the nearby village of Poleymieux, where André-Marie grew up. The house is today a national museum. Jean-Jacques Ampère had been greatly influenced by the educational theories of Rousseau and was determined to educate his son along the lines laid down in *Émile*. The method he seems to have followed was to expose his son to a considerable library and let him educate himself as his own tastes dictated. One of the first works Ampère read was Buffon's *Histoire naturelle,* which stimulated his lifelong interest in taxonomy. Probably the most important influence on him was the great *Encyclopédie*—even thirty years later he could recite many of the articles from memory. In his father's library he also discovered Antoine Laurent Thomas's eulogy of Descartes, which convinced him of the nobility of a life in science. It also introduced him to metaphysics, the one passion he sustained throughout his life.

Almost incidentally Ampère discovered and perfected his mathematical talents. As an infant, he was fascinated by numbers and taught himself the elements of number theory. Like the young Pascal, having been forbidden the rigors of geometry because of his tender years, he defied parental authority and worked out the early books of Euclid by himself.

When the librarian in Lyons informed him that the works by Euler and Bernoulli that he wished to read were in Latin, Ampère rushed home to learn this language. He soon became adept enough to read the books that interested him, but continued his studies to the point where he could write quite acceptable Latin verse.

Ampère's early education was also conducted in a deeply religious atmosphere. His mother, the former Jeanne Desutières-Sarcey, was a devout woman who saw to it that her son was thoroughly instructed in the Catholic faith. Throughout his life, Ampère reflected the double heritage of the *Encyclopédie* and Catholicism. He was almost constantly assailed by the doubts sown by the Encyclopedists and, just as constantly, renewed his faith. From this conflict came his concern for metaphysics, which shaped his approach to science.

Ampère's childhood ended in 1789 with the outbreak of the French Revolution. Although Poleymieux was a rural backwater, the events in Lyons soon involved the Ampère family. Jean-Jacques was called upon by his fellow citizens to assume the post of *juge de paix,* a post with important police powers. He met the threat of a Jacobin purge head-on by ordering the arrest of Joseph Chalier, the leading Jacobin of Lyons. Chalier was executed. When Lyons fell to the troops of the Republic, Jean-Jacques Ampère was tried and guillotined on 23 November 1793. The event struck André-Marie like a bolt of lightning. The world had always been remote; now it had moved to the very center of his life, and this sudden confrontation was more than he could immediately bear. For a year he retreated within himself, not speaking to anyone and trying desperately to understand what had happened. His contact with the outside world was minimal; only an interest in botany, stimulated by a reading of Rousseau's letters on the subject, seemed to survive.

It was in this extremely vulnerable emotional state that Ampère met the young lady who was to become his wife. Julie Carron was somewhat older than Ampère and as a member of a good bourgeois family must have seen Ampère's suit in a somewhat unfavorable light. Although the Ampères and the Carrons lived in neighboring villages and shared a common economic and social background, marriage seemed impossible. At twenty-two, Ampère had only a small patrimony and no trade or other special skill. He was also homely and rustic, characteristics that were hardly likely to attract someone accustomed to the society and usages of Lyons. Ampère's courtship, carefully documented in his journal, reveals an essential aspect of his character: he was an incurable romantic whose emotional life was both intense and simple. Having lost his heart to Julie, he had no choice but to pursue her until she finally consented to marry him. His joy, like his despair at the death of his father, was immoderate. So, in his science, Ampère was possessed by his own enthusiasm. He never laid out a course of experiments or line of thought; there would be a brilliant flash of insight that he would pursue feverishly to its conclusion.

On 7 August 1799 Ampère and Julie were wed. The next four years were the happiest of Ampère's life. At first he was able to make a modest living as a mathematics teacher in Lyons, where on 12 August 1800 his son, Jean-Jacques, was born. In February 1802 Ampère left Lyons to become professor of physics and chemistry at the *école centrale* of Bourg-en-Bresse, a position that provided him with more money and, more important, with the opportunity to prepare himself for a post in the new *lycée* that Napoleon intended to establish at Lyons. In April of that year he began work on an original paper on probability theory that, he was convinced, would make his reputation. Thus, everything concurred to make him feel the happiest of men. Then tragedy struck. Julie had been ill since the birth of their son, and on 13 July 1803 she died. Ampère was inconsolable, and began to cast about desperately for some way to leave Lyons and all its memories.

On the strength of his paper on probability, he was named *répétiteur* in mathematics at the École Polytechnique in Paris. Again his emotional state was extreme, and again he fell victim to it. Bored by his work at the École Polytechnique, lonely in a strange and sophisticated city, Ampère sought human companionship and was drawn into a family that appeared to offer him the emotional warmth he so desperately craved. On 1 August 1806 he married Jeanne Potot. The marriage began under inauspicious circumstances: his father-in-law had swindled him out of his patrimony and his wife had indicated that she was uninterested in bearing children. The marriage was a catastrophe from the very beginning. After the birth of a daughter, Albine, his wife and mother-in-law made life so unbearable for Ampère that he realized that his only recourse was a divorce. Albine joined Jean-Jacques in Ampère's household, now presided over by his mother and his aunt, who had come to Paris from Poleymieux.

In 1808 Ampère was named inspector general of the newly formed university system, a post he held, except for a few years in the 1820's, until his death. On 28 November 1814 he was named a member of the class of mathematics in the Institut Impérial. In September 1819 he was authorized to offer a course in philosophy at the University of Paris, and in 1820 he was named assistant professor (*professeur suppléant*) of astronomy. In August 1824 Ampère was elected to the chair of experimental physics at the Collège de France.

During these years, Ampère's domestic life continued in turmoil. His son, for whom he had great hopes, fell under the spell of Mme. Recamier, one of the great beauties of the Empire, and for twenty years was content to be in her entourage. His daughter, Albine, married an army officer who turned out to be a drunkard and a near maniac. There was, too, a constant anxiety about money. In 1836 Ampère's health failed and he died, alone, while on an inspection tour in Marseilles.

Ampère's personal misery had an important effect on his intellectual development. His deep religious faith was undoubtedly strengthened by the almost constant series of catastrophes with which he was afflicted. Each successive tragedy also reinforced his desire for absolute certainty in some area of his life. His son later remarked on this characteristic of his father's approach; he was never content with probabilities but always sought Truth. It is no coincidence that his first mathematical paper, "Des considérations sur la théorie mathématique du jeu" (1802), proved that a single player inevitably would lose in a game of chance if he were opposed by a group whose financial resources were infinitely larger than his own. The outcome was certain.

In science Ampère's search for certainty and the exigencies of his faith led him to devise a philosophy that determined the form of his scientific research. The dominant philosophy in France in the early years of the nineteenth century was that of the Abbé de Condillac and his disciples, dubbed *Idéologues* by Napoleon. It maintained that only sensations were real, thus leaving both God and the existence of an objective world open to doubt. Such a position was abhorrent to Ampère, and he cast about for an alternative view. He was one of the earliest Frenchmen to discover the works of Immanuel Kant. Although Kant's philosophy made it possible to retain one's religious faith, Ampère felt that his treatment of space, time, and causality implied the doubtful existence of an objective reality at a fundamental level.

Space and time, as Ampère interpreted Kant, became subjective modes of the human understanding, and Ampère, as a mathematician, could not accept this.

He therefore constructed his own philosophy. Its foundation was provided by his friend Maine de Biran, who felt he had successfully refuted David Hume's conclusion that *cause* simply meant succession of phenomena in time. The act of moving one's arm provided a firm proof that a cause explained an act and was not simply a description of succession. One wills the arm to move and one is conscious of the act of willing; the arm then moves. Therefore the arm moves *because* one wills it to. Ampère used this argument to prove the existence of an external world. If one's arm cannot move because it is, say, under a heavy table, then one becomes conscious of causes external to oneself. The arm does not move because the table prevents it from doing so. Thus Ampère carried causation from the psychological world to the physical world. Moreover, the resistance of the table proved, to Ampère's satisfaction, that matter does exist, for this external cause must be independent of our sensation of it. With similar arguments, Ampère was able to prove that the soul and God also must exist.

Ampère's philosophy permitted him to retain both a belief in God and a belief in the real existence of an objective nature. The next step was to determine what could be known about the physical world. Here again, Ampère's analysis contained highly idiosyncratic views on the nature of scientific explanation which were to be clearly illustrated in his own work. There are (and here the influence of Kant is obvious) two levels of knowledge of the external world. There are phenomena, presented to us directly through the senses, and there are noumena, the objective causes of phenomena. Noumena, according to Ampère, are known through the activity of the mind, which hypothesizes certain real, material entities whose properties can be used to account for phenomena. These two aspects of reality, however, are not all that we can know. We also can know relations (*rapports*) between phenomena and relations between noumena, and these relations are just as objectively real as the noumena. One example may suffice to illustrate this. It had been known since the end of the eighteenth century that two volumes of hydrogen combined with one volume of oxygen to form two volumes of water vapor. This is knowledge of a specific phenomenon.

In 1808 Gay-Lussac discovered that all gases combine in simple ratios, and thus was able to announce his law of combining volumes. The law states a relationship between phenomena and thereby extends our knowledge of the phenomenal world. In 1814

Ampère published his "Lettre de M. Ampère à M. le comte Berthollet sur la détermination des proportions dans lesquelles les corps se combinent d'après le nombre et la disposition respective des molécules dont leurs particules intégrantes sont composées."[1] It was an attempt to provide the noumenal, and therefore deeper, explanation of the phenomenal relations. From the theory of universal attraction used to account for the cohesion of bodies and the fact that light easily passes through transparent bodies, Ampère concluded that the attractive and repulsive forces associated with each molecule hold the ultimate molecules of bodies at distances from one another that are, as Ampère put it, "infinitely great in comparison to the dimensions of these molecules." This is knowledge of the noumena. It explains certain basic qualities of the observable world in terms of theoretical entities whose properties can be hypothesized from phenomena.

From the science of crystallography Ampère borrowed the idea of the integral particle, that is, the smallest particle of a crystal that has the form of the crystal. Ampère's molecules now were assumed to group themselves in various ways to form particles that had specific geometric forms. Thus there would be particles composed of four molecules that formed tetrahedrons (oxygen, nitrogen, and hydrogen), of eight molecules that formed an octahedron (chlorine), etc. These geometrical forms were of the greatest importance in Ampère's theory, for they allowed him to deal with the problem of elective affinity and also to deduce Avogadro's law. Ampère's particles were compound and could, therefore, be broken down into smaller parts. Thus, oxygen was composed of four molecules that could, and did, separate under certain conditions, with two molecules going one way and two the other. The rule was that only compounds whose molecules were regular polyhedrons could be formed. If a tetrahedron met an octahedron, there could not be a simple combination, for the result would be a bizarre (in Ampère's terms) geometrical figure. Two tetrahedrons could combine with one octahedron, however, since the result would be a dodecahedron.

Ampère's philosophy and its influence on his science are obvious here. The relations of noumena, in this case the association of molecules to form a geometrically regular form, are simply assumed. If Ampère had been asked what evidence he had for the existence of such forms, he would have replied that no evidence could be offered. One hypothesizes noumena and relations between them in order to give causal explanations of phenomena. There can be no "evidence" for the noumena; there can be only the greater or lesser success of the noumenal hypothesis in explaining what can be observed. The point is of central importance, for it permitted Ampère to assume whatever he wished about the noumena. His assumption of an electrodynamic molecule followed this pattern exactly.

Ampère's philosophical analysis also provided him with the key for his classification of the sciences, which he considered the capstone of his career. Like Kant, he was concerned with relating precisely what man could know with the sciences that dealt with each part of man's ability to know. The chart appended to the first volume of his *Essai sur la philosophie des sciences* (1834) seems, at first glance, to be a fantastic and uncorrelated list of possible objects of investigation. If Ampère's philosophical views are attended to, however, they all fall into a rather simple pattern. We may use general physics as an example. In Ampère's classification this is divided into two second-order sciences—elementary general physics and mathematical physics. Each of these, in turn, has two divisions. Elementary general physics consists of experimental physics and chemistry; mathematical physics is divided into stereonomy and atomology (Ampère's neologisms). Experimental physics deals with phenomena, i.e., with the accurate description of physical facts. Chemistry deals with the noumenal causes of the facts discovered by experimental physics. Stereonomy concerns the relations between phenomena, e.g., laws of the conduction of heat through a solid. Atomology explains these laws by demonstrating how they may be deduced from relations between the ultimate particles of matter. All other sciences are treated in this fashion and have exactly the same kind of fourfold division.

This classification reveals Ampère's far-ranging mind and permits us to understand his occasional excursions into botany, taxonomy, and even animal anatomy and physiology. He was, in large part, seeking confirmation for his philosophical analysis, rather than setting out on new scientific paths. By the time of his death, Ampère had found, to his great satisfaction, that his scheme did fit all the sciences and, in his *Essai sur la philosophie des sciences,* he maintained that the fit was too good to be coincidence; the classification must reflect truth. Once again he had found certainty where his predecessors had not.

Although the one continuing intellectual passion of Ampère's life from 1800 to his death was his philosophical system, these years were also devoted to scientific research of considerable originality. From 1800 to about 1814, he devoted himself primarily to mathematics. As his mathematical interests declined, he became fascinated with chemistry and, from 1808

to 1815, spent his spare time in chemical investigations. From 1820 to 1827, he founded and developed the science of electrodynamics, the scientific work for which he is best known and which earned him his place in the first rank of physicists.

Ampère was not a truly outstanding mathematician. His first paper showed considerable originality and, more revealingly, great ability as an algorist. Like Leonhard Euler, Ampère had the uncanny ability, found only in the born mathematician, to discover mathematical relations. His largest mathematical memoir, "Mémoire sur l'intégration des équations aux différences partielles" (1814), was on various means of integrating partial differential equations. Although one should not underestimate the utility of such works, they should not be put in the same class as, say, the invention of quaternions by Sir William Rowan Hamilton or the laying of rigorous foundations of the calculus by Augustin Cauchy.

Ampère's failure to achieve the early promise he had shown in mathematics was undoubtedly the result of his passion for metaphysics and the necessity of earning a living. But there was also the fact, worth noting here, that the French scientific system forced him to do mathematics when his interests were focused elsewhere. Having been classified as a mathematician, Ampère found himself unable to gain recognition as anything else until after his epoch-making papers on electrodynamics. The security that came with election to the Academy of Sciences was achieved by Ampère only at the cost of putting aside his chemical interests and writing a mathematical memoir for the express purpose of gaining entry to the Academy. Original mathematical work is rarely done under such conditions.

Ampère's interest in chemistry had been aroused in the days when he gave private lessons at Lyons. This interest continued to grow at Bourg-en-Bresse, where he mastered the subject, and it became most intense about 1808, when Humphry Davy was shaking the foundations of the orthodox chemistry of the French school. Ampère once described himself as credulous in matters of science, and this again reflected his philosophy. A new scientific idea could be immediately accepted as a hypothesis even if there was no evidence for it, just as a fundamental assumption could be made without evidence: the main criterion was whether it worked or not. Ampère was not committed to Lavoisier's system of chemistry.

When Davy announced the discovery of sodium and potassium, the orthodox were startled, if not dismayed. How could oxygen be the principle of acidity, as Lavoisier had insisted, if the oxides of potassium and sodium formed the strongest alkalies?

For Ampère there was no problem; he simply accepted the fact. If this fact were true, however, then the oxygen theory of acids was probably wrong. And if this were so, then the great riddle of muriatic acid could easily be solved. The green gas that was given off when muriatic acid was decomposed need not be a compound of some unknown base and oxygen; it could be an element. Thus, at the same time that Davy was questioning the compound nature of chlorine, Ampère had also concluded that it was an element. Unfortunately, and much to his later regret, he had neither the time nor the resources to prove this point, and the credit for the discovery of chlorine as an element went to Davy. Ampère was forestalled once again by Davy in 1813, when he brought Davy a sample of a new substance that Bernard Courtois had isolated from seaweed. Ampère had already seen its similarities to chlorine, but it was Davy who first publicly insisted upon its elemental character and named it iodine.

The noumenal aspect of chemistry fascinated Ampère. Although his derivation of Avogadro's law came three years after Avogadro had enunciated it, the law is known today in France as the Avogadro-Ampère law. This was Ampère's first excursion into molecular physics, and was followed almost immediately by a second. In 1815 he published a paper demonstrating the relation between Mariotte's (Boyle's) law and the volumes and pressures of gases at the same temperature. The paper is of some interest as a pioneer effort, along with Laplace's great papers on capillarity, in the application of mathematical analysis to the molecular realm.

In 1816 Ampère turned to the phenomenal relations of chemistry in a long paper on the natural classification of elementary bodies ("Essai d'une classification naturelle pour les corps simples"). Here he drew attention to the similarities between Lavoisier's and his followers' classification of elements in terms of their reactions with oxygen and Linnaeus' classification of plants in terms of their sexual organs. Bernard de Jussieu had successfully challenged Linnaeus with his natural system that took the whole plant into account and sought affinities between all parts of the plant, not just the flowers, as the basis of classification. Ampère now wished to do the same thing for chemistry. By discovering a natural classification, i.e., one that tied the elements together by real rather than artificial relations, Ampère hoped to provide a new insight into chemical reactions. His classificatory scheme, therefore, was not merely an ordering of the elements but, like the later periodic table of Dmitri Mendeleev, a true instrument of chemical research. Unfortunately, Ampère's system was as artificial as

Lavoisier's. Although he looked for more analogies among elements than Lavoisier had, the ones he selected offered little insight into the relations between the groups founded on them. The paper may be noted, however, as an early attempt to find relationships between the elements that would bring some order into the constantly growing number of elementary bodies.

By 1820 Ampère had achieved a certain reputation as both a mathematician and a somewhat heterodox chemist. Had he died before September of that year, he would be a minor figure in the history of science. It was the discovery of electromagnetism by Hans Christian Oersted in the spring of 1820 which opened up a whole new world to Ampère and gave him the opportunity to show the full power of his method of discovery. On 4 September 1820 François Arago reported Oersted's discovery to an astonished and skeptical meeting of the Académie des Sciences. Most of the members literally could not believe their ears; had not the great Coulomb proved to everyone's satisfaction in the 1780's that there could not be any interaction between electricity and magnetism? Ampère's credulity served him well here; he immediately accepted Oersted's discovery and turned his mind to it. On 18 September he read his first paper on the subject to the Académie; on 25 September and 9 October he continued the account of his discoveries. In these feverish weeks the science of electrodynamics was born.

There is some confusion over the precise nature of Ampère's first discovery. In the published memoir, "Mémoire sur l'action naturelle de deux courants électriques . . ." (1820), he stated that his mind leaped immediately from the existence of electromagnetism to the idea that currents traveling in circles through helices would act like magnets. This may have been suggested to him by consideration of terrestrial magnetism, in which circular currents seemed obvious. Ampère immediately applied his theory to the magnetism of the earth, and the genesis of electrodynamics may, indeed, have been as Ampère stated it. On the other hand, there is an account of the meetings of the Académie des Sciences at which Ampère spoke of his discoveries and presented a somewhat different order of discovery. It would appear that Oersted's discovery suggested to Ampère that two current-carrying wires might affect one another. It was this discovery that he announced to the Académie on 25 September.[2] Since the pattern of magnetic force around a current-carrying wire was circular, it was no great step for Ampère the geometer to visualize the resultant force if the wire were coiled into a helix. The mutual attraction and repulsion of two helices was also announced to the Académie on 25 September. What Ampère had done was to present a new theory of magnetism as electricity in motion.

From this point on, Ampère's researches followed three different but constantly intertwining paths. They conform exactly to his ideas on the nature of science and scientific explanation. The phenomenon of electromagnetism had been announced by Oersted; the relations of two current-carrying wires had been discovered by Ampère. It remained to explore these relations in complete and elaborate detail. Then, following his own philosophy, it was necessary for Ampère to seek the noumenal causes of the phenomena, which were found in his famous electrodynamic model and theory of the nature of electricity. Finally, Ampère had to discover the relations between the noumena from which all the phenomena could be deduced. Between 1820 and 1825 he successfully completed each of these tasks.

Ampère's first great memoir on electrodynamics was almost completely phenomenological, in his sense of the term. In a series of classical and simple experiments, he provided the factual evidence for his contention that magnetism was electricity in motion. He concluded his memoir with nine points that bear repetition here, since they sum up his early work.

1. Two electric currents attract one another when they move parallel to one another in the same direction; they repel one another when they move parallel but in opposite directions.

2. It follows that when the metallic wires through which they pass can turn only in parallel planes, each of the two currents tends to swing the other into a position parallel to it and pointing in the same direction.

3. These attractions and repulsions are absolutely different from the attractions and repulsions of ordinary [static] electricity.

4. All the phenomena presented by the mutual action of an electric current and a magnet discovered by M. Oersted . . . are covered by the law of attraction and of repulsion of two electric currents that has just been enunciated, if one admits that a magnet is only a collection of electric currents produced by the action of the particles of steel upon one another analogous to that of the elements of a voltaic pile, and which exist in planes perpendicular to the line which joins the two poles of the magnet.

5. When a magnet is in the position that it tends to take by the action of the terrestrial globe, these currents move in a sense opposite to the apparent motion of the sun; when one places the magnet in the opposite position so that the poles directed toward the poles of the earth are the same [S to S and N to N, not south-seeking to S, etc.] the same currents are found in the same direction as the apparent motion of the sun.

6. The known observed effects of the action of two magnets on one another obey the same law.

7. The same is true of the force that the terrestrial globe exerts on a magnet, if one admits electric currents in planes perpendicular to the direction of the declination needle, moving from east to west, above this direction.

8. There is nothing more in one pole of a magnet than in the other; the sole difference between them is that one is to the left and the other is to the right of the electric currents which give the magnetic properties to the steel.

9. Although Volta has proven that the two electricities, positive and negative, of the two ends of the pile attract and repel one another according to the same laws as the two electricities produced by means known before him, he has not by that demonstrated completely the identity of the fluids made manifest by the pile and by friction; this identity was proven, as much as a physical truth can be proven, when he showed that two bodies, one electrified by the contact of [two] metals, and the other by friction, acted upon each other in all circumstances as though both had been electrified by the pile or by the common electric machine [electrostatic generator]. The same kind of proof is applicable here to the identity of attractions and repulsions of electric currents and magnets.[3]

Here Ampère only hinted at the noumenal background. Like most Continental physicists, he felt that electrical phenomena could be explained only by two fluids and, as he pointed out in the paper, a current therefore had to consist of the positive fluid going in one direction and the negative fluid going in the other through the wire. His experiments had proved to him that this contrary motion of the two electrical fluids led to unique forces of attraction and repulsion in current-carrying wires, and his first paper was intended to describe these forces in qualitative terms. There was one problem: how could this explanation be extended to permanent magnets? The answer appeared deceptively simple: if magnetism were only electricity in motion, then there must be currents of electricity in ordinary bar magnets.

Once again Ampère's extraordinary willingness to frame *ad hoc* hypotheses is evident. Volta had suggested that the contact of two dissimilar metals would give rise to a current if the metals were connected by a fluid conductor. Ampère simply assumed that the contact of the molecules of iron in a bar magnet would give rise to a similar current. A magnet could, therefore, be viewed as a series of voltaic piles in which electrical currents moved concentrically around the axis of the magnet. Almost immediately, Ampère's friend Augustin Fresnel, the creator of the wave theory of light, pointed out that this hypothesis simply would not do. Iron was not a very good conductor of the electrical fluids and there should, therefore, be some heat generated if Ampère's views were correct. Magnets are not noticeably hotter than their surroundings and Ampère, when faced with this fact, had to abandon his noumenal explanation.

It was Fresnel who provided Ampère with a way out. Fresnel wrote in a note to Ampère that since nothing was known about the physics of molecules, why not assume currents of electricity around each molecule. Then, if these molecules could be aligned, the resultant of the molecular currents would be precisely the concentric currents required. Ampère immediately adopted his friend's suggestion, and the electrodynamic molecule was born. It is, however, a peculiar molecule. In some mysterious fashion, a molecule of iron decomposed the luminiferous ether that pervaded both space and matter into the two electrical fluids, its constituent elements. This decomposition took place *within* the molecule; the two electrical fluids poured out the top, flowed around the molecule, and reentered at the bottom. The net effect was that of a single fluid circling the molecule. These molecules, when aligned by the action of another magnet, formed a permanent magnet. Ampère did not say why molecules should act this way; for him it was enough that his electrodynamic model provided a noumenal foundation for electrodynamic phenomena.

There was no doubt that Ampère took his electrodynamic molecule seriously and expected others to do so too. In an answer to a letter from the Dutch physicist Van Beck, published in the *Journal de physique* in 1821, Ampère argued eloquently for his model, insisting that it could be used to explain not only magnetism but also chemical combination and elective affinity. In short, it was to be considered the foundation of a new theory of matter. This was one of the reasons why Ampère's theory of electrodynamics was not immediately and universally accepted. To accept it meant to accept as well a theory of the ultimate structure of matter itself.

Having established a noumenal foundation for electrodynamic phenomena, Ampère's next steps were to discover the relationships between the phenomena and to devise a theory from which these relationships could be mathematically deduced. This double task was undertaken in the years 1821–1825, and his success was reported in his greatest work, the *Mémoire sur la théorie mathématique des phénomènes électrodynamique, uniquement déduite de l'expérience* (1827). In this work, the *Principia* of electrodynamics, Ampère first described the laws of action of electric currents, which he had discovered from four extremely ingenious experiments. The measurement of

electrodynamic forces was very difficult, although it could be done, as J.-B. Biot and Félix Savart had shown in their formulation of the Biot-Savart law. Ampère realized, however, that much greater accuracy could be achieved if the experiments could be null experiments, in which the forces involved were in equilibrium.

The first experiment, to quote Ampère, "demonstrated the equality of the absolute value of the attraction and repulsion which is produced when a current flows first in one direction, then in the opposite direction in a fixed conductor which is left unchanged as to its orientation and at the same distance from the body on which it acts." The second "consists in the equality of the actions exerted on a mobile rectilinear conductor by two fixed conductors situated at equal distances from the first of which one is rectilinear and the other bent or contorted in any way whatsoever. . . ." The third case demonstrated "that a closed circuit of any form whatsoever cannot move any portion of a conducting wire forming an arc of a circle whose center lies on a fixed axis about which it may turn freely and which is perpendicular to the plane of the circle of which the arc is a part." Ampère rather casually mentioned at the end of the *Mémoire* that he had not actually performed the fourth experiment, which was intended to determine certain constants necessary for the solution of his mathematical equation. These constants, it would appear, had been found by measuring the action of a magnet and a current-carrying wire upon one another and were sufficiently accurate to permit Ampère to continue his researches.

From these cases of equilibrium, Ampère was able to deduce certain necessary consequences that permitted him to apply mathematics to the phenomena. It was time to turn to the noumena once again and to complete the edifice by deducing from the noumenal elements those mathematical relationships that had been indicated by experiment. The flow of an electrical current, it will be remembered, was a complicated process in Ampère's theory. Positive electricity was flowing in one direction in the wire while negative electricity flowed in the opposite direction. The luminiferous ether was a compound of these two fluids, so that it was constantly being formed from their union, only to be decomposed as each fluid went its way. Thus, at any moment in the wire there were elements of positive electricity, negative electricity, and the ether. Ampère's current element (*ids*), therefore, was not a mathematical fiction assumed out of mathematical necessity, but a real physical entity. What his experiments had done was to tell him the basic properties of this element. The force associated with the element is a central force, acting at a distance at right angles to the element's direction of flow. From this fact it was easy to deduce that the mutual action of two lengths of current-carrying wire is proportional to their length and to the intensities of the currents. Ampère was now prepared to give precise mathematical form to this action. As early as 1820, he had deduced a law of force between two current elements, ids and $i'ds'$. He gave the formula

$$F = \frac{i \cdot i' \cdot ds \cdot ds'}{r^2}$$
$$[\sin \theta \cdot \sin \theta' \cdot \cos \omega + k \cos \theta \cdot \cos \theta']$$

for the force between two current elements, making angles θ and θ' with the line joining them and the two planes containing this line and the two elements respectively making an angle ω with each other. At that time he had been unable to evaluate the constant k. By 1827 he was able to show that $k = -1/2$. The formula above could now be written

$$F = \frac{i \cdot i' \cdot ds \cdot ds'}{r^2}$$
$$[\sin \theta \cdot \sin \theta' \cdot \cos \omega - 1/2 \cos \theta \cdot \cos \theta'].$$

When integrated around a complete circuit (as in practice it must be), this formula is identical with that of Biot and Savart.

It was now possible for Ampère to attack the theory of magnetism quantitatively. He could show that his law of action of current elements led to the conclusion that the forces of a magnet composed of electrodynamic molecules should be directed toward the poles. He was also able to deduce Coulomb's law of magnetic action. In short, he was able to unify the fields of electricity and magnetism on a basic noumenal level. The theory was complete.

Not everyone accepted Ampère's theory. His primary opponent was Michael Faraday, who could not follow the mathematics and felt that the whole structure was based on *ad hoc* assumptions for which there was no evidence whatsoever. The phenomenal part was accepted; even in France the electrodynamic molecule was regarded with considerable suspicion. The idea, however, did not die with Ampère. It was accepted later in the century by Wilhelm Weber and became the basis of his theory of electromagnetism.

After 1827 Ampère's scientific activity declined sharply. These were the years of anxiety and fear for his daughter's well-being, as well as years of declining health. He produced an occasional paper but, by and large, after the great 1827 memoir Ampère's days as

a creative scientist were ended. He turned instead to the completion of his essay on the philosophy of science and his classification of the sciences. He must have derived some satisfaction from the fact that he had, almost single-handedly, created a new science to be placed in his taxonomic scheme.

NOTES

1. *Annales de chimie,* **90** (1814), 43 ff.
2. See *Bibliothèque universelle des sciences, belles-lettres, et arts,* **17** (1821), 83.
3. *Mémoires sur l'électrodynamique,* I (Paris, 1885), 48.

BIBLIOGRAPHY

I. ORIGINAL WORKS. The most important source for the life and work of Ampère is the forty cartons of documents in the archives of the Académie des Sciences in Paris. This material has been catalogued but never used. For Ampère's correspondence, see Louis de Launay, ed., *Correspondance du Grand Ampère,* 3 vols. (Paris, 1936–1943). It should be used with care, for there are many errors of transcription and it is not complete. It does, however, have a complete bibliography of Ampère's works at the end of the second volume. One should also consult *André-Marie Ampère et Jean-Jacques Ampère: Correspondance et souvenirs (de 1805 à 1864) recuellis par Madame H. C.[heuvreux]*, 2 vols. (Paris, 1875), and Mme. Cheuvreux's *Journal et correspondance d'André-Marie Ampère* (Paris, 1872). These volumes should be used with great caution, for Mme. Cheuvreux was not a scholar and changed the order of whole passages, sometimes inserting part of one letter in another for artistic reasons. Ampère's papers on electrodynamics were reprinted by the Société Française de Physique as *Mémoires sur l'électrodynamique,* 2 vols. (Paris, 1885–1887). The *Mémoire sur la théorie mathématique des phénomènes électrodynamiques, uniquement déduite de l'expérience* (Paris, 1827) was republished with a foreword by Edmond Bauer (Paris, 1958). Portions of this work and others of Ampère's papers on electrodynamics have been translated and appear in R. A. R. Tricker, ed., *Early Electrodynamics: The First Law of Circulation* (Oxford, 1965). This volume contains a long commentary by the editor that is of great value in explaining Ampère's theory.

For Ampère's philosophical development, see *Philosophie des deux Ampère publiée par J. Barthélemy Saint-Hilaire* (Paris, 1866), which contains a long essay by Jean-Jacques Ampère on his father's philosophy.

II. SECONDARY LITERATURE. There is no adequate biography of Ampère. C. A. Valson, *André-Marie Ampère* (Lyons, 1885), and Louis de Launay, *Le grand Ampère* (Paris, 1925), are the standard biographies, but neither discusses Ampère's work in any detail. The eulogy by François Arago provides a survey of Ampère's scientific achievement from the perspective of a century ago. See his *Oeuvres,* 17 vols. (Paris, 1854–1862), II, 1 ff. For some modern appreciations of Ampère's work, see the *Revue général de l'électricité,* **12** (1922), supplement. The entire issue is devoted to Ampère's work. For an interesting account of Ampère's early career, see Louis Mallez, *A.-M. Ampère, professeur à Bourg, membre de la Société d'Émulation de l'Ain, d'après des documents inédits* (Lyons, 1936).

For various aspects of Ampère's career, see Borislav Lorenz, *Die Philosophie André-Marie Ampères* (Berlin, 1908); and Maurice Lewandowski, *André-Marie Ampère. La science et la foi* (Paris, 1936). The *Bulletin de la Société des Amis d'André-Marie Ampère,* which appears irregularly, contains much Ampère lore. Two interesting sketches of Ampère are Henry James, "The Two Ampères," in *French Poets and Novelists* (London, 1878); and C. A. Sainte-Beuve, "M. Ampère," in *Portraits littéraires,* 3 vols. (Paris, 1862), I.

A discussion of Ampère's electrodynamic molecule is to be found in L. Pearce Williams, "Ampère's Electrodynamic Molecular Model," in *Contemporary Physics,* **4** (1962), 113 ff. For Ampère's relations with England, see K. R. and D. L. Gardiner, "André-Marie Ampère and His English Acquaintants," in *The British Journal for the History of Science,* **2** (1965), 235 ff.

L. PEARCE WILLIAMS

AMSLER (later **AMSLER-LAFFON**), **JAKOB** (*b.* Stalden bei Brugg, Switzerland, 16 November 1823; *d.* Schaffhausen, Switzerland, 3 January 1912), *mathematics, precision instruments.*

The son of a farmer, Amsler was educated at local schools before going on to study theology at the universities of Jena and Königsberg. At Königsberg he came under the influence of Franz Neumann, whose lectures and laboratory sessions he attended for seven semesters. After earning his doctorate in 1848, Amsler spent a year with Plantamour at the Geneva observatory; he went from there to Zurich, where he completed his *Habilitation* and began his teaching career. For four semesters he lectured on various topics in mathematics and mathematical physics, then in 1851 accepted a post at the Gymnasium in Schaffhausen. From this he hoped to gain some financial independence as well as an opportunity for more research. In 1854 Amsler married Elise Laffon, the daughter of a Schaffhausen druggist who was well known in Swiss scientific circles. Henceforth he used the double form Amsler-Laffon. The change applied to Jakob alone and was not adopted by his children.

Until 1854 Amsler's interests lay in the area of mathematical physics; he published articles on magnetic distribution, the theory of heat conduction, and the theory of attraction. One result of his work was a generalization of Ivory's theorem on the attraction of ellipsoids and of Poisson's extension of that theorem.

In 1854 Amsler turned his attention to precision mathematical instruments, and his research resulted in his major contribution to mathematics: the polar planimeter, a device for measuring areas enclosed by plane curves. Previous such instruments, most notably that of Oppikofer (1827), had been based on the Cartesian coordinate system and had combined bulkiness with high cost. Amsler eliminated these drawbacks by basing his planimeter on a polar coordinate system referred to a null circle as curvilinear axis. The instrument, described in "Ueber das Polarplanimeter" (1856), adapted easily to the determination of static and inertial moments and of the coefficients of Fourier series; it proved especially useful to shipbuilders and railroad engineers.

To capitalize on his inspiration, Amsler established his own precision tools workshop in 1854. From 1857 on, he devoted full time to the venture. At his death, the shop had produced 50,000 polar planimeters and 700 momentum planimeters. The polar planimeter marked the height of Amsler's career. His later research, mostly in the area of precision and engineering instruments, produced no comparable achievement, although it did bring Amsler recognition and prizes from world exhibitions at Vienna (1873) and Paris (1881, 1889), as well as a corresponding membership in the Paris Academy (1892). From 1848 until his death, Amsler was an active member of the Naturforschende Gesellschaft in Zurich.

BIBLIOGRAPHY

I. ORIGINAL WORKS. Amsler's writings include: "Zur Theorie der Verteilung des Magnetismus im weichen Eisen," in *Abhandlungen der naturforschenden Gesellschaft in Zürich* (1847), reprinted in *Neue Denkschriften der allgemeinen schweizerischen Gesellschaft für die gesammten Naturwissenschaften,* **10** (1849); "Methode, den Einfluss zu kompensieren, welchen die Eisenmassen eines Schiffes infolge der Verteilung der magnetischen Flüssigkeiten durch den Erdmagnetismus auf die Kompassnadel ausüben," in *Verhandlungen der schweizerischen naturforschenden Gesellschaft* (1848); "Ueber die klimatologischen Verhältnisse der Polargegenden" and "Ueber die Anwendung von Schwingungsbeobachtungen zur Bestimmung der spezifischen Wärme fester Körper bei konstantem Volumen," in *Mitteilungen der naturforschenden Gesellschaft in Zürich,* **2** (1850–1852), 314–315; "Neue geometrische und mechanische Eigenschaft der Niveauflächen," "Zur Theorie der Anziehung und der Wärme," and "Ueber die Gesetze der Wärmeleitung im Innern fester Körper, unter Berücksichtigung der durch ungleichförmige Erwärmung erzeugten Spannung," in *Crelle's Journal,* **42** (1851), the last reprinted in *Neue Denkschriften,* **12** (1852); "Ueber das Polarplanimeter," in *Dingler's Journal,* **140** (1856); "Ueber die mechanische Bestimmung des Flächeninhaltes, der statischen Momente und der Trägheitsmomente ebener Figuren, insbesondere über einen neuen Planimeter," in *Vierteljahrsschrift der naturforschenden Gesellschaft in Zürich,* **1** (1856), also printed separately (Schaffhausen, 1856); "Anwendung des Integrators (Momentumplanimeters) zur Berechnung des Auf- und Abtrages bei Anlage von Eisenbahnen, Strassen und Kanälen," a pamphlet (Zurich, 1875); "Der hydrometrische Flügel mit Zählwerk und elektrischer Zeichengebung," a pamphlet (Schaffhausen, 1877), reprinted in *Carls Repertorium,* **14** (1878); "Neuere Planimeterkonstruktionen," in *Zeitschrift für Instrumentkunde,* **4** (1884); and "Die neue Wasserwerksanlage in Schaffhausen und einige darauf bezügliche technische Fragen," in *Schweizerische Bauzeitung,* **16** (1890).

II. SECONDARY LITERATURE. See Poggendorf, Vols. III, IV, and V. The present article is based on the necrology by Ferdinand Rudio and Alfred Amsler in *Vierteljahrsschrift der naturforschenden Gesellschaft in Zürich,* **57** (1912), 1–17, and on the extensive study by Fr. Dubois, "Die Schöpfungen Jakob und Alfred Amsler's auf dem Gebiete der mathematischen Instrumente anhand der Ausstellung im Museum Allerheiligen systematisch dargestellt," in *Mitteilungen der naturforschenden Gesellschaft Schaffhausen,* **19** (1944), 209–273.

M. S. MAHONEY

ANARITIUS. See **al-Nayrīzī.**

ANATOLIUS OF ALEXANDRIA (*b.* Alexandria; *d.* Laodicea; *fl. ca.* A.D. 269), *mathematics, philosophy.*

The historian Eusebius, whose *Ecclesiastical History* provides what we know of Anatolius' life, says, "For his learning, secular education and philosophy [he] had attained the first place among our most illustrious contemporaries." Learned in arithmetic, geometry, astronomy, and other sciences both intellectual and natural, Anatolius was also outstanding in rhetoric. The Alexandrians deemed him worthy of heading the Aristotelian school in that city.

Bishop Theotecnus of Caesarea consecrated Anatolius as his successor, and he held office for a while in Caesarea. About A.D. 280, however, as he passed through Laodicea on his way to Antioch, he was retained by the inhabitants as their bishop, the previous bishop, also called Eusebius, having died. He remained bishop of Laodicea until his death some years later.

Anatolius' Christian and humanitarian character was much admired. During a siege of the Greek quarter of Alexandria by the Roman army, he attempted to make peace between the factions. He failed, but he succeeded in winning safe conduct from the besieged quarter for all noncombatants.

Anatolius put his knowledge of astronomy at the service of his religion in a treatise on the date of Easter. Eusebius gives the title of the work as *The Canons of Anatolius on the Pascha* and quotes several paragraphs that display Anatolius' grasp of astronomy in the discussion of the position of the sun and moon in the zodiac at the time of Easter. According to Eusebius, Anatolius did not write many books; but those that he did write were distinguished for eloquence and erudition, which is evident through his quotation of Philo, Josephus, and two of the seventy who translated the Old Testament into Greek during the third and second centuries B.C.

The only other work of Anatolius known to us by name is his *Introduction to Arithmetic.* In ten books, it seems to have been excerpted by the author of the curious writing entitled *Theologoumena arithmetica.* A Neoplatonic treatise, uncertainly attributed to Iamblichus, it is a discussion of each of the first ten natural numbers. It mixes accounts of truly arithmetical properties with mystical fancies. Many parts of the discussion are headed "of Anatolius." The character of its arithmetical lore may be illustrated by the following quotation from a part attributed to Anatolius: "[Four] is called 'justice' since its square is equal to the perimeter [i.e., $4 \times 4 = 16 = 4 + 4 + 4 + 4$]; of the numbers less than four the perimeter of the square is greater than the area, while of the greater the perimeter is less than the area."

In contrast with the flights of fancy preserved in *Theologoumena arithmetica,* some paragraphs of a writing of Anatolius are found in manuscripts of Hero of Alexander in which Anatolius deals soberly and sensibly, and in Aristotelian terms, with questions about mathematics, its name, its philosophical importance, and some of its methods. The structure of *Theologoumena arithmetica* and its selection of material from Anatolius suggest that Anatolius' *Introduction to Arithmetic* may have dealt with each of the first ten natural numbers. The Pythagoreanism or Neoplatonism manifested here was in the spirit of the times. Despite the number mysticism, however, Anatolius' competence in mathematics is clear and justifies the esteem in which Eusebius says he was held in Alexandria.

BIBLIOGRAPHY

No individual works of Anatolius' are known to exist today. Some paragraphs of a work by him are found in *Heronis Alexandrini geometricorum et stereometricorum reliquiae,* F. Hultsch, ed. (Berlin, 1864), pp. 276–280. A seeming use of excerpts from Anatolius' *Introduction to Arithmetic* is *Theologoumena arithmetica,* V. De Falco, ed.

(Leipzig, 1922). Two sources of information on the life of Anatolius are Eusebius, *The Ecclesiastical History*, H. J. Lawlor, trans., II (Cambridge-London, 1942), 228–238; and Pauly-Wissowa, eds., *Real-Enzyklopädie der Klassischen Altertumswissenschaft,* XII (Stuttgart, 1894–), col. 2073 f.

JOHN S. KIEFFER

ANAXAGORAS (*b.* Clazomenae, Lydia, 500 B.C.[?]; *d.* Lampsacus, Mysia, 428 B.C.[?]), *natural philosophy.*

Although he was born of wealthy parents, Anaxagoras neglected his inheritance to devote himself to natural philosophy. At the age of twenty, he traveled to Athens, where he spent the next thirty years. There he became a friend of Pericles and brought Ionian physical speculation to Athens at the height of its intellectual development. Subsequently he was prosecuted for impiety and banished[1] because, it was alleged, he held the sun to be a mass of red-hot stone. This charge doubtless was instigated by the political opponents of Pericles, who sought to attack him through his friendship with an atheistic scientist. Anaxagoras wrote only one treatise, completed after 467 B.C.

Like Empedocles, Anaxagoras sought to reconcile Parmenides' logic with the phenomena of multiplicity and change. Each maintained that there was never a unity in either the qualitative or the quantitative sense and postulated instead a plurality of eternal, qualitatively different substances that filled the whole of space. They accepted Parmenides' negation of coming-into-being and passing-away but replaced the former with the aggregation of their indestructible elements and the latter with their segregation. Motive forces were introduced to account for motion—a phenomenon whose validity had, prior to Parmenides, been taken for granted.

Anaxagoras evidently did not consider that Empedocles had fully satisfied the demands of Eleatic logic.[2] Empedocles had seen no objection to making secondary substances come into being as various combinations of his elements. A piece of flesh, according to him, consisted of the four elements juxtaposed in almost equal quantities. Theoretically, if it were divided, one would arrive at a minimum piece of flesh and thereafter at particles of the constituent elements. Thus, flesh originally came into being from the elements and, strictly speaking, from what is not flesh. Anaxagoras' own formulation of the problem is preserved: "How," he asks, "could hair come to be from what is not hair and flesh from what is not flesh?" (Diels and Kranz, B10). His answer was to claim that everything preexisted in our food. Thus, he denied the existence of elements simpler than and

prior to common natural substances and maintained that every natural substance must itself be elementary, since it cannot arise from what is not itself. Furthermore, to avoid being confuted by Zeno's paradoxes against plurality, he held that matter was infinitely divisible; that however far any piece of matter might be divided, there always resulted smaller parts of the same substance, each of which always contained portions of every other substance[3] and was itself capable of further division. Its predominant ingredients were responsible for its most distinctive features.

Initially, Anaxagoras held, all things were together in an apparently uniform, motionless mixture. Then Mind (Νοῦς) instituted a vortex, causing the dense, wet, cold, and dark matter to settle at the center and the rare, hot, and dry matter to take up peripheral positions as the sky. From the former, the disklike earth was compacted (Diels and Kranz, B15–16). The sun, moon, and stars, however, were torn from the earth and carried around, ignited by friction.[4]

Although strikingly rational, Anaxagoras' astronomy was not fruitful because it provided no stimulus to discover the laws of planetary motion. A more important contribution was his concept of a separate, immaterial moving cause, which paved the way for a fully teleological view of nature.[5] His theory of matter, however, was not influential, doubtless as much because of its subtlety and sophistication as because of its lack of economy.

NOTES

1. For the chronology of Anaxagoras' life see Taylor, Davison, and Guthrie.
2. For the relative dating of the works of these two see Longrigg, p. 173, n. 49.
3. The interpretation of Anaxagoras' theory is highly controversial. Certain scholars, most cogently Vlastos, reject this so-called naïve interpretation on the grounds that it involves a redundancy and an infinite regress. Their solution, although plausible, is, however, less in accordance with the fragments. On the question of the regress see especially Strang, pp. 101 ff.
4. The fall of the meteorite at Aegospotami in 467 B.C. probably suggested this theory. (It might be observed here that although Anaxagoras is commonly stated to have been the first to discover the true explanation of eclipses, there is evidence against his priority.)
5. For the reaction of Plato and Aristotle see *Phaedo* 97B and *Metaphysics* 985a18 ff. (Diels and Kranz, A47).

BIBLIOGRAPHY

The collected fragments and later testimony are in H. Diels and W. Kranz, *Die Fragmente der Vorsokratiker,* 6th ed. (Berlin, 1951–1952), II, 5–44.

Secondary literature includes C. Bailey, *The Greek*

Atomists and Epicurus (Oxford, 1928), pp. 537–556; D. Bargrave-Weaver, "The Cosmogony of Anaxagoras," in *Phronesis*, **4**, no. 2 (1959), 77–91; J. Burnet, *Early Greek Philosophy*, 4th ed. (London, 1930), pp. 251–275; W. Capelle, "Anaxagoras," in *Neue Jahrbücher für das klassische Altertum* (1919), 81–102, 169–198; F. M. Cleve, *The Philosophy of Anaxagoras* (New York, 1949); F. M. Cornford, "Anaxagoras' Theory of Matter," in *Classical Quarterly*, **24** (1930), 14–30, 83–95; J. A. Davison, "Protagoras, Democritus and Anaxagoras," *ibid.*, n.s. **3** (1953), 33–45; O. Gigon, "Zu Anaxagoras," in *Philologus*, **91** (1936–1937), 1–41; W. K. C. Guthrie, *A History of Greek Philosophy*, II (Cambridge, England, 1965), 266–338; G. S. Kirk and J. E. Raven, *The Presocratic Philosophers* (Cambridge, England, 1957), pp. 362–394; J. Longrigg, "Philosophy and Medicine: Some Early Interactions," in *Harvard Studies in Classical Philology*, **67** (1963), 147–175; R. Mathewson, "Aristotle and Anaxagoras: An Examination of F. M. Cornford's Interpretation," in *Classical Quarterly*, n.s. **8** (1958), 67–81; C. Mugler, "Le problème d'Anaxagore," in *Revue des études grecques*, **69** (1956), 314–376; A. L. Peck, "Anaxagoras: Predication as a Problem in Physics," in *Classical Quarterly*, **25** (1931), 27–37, 112–120; J. E. Raven, "The Basis of Anaxagoras' Cosmogony," *ibid.*, n.s. **4** (1954), 123–137; C. Strang, "The Physical Theory of Anaxagoras," in *Archiv für Geschichte der Philosophie*, **45**, 2 (1963), 101–118; P. Tannery, *Pour l'histoire de la science hellène*, 2nd ed. (Paris, 1930), pp. 275–303; A. E. Taylor, "On the Date of the Trial of Anaxagoras," in *Classical Quarterly*, **11** (1917), 81–87; G. Vlastos, "The Physical Theory of Anaxagoras," in *Philosophical Review*, **59** (1950), 31–57; and M. L. West, "Anaxagoras and the Meteorite of 467 B.C.," in *Journal of the British Astronomical Association*, **70** (1960), 368–369.

JAMES LONGRIGG

ANAXILAUS OF LARISSA (described by Eusebius as a Pythagorean magician who was banished from Italy by Augustus in Olympiad 188, 1 [28 B.C.]).

He wrote about the "magical" or peculiar effects of some minerals, herbs, and animal substances and of the drugs made with them; in this connection he is cited several times by Pliny. He seems to have been famous for his magical tricks, since he is mentioned as the author of *ludicra* ("sports" or "tricks") by Irenaeus and by Epiphanius. Anaxilaus may have been a source for Pliny in other instances where Pliny does not mention him by name, but it is impossible to prove it.

Because, in a magical papyrus now at Stockholm, Anaxilaus is reported as quoting a recipe of Pseudo-Democritus, Diels assumed that through Anaxilaus the author of the papyrus knew at least part of the treatise of Pseudo-Democritus on alchemy. Wellmann, through a comparison of Pliny's *Natural History* (XXV, 154), where Anaxilaus is mentioned, and

Dioscorides' *De materia medica* (IV, 79), infers that Anaxilaus was one of the authors used by Sextius Niger. Other passages, in Sextus Empiricus, Psellus, and others, that are parallel to passages where Anaxilaus is mentioned suggest that he was one of the important sources for magical and alchemical authors. The Anaxilaus mentioned by Diogenes Laertius (I, 107) may or may not be Anaxilaus of Larissa, but there is no reason to identify either with the Anaxilaïdes cited by Diogenes Laertius (III, 2) as the author of a work entitled *On Philosophers*, as Schwartz has suggested.

BIBLIOGRAPHY

H. Diels provides a review of Lagercrantz's book (see below) in *Deutsche Literaturzeitung*, **34** (1913), cols. 901–906. See also O. Lagercrantz, *Papyrus Graecus Holmiensis. Recepte für Silber, Steine und Purpur* (Uppsala-Leipzig, 1913); E. Schwartz, "Anaxilaides," in Pauly-Wissowa, *Real-Encyclopädie der klassischen Altertumswissenschaft*, I, 2 (Stuttgart, 1894), col. 2083; H. Stadler, *Die Quellen des Plinius im 19. Buche der naturalis historia*, inaugural dissertation (Munich, 1891), pp. 29–30; and M. Wellmann, "Sextius Niger. Eine Quellenuntersuchung zu Dioscorides," in *Hermes*, **24** (1889), 530–569; "Anaxilaos," in Pauly-Wissowa, *Real-Encyclopädie der klassischen Altertumswissenschaft*, I, 2 (Stuttgart, 1894), col. 2084; "Die ΦΥΣΙΚΑ des Bolos Demokritos und der Magier Anaxilaos aus Larissa, Teil I," in *Abhandlungen der Preussischen Akademie der Wissenschaften* (1928), philosophisch-historische Klasse, no. 7; see pp. 77–80 for a collection of the fragments of Anaxilaus.

Anaxilaus is mentioned in the following classical works: Epiphanius, *Contra haereses*, 34, 1; Eusebius, *Chronikon*, Schoene ed., II, 141; Irenaeus, *Contra haereses*, I, 13, 1; and Pliny, *Natural History*, XIX, 20; XXV, 154; XXVIII, 181; XXX, 74; XXXII, 141; XXXV, 175.

L. TARÁN

ANAXIMANDER, *astronomy, natural philosophy.*

There were at least two Anaximanders, both citizens of Miletus: the elder, who was born about 610 B.C. and who is said to have died shortly after 547/546 B.C. (i.e., in 546/545 B.C., the year of the fall of Sardis), and the younger, who is said to have been a historian, the author of *Interpretation of Pythagorean Symbols,* who lived toward the end of the fifth century B.C. We are concerned here with the older Anaximander. Of him we possess only one verbatim quotation, which is difficult to interpret with certainty, and several reports by later authors. Most of this indirect evidence, however, cannot be taken at its face value because it ultimately goes back to Theophrastus, who, like his teacher Aristotle, had the tendency to see and interpret the doctrines of pre-Aristotelian philosophers in the light of the problems, the terminology, and the positive doctrines of Aristotle's philosophy. Needless to say, the later doxographical reports also contain mistakes of their own making; and, in the case of the astronomical and mathematical data, later authors transferred the knowledge of what to them were obvious notions to the heroes of early Greek thought. Thus, for example, Anaximander is credited with the discovery of the equinoxes and of the obliquity of the ecliptic, attributions that are anachronistic and that contradict other notions that he is said to have held.

Fortunately, for Anaximander we possess information from a different tradition, the geographical. Thus, we know that he drew a map of the inhabited world and that he wrote a book in which he tried to explain the present state of the earth and of its inhabitants, especially the human race. For this purpose he advanced a cosmogony. According to Anaximander, at any given time there are an infinite number of worlds that have been separated off from the infinite, τὸ ᾽άπειρον, which is the source and reservoir of all things. These worlds come into being, and when they perish, they are reabsorbed into the infinite, which surrounds them and is eternal and ageless. Our world came into being when a mass of material was separated off from the infinite; a rotatory motion in a vortex caused the heavy materials to concentrate at the center, while masses of fire surrounded by air went to the periphery and later constituted the heavenly bodies. The sun and the moon are annular bodies constituted of fire surrounded by a mass of air. This mass of air has pipelike passages through which the light produced by the fire inside escapes, and this is the light the earth receives. In this way Anaximander perhaps accounted for the different shapes of the moon's face and also for eclipses. The earth, at the center of this world, has the shape of a rather flat cylinder. Animals originated from inanimate matter, by the action of the sun on water, and men originated from fish.

What is significant in all this is that Anaximander tried to explain all these different phenomena as the result of one law that rules everything; and it is this law that is preserved in the only verbatim quotation from Anaximander that we possess (here paraphrased): All things pass away into that from which they took their origin, the infinite, as it is necessary; for they make reparation to one another for their injustice in the fixed order of time. The extent and exact meaning of this quotation are controversial, but there can be no question that here we have an imper-

sonal law according to which all occurrences in the universe are explained. This all-inclusive, immanent law of nature is Anaximander's lasting contribution to human thought.

BIBLIOGRAPHY

The ancient sources are collected in H. Diels and W. Kranz, eds., *Die Fragmente der Vorsokratiker*, 6th ed., I (Berlin, 1951), 81–90.

Modern works dealing with Anaximander are J. Burnet, *Early Greek Philosophy*, 4th ed. (London, 1930), pp. 50–71; H. Cherniss, *Aristotle's Criticism of Presocratic Philosophy* (Baltimore, 1935), *passim*; and "The Characteristics and Effects of Presocratic Philosophy," in *Journal of the History of Ideas*, 12 (1951), 319–345; D. R. Dicks, "Solstices, Equinoxes, and the Presocratics," in *Journal of Hellenic Studies*, 86 (1966), 26–40; F. Dirlmeier, "Der Satz des Anaximandros von Milet," in *Rheinisches Museum*, 87 (1938), 376–382; W. A. Heidel, "The ΔINH in Anaximenes and Anaximander," in *Classical Philology*, 1 (1906), 279–282; "On Anaximander," *ibid.*, 7 (1912), 212–234; "On Certain Fragments of the Pre-Socratics," in *Proceedings of the American Academy of Arts and Sciences*, 48 (1913), 681–734, esp. 682–691; and "Anaximander's Book, the Earliest Known Geographical Treatise," *ibid.*, 56 (1921), 237–288; C. H. Kahn, *Anaximander and the Origins of Greek Cosmology* (New York, 1960); G. S. Kirk and J. E. Raven, *The Presocratic Philosophers* (Cambridge, 1957), pp. 99–142; A. Maddalena, *Ionici, testimonianze e frammenti* (Florence, 1963), pp. 76–157; J. B. McDiarmid, "Theophrastus on the Presocratic Causes," in *Harvard Studies in Classical Philology*, 61 (1953), 85–156; R. Mondolfo, *L'infinito nel pensiero dell'antichità classica* (Florence, 1956), pp. 188 ff.; and in his edition of E. Zeller's *Philosophie der Griechen, La filosofia dei greci nel suo sviluppo storico*, II (Florence, 1938), 135–205; and E. Zeller, *Die Philosophie der Griechen*, W. Nestle, ed., I (Leipzig, 1923), 270–315.

Additional bibliographies may be found in the works by Kahn and Maddalena cited above.

L. TARÁN

ANAXIMENES OF MILETUS (*fl.* 546/545 B.C.), *philosophy.*

The year in which Anaximenes is said to have flourished is that of the fall of Sardis, and therefore his chronology, which comes from Apollodorus, may be arbitrary. Anaximenes may or may not have been a student of Anaximander, but there can be no question that he was acquainted with Anaximander's book, since his cosmological and astronomical views are very close to those of Anaximander. His interests, however, seem to have been more restricted than those of Anaximander; but like the latter, Anaximenes thought that the source from which all things come into being is infinite. He further qualified this original substance by saying that it is air, for he had discovered a mechanism that could account for the transformation of one thing into another: the mechanism of condensation and rarefaction. When air is evenly distributed, it is invisible; when it is condensed, it becomes water; and when it is condensed further, it becomes earth and then stone. When, on the other hand, air is hot, it becomes rarefied and eventually becomes fire. Anaximenes seems to have been satisfied that the following "experiment," which proved to him that cold air is condensed and hot air is rarefied, corroborated his theory: When we expel air, it becomes cold if we press our lips, whereas it becomes hot if we open our mouths. This experiment, which is recounted—perhaps in Anaximenes' own words—by Plutarch, shows that for Anaximenes air is a substance composed of small, discrete particles: when the particles are compressed, we have water; when they are expanded by heat, we have hot air, fire, etc. This substance thus composed of discrete particles is not more air than water, earth, or fire, but Anaximenes seems to have named it "air" because air is the most widely distributed body in the universe and because breath is identified with the soul, which he believed holds living beings together.

On the basis of this analogy, Anaximenes seems to have believed that the cosmos breathes by inhaling the surrounding air. Consequently, what Anaximenes calls air should not be identified with a single substance that by qualitative alteration becomes all the things we see around us—as Aristotle, Theophrastus, and the doxographers believed he meant. Anaximenes seems also to have believed in an infinite number of worlds that come into being and pass away, to be reabsorbed into the infinite air that surrounds them and is in perpetual motion. We also find in Anaximenes the use of rotatory motion to explain the formation of our world: the big masses of air and water and the heavenly bodies are formed through the process of condensation and rarefaction; the earth, a flat disk at the center, is supported by air; and the same annular form is attributed to the heavenly bodies, which are carried around and supported by air. Since for Anaximenes the sun and the moon are formed out of fire, he must have been ignorant of the fact that the moon reflects the light of the sun. The heavenly bodies turn around the earth and become invisible because they are so far away and because the northern parts of the earth are elevated.

BIBLIOGRAPHY

The ancient sources are collected in Diels and Kranz, *Die Fragmente der Vorsokratiker*, 6th ed., I (Berlin, 1951), 90–96.

Modern works dealing with Anaximenes are J. Burnet, *Early Greek Philosophy*, 4th ed. (London, 1930), pp. 72–79; H. Cherniss, *Aristotle's Criticism of Presocratic Philosophy* (Baltimore, 1935); W. A. Heidel, "The ΔINH in Anaximenes and Anaximander," in *Classical Philology,* 1 (1906), 279–282; J. B. McDiarmid, "Theophrastus on the Presocratic Causes," in *Harvard Studies in Classical Philology,* 61 (1953), 85–156; A. Maddalena, *Ionici, testimonianze e frammenti* (Florence, 1963), with bibliography; and R. Mondolfo, in E. Zeller and R. Mondolfo, *La filosofia dei greci nel suo sviluppo storico,* pt. 1 (Florence, 1938), 206–238, with bibliography.

L. TARÁN

ANCEL, PAUL ALBERT (*b*. Nancy, France, 21 September 1873; *d*. Paris, France, 27 January 1961), *biology.*

Ancel became an intern in the Nancy hospitals in 1898 and received the M.D. in 1899 and the *docteur ès sciences* from the University of Nancy in 1903. The following year he was made *professeur agrégé* of anatomy at the Faculté de Médecine in Lyons. He then became *professeur titulaire* of anatomy at Nancy in 1908 and of embryology at Strasbourg in 1919. The chair of embryology in Strasbourg was the first of its kind in France. It demanded, both in teaching and in research, a complete reorientation, which Ancel accomplished superbly.

Ancel's numerous honors include corresponding membership in the Académie des Sciences of Paris, national corresponding membership in the Académie de Médecine, honorary foreign membership in the Académie Royale de Médecine Belge of Brussels, the Prix du Prince de Monaco of the Académie de Médecine (1937), and the Prix de la Fondation Singer Polignac (1950), both shared with Pol Bouin.

Ancel's work can be divided into three sections:

(1) His first publications sum up the observations of an anatomist trained in the operating room, but at the same time he carried on his research in cytology, which furnished the material for an important thesis on the hermaphroditic genital gland of the snail.

(2) Beginning in 1903, he collaborated for twenty-five years with Pol Bouin, first at Nancy and then at Strasbourg, in investigations on the physiology of reproduction in mammals. Their essential discoveries can be summed up as follows: In the male it is the

interstitial gland of the testis that produces a hormone responsible for the secondary sexual characteristics. In the female the internal secretion of the *corpus luteum* determines the preparation of the uterine mucosa for the nidation of the fertilized ovum, as well as the morphogenetic development of the mammary gland. These basic facts are still accepted, and Ancel and Bouin must figure in any history of sexual endocrinology. This science began, not around 1930 with the isolation of sex hormones, but in the first years of the twentieth century, through experimental investigations, among which those of Ancel and Bouin are of primary importance.

(3) Studies in experimental embryology and teratogenesis, started in Strasbourg as early as 1919, and continued by Ancel until his death, sometimes with various collaborators, constitute an important part of modern embryology. Ancel elucidated the determinism of bilateral symmetry in the amphibian embryo and gave a new scope to experimental teratogenesis, which had remained stagnant for scores of years, by trying out new and fruitful methods, such as the experimental production of monstrosities by precise and localized lesions and the use of chemistry in applying to the whole embryo, at a precise stage of development, substances having a specific action determined by previous tests. Ancel thus became one of the creators of present experimental embryology, and particularly of teratogenesis, by using physical and chemical means.

Of a determined and at times vehement character, Ancel did not fear discussion in order to defend university policy or conclusions reached through his investigations. He was most meticulous in preparing his courses, using blackboard diagrams as well as practical demonstrations in embryology. His scientific writings exceeded 300 memoranda, reports, and books, and his research, begun as early as his medical studies, covered nearly sixty years. After his retirement from teaching, Ancel continued his research at the Institut de Physico-Chimie Biologique in Paris until the eve of his death.

BIBLIOGRAPHY

For a complete list of Ancel's publications and references to his obituary notices, see Étienne Wolff, "Le Professeur Paul Ancel," in *Archives d'anatomie, d'histologie, d'embryologie normales et expérimentales,* supp. **44** (1961), 5–27.

MARC KLEIN

ANDERNACH, GUNTHER. See **Guenther, Johann.**

ANDERSON, ERNEST MASSON (*b.* Falkirk, Scotland, 9 August 1877; *d.* Edinburgh, Scotland, 8 August 1960), *geology.*

Anderson, a structural geologist, tectonist, and mathematical geophysicist, was a son of Rev. John Anderson and Annie Masson, daughter of a minister. He was educated at Dundee High School and Edinburgh University, from which he received the B.Sc. in 1897, the M.A. with first class honours in mathematics and natural philosophy in 1898, and the D.Sc. in 1933. In 1915 he married Alice Catherine Esson, by whom he had two daughters.

Anderson joined the Geological Survey of Great Britain in 1903. Except during 1916–1917, when he served in the army and was wounded in France, he worked in Scotland. Temporary ill health forced him to retire as a senior geologist in 1928.

He was a Christian free-thinker; self-effacing in spite of outstanding mathematical ability, he was characterized by his innate courtesy. Anderson was awarded three medals: by the Royal Society of Edinburgh, the Geological Society of London, and the Geological Society of Edinburgh.

Anderson contributed to many Geological Survey memoirs. His main scientific work stemmed from official problems but was done in leisure time and published almost entirely in other than governmental journals. This work concerned the dynamics of faulting and igneous intrusion, the lineation of schists, crustal heat and structure, and volcanism. After his retirement he expanded all these studies by mathematical analysis.

In 1905 Anderson gave the first explanation of the dynamic basis of the three main classes of faults—reversed, normal, and wrench (a term he preferred to "transcurrent" or "strike-slip"). He later extended his structural studies in discussions of the dynamics of intrusion of igneous sheets and dikes and of the formation of cauldron subsidences (1924, 1936, 1937, 1938). *The Dynamics of Faulting and Dyke Formation* (1942, 1951) has been acclaimed by W. B. Harland as a landmark in structural geology. E. S. Hills, however, has criticized some applications of Anderson's theories; H. Jeffreys has questioned certain of his views on fracture; and G. R. Robson and K. G. Barr have rejected a postulate in his theory of igneous intrusion.

Anderson's theory regarding lineation in schists of the Scottish Highlands was inspired by the work of his Geological Survey supervisor C. T. Clough. From kinematic analysis Anderson inferred that lineations, which may be due to subcrustal convection currents, are parallel to the direction of transport or shear, and that the planes of quartz and mica girdles are normal to that direction (1923, 1948, 1952). These unorthodox views were supported by A. Kvale and W. Q. Kennedy and criticized by G. Wilson and F. C. Phillips. E. S. Hills accepted Anderson's theory in part only.

Anderson's geophysical work stemmed from his early temperature studies in deep bores and colliery workings in Scotland (1909). He later amplified his discussion of heat flow in relation to Britain and the earth's crust in general (1934, 1938, 1940). His detailed criticism of the thermal earth-contraction theory (1934) led to his collaboration with W. Q. Kennedy; he and Kennedy suggested that basaltic magmas originate by the fusion of crustal layers at certain depths (1938). This idea has been used, with modifications, by A. F. Buddington, A. G. MacGregor, and F. Walker.

Anderson made an important contribution to mineral optics by giving the first fully satisfactory explanation of the "Becke line" effect seen in transparent mineral sections under the microscope (1910). He also dealt with other optical problems (1912, 1914, 1933).

BIBLIOGRAPHY

I. ORIGINAL WORKS. Anderson's writings include "The Dynamics of Faulting," in *Transactions of the Edinburgh Geological Society,* **8** (1905), 387–402; "On the Temperature-gradients of Deep Bores, With Special Reference to Those of the Balfour Bore, Cameron Bridge, Fifeshire," *ibid.,* **9** (1909), 167–178; in G. W. Grabham, "An Improved Form of Petrographical Microscope," in *Mineralogical Magazine,* **15** (1910), 342–343; "Are Eyes Ever Autophanous?" in *Nature,* **88** (1912), 484; "The Path of a Ray of Light in a Rotating Homogeneous and Isotropic Solid," in *Proceedings of the Royal Society of Edinburgh,* **34** (1914), 69–76; "The Geology of the Schists of the Schichallion District, Perthshire," in *Quarterly Journal of the Geological Society of London,* **79** (1923), 423–442; *In the Tertiary and Post-Tertiary Geology of Mull, Loch Aline and Oban,* Memoir of the Geological Survey (Edinburgh, 1924), pp. 11–12; "A Proposed Logarithmic Method of Calculating Exposures and Apertures," in *Photographic Journal* (Feb. 1933), 71–72; "Earth Contraction and Mountain Building," in *Gerlands Beiträge zur Geophysik,* **42** (1934), 133–159, and **43** (1934), 1–18; "The Dynamics of the Formation of Cone-sheets, Ring-dykes and Cauldron-subsidences," in *Proceedings of the Royal Society of Edinburgh,* **61** (1936), 128–157; "Cone-sheets and Ring-dykes: The Dynamical Explanation," in *Bulletin volcanologique,* 2nd Series, **1** (1937), 35–40; "Crustal Layers and the Origin of Magmas," *ibid.,* **3** (1938), 24–82, written with W. Q. Kennedy; "The Dynamics of Sheet Intrusion," in *Proceedings of the Royal Society of Edinburgh,* **58** (1938), 242–251; "The Loss of Heat by Conduction From the Earth's Crust in Britain," *ibid.,* **60** (1940), 192–209; *The Dynamics of*

Faulting and Dyke Formation, With Applications to Britain (Edinburgh and London, 1942; 2nd ed., rev., 1951); "On Lineation and Petrofabric Structure and the Shearing Movement by Which They Have Been Produced," in *Quarterly Journal of the Geological Society of London,* **104** (1948), 99–126; and "Lineation in Relation to Sub-crustal Convection Currents," in *Geological Magazine,* **89** (1952), 113–123.

II. SECONDARY LITERATURE. Writings that deal with Anderson or his work are A. F. Buddington, "Some Petrological Concepts and the Interior of the Earth," in *American Mineralogist,* **28** (1943), 119–140, esp. 137, 139; W. B. Harland, "The Dynamics of Faulting (A Review)," in *Geological Magazine,* **90** (1953), 300–301; E. S. Hills, *Elements of Structural Geology* (London, 1965), pp. 178, 426; H. Jeffreys, "Note on Fracture," in *Proceedings of the Royal Society of Edinburgh,* **56** (1936), 158–163; W. Q. Kennedy, discussion of Anderson's paper in *Quarterly Journal of the Geological Society of London,* **104** (1948), 131; A. Kvale, "Linear Structures and Their Relation to Movement in the Caledonides of Scandinavia and Scotland," *ibid.,* **109** (1953), 51–64, esp. 60, 62, 64; A. G. MacGregor, "Problems of Carboniferous-Permian Volcanicity in Scotland," *ibid.,* **104** (1948), 133–152, esp. 144–145, "Ernest Masson Anderson, M.A., D.Sc., F.G.S." (an obituary notice), in *Year Book of the Royal Society of Edinburgh* (Edinburgh, 1961), pp. 5–6, and "Ernest Masson Anderson" (an obituary notice), in *Proceedings of the Geological Society of London,* no. 1592 (1961), 137–138; F. C. Phillips, "Apparent Coincidences in the Life-history of the Moine Schists," in *Geological Magazine,* **88** (1951), 225–235; G. R. Robson and K. G. Barr, "The Effect of Stress on Faulting and Minor Intrusions in the Vicinity of a Magma Body," in *Bulletin volcanologique,* **27** (1964), 1–16; F. Walker, "The Part Played by Tholeiitic Magma in the Carbo-Permian Vulcanicity of Central Scotland," in *Mineralogical Magazine,* **34** (1965), 489–516, esp. 512–515; and G. Wilson, discussion of Anderson's paper in *Quarterly Journal of the Geological Society of London,* **104** (1948), 126–127.

A. G. MacGregor

ANDERSON, OSKAR JOHANN VIKTOR (*b.* Minsk, Russia, 2 August 1887; *d.* Munich, German Federal Republic, 12 February 1960), *mathematics.*

After studying for one term at the mathematical faculty of Kazan University, Anderson entered the economics faculty of the Petersburg Polytechnical Institute in 1907. He graduated in 1912 as a candidate in economics. His dissertation, in which he developed the variance-difference method for analyzing time series, was published in *Biometrika* (1914) almost simultaneously with similar work by W. S. Gosset.

Anderson was a pupil and an assistant of A. A. Tschuprow and always, even during the general excessive enthusiasm aroused by Karl Pearson's methods, considered himself a representative of the "Continental direction" of mathematical statistics exemplified by Lexis, Bortkiewicz, and Tschuprow. From 1912 until he left Russia in 1920, Anderson taught in commercial colleges at St. Petersburg and Kiev, and engaged in research. He participated in a study of the agriculture of Turkestan in 1915 using sampling methods—he was a pioneer in this field—and worked at the Demographical Institute of the Kiev Academy of Sciences in 1918.

After he left Russia, Anderson spent four years in Hungary, continuing his pedagogic and scientific activities. From 1924 to 1942 he lived in Bulgaria, where he was extraordinary professor of statistics and economic geography at the Varna Commercial College until 1929 and full professor from then on; a member of the Supreme Scientific Council of the Central Board of Statistics; and from 1935 director of the Statistical Institute of Economic Researches of Sofia University. Anderson was engaged mainly in the application of statistics to economics, and published a review of the general status of Bulgarian economics (1938). Subsequent economical-statistical investigations in Bulgaria were always conducted in the spirit of Andersonian traditions, and in this sense he founded a school in that country. Anderson also became internationally known: he published a primer (1935), delivered lectures at the London School of Economics in 1936, and was an adviser to the League of Nations and a charter member of the Econometric Society. He was also an honorary member of the Royal and West German Statistical Societies, the International Statistical Institute, and the American Statistical Association.

In 1942 Anderson accepted a professorship at the University of Kiel; from 1947 until his death he held the chair of statistics at the economics faculty of the University of Munich and was the recognized leader of West German statisticians. His pedagogic activities resulted in higher standards of statistical education for student economists in West Germany.

Besides developing the variance-difference method, Anderson did research in the quantity theory of money and in the index-number theory from the statistical viewpoint. Seeing no significant advantage in the application of classical mathematics to economics, he advocated the application of mathematical statistics. Anderson believed that the application of statistics distinguished modern economics from economics based on Robinson Crusoe theories and the *homo oeconomicus*. He especially believed that statistics, based on the law of large numbers and the sorting out of random deviations, is the only substitute for experimentation, which is impossible in economics. Sensibly estimating the difficulties in-

herent in economics as a science, Anderson was opposed to the use of "refined" statistical methods and to accepting preconditions regarding laws of distribution. This led him to nonparametric methods and to the necessity of causal analysis in economics.

BIBLIOGRAPHY

I. ORIGINAL WORKS. Anderson published some eighty books, papers, reports to national and international bodies, reviews, and obituaries, mainly in German and Bulgarian. He published three papers in Russian.

His books are *Einführung in die mathematische Statistik* (Vienna, 1935); *Struktur und Konjunktur der bulgarischen Volkswirtschaft* (Jena, 1938); and *Probleme der statistischen Methodenlehre in den Sozialwissenschaften,* 4th ed. (Würzburg, 1962). These books provide a sufficient overall notion of Anderson's work. Intended for a broad circle of readers with a preuniversity mathematical background, they are less known outside the German-speaking countries than they deserve to be.

Aside from the books, Anderson's main writings are in his selected works: *Ausgewählte Schriften,* 2 vols. (Tübingen, 1963). Forty-six works by Anderson are reprinted there, with translations into German if the originals are in Bulgarian. Vol. II contains a list of his other works (thirty-two items). This list is not complete, however, for Anderson published at least two more works.

II. SECONDARY LITERATURE. General information about Anderson can be found in Capelli, ed., *Bibliografie con brevi cenni biografici, Biblioteca di statistica,* II, pt. 1 (1959); and *Kürschners deutscher Gelehrten-Kalender* (Berlin, 1961). About fifteen obituaries of Anderson are listed with a biography in Vol. I of the *Ausgewählte Schriften.* Among the obituaries are E. M. Fels, in *Econometrica,* **29,** no. 1 (1961), 74–80; G. Tintner, in *American Statistical Association, Quarterly Publication,* **56,** no. 294 (1961), 273–280; and H. Wold, in *Annals of Mathematical Statistics,* **32,** no. 3 (1961), 651–660.

The most recent biography of Anderson is E. M. Fels, in the *International Encyclopedia of the Social Sciences* (New York, 1968).

O. B. SHEYNIN

ANDERSON, THOMAS (*b.* Leith, Scotland, 2 July 1819; *d.* Chiswick, England, 2 November 1874), *organic chemistry.*

The son of a physician in Leith, Anderson was educated at the high school there and at Edinburgh Academy. He then studied medicine at Edinburgh University, graduating in 1841. The subject of his doctoral thesis, the chemical changes accompanying nutrition and other physiological processes, shows the direction his interests were to take. He studied under Berzelius in Stockholm in 1842 and in the following year worked in Liebig's laboratory in Giessen; after visiting other European centers of chemical and medical research, he returned to Edinburgh. In 1845 he became a fellow of the Royal Society of Edinburgh, and in the following year he began lecturing in the extramural medical school in Edinburgh. When Thomas Thomson died in 1852, Anderson succeeded him as professor of chemistry at Glasgow, and in the same year he married Mary Barclay.

All Anderson's important work was done in the field of organic chemistry, but in addition to his pure research, he carried out numerous analyses of soils, manures, and cattle foods. As chemist to the Highland and Agricultural Society of Scotland, he examined the composition of wheat, beans, and turnips at various stages of growth, and the results were published in the Society's *Journal* over a period of twenty-five years. He also published a treatise on agricultural chemistry in 1860. His work was virtually brought to an end in 1869 by serious illness, and his last few years were marred by paralysis, deafness, and occasional delirium.

In Anderson's first important paper, read in 1846, he described how, on examining a mixture of bases derived from coal tar, he had found a minute quantity of pyrrole (discovered twelve years before by Runge) and, in attempting to separate it, had been led to the discovery of a new base, which he called picoline and found to be an isomer of aniline.

This was the first discovered member of the pyridine series of bases, and in a group of researches on the products of the distillation of bone oil (1848–1868) Anderson found pyridine itself and its methyl derivatives. In his first paper on these researches he described how, from 300 pounds of bone oil, he obtained less than two pounds of basic substances and, on distillation, found picoline and a substance he called *petinine* in the two most volatile fractions.

In subsequent researches Anderson realized that he was working with too little material, and he eventually distilled about 250 gallons of bone oil. Finding methylamine and propylamine, and possibly ethylamine, he concluded that his *petinine* was in fact butylamine—thus finding this substance shortly before Wurtz did. After the discovery of pyridine, lutidine, and collidine, in that order, he came to the conclusion that these new bases formed a homologous series and that they were derived "from ammonia by the replacement of its three atoms of hydrogen by as many different radicals" ("On the Products . . ." [1857], p. 230). The modern ring formula for pyridine was first published by Dewar in 1872.

Among his other researches, Anderson carried out a detailed investigation of codeine and other constituents of opium, in the course of which he elucidated the composition of a number of alkaloids; he also found the true constitution of anthracene.

Anderson was a painstaking worker and possessed considerable manipulative skill; the exposition of his results is marked by extreme lucidity.

BIBLIOGRAPHY

Anderson's major treatise was *Elements of Agricultural Chemistry* (Edinburgh, 1860). Most of his papers are listed in *The Royal Society Catalogue of Scientific Papers,* I (1867), 64–65. His papers on the pyridine bases are "On the Constitution and Properties of Picoline, a New Organic Base From Coal Tar," in *Transactions of the Royal Society of Edinburgh,* **16** (1849), 123–136; and "On the Products of the Destructive Distillation of Animal Substances," *ibid.,* 463–474; **20** (1853), 247–260; **21** (1857), 219–233, 571–595; and **25** (1869), 205–216.

An article on Anderson is E. J. Mills's obituary notice in *Journal of the Chemical Society,* **28** (1875), 1309–1313.

E. L. SCOTT

ANDOYER, HENRI (*b.* Paris, France, 1 October 1862; *d.* Paris, 12 June 1929), *astronomy, mathematics.*

Andoyer taught astronomy at the Sorbonne for thirty-seven years. His research dealt with celestial mechanics: perturbation theory, special cases of the three-body and of the *n*-body problem, and the motions of the moon. He developed special methods for use in computing ephemerides, the most elaborate one—for the moon—approximating E. W. Brown's definitive treatment but at a fraction of the labor.

Andoyer's interest in manipulating numbers began very early; his father's work as chief clerk at the Banque de France may have influenced him. He graduated at the top of his class in mathematical science at the École Normale Supérieure in 1884 and wrote his doctoral thesis (1887) on the theory of intermediate orbits as applied to the moon.

His first job took him to Toulouse, where besides continuing his theoretical studies he worked at the telescope, preparing a photographic map of the sky. In "Formules générales de la méchanique céleste" he showed how to solve the general equations of motion to any desired degree of accuracy in terms of trigonometric functions alone.

In 1892 Andoyer returned to Paris, where he began as a *maître de conférence* at the Sorbonne and became a full professor in 1903. Here he worked on special cases of the three-body problem, showing, for example, how to use the Lagrangian libration points (null points in a two-body gravitational field where a third body, of negligible mass, can remain more or less indefinitely) to make the periodic terms of the solution independent of time.

Next he attacked the problem of asteroids that, like Hecuba, move almost exactly twice as fast as Jupiter and hence are strongly perturbed. There followed an analysis of *n* bodies close to equilibrium points, which has been applied to problems of the general stability of the solar system.

In 1910 Andoyer became a member of the Bureau des Longitudes, where he succeeded to the editorship of *Connaissance des temps,* the French nautical almanac. During World War I, with most of the staff mobilized, he prepared many of the ephemerides himself. His *Nouvelles tables trigonométriques fondamentales,* prepared as an aid to computers, have values to fifteen decimal places. He must indeed have been, in the words of one of his students, *un calculateur formidable.*

In 1919 Andoyer became a member of the Académie Française.

BIBLIOGRAPHY

I. ORIGINAL WORKS. Andoyer's doctoral thesis, "Contributions à la théorie des orbites intermédiares," appeared in *Annales de la Faculté des Sciences de Toulouse,* **1** (1887), M.1–M.72. Other papers include "Sur les formules générales de la méchanique céleste," *ibid.,* **4** (1890), K.1–K.35; "Sur le calcul des équations de perturbations," in *Bulletin astronomique* (Paris), **19** (1902), 49–61; "Contribution à la théorie des petites planètes dont le moyen mouvement est sensiblement double de celui de Jupiter," *ibid.,* **20** (1903), 321–356; and "Sur les solutions périodiques voisines des positions d'équilibre relatif, dans le problème des *n* corps," *ibid.,* **23** (1906), 129–146.

The *Nouvelles tables trigonométriques fondamentales* was published in three volumes (Paris, 1915–1918). His lunar theory, a revision of Charles Delaunay's earlier work, appeared in four installments under the general title "Sur la théorie analytique du mouvement de la lune," in *Mémoires de l'Académie des Sciences,* 2nd series, **58**, no. 1 (1926), 1–30; **58**, no. 2 (1926), 1–69; **59**, no. 1 (1928), 1–98; and **59**, no. 3 (1928), 1–59.

Andoyer's lectures at the Sorbonne resulted in eight textbooks: four on mathematics, published in Paris from 1894 to 1898—*Cours de géométrie, Cours d'arithmétique, Cours d'algèbre,* and *Leçons élémentaires sur la théorie des formes et applications géométriques*; and four on astronomy —*Cours d'astronomie, Part I* (Paris, 1906; 3rd ed., 1923) and *Part II,* written with A. Lambert (Paris, 1907; 2nd ed., 1924), and *Cours de méchanique céleste, Part I* (Paris, 1923) and *Part II* (Paris, 1926).

II. SECONDARY LITERATURE. An obituary, with a portrait and a list of sixty-seven publications, appeared in *Bulletin astronomique* (Paris), 2nd series, **6** (1930), 129–145; two shorter memorials, with anecdotes, are in *Journal des observateurs* (Marseilles), **12** (15 November 1929), 193–198, and **13** (April 1930), 61–64.

SALLY H. DIEKE

ANDRÉ, CHARLES LOUIS FRANÇOIS (*b.* Chauny, Aisne, France, 18 March 1842; *d.* St. Genis-Laval, Rhône, France, 6 June 1912), *astronomy, meteorology.*

André worked on observational techniques for determining the distance to the sun—the problem of the solar parallax. In this connection he headed a French expedition sent to Nouméa in 1874 to observe a transit of Venus. Difficulties encountered in timing the transit led him to investigate sources of instrumental error. In later years he compiled statistics on the weather and climate of Lyons.

In 1864 André graduated from the École Normale Supérieure in Paris with a degree in physics. After teaching for a year in Nevers, he returned to Paris as an assistant astronomer under Urbain Leverrier, then director of the Paris Observatory.

His interest in methods of evaluating the solar parallax was shown in two papers written to acquaint French astronomers with work being done in this field by their colleagues in other countries. The first, "Sur la parallaxe du soleil déduite des observations méridiennes de Mars en 1862," was a summary of a cooperative effort, organized by Friedrich Winnecke, to measure the sun's distance by making meridian observations of Mars simultaneously from different latitudes on earth during the favorable opposition of 1862. The second, "Sur l'emploi des petites planètes pour la détermination de la parallaxe du soleil," discussed the merit of Johann Galle's suggestion that serial observations of asteroids would be even more profitable.

André was willing to go along with the majority, who favored observations of Venus made from widely separated places on earth on the approaching rare occasion when that planet would pass directly between earth and sun. But the failure in both 1761 and 1769 of France's previous attempts, made by Guillaume le Gentil de la Galaisière, reminded him how vulnerable the observing of so brief an occurrence as a transit could be. André therefore advocated a second program with asteroids. All that came of this was that André was chosen to head a Venus expedition and went to the French possession of New Caledonia for the transit of 9 December 1874. His results, when combined with those obtained in St. Paul, Minnesota, led to a solar parallax of 8.88″. This figure does not compare very favorably with the best modern value of 8.79415″, determined in 1961 by timing radar echoes from Venus, but André felt—as is now generally recognized—that he had isolated one major source of error: his observations led him to believe that the troublesome black drop effect, observed telescopically when the disc of Venus approached inner tangency with the solar limb, had its source in the instrument itself. He therefore investigated the effects of diffraction in optical instruments. With this work as his thesis, André was awarded a doctor's degree by the Sorbonne in 1876. He went to Ogden, Utah, to test his results at the transit of Mercury of 6 May 1878, but a snowstorm intervened.

On his return to France, André became a professor in the University of Lyons and director of the Lyons Observatory, for which he chose a new site at St.-Genis-Laval. Here he spent the remaining thirty-four years of his life. He was a corresponding member of the Académie Française and of the Bureau des Longitudes.

BIBLIOGRAPHY

I. ORIGINAL WORKS. André's works include "Sur la parallaxe du soleil déduite des observations méridiennes de Mars en 1862," in *Bulletin des sciences mathématiques et astronomiques, 2* (1871), 89–96; "Sur l'emploi des petites planètes pour la détermination de la parallaxe du soleil," *ibid.,* 3 (1872), 274–278; *L'astronomie pratique et les observatoires en Europe et en Amérique, depuis le milieu du 17e siècle jusqu'à nos jours,* 5 vols. (Paris, 1874–1878), Vols. III and IV written with A. Angot, Vol. V with G. Rayet and A. Angot; "Sur les documents scientifiques recueillis à Nouméa par la mission envoyée pour observer le passage de Vénus," in *Comptes rendus de l'Académie des Sciences (Paris),* **80** (1875), 1282–1285 and 1599; his thesis, "Diffraction dans les instruments d'optique; son influence sur les observations astronomiques," in *Annales scientifiques de l'École Normale Supérieure,* 2nd series, **5** (1876), 275–354; "Sur le passage de Vénus du 9 decembre 1874," in *Comptes rendus de l'Académie des Sciences (Paris),* **82** (1876), 205–208; "Resultats des observations du passage de Mercure, Ogden, Utah," *ibid.,* **86** (1878), 1380–1383; also several textbooks and works on meteorology, including *Recherches sur le climat du Lyonnais* (Lyons, 1880); and *Relations des phenomènes météorologiques déduites de leurs variations diurnes et annuelles* (Lyons, 1892). His papers, with the exception of a few published in *Comptes rendus de l'Académie des Sciences (Paris)* after 1900, are listed in the Royal Society of London's *Catalogue of Scientific Papers,* Vol. VII (London, 1877), Vol. IX (London, 1891), and Vol. XIII (Cambridge, 1914), where he is mistakenly identified as "l'abbé Charles André."

II. SECONDARY LITERATURE. An obituary, with portrait, appeared in *Bulletin de la Société des Amis de l'Université de Lyon* (1911–1912), 171–184; another, also in French,

in *Astronomische Nachrichten,* **192** (1912), no. 4595, cols. 187–188.

SALLY H. DIEKE

ANDREAE, JOHANN VALENTIN (*b.* Herrenberg, Württemberg, 17 August 1586; *d.* Stuttgart, Württemberg, 27 June 1654), *theology, Christian learning.*

Andreae's grandfather, Jacob Andreae, was professor of theology and chancellor of Tübingen University. The son of a smith, he has been called the Luther of Württemberg, and was the chief framer of the Formula of Concord (1577). Andreae's father, Johann, was a Lutheran minister, but seems to have neglected both his family and the ministry to pursue his interest in alchemy. After the father's death in 1601, Andreae's mother, Maria Moser Andreae, moved the family to Tübingen. She was also interested in the study of nature, and in her later years gained the position of court apothecary.

In poor health as a child, Andreae received his early education at home. Under the influence of his father and following the custom of the time, he was introduced to wide-ranging studies of classical authors and the secrets of nature. When he entered Tübingen University in 1601, he already had an avid interest in astronomy, mathematics, mechanics, music, and painting, and he had read Josephus, Livy, and Erasmus, as well as Sebastian Münster's *Cosmographia.* He pursued these interests at the university, where he found an intellectual milieu very similar to the one Kepler had entered in 1589: one characterized by Lutheran orthodoxy on the one hand and by growing interest in the book of nature and nature mysticism on the other. He received the B.A. in 1603 and the M.A. in 1605, and then officially took up the study of theology, without abandoning his earlier interests. Involvement in some student affair in violation of the university regulations caused him to be expelled in 1607, and he began five years of extensive travel interrupted by periods of residence and study in Tübingen and employment as a private tutor.

Among the teachers who especially influenced Andreae were two who had taught Kepler: the theologian Matthias Hafenreffer and the mathematician Michael Maestlin. In addition he became strongly indebted to another associate of Kepler's, Christoph Besold, who, although his subject was jurisprudence, took all knowledge for his province. Widely learned in languages, including Hebrew and probably Arabic, Besold read medieval philosophy, the Renaissance humanists, and the German mystics of the later Middle Ages, and admired Paracelsus, Ramón Lull, Nicholas of Cusa, and Pico della Mirandola. It was of great importance to Andreae that he had the use of Besold's extensive library. Well prepared in languages under Besold's guidance, Andreae traveled in Germany, France, northern Spain, Austria, Italy, and Switzerland. Early in 1611 he visited Lausanne and Geneva, whose Calvinistic social organization so greatly impressed him that he conceived the wish to introduce something similar into his own church. A year later he traveled to Rome through northern Italy, where he visited some of the Platonic academies. He found Rome so foreign to his temperament that he determined to devote his life to Lutheran theology and the service of his church.

Returning to Tübingen in 1612, Andreae studied theology under Hafenreffer, of whose dogmatics he published a synopsis, and mathematics under Maestlin, whose teaching he presented in the *Collectanea mathematica* (1614). In 1614 he become parson at Vaihingen and married Agnes Elisabeth Grüninger, who bore him nine children. During the years at Vaihingen (1614–1620) Andreae wrote most of the works for which he is remembered. The rest of his life was devoted to writing, the service of religion, and his efforts to create a Christian union. From 1620 to 1638 he was dean at Calw, where in September 1634, after the battle of Nördlingen, he lost practically all his manuscripts, his library, and a collection of art that included works by Dürer, Cranach, and Holbein. In 1639 he became court preacher and councillor in Stuttgart, and was in charge of the reorganization of the church in Württemberg. Suffering many disappointments in his efforts for the church and in failing health, he withdrew to Bebenhausen as bishop and abbot in 1650.

Andreae wrote a large number of small works, most of them in Latin; some were published anonymously, and several of them only years after their composition. Although his sole authorship of some works is contested, there is no doubt that he had a share in them. Their general aim was the universal spiritual reformation of mankind, a view shared by the intellectual community at Tübingen, of which he was the best-known and most influential representative. Dissatisfied with the increasing dryness and formality of the Lutheran orthodoxy, he wished to create a Christian union of all believers, joined in pious living and dedicated to the study of nature, reason, and the public welfare. These ideas were laid down in a number of works that show a strong debt to the chiliasm of Joachim of Fiore; to Paracelsus and the spiritual reformers of the late sixteenth century, especially Valentin Weigel; and to Campanella, whose manuscripts, which were brought to Tübingen around 1614 by Andreae's associate Tobias Adami,

had great influence there. On the pattern of the *Civitas soli,* Andreae wrote the typical Christian utopia in his *Reipublicae christianopolis descriptio* (1619). It was dedicated to Johann Arndt, whose *True Christianity* was the conceptual source of this new Jerusalem built against all sophistry. In this closely structured society all efforts are bent toward the attainment of the inward spiritual regeneration of each individual, with heavy emphasis on the study of nature, for which all citizens have a strong inclination. Since creation reveals the wisdom and benevolence of God, it is man's duty to study it closely, learn from it, and apply its lessons. The Book of Scripture is supplemented by the Book of Nature. The center of this society is its college, which offers a detailed division of the sciences and provision for their study, with correct observation and experiment playing a significant role. The pedagogical program includes universal education—even for girls—the study of the mother tongue, and knowledge of nature and the crafts, as well as physical training. It is strongly reminiscent of Bacon's *New Atlantis* (1627) and no less specific in its directions for the learned academy.

In 1619 and 1621 Andreae issued a call for the formation of such a society in his *Christianae societatis imago* and the *Christiani amoris dextera porrecta.* Both were presumed lost until recently found in the papers of Samuel Hartlib, in the original as well as in translations by John Hall, published at Cambridge in 1647 as *A Modell of a Christian Society* and *The Right Hand of Christian Love Offered.* Both have some connection with the Antilia scheme. In the *Modell,* Andreae says that man now lives in the old age of the world. He also explains that the naturalist is the "treasurer of nature," studying both the macrocosm and the microcosm, observing the "motions, differencies, uses, and excellencies of all creatures," and making them "as it were tributaries to mankind." Andreae is opposed to fables and sophistry, preferring things to words, experience to conjecture, and events to guesses. His aim is that all men may gain "the highest pitch of humane felicity" and "exhibit both in body and mind a perfect copy of Christian imitation." It is important for us to understand that the success of this and similar schemes did not depend on the formal organization of such a society: the reformation concerns the individual. The notion of the society is rather to be taken allegorically or metaphorically.

The same general inward reformation, Christian learning, and rejection of all false show of knowledge were also the aim of the works for which Andreae is best known. These are the three so-called original Rosicrucian writings, the *Fama fraternitatis* (1614), the *Confessio* (1615), and the *Chymische Hochzeit Christiani Rosencreutz* (1616). Andreae acknowledged authorship only of the last, written shortly before 1604, but he most likely also wrote the first two, between 1610 and 1612—which in any event came from his group at Tübingen. The *Fama* talks of Solomon as having reached greater wisdom and insight into creation than any man since Adam before the Fall. But, as the *Confessio* explains, God has willed that all men shall now, in the last age of the world, gain such universal knowledge as Adam possessed in "truth, light, life, and glory."

All three works were written in a satirical vein, but the fiction was mistaken for the truth and Andreae soon found himself compelled to reject them as a misunderstood joke; he did this in the *Turris Babel sive Judiciorum de fraternitate rosaceae crucis chaos* (1619). Hence all the mystification, which has not ceased to this day. There is no proof whatsoever that any fraternity existed before 1614 or that any has legitimately existed since according to the intent of the author. Andreae did not wish to promote occultism, esoteric mysteries, or secret societies—inward reform was mistaken for hidden organization.

Andreae exerted a considerable influence on Comenius, who declared that his interest in pansophy was first roused by the reading of Andreae. During his lifetime, Andreae had connections with a large number of men, including Kepler, Comenius, the circle around Samuel Hartlib and John Dury, and the learned Duke August of Braunschweig-Lüneburg-Wolfenbüttel. Through his devotion to Johann Arndt he also had some influence on what later became known as Pietism.

BIBLIOGRAPHY

There is no single comprehensive work on Andreae. His works are hard to come by, and the secondary literature is, with a few exceptions, beset with much confusion.

I. ORIGINAL WORKS. Much unpublished correspondence and some manuscripts are in the Herzog-August Bibliothek in Wolfenbüttel. Among Andreae's most important published works are *Vita ab ipso conscripta,* F. H. Rheinwald, ed. (Berlin, 1849), German translation by D. E. Seybold, in *Selbstbiographien berühmter Männer,* II (Winterthur, 1799); *Die chymische Hochzeit,* Alfons Rosenberg, ed. (Munich, 1957); *Confessio,* in Winfried Zeller, ed., *Der Protestantismus des 17. Jahrhunderts* (Bremen, 1962), pp. 170–185; *Christianopolis,* F. E. Held, ed. and trans. (New York, 1914); and *Christianae societatis imago* and *Christiani amoris dextera porrecta,* with John Hall's translations, in G. H. Turnbull, "Johann Valentin Andreae's Societas Christiana," in *Zeitschrift für deutsche Philologie,* **73** (1954), 407–432, and **74** (1955), 151–185.

II. SECONDARY LITERATURE. Works on Andreae are R. Kienast, *Johann Valentin Andreae und die vier echten Rosenkreutzer-Schriften* (Leipzig, 1926) (*Palaestra,* No. 152); Paul Joachimsen, "Johann Valentin Andreae un die evangelische Utopie," in *Zeitwende,* **2** (1926), 485–503, 623–642; Will-Erich Peuckert, *Die Rosenkreutzer* (Jena, 1928) and *Pansophie,* 2nd ed., rev. (Berlin, 1956); Heinrich Hermelink, *Geschichte der evangelischen Kirche in Württemberg* (Stuttgart, 1949), pp. 138–147; Hans Schick, *Das ältere Rosenkreuzertum* (Berlin, 1942); Paul Arnold, *Histoire des Rose-Croix* (Paris, 1955). The last two have good and extensive bibliographies. Arnold's book is the best introduction to Andreae, and it gives an excellent account of his times and the Tübingen milieu.

HANS AARSLEFF

ANDREWS, THOMAS (*b.* Belfast, Ireland, 19 December 1813; *d.* Belfast, 26 November 1885), *chemistry.*

The eldest son of Thomas John Andrews, a linen merchant, and Elizabeth Stevenson, Andrews was first educated at the Belfast Academy and the Belfast Academical Institution. After working for a short time in his father's office in 1828, he studied chemistry at Glasgow and then spent a short period in Dumas's laboratory in Paris in 1830. He studied medicine for four years at Dublin and for a year at Edinburgh, where he received the M.D. in 1835. On qualifying, he established a medical practice in Belfast and at the same time was appointed the first professor of chemistry at the Belfast Academical Institution. In 1842 Andrews married Jane Walker, and three years later gave up both his medical practice and his teaching post to become the first vice-president of Queen's College, Belfast. He also became professor of chemistry at Belfast when teaching started in 1849, and did not retire until 1879. In June 1849 he was elected a fellow of the Royal Society.

Andrews was noted for his manipulative skill and ingenuity in solving practical problems; he constructed much of his own apparatus. He was a good university administrator and keenly interested in social and political problems. He published two pamphlets, *Studium generale* and *The Church in Ireland,* which he called "chapters of contemporary history."

After some early work extending Schönbein's discoveries regarding passivity of metals, Andrews turned his attention to thermochemistry and, in a series of papers read in the period 1841–1848, gave details of experiments, many of them remarkably accurate, on heats of neutralization, heats of formation of water and other oxides and of metallic halides, and on the heat evolved when one metal replaces another in solutions. His work was begun at about the same time as that of Hess, but although they obtained similar results, their conclusions did not always agree.

Andrews subsequently turned his attention to the problem of the constitution of ozone. This had been investigated by a number of chemists, including Schönbein, its discoverer. Its nature was still unknown, however, and it was by no means certain that the ozone obtained from different sources was one and the same substance; it was thought by some to contain hydrogen. Andrews says his researches extended over four or five years, and he finally reached the conclusion that all the supposed varieties of ozone were identical and that it was in fact oxygen in an altered or allotropic condition. The investigation was continued in collaboration with P. G. Tait, but their attempts to determine the density of ozone proved abortive. This was because of their assumption that those reagents which were known to remove the ozonic properties from a mixture of ozone and oxygen actually combined with the ozone; they did not realize that the reagent removed an atom of oxygen from a molecule of ozone, leaving a molecule of oxygen, so that no volume change took place. Since a measurable weight of ozone thus appeared to occupy zero volume, it seemed that its density was infinite. This perplexing result (which they came near to explaining toward the end of their joint paper of 1860) led, however, to a proposal of the true solution by Odling in 1861; and the suggested formula O_3 was eventually established by Jacques Soret in 1866 and confirmed by B. C. Brodie in 1872.

Andrews is best known for his studies on the continuity of the gaseous and liquid states, and in particular for his discovery of the critical temperature of carbon dioxide in 1861. His researches formed the subject of the Bakerian lectures for 1869 and 1876; a further paper was published posthumously in 1887. The first printed account of his work appeared as a result of a communication from Andrews to W. A. Miller, who published it in his textbook (1863). After a graphic description of the appearance of carbon dioxide in a state intermediate between gas and liquid, he concludes "that there exists for every liquid a temperature at which no amount of pressure is sufficient to retain it in the liquid form" (in W. A. Miller, *Elements of Chemistry*, 3rd ed. [London, 1863], I, 328–329). He expressed the full implications of his discovery some ten years after his first experiments when, in 1871, he wrote: "We may yet live to see, or at least we may feel with some confidence that those who come after us will see, such bodies as oxygen and hydrogen in the liquid, perhaps even in the solid state" (*Scientific Papers*, p. lx).

BIBLIOGRAPHY

I. ORIGINAL WORKS. *Studium generale* (London, 1867) is severely critical of the policy of awarding external degrees without compulsory residence; Andrews argues for the establishment of more universities but insists they should be independent of each other and free from governmental or ecclesiastical control. *The Church in Ireland* (London, 1869) is a plea for religious toleration and an argument for the disestablishment of the Church of Ireland. Andrews' papers, with their original locations, are collected in *The Scientific Papers of the Late Thomas Andrews, M.D., F.R.S., With a Memoir*, P. G. Tait and A. Crum Brown, eds. (London, 1889). See also *The Royal Society Catalogue of Scientific Papers*, I (1867), 69–70.

II. SECONDARY LITERATURE. The memoir by Tait and Crum Brown (see above) is a biographical sketch and an appraisal of Andrews' work; it contains numerous extracts from his letters. See also Hugo Müller, in *Journal of the Chemical Society*, **49** (1886), 342–344. A more recent estimate of his work is C. L. Wilson, "The Queen's University of Belfast," in *Journal of the Royal Institute of Chemistry*, **81** (1957), 16–29, but he is concerned primarily with the history of the chemical school at Belfast University. See also Henry Riddell, in *Proceedings of the Belfast Natural History and Philosophical Society* (1921), 107–138.

E. L. SCOTT

ANDRUSOV, NIKOLAI IVANOVICH (*b.* Odessa, Russia, 19 December 1861; *d.* Prague, Czechoslovakia, 27 April 1924), *geology, paleontology.*

His father, Ivan Andreevich Andrusov, a navigator for a steamship company, died in a shipwreck on the Black Sea in 1870. His mother, Elena Filippovna Belaya, was the daughter of a merchant. There were five other children, two boys and three girls.

While still a Gymnasium student, Andrusov became interested in geology. During excursions throughout the Kerch Peninsula, where he spent his childhood, he familiarized himself with the geological structure of the area and collected rocks and fossils. Upon graduating from the Kerch Gymnasium in 1880, Andrusov entered Novorossiysk University in Odessa, where among his instructors were the prominent biologists I. I. Mechnikov and V. O. Kovalevski. During his first two years there he concentrated on zoology; but then, as in his Gymnasium years, he returned to geology and seriously studied paleontology. The Novorossiysk Society of Naturalists, having followed Andrusov's activities, annually subsidized his trips to the Crimea, on which he collected both geological and zoological material.

In 1884 Andrusov graduated from the university with excellent marks, but he was not appointed to the faculty because a year before his graduation he had signed a collective protest against the dismissal of Mechnikov. Through the vigorous efforts of his friends, Andrusov went abroad for two years, where he studied in Vienna and Munich under M. Neumayr, E. Suess, K. Zittel, and several other prominent geologists. During the summers he undertook scientific expeditions to the Tyrol, Croatia, and Italy.

Upon returning to Russia, Andrusov received a position at Petersburg University and remained there for the next four years. In 1887 the Petersburg Society of Naturalists sent him to the Transcaspian region for geological exploration and prospecting in Mangyshlak and Ust Urt (between the Caspian and Aral seas). The following summer he led a hydrogeological expedition to the vicinity of Kerch, and in 1889 he was made university laboratory assistant. Also in 1889 Andrusov married Nadezhda Genrikhovna (Andreevna) Schliemann, daughter of the famous archaeologist Heinrich Schliemann, who had discovered the remains of Troy.

In February 1890 at Petersburg University Andrusov defended his master's dissertation, based on his researches on the fauna in Kerch limestones. He then received the post of assistant professor of geology at Novorossiysk University. That summer Andrusov participated in an expedition aboard the research vessel *Chernomorets,* which was equipped by the Russian Geographical Society and the Maritime Ministry for studying the depths of the Black Sea. In the winter of 1891 he and his family went abroad for two years. He worked in the museums of Paris, Vienna, Zagreb, and Zurich, preparing a monograph on saltwater fauna (*Dreissensidae and Cardeidae*).

Andrusov returned to Russia in 1893. After receiving the post of assistant professor at Petersburg University, he began to lecture on paleontology. During the next three summers he made expeditions along the coastline of the Bay of Kara-Bogaz-Gol, in the Balkans, and in the regions of the Inlet of Baku. He also measured the depths of the Sea of Marmara.

In 1896 Andrusov was appointed *professeur extraordinaire* at the University of Yuriev. The following year he defended his doctoral dissertation on fossils and living dreissenoids, for which the Academy of Sciences awarded him the Lomonosov Prize.

While working in Yuriev, Andrusov continued his study of the geology and Neocene fauna of the Transcaspian region, Azerbaijan, Northern Caucasus, and the Crimea, making trips each summer to southern Russia.

In 1905 Andrusov was chosen full professor at the University of Kiev. During the next seven years he held the chair of geology and paleontology at the university and was also president of the Kiev Society of Naturalists. There gathered around him a group of talented young scientists whose activity with him was the start of the Kiev scientific school of geology.

In 1912 Andrusov was appointed geologist on the Geological Committee and professor at the Bestuzhev Higher Women's School in Petersburg. Taking note of his scientific merits, the Academy of Sciences in Petersburg elected him a corresponding member in 1910 and an academician in 1914. He next became director of the Peter I Geological Museum of the Academy of Sciences.

During World War I, Andrusov helped to create, and served on, a commission for studying Russia's natural resources. He was elected a full member of the Ukrainian Academy of Sciences in 1918 and was made professor at Tavricheski (Tauris) University in Simferopol, where he gathered around him such eminent scientists as V. I. Vernadski and V. A. Obruchev.

A year later Andrusov suffered a serious stroke. When he had partially recovered, his wife took him to Paris to recuperate. He taught at the Sorbonne for several years and then moved to Prague, where he died shortly afterward.

Andrusov's research trips extended throughout the wide expanses of southern Europe and central Asia: the Caucasus, the Crimea, the Transcaspian region, Rumania, the Balkan Peninsula, and Italy. Thus he was able to compare deposits of the same age in various regions. While studying paleontological remains he did not limit himself to his own collections, but made extensive use of those in various museums.

Among the research projects of his early period, a prominent place belongs to his oceanographic work—Andrusov was one of the initiators of this kind of research. He sailed the Black Sea, the Sea of Marmara, and the Caspian Sea, studying their depths, their currents, and the temperature and composition of the water at different depths and in various regions. But his chief attention was directed to recent bottom sediments and outcrops of bedrock. In the process of Andrusov's oceanographic work it was established that the lower portions of the Black Sea were contaminated with hydrogen sulfide. Great scientific interest was generated by his discovery, on the bottom of the Black Sea, of deposits with post-Tertiary fauna of the Caspian type. This find served as the basis for his later interesting paleogeographic reconstructions.

While still a youth exploring the length and breadth of the Kerch Peninsula, Andrusov noticed fossil reefs of a peculiar structure and with strange organic remains embedded in them. In his subsequent investigations on the Kerch Peninsula, and also on the Taman Peninsula, he established that prominent among the reef-building organisms present were those lime-secreting attached forms which, under the conditions of burial, retained the position they occupied during their life cycles. Such structures are characterized by the absence of lamination and by a more rapid growth vertically than laterally. Andrusov gave the name "onkoids" to those types of limestone that consist of reef-building organisms developing in their place of habitation and that are frequently called bioherms. These peculiar structures are less varied in facies and are of a smaller size than in presently existing reefs. Andrusov also studied the organic limestones found in other regions, and has given a detailed monographic description of the nubecularian limestone formations in Moldavia and Mangyshlak.

The major part of Andrusov's work was devoted to the Neocene period in southern Russia. Throughout all his life as a researcher he studied these deposits and the fauna embedded in them with exceptional thoroughness and detail. Thus, his monograph devoted to a paleontological description of the so-called Mediterranean stage of the northern Black Sea environs, Miocene and Pliocene deposits of the eastern part of the Caucasus and Transcaspian area, was significant for decades. Andrusov's study of mollusks in marine basins and closed basins with abnormal salinity, which periodically appeared in Neocene times within the boundaries of the Ponto-Caspian region, was especially important.

Andrusov distinguished and described a large number of new species, many of which were accepted as key fossils for different stages of the Neocene period. Relying on paleontological data, he established a detailed subdivision of Tertiary deposits in the oil-bearing regions of the Caucasus, defining most of the presently existing stratigraphic units: the Tarkhanski, Chokrak, Karagan, and Konka horizons; the Akchagylian and Apsheronian stages; and the Kuyalinik beds. He also established the extent of the Sarmatian and Pontian stages.

A significant place in Andrusov's paleontological-stratigraphical works was allotted to the elucidation of the paleogeographic conditions of the period under study. Those of his works that deal with this elucidation contain brilliant models of analysis of facies relationships and ecological features in the habitat of fossil organisms. Andrusov endeavored to establish the composition of the population of each paleogeographic zone by species and the interrelation of various forms that have a common habitat. That is, he studied not simply the fauna of any one horizon but the biocenosis that characterizes it.

Andrusov regarded the environment of animals and plants as the decisive factor in organic evolution, and in many respects his work was conducive to the formulation, at the beginning of the twentieth century, of a new direction in geology: paleoecology.

Besides paleontological-stratigraphical and paleogeographical works, a prominent place in Andrusov's writing is occupied by his studies of regional geology—works that, as a rule, throw light on the tectonic structure of a region. Of special interest in this connection is his essay on the geotectonics of the Kerch Peninsula and an examination of the conditions for formation of submarine terraces. A series of his scientific papers concerns the origin of oil and describes the mud volcanoes of southeastern Caucasus.

Andrusov worked with great energy in the Society of Naturalists at the universities of Yuriev and Kiev. He was one of the organizers of the seventh session of the International Geological Congress (convened in Russia in 1897), and he participated in its activities. He was also the founder of the journal *Geologicheski vestnik* ("Geological Herald") and was its editor for a number of years. Andrusov wrote more than 120 scientific works, the great majority of which received wide dissemination among paleontologists and stratigraphers in many countries.

Andrusov is recognized as the founder of the stratigraphy of the Neocene deposits in southern Russia and contiguous territories; and the schema he worked out for the subdivision of Upper Tertiary deposits has become the standard for all investigators of the Cenozoic era.

BIBLIOGRAPHY

Among Andrusov's writings are "Kerchenski izvestniak i ego fauna" ("Kerch Limestone and Its Fauna"), in *Zapiski S. Peterburgskogo Mineralogicheskogo Obschestva* (*Memoirs of the St. Petersburg Mineralogical Society*), **26**, sec. 2 (1890), 193–345; "Die südrussische Neogenablagerungen," *ibid.*, **34**, sec. 2 (1896), 195–295; **36**, sec. 1 (1899), 101–170; **39**, sec. 2 (1902), 337–495; **44** (1906), 289–499; "Iskopaemye i zhivuschie Dreissensidae Evrazii" ("The Fossil and Living Dreissensidae of Eurasia"), in *Trudy S. Peterburgskogo Obschestva estestvoispytatelei* (*Transactions of the St. Petersburg Society of Naturalists*), **25**, div. of geol. and miner., I–IV, 1–683, 1 map, 20 plates; *Die fossilen Bryozoenriffe der Halbinseln Kertsch und Taman*, 3 vols. (Kiev, 1909–1912); "Apsheronski yarus" ("The Apsheronian Stage"), in *Trudy Geologicheskogo Komiteta* (*Transactions of the Geological Committee*), **110** (1923), I–VI, 1–294; *Vospominaniya, 1871–1890* ("Remembrances, 1871–1890" [Paris, 1923]), 1–198; *Izbrannye trudy v 4 tomakh* ("Selected Works in Four Volumes" [Moscow, 1961–1965]).

V. V. TIKHOMIROV

ANGELI, STEFANO DEGLI (*b.* Venice, Italy, 21 September 1623; *d.* Venice, 11 October 1697), *mathematics, physics.*

Born Francesco degli Angeli, he entered the Order of the Gesuati of Saint Jerolamen. At twenty-one he was appointed reader of literature, philosophy, and theology in the faculty of his order at Ferrara. He remained in Ferrara for about three years, although he was in poor health, until his physicians concluded that the climate of the city was harmful to him. He was then transferred to Bologna, where he developed a deep interest in mathematics under the guidance of a member of the same religious order, Bonaventura Cavalieri, who taught at the University of Bologna. Cavalieri was soon able to appreciate Angeli's ability, and encouraged him in his studies and mathematical researches.

Toward the end of his life, when he was gravely ill, Cavalieri entrusted Angeli with the task of correcting and publishing his last work, *Exercitationes geometricae sex* (1647). After Cavalieri's death in 1647, Angeli was offered the opportunity to succeed his master as professor of mathematics, but he was too modest to accept. Instead, he went to Rome, where he zealously continued his mathematical studies and his religious activity. About 1652 he was appointed prior of the monastery of the Gesuati in Venice, and shortly afterward he was given the post of provincial definer, a position he held until Pope Clement IX suppressed the order in 1668. On 2 January 1663 the Republic of Venice offered him the professorship of mathematics at the University of Padua, a post that had been held by Galileo, which he filled until his death. The mathematician Jacopo Riccati was among Angeli's pupils.

Angeli's studies in mathematics include a further development of the methods of indivisibles—methods introduced by Cavalieri and Evangelista Torricelli—to solve problems dealing with infinitesimals and with the areas, volumes, and centers of gravity of given geometric figures. His mathematical works echo the polemics that took place in the seventeenth century between supporters of the method of indivisibles and those such as Paul Guldin and Andreas Tacquet, who defended the more rigorous but less cogent exhaustive method of the ancients. "Lectori benevolo," the introduction to Angeli's *De infitinitis parabolis* (1654), is interesting in this connection. To those who opposed Cavalieri's method by asserting that the continuous is not composed of indivisibles, Angeli replied, in agreement with his master, that the method in question does not depend on the composition of the continuous.

Angeli's work on mathematics, *De infinitorum spiralium spatiorum mensura* (1660), deals with curves that constitute a generalization of Archimedes' spiral. A moving point describes one of these curves when it is acted upon by two movements, one uniform and rectilinear starting from a point *A*, and the other rotational around the same point *A*. If the rotational motion is also uniform, one obtains Archimedes' spiral; if, on the other hand, it varies, the general condition studied by Angeli results. In particular, if the angles described by the rotational motion are proportional to the squares of the times, one obtains a quadratic spiral; if these angles are proportional to the cubes of the times, one obtains a cubic spiral, and so on. The *De infinitorum spiralium* is devoted to the areas of the figures bounded by arcs of these curves and to the centers of gravity of the figures themselves.

In his *De infinitarum cochlearum mensuris ac centris gravitatis* (1661), Angeli begins with the definition of the solid that he called a *cochlea* and with the results of the problem published by Torricelli:[1] Consider in a given plane a figure, *F*, with nonzero area, and a straight line, *a*. Let *F* be subjected to a double motion; a rotational motion around *a* and a translation motion along the *a* direction. The solid thus obtained is a cochlea. Torricelli concluded that the volume of the cochlea is equivalent to that of a rotational solid; he had intended to devote a small volume to the later developments of the cochlea, especially regarding centers of gravity, but he died before completing it. In *De infinitarum cochlearum* Angeli seeks to carry out Torricelli's plan.

In questions dealing with infinitesimals, Angeli remained faithful to the indivisibles of the school of Galileo. Indeed, he proves to be unfamiliar with the points of view that follow from the analytic geometry of Descartes and the infinitesimal calculus of Newton and Leibniz, even though he had read Newton's *Naturalis philosophiae principia mathematica.*

Four of Angeli's minor works, in the form of dialogues that reflect Galileo's style, form a lively but cautious polemic on the problems of the Ptolemaic and Copernican cosmological systems. G. B. Riccioli, in his *Almagestum novum,* had formulated some arguments against the Copernican system. Angeli asserted that "the earth is motionless, but Riccioli's reasons do not prove the point," and he devoted the first of these studies (1667) to demonstrating that Riccioli's anti-Copernican arguments were without foundation. Angeli replied to Riccioli's arguments with another work in 1668. G. A. Borelli, who later participated in the polemic, rejected Riccioli's arguments and pointed out that if Angeli's views were correct, falling bodies should follow a vertical trajectory in the hypothesis of the earth's motion as well. In addition, he held that there must be a deviation to the east (as was experimentally proved by G. B. Guglielmini in 1791).[2]

Angeli's *Della gravità dell'aria e fluidi* is largely experimental in character. In it he examines the fluid statics, based on Archimedes' principle and on Torricelli's experiments. It also contains theories of capillary attraction.

In Angeli's works on physics, there are many references to Galileo's mechanics, as well as his acceptance of the experimental method.

NOTES

1. Torricelli's *Opere,* I, pt. 1 (Faenza, 1919), 223–230.
2. M. Gliozzi, *Storia della fisica,* Vol. II of *Storia delle scienze* (Turin, 1962), p. 89.

BIBLIOGRAPHY

I. ORIGINAL WORKS. Angeli's works, all of which are in the library of the University of Padua, are *De infinitis parabolis, de infinitisque solidis* (Venice, 1654); *Problemata geometrica sexaginta* (Venice, 1658); *Miscellanaeum hyperbolicum et parabolicum* (Venice, 1659); *De infinitorum spiralium spatiorum mensura, opusculum geometricum* (Venice, 1660); *Miscellanaeum geometricum* (Venice, 1660); *De infinitarum cochlearum mensuris ac centris gravitatis* (Venice, 1661); *De superficie ungulae et de quartis liliorum parabolicorum et cycloidalium* (Venice, 1661); *Accessionis ad steriometriam, et mecanicam,* I (Venice, 1662); *De infinitis parabolis liber quintus* (Venice, 1663); *Considerationi sopra la forza di alcune ragioni fisico-mattematiche, addotte dal M. R. P. Gio. Battista Riccioli, . . . nel suo Almagesto nuovo, et astronomia riformata contro il sistema copernicano* (Venice, 1667); *De infinitis spirabilibus inversis, infinitisque hyperbolis* (Padua, 1667); *Seconde considerationi sopra la forza dell'argomento fisico-mattematico del M. R. P. Gio. Battista Riccioli, . . . contro il moto diurno della terra* (Padua, 1668); *Terze considerationi sopra una lettera del molto illustre et eccellentissimo Signor Gio. Alfonso Borelli* (Venice, 1668); *Quarte considerationi sopra la conformatione d'una sentenza del Signor Gio. Alfonso Borelli* (Padua, 1669); *Della gravità dell'aria e fluidi* (Padua, 1671–1672).

II. SECONDARY LITERATURE. Works on Angeli are J. E. Montucla, *Histoire des mathématiques* (Paris, 1758), I, 537; II, 69; A. G. Kästner, *Geschichte der Mathematik,* III (Göttingen, 1798), 212–215; P. Magrini, "Sulla vita e sulle opere del P. Stefano degli Angeli," in *Giornale arcadico di scienze lettere ed arti,* **190** (July-August 1864), 205–237, also printed separately (Rome, 1866); M. Cantor, *Vorlesungen über Geschichte der Mathematik,* II (Leipzig, 1892), 820–821; P. Riccardi, *Biblioteca matematica italiana* (Modena, 1893), I, cols. 33–36 and IV, s.6 col. 181; G. Favaro, "Amici e corrispondenti di G. Galilei," in *Atti dell'Istituto veneto,* **72,** no. 2 (1912–1913), 46, and "I successori di Galileo nello studio di Padova," in *Nuovo archivio veneto,* n. s. **33** (1917), 117–121; G. Loria, *Storia delle matematiche,* II (Turin, 1931), 417–418, 425, 429; A. A. Michieli, "Un maestro di Jacopo Riccati," in *Atti dell'Istituto veneto, classe di scienze morali e lettere,* **107** (1948-1949), 73–81; and M. Gliozzi, "Angeli, Stefano degli," in *Dizionario biografico degli Italiani,* III (Rome, 1961), 205–206.

ETTORE CARRUCCIO

ANGELUS (ENGEL), JOHANNES (*b.* Aichach, Germany, 2 March 1453 [?]; *d.* Vienna, Austria, 29 September 1512), *astronomy.*

Although Angelus has been mentioned by many competent authors, reliable information about his life is scarce. From a few fairly certain dates the following sketch may be drawn.

In 1468 Angelus began his studies at the University of Vienna as a pupil of the famous astronomer Regiomontanus. In January 1471 he received the baccalaureate and most probably continued his studies in Italy. After having received the master's degree in liberal arts and the doctorate in medicine, Angelus returned to Bavaria, where he subsisted by practicing medicine and astrology in Augsburg. There, in 1489, he published his *Ephemerides*—astronomical predictions of the phases of the moon, eclipses, and planetary phenomena—based on Regiomontanus' improved tables. In the same year he published a revised translation of Abū Maʿshar's eight-volume work *De magnis conjunctionibus,* for speculations on the alleged effects of conjunctions of Jupiter with Saturn were then in vogue. Angelus also wrote a treatise on calendar reform and many astrological prognostica.

Apparently in Italy again about 1494, Angelus published an astrological volume containing two treatises, "Astrolabium planum" and "De nativitatibus." In the same year he was made a member of the Faculty of Liberal Arts at the University of Vienna, where he spent the rest of his life improving Peuerbach's planetary tables. Even if he had succeeded in accomplishing this work before his death, it would not essentially have influenced the subsequent development of astronomy, since at nearly the same time Copernicus wrote his first *Commentariolus* on the heliocentric system. But, according to Tannstetter, among his contemporaries Angelus was esteemed as an "excellent astronomer."

BIBLIOGRAPHY

I. ORIGINAL WORKS. Angelus' writings are *Albumazaris de magnis conjunctionibus* (Augsburg, 1489); *Ephemerides* (Augsburg, 1489); and a volume containing "Astrolabium planum cum aequationibus domorum coeli" and "Tractatus de nativitatibus" (Venice, 1494).

II. SECONDARY LITERATURE. A short, firsthand report is given by George Tannstetter in the introduction to his ed. of *Tabulae eclypsium magistri Georgij Peurbachij* (Vienna, 1514). See also Carl Bruhns, "Johann Angelus," in *Neue deutsche Biographie*, I (1875), 457; Christian Gottlieb Jöcher, in *Allgemeines Gelehrten-Lexikon*, I (1750), 415; and Poggendorff, I, 47, 1528.

KONRADIN FERRARI D'OCCHIEPPO

ÅNGSTRÖM, ANDERS JONAS (*b.* Lögdö, Medelpad, Sweden, 13 August 1814; *d.* Uppsala, Sweden, 21 June 1874), *astronomy, physics.*

Ångström was the second son of Johan Ångström, a minister. He attended elementary and secondary schools in Härnösand, then began his studies in mathematics and physics at the University of Uppsala in 1833. In 1839 he received a doctorate with a dissertation on the optics of conical refraction, and then became a lecturer in physics at Uppsala. He went to Stockholm Observatory in 1842 in order to gain experience in practical astronomy, and the following year he was appointed assistant professor of astronomy at Uppsala Observatory. He was professor of physics at Uppsala from 1858 until his death. His most important physical papers are those on spectroscopy, but he also wrote on terrestrial magnetism and the conduction of heat.

In February 1853 Ångström presented his "Optiska undersökningar" ("Optical Researches") before the Stockholm Academy of Science. In this work, he observed that the spectrum of an alloy of two metals contained the spectrum of each of the constituent metals and that an electric spark yielded two superimposed spectra, one from the metal of the electrodes and the other from the gas through which it passed. He also compared terrestrial emission spectra with the dark lines of the solar spectrum and concluded that a terrestrial spectrum was essentially a reversal of a portion of the solar spectrum. Proceeding from Euler's resonance theory, Ångström deduced that an incandescent gas should emit spectral lines of the same wavelengths as those it absorbed, thus proposing a relationship between the emission and absorption spectra of a chemical element that was more fully and effectively presented by Gustav Robert Kirchhoff several years later. This work establishes Ångström as one of several significant predecessors of Kirchhoff in formulating the foundations of modern spectroscopy.

After 1861 Ångström intensively studied the spectrum of the sun, noting the presence of hydrogen in the solar atmosphere and confirming the probable existence there of a number of other elements. In 1868 he published his monumental *Recherches sur le spectre solaire,* which contained an atlas of the solar spectrum with measurements of the wavelengths of approximately a thousand lines determined by the use of diffraction gratings. Ångström expressed his results in units of one ten-millionth of a millimeter—a unit of length that has been named the angstrom unit in his honor.

In order to have a precise basis for the new science of spectroscopy, accepted standards were needed. In 1861 Kirchhoff made a map of the solar spectrum and labeled lines with the corresponding scale readings of his own prismatic instrument. These rapidly became the almost universally accepted manner of designating spectral lines, but they were inconvenient because each observer had to correlate his own readings with those of the arbitrary Kirchhoff scale. Ångström's wavelength measurements provided a more precise and convenient reference and, after 1868, became a competing authoritative standard. Unfortunately, as was noted later, the length of the Uppsala meter was not 999.81 millimeters, the value used by Ångström, but 999.94 millimeters. Eventually Ångström's scale was replaced as the accepted standard by the more precise tables published by Henry Augustus Rowland between 1887 and 1893.

In 1867 Ångström was the first to examine the spectrum of the aurora borealis. A work on the spectra of the metalloids, which was begun some years previously, was completed by Tobias Robert Thalén, who actively assisted Ångström for many years, and was published in 1875. In opposition to the view that a given chemical element had a multiplicity of spectra, depending upon conditions, Ångström remained a strong defender of the opinion that each chemical element had a single characteristic spectrum that remained essentially unchanged.

Ångström's scientific merit was widely recognized. He twice shared the Wallmarsh Prize of the Royal Academy of Stockholm, and in 1872 he was awarded the Rumford Medal of the Royal Society of London. He was a member of scientific societies in Uppsala, Stockholm, Copenhagen, Berlin, Paris, and London, among others. Late in Ångström's life, his scientific work had to compete with various administrative duties. He was secretary of the Uppsala Scientific Society (1867–1874), a member of the Administrative Council of the city of Uppsala (1868–1873), and served the university as president of the Council of Economic Administration (1869–1874) and rector (1870–1871).

BIBLIOGRAPHY

I. ORIGINAL WORKS. Ångström's two most important spectral publications are "Optiska undersökningar," in *Philosophical Magazine,* **9** (1855), 327–342; and *Recherches sur le spectre solaire* (Uppsala, 1868). Other articles of significance are "On the Fraunhofer Lines Visible in the Solar Spectrum," in *Philosophical Magazine,* **24** (1862), 1–11; "New Method of Determining the Thermal Conductivity of Bodies," *ibid.,* **25** (1863), 130–142; "Spectrum of the Aurora Borealis," *ibid.,* **38** (1869), 246–247; "On the Spectra of the Simple Gases," *ibid.,* **42** (1871), 395–399; and, with T. R. Thalén, "Recherches sur les spectres des metalloïdes," in *Nova acta Societatis Regiae scientiarum upsaliensis,* **9** (1875), article 9.

II. SECONDARY LITERATURE. A short biography of value is that by Anna Beckman in *Swedish Men of Science 1650–1950,* edited by Sten Lindroth and translated from the Swedish by Burnett Anderson (Stockholm, 1952), pp. 193–203. Two contemporary unsigned biographical obituaries are in *Nature,* **10** (10 September 1874), 376–377; and *Proceedings of the Royal Society of London,* **25** (1877), xviii–xxii.

C. L. MAIER

ANGUILLARA, LUIGI (real name, **Luigi Squalermo**) (*b.* Anguillara, Sabazia, Italy, *ca.* 1512; *d.* Ferrara, Italy, September 1570), *botany.*

Little is known of Anguillara's early life. In 1539 he became associated with Luca Ghini at the latter's private botanical garden, first in Bologna, then in Pisa in 1544. Two years later, on 20 August 1546, Anguillara became the first director of the botanical garden in Padua, the oldest of its kind in Europe. He remained at Padua, supervising a garden that received favorable notice from many distinguished visitors, until 1561; then, having incurred the displeasure of Aldrovandi and Mattioli, he moved to Ferrara. He became herbalist to the duke of Ferrara and continued his botanical travels; whether he also taught medicine at Ferrara is unclear. He probably died of the plague, notwithstanding his efforts to prepare an antidote of theriaca.

Anguillara's only known book, the *Semplici,* was written over a long period (1549–1560). It is divided into fourteen *pareri* ("opinions"), each of which is dedicated to a contemporary Italian physician. Following the usual procedure of the times, the book is devoted principally to the identification of the plants known to Dioscorides and the other ancient writers on materia medica. Because of his travels in Greece, Italy, France, and Asia Minor and his great personal knowledge of plant life throughout the Mediterranean basin, Anguillara was among the best-equipped of sixteenth-century botanists to make such a study.

Approximately 1,540 plants are discussed by Anguillara, but in no discernible systematic order. Each plant is described, its classical name established (often with vernacular synonyms appended), and its medical and alimentary uses mentioned, along with its habitat, literary references, and the location where Anguillara found it. The descriptions are sufficiently full and accurate that the majority of his plants have been identified by modern historians of botany. Frequently cited by seventeenth-century botanists, the *Semplici* still remains an important source for historical nomenclature and floristic studies. He is commemorated today by the genus *Anguillaria* (*Liliaceae*) named in his honor by Robert Brown (1810).

BIBLIOGRAPHY

Anguillara's only known work is *Semplici . . . liquali in piu pareri a diversi nobili huomini scritti appaiono, et nuovamente da m. Giovanni Marinello mandati in luce* (Venice, 1561); trans. into Latin, with notes, by Gaspard Bauhin (Basel, 1593).

Works on Anguillara are Ettore De Toni, "Luigi Anguillara e Pietro Antonio Michiel," in *Annali di botanica,* **8** (1910), 617–685, an identification of the plants in the herbarium of P. A. Michiel (1510–1576), the dedicatee of the second *pareri,* based on Anguillara's *Semplici,* whose nomenclature was often used by Michiel; Giovanni Battista De Toni, "Nuovi documenti intorno Luigi Anguillara, primo prefetto dell' Orto Botanico di Padova," in *Atti del Istituto veneto di scienze, lettere ed arti,* **70**, no. 2 (1910–1911), 289–307, which contains eleven letters by Anguillara and a legal document concerning his salary; and "Luigi Anguillara," in Aldo Mieli, ed., *Gli scienziati italiani dall'inizio del medio evo ai nostri giorni,* I, pt. 1 (Rome, 1921), 76–78, a biographical account, with secondary bibliography (p. 77 contains a reference to two unpublished MSS of Anguillara in Bologna); Ludovic Legré, "La botanique en Provence au XVIᵉ siècle," in *Bulletin de la Société botanique de France,* **46** (1899), xxxiii–lxi, pp. xxxiii–li devoted to the identification of some of the more notable plants described by Anguillara on his botanizing expedition in southern France; and *La botanique en Provence au XVIᵉ siècle: Louis Anguillara, Pierre Belon, Charles de l'Escluse, Antoine Constantin* (Marseilles, 1901), Vol. V in a series of books by Legré, pp. 9–34 a reprint of the author's earlier article; Ernst H. F. Meyer, *Geschichte der Botanik,* 4 vols. (Königsberg, 1854–1857), IV, 378–383; and Kurt Sprengel, *Geschichte der Botanik,* 2 vols. (Altenburg-Leipzig, 1817–1818), I, 289–293.

JERRY STANNARD

ANSCHÜTZ, RICHARD (*b.* Darmstadt, Germany, 10 March 1852; *d.* Darmstadt, 3 January 1937), *chemistry.*

The son of a German officer, Anschütz was imbued with a deep sense of simplicity, responsibility, and duty. Excelling in mathematics and the natural sciences, he graduated from the Gymnasium of his native city at eighteen and began to study engineering at the Technische Hochschule in Darmstadt. At the end of his first semester he changed his course of studies in order to concentrate on chemistry, to which he devoted four semesters. He then matriculated at the University of Heidelberg, from which he obtained the Ph.D. on 24 February 1874, and went on to Tübingen in order to round out his studies in chemistry under Rudolf Fittig.

Soon a fortunate event gave a decisive turn to his career. Having learned that August Kekulé sought a new assistant, Fittig urged Anschütz to apply for the post. At the time Kekulé was the grand master of organic chemistry and for several years had headed the Institute of Chemistry of the University of Bonn, which had become the mecca for chemists. Young Anschütz, barely twenty-three, was admitted to residence and given an assistantship. Since Kekulé gave his assistants great freedom, Anschütz was able to choose among many subjects and to complete his projects either by himself or in collaboration with other chemists or students who used the laboratory.

Anschütz rose through the academic ranks in Bonn. He was an instructor in 1878; *Unterrichtsassistent* in 1882, succeeding Claisen; associate professor in 1889, after Wallach moved to Göttingen; full professor in charge of the Chemical Institute in 1898, following the death of Kekulé; and rector of the university during World War I. He remained director of research until his retirement in 1922. Subsequently, he did important biobibliographical research on Couper and Loschmidt, both little known at that time. He wrote *August Kekulé, Leben und Wirken* (1929) and composed obituaries of L. Claisen and W. Körner.

For fifty years Anschütz was able to dedicate himself to research. A talented experimenter, he successfully combined physical methods and chemical synthesis as a means of establishing chemical structure. He also pioneered in methods of vacuum distillation (1887).

Anschütz' major publications all dealt with organic chemistry. His earliest contributions, on polybasic acids, were closely related to Kekulé's experiments on unsaturated dibasic acids. The isomerism of maleic and fumaric acids was the starting point, but Anschütz' preoccupation with it lasted almost the rest of his life. He expressed his views on this subject in articles published in *Liebig's Annalen* (1887, 1889,

1928) under the title "Zur Geschichte der Isomerie der Fumarsäure und der Maleinsäure."

In his research on oxalic acid and its derivatives, Anschütz recognized the value of using oxalic acid as a dehydrating agent in the preparation of the anhydrides of dicarboxylic acids from the corresponding chlorides. By distilling under reduced pressure, he succeeded in isolating new oxalic acid esters, such as dichloroxalic ester and tetraorthoxalic ester.

In 1883, in collaboration with F. Eltzbacher, Anschütz synthesized anthracene by the action of aluminum chloride on a mixture of benzene and acetylene tetrabromide, thus providing a confirmation of the formula proposed by Graebe and Liebermann. Using carbon disulfide as a solvent in reactions of aluminum chloride with aromatic hydrocarbons, Anschütz studied the shifting of alkyl side chains on the ring. These important studies, carried out between 1882 and 1885, became the subjects of doctoral dissertations sponsored by Anschütz.

In other experiments (beginning in 1885) involving the action of phosphorus chloride on phenol, phenolcarbonic acids, and phenolsulfuric acids, Anschütz furnished a confirmation of the analogy between phenolcarbonic and phenolsulfuric acids, which had been indicated by Kekulé as early as 1867. In 1893 Anschütz succeeded in clarifying the action of phosphorus oxychloride on salicylic acid. This, in turn, led to his research on salicylides, dithiosalicylides, and sulfonylides. One of the results of this work was the discovery of a crystalline salicylide chloroform that is one-third chloroform by weight. From it chloroform of high purity can be extracted. This chloroform, named "Anschütz," is used for narcosis.

In his work on dioxytartaric acid and tartrazine Anschütz was able to furnish proof that tartrazine is not an osazone, as Ziegler had assumed, but a derivative of pyrazoline.

In collaboration with his pupils Anschütz wrote many papers on the tetronic and benzotetronic acids. He proposed the name "benzotetronic acid" for β-hydroxycoumarin in order to stress the analogy with tetronic acid, in which methylene is replaced by phenylene. New syntheses of coumarin and of tetronic acid itself were realized, and dimethyltetramic acid was also produced in pure form.

BIBLIOGRAPHY

I. Original Works. Most of Anschütz' original articles were published between 1876 and 1936 in *Liebigs Annalen der Chemie* and in the *Berichte der Deutschen chemischen Gesellschaft;* Poggendorff provides a partial list. His books are *Die Destillation unter vermindertem Druck im Laboratorium* (Bonn, 1887); with V. von Richter, *Lehrbuch der organischen Chemie* (Bonn, 1894; 12th ed., 1935); *August Kekulé, Leben und Wirken* (Berlin, 1929).

II. SECONDARY LITERATURE. Hans Meerwein, "Richard Anschütz zum Gedächtnis," in *Berichte der Deutschen chemischen Gesellschaft,* **74A** (1941), 29-74.

JEAN GILLIS

ANTHELME, VOITURET (*b.* Chatenay-Vaudin, France, *ca.* 1618; *d.* Dijon, France, 14 December 1683), *astronomy.*

Anthelme, a Carthusian monk often confused with Father Pierre Antelme (1598–1668), spent a great deal of time looking for celestial changes and for comets. He concentrated on the constellations Cygnus and Cassiopeia and, consequently, discovered the nova Variable R Volpecula, which was observed between 1670 and 1672. In pursuing his interest in celestial changes, he prepared one of the first ephemerides of a variable star, dealing with Mira Ceti, whose light varied in intensity and disappeared for long periods of time. In his view, this star was a slowly spinning sphere having on half of its surface a pear-shaped light source whose axis of symmetry lay along the sphere's equator.

The appearance of a comet in 1680 occasioned the treatise *Explication de la comète* (1681). No extant copy of it is known, but the *Journal des sçavans* gives an account of it. Anthelme thought that it was the same comet as that of April 1665, for it followed the same path and had the same daily motion. Therefore, comets obeyed the same regular laws as other heavenly bodies. Furthermore, the orbits of comets had their centers quite far from the earth and such small curvatures that many considered them to be straight lines. Anthelme rejected the Cartesian interpretation that comets were stars detached from a large vortex. He also assumed that they were diaphanous bodies that transmitted the sun's rays.

Little else is known about Anthelme. The star catalog he prepared reveals the extent of his knowledge. He had a prominent reputation, for the *Journal des sçavans* delayed publication in order to review his treatise on the comet of 1680, and Edme Mariotte corresponded with him. Although his career extended well into the period of precision astronomy, he continued to use traditional open sights as did Johannes Hevelius.

BIBLIOGRAPHY

I. ORIGINAL WORKS. Anthelme's works are "Catalogue des noms, grandeurs et positions des estoiles, corrigées et calculées par longitudes et latitudes pour l'an 1700," in Augustin Royer, ed., *Cartes du ciel réduites en quatre tables, contenant toutes les constellations, avec un catalogue . . . en latin le français à costé* (Paris, 1679); and *Explication de la comète qui a paru sur la fin de l'année 1680, et au commencement de celleci 1681; avec une table, qui marque le jour qu'elle a commencé a paroitre, et le jour qu'elle finira, la somme de ses mouvemens, sa longitude et sa latitude* (Dijon, 1681); a possible work is *Observations faites à Dijon sur la comète de cette présente année 1682* (Dijon, 1682). The treatise *Discours sur la comète qui a paru l'an 1664 et 1665,* attributed to Anthelme, is probably by Jacques de Billy; and P. Bayle's *Pensées diverses écrites à un docteur de Sorbonne à l'occasion de la comète . . . 1680* is falsely attributed to Anthelme.

II. SECONDARY LITERATURE. Works on Anthelme are "An Account From Paris, in Two Letters to the Publisher, Dated July 5 and July 19 1670 Concerning the Earlier Discovery of the Same New Star, Which Is Described in the Precedent Letter [of Hevelius]," in *Philosophical Transactions,* **5** (14 November 1670), 2092; review of *Explication de la Comète,* in *Journal des sçavans* (24 February 1681), 49–52; S.-M. Autore, *Bibliotheca cartusiano mariano* (Monstroli, 1890); P. Delamare, "Mémoires," in "Mémoires commencés en l'an 1682," II, 73 (MS, Dijon, Bibliothèque Publique, 839 bis); "An Extract of a Letter of M. Hevelius, . . . Concerning a New Star . . . ," in *Philosophical Transactions,* **5** (14 November 1670), 2087–2091; P. Humbert, "Les Astronomers français de 1610 à 1667 . . . ," in Société d'Études Scientifiques et Archéologiques de Draguignan, *Mémoires,* **63** (1942), 1–72, "Don Anthelme . . . ," in *Archives internationales d'histoire des sciences,* **6** (1949), 303–311, "À propos de Mira Ceti," in *Ciel et terre,* **50** (1939), 379–380, and "Encore à propos de Mira Ceti," *ibid.,* **51** (1940), 77–79; Christian Huygens, *Oeuvres* (La Haye, 1897), VII; C. Monget, *La Chartreuse de Dijon . . .* (Montreuil-sur-Mer, 1901), II, 345; "Observation d'une étoile nouvellement découverte proche la constellation du Cygne, par Dom Anthelme Cartreux," in *Mémoires de l'Académie Royale des Sciences,* **10** (1730), 496–501, and Fig. 2, pl. 2, p. 542; and E. Pigott, "Observations and Remarks on Those Stars Which the Astronomers of the Last Century Suspected to be Changeable," in *Philosophical Transactions,* **76**, pt. 1 (1786), 189–220.

ROBERT M. McKEON

ANTHEMIUS OF TRALLES (*fl.* sixth century A.D., in the time of Justinian), *architecture, mathematics.*

The son of Stephanus, a physician, Anthemius came from a learned family of Tralles in western Asia Minor. One of his brothers, Metrodorus, was a man of letters; another, Olympius, was a lawyer; and two others, Dioscorus and Alexander, were physicians. Together with Isidorus of Miletus and under the patronage of Justinian, Anthemius undertook in A.D. 532 the replacing of the old church of Hagia Sophia in Constantinople. Anthemius and Isidorus are said also to have been employed by Justinian in the repair of the flood defenses at Daras. An anecdote relates that Anthemius persecuted a neighbor and rival, Zenon, by reflecting sunlight into his house. He also produced the impression of an earthquake in Zenon's house by the use of steam led under pressure through pipes connected to a boiler.

Anthemius' interest in conic sections as well as in reflectors is shown by the work *On Remarkable Mechanical Devices* (first edited in modern times by L. Dupuy in 1777, although it was known to Ibn al-Haytham [Alhazen] and Vitello). A mathematical fragment from Bobbio concerned with parabolic burning mirrors is sometimes attributed to Anthemius but may well be of early Hellenistic origin. Eutocius dedicated his *Commentaries* on Books I to IV of the *Conics* of Apollonius to Anthemius. The problem of how to contrive that at any hour and season a ray of the sun, passing through a small aperture, shall fall in a given spot without moving away was solved by Anthemius. He describes the construction of an elliptical reflector with one focus at the aperture and the other at the point to which the ray is to be reflected. Both winter and equinoctial rays are considered. In his treatment, Anthemius incidentally mentions the construction of an ellipse by means of a loop of string drawn closely around the foci. He also uses a proposition not made explicit in the *Conics*: that the straight line joining the focus to the intersection of two tangents bisects the angle between the two straight lines joining the focus to the two points of contact. Another construction shows how parallel rays may be reflected to one point at the focus of a parabolic reflector.

BIBLIOGRAPHY

Procopius, *De aedificiis,* edit. of H. B. Dewing, in Loeb Classical Library, Vol. VII (London-Cambridge, Mass., 1960). Agathias, *Historiae* 5. 6–9; F. Hultsch, in Pauly-Wissowa, *Real-Encyclopädie,* I, pt. 2 (Stuttgart, 1894), cols. 2368–2369; J. L. Heiberg, *Mathematici Graeci Minores* (Copenhagen, 1927); G. L. Huxley, *Anthemius of Tralles* (Cambridge, Mass., 1959); T. L. Heath, *Bibliotheca Mathematica,* **7,** ser. 3 (1907), 225–233.

G. L. HUXLEY

ANTIGONE OF CARYSTUS. See Diocles Carystius.

ANTIPHON (lived in Athens in the second half of the fifth century B.C.), *mathematics, cosmology, psychology.*

Antiphon was the first native Athenian to be classed as a "Sophist" in the sense of "professional teacher of young men." Unfortunately little is known for certain of his life, or even of his identity. The grammarian Didymus Chalcenterus, writing in the late first century B.C., distinguished two "Sophistic" Antiphons at Athens in the fifth century B.C. The first was Antiphon the orator, sometimes called Antiphon of Rhamnus, the author of the surviving *Tetralogies,* which are specimen outline speeches for the prosecution and the defense in certain real or imaginary cases of murder; he took part in Athenian politics and was condemned to death in 410 B.C. after the overthrow of the oligarchic conspiracy at Athens (Thucydides VIII, 68). The other was Antiphon the diviner and interpreter of dreams, author of the treatises *On Truth, On Concord,* and *The Statesman.*

This distinction between two Antiphons was repeated by Hermogenes in the second century A.D., but he based the distinction on a supposed difference in the style of writing in the *Tetralogies* compared with the other works; he may have had no other grounds. Caecilius of Calacte, probably writing just slightly later than Didymus, seems to have known nothing of such a distinction, and he is the source of the alternative tradition preserved in Pseudo-Plutarch's *Lives of the Ten Orators,* which assumes a single Antiphon who was the subject of conflicting stories.

Modern scholars are divided, and some follow the approach of Didymus, distinguishing at least three different Antiphons, who, it is supposed, were later confused. Others adopt a view like that of Caecilius, concluding that at least the orator and the Sophist were one and the same person. Something is known of the political career of Antiphon the orator, and if the identification is sound, we would at least know that the Sophist had belonged to the extreme right wing in politics and probably met his death in 410 B.C. The identification must remain uncertain, however, and virtually nothing is known of the life of Antiphon the Sophist if he was not the same person as the orator.

Four works are clearly ascribed to Antiphon the Sophist (*On Truth, On Concord, The Statesman, On Interpretation of Dreams*), and a fifth (*The Art of Avoiding Pain*) may also be his. Of these works only brief quotations remain, aside from some important papyrus fragments of *On Truth* found at Oxyrhynchus in Egypt; but it seems likely that most of them were still known in the first century A.D.

On Truth comprised two books. Its title suggests the first part of Parmenides' poem "On Nature" (written at least a generation before Antiphon), commonly referred to as "The Way of Truth" and dealing with the doctrine of One Being as the sole reality, as against the (unreal) multiplicity of the phenomenal world. But since Protagoras the Sophist, roughly contemporary with Antiphon, also used the title *Truth* for a work in which he rejected the One Being of Parmenides and preferred instead the "truth" of every individual's sensations, we cannot infer from the title what position Antiphon adopted about the status of the phenomenal world. The first surviving fragment of Antiphon in the collection by Hermann Diels and Walther Kranz may hold the answer to this question, but the text is so corrupt that its meaning must remain wholly uncertain.

More helpful as evidence is the attempt to square the circle recorded by Aristotle (*Physics* A, 185a14). It is clear from Aristophanes (*The Birds,* 1004) that the squaring of the circle was a standard problem in the late fifth century B.C. The problem was to construct, by means of compass and ruler only, a square with an area equal to that of a given circle. Since any rectilinear figure could quite easily be converted into a square of the same area, the problem in practice was that of reducing the area of a circle to an equal area bounded by straight lines. In the third century B.C., Archimedes, in his *On the Measurement of the Circle* (Prop. I), showed that this requirement was satisfied by a right-angled triangle with one side adjacent to the right angle equal to the radius and the other adjacent side equal to the circumference. The problem is now known to be incapable of solution by the use of ruler and compass alone.

Aristotle was aware of three attempts to solve this problem in its original form. One he seems to have attributed, perhaps mistakenly (see full discussion in W. D. Ross, *Aristotle's Physics* [Oxford, 1936], pp. 463–466), to Hippocrates of Chios about the middle of the fifth century B.C. According to this attempt, it was mistakenly concluded from the possibility of squaring the lune on the side of the square inscribed in a circle that the circle could be completely divided into lunes similar to the one thus squared. Another was by a certain Bryson, who simply argued that since a polygon inscribed within a circle is smaller than the circle and a polygon circumscribing a circle will be larger than the circle, there must be a polygon intermediate in size that will be equal to the circle; however, he did not have anything to say about how such a polygon could be constructed diagrammatically. Antiphon's method is explained slightly differently by each of two commentators on Aristotle. According to Simplicius, he proposed to inscribe a polygon such as a square within the circle and, on each of its sides, to build two chords meeting midway

on the circumference above the side. The process must be continued with each of the sides of the resulting octagon, and so on with subsequent polygons, until the sides are so small that they coincide with their respective sections of the circumference. According to the Neoplatonist Themistius (A.D. 320–390), the polygon is an equilateral triangle, but otherwise his account of the procedure is the same.

In modern times it has often been supposed that Antiphon was simply making a bad mistake in geometry by supposing that any approximation could ever amount to coincidence between a polygon with however many sides and the continuously curved circumference of a true circle. At the same time, his method has been considered of interest as anticipating the method of exhaustion used by Euclid (XII, 2) and the method of approximation of Archimedes. This may not be the right view to take. Antiphon appears to have believed that complete coincidence could be achieved by his method, and Aristotle treats this not as a mistake in geometry, but as nongeometrical in its approach, in that it did not proceed on geometrical assumptions. This may mean that Antiphon regarded the circle itself as a polygon with a very large (or possibly infinite) number of sides. Such a view is implied in the doctrine of Protagoras that the tangent touches a circle not at a single point only, but over a series of points, as we see with our eyes in the case of drawn tangents and circles. This would suggest that Antiphon, like Protagoras, may have considered the world of phenomena more real than the "truth" of Parmenides.

It is probable that Antiphon, like most of the pre-Socratics, discussed in detail the physical formation of the universe and the nature of the heavenly bodies, but only small details of his doctrines survive. He seems to have related the rising and setting of the sun to changes in the air surrounding the earth (fr. 26); he regarded the moon as the source of its own light (fr. 27) and as undergoing eclipse by some kind of turning of its bowl (fr. 28). He appears to have held a doctrine of opposite qualities (such as hot and cold) acting as primary substances or elements (frs. 26, 29, 32) and also as determining human physiology (fr. 29*a*; Diels and Kranz II, 426).

Antiphon's most famous doctrine is his opposition of nature and convention. In fr. 15 he opposes manufactured articles to the "natural" materials of which they are made; and he is often interpreted as preferring things that exist by nature to those that exist merely by convention and, thus, as setting up the selfish "natural" impulses of the individual as norms superior to the laws of the community. But in *On Concord* he defends the authority of the community as a safeguard against anarchy (fr. 61) and recommends the ideals of concord and self-restraint both within communities and within the individual soul. Most probably he was only concerned to criticize the laws of a city by asking whether or not they satisfy the "natural" needs of the individual. Thus, in *On Truth* he argues that there is a basic human nature common to Greeks and barbarians, and in the *Art of Avoiding Pain,* if it is his, he was probably also concerned with ways in which the individual could achieve the fulfillment of his nature without having to suffer.

BIBLIOGRAPHY

I. ORIGINAL WORKS. For fragments and testimonia in Greek, see Hermann Diels and Walther Kranz, eds., *Die Fragmente der Vorsokratiker,* 7th ed., II (Berlin, 1954), 334–370. Antonio Battegazzore and Mario Untersteiner, eds., *Sofisti, testimonianze e frammenti* (Florence, 1962), fasc. IV, has, in addition to the Greek, a bibliography, Italian translation, and commentary. An English translation of the fragments can be found in Kathleen Freeman, *Ancilla to the Pre-Socratic Philosophers* (Oxford, 1948). For text and English translation of the *Tetralogies* of Antiphon the orator, see Kenneth John Maidment, *Minor Attic Orators,* Vol. I (London-New York, 1941), which is part of the Loeb Classical Library.

II. SECONDARY LITERATURE. For interpretations, see Ettore Bignone, *Studi sul pensiero antico* (Naples, 1938), chs. 1–3; and, in English, Mario Untersteiner, *The Sophists* (Oxford, 1954).

G. B. KERFERD

ANTONIADI, EUGÈNE M. (*b.* Constantinople [now Istanbul], Turkey, 1870; *d.* Meudon, France, 10 February 1944), *astronomy.*

Born of a Greek family, Antoniadi was more than a professional astronomer; he was an astrophile. At the age of eighteen, using very modest instruments, he began his long series of observations in Constantinople and on the island of Prinkipe. He published these observations, and most of his others, in Camille Flammarion's review *L'astronomie,* the bulletin of the Astronomical Society of France. A frequent and diligent observer, Antoniadi was also an artist. His drawings from observation far surpass those of many other astronomers who lacked his artistic ability.

In 1893 Antoniadi was Flammarion's guest in his private observatory at Juvisy, near Paris. Here he was able to employ a forty-two-centimeter equatorial to observe Mars, which was his chief concern. As a result of his research he was appointed director of the section on Mars of the British Astronomical Association.

In 1909 H. Deslandres, director of the observatory at Meudon, authorized him to make use of the large telescope there, which led Antoniadi to make important discoveries regarding the constitution of the surface details of Mars. This was possible because in that year the planet, in a close opposition, was in an extremely favorable position to be observed. Antoniadi's excellent drawings of that particular opposition and of those that followed revealed that the strange network of geometrical "canals," which some observers had thought to be man-made, are no more than an effect produced by very minute details. It was his conclusion that 70 percent of the canals are irregular dark bands, more or less continuous and scattered with small spots that vary in width and appearance; 21 percent are irregular lines of gray, diffuse spots; 9 percent are isolated and complex nuclei. Antoniadi's drawings, reproduced in his major work, show terrain covered with sparse vegetation, volcanic soil, and vast deserts.

During the opposition of 1924 Antoniadi observed, among other things, shining protuberances on the edge of the planet, precisely on the configuration called Hellas. The highest point of these protuberances seemed to oscillate, over a period of four days, eight to twenty kilometers above the surface of the planet. By observing the apparent motion of the various details of Mars, Antoniadi also was able to confirm the period of rotation about its axis, which had been determined by Giovanni Schiaparelli.

In later life Antoniadi became interested in the history of Greek and Egyptian astronomy; the results of his studies were published in *L'astronomie* and in his *L'astronomie égyptienne.* In addition, outside the field of astronomy, he conducted important archeological studies on the basilica of Saint Sophia in Constantinople, which were published in 1907. The French government awarded him the Cross of Chevalier of the Legion of Honor, and in 1928 he became a French citizen.

BIBLIOGRAPHY

Antoniadi's major work is *La planète Mars* (Paris, 1930). Also see *L'astronomie,* **58** (1944), 58; and G. Abetti, *Storia dell'astronomia* (Florence, 1963). Antoniadi's major contributions to periodicals are to be found primarily in the *Bulletin de la Société astronomique de France* and in the *Journal of the British Astronomical Association.*

GIORGIO ABETTI

ANUCHIN, DMITRII NIKOLAEVICH (*b.* St. Petersburg, Russia, 8 September 1843; *d.* Moscow, Union of Soviet Socialist Republics, 4 June 1923), *geography, anthropology, ethnography.*

Anuchin's father was a soldier; his mother, the daughter of a peasant. He studied at the Physics and Mathematics Faculty of Moscow University, where Darwin's concept of evolution and the mutual influence of natural phenomena were advocated and became the basis for his scientific research.

Anuchin was attracted to anthropology and ethnography, and after graduating from the university he became secretary of the Society for the Acclimatization of Animals and Plants. He published his first scientific papers on observations of several little-studied animals. During the 1870's he worked seriously on anthropological and ethnographical problems, publishing papers on anthropomorphic monkeys and lower forms of man, and on the ethnography of Siberia; he also prepared his master's dissertation. In recognition of his work, Moscow University invited Anuchin to head the department of anthropology, and in 1876 he was sent to Paris and other European university cities. For more than two years he studied museums of anthropology, listened to the lectures of leading scientists, and worked in their laboratories. He also organized the Russian section of the World Anthropological Exhibition held in Paris in 1878.

In the school year 1879–1880 Anuchin instituted Russia's first elective course in physical anthropology. In January 1881 he defended his master's dissertation, "O nekotorykh anomalijakh chelovecheskogo cherepa i preimushchestvenno ob ikh rasprostranenii po rasam" ("On Several Anomalies of the Human Cranium, Primarily on Their Prevalence According to Race"). From 1884 on, he headed the newly organized department of geography and ethnography, where he gave the first Russian lecture course on the history of geography; he also taught several courses in physical geography and specific geography (of Russia and Asia, among other areas). His study of the geographical distribution of Russia's male population according to height (1889), a notable contribution to science, led Moscow University to award him the doctor of geography, *honoris causa.*

In 1890 Anuchin was elected president of the Society of Lovers of Natural Science, Anthropology, and Ethnography, in which he brought together the few influences in Moscow making for geographical research. In the same year he organized an expedition to study the upper reaches of the Dnieper, Western Dvina, and Volga rivers. The results of his orographical investigations and his study of the lakes of the area were highly valued by Russian and foreign scholars.

Anuchin achieved wide fame as the founder and editor of the journal *Zemlevedenie* ("Geography"). The publication of this journal (from 1894 on) and the activities of the geographic section of the Society of Lovers of Natural Science made Moscow the second most important center of geographic thought in Russia. Since Anuchin had created an important school of geography, he was elected a member of the Academy of Sciences in St. Petersburg in 1896; two years later he became an honored member.

After the October Revolution, Anuchin continued to work fruitfully, devoting all his strength and knowledge to the construction of the new society. He participated in the establishment of the government, especially in Gosplan (State Planning Committee of the U.S.S.R.). Upon Lenin's recommendation, Anuchin's services were enlisted in the compilation and editing of the first Soviet world atlas, the *Atlas mira.*

Anuchin often participated in international congresses of geography, anthropology, and archaeology. His name was immortalized in the names of geographical features—for example, a glacier on Novaya Zemlya, a mountain in the northern Urals, and an island and strait in the Malaya Kuril'skaya (Lesser Kurile Islands)—and in the establishment of the D. N. Anuchin Prize for the best scientific work in geography, awarded by Moscow University. He was a materialist and a convinced Darwinist, and the methodological principles of these philosophies permeated all his work, both theoretical and practical.

Anuchin understood the science of geography in a broad sense. As early as 1885 he considered it an independent branch of knowledge, on the boundary between natural science and the humanities. He classified it as follows:

I. General geography.
   A. Geography of inorganic nature (physical geography).
      1. Meteorology (climatology).
      2. Hydrography (oceanography).
      3. Orography.
   B. Geography of organic nature (biogeography).
      1. Geography of plants.
      2. Geography of animals.
   C. Anthropogeography.
II. Specific geography (geography of countries).

Anuchin was a critic of the ideas of Humboldt and Karl Ritter, the most eminent geographers of the first half of the nineteenth century. He noted that Humboldt's ideas were more advanced than Ritter's and pointed out the weakness of Ritter's methodological views, which were theologically oriented.

Reevaluating and defining his views on the nature and problems of geography more precisely, Anuchin stood fast by his early positions. He was sympathetic to Richtofen's views and criticized G. Gerland's views as one-sided and as reducing geography to geophysics. At the beginning of the twentieth century, Hettner won many followers for his theory that geography was a chronological science "of the expanse of the earth's surface according to its material composition." According to Hettner, questions of the essence of objects and phenomena, as well as questions of development, were alien to the science of geography. Anuchin's theoretical views were the direct opposite of Hettner's:

> The subject of geography has remained the same for all times: our planet, the earth, and its relation to the other heavenly bodies, but more importantly, the earth in and of itself, especially its surface, which serves as the arena of various cosmic and telluric forces, as the result of which her atmosphere, hydrosphere, lithosphere, and pediosphere, as well as—one can express it thusly—her biosphere and anthroposphere were established [*Geograficheskie raboty*, pp. 291-292].

Emphasizing the constant changes in the earth's surface, Anuchin wrote, "a proper understanding of a country's surface forms, its landscapes, and its phenomena of life can be obtained only by means of an inquiry into its past and the study of those processes which elicited the consequent transformation" (*ibid.*, p. 314).

Thus, Anuchin believed that geography should concern the surface of the earth, with its inorganic nature and its variegated animal world (including man), and the relationship between them. Geography should analyze the phenomena of the surface of the earth, compare their alterations, place them within a system, and strive for an explanation of the connection between them and an elucidation of their origin. He considered the historically established separation of geography into general and specific spheres as the basis for its further development.

Anuchin's basic works in general geography—including "Rel'ef poverkhnosti Evropejskoj Rossii" ("Surface Relief of European Russia," 1895), "Sushcha" ("Land," 1895), and *Verkhnevolzhskie ozera i verkhov'ja Zapadnoj Dviny* ("The Upper Volga Lakes and the Upper Reaches of the Western Dvina," 1897)—played an important role in the development of geomorphology and hydrology. In studying the surface of the earth, Anuchin started from the basic methodological principle of geomorphology—the present relief of the earth is the result of endogenous and exogenous forces over a long period of time. Accordingly, he opposed the theory that mountains were formed as the result of the cooling of the earth. Anuchin considered the endogenic forces of the earth as the basic and decisive factor in the formation of mountains. He placed the origin of the internal energy of the earth "in the pressure of strata and especially in radioactive substances, which are capable of giving off heat" (*Lektsii po fizicheskoj geografii*, p. 33). In addition, he recognized the significant role of exogenous forces in relief formation. Anuchin distinguished three basic relief types on the basis of geological structures and the degree of erosion of a mountainous terrain: mountains, hills, and plains; in each of these categories he distinguished the different surface forms. He was thus the first to formulate the basic elements of modern orography.

Anuchin had many valuable ideas in hydrology, especially in limnology. He viewed lakes as a complex element of the landscape and therefore thoroughly studied their surrounding territory. He did not accept Forel's hypothesis of the autonomy of lakes as absolute; rather, he developed another aspect of the study of lakes—the view that lakes were related to other geographical conditions. Anuchin associated lake formation with the genesis of hollows in the watershed areas of Russia's plain that have a moraine-hilly surface.

Anuchin analyzed the distribution of lakes and the genesis of lake beds; he also classified lakes and noted their tendency to decrease in size and disappear. But, most important, he paved the way for his many students and is rightly acclaimed as one of the founders of limnology in Russia. From the end of the nineteenth century, the lakes of European Russia, central Asia, and Siberia were systematically studied by his followers. The classic publication on the investigation of lakes was L. C. Berg's monograph *Aral'skoe more* ("The Aral Sea," 1908).

Having accepted the advanced anthropological ideas of scientists in France and other countries, Anuchin developed them further and created a school of Russian anthropologists. He conceived of anthropology as a vast complex of knowledge about man—his physical nature and his daily life and activity, both modern and past, especially the prehistoric. The origin of man, with which his first studies on anthropoid apes (1874) were concerned, was included by Anuchin within the realm of anthropology. These ideas were later generalized in his "Proiskhozhdenie cheloveka" ("The Origin of Man," 1922).

Anuchin's studies of man's racial types were also significant. He thought that all human physical types (races) were essentially transitions from some types toward others: "Mankind represents properly one form. . . . In other words, all mankind proceeds from the same ancestors, whose descendants only gradually formed different races" ("O zadachakh i metodakh antropologii," p. 69). Anuchin decisively rejected the view that the human races originated from distinct apelike ancestors. He wrote several fundamental works on the physical types of various nationalities, among them a monograph on the Ainu people (1876).

Anuchin's works on ethnography were distinguished by originality and strict adherence to scientific method. Such works as the comparative study of bows and arrows (1881), "Sani, lad'ja i koni, kak prinadlezhnosti pokhoronnogo obrjada" ("Sleighs, Large Boats, and Horses as Appurtenances of Funeral Rites," 1890), and "K istorii oznakomlenija s Sibir'ju do Ermaka" ("Toward the History of the Acquaintance with Siberia Before Ermak," 1890) are regarded as models of scientific creativity. Anuchin was also interested in the origin of domestic animals as the basis of one of the most important branches of agricultural economics.

Anuchin did work in the history of science, writing original studies of Lomonosov, Darwin, Humboldt, Miklukho-Maklaja, and others. He published approximately a thousand papers.

BIBLIOGRAPHY

I. ORIGINAL WORKS. Anuchin's writings include "Antropomorfnye obez'jany i nizshie tipy chelovechestva" ("Anthropoid Apes and Lower Types of Man"), in *Priroda*, no. 1 (1874), 185–280; no. 3 (1874), 220–276; no. 4 (1874), 81–141; "Materialy dlja antropologii Vostochnoj Azii. Plemja Ajnov" ("Materials for the Anthropology of Eastern Asia. The Ainu Tribe"), in *Izvêstīya Imperatorskago obshchestva lyubiteleĭ estestvoznanīya, antropologīi i étnografīi. Trudȳ antropologicheskago otdela,* **20,** no. 2 (1876), 79–204; *Antropologija, ee zadachi i metody* ("Anthropology, Its Problems and Methods"; Moscow, 1879); "O nekotorykh anomalijakh chelovecheskogo cherepa i preimushchestvenno ob ikh rasprostranenii po rasam" ("On Several Anomalies of the Human Cranium, Primarily on Their Prevalence According to Race") in *Izvêstīya Imperatorskago obshchestva lyubiteleĭ estestvoznanīya, antropologīi i étnografīi. Trudȳ antropologicheskago otdela,* **6** (1880); *Kurs lektsij po istorii zemlevedinija* ("Lecture Course on the History of Geography"; Moscow, 1885); *Kurs lektsij po obshchej geografii* ("Lecture Course in General Geography"; Moscow, 1887); *O geograficheskom raspredelenii rosta muzhskogo naselenija Rossii* ("On the Geographic Distribution of the Height of Russia's Male Population"; St. Petersburg, 1889); "Rel'ef poverkhnosti Evropejskoj Rossii v posledovatel'nom razvitii o nem predstavlenii" ("The Surface Relief of European Russia in the Chronological Development of Its Mapping"), in *Zemlevedenie,* **2,** no. 1 (1895), 77–126, and no. 4 (1895), 65–124, also in *Rel'ef Evropejskoj chasti SSSR* (see below), pp. 35–147; *Verkhnevolzhskie ozera i verkhov'ja Zapadnoj Dviny. Rekognostsirovki i issledovanija 1894–1895 gg.* ("The Upper Volga Lakes and the Upper Reaches of the Western Dvina. Reconnaissance and Study in 1894–1895"; Moscow, 1897); "O zadachakh i metodakh antropologii" ("On the Problems and Methods of Anthropology"), in *Russkij antropologicheskij zhurnal,* **9,** no. 1 (1902), 62–88; *Japonija i japontsy* ("Japan and the Japanese"; Moscow, 1907); "Proiskhozdhenie cheloveka i ego istoricheskie predke" ("The Origin of Man and His Historical Predecessors"), in *Itogi nauki v teorii i pratike,* VI (Moscow, 1912), 691–784; *Lektsii po fizicheskoj geografii* ("Lectures on Physical Geography"; Moscow, 1916); *Proiskhozhdenie cheloveka* ("The Origin of Man"; Moscow, 1922; 3rd ed., Moscow–Leningrad, 1927); *Rel'ef Evropejskoj chasti SSSR* ("Relief of the European Sector of the U.S.S.R."; Moscow, 1948), written with A. A. Borzov; *Izbrannye geograficheskie raboty* ("Selected Geographical Works"), L. S. Berg, gen. ed. (Moscow, 1949); *O ljudjakh russkoj nauki i kul'tury* ("On Men of Russian Sciences and Culture"; Moscow, 1950, 1952); *Geograficheskie raboty* ("Geographical Works"), A. A. Grigor'ev, ed. (Moscow, 1954), with bibliography; and *Ljudi zarubezhnoj nauki i kul'tury* ("Men of Foreign Science and Culture"; Moscow, 1960).

II. SECONDARY LITERATURE. Works on Anuchin are V. V. Bogdanov, *D. N. Anuchin. Antropolog i geograf* ("D. N. Anuchin, Anthropologist and Geographer"; Moscow, 1941), with bibliography; *Sbornik v chest semidesjatiletija prof. D. N. Anuchina* ("Collection in Honor of the Seventieth Birthday of Professor D. N. Anuchin"; Moscow, 1913); V. A. Esakov, *D. N. Anuchin i sozdanie russkoj universitetskoj geograficheskoj shkoly* ("D. N. Anuchin and the Creation of the Russian University School of Geography"; Moscow, 1955); A. A. Grigor'ev, "D. N. Anuchin," in *Ljudi russkoj nauki* ("Men of Russian Science"), I (Moscow–Leningrad, 1948), 599–605; 2nd ed., II (1962), 508–515; G. V. Karpov, *Put' uchenogo* ("The Path of a Scientist"; Moscow, 1958); *Pamjati D. N. Anuchina (1843–1923)* ("In Memory of D. N. Anuchin [1843–1923]"), in *Trudȳ Instituta étnografii imeni N. N. Miklukho-Maklaja. Akademiya nauk SSR,* n.s. **1** (1947); and A. I. Solov'ev, "D. N. Anuchin, ego osnovnye geograficheskie idei i ego rol' v razvitii russkoj geografii" ("D. N. Anuchin, His Basic Geographical Ideas and his Role in the Development of Russian Geography"), in *Voprosy geografii,* **9** (1948), 9–28.

V. A. ESAKOV

ANVILLE, JEAN-BAPTISTE BOURGUIGNON D' (*b.* Paris, France, 11 July 1697; *d.* Paris, 28 January 1782), *cartography.*

D'Anville was the son of Hubert Bourguignon and

Charlotte Vaugon. About 1730 he married Charlotte Testard, who bore him two daughters. He was secretary to the duke of Orléans (regent during the minority of Louis XV) and was named royal geographer as early as 1717. Having been elected to the Académie des Inscriptions et Belles-Lettres in 1754, he succeeded Buache as chief royal geographer in 1773 and as assistant geographer to the Académie Royale des Sciences.

D'Anville contributed greatly to the renaissance of geography and cartography in France in the eighteenth century. He was the author of 211 maps or plans, and from his first publications he demonstrated great intellectual honesty by leaving unknown territories (the interior of Africa, America, and Asia) blank, contrary to the practice of many cartographers, who used ornaments—the less their knowledge of a territory, the greater the ornamentation.

Furthermore, his maps were solidly based on triangulation nets. As a result, the maps of China, drawn at the request of the Jesuits for Father du Halde's history, after reports of their missionaries, were the first to give an accurate indication of the Pacific coastline (the Yellow Sea and its gulfs and headlands and the Molucca Islands). D'Anville also drew maps of France for Longuerue's *Description de la France* (1719), and maps of Africa and Santo Domingo.

He made studies of ancient measurements in several memoirs and in his *Traité des mesures itinéraires anciennes et modernes* (1769). Comparing them with modern figures, he established remarkably accurate maps for Rollin's *Histoire ancienne,* Rollin and Crevier's *Histoire romaine,* and the *Histoire des empereurs romains.* His maps were greatly appreciated by geographers and navigators, and their exactness was confirmed for Italy by the geodesic operations carried out under the pontificate of Benedict XIV, and for Egypt during Napoleon's campaign in 1799. D'Anville was less successful in his studies of the figure of the earth, and his two memoirs on that subject (1735, 1736) contain some erroneous conclusions. In 1780 d'Anville gave the king his remarkable collection of 10,000 maps, which were both engraved and in manuscript. This collection is now in the Bibliothèque Nationale. In spite of delicate health d'Anville lived until his eighty-fifth year, having devoted his life almost wholly to his work and having published, besides his maps, numerous articles on geography and cartography.

BIBLIOGRAPHY

I. ORIGINAL WORKS. The complete bibliography is in L.-C.-J. de Manne, *Notice des ouvrages de M. d'Anville* (see below). The works most important to understanding his achievements in cartography are *Mémoire instructif pour dresser sur lieux des cartes particulières et topographiques d'un canton de pays . . .* (Paris, 1743); *Géographie ancienne abrégée* (Paris, 1769); *Traité des mesures itinéraires anciennes et modernes* (Paris, 1769); and *Considérations générales sur l'étude et les connaissances que demande la composition des ouvrages de géographie* (Paris, 1777). Manne prepared an ed. of the *Oeuvres de d'Anville* in 6 vols., only 2 of which appeared, with an atlas (Paris, 1834).

II. SECONDARY LITERATURE. Works on d'Anville are Condorcet, "Éloge de d'Anville," in *Oeuvres de Condorcet,* II (Paris, 1847), 528 ff.; M. Dancier, "Éloge de d'Anville," in *Oeuvres de d'Anville,* I, i–xvii; C. Du Bus, "La collection d'Anville à la Bibliothèque Nationale," in *Bulletin de géographie historique,* 41 (1926–1929), 93 ff.; F. Hoefer, in *Nouvelle biographie générale,* II (1852), cols. 368–370; L.-C.-J. de Manne, *Notice des ouvrages de M. d'Anville* (Paris, 1802); Michaud, in *Biographie universelle,* II, 97–98; N. Nielsen, *Géomètres français du dix-huitième siècle* (Paris, 1935), pp. 24–25; Poggendorff, I, 51; and M. Prévost, in *Dictionnaire de biographie française,* III, cols. 84–86.

JULIETTE TATON

APÁTHY, STEPHAN (*b.* Budapest, Austria-Hungary, 4 January 1863; *d.* Szeged, Hungary, 27 September 1922), *medical science, histology, zoology.*

Apáthy's father, István, was a professor at the University of Budapest and a famous expert in international law. Apáthy attended high school in Budapest and then studied medicine at the university. As a student he worked from 1883 to 1884 at the Institute of Pathology, where his interest in histology was awakened; in 1884 he published a paper dealing with the microscopic anatomy of naiades. He was known as the leader of a progressive student movement, and wrote poetry and essays on social themes. After obtaining his doctor's degree in 1885, he became assistant to Theodor Margó at the Institute of Zoology and Comparative Anatomy in Budapest, where he improved his knowledge of histology.

From 1886 to 1889 Apáthy had a scholarship to the marine biological laboratory in Naples, where he worked under Anton Dohrn. During this period he published seventeen papers and traveled in several European countries. In 1890 he was appointed professor of zoology, and a few years later became professor of histology and embryology at Kolozsvár in Transylvania (now Cluj, Rumania), where he established a modern institute that became a famous international histological research center. In 1895 Apáthy was elected a corresponding member of the Hungarian Academy of Sciences, and in 1905 he was appointed an honorary foreign member of the Royal Medicinal Academy of Belgium.

From his youth Apáthy had opposed the official policies of Vienna and Budapest. Unfortunately, after

World War I he devoted more time to politics than to science. When Transylvania became part of Rumania, the government of the newly created Hungarian Republic appointed Apáthy as government commissioner of Transylvanian affairs to the Rumanian National Committee in Sibiu because of his progressive ideas and scientific reputation. He was, as a commissioner and representative spokesman of a defeated country, imprisoned by the Rumanians in Sibiu, but they, respecting his scientific reputation and patriotism, set him free again. He was even allowed to take all of his research material, collections, microscopes, and such. Apáthy returned to Hungary as professor of zoology at Szeged University, where he founded another modern institute. His health was impaired, however, and he died soon after.

Apáthy's scientific achievements were in three fields: zoology, neurohistology, and microscopic technique. In zoology his most important contributions concerned the systematic and comparative anatomy of Hirudinea, especially of their nervous system.

In neurohistology Apáthy defended the concept of a continuous network of neurofibrils, passing from one neuron to another. The first research worker in this field, he found, with the aid of his original impregnation containing gold chloride, a network of finest neurofibrils in the intestine wall of marine Hirudines. According to his interpretation of his microscopic examination of the whole thickness of the intestinal wall—not, unfortunately, in microscopic sections—these neurofibrils are closely connected with all other cells of the intestinal wall tissues and pass from one neuron to another.

Apáthy considered the neurofibrils to be a connected system, forming an intimate unity with the various tissues penetrated by them. Consequently, he advanced the assumption of the continuity of neurofibrils in the whole animal body. To this idea Apáthy applied all his interpretations, and his further scientific work was given over, for the most part, to the proof and the polemic defense of his view. He published a series of papers opposing the views of Santiago Ramón y Cajal, Joseph Gerlach, Wilhelm Waldeyer, and others, in which he perseverantly tried to prove that the neurons are not merely apposed to each other and that the nervous irritation from one individual neuron to the other is not realized through its transfer *per contiguitatem,* but that the whole nervous system is connected continuously by means of reticularly arranged neurofibrils. Unfortunately he extended his observations, made on invertebrate nervous systems with a specific microscopic feature and function, to the whole class of vertebrates, thus leaving his hypothesis open to attack.

The prolonged controversy contributed, by the response in the world and the tough bilateral polemics lasting many years, to many new and important findings in the field of neurology. This controversy has recently been settled in favor of the neuron theory through electron microscopy. Apáthy always interpreted his morphological findings functionally, and thanks to him many scientists in other branches of biology (e.g., physiology, pathophysiology, neurology, pharmacology) were induced to extend his research. Apáthy is for these reasons to be considered the founder of the modern trends in neurohistology.

Apáthy's work in microscopic technique constituted a great contribution to the development of modern histological techniques. His improvements in the fixation of tissues—in embedding them in paraffin, gelatine, or celloidin; in sectioning and staining them, or impregnating them with gold salts, or both—meant a great advance in histology and furnished many good results. Apáthy's *Die Mikrotechnik der thierischen Morphologie* was an indispensable handbook for two generations of histologists. His greatest achievement is that he made microscopic technique a scientific method, based not only on empirical knowledge but also on systematic comparisons and investigations.

BIBLIOGRAPHY

I. ORIGINAL WORKS. Lists of Apáthy's works may be found in Ambrus Ábráham, "Stephan von Apáthy" (see below), and in Ferenc Kiss, "Stephan von Apáthy als Neurolog" (see below).

II. SECONDARY LITERATURE. There is no biography of Apáthy, but information on his life and work may be found in the following papers: Ambrus Ábráham, "Apáthy István," in *Communicationes ex Bibliotheca Historiae Medicae Hungarica,* 25 (1962), 13–24, and "Stephan von Apáthy," in H. Freud and A. Berg, *Geschichte der Mikroskopie* (Frankfurt am Main, 1963), pp. 65–75; Ferenc Kiss, "Stephan von Apáthy als Neurolog," in *Communicationes ex Bibliotheca Historiae Medicae Hungarica,* 3 (1956), 1–64, and "Apáthy István nehézségei" ("The Difficulties of István Apáthy"), *ibid.,* 36–41; Gábor Kolosváry, "Apáthy mint rendszerezö elme a zoológiában források és személyes kapcsolat alapján" ("Apáthy's Contribution to Zoology, Based on Works of Reference and Personal Recollections"), *ibid.,* 25 (1962), 29–35; Maria Koszoru, "Apáthy István korának társadalma és a tudós szociálpolitikai munkássága" ("István Apáthy, the Society of His Time and the Social-Political Activities of the Scientist"), *ibid.,* 53–57; Endre Réti, "Apáthy István emberi jelentosege" ("The Human Importance of István Apáthy"), *ibid.,* 42–49, and "Darwinista humanizmus Apáthy és Lenhossék szemléletében"—"Darvinističeskij gumanism vo vzljadach Apati i Lenchoseka" ("Apáthy's and Lenhossék's Opinion About Darwinian Humanism"), *ibid.,* 27 (1963), 111–116, 117–122; and Gylyás Pál, *Magyar irók élete és munkái* (Budapest, 1939).

JOSEF SAJNER

APELT, ERNST FRIEDRICH (*b.* Reichenau bei Zittau, Germany, 3 March 1812; *d.* Oppelsdorf, Germany, 27 October 1859), *philosophy, history of science.*

Following a conventional education at a Dorfschule in Reichenau from 1818 to 1822 and at a Bürgerschule in Zittau from 1822 to 1824, Apelt was admitted to the Gymnasium in Zittau, where he studied natural science. An early interest in mathematics led him to speculate on cosmological and philosophical questions, and his teachers directed him to Jakob Fries's *Neue Kritik der Vernunft.* With characteristic aplomb, he wrote to Fries, commenting on several passages in the *Neue Kritik;* as a result, he was invited to study at the University of Jena.

Under Fries's tutelage there from 1831 to 1833, Apelt read mathematics and philosophy. He continued his studies at Leipzig until 1835, specializing in astronomy and physics under the direction of A. F. Moebius. After a brief period in his father's business, in 1839 he became a *Privatdozent* at Jena, where he spent the rest of his life. Apelt lectured initially on mathematics and astronomy, later turning to philosophy. A prolific writer, his inaugural dissertation (*De viribus naturae primitivis*, 1839) was followed in quick succession by a number of important works on metaphysics, epistemology, and history of science: *Die Epochen der Geschichte der Menschheit* (1845–1846), *Johann Keplers Weltansicht* (1849), *Die Reformation der Sternkunde* (1852), *Theorie der Induction* (1854), *Metaphysik* (1857), and the posthumously published *Religionsphilosophie* (1860).

Although his direct contributions to science were slight, Apelt's influence on German history and philosophy of science was far-reaching. His general approach was much like that of Fries and other first-generation Neo-Kantians: philosophy was conceived of as an analysis of knowledge and reason by the critical method. Apelt's special contribution to the Kantian tradition was his insistence, both by precept and by example, that scientific knowledge should be the epistemologist's touchstone and that a careful historical scrutiny of the sciences should be absolutely essential for epistemology. His most important work in the philosophy of science was his *Theorie der Induction,* which was prompted in part by the controversy then raging among Comte, Mill, Herschel, and Whewell about scientific method in general and induction in particular. Apelt's views are probably closest to those of Whewell, which is hardly surprising in view of their common Kantian orientation. Like Whewell, he drew extensively on case studies from the history of science to support his methodological analyses. Moreover, his *Theorie der Induction* in-

cludes a lengthy analysis of mathematical induction and the foundations of mathematical inference. Apelt must be regarded as one of the two leading German methodologists of the period, Justus von Liebig being the other. His historical writings were concerned primarily with astronomy and cosmology; his books and monographs dealt with the Copernican revolution, Greek astronomy, Kepler's natural philosophy, and the scientific work of F. H. Jacobi.

BIBLIOGRAPHY

I. ORIGINAL WORKS. Apelt's works are *De viribus naturae primitivis* (Jena, 1839); "Die Conjunktion des Jupiter und Saturn und ihr Zusammenhang mit den Prophezeihungen des Peter d'Ailln und Nostradamus," in *Zeitschrift Minerva* (July 1840), pp. 1–37; "Ernst Reinhold und die Kantische Philosophie," in *Kritik der Erkenntnistheorie,* **1** (1840), 74–103; *Die Epochen der Geschichte der Menschheit,* 2 vols. (Jena, 1845–1846); *Wie muss das Glaubensbekenntnis beschaffen sein, das zur Vereinigung aller Confessionen führen soll?* (Jena, 1846); "Die Sternhimmel," in *Zeitschrift Minerva* (Jan. 1847), 145–174; "Untersuchungen über die Philosophie und Physik der Alten," in *Abhandlungen der Fries'schen Schule,* I (Leipzig, 1847), 31–144; "Erwiederung auf H. Ritters Recension des ersten Hefts," *ibid.,* II (Leipzig, 1849), 1–26; "Die Sphärentheorie des Eudoxus und Aristoteles," *ibid.,* 27–49; "Die Entdeckung von Amerika: eine historische Skizze," *ibid.,* 51–78; "Bemerkungen über F. H. Jacobi und seine Lehre," *ibid.,* 79–88; "Metaphysische Betrachtungen über die Welt," *ibid.,* 89–105; *Parmenides et Empedoclis doctrina de mundi structura* (Jena, 1847); *Johann Keplers astronomische Weltansicht* (Leipzig, 1849); *Die Reformation der Sternkunde* (Jena, 1852); *Die Theorie der Induction* (Jena, 1854); *Metaphysik* (Leipzig, 1857); and *Religionsphilosophie* (Leipzig, 1860).

II. SECONDARY LITERATURE. The only detailed recent studies of Apelt's work are by W. Gresky: *Die Ausgangspunkte der Philosophie Ernst Friedrich Apelts* (Würzburg, 1936); and "21 Briefe von Hermann Lotze an Ernst Friedrich Apelt (1835–1841)," in *Blätter für deutsche Philosophie,* **10** (1936), 319–331; **11** (1937), 184–203.

L. L. LAUDAN

APIAN, PETER, also known as **Petrus Apianus, Peter Bienewitz** (or **Bennewitz**) (*b.* Leisnig, Germany, 16 April 1495; *d.* Ingolstadt, Germany, 21 April 1552), *astronomy, geography.*

Apian was a pioneer in astronomical and geographical instrumentation, and one of the most successful popularizers of these subjects during the sixteenth century. He studied mathematics and astronomy at Leipzig and Vienna, and quickly established a reputation as an outstanding mathematician. His first work was *Typus orbis universalis,* a world map, based on the work of Martin Waldseemüller, which illustrated the 1520 Vienna edition of Solinus' *Polyhistor seu de mirabilibus mundi*. The following year he published the *Isagoge*, a commentary on the *Typus* and on geography.

Apian's first major work, *Cosmographia seu descriptio totius orbis* (1524), was based on Ptolemy. Starting with the distinction between cosmography, geography, and chorography, and using an ingenious and simple diagram, the book defines terrestrial grids; describes the use of maps and simple surveying; defines weather and climate; and provides thumbnail sketches of the continents. In its later form, as modified by Gemma Frisius, the *Cosmographia* was one of the most popular texts of the time and was translated into all major European languages. The success of this and his previous works led to Apian's appointment as professor of mathematics at the University of Ingolstadt, where he remained until his death. He was knighted by Charles V.

In his *Cosmographia*, Apian suggests the use of lunar distances to measure longitude; in his second major work, *Astronomicon Caesareum* (1540), he supports the use of solar eclipses for that purpose. The *Astronomicon* is notable for Apian's pioneer observations of comets (he describes the appearances and characteristics of five comets, including Halley's) and his statement that comets point their tails away from the sun. Also important is his imaginative use of simple mechanical devices, particularly valvelles, to provide information on the position and movement of celestial bodies. Of greater scientific significance, however, is Apian's *Instrumentum sinuum sive primi mobilis* (1534), where he calculates sines for every minute, with the radius divided decimally. These are the first such tables ever printed.

Apian's contribution to cartography was as a compiler and publisher, rather than as a mapmaker. His cordiform world map and maps of Hungary and France survive; his large-scale map of Europe (1534), the first of its kind, is lost. He also designed a quadrant and an armillary sphere that were popular in his day.

BIBLIOGRAPHY

The best list of Apian's writings is F. Van Ortroy, "Bibliographie de l'oeuvre de Pierre Apian," in *Bibliographie moderne* (Mar.–Oct. 1901).

The standard biographical source is S. Günther, "Peter und Phillipp Apian: Zwei deutsche Mathematiker und Kartographen," in *Abhandlungen der Königlich böhmischen Gesellschaft der Wissenschaften*, 6th ser., **11** (1882).

GEORGE KISH

APOLLONIUS OF PERGA (*b*. second half of third century B.C.; *d*. early second century B.C.), *mathematical sciences.*

Very little is known of the life of Apollonius. The surviving references from antiquity are meager and in part untrustworthy. He is said to have been born at Perga (Greek Πέργη), a small Greek city in southern Asia Minor, when Ptolemy Euergetes was king of Egypt (i.e., between 246 and 221 B.C.)[1] and to have become famous for his astronomical studies in the time of Ptolemy Philopator, who reigned from 221 to 205 B.C.[2] Little credence can be attached to the statement in Pappus that he studied for a long time with the pupils of Euclid in Alexandria.[3] The best evidence for his life is contained in his own prefaces to the various books of his *Conics*. From these it is clear that he was for some time domiciled at Alexandria and that he visited Pergamum and Ephesus.

The prefaces of the first three books are addressed to one Eudemus of Pergamum. Since the Preface to Book II states that he is sending the book by the hands of his son Apollonius, he must have been of mature age at the time of its composition.[4] We are told in the Preface to Book IV that Eudemus is now dead;[5] this and the remaining books are addressed to one Attalus. The latter is commonly identified with King Attalus I of Pergamum (reigned 241–197 B.C.); but it is highly unlikely that Apollonius would have neglected current etiquette so grossly as to omit the title of "King" (βασιλεύς) when addressing the monarch, and Attalus was a common name among those of Macedonian descent. However, a chronological inference can be made from a passage in the Preface to Book II, where Apollonius says, ". . . and if Philonides the geometer, whom I introduced to you in Ephesus, should happen to visit the neighborhood of Pergamum, give him a copy [of this book]."[6] Philonides, as we learn from a fragmentary biography preserved on a papyrus and from two inscriptions, was an Epicurean mathematician and philosopher who was personally known to the Seleucid kings Antiochus IV Epiphanes (reigned 175–163 B.C.) and Demetrius I Soter (162–150 B.C.). Eudemus was the first teacher of Philonides. Thus the introduction of the young Philonides to Eudemus probably took place early in the second century B.C. The *Conics* were composed about the same time. Since Apollonius was then old enough to have a grown son, it is reasonable to accept the birth date given by Eutocius and to place the period of Apollonius' activity in the late third and early second centuries B.C. This fits well with the internal evidence which his works provide on his relationship to Archimedes (who died an old man in 212–211 B.C.); Apollonius appears at times to be developing and improving on ideas that were originally conceived by Archimedes (for examples see p. 189). It is true that Apollonius does not mention Archimedes in his extant works; he does, however, refer to Conon, an older (?) contemporary and correspondent of Archimedes, as a predecessor in the theory of conic sections.[7]

Of Apollonius' numerous works in a number of different mathematical fields, only two survive, although we have a good idea of the content of several others from the account of them in the encyclopedic work of Pappus (fourth century A.D.). But it is impossible to establish any kind of relative chronology for his works or to trace the development of his ideas. The sole chronological datum is that already established, that the *Conics* in the form that we have them are the work of his mature years. Thus the order in which his works are treated here is an arbitrary one.

The work on which Apollonius' modern fame rests, the *Conics* (κωνικά), was originally in eight books. Books I–IV survive in the original Greek, Books V–VII only in Arabic translation. Book VIII is lost, but some idea of its contents can be gained from the lemmas to it given by Pappus.[8] Apollonius recounts the genesis of his *Conics* in the Preface to Book I[9]: he had originally composed a treatise on conic sections in eight books at the instance of one Naucrates, a geometer, who was visiting him in Alexandria; this had been composed rather hurriedly because Naucrates was about to sail. Apollonius now takes the opportunity to write a revised version. It is this revised version that constitutes the *Conics* as we know it.

In order to estimate properly Apollonius' achievement in the *Conics,* it is necessary to know what stage the study of the subject had reached before him. Unfortunately, since his work became the classic textbook on the subject, its predecessors failed to survive the Byzantine era. We know of them only from the scattered reports of later writers. It is certain, however, that investigation into the mathematical properties of conic sections had begun in the Greek world at least as early as the middle of the fourth century B.C., and that by 300 B.C. or soon after, textbooks on the subject had been written (we hear of such by Aristaeus and by Euclid). Our best evidence for the content of these textbooks comes from the works of Archimedes. Many of these are concerned with problems involving conic sections, mostly of a very specialized nature; but Archimedes makes use of a number of more elementary propositions in the theory of conics, which he states without proof. We may assume that these propositions were already well known. On occasion Archimedes actually states that such and such a proposition is proved "in the

Elements of Conics" (ἐν τοῖς κωνικοῖς στοιχείοις).[10] Let us leave aside the question of what work(s) he is referring to by this title; it is clear that in his time there was already in existence a corpus of elementary theorems on conic sections. Drawing mainly on the works of Archimedes, we can characterize the approach to the theory of conics before Apollonius as follows.

The three curves now known as parabola, hyperbola, and ellipse were obtained by cutting a right circular cone by a plane at right angles to a generator of the cone. According to whether the cone has a right angle, an obtuse angle, or an acute angle at its vertex, the resultant section is respectively a parabola, a hyperbola, or an ellipse. These sections were therefore named by the earlier Greek investigators "section of a right-angled cone," "section of an obtuse-angled cone," and "section of an acute-angled cone," respectively; those appellations are still given to them by Archimedes (although we know that he was well aware that they can be generated by methods other than the above). With the above method of generation, it is possible to characterize each of the curves by what is known in Greek as a σύμπτωμα, i.e., a constant relationship between certain magnitudes which vary according to the position of an arbitrary point taken on the curve (this corresponds to the equation of the curve in modern terms). For the parabola (see Figure 1), for an arbitrary point K, $KL^2 = 2\,AZ \cdot ZL$ (for suggested proofs of this and the σύμπτωμα of hyperbola and ellipse, see Dijksterhuis, *Archimedes,* pp. 57–59, whom I follow closely here). In algebraic notation, if $KL = y$, $ZL = x$, $2\,AZ = p$, we get the characteristic equation of the parabola $y^2 = px$. Archimedes frequently uses this relationship in the parabola and calls the parameter p "the double of the distance to the axis" (ἁ διπλασία τᾶς μέχρι τοῦ ἄξονος)[11] exactly describing $2\,ZA$ in Figure 1 ("axis" refers to the axis of the *cone*). For the hyperbola and ellipse the following σύμπτωμα can be derived (see Figures 2 and 3):

$$\frac{KL^2}{ZL \cdot PL} = \frac{2\,ZF}{PZ};$$

in algebraic notation, if $KL = y$, $ZL = x_1$, $PL = x_2$, $2\,ZF = p$, $PZ = a$,

$$\frac{y^2}{x_1 x_2} = \frac{p}{a} = \text{constant}.$$

This is found in Archimedes in the form equivalent to

$$\frac{y^2}{x_1 x_2} = \frac{y'^2}{x'_1 x'_2}.{}^{12}$$

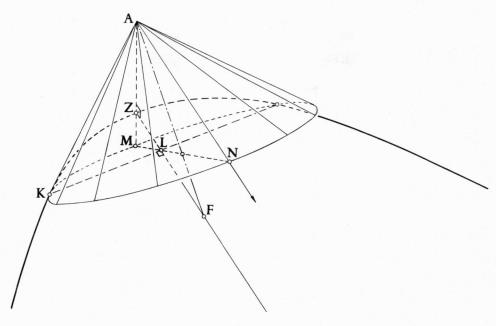

FIGURE   1

It is to be noted that in this system *ZL* always lies on the axis of the section and that *KL* is always at right angles to it. In other words, it is a system of "orthogonal conjugation."

Apollonius' approach is radically different. He generates all three curves from the double oblique circular cone, as follows: in Figures 4, 5, and 6 *ZDE* is the cutting plane. We now cut the cone with another plane orthogonal to the first and passing through the axis of the cone; this is known as the axial triangle (*ABG*); the latter must intersect the base of the cone in a diameter (*BG*) orthogonal to the line in which

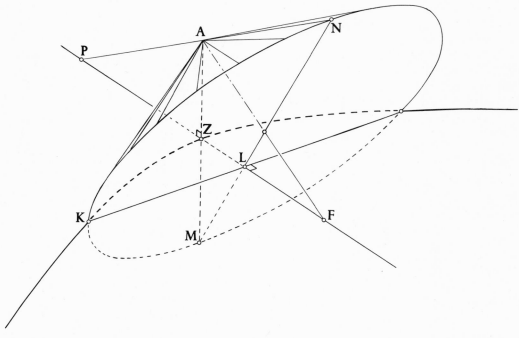

FIGURE   2

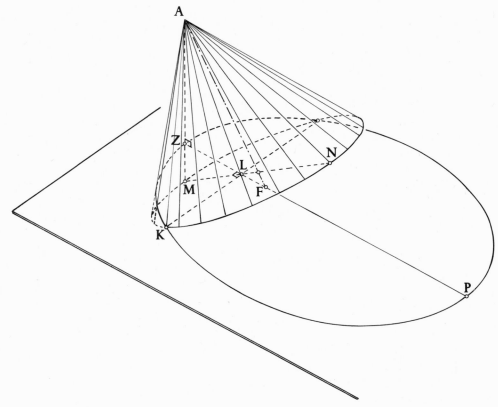

FIGURE 3

the cutting plane intersects it (or its extension); it intersects the cutting plane in a straight line *ZH*. Then, if we neglect the trivial cases where the cutting plane generates a circle, a straight line, a pair of straight lines, or a point, there are three possibilities:

(*a*) The line *ZH* in which the cutting plane intersects the axial triangle intersects only one of the two sides of the axial triangle, *AB, AG*; i.e., it is parallel to the other side (Figure 4).

(*b*) *ZH* intersects one side of the axial triangle below the vertex *A* and the other (extended) above it (Figure 5).

(*c*) *ZH* intersects both sides of the axial triangle below *A* (Figure 6).

In all three cases, for an arbitrary point *K* on the curve,

(1) $$KL^2 = ML \cdot LN.$$

Furthermore, in case (*a*),

(2) $$\frac{ML}{LZ} = \frac{BG}{AG} \text{ and } \frac{LN}{BG} = \frac{AZ}{AB}.$$

If we now construct a line length Θ such that $\Theta = BG^2 \cdot AZ/AB \cdot AG$, it follows from (1) and (2) that $KL^2 = LZ \cdot \Theta$. Since none of its constituent parts is dependent on the position of *K*, Θ is a constant. In algebraic terms, if $KL = y$, $LZ = x$, and $\Theta = p$, then $y^2 = px$. In cases (*b*) and (*c*),

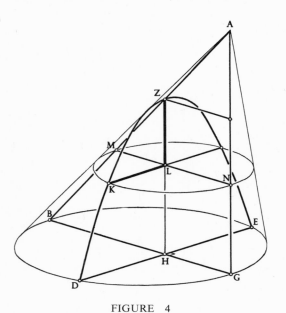

FIGURE 4

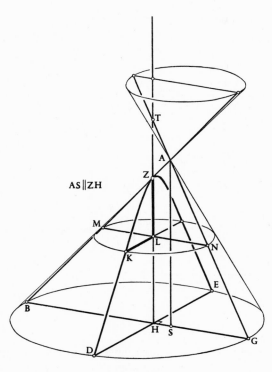

AS∥ZH

FIGURE 5

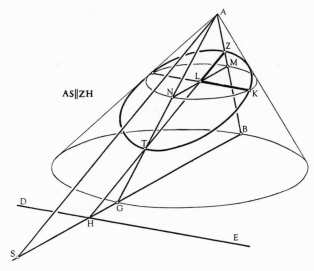

AS∥ZH

FIGURE 6

(3) $$\frac{ML}{LZ} = \frac{BS}{AS} \text{ and } \frac{LN}{LT} = \frac{SG}{AS}.$$

If we now construct a line length Ξ such that $\Xi = BS \cdot SG \cdot ZT/AS^2$, it follows from (1) and (3) that

$$KL^2 = \Xi \cdot \frac{LZ \cdot LT}{ZT}.$$

Thus

$$KL^2 = \Xi \cdot \frac{LZ(LZ + ZT)}{ZT} \text{ for case } (b)$$

and

$$KL^2 = \Xi \cdot \frac{LZ(LZ - ZT)}{ZT} \text{ for case } (c).$$

In algebraic terms, if $KL = y$, $LZ = x$, $\Xi = p$, and $ZT = a$,

$$y^2 = x\left(p + \frac{p}{a}x\right) \text{ for case } (b),$$

$$y^2 = x\left(p - \frac{p}{a}x\right) \text{ for case } (c).$$

The advantage of such formulation of the συμπτώματα of the curves from the point of view of classical Greek geometry is that now all three curves can be determined by the method of "application of areas," which is the Euclidean way of geometrically formulating problems that we usually express algebraically by equations of second degree. For instance, Euclid (VI, 28) propounds the problem "To a given straight line to apply a parallelogram equal to a given area and falling short of it by a parallelogrammic figure similar to a given one." (See Figure 7, where for simplicity rectangles have been substituted for parallelograms.) Then the problem is to apply to a line of given length b a rectangle of given area A and side x such that the rectangle falls short of the rectangle bx by a rectangle similar to another with sides c, d. This is equivalent to solving the equation

$$bx - \frac{c}{d}x^2 = A.$$

Compare the similar problem Euclid VI, 29: "To a given straight line to apply a parallelogram equal to a given area and exceeding it by a parallelogrammic figure similar to a given one."

This method is used by Apollonius to express the συμπτώματα of the three curves, as follows (see Figures 8–10).

For case (a) (Figure 8), a rectangle of side x (equal to the abscissa) is applied (παραβάλλεται) to the line-length p (defined as above): this rectangle is equal to the square on the ordinate y. The section is accordingly called parabola (παραβολή, meaning "exact application").

For case (b) (Figure 9), there is applied to p a rectangle, of side x, equal to y^2 and exceeding

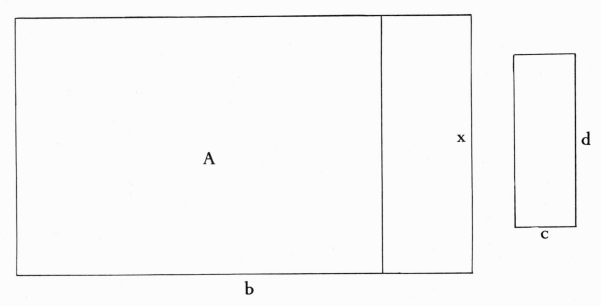

FIGURE 7

($\acute{v}\pi\epsilon\rho\beta\acute{a}\lambda\lambda o\nu$) p by a rectangle similar to p/a. The section is accordingly named hyperbola ($\acute{v}\pi\epsilon\rho\beta o\lambda\acute{\eta}$, meaning "excess").

For case (*c*) (Figure 10) there is applied to p a rectangle of side x, equal to y^2 and falling short ($\acute{\epsilon}\lambda\lambda\epsilon\hat{\iota}\pi o\nu$) of p by a rectangle similar to p/a. The section is accordingly named ellipse ($\acute{\epsilon}\lambda\lambda\epsilon\iota\psi\iota s$, meaning "falling short").

This approach has several advantages over the older one. First, all three curves can be represented by the method of "application of areas" favored by classical Greek geometry (it has been appropriately termed "geometrical algebra" in recent times); the older approach allowed this to be done only for the parabola. In modern terms, Apollonius refers the equation of all three curves to a coordinate system of which one axis is a given diameter of the curve and the other the tangent at one end of that diameter. This brings us to a second advantage: Apollonius' method of generating the curves immediately pro-

duces oblique conjugation, whereas the older method produces orthogonal conjugation. As we shall see, oblique conjugation was not entirely unknown to earlier geometers; but it is typical of Apollonius' approach that he immediately develops the most general formulation. It is therefore a logical step, given this approach, for Apollonius to prove (I,50 and the preceding propositions) that a $\sigma\acute{v}\mu\pi\tau\omega\mu\alpha$ equivalent to those derived above can be established for any diameter of a conic and its ordinates: in modern terms, the coordinates of the curves can be transposed to any diameter and its tangent.

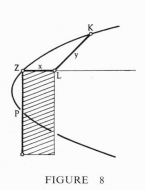

FIGURE 8

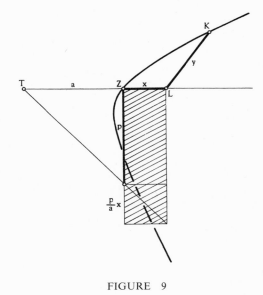

FIGURE 9

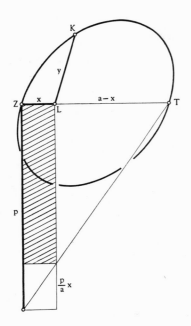

FIGURE 10

We cannot doubt that Apollonius' approach to the generation and basic definition of the conic sections, as outlined above, was radically new. It is not easy to determine how much of the *content* of the *Conics* is new. It is likely that a good deal of the nomenclature that his work made standard was introduced by him; in particular, the terms "parabola," "hyperbola," and "ellipse" make sense only in terms of Apollonius' method. To the parameter which we have called *p* he gave the name 'ορθία ("orthogonal side" [of a rectangle]), referring to its use in the "application": this term survives in the modern *latus rectum*. He defines "diameter" as *any* line bisecting a system of parallel chords in a conic, in accordance with the new generality of his coordinate system: this differs from the old meaning of "diameter" of a conic section (exemplified in Archimedes), which is (in Apollonian and modern terminology) the axis. But though this new terminology reflects the new approach, it does not in itself exclude the possibility that many of Apollonius' results in the *Conics* were already known to his predecessors. That this is true at least for the first four books is suggested by his own Preface to Book I. He says there:[13]

> The first four books constitute an elementary introduction. The first contains the methods of generating the three sections and their basic properties (συμπτώματα), developed more fully and more generally (καθόλου μᾶλλον) than in the writings of others; the second contains the properties of the diameter and axes of the sections, the asymptotes, and other things . . . ;

the third contains many surprising theorems useful for the syntheses of solid loci and for determinations of the possibilities of solutions (διορισμούς); of the latter the greater part and the most beautiful are new. It was the discovery of these that made me aware that Euclid has not worked out the whole of the locus for three and four lines,[14] but only a fortuitous part of it, and that not very happily; for it was not possible to complete the synthesis without my additional discoveries. The fourth book deals with how many ways the conic sections can meet one another and the circumference of the circle, and other additional matters, neither of which has been treated by my predecessors, namely in how many points a conic section or circumference of a circle can meet another. The remaining books are particular extensions (περιουσιαστικώτερα); one of them [V] deals somewhat fully with minima and maxima, another [VI] with equal and similar conic sections, another [VII] with theorems concerning determinations (διοριστικῶν), another [VIII] with determinate conic problems.

From this one gets the impression that Books I–IV, apart from the subjects specifically singled out as original, are merely reworkings of the results of Apollonius' predecessors. This is confirmed by the statement of Pappus, who says that Apollonius supplemented the four books of Euclid's *Conics* (which Pappus *may* have known) and added four more books.[15]

Apollonius also claims to have worked out the methods of generating the sections and setting out their συμπτώματα "more fully and more generally" than his predecessors. The description "more generally" is eminently justified by our comparison of the two methods. However, it is not clear to what "more fully" ('επὶ πλέον) refers. Neugebauer suggests that Apollonius meant his introduction of conjugate hyperbolas (conjugate diameters in ellipse and hyperbola are dealt with in I, 15–16).[16] At least as probable is a more radical alternative, rejected by Neugebauer, that Apollonius is referring to his treatment of the two branches of the hyperbola as a unit (exemplified in I, 16 and frequently later). It is true that Apollonius applies the name "hyperbola" only to a single branch of the curve (he refers to the two branches as the "opposite *sections*" [τομαὶ 'αντικείμεναι]); it is also true that in his own Preface to Book IV[17] he reveals that at least Nicoteles among his predecessors had considered the two branches together; but Apollonius' very definition of a conic surface[18] as the surface *on both sides* of the vertex is significant in this context; and it is unlikely that any of his predecessors had *systematically* developed the theory of both branches of the hyperbola. Here again, then, we may reasonably regard Apollonius as an innovator in his *method*. But we are not justified in assuming that any of the

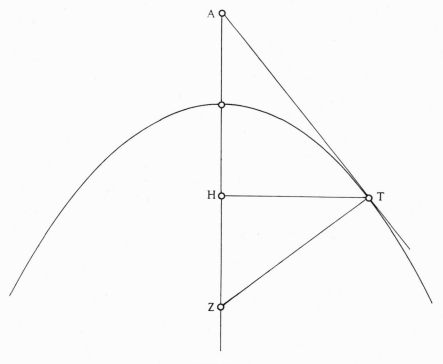

FIGURE 11

results stated in the first four books were unknown before Apollonius, except where he specifically states this. In this part of the work we must see him rather as organizing the results of his predecessors, consisting in part of haphazard and disconnected sets of theorems, into an exposition ordered rationally according to his own very general method. His mastery is such that it seems impossible to separate different sources (as one can, for instance, in the comparable work of Euclid on elementary geometry).

Nevertheless, we may suspect that Archimedes, could he have read Books I–IV of the *Conics,* would have found few results in them that were not already familiar to him (although he might well have been surprised by the order and mutual connection of the theorems). The predecessors of Archimedes were already aware that conic sections could be generated by methods other than that described on p. 180. Euclid states that an ellipse can be produced by cutting a cylinder by a plane not parallel to the base.[19] Archimedes himself certainly knew that there were many different ways of generating the sections from a cone. The best proof of this is *De conoidibus et sphaeroidibus* VII–IX, in which it is shown that for any ellipse it is possible to find an *oblique* circular cone from which that ellipse can be generated. Furthermore, it is certain that the essential properties of the oblique conjugation of at least the parabola were known to

Apollonius' predecessors; for that is the essence of propositions I–III of Archimedes' *Quadrature of the Parabola,* which he states are proved "in the Elements of Conics."[20] In *De conoidibus et sphaeroidibus* III, Archimedes states "If two tangents be drawn from the same point to *any* conic, and two chords be drawn inside the section parallel to the two tangents and intersecting one another, the product of the two parts of each chord [formed by the intersection] will have the same ratio to one another as the squares on the tangents. . . . this is proved in the Elements of Conics."[21] It is plausible to interpret this, with Dijksterhuis, as treatment of all three sections in oblique conjugation.[22]

It is probable then that much of the contents of Books I–IV was already known before Apollonius. Conversely, Apollonius did not include in the "elementary introduction" of Books I–IV all theorems on conics known to his predecessors. For example, in a parabola the subnormal to any tangent formed on the diameter (*HZ* in Figure 11) is constant and equal to half the parameter *p*. This is assumed without proof by Archimedes[23] and by Diocles (perhaps a contemporary of Apollonius) in his proof of the focal property of the parabola in his work *On Burning Mirrors.*[24] We can therefore be sure that it was a well-known theorem in the *Elements of Conics.* Yet in Apollonius it can be found only by combining the results of propositions 13 and 27 of Book V, one of the "particular extensions."

If Apollonius omitted some of his predecessors' results from the elementary section, we must not be surprised if he omitted altogether some results with which he was perfectly familiar: his aim was not to compile an encyclopedia of all possible theorems on conic sections, but to write a systematic textbook on the "elements" and to add some more advanced theory which he happened to have elaborated. The question has often been raised in modern times why there is no mention in the *Conics* of the focus of the parabola. The focal properties of hyperbola and ellipse are treated in III, 45–52: Apollonius proves, *inter alia,* that the focal distances at any point make equal angles with the tangent at that point and that their sum (for the ellipse) or difference (for the hyperbola) is constant. There is no mention of directrix, and from the *Conics* we might conclude that Apollonius was totally ignorant of the focus-directrix property of conic sections. However, it happens that Pappus proves at length that if a point moves in such a way that the ratio of its distance from a fixed point and its orthogonal distance from a fixed straight line is constant, then the locus of that point is a conic section; and that according as the ratio is equal to, greater than, or less than unity, the section will be respectively a parabola, a hyperbola, or an ellipse.[25] This amounts to the generation of the sections from focus and directrix. Pappus gives this proof as a lemma to Euclid's (lost) book *On Surface Loci;* hence, it has been plausibly concluded that the proposition was there stated without proof by Euclid.[26] If that is so, here is a whole topic in the theory of conics that must have been completely familiar to Apollonius, yet which he omits altogether. Thus the lack of any mention of the focus of the parabola in the *Conics* is not an argument for Apollonius' ignorance of it. I agree with those who argue on a priori grounds that he must have known of it.[27] Since he very probably dealt with it in his work(s) on burning mirrors (see p. 189) there was all the more justification for omitting it from the *Conics.* In any case, we now have a proof of it, by Diocles, very close to the time of Apollonius. Since Diocles further informs us that a parabolic burning mirror was constructed by Dositheus, who corresponded with Archimedes, it is highly probable that the focal property of the parabola was well known *before* Apollonius.

For a detailed summary of the contents of the *Conics,* the reader is referred to the works of Zeuthen and Heath listed in the Bibliography. Here we will only supplement Apollonius' own description quoted above by noting that Book III deals with theorems on the rectangles contained by the segments of intersecting chords of a conic (an extension to conics of that proved by Euclid for chords in a circle), with the harmonic properties of pole and polar (to use the modern terms: there are no equivalent ancient ones), with focal properties (discussed above), and finally with propositions relevant to the locus for three and four lines (see n. 14). Of Books V–VII, which are, to judge from Apollonius' own account, largely original, Book V is that which has particularly evoked the admiration of modern mathematicians: it deals with normals to conics, when drawn as maximum and minimum straight lines from particular points or sets of points to the curve. Apollonius finally proves, in effect, that there exists on either side of the axis of a conic a series of points from which one can draw only one normal to the opposite side of the curve, and shows how to construct such points: these points form the curve known, in modern terms, as the *evolute* of the conic in question. Book VII is concerned mainly with propositions about inequalities between various functions of conjugate diameters. Book VIII is lost, but an attempt at restoration from Pappus' lemmas to it was made by Halley in his edition of the *Conics.* If he is right, it contained problems concerning conjugate diameters whose functions (as "determined" in Book VII) have given values.

For a modern reader, the *Conics* is among the most difficult mathematical works of antiquity. Both form and content are far from tractable. The author's rigorous rhetorical exposition is wearing for those used to modern symbolism. Unlike the works of Archimedes, the treatise does not immediately impress the reader with its mathematical brilliance. Apollonius has, in a way, suffered from his own success: his treatise became canonical and eliminated its predecessors, so that we cannot judge by direct comparison its superiority to them in mathematical rigor, consistency, and generality. But the work amply repays closer study; and the attention paid to it by some of the most eminent mathematicians of the seventeenth century (one need mention only Fermat, Newton, and Halley) reinforces the verdict of Apollonius' contemporaries, who, according to Geminus, in admiration for his *Conics* gave him the title of The Great Geometer.[28]

In Book VII of his mathematical thesaurus, Pappus includes summaries of and lemmas to six other works of Apollonius besides the *Conics.* Pappus' account is sufficiently detailed to permit tentative reconstructions of these works, all but one of which are entirely lost. All belong to "higher geometry," and all consisted of exhaustive discussion of the particular cases of one or a few general problems. The contrast with

Apollonius' approach in the *Conics,* where he strives for generality of treatment, is notable. A brief indication of the problem(s) discussed in these works follows.

(1) *Cutting off of a Ratio* (λόγου ᾽αποτομή), in two books, is the only surviving work of Apollonius apart from the *Conics.* However, it is preserved only in an Arabic version which, by comparison with Pappus' summary, appears to be an adaptation rather than a literal translation. Pappus describes the general problem as follows: "To draw through a given point a straight line to cut off from two given straight lines two sections measured from given points on the two given lines so that the two sections cut off have a given ratio."[29] Apollonius discusses particular cases before proceeding to the more general (e.g., in every case discussed in Book I the two given lines are supposed to be parallel) and solves every case by the classical method of "analysis" (in the Greek sense). That is, the problem is presumed solved, and from the solution is deduced some other condition that is easily constructible. Then, by "synthesis" from this latter construction, the original condition is constructed. We may presume that Apollonius followed the same method in all six of these works, especially since Book VII of Pappus was named ᾽αναλυόμενος ("Field of Analysis"). In the *Cutting off of a Ratio* the problem was reduced to one of "application of an area." Zeuthen[30] points out the relevance of this work to *Conics* III, 41: If one regards the theorem proved there as a method of drawing a tangent to a given point in a parabola by determining the intercepts it makes on two other tangents to the curve, that is exactly the problem discussed by Apollonius in this work. Although there is no mention in it of conic sections, the connection is surely not a fortuitous one. In fact, many of the problems discussed by Apollonius in the six works summarized in Book VII of Pappus can be reduced to problems connected with conics. (This helps to explain the great interest shown in this part of Pappus' work by mathematicians of the sixteenth and seventeenth centuries.)

(2) *Cutting off of an Area* (χωρίον ᾽αποτομή), in two books, has a general problem similar to that of the preceding work. But in this case the intercepts cut off from the two given lines must have a given product (in Greek terms, contain a given rectangle) instead of a given proportion.[31] Here again Zeuthen has shown that *Conics* III, 42 and 43, which concern tangents drawn to ellipse and hyperbola, are equivalent to particular cases of the problem discussed by Apollonius in this work.[32]

(3) *Determinate Section* (διωρισμένη τομή) deals with the following general problem: Given four points—*A, B, C, D*—on a straight line *l,* to determine a point *P* on that line such that the ratio $AP \cdot CP / BP \cdot DP$ has a given value.[33] Since this comparatively simple problem was discussed at some length by Apollonius, Zeuthen conjectured—plausibly—that he was concerned to find the limits of possibility of a solution for the various possible arrangements of the points (e.g., when two coincide).[34] We know from Pappus' account that it dealt, among other things, with maxima and minima. Whether, as Zeuthen claims, the work amounted to "a complete theory of involution" cannot be decided on existing evidence. But it is a fact that the general problem is the same as determining the intersection of the line *l* and the conic that is the "locus for four lines," the four lines passing through *A, B, C,* and *D*; and Apollonius must have known this. Here again, then, is a connection with the theory of conics.

(4) *Tangencies* (᾽επαφαί), in two books, deals with the general problem characterized by Pappus[35] as follows: "Given three elements, either points, lines or circles (or a mixture), to draw a circle tangent to each of the three elements (or through them if they are points)." There are ten possible different combinations of elements, and Apollonius dealt with all eight that had not already been treated by Euclid. The particular case of drawing a circle to touch three given circles attracted the interest of Vieta and Newton, among others. Although one of Newton's solutions[36] was obtained by the intersection of two hyperbolas, and solutions to other cases can also be represented as problems in conics, Apollonius seems to have used only straight-edge and compass constructions throughout. Zeuthen provides a plausible solution to the three-circle problem reconstructed from Pappus' lemmas to this work.[37]

(5) *Inclinations* (νεύσεις), in two books, is described by Pappus on pages 670–672 of the Hultsch edition. In Greek geometry, a νεῦσις problem is one that consists in placing a straight line of given length between two given lines (not necessarily straight) so that it is inclined (νεύει) toward a given point. Pappus tells us that in this work Apollonius restricted himself to certain "plane" problems, i.e., ones that can be solved with straight-edge and compass alone. The particular problems treated by Apollonius can be reconstructed with some probability from Pappus' account.

(6) *Plane Loci* (τόποι ᾽επίπεδοι), in two books, is described on pages 660–670 of Pappus. "Plane loci" in Greek terminology are loci that are either straight lines or circles. In this work, Apollonius investigated

certain conditions that give rise to such plane loci. From them one can easily derive the equation for straight line and circle in Cartesian coordinates.[38]

A number of other works by Apollonius in the field of pure mathematics are known to us from remarks by later writers, but detailed information about the contents is available for only one of these: a work described by Pappus in Book II of his *Collectio*.[39] Since the beginning of Pappus' description is lost, the title of the work is unknown. It expounds a method of expressing very large numbers by what is in effect a place-value system with base 10,000. This way of overcoming the limitations of the Greek alphabetic numeral system, although ingenious, is not surprising, since Archimedes had already done the same thing in his ψαμμίτης (or "Sand Reckoner").[40] Archimedes' base is 10,000². It is clear that Apollonius' work was a refinement on the same idea, with detailed rules of the application of the system to practical calculation. Besides this we hear of works on the cylindrical helix (κοχλίας);[41] on the ratio between dodecahedron and eicosahedron inscribed in the same sphere;[42] and a general treatise (καθόλου πραγματεία).[43] It seems probable that the latter dealt with the foundations of geometry, and that to it are to be assigned the several remarks of Apollonius on that subject quoted by Proclus in his commentary on the first book of Euclid (see Friedlein's Index).

Thus Apollonius' activity covered all branches of geometry known in his time. He also extended the theory of irrationals developed in Book X of Euclid, for several sources mention a work of his on unordered irrationals (περὶ τῶν ἀτάκτων ἀλόγων).[44] The only information as to the nature of this work comes from Pappus' commentary on Euclid X, preserved in Arabic translation;[45] but the exact connotation of "unordered irrationals" remains obscure. Finally, Eutocius, in his commentary on Archimedes' *Measurement of a Circle*,[46] informs us that in a work called ὠκυτόκιον, meaning "rapid hatching" or "quick delivery," Apollonius calculated limits for π that were closer than Archimedes' limits of 3-1/7 and 3-10/71. He does not tell us what Apollonius' limits were; it is possible to derive closer limits merely by extending Archimedes' method of inscribing and circumscribing regular 96-gons to polygons with an ever greater number of sides (as was frequently done in the sixteenth and seventeenth centuries).[47] Very probably this was Apollonius' procedure, but that cannot be proved.

In applied mathematics, Apollonius wrote at least one work on optics. The evidence comes from a late Greek mathematical work preserved only fragmen-
tarily in a palimpsest (the "Bobbio Mathematical Fragment"). Unfortunately, the text is only partly legible at the crucial point,[48] but it is clear that Apollonius wrote a work entitled *On the Burning Mirror* (περὶ τοῦ πυρ⟨ε⟩ίου), in which he showed to what points parallel rays striking a spherical mirror would be reflected. The same passage also appears to say that in another work, entitled *To the Writers on Catoptrics* (πρὸς τοὺς κατοπτρικούς), Apollonius proved that the supposition of older writers that such rays would be reflected to the center of sphericity is wrong. The relevance of his work on conics to the subject of burning mirrors is obvious. We may conjecture with confidence that Apollonius treated of parabolic as well as of spherical burning mirrors. But the whole history of this subject in antiquity is still wrapped in obscurity.

Several sources indicate that Apollonius was noted for his astronomical studies and publications. Ptolemaeus Chennus (see n. 2) made the statement that Apollonius was called Epsilon, because the shape of the Greek letter ε is similar to that of the moon, to which Apollonius devoted his most careful study. This fatuous remark incidentally discloses some valuable information. "Hippolytus," in a list of distances to various celestial bodies according to different authorities, says that Apollonius stated that the distance to the moon from the earth is 5,000,000 stades (roughly 600,000 miles).[49] But the only specific information about Apollonius' astronomical studies is given by Ptolemy (fl. A.D. 140) in the *Almagest*.[50] While discussing the determination of the "station" of a planet (the point where it begins or ends its apparent retrogradation), he states that Apollonius proved the following theorem. In Figure 12, *O* is the observer (earth), the center of a circle on the circumference of which moves an epicycle, center *C*, with (angular) velocity v_1; the planet moves on the circumference of the epicycle about *C* with velocity v_2, and in the same sense as *C* moves about *O*. Then Apollonius' theorem states that if a line *OBAD* is drawn from *O* to cut the circle at *B* and *D*, such that

$$\frac{\frac{1}{2}BD}{BO} = \frac{v_1}{v_2},$$

B will be that point on the epicycle at which the planet is stationary. Ptolemy also indicates that Apollonius proved it both for the epicycle model and for an equivalent eccenter model (depicted in Figure 13; here the planet *P* moves on a circle, center *M*, eccentric to the earth *O*, such that $OM/MP = CD/OC$ in Figure 12; *M* moves about *O* with speed $[v_1 + v_2]$,

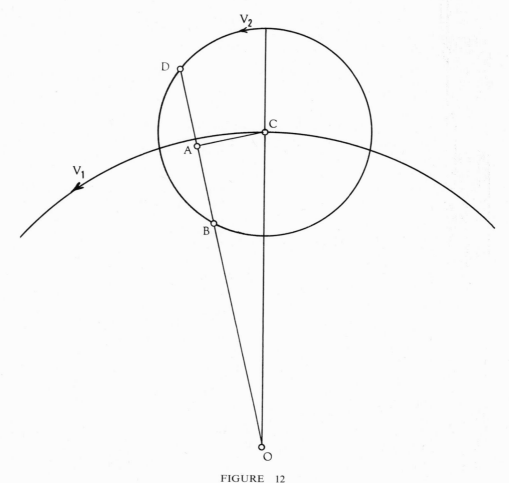

FIGURE 12

P about *M* with speed v_1). Even this much information is valuable, for it shows that Apollonius had already gone far in the application of geometrical models to explain planetary phenomena, and that he must have been acquainted with the equivalence of epicyclic and eccentric models (demonstrated by Ptolemy in *Almagest* III, 3); yet he was still operating with a simple epicycle/eccentric for the planets, although this would, for instance, entail that the length of the retrograde arc of a planet is constant, which is notoriously not the case. Neugebauer (see Bibliography) supposes, however, that the whole of the passage in which Ptolemy himself proves the above theorem is taken from Apollonius. That proof combines the two models of epicycle and eccenter in one by the ingenious device of using the same circle as both epicycle and eccenter; in other words, the epicycle model is transformed into the eccentric model by inversion on a circle. The procedure is worthy of Apollonius, and is indeed a particular case of the pole-polar relationship treated in *Conics* III, 37. But

Ptolemy (who of all ancient authors is most inclined to give credit where it is due) seems to introduce this device as his own,[51] and to return to Apollonius only later.[52] Fortunately, this uncertainty does not affect the main point: that Apollonius represents an important stage in the history of the adaptation of geometrical models to planetary theories. His real importance may have been much greater than we can ever know, since not only his astronomical works, but also those of his successor in the field, Hipparchus (*fl.* 130 B.C.), are lost.

It is not clear how far Apollonius applied his theoretical astronomical models to practical prediction (i.e., assigned sizes to the geometrical quantities and velocities). For the fact that he "calculated" the absolute distance of the moon need imply no more than imitation of the crude methods of Aristarchus of Samos (early third century B.C.); for "Hippolytus" also lists figures for distances in stades between the spheres of the heavenly bodies as given by Archimedes which cannot be reconciled with any rational astronomical

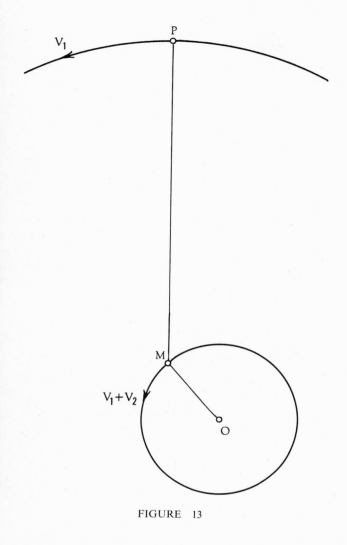

FIGURE   13

his *Conics* became the standard treatise on the subject, and were duly provided with elementary commentaries and annotations by succeeding generations. We hear of such commentaries by Serenus (fourth century A.D.?) and Hypatia (*d*. A.D. 415). The commentary of Eutocius (early sixth century A.D.) survives, but it is entirely superficial. Of surviving writers, the only one with the mathematical ability to comprehend Apollonius' results well enough to extend them significantly is Pappus (*fl*. A.D. 320), to whom we owe what knowledge we have of the range of Apollonius' activity in this branch of mathematics. The general decline of interest in the subject in Byzantium is reflected in the fact that of all Apollonius' works only *Conics* I–IV continued to be copied (because they were used as a textbook). A good deal more of his work passed into Islamic mathematics in Arabic translation, and resulted in several competent treatises on conics written in Arabic; but so far as is known, no major advances were made. (Ibn al-Haytham discusses the focus of the parabola in his work on parabolic burning mirrors;[56] but this, too, may be ultimately dependent on Greek sources.) The first real impulse toward advances in mathematics given by study of the works of Apollonius occurred in Europe in the sixteenth and early seventeenth centuries. The *Conics* were important, but at least as fruitful were Pappus' reports on the lost works, available in the excellent Latin translation by Commandino, published in 1588. (We must remember in this context that Books V–VII of the *Conics* were not generally available in Europe until 1661,[57] too late to make a real impact on the subject.) The number of "restorations" of the lost works of Apollonius made in the late sixteenth and early seventeenth centuries, some by outstanding mathematicians (e.g., Vieta, whose *Apollonius Gallus* [1600] is a reconstruction of the *Tangencies,* and Fermat, who reconstructed the *Plane Loci*) attests to the lively interest that Pappus' account excited. It is hard to underestimate the effect of Apollonius on the brilliant French mathematicians of the seventeenth century, Descartes, Mersenne, Fermat, and even Desargues and Pascal, despite their very different approach. Newton's notorious predilection for the study of conics, using Apollonian methods, was not a chance personal taste. But after him the analytic methods invented by Descartes brought about a lack of interest in Apollonius which was general among creative mathematicians for most of the eighteenth century. It was not until Poncelet's work in the early nineteenth century, picking up that of Desargues, Pascal, and la Hire, revived the study of projective geometry that the relevance of much of Apollonius' work to some basic modern theory was

system.[53] We should not assume without evidence that Apollonius had any better basis for his lunar distance. There is, however, a passage in the astrologer Vettius Valens (*fl*. A.D. 160) that has been taken to show that Apollonius actually constructed solar and lunar tables.[54] The author says that he has used the tables of Hipparchus for the sun; of Sudines, Kidenas, and Apollonius for the moon; and also of Apollonius for both. But there is no certainty that "Apollonius" here refers to Apollonius of Perga. At least as likely is the suggestion of Kroll that it may be Apollonius of Mynda, who is known to us only from a passage of Seneca, from which it appears that he claimed to have studied with the "Chaldaeans" and that he was "very experienced in the examination of horoscopes."[55] The Apollonius of the Vettius Valens passage is also associated with Babylonian names and practices.

Although the mathematical stature of Apollonius was recognized in antiquity, he had no worthy successor in pure mathematics. The first four books of realized. It is no accident that the most illuminating accounts of Apollonius' geometrical work have been written by mathematicians who were themselves leading exponents of the revived "synthetic" geometry, Chasles and Zeuthen.

The contribution of Apollonius to the development of astronomy, although far less obvious to us now, may have been equally important but, unlike his geometrical work, it had an immediate effect on the progress of the subject. Hipparchus and Ptolemy absorbed his work and improved on it. The result, the Ptolemaic system, is one of the most impressive monuments of ancient science (and certainly the longest-lived), and Apollonius' work contributed some of its essential parts.

NOTES

1. Eutocius, *Commentary,* Heiberg, II, 168, quoting one Heraclius.
2. Photius, *Bibliotheca,* p. 151b18 Bekker, quoting the dubious authority Ptolemaeus Chennus of the second century A.D.
3. Pappus, *Collectio* VII, Hultsch, p. 678.
4. Heiberg, I, 192.
5. *Ibid.,* II, 2.
6. *Ibid.,* I, 192.
7. *Ibid.,* Preface to Bk. IV, II, 2, 4.
8. Pappus, *Collectio* VII, Hultsch, p. 990 ff.
9. Heiberg, I, 2.
10. *De quadratura parabolae* III, Heiberg, II², 268; *cf. De conoidibus et sphaeroidibus* III, Heiberg, I², 270.
11. E.g., *De conoidibus et sphaeroidibus* III, Heiberg, I², 272.
12. For the ellipse, see, e.g. *De conoidibus et sphaeroidibus* VIII, Heiberg, I², 294, 22–26; for the hyperbola, *ibid.* XXV, Heiberg, I², 376, 19–23.
13. Heiberg, I, 2, 4.
14. In modern terms, the locus for four lines is the locus of a point whose distances x, y, z, u from four given straight lines, measured along a given axis, satisfy the equation $xz/yu = $ constant. This locus is a conic. (The locus for three lines is just a particular case of the above: for the distances x, y, z from three lines, $xz/y^2 = $ constant.) This is, in modern terms, an *anharmonic* ratio: it can be shown that the theorem that this locus is a conic is equivalent to some basic theorems of projective geometry. (See Michel Chasles, *Aperçu historique,* pp. 58, 354 ff.)
15. *Collectio* VII, Hultsch, p. 672.
16. "Apollonius-Studien," p. 219.
17. Heiberg, II, 2.
18. *Ibid.,* I, 6.
19. *Phaenomena,* ed. H. Menge (*Euclidis Opera Omnia* VIII) (Leipzig, 1916), p. 6.
20. Heiberg, II², 266–268.
21. *Ibid.,* I², 270.
22. Dijksterhuis, *Archimedes,* pp. 66, n.1, 106.
23. *De corporibus fluitantibus* II, 4, Heiberg, II², 357.
24. Chester Beatty MS. Ar. 5255, f.4v.
25. *Collectio* VII, Hultsch, pp. 1006–1014.
26. See, e.g., Zeuthen, *Kegelschnitte,* p. 367 ff.
27. For a method of proving the focal property of the parabola exactly parallel to Apollonius' procedure for those of hyperbola and ellipse, see Neugebauer, "Apollonius-Studien," pp. 241–242.
28. Eutocius, *Commentary,* Heiberg, II, 170.
29. Hultsch, p. 640.
30. *Kegelschnitte,* p. 345.

31. See Pappus, ed. Hultsch, pp. 640–642.
32. *Kegelschnitte,* p. 345 ff.
33. Pappus, ed. Hultsch, pp. 642–644.
34. *Kegelschnitte,* p. 196 ff.
35. Hultsch, p. 644.
36. *Principia,* Bk., I, Lemma XVI (Motte-Cajori trans., pp. 72–73).
37. *Kegelschnitte,* p. 381 ff.
38. See T. L. Heath, *A History of Greek Mathematics,* II, 187–189.
39. Hultsch, p. 2 ff.
40. Heiberg, II², 216 ff.
41. Proclus, *Commentary on Euclid,* ed. Friedlein, p. 105.
42. "Euclid," Bk. XIV, ed. Heiberg, V, 2: the problem is solved by the author of this part of the *Elements,* a man named Hypsicles (*fl. ca.* 150 B.C.), but we cannot tell exactly how much he owes to Apollonius.
43. See the commentary on Euclid's *Data* by Marinus (fifth century A.D.), in *Euclidis opera,* ed. Heiberg-Menge, VI, 234.
44. Proclus, *op. cit.,* p. 74.
45. Ed. Junge-Thomson, p. 219.
46. *Archimedis opera,* ed. Heiberg, III², 258.
47. See E. W. Hobson, *Squaring the Circle* (Cambridge, 1913), pp. 26–28.
48. *Mathematici Graeci Minores,* ed. Heiberg, p. 88.
49. *Refutation of all Heresies* IV, 8, ed. Wendland, III, 41.
50. XII, 1, ed. Heiberg, II, 450 ff.
51. *Ibid.,* pp. 451, 22.
52. *Ibid.,* pp. 456, 9.
53. *Refutation,* ed. Wendland, pp. 41–42.
54. *Anthologiae* XI 11, ed. Kroll, 354.
55. *Quaestiones naturales* VII, 4, 1, ed. Oltramare, II, 304.
56. Ed. Heiberg-Wiedemann, in *Bibliotheca mathematica,* **10** (1910), 201–237.
57. 1661 is the date of the publication at Florence of Abraham Ecchellensis' unsatisfactory version. Some knowledge of it had trickled out before, for Mersenne mentions some of the propositions in a book published in 1644 (see Introduction, xlvi, of ver Eecke's translation of the *Conics*).

BIBLIOGRAPHY

Ancient sources for Apollonius' life include the Prefaces to Books I, II, IV, V, VI, and VII of the *Conics* (in editions of Heiberg and Halley); Eutocius, *Commentary on Apollonius* I (in Heiberg, II, 168, 170); Pappus, *Collectio* VII (Hultsch, p. 678); Photius, *Bibliotheca,* ed. Bekker (Berlin, 1824–1825), p. 151b18. The fragmentary papyrus containing the life of Philonides is edited by Wilhelm Crönert in "Der Epikureer Philonides," in *Sitzungsberichte der Königlich Preussischen Akademie der Wissenschaften zu Berlin,* Jahrgang 1900.2, pp. 942–959. Crönert there points out the importance of this text for dating Apollonius. See further R. Philippson, article "Philonides 5," in *Real-Encyclopädie,* XX.1 (Stuttgart, 1941), cols. 63 ff. A convenient summary of the evidence is given by George Huxley in "Friends and Contemporaries of Apollonius of Perge," in *Greek, Roman and Byzantine Studies,* **4** (1963), 100–103.

A critical text of books I–IV of the *Conics* (with Latin translation) and Eutocius' commentary was published by J. L. Heiberg, *Apollonii Pergaei quae Graece exstant cum commentariis antiquis,* 2 vols. (Leipzig, 1891–1893). Of the Arabic version, only part of Book V has been published, with German translation, by L. Nix, *Das Fünfte Buch der Conica des Apollonius von Perga in der Arabischen Uebersetzung des Thabit ibn Corrah* (Leipzig, 1889). For the rest of Books V–VII the basis is still Edmund Halley's Latin translation from the Arabic in the first edition of the Greek text (Oxford, 1710). The most influential translation was Commandino's Latin version of the first four books (Bologna, 1566). For other editions and early versions and a history of the text, see Heiberg, II, lvii ff. The best modern translation is the French version of all seven books (from the Greek for I–IV and from Halley's Latin for V–VII) by Paul ver Eecke, *Les coniques d'Apollonius de Perge* (Bruges, 1923; reprinted Paris, 1963); the introduction gives a good survey of the work of Apollonius. T. L. Heath's *Apollonius of Perga* (Cambridge, 1896; reprinted 1961) is a free adaptation of the *Conics* rather than a translation. The fundamental modern work on Apollonius (and the ancient theory of conics in general) is H. G. Zeuthen, *Die Lehre von den Kegelschnitten im Altertum* (Copenhagen, 1886; reprinted Hildesheim, 1966), originally published in Danish. It is indispensable for anyone who wishes to make a serious effort to understand the methods underlying the *Conics.* The Introduction of Heath's *Apollonius* is valuable for those who cannot read Zeuthen. A useful summary of the contents of the *Conics* is provided by T. L. Heath, *A History of Greek Mathematics* (Oxford, 1921), II, 126–175. O. Neugebauer's "Apollonius-Studien," in *Quellen und Studien zur Geschichte der Mathematik*, Abteilung B: Studien Band 2 (1933), pp. 215–253, a subtle analysis of some parts of the *Conics,* attempts to trace certain "algebraic" procedures of Apollonius.

On the theory of conic sections before Apollonius, Zeuthen is again the best guide. On Archimedes in particular, J. L. Heiberg, "Die Kenntnisse des Archimedes über die Kegelschnitte," in *Zeitschrift für Mathematik und Physik,* **25** (1880), Hist.-lit. Abt., 41–67, is a careful collection of the relevant passages. In English, an account of pre-Apollonian conic theory is provided by Heath, *A History of Greek Mathematics,* II, 110–126; and E. J. Dijksterhuis, *Archimedes* (Copenhagen, 1956), ch. 3, gives an illuminating comparison between the Apollonian and Archimedean approaches. Another relevant work is Diocles' "On Burning Mirrors," which is extant only in Arabic translation. The sole known manuscript is Chester Beatty Arabic no. 5255, ff. 1–26, in the Chester Beatty Library, Dublin. An edition is being prepared by G. J. Toomer.

The Arabic text of *Cutting off of a Ratio* has never been printed. Halley printed a Latin version, together with a restoration of *Cutting off of an Area,* in *Apollonii Pergaei De sectione rationis libri duo* (Oxford, 1706); see also W. A. Diesterweg, *Die Bücher des Apollonius von Perga De Sectione Rationis* (Berlin, 1824), adapted from Halley's Latin.

Ancient texts giving information on lost mathematical works of Apollonius are the commentary of Proclus (fifth century A.D.) on Euclid Book I, edited by G. Friedlein, *Procli Diadochi in primum Euclidis Elementorum librum* (Leipzig, 1873); and *The Commentary of Pappus on Book X of Euclid's Elements,* ed. G. Junge and W. Thomson (Cambridge, Mass., 1930); but the most important is in Book VII of Pappus' *Collectio,* ed. Fr. Hultsch, *Pappi Alexandrini Collectionis quae supersunt,* 3 vols. (Berlin,

1876–1878). There is a good French translation of this work by P. ver Eecke, 2 vols. (Paris-Bruges, 1933). In modern times many attempts have been made at restoration of lost works of Apollonius on the basis of Pappus' account. Here we mention only the following: for the *Determinate Section,* Willebrordus Snellius, *Apollonius Batavus* (Leyden, 1608), and Robert Simson, in *Opera quaedam reliqua* (Glasgow, 1776); for the *Tangencies*—apart from Vieta's *Apollonius Gallus* (Paris, 1600)—J. Lawson, *The Two Books of Apollonius Pergaeus Concerning Tangencies* (Cambridge, 1764); for the *Inclinations,* Samuel Horsley, *Apollonii Pergaei inclinationum libri duo* (Oxford, 1770); for the *Plane Loci,* Pierre de Fermat, *Oeuvres,* P. Tannery and C. H. Henry, eds., I (Paris, 1891), 3–51, and Robert Simson, *Apollonii Pergaei locorum planorum libri II restituti* (Glasgow, 1749).

For other restorations of all the above see the Introduction to ver Eecke's translation of the *Conics,* pp. xxii–xxxiv. A good account of the probable contents of all six works is given by Heath, *A History of Greek Mathematics,* II, 175 ff. This is heavily dependent on Zeuthen's *Kegelschnitte;* the Index to the 1966 reprint of the latter is the most convenient guide to Zeuthen's scattered treatment of these lost works. F. Woepcke, "Essai d'une restitution de travaux perdus d'Apollonius sur les quantités irrationelles," in *Mémoires présentées à l'Académie des Sciences,* **14** (Paris, 1856), 658–720, is devoted to the work on unordered irrationals; see also T. L. Heath, *The Thirteen Books of Euclid's Elements Translated,* III (2nd ed., Cambridge, 1925), 255–259.

Ancient texts relevant to Apollonius' astronomical works are "Hippolytus," *Refutatio omnium haeresium,* ed. P. Wendland, Hippolytus Werke III (Leipzig, 1916), IV 8–10; Vettius Valens, *Anthologiarum libri,* ed. W. Kroll (Berlin, 1908), IX, 11; Seneca, *Quaestiones naturales,* ed. P. Oltramare, 2 vols. (Paris, 1961), VII, 4, 1; and especially Ptolemy, *Almagest* XII, 1, ed. J. L. Heiberg, in *Claudii Ptolemaei syntaxis mathematica,* 2 vols. (Leipzig, 1898–1903).

For Apollonius' astronomical work, see O. Neugebauer, "Apollonius' Planetary Theory," in *Communications on Pure and Applied Mathematics,* **8** (1955), 641–648, and "The Equivalence of Eccentric and Epicyclic Motion According to Apollonius," in *Scripta mathematica,* **24** (1959), 5–21.

No detailed account of the influence of Apollonius on later mathematics exists. Much interesting information can be found in ver Eecke's introduction to his translation. The best guide is Michel Chasles, *Aperçu historique sur l'origine et le développement des méthodes en géométrie* (Paris, 1837; reprinted 1875), a work which is also remarkable for its treatment of Apollonius in the light of nineteenth-century synthetic geometry.

G. J. TOOMER

APPELL, PAUL (-ÉMILE) (*b.* Strasbourg, France, 27 September 1855; *d.* Paris, France, 24 October 1930), *mathematics, mathematical physics.*

Appell's parents, Jean-Pierre Appell and Elizabeth

Müller, were Catholic Alsatians ardently loyal to revolutionary France. The family lived in a corner of the great Ritterhus, formerly a knightly lodge, where the master-dyer father and two sons by a previous marriage managed production while the mother, her sister, and a stepdaughter tended the store. Paul accepted the family ambition and patriotism but rejected Catholic piety. His character was forged by a forced move from the Ritterhus in 1866, his father's death in 1867, transfer from a religious school to the *lycée* at his own insistence in 1869, bitter experiences in the siege of Strasbourg in 1870, and a close relationship with the younger of his half brothers, Charles, who served in the Foreign Legion, fought as an irregular in 1870–1871, and in 1889 was sentenced to ten years' confinement for anti-German activities. When Appell went to Nancy in 1871 to prepare for the university and to assume French citizenship in 1872, he was carrying the hopes of his family, who remained behind in Strasbourg as German subjects.

Blessed with unbounded energy, this attractive outsider with an accent moved rapidly toward the inner circles of French mathematics. At Nancy, he and Henri Poincaré formed a friendship that lasted until the latter's death. In 1873 he entered the École Normale, from which he graduated first in the class of 1876, three months after earning his doctorate. From this time on, Appell maintained an amazing level of activity in teaching, research, editing, and public service. He typically held several teaching posts at the same time, including the chair of mechanics at the Sorbonne from 1885. He was elected to the Académie des Sciences in 1892. He served as dean of the Faculty of Science of the University of Paris from 1903 to 1920 and as rector from 1920 to 1925. In various government posts, including membership in the Conseil Supérieure d'Instruction Publique, he was an exponent of educational reform and initiator of numerous large-scale projects, including the Cité Universitaire.

In 1881 he married Amelie, daughter of the archaeologist Alexandre Bertrand, niece of the mathematicians Joseph Bertrand and Charles Hermité, and a cousin of Appell's classmate and friend Émile Picard. Their son became a deputy and undersecretary of state. Two of their three daughters married the academicians Émile Borel and J. E. Duclaux. The household included Paul's mother, who had joined him in 1877 and remained until her death in 1902. In his *Souvenirs* (p. 180) he described his life as "flowing tranquilly between teaching, mathematical work and vacations in Alsace" at the maternal home

in Klingenthal, but he found energy to support vigorously the movement for women's rights, to carry from Alsace his brother's reports destined for the French War Office, and to defend his fellow Alsatian Dreyfus and serve on an expert commission whose ruling played a key role in his final rehabilitation. During World War I he founded and led the Secours National, a semiofficial organization uniting all religious and political groups to aid civilian victims. He described the return of the tricolor to Alsace as the fulfillment of his "lifelong goal" and felt that Germany had been treated too easily. He served as secretary-general of the French Association for the League of Nations.

Appell's first paper (1876) was his thesis on projective geometry in the tradition of Chasles, but at the suggestion of his teachers he turned to algebraic functions, differential equations, and complex analysis. He generalized many classical results (e.g., the theories of elliptic and of hypergeometric functions) to the case of two or more variables. From the first his work was close to physical ideas. For example, in 1878 he noted the physical significance of the imaginary period of elliptic functions in the solution of the pendulum problem, and thus showed that double periodicity follows from physical considerations. In 1880 he wrote on a sequence of functions (now called the Appell polynomials) satisfying the condition that the derivative of the nth function is n times the previous one.

In 1885 Appell was awarded half the Bordin Prize for solving the problem of "cutting and filling" (*deblais et remblais*) originally posed by Monge: To move a given region into another of equal volume so as to minimize the integral of the element of volume times the distance between its old and new positions. In 1889 he won second place (after Poincaré) in a competition sponsored by King Oscar II of Sweden: To find an effective method of calculating the Fourier coefficients in the expansion of quadruply periodic functions of two complex variables.

The flow of papers continued, augmented by treatises, textbooks, and popularizations and seemingly unaffected by other responsibilities. Although Appell never lost his interest in "pure" analysis and geometry, his activity continued to shift toward mechanics, and in 1893 Volume I of the monumental *Traité de mécanique rationnelle* appeared. Volume V (1921) included the mathematics required for relativity, but the treatise is essentially an exposition of classical mechanics of the late nineteenth century. It contains many of Appell's contributions, including his equations of motion valid for both holonomic and nonholonomic systems, which have not displaced the classical Lagrangian system in spite of undoubted advantages.

It is difficult to do justice to Appell's work because it lacks central themes, seminal ideas, and dramatic results. In 1925 he wrote: "I always had little taste for developing general theories and preferred to study limited and precise questions that might open new paths" ("Notice," p. 162). Indeed, his scientific work consists of a series of brilliant solutions of particular problems, some of the greatest difficulty. He was a technician who used the classical methods of his time to answer open questions, work out details, and make natural extensions in the mainstream of the late nineteenth century; but his work did not open new doors, as he hoped. On the contrary, he does not seem to have looked down any of the new paths that were leading to a period of unbridled abstraction and generalization. During the last half of his career he was a pillar of a backward-looking establishment that was to give way to Nicolas Bourbaki, a namesake of a general who was one of his boyhood heroes.

BIBLIOGRAPHY

I. ORIGINAL WORKS. Appell's "Notice sur les travaux scientifiques," in *Acta mathematica,* **45** (1925), 161–285, describes 140 publications in analysis, 30 in geometry, and 87 in mechanics. The most notable are *Notice sur les travaux* (Paris, 1884, 1889, 1892), written to support his candidacy for the Académie; "Sur les intégrales des fonctions à multiplicateurs," in *Acta mathematica,* **13** (1890); *Traité de mécanique rationnelle,* 5 vols. (Paris, 1893–1921 and later eds.); *Théorie des fonctions algébriques et de leurs intégrales* (Paris, 1895, 1922), written with E. Goursat; and *Principes de la théorie des fonctions elliptiques et applications* (Paris, 1897), written with E. Lacour.

Not listed in the "Notice" are numerous elementary textbooks, popularizations, addresses and papers on history and education, and several later publications, including *Sur une forme générale des équations de la dynamique,* Mémorial des Sciences Mathématiques (Paris, 1925); *Sur les fonctions hypergéométriques de plusieurs variables, les polynomes d'Hermite et autres fonctions sphériques dans l'hyperspace, ibid.* (Paris, 1925); *Henri Poincaré* (Paris, 1925); *Fonctions hypergéométriques et hypersphériques. Polynomes d'Hermite* (Paris, 1926), written with M. J. Kampé de Feriet; *Le problème géométrique des deblais et remblais,* Mémorial des Sciences Mathématiques (Paris, 1928); *Sur la décomposition d'une fonction en éléments simples, ibid.* (Paris, 1929); and "Sur la constante d'Euler," in *Enseignement mathématique,* **29** (1930), 5–6, apparently his last paper, a follow-up to one on the same subject, *ibid.,* **26** (1927), 11–14, which had been welcomed by the editor with a note observing that "a great source of light is still burning."

II. SECONDARY LITERATURE. Appell's life and work are unusually well documented by his four *notices* mentioned above; his charming and revealing autobiography, *Souvenirs d'un alsacien 1858–1922* (Paris, 1923); and E. Lebon, *Biographie et bibliographie analytique des écrits de Paul Appell* (Paris, 1910), which gives many biographical details and seems to have been written with Appell's collaboration. Other biographical articles rely on these sources, but some of them contain personal recollections or other interesting information, notably *Cinquantenaire scientifique de Paul Appell* (Paris, 1927); "Centenaire de la naissance de Paul Appell," in *Annales de l'Université de Paris,* **26**, no. 1 (1956), 13–31; A. Buhl, in *Enseignement mathématique,* **26** (1927), 5–11; **30** (1931), 5–21; **33** (1934), 229–231; T. Levi-Civita, in *Rendiconti Accademia dei Lincei,* 6th ser., **13** (1931), 241–242; and Raymond Poincaré, in *Annales de l'Université de Paris,* **5** (1930), 463–477.

KENNETH O. MAY

APPLETON, EDWARD VICTOR (*b.* Bradford, Yorkshire, England, 6 September 1892; *d.* Edinburgh, Scotland, 21 April 1965), *radio physics.*

Appleton showed exceptional promise as a boy, matriculating at the University of London at sixteen and winning a scholarship to St. John's College, Cambridge, at eighteen. He graduated with first class honours in physics in 1913 and started postgraduate work in crystallography under William Henry Bragg. Shortly after the outbreak of World War I he became a signals officer in the Royal Engineers, an assignment that aroused his interest in radio.

Upon his return to Cambridge after the war, Appleton first investigated vacuum tubes at the Cavendish Laboratory with Balthazar van der Pol, Jr., and later wrote a monograph on the subject, *Thermionic Vacuum Tubes* (1932). He next turned to the study of the fading of radio signals. In 1924, when he was only thirty-two, he became Wheatstone professor of physics at King's College of the University of London, where he remained for twelve years. During the first year, he and Miles Barnett, a graduate student from New Zealand, performed a crucial experiment that led to a measurement of the height of the reflecting atmospheric layer of ionized gases, which had been postulated by Oliver Heaviside and A. E. Kennelly in explanation of the first transatlantic radio transmission by Guglielmo Marconi in 1901. In the experiment, the frequency of the new British Broadcasting Company transmitter at Bournemouth was periodically varied after broadcasting hours at a constant rate, so that the interference between the direct (ground) and reflected (sky) waves resulted in a regular fading in and out at a site about 100 kilometers away, in a manner analogous to the behavior of optical interference fringes.

Appleton's experimental proof that the Kennelly-Heaviside, or *E*, layer really existed, a scientific accomplishment of the highest order, was honored by his election as fellow of the Royal Society (1927), a knighthood (1941), and the Nobel Prize in physics (1947), "for his investigation of the physics of the upper atmosphere, especially for the discovery of the so-called Appleton layers." The last refers to the later discoveries of a second (*F*) layer at more than twice the height of the *E* layer and a third (*D*) layer below the *E* layer. Besides discovering these layers, Appleton and his co-workers showed that the sky wave generally was elliptically polarized, and calculated the reflection coefficients and electron densities of the layers and their diurnal and seasonal variations. His work may also be considered to be of prime technological significance, not only in regard to radio transmission but also as a milestone in the development of radar; the determination of the height of the *E* layer was the first distance measurement made by radio, a technique that was closely followed by Robert Alexander Watson-Watt, the British radar pioneer, who had collaborated with Appleton in atmospheric research and had many subsequent professional contacts with him. The rest of Appleton's life was spent in research flowing from his own discoveries, an endeavor in which he continued to maintain a degree of involvement that was astonishing in view of the many other duties thrust upon him.

Following a three-year tenure as Jacksonian professor of natural philosophy at the University of Cambridge, Appleton was appointed secretary of the government's Department of Scientific and Industrial Research. In 1949 he was made principal and vice-chancellor of the University of Edinburgh, where he remained until his death. Appleton was a great international figure: his first paper on the ionosphere was published in a Dutch journal (in Dutch); he served as vice-president of the (U.S.) Institute of Radio Engineers in 1932; he was president of the International Scientific Radio Union (URSI) from 1934 to 1952; and he was instrumental in organizing the first International Geophysical Year in 1957, a year of maximum sunspot activity. After moving to Edinburgh, he founded the *Journal of Atmospheric Research* (affectionately known as "Appleton's Journal") and served as its editor-in-chief for the rest of his life.

Appleton married Jessie Longson in 1915; they had two daughters, Marjery and Rosalind. A month before his death, Appleton, a widower since 1964, married Mrs. Helen F. Allison, who had been his private secretary for thirteen years.

BIBLIOGRAPHY

A list of Appleton's honors, decorations, medals, and the most important papers he wrote and collaborated in (a total of 140) appears in the obituary by his long-time associate, J. A. Ratcliffe, in *Biographical Memoirs of Fellows of the Royal Society,* **12** (1966), 1–21. See also obituaries in *The Times* (London), 23 April 1965; and in *Science and Culture,* **31** (1965), 348–350.

CHARLES SÜSSKIND

AQUINAS, SAINT THOMAS (*b.* Roccasecca, near Monte Cassino, Italy, *ca.* 1225; *d.* Fossanuova, near Maenza, Italy, 7 March 1274), *not a scientist in the modern sense, but a philosopher and theologian whose synthesis of Christian revelation with Aristotelian science has influenced all areas of knowledge—including modern science, especially in its early development.*

Thomas, the youngest of nine children, was born in the castle of the Aquino family. His father, Landolfo, and his older brothers served the Holy Roman Emperor, Frederick II, then warring against the papacy; his mother, Teodora of Chieti, was a Lombard. The family's political situation was precarious, and in 1231 Thomas was placed in the abbey of Monte Cassino for his elementary education. When the abbey was occupied by Frederick's troops in 1239, Thomas was sent to finish his studies at the recently founded University of Naples; his teachers there were Master Martin in grammar and logic and Peter of Ireland in natural science.

Thomas entered the Dominican order at Naples in 1244, against his family's wishes, and was sent to Paris, and then to Cologne, for further studies (1245–1252). The Dominicans at the time were in the forefront of intellectual life; in natural science, groups of friars were synthesizing the heritage of Greece and Rome, which soon appeared in the encyclopedias of Thomas of Cantimpré and Vincent of Beauvais. Albertus Magnus, earlier recruited into the order by Jordan of Saxony, was himself paraphrasing in Latin all of the works of Aristotle that had just been brought to the West, thus rendering them intelligible to the younger friars. Studying under Albert, possibly at Paris and certainly at Cologne (1248–1252), Thomas was soon abreast of the most advanced scholarship of his time, including the major Greek, Arab, and Latin sources that were to revivify the intellectual life of the Middle Ages.

Sent to Paris "to read the *Sentences*" at the priory of Saint-Jacques in 1252, Thomas quickly demonstrated his proficiency as a theologian. There was, however, growing jealousy and antipathy toward the friars (both Dominican and Franciscan) among the secular masters at the University of Paris, and in 1256 the intervention of Pope Alexander IV was required before Thomas and the Franciscan Bonaventure were accepted as masters at the university. During or before this, his first Paris professorship (1256–1259), Thomas composed his commentary on the *Sentences,* some smaller treatises—including the highly original *De ente et essentia* ("On Being and Essence")—and the disputed question *On Truth;* he also began work on the *Summa contra gentiles,* of special importance for its evaluation of Arab thought.

From 1259 to 1268 he was back in Italy, first at Anagni and at Orvieto, where he was associated with the papal courts of Alexander IV and Urban IV, respectively; then at Rome (1265–1267), where he taught at the Dominican priory of Santa Sabina and began his famous *Summa theologiae;* and finally at Viterbo, where he served at the court of Clement IV.

Then, in 1268 or 1269, possibly because of disputes at the University of Paris over the Aristotelianism which he and Albert had introduced, Thomas returned to Paris for a somewhat unusual second professorship (1269–1272). Here he combated both the traditional Augustinian orthodoxy being fostered by such Franciscans as Bonaventure and John Peckham and the heterodox Aristotelianism of Siger of Brabant and his associates, who are usually referred to as Latin Averroists. One of the key issues in the dispute was Thomas' teaching that the world's creation in time cannot be demonstrated by reason alone, since there is no philosophical repugnance in a created universe's having existed from eternity—a thesis with important ramifications for later medieval concepts of infinity.

The condemnation, in 1270, of certain Averroist theses by Étienne Tempier, bishop of Paris, is regarded by some scholars as directed, at least implicitly, against Aquinas' teaching. Of the later condemnation, in 1277, there can be no doubt that two propositions concern matters taught by Thomas, including his thesis on the unicity of the substantial form in man, which bears on the problem of the presence of elements in compounds. Such controversies drew a series of polemical treatises from Aquinas' pen, including *De aeternitate mundi contra murmurantes* ("On the Eternity of the Universe, Against the 'Murmurers'" [i.e., the traditionalist Augustinians]) and *De unitate intellectus contra Averroistas* ("On the Unity of the Intellect, Against the Averroists"). The intellectual ferment also stimulated him to further efforts at philosophical and theological synthesis. During these years he elaborated most of his detailed commentaries on Aristotle and worked steadily on the *Summa theologiae.*

After his second Paris professorship was concluded in 1272, Thomas returned to Italy, this time to Naples,

to erect a Dominican *studium* near the university there. He lectured, directed disputations, and continued writing; but the pace of his work slowed noticeably, partly because of failing health. He suspended all writing activity late in 1273 and died a few months later, while en route to the second Council of Lyons. He was canonized on 18 July 1323 and subsequently was approved by the Roman Catholic Church as its most representative teacher.

Today the name of Thomas is so associated with Catholic orthodoxy that one tends to forget that he was an innovator. In an atmosphere dominated by faith, especially at the University of Paris, he took the leadership in championing the cause of reason. Almost single-handedly he turned the theologians of that university to a study of the pagan Aristotle, to the use of what was then a rigorous scientific method, learned from investigating the world of nature, for probing the mysteries of revelation. Opposing the popular teaching that all knowledge comes by divine illumination, he allowed that man, by sense observation and through the use of unaided reason, could arrive at truth and certitude.

It would be a mistake, of course, to urge that Aquinas' main concern was with the physical universe. Rather, he was preoccupied with questions about God, the angels, and man; first and foremost he was a metaphysician and a theologian. Yet there can be no doubt that, like Aristotle, his approach to metaphysical problems was through the physical sciences. Like St. Paul, he firmly believed that the invisible things of God are seen through his visible creation, provided it is rightly understood (Romans 1:20). So convinced of this was he that in his later life he turned from his unfinished *Summa theologiae* to comment on all the physical works of Aristotle. He probably completed his exposition of *De caelo et mundo,* one of his best works as a commentator, at Naples (1272–1273) and ceased commenting on *De generatione et corruptione* and the *Meteorologica* only shortly before his death.

Furthermore, for a man not usually recognized as a scientist, he made noteworthy contributions to medieval science. These can best be indicated by summarizing his more significant teachings relating to the medieval counterparts of physics, astronomy, chemistry, and the life sciences.

In the high scholastic period, foundations were laid for later medieval discussions that adumbrated the distinction in modern mechanics between kinematics and dynamics. The kinematical content of Thomas' teaching is meager, although he did hold that velocity is a mode of continuous quantity and thus is capable of intensification in the same manner as qualities, thereby allowing for the type of comparison between qualitative change and local motion later made by Nicole Oresme.

In dynamics, he inaugurated some new directions in the study of causality affecting gravitational and projectile motions. Aquinas would probably look askance at the tendency of present-day historians of science to identify Aristotle's motive powers and resistances with forces and to represent Aristotle's teaching with precise dynamical equations. His own exegesis of the relevant Aristotelian texts, as opposed to that of Averroës and Avempace, discounts any demonstrative intent on Aristotle's part and interprets his statements as dialectical efforts to confute his atomist opponents.

Thus, on the disputed question whether motion through a vacuum would take place instantaneously, Thomas did not follow Aristotle literally. He insisted that if, by an impossibility, a vacuum were to exist, motion through it would still take time—that the temporal character of the motion does not arise uniquely from external resistance but, rather, from the proportion of the mover to the moved (which prevents the movements of the heavens from being instantaneous, although they are not impeded by resistance) and also from the continuity of the distance being traversed. The latter reason, particularly, provoked speculation among fourteenth-century thinkers; some, such as Oresme, saw no necessary connection between spatial continuity and velocity limitation and were led on this account to seek some type of resistance internal to the moving body—thereby foreshadowing the modern concept of inertia.

Thomas' analysis of gravitation is basically Aristotelian, yet it differs in significant respects from that of other commentators. Like all medieval thinkers, he regarded gravitation as the natural motion of a heavy body to its proper place. For Thomas, however, nature was a relational concept, and thus he disagreed with those who defined it as a *vis insita* or as something absolute; it is a principle of motion, either actively or passively, depending on the particular motion that results.

Aquinas held that the body's gravity is the proximate cause of its falling, but only in the manner of a "passive principle." He rejected Averroës' teaching that the medium through which the body falls plays an essential role in its motion and that there is an active source of such motion within the body, whether this be its gravity or its substantial form. In this respect, Aquinas was also at variance with the later teaching of Walter Burley and the Paris terminists, all of whom saw the cause of falling as some type of active force within the body itself, thereby fore-

shadowing animist theories of gravitation such as subsequently proposed by William Gilbert. Again, Thomas disagreed with Bonaventure and Roger Bacon, who regarded place as exerting some type of repulsive or attractive influence on the falling body; for Thomas, there was no repulsion involved, and the attractive aspect of place was sufficiently accounted for by its being the end, or final cause, of the body's movement. Here Thomas implicitly rejected the absolute space and attractive forces later proposed by the Newtonians; his own analysis, it has been remarked, shows more affinity with the ideas behind Einstein's theory of general relativity, although the two are so remote in thought context as to defy any attempt at detailed comparison.

On the subject of *impetus,* authors are divided as to Thomas' teaching. Certainly he has no treatment of the concept to match that found later in Franciscus de Marcia, Jean Buridan, and Oresme, nor does he use it to explain any details of projectile or gravitational motion. In his later writings, particularly the commentaries on the *Physics* and the *De caelo,* Thomas clearly defends the original Aristotelian teaching on the proximate cause of projectile motion. In some earlier writings, on the other hand, he speaks of a *virtus* in the projectile, and, in one text of the *Physics* commentary, discussing the case of a ball that bounces back from a wall, he mentions that the *impetus* is given not by the wall but by the thrower. Later Thomists, such as Joannes Capreolus and Domingo de Soto, had no difficulty in assimilating a fully developed *impetus* theory to Thomas' teaching, evidently regarding the Aristotelian element in his expositions as reflecting his role as a commentator more than his personal views.

Aquinas took up the problems of the magnet, of tidal variations, and of other "occult" phenomena in a letter entitled *De occultis operationibus naturae* ("On the Occult Workings of Nature"), whose very title shows his preoccupation with reducing all of these phenomena to natural, as opposed to supramundane, causes. Significantly, Thomas' analysis of magnetism was known to Gilbert and was praised by him.

Commenting as he did on the *De caelo* and also, in his theological writings, on the cosmogony detailed in Genesis, Thomas could not help but evaluate the astronomical theories of his contemporaries. He contributed nothing new by way of observational data, nor did he evolve any new theories of the heavens, but his work has an importance nonetheless, if only to show the care with which he assessed the current state of astronomical science. His view of the structure of the universe was basically Aristotelian; he knew of two theories to account for the phenomena of the heavens, both geocentric in the broad sense: that of Eudoxus, Callippus, and Aristotle, and that of Ptolemy. Aquinas generally employed the Eudoxian terminology; he mentions the Ptolemaic system at least eleven times, and five of these are in his late commentary on the *De caelo.* In most of his references to the Eudoxian or Ptolemaic systems, he refrains from expressing any preference; clearly, he was aware of the hypothetical character of both. At least once, commenting on Ptolemy's cumbersome theory of eccentrics and epicycles, he voices the expectation that this theory will one day be superseded by a simpler explanation.

The astronomical data reported by Aquinas, according to an extensive analysis by Thomas Litt, were those of a well-informed thirteenth-century writer; he errs in one or two particulars, but on matters of little theoretical consequence. His treatise on comets, included in a work by Lynn Thorndike, is one of the most balanced in the high Middle Ages, rejecting fanciful explanations and pointing out how little is actually known about these occurrences.

In his more philosophical views, however, Thomas was not so fortunate. He believed in the existence of spheres that transport the heavenly bodies and, with his contemporaries, regarded such bodies as incorruptible. He was convinced also of the existence of an empyrean heaven, the dwelling place of the blessed and known only through revelation, but nonetheless included in the corporeal universe. He accorded an extensive causality to the heavenly bodies, while excepting from this all actions that are properly human (i.e., that arise from man's intelligence and deliberate will) and completely fortuitous events, so as to discourage any naïve credence in the astrologers of his day.

Aquinas has no treatment of alchemy to match that of his teacher Albertus Magnus, but he does discuss one topic that had important bearing on later views of the structure of matter, that of the presence of elements in compounds. Earlier thinkers, attempting to puzzle out Aristotle's cryptic texts, favored one of two explanations of elemental presence offered by Avicenna and Averroës, respectively. Dissatisfied with both, Aquinas formulated a third position, which soon became the most popular among the Schoolmen. He taught that the elements do not remain actually in the compound, but that their qualities give rise to "intermediate qualities" that participate somewhat in each extreme; these intermediate qualities are in turn proper dispositions for a new substantial form, that of the compound, which is generated through the alteration that takes place. Since the elemental qualities remain "in some way" in the compound, one can say also that the substantial forms of the elements are present there, too—not actually, but virtually.

The subsequent influence of Thomas' teaching has been traced in considerable detail by Anneliese Maier, who characterizes it as inaugurating a modern direction that dominated treatments of the problem in later Scholasticism (*Studien* III, pp. 89–140). Duns Scotus and his school, particularly, became enamored of the theory and attempted a consistent development of its ramifications. Nominalists such as William of Ockham and Gregory of Rimini took it up, too, as did such Paris terminists as Buridan, Oresme, Albert of Saxony, and Marsilius of Inghen. The basic explanation continued to be taught through the sixteenth century and, coupled with Aristotelian teaching on *minima naturalia,* became the major alternative to a simplistic atomist view of the structure of matter before the advent of modern chemistry.

In biology and psychology, Aquinas followed Aristotle, Galen, and the medieval Arab tradition; his work is noteworthy more for its philosophical consistency than for its scientific detail. He wrote commentaries on Aristotle's *De anima, De sensu et sensato,* and *De memoria et reminiscentia,* all based on the texts of William of Moerbeke, his fellow Dominican. Also, *ca.* 1270, he composed a letter to a Master Philippus, who seems to have been a physician and professor at Bologna and Naples, on the motion of the heart (*De motu cordis*), explaining how the principle "Whatever is moved, is moved by another" is saved in this phenomenon. Like his contemporaries, he believed in spontaneous generation and countenanced a qualified type of evolution in the initial formation of creatures. Catholic thinkers, on the basis of his philosophy, have been more open to evolutionary theories than have fundamentalists, who follow a strict, literal interpretation of the text of Genesis.

Thomas was a mild man, objective and impersonal in his writing, more cautious than most in giving credence to reported facts. He showed neither the irascible temperament of Roger Bacon, nor the subtle questioning of Duns Scotus, nor the pious mysticism of Bonaventure. Calm and methodical in his approach, proceeding logically, step by step, he offered proof where it could be adduced, appealing to experience, observation, analysis, and (last of all) authority. He appreciated the importance of textual criticism, and possibly was one of the instigators of Moerbeke's many Latin translations of scientific treatises from the original Greek. He had a penetrating intellect and a strong religious faith, both of which led him to seek a complete integration of all knowledge, divine as well as human. Working with the science of his time, he succeeded admirably in this attempt, thus providing a striking example for all who were to be similarly motivated in the ages to come.

BIBLIOGRAPHY

I. ORIGINAL WORKS. Standard editions of Aquinas are the Leonine edition, *S. Thomae Aquinatis opera omnia, iussu Leonis XIII edita* (Rome, 1882–　), a critical edition still in process (American section of the Leonine Commission at Yale University, New Haven, Conn.); Parma edition, *S. Thomae opera omnia,* 25 vols. (Parma, 1852–1873; photographically reproduced, New York, 1948–1949); Vivès edition, *D. Thomae Aquinatis opera omnia,* S. E. Fretté and P. Maré, eds., 32 vols. (Paris, 1871–1880).

English translations of major works include *Summa theologiae,* trans. and commentary, T. Gilby et al., eds., 60 vols. planned (New York-London, 1964–　); *Summa theologiae,* English Dominicans trans., 22 vols., 2nd ed. (New York-London, 1912–1936); *Summa contra gentiles (On the Truth of the Catholic Faith),* A. C. Pegis et al., trans., 5 vols. (New York, 1955–1956); *De veritate (Truth),* R. W. Mulligan et al., trans., 3 vols. (Chicago, 1952–1954).

English translations of scientific writings include *Commentary on Aristotle's Physics,* R. J. Blackwell et al., trans. (New Haven, Conn., 1963); *Exposition of Aristotle's Treatise On the Heavens,* R. F. Larcher and P. H. Conway, trans. (Columbus, Ohio, 1963–1964), mimeographed, available from College of St. Mary of the Springs, Columbus; *Exposition of Aristotle's Treatise On Generation and Corruption,* Bk. I, chs. 1–5, R. F. Larcher and P. H. Conway, trans. (Columbus, Ohio, 1964)—as above; *Exposition of Aristotle's Treatise On Meteorology,* Bks. I–II, chs. 1–5, R. F. Larcher and P. H. Conway, trans. (Columbus, Ohio, 1964)—as above. Excerpt on comets in Lynn Thorndike, *Latin Treatises on Comets Between 1238 and 1368 A.D.* (Chicago, 1950), pp. 77–86. *Aristotle's De Anima With the Commentary of St. Thomas Aquinas,* K. Foster and S. Humphries, trans. (New Haven, Conn., 1951); *Exposition of the Posterior Analytics of Aristotle,* P. Conway, trans. (Quebec, 1956)—mimeographed, available from La Librairie Philosophique M. Doyon, Quebec, Canada; *The Letter of St. Thomas Aquinas De Occultis Operibus Naturae,* with a commentary, J. B. McAllister, trans., The Catholic University of America Philosophical Studies, **42** (Washington, D. C., 1939).

II. SECONDARY LITERATURE. General works on Aquinas include V. J. Bourke, *Aquinas's Search for Wisdom* (Milwaukee, 1965), an excellent biography; M. D. Chenu, *Toward Understanding St. Thomas,* A. M. Landry and D. Hughes, trans. (Chicago, 1964), a good introduction to Thomas' intellectual milieu; K. Foster, ed. and trans., *The Life of Saint Thomas Aquinas: Biographical Documents* (Baltimore, 1959); W. A. Wallace and J. A. Weisheipl, "Thomas Aquinas, St.," in *The New Catholic Encyclopedia* (New York, 1967), a compendious survey of his life and works.

Aquinas' scientific work is discussed in Thomas Litt, *Les corps célestes dans l'univers de saint Thomas d'Aquin,* Phi-losophes Médiévaux, VII (Louvain-Paris, 1963), the best on Thomas' astronomy; Anneliese Maier, *Studien zur Naturphilosophie der Spätscholastik,* I, *Die Vorläufer Galileis im 14. Jahrhundert,* Edizioni di storia e letteratura, **22** (Rome, 1949); II, *Zwei Grundprobleme der scholastischen Naturphilosophie,* Edizioni . . ., **37** (Rome, 1951); III, *An der Grenze von Scholastik und Naturwissenschaft,* Edizioni . . ., **41** (Rome, 1952); IV, *Metaphysische Hintergründe der spätscholastischen Naturphilosophie,* Edizioni . . ., **52** (Rome, 1955); V. *Zwischen Philosophie und Mechanik,* Edizioni . . ., **69** (Rome, 1958). These are the most complete sources; consult the index of each volume under "Thomas von Aquin." Some of this material is summarized in English in E. J. Dijksterhuis, *The Mechanization of the World Picture,* C. Dikshoorn, trans. (Oxford, 1961); W. A. Wallace, ed. and trans., *Cosmogony,* Vol. X of Aquinas' *Summa theologiae* (New York-London, 1967), with notes and appendices on Thomas' science and its background.

WILLIAM A. WALLACE, O. P.

ARAGO, DOMINIQUE FRANÇOIS JEAN (*b.* Estagel, France, 26 February 1786; *d.* Paris, France, 2 October 1853), *physics, astronomy.*

Arago was the eldest son of Marie Roig and François Bonaventure Arago, a modest landowner of Catalonian origin who became mayor of Estagel in 1789. The family moved to Perpignan in 1795, when Arago's father was named cashier at the mint. There Arago completed the usual classical education and set his sights on a military career in the artillery. He prepared for admission to the École Polytechnique by mastering the works of Euler, Lagrange, and Laplace, and passed the entrance examination with great distinction in 1803. After two years at the head of his class, he was named secretary of the Bureau des Longitudes and sent to Spain with Biot on a geodetic expedition. After being held prisoner in Spain and Algeria, he returned in June 1809 to France, where he was welcomed into the Société d'Arcueil. He was elected to the Institut de France as an astronomer on 18 September 1809 and in that year also succeeded Monge as professor of descriptive geometry at the École Polytechnique, where he taught a variety of subjects until his resignation in 1830. At the request of the Bureau des Longitudes, which placed the Paris Observatory under his direction, Arago also taught astronomy to the general public at the observatory from 1813 to 1846. He was the main contributor to the *Annuaire du Bureau des Longitudes* for more than forty years and coeditor, with Gay-Lussac, of the *Annales de chimie et physique* from 1816 to 1840. He was a member of most of the important scientific societies, receiving the Royal Society's Copley Medal in 1825 and being elected perpetual secretary of the

Académie des Sciences, replacing Fourier, on 7 June 1830.

Arago was at once volatile and warm-hearted in his personal relations. He either forged strong bonds with fellow scientists or engaged in sharp polemics that often were provoked by priority controversies. Among his closest friends were Alexander von Humboldt, with whom he shared a room in Paris from 1809 to 1811, Gay-Lussac, and Malus; and among his relatives, the physicist Alexis Petit and the astronomer Claude L. Mathieu. He had a stormy relationship with Biot, Thomas Young, and Brewster, but it did not blind him to their scientific merits. In both his writings and his public appearances, Arago conveyed a contagious sense of excitement that won him a large following. His personal style, which spilled over into his work habits, was that of a romantic—restless, inquisitive, volatile, and constantly bubbling with enthusiasm and optimism. Married in 1811, Arago had three sons and lived in an apartment at the observatory. In his later years he gradually lost his eyesight, went blind, and was reduced to dictating to his students.

Arago's most important original work in science was carried out before 1830, for his younger brothers, particularly Étienne, drew him into politics following the July Revolution of 1830. He was repeatedly elected deputy for his native department (Pyrénées-Orientales) and for Paris between 1830 and 1852, and sat on the left in the Chamber of Deputies, delivering influential speeches on educational reform, freedom of the press, and the application of scientific knowledge to technological progress, particularly concerning canals, steam engines, railroads, the electric telegraph, and photography. He also was twice named president of the Paris Municipal Council. The peak of Arago's political career came after the February Revolution of 1848, when he was made a member of the provisional government and was named, successively, minister of the navy and the army and president of the Executive Committee. As minister he signed decrees outlawing corporal punishment and improving the rations of sailors on the high seas, and abolishing slavery in the French colonies. His politics were those of a constitutional liberal, passionately concerned with social reform (he helped found La réforme in 1843), freedom of association, and education of the lower classes. He was, however, violently opposed to mob rule and to the socialistic programs espoused by Louis Blanqui, Alexandre Ledru-Rollin, and Louis Blanc. Arago's effective political career ended following his loss of control over the revolutionaries during the June days of 1848.

Arago's scientific life was dominated by a persistent interest in physical phenomena related to electricity, magnetism, and, above all, to light. His earliest investigations with Biot in 1805 and 1806 continued the work of Borda on the factors affecting the refraction of light passing through the atmosphere of the earth. They helped to verify the formulas given in Laplace's *Mécanique céleste,* which were based on the assumption that the atmosphere is composed of concentric rings of a mixture of oxygen and nitrogen, with density as a function of altitude. Biot and Arago showed experimentally that temperature and pressure were significant variables, whereas humidity and the traces of carbon dioxide in the atmosphere could be disregarded. But when Arago extended his investigations to refraction in liquids and solids—with Petit in 1813 and Fresnel in 1815—he recognized the failure of the current theory of emission and particulate attraction to account for the empirical formulas he derived. After his return from the geodetic expedition to extend meridian triangulations from Barcelona to the Balearic Islands, Arago became a vocal critic of the Newtonian emission theory and, by 1816, an ardent supporter of the undulatory theory.

The original source of Arago's interest was Thomas Young's classic paper of 1801 on the color of thin glass plates and the discovery of polarization by Malus in 1808. Arago continued their independent investigations by passing beams of polarized light through a variety of gaseous and crystalline substances at various degrees of incidence to study the light's properties. His results, which suggested the usefulness of the undulatory theory, included the discovery of chromatic polarization by the use of thin mica plates (1811), rediscovered independently by Brewster; the elaboration of the conditions necessary to produce Newton's rings (1811); and the observation of special cases of rotary polarization (1812), which were shortly thereafter made a general law of optics by Biot.

It was this series of disparate experiments that caused Fresnel to write to Arago in 1815 to announce his theory of stellar aberration and the explanation of diffraction phenomena by undulatory principles. Although Fresnel's "discoveries" had retraced the work of Bradley and Thomas Young, Arago urged him to pursue his investigations and agreed to collaborate with the young engineer. Together they published a series of papers advocating the undulatory theory of light, answering one by one the criticisms of the partisans of emission theory, especially Arago's colleagues and former friends, Laplace and Biot. In this collaborative enterprise Fresnel supplied the crucial mathematical analyses and the seminal concept of transverse waves, while Arago contributed his encyclopedic command of the current literature in optics, his critical powers, and a significant number of experimental insights and actual experiments.

Above all, Arago functioned as a catalytic agent and public defender of the new theory, and eventually as its major historian. In 1824 he wrote an important article on polarization, translated by Young for the *Encyclopaedia Britannica,* and later wrote detailed and moving biographical notices of Fresnel (1830), Young (1832), and Malus (1853), sprinkled with personal anecdotes of great significance. It was Arago who, in 1838, borrowing and amplifying the idea and apparatus from Wheatstone's experiments for measuring the speed of electricity, suggested the "crucial experiment" to decide between the corpuscular and undulatory theories of light by comparing the speed of light in water and in air. The experiment, which vindicated the undulatory position, was carried out by Foucault in 1850 and announced to the Academy in Arago's presence.

Arago was also concerned with optical instruments that proved useful for a variety of purposes, in physics and meteorology as well as in astronomy, for which they were mainly devised. In 1811 he invented the polariscope to determine the degree of polarization of light rays by passing them successively through a mica or rock-crystal polarizer and an Iceland spar analyzer. With the addition of a series of properly graduated plates that could be inclined at will with reference to the incident ray, Arago transformed his polariscope into a polarimeter, which he used to verify one of the few mathematically expressed laws he discovered: the cosine-squared law for calculating the intensity of the ordinary ray in double refraction. In 1833 he derived from it the ratio of the amount of polarized light to neutral light: $\cos 2i$ for the ordinary ray and $2 \sin^2 i$ for the extraordinary ray, where i is the angle between the rock-crystal polarizer and the plane of polarization of the incident ray. With the polarimeter, he was able to differentiate between light emanating from solid and liquid surfaces, polarized by reflection and from incandescent gases, and to determine that the edge of the sun is gaseous. The polarimeter also suggested to him ways to determine polarization of the corona during total eclipses, to determine that rays from the sun's halo are refracted but not reflected, to observe the nature of a comet's tail, and to calculate the height of isolated clouds.

In 1815 Arago built a primitive cyanometer to measure the degree of blueness of the atmosphere, which was later adapted for use in hydrographical determinations of the depth of the sea. In 1833 he proposed a photometer to measure comparative intensities of stellar light; his student Paul Ernest Laugier later employed it. He also perfected an ocular micrometer for measuring small angles, which was erroneously attributed to William Pearson. The workings of all these instruments, based upon polarization phenomena, were expounded with great clarity and enthusiasm in Arago's public lectures at the observatory, published posthumously as *Astronomie populaire.*

As a young astronomer and member of the Bureau des Longitudes, Arago made numerous observations and important theoretical proposals. Among them were the explanation of the scintillation of stars by the use of interference phenomena and the realization of the asymmetry of the layers of atmosphere with reference to the observer. In his later years he made some important remarks on solar appendages noticed during the 1842 eclipse, which he observed with Laugier and Mauvais. But it was even more by the stimulus he gave younger astronomers—including Paul Laugier, Félix Mauvais, Jean Goujon, Jules Jamin, Hervé Faye, and Charles Mathieu—that Arago made his reputation as an astronomer. It also was Arago who urged Leverrier, his successor as director of the observatory, to take up Bouvard's work on the tables of Uranus. These investigations eventually led to the prediction of the existence and position of Neptune. Arago was also attentive to instrument makers, being responsible for promoting the precision work of Henri Gambey and Louis Bréguet. He was proud that during his tenure at the observatory most of its late eighteenth-century, English-made instruments were gradually replaced by better, French apparatus.

In 1820 Arago interrupted his optical work to play a significant role in the elaboration of electrodynamic and electromagnetic theories. Invited to the La Rive laboratory in Geneva to witness the verification of Oersted's experiments linking electricity to magnetism, he immediately acquired a passionate interest in the subject, displaying what Humboldt characterized as "the intolerance of a new convert." Arago repeated the Geneva experiments at the Paris Academy on 11 September 1820, thereby inspiring Ampère to elaborate his electrodynamic theory of electricity and magnetism. Although the two scientists did not write joint papers, they were in constant and friendly communication, often working in each other's laboratories. Just as Arago had been the champion of Fresnel's theories in 1815, so now did he propagandize Ampère's new theory and vehemently support his novel views. Because of his loyalty to Ampère, Arago was never fully able to appreciate or accept the rival theory of Faraday.

Arago also made several important contributions to electromagnetism on his own. On 20 September 1820 he announced the discovery of the temporary magnetization of soft iron by an electric current, which suggested to Ampère a theory about the nature of magnetic "currents" and provided the technological key to the electric telegraph. Ampère calculated that the magnetic power could be multiplied by twisting the current-carrying wire into a helix, and with Arago he carried out the first experiments on primitive solenoids. In his historical articles Arago was always careful to credit Ampère with the major share of this discovery, which ultimately depended upon Ampère's mathematical theory. In 1822, while he and Humboldt were measuring the magnetic intensity of a hill at Greenwich, Arago casually noticed the dampening effect that metallic substances had on the oscillations of the compass needle. After a delay of several years, during which he worked on the speed of sound and the crystalline nature of ice, and wrote up his observations on the chemical and thermal effects of light, Arago recognized the importance of his original observation at Greenwich. He announced that the rotation of nonmagnetic metallic substances (especially copper) created a magnetic effect on a magnetized needle. Known as Arago's "disc" or "wheel," it was the discovery of this effect that won him the Copley Medal in 1825. John Herschel and Babbage attempted to explain the phenomenon on the basis of Ampère's theory, but it was Faraday who in 1831 explained it by his theory of induction. By this time Arago had abandoned electrical research and had turned to other, more eclectic concerns.

In 1824 Arago was a member of an academic commission to study steam pressure, with the aim of reducing the dangers of explosion in steam engines. He and Dulong prepared elaborate apparatus for measuring pressure under high temperatures, verifying Boyle's law for values up to 24 atmospheres. Through his long-standing friendship with Humboldt, Arago was led to write popular articles on meteorology and physical geography, which ranged from discussions of the temperature of the earth, the seas, and the atmosphere to earthquakes and magnetic variations on the earth. He was particularly influential in propagating Humboldt's concept of isothermal lines and in setting down the purposes of and data required from scientific expeditions. In 1839 Arago took a personal interest in announcing and popularizing the inventions of Niepce and Daguerre, who were awarded government pensions as a result of Arago's recognition of their inventions' potential significance.

In his last years, while his sight was failing him,

Arago continued to discharge his duties as perpetual secretary of the Academy by summarizing the achievements of other scientists and by suggesting new experiments that he himself could not carry out. Surrounded by a group of devoted younger scientists who wrote, observed, and experimented for him, Arago never lost his mental energies and his ability to stimulate his colleagues and excite the public about the progress of science.

BIBLIOGRAPHY

I. ORIGINAL WORKS. Arago published no single scientific treatise of major significance during his lifetime. After the June days of 1848 he began arranging his papers in preparation for a complete edition. It was published posthumously as *Oeuvres de François Arago,* J. A. Barral, ed., 17 vols. (Paris, 1854–1862; 2nd ed., 1865), with an introduction by Humboldt. It contains most of his published articles (somewhat edited) and reports, the revised portions of his lectures (*Astronomie populaire*), and many previously unpublished notes. Missing is the *Recueil d'observations géodésiques, astronomiques et physiques en Espagne, en France, en Angleterre et en Écosse, pour déterminer la variation de la pesanteur et des degrés terrestres sur le prolongement du méridien de Paris* (Paris, 1821), written with Biot, and a number of reports prepared for the Academy, which are printed in the *Procès-verbaux des séances de l'Académie,* 10 vols. (Hendaye, 1910–1922), for the period until 1835 and unpublished in the archives of the Academy thereafter. Arago also collaborated with Bouvard, Mathieu, and Nicollet in preparing *Observations astronomiques, faites à l'Observatoire royal de Paris,* 2 vols. (Paris, 1825–1838). He annotated and edited Alexandre Bertrand, *Lettres sur les révolutions du globe* (5th ed., Paris, 1839); Jacques Étienne Victor Arago, *Souvenirs d'un aveugle,* 2 vols. (Paris, 1842–1843); and Condorcet, *Oeuvres,* 12 vols. (Paris, 1847–1849).

Of Arago's voluminous correspondence, only a small portion has been published: *Correspondance d'Alexandre de Humboldt avec François Arago (1809–1853),* E. T. Hamy, ed. (Paris, 1908). The library of the Paris Observatory has over 50 unpublished letters (B4 9–12) and most of his MS notes and observations related to astronomy (C6 8–11, E1 19, E3 4–13). An important correspondence with Thomas Young is at the British Museum (Add. MSS 34613) and at the Royal Society Library.

II. SECONDARY LITERATURE. The best biography is still Maurice Daumas, *Arago* (Paris, 1943), despite its meager scholarly apparatus. In addition to the works cited in Daumas's bibliographical essay, pp. 273–275, and in Horace Chauvet, *François Arago et son temps* (Perpignan, 1954), consult Maurice Crosland, *The Society of Arcueil* (London, 1967), *passim.*

ROGER HAHN

ARANZIO, GIULIO CESARE (*b.* Bologna, Italy, *ca.* 1529/1530; *d.* Bologna, 7 April 1589), *surgery, anatomy.*

Since Aranzio's parents, Ottaviano di Jacopo and Maria Maggi, were poor, he was aided in his medical education by his maternal uncle, Bartolomeo Maggi (1477–1552), lecturer in surgery at the University of Bologna and principal court physician of Julius III. He was a favorite pupil of this uncle, whom he loved and esteemed so highly that he assumed his surname, calling himself Giulio Cesare Aranzio Maggio. He studied at the University of Padua, where in 1548, at nineteen, he made his first anatomical discovery: the elevator muscle of the upper eyelid. He received his degree at Bologna on 20 May 1556, and shortly thereafter, at the age of twenty-seven, he became lecturer in medicine and surgery at the same university.

The excellent scientific and practical preparation Aranzio had received from his uncle immediately brought him fame. He discovered the *pedes hippocamp;* the cerebellum cistern; and the fourth ventricle, the arterial duct between the aorta and the pulmonary duct, which discovery was erroneously attributed to Leonardo Botallo.

In 1564 Aranzio published *De humano foetu opusculum,* and fifteen years later his *Observationes anatomicae* appeared. In these he presented the new direction of anatomy, based not merely on simple description of the organs of the body but also on experimental investigations of their functions.

Aranzio was the first lecturer at the University of Bologna to hold a separate professorship of anatomy; prior to him, instruction was given by lecturers in surgery. He himself began as a lecturer in surgery, but in 1570 he was able to have the two subjects separated so that each would have its own professorship. He held both professorships all his life, beloved and esteemed by his students.

Aranzio's *De tumoribus secundum locus affectum* (1571) is devoted to surgical subjects and gives a very good idea of the quality of his surgical lectures. He performed rhinoplastic surgery several years before Gaspare Tagliacozzi, but he wrote nothing on these operations. One of his pupils, Oczok Wojciech, who graduated from Bologna in 1569, did publish *Przymiot* (Cracow, 1581), a treatise on syphilis, however. In this treatise, in discussing the loss of the nose as the result of an attack of syphilis, he mentions rhinoplastic surgery and then states that in Bologna he frequently saw Aranzio perform such surgery successfully by using the "skin of the arm." It was Tagliacozzi, though, who gave the first scientific description of facial plastic surgery, illustrating the account with splendid charts.

BIBLIOGRAPHY

I. ORIGINAL WORKS. Aranzio's writings are *De humano foetu opusculum* (Rome, 1564; Venice, 1571; Basel, 1579); *De tumoribus secundum locus affectum* (Bologna, 1571); and *Observationes anatomicae* (Basel, 1579; Venice, 1587, 1595).

II. SECONDARY LITERATURE. Works on Aranzio are A. Malati Benedicenti, *Medici e farmacisti,* 2 vols. (Milan, 1947); T. G. Benedict, *Collectanea ad historiam rinoplastices Italorum* (Bratislava, 1843); *Biographie medicale: Dizionario delle scienze mediche* (Paris, 1820–1825); A. Castiglioni, "La scuola bolognese e la rinascita dell'anatomia," in *Annali Merck* (1931); U. Cesarano, "Giulio Cesare Aranzi," in *Comune di Bologna,* **1** (1929); E. Dall'Osso, "Giulio Cesare Aranzio e la rinoplastica," in *Annali di medicina navale e tropicale,* **61**, no. 5 (Sept.–Oct. 1956), and "Un contributo al pensiero scientifico di Giulio Cesare Aranzio: la sua opera chirurgica," *ibid.,* no. 6 (Nov.–Dec. 1956); O. Dezeimeris and Rainge-Delorme, *Dizionario storico della medicina antica e moderna* (Paris, 1828–1829); *Dizionario classico di medicina interna ed esterna* (Milan, 1838–1847); G. Fantuzzi, "Aranzio," in *Notizie degli scrittori bolognesi,* I (Bologna, 1790); A. Gallassi, "Chirurgia plastica. Ars medica per saecula," in *Collana di studi e ricerche* (Bologna, 1950–1951); G. Marini, *Degli archiatri pontifici* (Rome, 1784); G. Martinotti, *L'insegnamento dell'anatomia a Bologna prima del secolo XIX* (Bologna, 1910); G. M. Mazzucchelli, *Gli scrittori d'Italia* (Brescia, 1753); M. Medici, *Compendio storico della scuola anatomica di Bologna* (Bologna, 1857); L. Münster, "Un precursore bolognese della rinoplastica del '400," in *Atti del 1º Convegno Società Medica Italo-Svizzera* (Bologna, 1953); A. Pazzini, *Storia della medicina* (Milan, 1947), *Bio-bibliografia di storia della chirurgia* (Rome, 1948), and "Breve storia della rinoplastica," in *La chirurgia plastica,* **1**, no. 1; A. Sorbelli and L. Simeoni, *Storia dell'Università di Bologna* (Bologna, 1949); and J. P. Webster and M. Tesch Gnudi, *The Life and Times of M. Gaspare Tagliacozzi* (New York-Bologna, 1953).

EUGENIO DALL'OSSO

ARATUS OF SOLI (*b.* Soli, Cilicia, *ca.* 310 B.C.; *d.* *ca.* 240/239 B.C.), *astronomy.*

Although we possess four anonymous "lives" and a biography by Suidas, we are poorly informed about Aratus' life. The letters supposedly by him that are in the first life, edited by Westermann, are most probably spurious. Aratus went to Athens as a young man and there became acquainted with Stoicism. He then spent some time in Macedon at the court of Antigonus Gonatas (276–239 B.C.) and in Syria with Antiochus I. He is said to have prepared an edition of Homer's *Odyssey* and of the *Iliad.* Aratus was the author of several poems that are now lost: *Hymn to Pan,* celebrating the marriage of Antigonus Gonatas to Phile, half sister of Antiochus; *epideceia* addressed to his friends (and one to his brother); *Ostologia,* which seem to have been poems on medical subjects; and *Catalepton,* a collection of poems from which Strabo quotes two hexameters. Two of his epigrams are in *Anthologia Palatina* (XI, 437; XII, 129).

Aratus' only extant work is *Phaenomena,* a poem in 1,154 hexameters. After a prelude (lines 1–18) consisting of a hymn to Zeus, he describes the northern (19–320) and the southern (320–453) constellations. He refrains from giving an explanation of the planetary movements (454–461), apparently because of their complicated nature and the difficulty of calculating their conjunction (an allusion to the great year). Next (462–558) Aratus describes the circles of the celestial sphere and then (559–757) deals with the calendar: the hours of the risings and settings of stars (559–732), the days of the lunar month (733–739), the seasons (740–751), and the Metonic cycle (752–757). The second part of the poem (758–1154) deals with weather signs and is an integral part of it even though some ancient commentators give it a separate title (*Prognosis*). After a transitional part (758–772), in which he again emphasizes the power of all-pervading Zeus, Aratus deals with the signs derived from the observation of the different celestial phenomena (the stars, the sun, etc.); he ends with a description of the signs that depend on terrestrial phenomena. He concludes his poem (1142–1154) with an invitation to observe all these signs during the whole year, certain that we will not, by doing so, reach unwarranted conclusions.

The *Phaenomena* became famous as soon as it was published, as may be seen from the epigrams that Callimachus (*Anthologia Palatina* IX, 507) and Leonidas of Tarentum (*Anthologia Palatina* IX, 25) dedicate to Aratus. The poem was translated into Latin by Cicero and by Germanicus; Avienus translated it in the fourth century, and there is extant a seventh-century translation into barbarous Latin. The *Phaenomena* is cited by many authors, both Greek and Latin, and remained fashionable until the sixteenth century, as may be seen by the numerous manuscripts that have come down to us. It possesses some literary value and is indebted mainly to Hesiod and Homer for vocabulary and syntax. Aratus' adherence to Stoicism is patent throughout the poem, especially in the opening hymn to Zeus, who stands for the Stoic pantheistic divinity. From an astronomical standpoint the poem contains many errors, more than were in its source, the *Phaenomena* of Eudoxus of Cnidos. That this work of Eudoxus' was the source for Aratus, at least for the first part of the poem, we know from the commentary that Hipparchus devoted to both works. Aratus' source for the second part may

have been the same or another work by Eudoxus, but a work by Theophrastus dealing with meteorology (now lost) has also been suggested. Two manuscripts now at the Vatican give the names of twenty-seven commentators on Aratus.

BIBLIOGRAPHY

The most important editions of Aratus are those of E. Maass, *Arati Phaenomena* (Berlin, 1893; repr. 1955); and J. Martin, *Arati Phaenomena* (Florence, 1956); the latter contains an extensive commentary and a translation, both in French. For a translation into English, see that of G. R. Mair in the Loeb Classical Library's *Callimachus, Lycophron, Aratus* (London, 1921). On Aratus' life, text tradition, and influence, see J. Martin, *Histoire du texte des Phénomènes d'Aratos* (Paris, 1956). The texts of the four lives and of Suidas' biography are in A. Westermann, *BIOGRAPHOI. Vitarum scriptores Graeci minores* (Brunswick, 1845; repr. Amsterdam, 1964), pp. 52–61; see also Suidas, *s.n.* Aratus (A. Adler, ed.). For the commentaries and scholia, see E. Maass, *Aratea* (Berlin, 1892), and *Commentariorum in Aratum reliquiae* (Berlin, 1898; repr. 1958); and C. Manitius, *Hipparchi in Arati et Eudoxi Phaenomena commentariorum libri tres* (Leipzig, 1894). See also W. von Christ and W. Schmid, *Geschichte der griechischen Literatur,* pt. 2, 1st half (Munich, 1920), 163–167; G. Knaack, "Aratos," no. 6, in Pauly-Wissowa, *Real-Encyclopädie,* II, pt. 1 (1894), cols. 391–399; F. Susemihl, *Geschichte der griechischen Literatur in der Alexandrinerzeit,* I (Leipzig, 1891), 284–299; and M. Erren, *Die Phainomena des Aratos von Soloi* (Wiesbaden, 1967).

L. TARÁN

ARBER, AGNES ROBERTSON (*b.* London, England, 23 February 1879; *d.* Cambridge, England, 22 March 1960), *botany.*

Agnes Robertson's interest in botany developed strongly at school in northern London and later at University College, London, and the Botany School, Cambridge. She was particularly influenced by her friend and teacher, Ethel Sargant, who excited her interest in comparative plant anatomy. In 1909 she married E. A. N. Arber, demonstrator in paleobotany at Cambridge University.

At the suggestion of A. C. Seward, Mrs. Arber engaged in the study of early printed herbals, and her book on them (1912) became a standard work. It was revised and largely rewritten for the 1938 edition.

She published many papers on comparative anatomy, especially of the monocotyledons, and coordinated her results in three books, the first of which was *Water Plants: A Study of Aquatic Angiosperms.*

The second, *Monocotyledons: A Morphological Study,* was noted for its illumination of the so-called phyllode theory of the origin of the monocotyledonous leaf. The third, *The Gramineae,* was like *Water Plants* in that it embraced a very wide botanical approach.

In the later years of her life Mrs. Arber published three books that reflect the way she had then turned to consideration of scientific thought in relation to philosophy and metaphysics.

Agnes Arber was in the vanguard of the movement of women into scientific research: she was the first woman botanist to be made a fellow of the Royal Society and she received the Gold Medal of the Linnean Society in 1948. Throughout her life she had few formal contacts with college or university, choosing to work largely by herself. She was nonetheless kindly, helpful, and gracious, and certainly deserved A. G. Tansley's tribute (1952): "Dr. Agnes Arber is the most distinguished as well as the most erudite of British plant morphologists."

BIBLIOGRAPHY

I. ORIGINAL WORKS. Between 1902 and 1957 Agnes Arber published in scientific periodicals some eighty-four original papers, the bulk of them in the field of comparative plant anatomy. They are listed in full in H. Hamshaw Thomas' obituary notice (see below). In addition she published *Herbals: Their Origin and Evolution* (Cambridge, 1912, 2nd rev. ed. 1938); *Water Plants: A Study of Aquatic Angiosperms* (Cambridge, 1920); *Monocotyledons: A Morphological Study* (Cambridge, 1925); *The Gramineae: A Study of Cereal, Bamboo and Grass* (Cambridge, 1934); *The Natural Philosophy of Plant Form* (Cambridge, 1950); *The Mind and the Eye: A Study of the Biologist's Standpoint* (Cambridge, 1954); and *The Manifold and the One* (London, 1957).

II. SECONDARY LITERATURE. The most comprehensive biography is that by H. Hamshaw Thomas, in *Biographical Memoirs of Fellows of the Royal Society,* **6** (1960), 1–11. Shorter obituaries appeared in *Taxon,* **9** (1960), 261–263; *Proceedings of The Linnean Society of London,* **172** (1961), 128; and *Phytomorphology,* **11** (1961), 197–198.

HARRY GODWIN

ARBOGAST, LOUIS FRANÇOIS ANTOINE (*b.* Mutzig, Alsace, 4 October 1759; *d.* Strasbourg, France, 18 April 1803), *mathematics.*

There is no exact information on Arbogast's early years nor on his studies. He is registered as a nonpleading lawyer to the Sovereign Council of Alsace about 1780, and it is known that he taught mathematics at the Collège de Colmar about 1787. In 1789 he moved to Strasbourg, where he taught the same subject at the École d'Artillerie. He also was professor of physics at the Collège Royal, and after it was nationalized he served as director from April to October 1791. He then became rector of the University of Strasbourg. In 1790 he joined the society known as the Amis de la Constitution. He was a noted person in the Commune of Strasbourg, and in 1791 was elected a deputy to the Assemblée Législative and, in the following year, deputy from Haguenau to the Convention Nationale.

At the first of these assemblies, he and Gilbert Romme, Condorcet's closest collaborator, were on the committee of public instruction. Arbogast was the author of the general plan for public schools at all levels, which was brought before the convention but not adopted. He was responsible for the law introducing the decimal metric system in the whole of the French Republic.

Arbogast and his Alsatian colleagues were responsible for making the two assemblies aware of the efforts in Alsace toward building up a teaching force, as well as introducing the methods of pedagogy used in Germany. This information was useful in the establishment of the École Normale in the year III (1795).

Although he had been made *instituteur d'analyse* (probably professor of calculus) at the École Centrale de Paris (now École Polytechnique) in 1794, Arbogast taught only at the École Préparatoire. In this temporary institution an accelerated course of three months was given to 392 students before they were divided into three groups, which then proceeded to finish their studies in one, two, or three years.

In July 1795 Arbogast was entrusted with the planning of the École Centrale du Bas-Rhin, which replaced the abolished university. There he held the chair of mathematics from 1796 until 1802.

Arbogast was elected corresponding member of the Académie des Sciences in 1792 and an associate nonresident member of the Institut National (mathematics section, first class) four years later.

Arbogast's interest in the history of mathematics led to his classification of papers left by Marin Mersenne. He also amassed an important collection of manuscripts that are for the most part copies, in his writing, of the originals of memoirs or letters of Pierre Fermat, René Descartes, Jean Bernoulli, Pierre Varignon, Guillaume de L'Hospital, and others. At Arbogast's death these manuscripts were collected by his friend Français. They were bought in 1839 by Guglielmo Libri, the inspector of libraries, from a bookseller in Metz. After Libri's committal for trial on charges of malfeasance, his escape, and the seizure of his property, some of Arbogast's copies were deposited at the Bibliothèque Nationale in Paris. Other documents sold by the unscrupulous historian of science to Lord Ashburnham have also come to rest there. Other copies are now in the Laurenziana Library, Florence. The collection gathered by Arbogast became extremely valuable when definitive editions of the complete works of Fermat and Descartes, and of Mersenne's correspondence, were published.

In 1787 Arbogast took part in a competition organized by the Academy of St. Petersburg on "the arbitrary functions introduced by the integration of differential equations which have more than two variables," the question being "Do they belong to any curves or surfaces either algebraic, transcendental, or mechanical, either discontinuous or produced by a simple movement of the hand? Or shouldn't they legitimately be applied only to continuous curves susceptible of being expressed by algebraic or transcendental equations?"

The Academy was thus requesting a drastic settlement of the dispute between Jean d'Alembert, who adopted the second point of view, and Leonhard Euler, partisan of the first.

Arbogast won the prize and was even bolder than Euler in his conclusions. He showed that arbitrary functions may tolerate not only discontinuities in the Eulerian sense of the term, but also "combinations of several portions of different curves or those drawn by the free movement of the hand," that is, discontinuities in the sense afterward used by Augustin Cauchy.

Two years later, Arbogast sent a report to the Académie des Sciences de Paris on the new principles of differential calculus. This was never published, but Joseph Lagrange mentions it in 1797 as setting forth the same idea that he had developed in 1772, an idea that is the fundamental principle of his theory of analytic functions, "with its own developments and applications."

In speaking of his report in the Preface to *Calcul des dérivations,* Arbogast recalled the general ideas that anticipate Cauchy's and Niels Abel's ideas on the convergence of series. He added, "It caused me to reflect on fundamental principles . . . I then foresaw the birth of the first inkling of the ideas and methods which, when developed and extended, formed the substance of calculus of derivatives."

The principal aim of the calculus of derivatives, as Arbogast understood it, was to give simple and precise rules for finding series expansions. In order not to stay in the domain of pure theory, he used his rapid methods to find important formulas that were reached more laboriously by some of the great geometers.

Arbogast's work is dominated by a general idea that has become increasingly important in science and that until then had barely been anticipated: operational calculus. His only followers in this field were the brothers Français, then François Servois. But he was part of a vast mathematical movement that later included such names as Cauchy, George Boole, Sir William Rowan Hamilton, and Hermann Grassmann.

Arbogast clearly saw the difference that should be made between function and operation. When he defined his method of the "separation of the scale of operations," he said (*Traité des dérivations,* Preface):

This method is generally thought of as separating from the functions of variables when possible, the operational signs which affect this function. Then of treating the expressions formed by these signs applied to any quantity whatsoever, an expression which I have called a scale of operation, to treat it, I say, nevertheless as if the operational signs which compose it were quantities, then to multiply the result by the function.

Arbogast appears in his mathematical work as a philosophical thinker whose ideas prefigured many mathematical notions of modern times, such as the introduction into analysis of discontinuous functions, the limitation of certain methods of algebra to what are today known as holomorphic functions, the necessity for care in the use of infinite series, and the conception of calculus as operational symbols, disregarding the quantities or functions on which they are based.

BIBLIOGRAPHY

I. ORIGINAL WORKS. Arbogast's works include "Essai sur de nouveaux principes du calcul différentiel et intégral indépendant de la théorie des infiniment petits et de celle des limites; mémoire envoyé à l'Académie des Sciences de Paris au printemps 1789" (unpublished); *Mémoire sur la nature des fonctions arbitraires qui entrent dans les intégrales des équations aux dérivées partielles. Présenté a l'Académie Impériale de Pétersbourg pour concourir au Prix proposé en 1787 et couronné dans l'Assemblée du 29 novembre 1790. Par M. ARBOGAST, professeur de mathématiques à Colmar* (St. Petersburg, 1791); and *Du calcul des dérivations et de ses usages dans la théorie des suites et dans le calcul différentiel* (Strasbourg, 1800).

II. SECONDARY LITERATURE. Works concerning Arbogast or his work are Paul Dupuy, *L'École Normale de l'an III* (Paris, 1895), p. 28; Maurice Fréchet, "Biographie du mathematicien alsacien Arbogast," in *Thales,* **4** (1937-1939), 43-55; Joseph Lagrange, *Théories des fonctions analytiques* (Paris, 1797), Introduction; Niels Nielsen, *Géomètres français sous la Révolution* (Copenhagen, 1929), pp. 1-5; Paul Tannery, *Mémoires scientifiques,* VI (Paris,

1926), 157; and K. Zimmermann, dissertation (Heidelberg, 1934).

JEAN ITARD

ARBOS, PHILIPPE (*b.* Mosset, France, 30 July 1882; *d.* Andancette, Drôme, France, 28 October 1956), *geography.*

The son of schoolteachers, Arbos was admitted in 1904, after secondary schooling at Perpignan, to the École Normale Supérieure. Among his teachers there was Vidal de la Blache, who was trying to free geography from its subordination to history (it was restricted to mere enumeration) and transform it into an autonomous science, and to link the study of the physical environment to that of human activities. Before Arbos, he had taught Raoul Blanchard, Jean Brunhes, Emmanuel de Martonne, and others who were to be among the masters of the French school of geography.

In 1907, after passing his *agrégation* in both history and geography, Arbos became a professor at the Grenoble *lycée.* Under the direction of Raoul Blanchard, in 1912 he began a doctoral thesis on pastoral life in the French Alps, a work that took ten years to complete (he visited all the valleys and nearly all the townships of the Alps) and became a model for similar studies. Indeed, he clarified the general principles of pastoral life, little known and poorly understood until then. The newness of the subject, the soundness of the information, and the depth of treatment accorded this thesis inspired a whole school of research.

Arbos made the University of Clermont-Ferrand, where he became lecturer in 1919 and served as professor from 1922 to 1952, a center for geographical studies. His study of the urban geography of Clermont-Ferrand (1930) has not become outdated, and his book on the Auvergne (1946) is a classic of regional geography. His great interest was the geography of the Massif Central, and toward the end of his life he contributed a lengthy article on it to Larousse's *La France* (1951). Arbos's scientific writing also includes a great many articles and notes in *Revue de géographie alpine* and *Annales de géographie.* Greatly admired abroad, he lectured in Belgium, the United States, and Brazil.

An excellent teacher, Arbos made a point of being available to his students every day. He developed methods of study in the field by increasing the number of field trips, and taught his students the need for solid groundwork and concern for precision, as well as breadth of view and the need to synthesize. Having had excellent literary training, he accustomed his students to the skill and the rigor of his presentation. Many of his students were teachers, and besides influencing them, Arbos had the pleasure of seeing his methods of instruction spread to the secondary and even to the primary level of instruction.

BIBLIOGRAPHY

I. ORIGINAL WORKS. Arbos's writings include *La vie pastorale dans les Alpes françaises* (Paris, 1922); *Étude de géographie urbaine: Clermont-Ferrand* (Clermont-Ferrand, 1930); *L'Auvergne* (Paris, 1946); and "Le Massif Central," in *La France* (Paris, 1951), pp. 25–111. *Mélanges géographiques offerts à Ph. Arbos* (Clermont-Ferrand, 1953) contains three articles by Arbos.

II. SECONDARY LITERATURE. Obituaries of Arbos are R. Blanchard, in *Revue de géographie,* **32** (1957), 57–58; D. Faucher, in *Revue de géographie des Pyrénées et du Sud-ouest,* **27** (1956), 418; and M. Sorre, in *Annales de géographie,* **32** (1957), 182–183.

JULIETTE TATON

ARBUTHNOT, JOHN (*b.* Arbuthnot, Kinkardineshire, Scotland, 29 April 1667; *d.* London, 27 February 1735), *mathematical statistics.*

The son of a Scottish Episcopal clergyman, Arbuthnot studied at Aberdeen, took his doctor's degree in medicine at St. Andrews in 1696, and settled in London in 1697. He was elected a fellow of the Royal Society in 1704 and was appointed a physician extraordinary to Queen Anne in 1705 (he became ordinary physician in 1709). The Royal College of Physicians elected him a fellow in 1710.

Arbuthnot wrote a few scientific and medical essays, but he became especially famous for his political satires. He was a close friend of the wits and literary men of his day: with Swift, Pope, John Gay, and Thomas Parnell he was a member of the Scriblerus Club. Of the characters in his political novels, the one that has survived is John Bull.

Arbuthnot was well acquainted with the theory of probability. It is certain that he published an English translation of Christian Huygens' *De ratiociniis in ludo aleae* (probably to be identified with a work said to have appeared in 1692, and with the first edition of part of an anonymous work that appeared in a fourth edition in 1738 in London under the title *Of the Laws of Chance . . .*). His scientific importance, however, resides in a short paper in the *Philosophical Transactions of the Royal Society,* which has been taken as the very origin of mathematical statistics. Entitled "An Argument for Divine Providence, Taken From the Constant Regularity Observ'd in the Birth of Both Sexes," it begins:

Among innumerable footsteps of divine providence to be found in the works of nature, there is a very remarkable one to be observed in the exact balance that is maintained, between the numbers of men and women; for by this means it is provided, that the species never may fail, nor perish, since every male may have its female, and of proportionable age. This equality of males and females is not the effect of chance but divine providence, working for a good end, which I thus demonstrate.

He first shows by numerical examples that if sex is determined by a die with two sides, *M* and *F*, it is quite improbable that in a large number of tosses there will be as many *M* as *F*. However, it is also quite improbable that the number of *M* will greatly exceed that of *F*. Nevertheless, there are more male infants born than female infants—clearly through divine providence—to make good the greater losses of males in external accidents. In every year from 1629 to 1710, there were more males christened in London than females—as if 82 tosses of the die would all show *M*. Such an event has a very poor probability: 2^{-82}. Therefore it cannot have been produced by chance; it must have been produced by providence.

Arbuthnot's argument is the first known example of a mathematical statistical inference and, in fact, is the ancestor of modern statistical reasoning. It immediately drew the attention of Continental scientists, particularly the Dutch physicist 's Gravesande, as is shown by contemporary correspondence. Daniel Bernoulli used it in 1732 to show that it could not be by chance that the planetary orbits are only slightly inclined to the ecliptic. In 1757 John Michell proved the existence of double stars by showing that stars are found close to each other more often than mere chance would allow.

Condorcet applied the argument to test the veracity of the tradition of Roman history that seven kings had reigned for a total of 257 years. Laplace, in his classic work, reconsidered such applications and added many new ones. This crude argument, although now greatly refined, is still the basis of statistical inference.

BIBLIOGRAPHY

Arbuthnot's major paper, "An Argument for Divine Providence, Taken from the Constant Regularity Observ'd in the Birth of Both Sexes," is found in *Philosophical Transactions of the Royal Society*, **27** (1710–1712), 186–190. See also G. A. Aitken, *The Life and Works of John Arbuthnot* (Oxford, 1892); L. M. Beattie, *John Arbuthnot* (Cambridge, Mass., 1935); Daniel Bernoulli, in *Recueil des pièces qui ont remporté le prix double de l'Académie Royale des Sciences*, **3** (1734), 95–144; M. J. A. N. C. le Marquis de Condorcet, in *Histoire de l'Académie* (Paris, 1784), pp. 454–468; Hans Freudenthal, "Introductory Address," in *Quantitative Methods in Pharmacology* (Amsterdam, 1961), and "De eerste ontmoeting tussen de wiskunde en de sociale wetenschappen," in *Verhandelingen van de Koninklijke Vlaamse Akademie, Klasse Wetenschappen*, **28** (1966), 3–51; W. J. 's Gravesande, *Oeuvres philosophiques et mathématiques*, II (Amsterdam, 1774), 221–248; P. S. Laplace, *Théorie analytique de la probabilité*, 2nd ed. (Paris, 1820); John Michell, in *Philosophical Transactions of the Royal Society*, **57**, no. 1 (1767), 234–264; and I. Todhunter, *A History of the Mathematical Theory of Probability* (Cambridge, 1865; repr. New York, 1949).

HANS FREUDENTHAL

ARCHIAC, ÉTIENNE-JULES-ADOLPHE DESMIER (or **DEXMIER**) **DE SAINT-SIMON, VICOMTE D'** (*b.* Rheims, France, 24 September 1802; *d.* Paris, France, 24 or 25 December 1868), *geology, paleontology.*

Registered as the natural son of Marie-Elisabeth-Françoise Commelin, Adolphe was acknowledged by his father, Étienne-Louis-Marie Dexmier d'Archiac de Saint-Simon, a former cavalry captain who was an impoverished descendant of an ancient noble family from Angoumois.

After a childhood spent at Mesbrecourt, Aisne, d'Archiac entered the school for pages at Versailles and prepared for the military academy at Saint-Cyr, to which he was admitted in November 1819. He was appointed second lieutenant in the cavalry in 1821 and promoted to first lieutenant in 1827. In 1830, shortly before the July Revolution, d'Archiac published a pamphlet that showed his attachment to the *ancien régime* and expressed his aversion to the nobility of the Empire and to the bourgeoisie. He was placed on leave pay (about half the pay of a soldier on active duty) on 1 October 1830 because of this attachment to the Bourbon cause. The amount he received enabled him to subsist without working for a living.

How he came to study the geology of sedimentary formations is unknown. On 4 September 1832, at the annual extraordinary meeting of the Geological Society at Caen, he arranged to be introduced by Graves, secretary-general of the prefecture of Oise, and by Mutel-Delisle, a Paris attorney—a choice of sponsorship that reveals his lack of connections in the teaching profession. D'Archiac then declared that he had renounced his military career in order to devote himself to geology.

Leaving the study of eruptive and volcanic formations to the mining engineers, d'Archiac concentrated on sedimentary formations. His curiosity first led him to study two regions through which he had traveled in his youth: Aisne and Charente. From the beginning of his surveys in Aisne he undertook to make detailed sections and to collect fauna, which he carefully catalogued layer by layer. In 1835 he published a summary of his research as well as "Note sur la position du calcaire de Château-Landon." Following these publications, the Ministry of Public Works commissioned him to make a geological map of Aisne. His search for correlations led him to England for two months in 1837 and, the following year, to Brussels and Düsseldorf. He followed the lignite deposits from the Soissons region to Berkshire and established that they were of the same age and belonged at the level of the plastic clay of the Paris basin, as had already been indicated by Alexandre Brongniart and Élie de Beaumont.

His "Essais sur la coordination des terrains tertiaires du nord de la France, de la Belgique et de l'Angleterre" appeared in 1839. In 1843 he published a geological map of Aisne on the scale of 1:160,000 in a serial monograph, in which he described the physical features of the department as well as its hydrography, industries, and meteorology. Above all, he classified its formations into five groups: Transitional, Oolitic, Cretaceous, Tertiary, and Diluvial. In these he distinguished separate strata and determined their fossil contents. The "Essais" was followed by another work dealing with the Cretaceous formation of the southwestern, northern, and northwestern slopes of the French central plateau. D'Archiac subdivided the Cretaceous formation into four groups (Neocomian, green sandstone, tufa chalk, white chalk), which were further subdivided into stages.

Approaching problems of narrower scope with the same meticulous care, d'Archiac published notes on the petrographic features of Silurian and Carboniferous limestones, on the fossilization of echinoderms, the serpentine rocks of Limousin, pelagic formations, and the comparative geographic distribution of Paleozoic and contemporary mollusks. His last surveying trips during the summers of 1853–1856 and 1858 were devoted to the Corbières region, little known until then. In 1854 he published *Coupe géologique des environs des Bains de Rennes (Aude), suivie de la description de quelques fossiles de cette localité.* On 16 March 1857 he presented to the Geological Society his newly completed geological map of the regions adjacent to Aude and Pyrénées-Orientales.

D'Archiac did not restrict himself to fauna that he himself had collected. In 1842, in collaboration with his friend Edouard de Verneuil, he published a description of Devonian fossils of the Rhineland. Three years later the two naturalists described the fauna brought back by Adrien Paillette, who had prospected the Primary formations of Asturias. When the Geological Society received an important collection of "tourtia" (a glauconite conglomerate of quartz pebbles, deposited by the Cenomanian transgression in Hainaut and Flanders) from Belgium, d'Archiac undertook a study of it that was published in 1846–1847.

He was particularly interested in *Nummulites.* In 1846 and 1850 he described and illustrated finds made by geologists at Bayonne and Dax. In 1853 he published, in collaboration with Jules Haime, *Description des animaux fossiles du groupe nummulitique de l'Inde, précédée d'un résumé géologique et d'une monographie des Nummulites.* This work, containing illustrations of 352 species or varieties received by the Geological Society of London, has remained the basic work for every paleontological laboratory interested in the determination of Foraminifera. In 1866 d'Archiac, in collaboration with Verneuil and Paul Fischer, described the fossils brought back from Asiatic Turkey by the Russian geographer Pëtr Tschichatschew. The following year he made public the findings of Auguste Viquesnel in European Turkey.

D'Archiac published most of his articles and memoirs in the *Bulletin* or the *Mémoires* of the Geological Society. Named the society's deputy secretary in 1836 and its secretary in 1838, he served as president in 1844, 1849, and 1854. In March 1842 the society commissioned him to present an analysis of papers published since 1834, the review for the previous publications having been Ami Boué's work. In 1847 d'Archiac began publication of *Histoire des progrès de la géologie* with Volume I (*Cosmogénie et géogénie, physique du globe, géographie physique, terrain moderne*) and announced that three additional volumes would complete the work. Geology developed so rapidly, however, that it soon outdistanced his plans. D'Archiac's abstracts make up eight other volumes published between 1848 and 1860 and terminate with the Triassic, leaving out older formations. These nine volumes are a remarkable collection of learning that is still highly appreciated by geologists.

D'Archiac was elected a member of the Académie des Sciences, Section for Mineralogy, on 27 April 1857, to replace Constant Prevost. When d'Orbigny's death left vacant the chair of paleontology at the Muséum d'Histoire Naturelle, d'Archiac, supported by the assembly of the professors of the museum and by the Academy of Sciences, offered himself as a candidate on 28 September 1857 and wrote:

> In summing up, the Museum's course in paleontology, in order to be truly useful and to respond to present

needs and clearly evident scientific tendencies, should have as its aim not so much making known the zoological or anatomical characteristics of the organic fossil forms . . . as demonstrating the relationships of these forms to the earth strata and the manner in which they are distributed therein, and searching for the overall laws that have governed the succession of beings in the course of time, as well as the causes that have modified these laws for short periods of time [Archives Nationales, F17.20036].

Despite his exceptional qualifications, the authorities were slow to decide. A first appeal by d'Archiac served merely to add another document to his file. A second appeal brought his appointment on 14 June 1861. "Précis de l'histoire de la paléontologie stratigraphique" was the subject of his first course.

Among the subjects d'Archiac treated was a lively critique of Darwin's *On the Origin of Species,* the first French translation of which had just appeared and in which the term *élection* had been preferred to *sélection.* Accustomed to accuracy, d'Archiac stressed the vagueness and gratuitousness of numerous claims made by the English author. "The sad impressions of fatalism prevail from beginning to end in Darwin's book," he wrote (*Cours de paléontologie stratigraphique,* II, 113), but by 1866 he had become an evolutionist:

> The present state of the earth is only the consequence of its past—and this holds true for the organic as well as the inorganic realm. The animals and plants surrounding us and among which we live are only the descendants or the representatives of those which have preceded us. The living forms, as well as those which are extinct, are all part of a continuous chain [*Géologie et paléontologie,* p. 345].

D'Archiac, who remained single, lived alone and had no close ties. The frantic work that enabled him to rank among the leading scientists was his consolation. His physical stamina, which had sustained him as long as he engaged in surveying trips, finally began to fail. On 24 December 1868, apparently in the grip of a severe depression, he submitted his resignation as academician and professor to Victor Duruy, minister of public education, and left his home. It is believed that within the next few hours he threw himself into the Seine, from which his body was recovered at Meulan on 30 May 1869.

BIBLIOGRAPHY

I. ORIGINAL WORKS. D'Archiac's major writing is *Histoire des progrès de la géologie de 1834 à 1845,* in 9 vols., all pub. in Paris: I, *Cosmogénie et géogénie, physique du globe, géographie physique, terrain moderne* (1847); II, pt. 1, *Terrain quaternaire ou diluvien* (1848); II, pt. 2, *Terrain tertiaire* (1849); III, *Formation nummulitique. Roches ignées ou pyrogènes des époques quaternaire et tertiaire* (1850); IV, *Formation crétacée, l^re partie* (1851); V, *Formation crétacée, 2e partie* (1853); VI, *Formation jurassique, l^re partie* (1856); VII, *Formation jurassique, 2e partie* (1857); and VIII, *Formation triasique* (1860).

His other works include "Résumé d'un mémoire sur une partie des terrains tertiaires inférieurs du département de l'Aisne," in *Bulletin de la Société géologique de France,* **6** (1835), 240–247; "Note sur la position du calcaire de Château-Landon," *ibid.,* **7** (1835), 30–35; "Mémoire sur la formation crétacée du sud-ouest de la France," in *Mémoires de la Société géologique de France,* **2,** pt. 2 (1837), 157–192; "Note sur les sables et grès moyens tertiaires," in *Bulletin de la Société géologique de France,* **9** (1837), 54–73; "Observations sur les lignites tertiaires du nord de la France et de l'Angleterre," *ibid.,* **9** (1838), 103–106; "Observations sur le groupe moyen de la formation crétacée," in *Mémoires de la Société géologique de France,* **3,** pt. 1 (1838), 261–311; "Essais sur la coordination des terrains tertiaires du nord de la France, de la Belgique et de l'Angleterre," in *Bulletin de la Société géologique de France,* **10** (1839), 168–225, a German translation is in Leonhard and Bronn's *Neues Jahrbuch für Mineralogie* (Stuttgart, 1839); *Discours sur l'ensemble des phénomènes qui se sont manifestés à la surface du globe, depuis son origine jusqu'à l'époque actuelle* (Paris, 1840); "Description géologique du département de l'Aisne," in *Mémoires de la Société géologique de France,* **5,** pt. 2 (1843), 129–421; "Études sur la formation crétacée des versants sud-ouest, nord et nord-ouest du plateau central de la France," pt. 1 in *Annales des sciences géologiques,* **2** (1843), 121–143, 169–191; pt. 2 in *Mémoires de la Société géologique de France,* 2nd ser., **2,** pt. 1 (1846), 1–148; "Description des fossiles recueillis par M. Thorent, dans les couches à *Nummulines* des environs de Bayonne," *ibid.,* 189–217; "Rapport sur les fossiles du Tourtia, légués par M. Léveillé à la Société géologique de France," *ibid.,* pt. 2 (1847), 291–351; *Notice sur les travaux géologiques de M. d'Archiac* (Paris, 1847); "Description des fossiles du groupe nummulitique recueillis par M. S.-P. Pratt et M. J. Delbos aux environs de Bayonne et de Dax," in *Mémoires de la Société géologique de France,* 2nd ser., **3,** pt. 2 (1850), 397–456; *Liste bibliographique par ordre de dates des travaux géologiques de M. d'Archiac* (Paris, 1856); "Les Corbières. Études géologiques d'une partie des départements de l'Aude et des Pyrénées-Orientales," in *Mémoires de la Société géologique de France,* 2nd ser., **6,** pt. 2 (1859); *Cours de paléontologie stratigraphique professé au Muséum d'Histoire Naturelle,* 2 vols.: I, *Précis de l'histoire de la paléontologie stratigraphique* (Paris, 1862); II, *Connaissances générales qui doivent précéder l'étude de la paléontologie stratigraphique et des phénomènes organiques qui s'y rattachent* (Paris, 1864); *Leçons sur la faune quaternaire* (Paris, 1865); *Géologie et paléontologie* (Paris, 1866); "Paléontologie," in Auguste Viquesnel, *Voyage dans la Turquie d'Europe,* II (Paris, 1868), 449–481; and *Paléontologie de la France* (Paris, 1868).

Works written with others are "On the Fossils of the Older Deposits in the Rhenish Provinces; Preceded by a General Survey of the Fauna of the Paleozoic Rocks, and Followed by a Tabular List of the Organic Remains of the Devonian System in Europe," in *Transactions of the Geological Society of London,* **6** (1842), 303–410, written with Edouard de Verneuil, trans. into German by G. von Leonhard (Stuttgart, 1844); *Description des animaux fossiles du groupe nummulitique de l'Inde, précédée d'un résumé géologique et d'une monographie des Nummulites* (Paris, 1853), written with Jules Haime; and "Paléontologie de l'Asie Mineure," written with Verneuil and Paul Fischer, in Pëtr Tschichatschew, *Asie Mineure. Description physique de cette contrée,* IV (Paris, 1869), 83–234, 393–420.

II. SECONDARY LITERATURE. An article on d'Archiac is Albert Gaudry, "Notice sur les travaux scientifiques de d'Archiac," in *Bulletin de la Société géologique de France,* 3rd ser., **2** (1874), 230–244. Source material may be found in Archives de la Guerre, Vincennes, d'Archiac's file; Archives Nationales, Paris, F17.13566 and F17.20036; and the archives of the Académie des Sciences, which has d'Archiac's papers that were turned over to it in 1960 by the Société Géologique de France, including 987 letters written to d'Archiac.

ARTHUR BIREMBAUT

ARCHIGENES (*b.* Apameia, Syria, *ca.* A.D. 54; *fl.* Rome, 98–117), *medicine.*

Archigenes was the son of Philippos and pupil of Agathinos; he practiced medicine in Rome during the reign of Trajan and achieved sufficient popularity to be mentioned by the poet Juvenal (VI, 236; XIII, 98; XIV, 252).

Nearly all of his many and varied writings have been lost, and their contents can be reconstructed only approximately from the fragments preserved in Galen and later medical writers. According to Galen, Archigenes belonged to the eclectic school; the surviving fragments indicate, however, that he was influenced considerably by the doctrines of the pneumatic school. His main contributions were in pathology, surgery, and therapeutics.

Archigenes' main work in general medicine was the semidiagnostic Περὶ τόπων πεπονθότων ("On Places Affected"), in which he sought to explain the causes of diseases by concentrating upon their localized manifestations. Although he seems to have had a vague idea of the difference between a generalized, systemic disease and the locally painful injury or infection, it is difficult, as Galen noted, to understand him because of his tendency to designate the types of pain associated with local inflammations by separate names. Certain inconsistencies in Archigenes' medical theories were probably the result of his reliance on Stoic doctrines. Thus, his belief that the

hegemonikon (ruling principle) was located in the heart did not prevent him from treating loss of memory by local applications to the head. Because he discussed the role of the nerves and arteries in the pneuma's transmission of pain throughout the body, it is not surprising that he devoted a special treatise to the pulse. His Περὶ τῶν σφυγμῶν ("On the Pulses") was frequently cited by Galen, who also wrote a commentary on it and probably took some of his ideas on the pulse from it.

Among the titles preserved of Archigenes' other writings, several pertain to more specific diseases. Acute and chronic diseases were distinguished, and a separate treatise was written on the signs of fevers. At least some of the conditions underlying the feverish symptoms were treated by surgery. Archigenes described an amputation of a gangrenous limb that used both ligatures and cauterization. He noted the importance and location of tendons, and perhaps of nerves, in surgical repair. He described cancer of the breast and employed a speculum in the examination of uterine tumors.

In antiquity, Archigenes was highly regarded for his writings on therapeutics and materia medica. Numerous fragments are preserved from his Περὶ τῶν κατὰγένος φαρμάκον ("On Drugs According to Their Nature"). Two other writings are known by title: Περὶ καστορίου χρήσεως ("On the Use of Castoreum") and Περὶ τῆς δόσεως τοῦ ἑλλβόρου ("On the Giving of Hellebore"), but these may have been portions of a larger work. Some of his prescriptions have been preserved in Galen and Alexander of Tralles. For epilepsy he resorted to amulets, and he relied heavily on animal substances in his compound drugs. In accordance with the prevailing humoral-pneumatic doctrines, the purpose of therapy was to control the δυσκρασίαι ("bad temperaments") by neutralizing them.

BIBLIOGRAPHY

Cesare Brescia, ed., *Frammenti medicinali di Archigene* (Naples, 1955), consists of three short tracts edited from MS Vat. Pal. 199.

Additional writings on Archigenes are E. Gurlt, *Geschichte der Chirurgie und ihrer Ausübung,* I (Berlin, 1898), 411–414; Alessandro Olivieri, "Frammenti di Archigene," in *Memorie dell'Accademia di Archeologia, Lettere e Belle Arti di Napoli,* **6** (1942), 120–122; Erwin Rohde, "Aelius Promotus," in *Rheinisches Museum für Philologie,* **28** (1873), 264–290, an analysis of a tract on poisonous drugs, part of which has been attributed to Archigenes; and Max Wellmann, "Die pneumatische Schule bis auf Archigenes," in *Philologische Untersuchungen,* **14** (1895), a fundamental study that lists sources for and titles of thirteen of Archigenes' lost writings, and "Archigenes," in Pauly-Wissowa, *Real-Encyclopädie der classischen Altertumswissenschaft*, II (1896), cols. 484–486.

JERRY STANNARD

ARCHIMEDES (*b.* Syracuse, *ca.* 287 B.C.; *d.* Syracuse, 212 B.C.), *mathematics, mechanics.*

Few details remain of the life of antiquity's most celebrated mathematician. A biography by his friend Heracleides has not survived. That his father was the astronomer Phidias we know from Archimedes himself in his *The Sandreckoner* (Sect. I. 9). Archimedes was perhaps a kinsman of the ruler of Syracuse, King Hieron II (as Plutarch and Polybius suggest). At least he was on intimate terms with Hieron, to whose son Gelon he dedicated *The Sandreckoner*. Archimedes almost certainly visited Alexandria, where no doubt he studied with the successors of Euclid and played an important role in the further development of Euclidian mathematics. This visit is rendered almost certain by his custom of addressing his mathematical discoveries to mathematicians who are known to have lived in Alexandria, such as Conon, Dositheus, and Eratosthenes. At any rate Archimedes returned to Syracuse, composed most of his works there, and died there during its capture by the Romans in 212 B.C. Archimedes' approximate birth date of 287 B.C. is conjectured on the basis of a remark by the Byzantine poet and historian of the twelfth century, John Tzetzes, who declared (*Chiliad* 2, hist. 35) that Archimedes "worked at geometry until old age, surviving seventy-five years." There are picturesque accounts of Archimedes' death by Livy, Plutarch, Valerius Maximus, and Tzetzes, which vary in detail but agree that he was killed by a Roman soldier. In most accounts he is pictured as being engaged in mathematics at the time of his death. Plutarch tells us (*Marcellus,* Ch. XVII) that Archimedes "is said to have asked his friends and kinsmen to place on his grave after his death a cylinder circumscribing a sphere, with an inscription giving the ratio by which the including solid exceeds the included." And indeed Cicero (see *Tusculan Disputations,* V, xxiii, 64–66), when he was Quaestor in Sicily in 75 B.C.,

> . . . tracked out his grave. . . . and found it enclosed all around and covered with brambles and thickets; for I remembered certain doggerel lines inscribed, as I had heard, upon his tomb, which stated that a sphere along with a cylinder had been put upon the top of his grave. Accordingly, after taking a good look all around (for there are a great quantity of graves at the Agrigentine Gate), I noticed a small column arising a little above the bushes, on which there was the figure of a sphere

> and a cylinder. . . . Slaves were sent in with sickles. . . and when a passage to the place was opened we approached the pedestal in front of us; the epigram was traceable with about half of the lines legible, as the latter portion was worn away.

No surviving bust can be certainly identified as being of Archimedes, although a portrait on a Sicilian coin (whatever its date) is definitely his. A well-known mosaic showing Archimedes before a calculating board with a Roman soldier standing over him was once thought to be a genuine survival from Herculaneum but is now considered to be of Renaissance origin.

Mechanical Inventions. While Archimedes' place in the history of science rests on a remarkable collection of mathematical works, his reputation in antiquity was also founded upon a series of mechanical contrivances which he is supposed to have invented and which the researches of A. G. Drachmann tend in part to confirm as Archimedean inventions. One of these is the water snail, a screwlike device to raise water for the purpose of irrigation, which, Diodorus Siculus tells us (*Bibl. hist.,* V, Ch. 37), Archimedes invented in Egypt. We are further told by Atheneus that an endless screw invented by Archimedes was used to launch a ship. He is also credited with the invention of the compound pulley. Some such device is the object of the story told by Plutarch in his life of *Marcellus* (Ch. XIV). When asked by Hieron to show him how a great weight could be moved by a small force, Archimedes "fixed upon a three-masted merchantman of the royal fleet, which had been dragged ashore by the great labors of many men, and after putting on board many passengers and the customary freight, he seated himself at a distance from her, and without any great effort, but quietly setting in motion a system of compound pulleys, drew her towards him smoothly and evenly, as though she were gliding through the water." It is in connection with this story that Plutarch tells us of the supposed remark of Archimedes to the effect that "if there were another world, and he could go to it, he could move this one," a remark known in more familiar form from Pappus of Alexandria (*Collectio,* Bk. VIII, Prop. 11): "Give me a place to stand on, and I will move the earth." Of doubtful authenticity is the oft-quoted story told by Vitruvius (*De architectura,* Bk. IX, Ch. 3) that Hieron wished Archimedes to check whether a certain crown or wreath was of pure gold, or whether the goldsmith had fraudulently alloyed it with some silver.

While Archimedes was turning the problem over, he chanced to come to the place of bathing, and there,

213

as he was sitting down in the tub, he noticed that the amount of water which flowed over by the tub was equal to the amount by which his body was immersed. This indicated to him a method of solving the problem, and he did not delay, but in his joy leapt out of the tub, and, rushing naked towards his home, he cried out in a loud voice that he had found what he sought, for as he ran he repeatedly shouted in Greek, *heurēka, heurēka.*

Much more generally credited is the assertion of Pappus that Archimedes wrote a book *On Sphere-making,* a work which presumably told how to construct a model planetarium representing the apparent motions of the sun, moon, and planets, and perhaps also a closed star globe representing the constellations. At least, we are told by Cicero (*De re publica,* I, XIV, 21–22) that Marcellus took as booty from the sack of Syracuse both types of instruments constructed by Archimedes:

> For Gallus told us that the other kind of celestial globe [that Marcellus brought back and placed in the Temple of Virtue], which was solid and contained no hollow space, was a very early invention, the first one of that kind having been constructed by Thales of Miletus, and later marked by Eudoxus of Cnidus . . . with the constellations and stars which are fixed in the sky. . . . But this newer kind of globe, he said, on which were delineated the motions of the sun and moon and of those five stars which are called the wanderers . . . contained more than could be shown on a solid globe, and the invention of Archimedes deserved special admiration because he had thought out a way to represent accurately by a single device for turning the globe those various and divergent courses with their different rates of speed.

Finally, there are references by Polybius, Livy, Plutarch, and others to fabulous ballistic instruments constructed by Archimedes to help repel Marcellus. One other defensive device often mentioned but of exceedingly doubtful existence was a burning mirror or combination of mirrors.

We have no way to know for sure of Archimedes' attitude toward his inventions. One supposes that Plutarch's famous eulogy of Archimedes' disdain for the practical was an invention of Plutarch and simply reflected the awe in which Archimedes' theoretical discoveries were held. Plutarch (*Marcellus,* Ch. XVII) exclaims:

> And yet Archimedes possessed such a lofty spirit, so profound a soul, and such a wealth of scientific theory, that although his inventions had won for him a name and fame for superhuman sagacity, he would not consent to leave behind him any treatise on this subject, but regarding the work of an engineer and every art

that ministers to the needs of life as ignoble and vulgar, he devoted his earnest efforts only to those studies the subtlety and charm of which are not affected by the claims of necessity. These studies, he thought, are not to be compared with any others; in them, the subject matter vies with the demonstration, the former supplying grandeur and beauty, the latter precision and surpassing power. For it is not possible to find in geometry more profound and difficult questions treated in simpler and purer terms. Some attribute this success to his natural endowments; others think it due to excessive labor that everything he did seemed to have been performed without labor and with ease. For no one could by his own efforts discover the proof, and yet as soon as he learns it from him, he thinks he might have discovered it himself, so smooth and rapid is the path by which he leads one to the desired conclusion.

Mathematical Works. The mathematical works of Archimedes that have come down to us can be loosely classified in three groups (Arabic numbers have been added to indicate, where possible, their chronological order). The first group consists of those that have as their major objective the proof of theorems relative to the areas and volumes of figures bounded by curved lines and surfaces. In this group we can place *On the Sphere and the Cylinder* (5); *On the Measurement of the Circle* (9); *On Conoids and Spheroids* (7); *On Spirals* (6); and *On the Quadrature of the Parabola* (2), which, in respect to its Propositions 1–17, belongs also to the second category of works. The second group comprises works that lead to a geometrical analysis of statical and hydrostatical problems and the use of statics in geometry: *On the Equilibrium of Planes,* Book I (1), Book II (3); *On Floating Bodies* (8); *On the Method of Mechanical Theorems* (4); and the aforementioned propositions from *On the Quadrature of the Parabola* (2). Miscellaneous mathematical works constitute the third group: *The Sandreckoner* (10); *The Cattle-Problem*; and the fragmentary *Stomachion.* Several other works not now extant are alluded to by Greek authors (see Heiberg, ed., *Archimedis opera,* II, 536–554). For example, there appear to have been various works on mechanics that have some unknown relationship to *On the Equilibrium of Planes.* Among these are a possible work on *Elements of Mechanics* (perhaps containing an earlier section on centers of gravity, which, however, may have been merely a separate work written before *Equilibrium of Planes,* Book I), a tract *On Balances,* and possibly one *On Uprights.* Archimedes also seems to have written a tract *On Polyhedra,* perhaps one *On Blocks and Cylinders,* certainly one on *Archai* or *The Naming of Numbers* (a work preliminary to *The Sandreckoner*), and a work on *Optics* or *Catoptrics.* Other works are attributed to Archimedes by Arabic authors, and, for the most part, are extant in Arabic manuscripts (the titles for which manuscripts are known are indicated by an asterisk; see Bibliography): *The Lemmata**, or *Liber assumptorum* (in its present form certainly not by Archimedes since his name is cited in the proofs), *On Water Clocks**, *On Touching Circles**, *On Parallel Lines*, *On Triangles**, *On the Properties of the Right Triangle**, *On Data*, and *On the Division of the Circle into Seven Equal Parts**.

But even the genuine extant works are by no means in their original form. For example, *On the Equilibrium of Planes*, Book I, is possibly an excerpt from the presumably longer *Elements of Mechanics* mentioned above and is clearly distinct from Book II, which was apparently written later. A solution promised by Archimedes in *On the Sphere and the Cylinder* (Bk. II, Prop. 4) was already missing by the second century A.D. *On the Measurement of the Circle* was certainly in a much different form originally, with Proposition II probably not a part of it (and even if it were, it would have to follow the present Proposition III, since it depends on it). The word *paraboles* in the extant title of *On the Quadrature of the Parabola* could hardly have been in the original title, since that word was not yet used in Archimedes' work in the sense of a conic section. Finally, the tracts *On the Sphere and the Cylinder* and *On the Measurement of the Circle* have been almost completely purged of their original Sicilian-Doric dialect, while the rest of his works have suffered in varying degrees this same kind of linguistic transformation.

In proving theorems relative to the area or volume of figures bounded by curved lines or surfaces, Archimedes employs the so-called Lemma of Archimedes or some similar lemma, together with a technique of proof that is generally called the "method of exhaustion," and other special Greek devices such as *neuseis*, and principles taken over from statics. These various mathematical techniques are coupled with an extensive knowledge of the mathematical works of his predecessors, including those of Eudoxus, Euclid, Aristeus, and others. The Lemma of Archimedes (*On the Sphere and Cylinder*, Assumption 5; cf. the Preface to *On the Quadrature of the Parabola* and the Preface to *On Spirals*) assumes "that of two unequal lines, unequal surfaces, and unequal solids the greater exceeds the lesser by an amount such that, when added to itself, it may exceed any assigned magnitude of the type of magnitudes compared with one another." This has on occasion been loosely identified with Definition 4 of Book V of the *Elements* of Euclid (often called the axiom of Eudoxus): "Magnitudes are said to have a ratio to one another which are capable, when multiplied, of exceeding one another."

But the intent of Archimedes' assumption appears to be that if there are two unequal magnitudes capable of having a ratio in the Euclidian sense, then their difference will have a ratio (in the Euclidian sense) with any magnitude of the same kind as the two initial magnitudes. This lemma has been interpreted as excluding actual infinitesimals, so that the difference of two lines will always be a line and never a point, the difference between surfaces always a surface and never a line, and the difference between solids always a solid and never a surface. The exhaustion procedure often uses a somewhat different lemma represented by Proposition X.1 of the *Elements* of Euclid: "Two unequal magnitudes being set out, if from the greater there be subtracted a magnitude greater than its half, and from that which is left a magnitude greater than its half, and if this process be repeated continually, there will be left some magnitude which will be less than the lesser magnitude set out." This obviously reflects the further idea of the continuous divisibility of a continuum. One could say that the Lemma of Archimedes justifies this further lemma in the sense that no matter how far the procedure of subtracting more than half of the larger of the magnitudes set out is taken (or also no matter how far the procedure of subtracting one-half the larger magnitude, described in the corollary to Proposition X.1, is taken), the magnitude resulting from the successive division (which magnitude being conceived as the difference of two magnitudes) will always be capable of having a ratio in the Euclidian sense with the smaller of the magnitudes set out. Hence one such remainder will some time be in a relationship of "less than" to the lesser of the magnitudes set out.

The method of exhaustion, widely used by Archimedes, was perhaps invented by Eudoxus. It was used on occasion by Euclid in his *Elements* (for example, in Proposition XII.2). Proof by exhaustion (the name is often criticized since the purpose of the technique is to avoid assuming the complete exhaustion of an area or a volume; Dijksterhuis prefers the somewhat anachronistic expression "indirect passage to the limit") is an indirect proof by reduction to absurdity. That is to say, if the theorem is of the form $A = B$, it is held to be true by showing that to assume its opposite, namely that A is not equal to B, is impossible since it leads to contradictions. The method has several forms. Following Dijksterhuis, we can label the two main types: the compression method and the approximation method. The former is the most widely used and exists in two forms, one that depends upon taking decreasing differences and one that depends on taking decreasing ratios. The fundamental procedure of both the "difference" and the "ratio" forms starts with the successive inscription and circumscription of regular figures within or without the figure for which the area or volume is sought. Then in the "difference" method the area or volume of the inscribed or circumscribed figure is regularly increased or decreased until the difference between the desired area or volume and the inscribed or circumscribed figure is less than any preassigned magnitude. Or to put it more specifically, if the theorem is of the form $A = B$, A being the curvilinear figure sought and B a regular rectilinear figure the formula for the magnitude of which is known, and we assume that A is greater than B, then by the exhaustion procedure and its basic lemma we can construct some regular rectilinear inscribed figure P such that P is greater than B; but it is obvious that P, an included figure, is in fact always less than B. Since P cannot be both greater and less than B, the assumption from which the contradiction evolved (namely, that A is greater than B) must be false. Similarly, if A is assumed to be less than B, we can by the exhaustion technique and the basic lemma find a circumscribed figure P that is less than B, which P (as an including figure) must always be greater than B. Thus the assumption of A less than B must also be false. Hence, it is now evident that, since A is neither greater nor less than B, it must be equal to B. An example of the exhaustion procedure in its "difference" form is to be found in *On the Measurement of the Circle:* [1]

Proposition 1

The area of any circle is equal to a right-angled triangle in which one of the sides about the right angle is equal to the radius, and the other to the circumference, of the circle.

Let $ABCD$ be the given circle, K the triangle described.

Then, if the circle is not equal to K, it must be either greater or less.

I. If possible, let the circle be greater than K.

Inscribe a square $ABCD$, bisect the arcs AB, BC, CD, DA, then bisect (if necessary) the halves, and so on, until the sides of the inscribed polygon whose angular points are the points of division subtend segments whose sum is less than the excess of the area of the circle over K.

Thus the area of the polygon is greater than K.

Let AE be any side of it, and ON the perpendicular on AE from the centre O.

Then ON is less than the radius of the circle and therefore less than one of the sides about the right angle in K. Also the perimeter of the polygon is less than the circumference of the circle, i.e. less than the other side about the right angle in K.

Therefore the area of the polygon is less than K; which is inconsistent with the hypothesis.

Thus the area of the circle is not greater than K.

II. If possible, let the circle be less than K.

Circumscribe a square, and let two adjacent sides, touching the circle in E, H, meet in T. Bisect the arcs between adjacent points of contact and draw the tangents at the points of bisection. Let A be the middle point of the arc EH, and FAG the tangent at A.

Then the angle TAG is a right angle.

Therefore $$TG > GA$$ $$> GH.$$

It follows that the triangle FTG is greater than half the area $TEAH$.

Similarly, if the arc AH be bisected and the tangent at the point of bisection be drawn, it will cut off from the area GAH more than one-half.

Thus, by continuing the process, we shall ultimately arrive at a circumscribed polygon such that the spaces intercepted between it and the circle are together less than the excess of K over the area of the circle.

Thus the area of the polygon will be less than K.

Now, since the perpendicular from O on any side of the polygon is equal to the radius of the circle, while the perimeter of the polygon is greater than the circum-

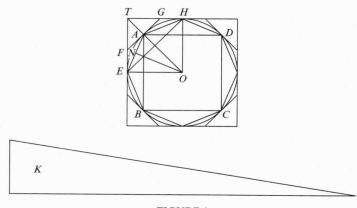

FIGURE 1

ference of the circle, it follows that the area of the polygon is greater than the triangle K; which is impossible.

Therefore the area of the circle is not less than K.

Since then the area of the circle is neither greater nor less than K, it is equal to it.

Other examples of the "difference" form of the exhaustion method are found in *On Conoids and Spheroids* (Props. 22, 26, 28, 30), *On Spiral Lines* (Props. 24, 25), and *On the Quadrature of the Parabola* (Prop. 16).

The "ratio" form of the exhaustion method is quite similar to the "difference" form except that in the first part of the proof, where the known figure is said to be less than the figure sought, the ratio of circumscribed polygon to inscribed polygon is decreased until it is less than the ratio of the figure sought to the known figure, and in the second part the ratio of circumscribed polygon to inscribed polygon is decreased until it is less than the ratio of the known figure to the figure sought. In each part a contradiction is shown to follow the assumption. And thus the assumption of each part must be false, namely, that the known figure is either greater or less than the figure sought. Consequently, the known figure must be equal to the figure sought. An example of the "ratio" form appears in *On the Sphere and the Cylinder* (Bk. I):[2]

Proposition 14

The surface of any isosceles cone excluding the base is equal to a circle whose radius is a mean proportional between the side of the cone [a generator] and the radius of the circle which is the base of the cone.

Let the circle A be the base of the cone; draw C equal to the radius of the circle, and D equal to the side of the cone, and let E be a mean proportional between C, D.

Draw a circle B with radius equal to E.

Then shall B be equal to the surface of the cone (excluding the base), which we will call S.

If not, B must be either greater or less than S.

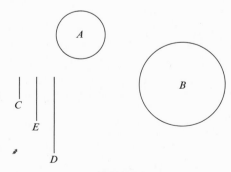

FIGURE 2

I. Suppose $B < S$.

Let a regular polygon be described about B and a similar one inscribed in it such that the former has to the latter a ratio less than the ratio $S:B$.

Describe about A another similar polygon, and on it set up a pyramid with apex the same as that of the cone.

Then (polygon about A):(polygon about B)

$= C^2:E^2$

$= C:D$

$=$ (polygon about A):(surface of pyramid excluding base). Therefore

(surface of pyramid) $=$ (polygon about B).

Now (polygon about B):(polygon in B) $< S:B$.

Therefore

(surface of pyramid):(polygon in B) $< S:B$,

which is impossible (because the surface of the pyramid is greater than S, while the polygon in B is less than B).

Hence $B \not< S$.

II. Suppose $B > S$.

Take regular polygons circumscribed and inscribed to B such that the ratio of the former to the latter is less than the ratio $B:S$.

Inscribe in A a similar polygon to that inscribed in B, and erect a pyramid on the polygon inscribed in A with apex the same as that of the cone.

In this case

(polygon in A):(polygon in B) $= C^2:E^2$

$= C:D$

$>$ (polygon in A):(surface of pyramid excluding base).

This is clear because the ratio of C to D is greater than the ratio of the perpendicular from the center of A on a side of the polygon to the perpendicular from the apex of the cone on the same side.

Therefore

(surface of pyramid) $>$ (polygon in B).

But (polygon about B):(polygon in B) $< B:S$.

Therefore, *a fortiori*,

(polygon about B):(surface of pyramid) $< B:S$; which is impossible.

Since therefore B is neither greater nor less than S,

$$B = S.$$

Other examples of the "ratio" form of the exhaustion method are found in *On the Sphere and the Cylinder*, (Bk. I, Props. 13, 33, 34, 42, 44.)

As indicated earlier, in addition to the two forms of the compression method of exhaustion, Archimedes used a further technique which we may call the approximation method. This is used on only one occasion, namely, in *On the Quadrature of the Parabola* (Props. 18–24). It consists in approximating from below the area of a parabolic segment. That is to say, Archimedes continually "exhausts" the parabola by drawing first a triangle in the segment with the same base and vertex as the segment. On each side of the triangle we again construct triangles. This process is continued as far as we like. Thus if A_1 is the area of the original triangle, we have a series of inscribed triangles whose sum converges toward the area of parabolic segment: A_1, $1/4 A_1$, $(1/4)^2 A_1$, $\cdots$ (in the accompanying figure A_1 is $\triangle PQq$ and $1/4 A_1$ or A_2 is the sum of triangles Prq and PRQ and A_3 is the sum of the next set of inscribed triangles—not shown on the diagram but equal to $[1/4]^2 A_1$). In order to prove that K, the area of the parabolic segment, is equal to $4/3 A_1$, Archimedes first proves in Proposition 22 that the sum of any finite number of terms of this series is less than the area of the parabolic segment. He then proves in Proposition 23 that if we have a series of terms A_1, A_2, A_3, $\cdots$ such as those given above, that is, with $A_1 = 4A_2$, $A_2 = 4A_3$, $\cdots$, then

$$A_1 + A_2 + A_3 + \cdots + A_n + \frac{1}{3} \cdot A_n = \frac{4}{3} \cdot A_1,$$

or

$$A_1 \left[1 + \frac{1}{4} + \left(\frac{1}{4} \right)^2 + \cdots + \left(\frac{1}{4} \right)^{n-1} + \frac{1}{3} \cdot \left(\frac{1}{4} \right)^{n-1} \right]$$
$$= \frac{4}{3} \cdot A_1$$

With modern techniques of series summation we would simply say that as n increases indefinitely $(1/4)^{n-1}$ becomes infinitely small and the series in brackets tends toward $4/3$ as a limit and thus the parabolic segment equals $4/3 \cdot A_1$. But Archimedes followed the Greek *reductio* procedure. Hence he showed that if we assume $K > 4/3 \cdot A_1$ on the basis of a corollary to Proposition 20, namely, that by the successive inscription of triangles "it is possible to inscribe in the parabolic segment a polygon such that the segments left over are together less than any assigned area" (which is itself based on Euclid, *Elements* X.1), a contradiction will ensue. Similarly, a contradiction results from the assumption of $K < 4/3 \cdot A_1$. Here in brief is the final step of the proof (the reader is reminded that the terms A_1, A_2, A_3, $\cdots$, A_n, which were used above, are actually rendered by A, B, C, $\cdots$, X):[3]

Proposition 24

Every segment bounded by a parabola and a chord Qq is equal to four-thirds of the triangle which has the same base as the segment and equal height.

Suppose $\qquad K = \frac{4}{3} \triangle PQq,$

where P is the vertex of the segment; and we have then to prove that the area of the segment is equal to K.

For, if the segment be not equal to K, it must either be greater or less.

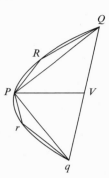

FIGURE 3

I. Suppose the area of the segment greater than K.

If then we inscribe in the segments cut off by PQ, Pq triangles which have the same base and equal height, i.e. triangles with the same vertices R, r as those of the segments, and if in the remaining segments we inscribe triangles in the same manner, and so on, we shall finally have segments remaining whose sum is less than the area by which the segment PQq exceeds K [Prop. 20 Cor.].

Therefore the polygon so formed must be greater than the area K; which is impossible, since [Prop. 23]

$$A + B + C + \cdots + Z < \frac{4}{3} A,$$

where $\qquad A = \triangle PQq.$

Thus the area of the segment cannot be greater than K.

II. Suppose, if possible, that the area of the segment is less than K.

If then $\triangle PQq = A$, $B = 1/4 A$, $C = 1/4 B$, and so on, until we arrive at an area X such that X is less than the difference between K and the segment, we have

$$A + B + C + \cdots + X + \frac{1}{3} X = \frac{4}{3} A \qquad \text{[Prop. 23]}$$
$$= K.$$

Now, since K exceeds $A + B + C + \cdots + X$ by an area less than X, and the area of the segment by an area greater than X, it follows that

$$A + B + C + \cdots + X > \text{(the segment)};$$

which is impossible, by Prop. 22. . . .

Hence the segment is not less than K.

Thus, since the segment is neither greater nor less than K,

$$(\text{area of segment } PQq) = K = \frac{4}{3} \triangle PQq.$$

In the initial remarks on the basic methods of Archimedes, it was noted that Archimedes sometimes used the technique of a *neusis* ("verging") construction. Pappus defined a *neusis* construction as "Two lines being given in position, to place between them a straight line given in length and verging towards a given point." He also noted that "a line is said to verge towards a point, if being produced, it reaches the point." No doubt "insertion" describes the mathematical meaning better than "verging" or "inclination," but "insertion" fails to render the additional condition of inclining or verging toward a point just as the name *neusis* in expressing the "verging" condition fails to render the crucial condition of insertion. At any rate, the *neusis* construction can be thought of as being accomplished mechanically by marking the termini of the linear insertion on a ruler and shifting that ruler until the termini of the insertion lie on the given curve or curves while the ruler passes through the verging point. In terms of mathematical theory most of the Greek *neuseis* require a solution by means of conics or other higher curves. *Neusis* constructions are indicated by Archimedes in *On Spirals* (Props. 5–9). They are assumed as possible without any explanation. The simplest case may be illustrated as follows: [4]

Proposition 5

Given a circle with center O, and the tangent to it at a point A, it is possible to draw from O a straight line OPF, meeting the circle in P and the tangent in F, such that, if c be the circumference of any given circle whatever,

$$FP:OP < (\text{arc } AP): c.$$

Take a straight line, as D, greater than the circumference c. [Prop. 3]

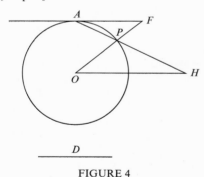

FIGURE 4

Through O draw OH parallel to the given tangent, and draw through A a line APH, meeting the circle in P and OH in H, such that the portion PH intercepted between the circle and the line OH may be equal to D [literally: "let PH be placed equal to D, verging toward A"]. Join OP and produce it to meet the tangent in F.

Then $FP:OP = AP:PH$, by parallels,
                 $= AP:D$
                 $< (\text{arc } AP):c.$

With the various methods that have been described and others, Archimedes was able to demonstrate a whole host of theorems that became a basic part of geometry. Examples beyond those already quoted follow: "The surface of any sphere is equal to four times the greatest circle in it" (*On the Sphere and the Cylinder,* Bk. I, Prop. 23); this is equivalent to the modern formulation $S = 4\pi r^2$. "Any sphere is equal to four times the cone which has its base equal to the greatest circle in the sphere and its height equal to the radius of the sphere" (*ibid.,* Prop. 34); its corollary that "every cylinder whose base is the greatest circle in a sphere and whose height is equal to the diameter of the sphere is 3/2 of the sphere and its surface together with its base is 3/2 of the surface of the sphere" is the proposition illustrated on the tombstone of Archimedes, as was noted above. The modern equivalent of Proposition 34 is $V = 4/3 \,\pi r^3$. "Any right or oblique segment of a paraboloid of revolution is half again as large as the cone or segment of a cone which has the same base and the same axis" (*On Conoids and Spheroids,* Props. 21–22). He was also able by his investigation of what are now known as Archimedean spirals not only to accomplish their quadrature (*On Spirals,* Props. 24–28), but, in preparation therefore, to perform the crucial rectification of the circumference of a circle. This, then, would allow for the construction of the right triangle equal to a circle that is the object of *On the Measurement of a Circle* (Prop. I), above. This rectification is accomplished in *On Spirals* (Prop. 18): "If a straight line is tangent to the extremity of a spiral described in the first revolution, and if from the point of origin of the spiral one erects a perpendicular on the initial line of revolution, the perpendicular will meet the tangent so that the line intercepted between the tangent and the origin of the spiral will be equal to the circumference of the first circle" (see Fig. 5).

It has also been remarked earlier that Archimedes employed statical procedures in the solution of geometrical problems and the demonstration of theorems. These procedures are evident in *On the Quadrature of the Parabola* (Props. 6–16) and also in *On the Method.* We have already seen that in the latter part of *On the Quadrature of the Parabola* Archimedes demonstrated the quadrature of the parabola by purely geometric methods. In the first part of the tract he demonstrated the same thing by means of a balancing method. By the use of the law of the lever and a knowledge of the centers of gravity of triangles and trapezia, coupled with a *reductio* procedure, the quadrature is demonstrated. In *On the Method* the same statical procedures are used; but, in addition, an entirely new assumption is joined with them, namely, that a plane figure can be considered as the summation of its line elements (presumably infinite in number) and that a volumetric figure can be

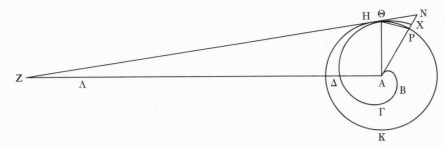

FIGURE 5

considered as the summation of its plane elements. The important point regarding this work is that it gives us a rare insight into Archimedes' procedures for discovering the theorems to be proved. The formal, indirect procedures that appear in demonstrations in the great body of Archimedes' works tell us little as to how the theorems to be proved were discovered. To be sure, sometimes he no doubt proved theorems that he had inherited with inadequate proof from his predecessors (such was perhaps the case of the theorem on the area of the circle, which he proved simply and elegantly in *On the Measurement of the Circle* [Prop. 1], as has been seen). But often we are told by him what his own discoveries were, and their relation to the discoveries of his predecessors, as, for example, those of Eudoxus. In the Preface of Book I of *On the Sphere and the Cylinder,* he characterizes his discoveries by comparing them with some established theorems of Eudoxus:[5]

> Now these properties were all along naturally inherent in the figures referred to . . ., but remained unknown to those who were before my time engaged in the study of geometry. Having, however, now discovered that the properties are true of these figures, I cannot feel any hesitation in setting them side by side both with my former investigations and with those of the theorems of Eudoxus on solids which are held to be most irrefragably established, namely, that any pyramid is one third part of the prism which has the same base with the pyramid and equal height, and that any cone is one third part of the cylinder which has the same base with the cone and equal height. For, though these properties also were naturally inherent in the figures all along, yet they were in fact unknown to all the many able geometers who lived before Eudoxus, and had not been observed by anyone. Now, however, it will be open to those who possess the requisite ability to examine these discoveries of mine.

Some of the mystery surrounding Archimedes' methods of discovery was, then, dissipated by the discovery and publication of *On the Method of Mechanical Theorems.* For example, we can see in Proposition 2 how it was that Archimedes discovered by the "method" the theorems relative to the area and volume of a sphere that he was later to prove by strict geometrical methods in *On the Sphere and the Cylinder:*[6]

Proposition 2

We can investigate by the same method the propositions that

(*1*) *Any sphere is* (*in respect of solid content*) *four times the cone with base equal to a great circle of the sphere and height equal to its radius; and*

(*2*) *the cylinder with base equal to a great circle of the sphere and height equal to the diameter is 1-1/2 times the sphere.*

(1) Let *ABCD* be a great circle of a sphere, and *AC, BD* diameters at right angles to one another.

Let a circle be drawn about *BD* as diameter and in a plane perpendicular to *AC*, and on this circle as base let a cone be described with *A* as vertex. Let the surface of this cone be produced and then cut by a plane through *C* parallel to its base; the section will be a circle on *EF* as diameter. On this circle as base let a cylinder be erected with height and axis *AC*, and produce *CA* to *H*, making *AH* equal to *CA*.

Let *CH* be regarded as the bar of a balance, *A* being its middle point.

Draw any straight line *MN* in the plane of the circle *ABCD* and parallel to *BD*. Let *MN* meet the circle in *O, P*, the diameter *AC* in *S*, and the straight lines *AE, AF* in *Q, R* respectively. Join *AO*.

Through *MN* draw a plane at right angles to *AC*; this plane will cut the cylinder in a circle with diameter *MN*, the sphere in a circle with diameter *OP*, and the cone in a circle with diameter *QR*.

Now, since *MS* = *AC*, and *QS* = *AS*,

$$MS \cdot SQ = CA \cdot AS$$
$$= AO^2$$
$$= OS^2 + SQ^2.$$

And, since *HA* = *AC*,

$$HA:AS = CA:AS$$
$$= MS:SQ$$
$$= MS^2:MS \cdot SQ$$
$$= MS^2:(OS^2 + SQ^2), \text{ from above,}$$
$$= MN^2:(OP^2 + QR^2)$$
$$= \text{(circle, diam. } MN\text{):(circle, diam. } OP$$
$$+ \text{ circle, diam. } QR\text{).}$$

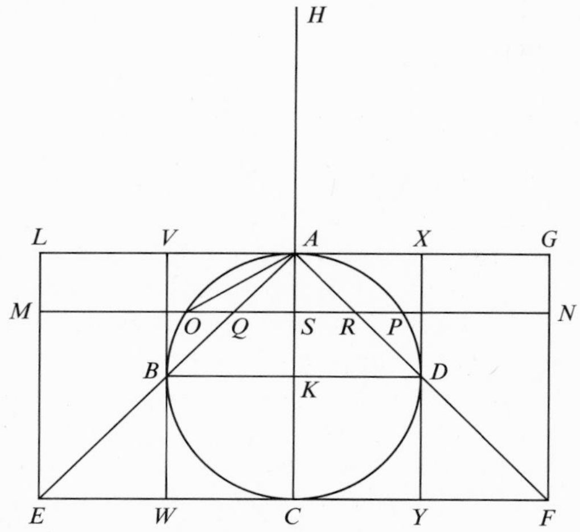

FIGURE 6

That is,

$HA:AS$ = (circle in cylinder):(circle in sphere + circle in cone).

Therefore the circle in the cylinder, placed where it is, is in equilibrium, about A, with the circle in the sphere together with the circle in the cone, if both the latter circles are placed with their centers of gravity at H.

Similarly for the three corresponding sections made by a plane perpendicular to AC and passing through any other straight line in the parallelogram LF parallel to EF.

If we deal in the same way with all the sets of three circles in which planes perpendicular to AC cut the cylinder, the sphere and the cone, and which make up those solids respectively, it follows that the cylinder, in the place where it is, will be in equilibrium about A with the sphere and the cone together, when both are placed with their centers of gravity at H.

Therefore, since K is the center of gravity of the cylinder,

$$HA:AK = \text{(cylinder)}:\text{(sphere} + \text{cone } AEF).$$

But $HA = 2AK$;
therefore cylinder = 2 (sphere + cone AEF).

Now cylinder = 3 (cone AEF); [Eucl. XII. 10]

therefore cone AEF = 2 (sphere).

But, since $EF = 2BD$,

cone AEF = 8 (cone ABD);
therefore sphere = 4 (cone ABD).

(2) Through B, D draw VBW, XDY parallel to AC; and imagine a cylinder which has AC for axis and the circles on VX, WY as diameters for bases.

Then

cylinder VY = 2 (cylinder VD)
= 6 (cone ABD)   [Eucl. XII. 10]
= $\frac{3}{2}$ (sphere), from above.

Q.E.D.

From this theorem, to the effect that a sphere is four times as great as the cone with a great circle of the sphere as base and with height equal to the radius of the sphere, I conceived the notion that the surface of any sphere is four times as great as a great circle in it; for, judging from the fact that any circle is equal to a triangle with base equal to the circumference and height equal to the radius of the circle, I apprehended that, in like manner, any sphere is equal to a cone with base equal to the surface of the sphere and height equal to the radius.

It should be observed in regard to this quotation that the basic volumetric theorem was discovered prior to the surface theorem, although in their later formal presentation in *On the Sphere and the Cylinder,* the theorem for the surface of a sphere is proved first. By using the "method" Archimedes also gave another "proof" of the quadrature of the parabola—already twice proved in *On the Quadrature of the Parabola*—and he remarks in his preface (see the quotation below) that he originally discovered this theorem by the method. Finally, in connection with *On the Method,* it is necessary to remark that Archimedes considered the method inadequate for formal demonstration, even if it did provide him with the theorems to be proved more rigorously. One supposes that it was the additional assumption considering the figures as the summation of their infinitesimal elements that provoked Archimedes' cautionary attitude, which he presents so lucidly in his introductory remarks to Eratosthenes: [7]

Seeing moreover in you, as I say, an earnest student, a man of considerable eminence in philosophy, and an admirer [of mathematical inquiry], I thought fit to write out for you and explain in detail in the same book the peculiarity of a certain method, by which it will be possible for you to get a start to enable you to investigate some of the problems in mathematics by means of mechanics. This procedure is, I am persuaded, no less useful even for the proof of the theorems themselves; for certain things first became clear to me by a mechanical method, although they had to be demonstrated by geometry afterwards because their investigation by the said method did not furnish an actual demonstration. But it is of course easier, when we have previously acquired, by the method, some knowledge of the questions, to supply the proof than it is to find it without any previous knowledge. This is a reason why, in the case of the theorems the proof of which Eudoxus was the first to discover, namely that the cone is a third part of the cylinder, and the pyramid of the prism, having the same base and equal height, we should give no small share of the credit to Democritus who was the first to make the assertion with regard to the said figure though he did not prove it. I am myself in the position of having first made the discovery of the theorem now to be published [by the method indicated], and I deem it necessary to expound the method partly because I have already spoken of it and I do not want to be thought to have uttered vain words, but equally because I am persuaded that it will be of no little service to mathematics; for I apprehend that some, either of my contemporaries or of my successors, will, by means of the method when once established, be able to discover other theorems in addition, which have not yet occurred to me.

While Archimedes' investigations were primarily in geometry and mechanics reduced to geometry, he made some important excursions into numerical calculation, although the methods he used are by no means clear. In *On the Measurement of the Circle* (Prop. 3), he calculated the ratio of circumference to diameter (not called π until early modern times) as being less than 3-1/7 and greater than 3-10/71. In the course of this proof Archimedes showed that he had an accurate method of approximating the roots of large numbers. It is also of interest that he there gave an approximation for $\sqrt{3}$, namely, $1351/780 > \sqrt{3} > 265/153$. How he computed this has been much disputed. In the tract known as *The Sandreckoner,* Archimedes presented a system to represent large numbers, a system that allows him to express a number P^{10^8}, where P itself is $(10^8)^{10^8}$. He invented this system to express numbers of the sort that, in his words, "exceed not only the number of the mass of sand equal in magnitude to the earth . . ., but also that of a mass equal in magnitude to the universe." Actually, the number he finds that would approximate the number of grains of sand to fill the universe is a mere 10^{63}, and thus does not require the higher orders described in his system. Incidentally, it is in this work that we have one of the few antique references to Aristarchus' heliocentric system.

In the development of physical science, Archimedes is celebrated as the first to apply geometry successfully to statics and hydrostatics. In his *On the Equilibrium of Planes* (Bk. I, Props. 6–7), he proved the law of the lever in a purely geometrical manner. His weights had become geometrical magnitudes possessing weight and acting perpendicularly to the balance beam, itself conceived of as a weightless geometrical line. His crucial assumption was the special case of the equilibrium of the balance of equal arm length supporting equal weights. This postulate, although it may ultimately rest on experience, in the context of a mathematical proof appears to be a basic appeal to geometrical symmetry. In demonstrating Proposition 6, "Commensurable magnitudes are in equilib-

rium at distances reciprocally proportional to their weights," his major objective was to reduce the general case of unequal weights at inversely proportional distances to the special case of equal weights at equal distances. This was done by (1) converting the weightless beam of unequal arm lengths into a beam of equal arm lengths, and then (2) distributing the unequal weights, analyzed into rational component parts over the extended beam uniformly so that we have a case of equal weights at equal distances. Finally (3) the proof utilized propositions concerning centers of gravity (which in part appear to have been proved elsewhere by Archimedes) to show that the case of the uniformly distributed parts of the unequal weights over the extended beam is in fact identical with the case of the composite weights concentrated on the arms at unequal lengths. Further, it is shown in Proposition 7 that if the theorem is true for rational magnitudes, it is true for irrational magnitudes as well (although the incompleteness of this latter proof has been much discussed). The severest criticism of the proof of Proposition 6 is, of course, the classic discussion by Ernst Mach in his *Science of Mechanics,* which stresses two general points: (1) experience must have played a predominant role in the proof and its postulates in spite of its mathematical-deductive form; and (2) any attempt to go from the special case of the lever to the general case by replacing expanded weights on a lever arm with a weight concentrated at their center of gravity must assume that which has to be proved, namely, the principle of static moment. This criticism has given rise to an extensive literature and stimulated some successful defenses of Archimedes, and this body of literature has been keenly analyzed by E. J. Dijksterhuis (*Archimedes,* pp. 289–304). It has been pointed out further, and with some justification, that Proposition 6 with its proof, even if sound, only establishes that the inverse proportionality of weights and arm lengths is a sufficient condition for the equilibrium of a lever supported in its center of gravity under the influence of two weights on either side of the fulcrum. It is evident that he should also have shown that the condition is a necessary one, since he repeatedly applies the inverse proportionality as a necessary condition of equilibrium. But this is easily done and so may have appeared trivial to Archimedes. The succeeding propositions in Book I of *On the Equilibrium of Planes* show that Archimedes conceived of this part of the work as preparatory to his use of statics in his investigation of geometry of the sort that we have described in *On the Quadrature of the Parabola* and *On the Method.*

In his *On Floating Bodies,* the emphasis is once

more largely on geometrical analysis. In Book I, a somewhat obscure concept of hydrostatic pressure is presented as his basic postulate:[8]

> Let it be granted that the fluid is of such a nature that of the parts of it which are at the same level and adjacent to one another that which is pressed the less is pushed away by that which is pressed the more, and that each of its parts is pressed by the fluid which is vertically above it, if the fluid is not shut up in anything and is not compressed by anything else.

As his propositions are analyzed, we see that Archimedes essentially maintained an Aristotelian concept of weight directed downward toward the center of the earth conceived of as the center of the world. In fact, he goes further by imagining the earth removed and so fluids are presented as part of a fluid sphere all of whose parts weigh downward convergently toward the center of the sphere. The surface of the sphere is then imagined as being divided into an equal number of parts which are the bases of conical sectors having the center of the sphere as their vertex. Thus the water in each sector weighs downward toward the center. Then if a solid is added to a sector, increasing the pressure on it, the pressure is transmitted down through the center of the sphere and back upward on an adjacent sector and the fluid in that adjacent sector is forced upward to equalize the level of adjacent sectors. The influence on other than adjacent sectors is ignored. It is probable that Archimedes did not have the concept of hydrostatic paradox formulated by Stevin, which held that at any given point of the fluid the pressure is a constant magnitude that acts perpendicularly on any plane through that point. But, by his procedures, Archimedes was able to formulate propositions concerning the relative immersion in a fluid of solids less dense than, as dense as, and more dense than the fluid in which they are placed. Proposition 7 relating to solids denser than the fluid expresses the so-called "principle of Archimedes" in this fashion: "Solids heavier than the fluid, when thrown into the fluid, will be driven downward as far as they can sink, and they will be lighter [when weighed] in the fluid [than their weight in air] by the weight of the portion of fluid having the same volume as the solid." This is usually more succinctly expressed by saying that such solids will be lighter in the fluid by the weight of the fluid displaced. Book II, which investigates the different positions in which a right segment of a paraboloid can float in a fluid, is a brilliant geometrical tour de force. In it Archimedes returns to the basic assumption found in *On the Equilibrium of Planes, On the Quadrature of the Parab-*

ola, and *On the Method,* namely, that weight verticals are to be conceived of as parallel rather than as convergent at the center of a fluid sphere.

Influence. Unlike the *Elements* of Euclid, the works of Archimedes were not widely known in antiquity. Our present knowledge of his works depends largely on the interest taken in them at Constantinople from the sixth through the tenth centuries. It is true that before that time individual works of Archimedes were obviously studied at Alexandria, since Archimedes was often quoted by three eminent mathematicians of Alexandria: Hero, Pappus, and Theon. But it is with the activity of Eutocius of Ascalon, who was born toward the end of the fifth century and studied at Alexandria, that the textual history of a collected edition of Archimedes properly begins. Eutocius composed commentaries on three of Archimedes' works: *On the Sphere and the Cylinder, On the Measurement of the Circle,* and *On the Equilibrium of Planes.* These were no doubt the most popular of Archimedes' works at that time. The *Commentary on the Sphere and the Cylinder* is a rich work for historical references to Greek geometry. For example, in an extended comment to Book II, Proposition 1, Eutocius presents manifold solutions of earlier geometers to the problem of finding two mean proportionals between two given lines. *The Commentary on the Measurement of the Circle* is of interest in its detailed expansion of Archimedes' calculation of π. The works of Archimedes and the commentaries of Eutocius were studied and taught by Isidore of Miletus and Anthemius of Tralles, Justinian's architects of Hagia Sophia in Constantinople. It was apparently Isidore who was responsible for the first collected edition of at least the three works commented on by Eutocius as well as the commentaries. Later Byzantine authors seem gradually to have added other works to this first collected edition until the ninth century when the educational reformer Leon of Thessalonica produced the compilation represented by Greek manuscript A (adopting the designation used by the editor, J. L. Heiberg). Manuscript A contained all of the Greek works now known excepting *On Floating Bodies, On the Method, Stomachion,* and *The Cattle Problem.* This was one of the two manuscripts available to William of Moerbeke when he made his Latin translations in 1269. It was the source, directly or indirectly, of all of the Renaissance copies of Archimedes. A second Byzantine manuscript, designated as B, included only the mechanical works: *On the Equilibrium of Planes, On the Quadrature of the Parabola,* and *On Floating Bodies* (and possibly *On Spirals*). It too was available to Moerbeke. But it disappears after an early fourteenth-century reference. Finally, we can mention a third Byzantine manuscript, C, a palimpsest whose Archimedean parts are in a hand of the tenth century. It was not available to the Latin West in the Middle Ages, or indeed in modern times until its identification by Heiberg in 1906 at Constantinople (where it had been brought from Jerusalem). It contains large parts of *On the Sphere and the Cylinder,* almost all of *On Spirals,* some parts of *On the Measurement of the Circle* and *On the Equilibrium of Planes,* and a part of the *Stomachion.* More important, it contains most of the Greek text of *On Floating Bodies* (a text unavailable in Greek since the disappearance of manuscript B) and a great part of *On the Method of Mechanical Theorems,* hitherto known only by hearsay. (Hero mentions it in his *Metrica,* and the Byzantine lexicographer Suidas declares that Theodosius wrote a commentary on it.)

At about the same time that Archimedes was being studied in ninth-century Byzantium, he was also finding a place among the Arabs. The Arabic Archimedes has been studied in only a preliminary fashion, but it seems unlikely that the Arabs possessed any manuscript of his works as complete as manuscript A. Still, they often brilliantly exploited the methods of Archimedes and brought to bear their fine knowledge of conic sections on Archimedean problems. The Arabic Archimedes consisted of the following works: (1) *On the Sphere and the Cylinder* and at least a part of Eutocius' commentary on it. This work seems to have existed in a poor, early ninth-century translation, revised in the late ninth century, first by Isḥāq ibn Ḥunayn and then by Thābit ibn Qurra. It was reedited by Nasīr ad-Dīn al-Ṭūsī in the thirteenth century and was on occasion paraphrased and commented on by other Arabic authors (see Archimedes in Index of Suter's "Die Mathematiker und Astronomen"). (2) *On the Measurement of the Circle,* translated by Thābit ibn Qurra and reedited by al-Ṭūsī. Perhaps the commentary on it by Eutocius was also translated, for the extended calculation of π found in the geometrical tract of the ninth-century Arabic mathematicians the Banū Mūsā bears some resemblance to that present in the commentary of Eutocius. (3) A fragment of *On Floating Bodies,* consisting of a definition of specific gravity not present in the Greek text, a better version of the basic postulate (described above) than exists in the Greek text, and the enunciations without proofs of seven of the nine propositions of Book I and the first proposition of Book II. (4) Perhaps *On the Quadrature of the Parabola*—at least this problem received the attention of Thābit ibn Qurra. (5) Some indirect material from *On the Equilibrium of Planes* found in other mechanical works translated into Arabic (such as

Hero's *Mechanics,* the so-called Euclid tract *On the Balance,* the *Liber karastonis,* etc.). (6) In addition, various other works attributed to Archimedes by the Arabs and for which there is no extant Greek text (see list above in "Mathematical Works"). Of the additional works, we can single out the *Lemmata* (*Liber assumptorum*), for, although it cannot have come directly from Archimedes in its present form, in the opinion of experts several of its propositions are Archimedean in character. One such proposition was Proposition 8, which employed a *neusis* construction like those used by Archimedes:[9]

Proposition 8

If we let line *AB* be led everywhere in the circle and extended rectilinearly [see Fig. 7], and if *BC* is posited as equal to the radius of the circle, and *C* is connected to the center of the circle *D,* and the line (*CD*) is produced to *E,* arc *AE* will be triple arc *BF.* Therefore, let us draw *EG* parallel to *AB* and join *DB* and *DG.* And because the two angles *DEG, DGE* are equal, $\angle GDC = 2 \angle DEG$. And because $\angle BDC = \angle BCD$ and $\angle CEG = \angle ACE$, $\angle GDC = 2 \angle CDB$ and $\angle BDG = 3 \angle BDC$, and arc *BG* = arc *AE,* and arc *AE* = 3 arc *BF;* and this is what we wished.

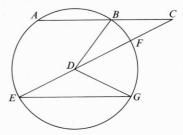

FIGURE 7

This proposition shows, then, that if one finds the position and condition of line *ABC* such that it is drawn through *A,* meets the circle again in *B,* and its extension *BC* equals the radius, this will give the trisection of the given angle *BDG.* It thus demonstrates the equivalence of a *neusis* and the trisection problem—but without solving the *neusis* (which could be solved by the construction of a conchoid to a circular base).

Special mention should also be made of the *Book on the Division of the Circle into Seven Equal Parts,* attributed to Archimedes by the Arabs, for its remarkable construction of a regular heptagon. This work stimulated a whole series of Arabic studies of this problem, including one by the famous Ibn al-Haytham (Alhazen). Propositions 16 and 17, leading to that construction, are given here in toto:[10]

Proposition 16

Let us construct square *ABCD* [Fig. 8] and extend side *AB* directly toward *H.* Then we draw the diagonal

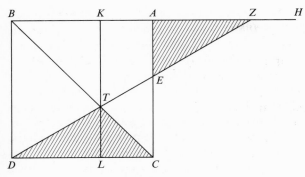

FIGURE 8

BC. We lay one end of a rule on point *D*. Its other end we make meet extension *AH* at a point *Z* such that $\triangle AZE = \triangle CTD$. Further, we draw the straight line *KTL* through *T* and parallel to *AC*. And now I say that $AB \cdot KB = AZ^2$ and $ZK \cdot AK = KB^2$ and, in addition, each of the two lines *AZ* and $KB > AK$.

Proof:

(1) $CD \cdot TL = AZ \cdot AE$ \qquad [given] \qquad Hence

(2) $\dfrac{CD(=AB)}{AZ} = \dfrac{AE}{TL}$

Since $\triangle ZAE \sim \triangle ZKT \sim \triangle TLD$, hence

(3) $\dfrac{AE}{TL} = \dfrac{AZ}{LD(=KB)}, \dfrac{AB}{AZ} = \dfrac{AZ}{KB}$, and

$\dfrac{TL(=AK)}{KT(=KB)} = \dfrac{LD(=KB)}{ZK}$. Therefore

(4) $AB \cdot KB = AZ^2$ \qquad and
$ZK \cdot AK = KB^2$

and each of the lines *AZ* and $KB > AK$. \qquad Q.E.D.

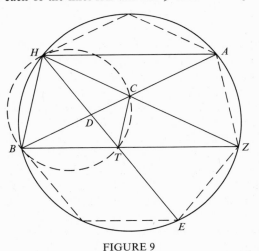

FIGURE 9

Proposition 17

We now wish to divide the circle into seven equal parts (Fig. 9). We draw the line segment *AB*, which we set out as known. We mark on it two points *C* and *D*, such that $AD \cdot CD = DB^2$ and $CB \cdot BD = AC^2$ and in addition each of the two segments *AC* and $DB > CD$,

following the preceding proposition [i.e., Prop. 16]. Out of lines *AC, CD* and *BD* we construct $\triangle CHD$. Accordingly $CH = AC$, $DH = DB$ and $CD = CD$. Then we circumscribe about $\triangle AHB$ the circle *AHBEZ* and we extend lines *HC* and *HD* directly up to the circumference of the circle. On their intersection with the circumference lie the points *Z* and *E*. We join *B* with *Z*. Lines *BZ* and *HE* intersect in *T*. We also draw *CT*. Since $AC = CH$, hence $\angle HAC = \angle AHC$, and arc $AZ =$ arc *HB*. And, indeed, $AD \cdot CD = DB^2 = DH^2$ and [by Euclid, VI.8] $\triangle AHD \sim \triangle CHD$; consequently $\angle DAH = \angle CHD$, or arc $ZE =$ arc *BH*. Hence *BH, AZ* and *ZE* are three equal arcs. Further, *ZB* is parallel to *AH*, $\angle CAH = \angle CHD = \angle TBD$; $HD = DB$, $CD = DT$, $CH = BT$. Hence, [since the products of the parts of these diagonals are equal], the 4 points *B, H, C* and *T* lie in the circumference of one and the same circle. From the similarity of triangles *HBC* and *HBT*, it follows that $CB \cdot DB = HC^2 = AC^2$ [or $HT/HC = HC/HD$] and from the similarity of $\triangle THC$ and $\triangle CHD$, it follows that $TH \cdot HD = HC^2$. And further $CB = TH$ [these being equal diagonals in the quadrilateral] and $\angle DCH = \angle HTC = 2\angle CAH$. [The equality of the first two angles arises from the similarity of triangles *THC* and *CHD*. Their equality with $2\angle CAH$ arises as follows: (1) $AHD = 2\angle CAH$, for $\angle CAH = \angle CHD = \angle CHA$ and $\angle AHD = \angle CHA + \angle CHD$; (2) $\angle AHD = \angle BTH$, for parallel lines cut by a third line produce equal alternate angles; (3) $\angle BTH = \angle DCH$, from similar triangles; (4) hence $\angle DCH = 2\angle CAH$.] [And since $\angle HBA = \angle DCH$, hence $\angle HBA = 2\angle CAH$.] Consequently, arc $AH = 2$ arc *BH*. Since $\angle DHB = \angle DBH$, consequently arc $EB = 2$ arc *HB*. Hence, each of arcs *AH* and *EB* equals 2 arc *HB*, and accordingly the circle *AHBEZ* is divided into seven equal parts. Q.E.D. And praise be to the one God, etc.

The key to the whole procedure is, of course, the *neusis* presented in Proposition 16 (see Fig. 8) that would allow us in a similar fashion to find the points *C* and *D* in Proposition 17 (see Fig. 9). In Proposition 16 the *neusis* consisted in drawing a line from *D* to intersect the extension of *AB* in point *Z* such that $\triangle AZE = \triangle CTD$. The way in which the *neusis* was solved by Archimedes (or whoever was the author of this tract) is not known. Ibn al-Haytham, in his later treatment of the heptagon, mentions the Archimedean *neusis* but then goes on to show that one does not need the Archimedean square of Proposition 16. Rather he shows that points *C* and *D* in Proposition 17 can be found by the intersection of a parabola and a hyperbola.[11] It should be observed that all but two of Propositions 1–13 in this tract concern right triangles, and those two are necessary for propositions concerning right triangles. It seems probable, therefore, that Propositions 1–13 comprise the so-called *On the Properties of the Right Triangle* attributed in the *Fihrist* to Archimedes (although at least some of these propositions are Arabic interpolations). Incidentally, Propositions 7–10 have as their objective the formulation $K = (s - a) \cdot (s - c)$, where K is the area and a and c are the sides including the right angle and s is the semiperimeter, and Proposition 13 has as its objective $K = s(s - b)$, where b is the hypotenuse. Hence, if we multiply the two formulations, we have

$$K^2 = s(s - a) \cdot (s - b) \cdot (s - c)$$

or $\quad K = \sqrt{s(s - a) \cdot (s - b) \cdot (s - c)},$

Hero's formula for the area of a triangle in terms of its sides—at least in the case of a right triangle. Interestingly, the Arab scholar al-Bīrūnī attributed the general Heronian formula to Archimedes. Propositions 14 and 15 of the tract make no reference to Propositions 1–13 and concern chords. Each leads to a formulation in terms of chords equivalent to $\sin A/2 = \sqrt{(1 - \cos A)/2}$. Thus Propositions 14–15 seem to be from some other work (and at least Proposition 15 is an Arabic interpolation). If Proposition 14 was in the Greek text translated by Thābit ibn Qurra and does go back to Archimedes, then we would have to conclude that this formula was his discovery rather than Ptolemy's, as it is usually assumed to be.

The Latin West received its knowledge of Archimedes from both the sources just described: Byzantium and Islam. There is no trace of the earlier translations imputed by Cassiodorus to Boethius. Such knowledge that was had in the West before the twelfth century consisted of some rather general hydrostatic information that may have indirectly had its source in Archimedes. It was in the twelfth century that the translation of Archimedean texts from the Arabic first began. The small tract *On the Measurement of the Circle* was twice translated from the Arabic. The first translation was a rather defective one and was possibly executed by Plato of Tivoli. There are many numerical errors in the extant copies of it and the second half of Proposition 3 is missing. The second translation was almost certainly done by the twelfth century's foremost translator, Gerard of Cremona. The Arabic text from which he worked (without doubt the text of Thābit ibn Qurra) included a corollary on the area of a sector of a circle attributed by Hero to Archimedes but missing from our extant Greek text.

Not only was Gerard's translation widely quoted by medieval geometers such as Gerard of Brussels, Roger Bacon, and Thomas Bradwardine, it also served as the point of departure for a whole series of emended versions and paraphrases of the tract in the course of the thirteenth and fourteenth centuries. Among these are the so-called Naples, Cambridge, Florence, and Gordanus versions of the thirteenth century; and the Corpus Christi, Munich, and Albert of Saxony versions of the fourteenth. These versions were expanded by including pertinent references to Euclid and the spelling-out of the geometrical steps only implied in the Archimedean text. In addition, we see attempts to specify the postulates that underlie the proof of Proposition I. For example, in the Cambridge version three postulates (*petitiones*) introduce the text: [12] "[1] There is some curved line equal to any straight line and some straight line to any curved line. [2] Any chord is less than its arc. [3] The perimeter of any including figure is greater than the perimeter of the included figure." Furthermore, self-conscious attention was given in some versions to the logical nature of the proof of Proposition I. Thus, the Naples version immediately announced that the proof was to be *per impossibile,* i.e., by reduction to absurdity. In the Gordanus, Corpus Christi, and Munich versions we see a tendency to elaborate the proofs in the manner of scholastic tracts. The culmination of this kind of elaboration appeared in the *Questio de quadratura circuli* of Albert of Saxony, composed some time in the third quarter of the fourteenth century. The Hellenistic mathematical form of the original text was submerged in an intricate scholastic structure that included multiple terminological distinctions and the argument and counterargument technique represented by initial arguments ("principal reasons") and their final refutations.

Another trend in the later versions was the introduction of rather foolish physical justifications for postulates. In the Corpus Christi version, the second postulate to the effect that a straight line may be equal to a curved line is supported by the statement that "if a hair or silk thread is bent around circumference-wise in a plane surface and then afterwards is extended in a straight line, who will doubt—unless he is hare-brained—that the hair or thread is the same whether it is bent circumference-wise or extended in a straight line and is just as long the one time as the other." Similarly, Albert of Saxony, in his *Questio,* declared that a sphere can be "cubed" since the contents of a spherical vase can be poured into a cubical vase. Incidentally, Albert based his proof of the quadrature of the circle not directly on Proposition X.1 of the *Elements,* as was the case in the other medieval versions of *On the Measurement of the Circle,* but rather on a "betweenness" postulate: "I suppose that with two continuous [and comparable] quantities proposed, a magnitude greater than the 'lesser' can be cut from the 'greater.'" A similar postulate was employed in still another fourteenth-century version of the *De mensura circuli* called the Pseudo-Bradwardine version. Finally, in regard to the manifold medieval versions of *On the Measurement of the Circle,* it can be noted that the Florence version of Proposition 3 contained a detailed elaboration of the calculation of π. One might have supposed that the author had consulted Eutocius' commentary, except that his arithmetical procedures differed widely from those used by Eutocius. Furthermore, no translation of Eutocius' commentary appears to have been made before 1450, and the Florence version certainly must be dated before 1400.

In addition to his translation of *On the Measurement of the Circle,* Gerard of Cremona also translated the geometrical *Discourse of the Sons of Moses (Verba filiorum)* composed by the Banū Mūsā. This Latin translation was of particular importance for the introduction of Archimedes into the West. We can single out these contributions of the treatise: (1) A proof of Proposition I of *On the Measurement of the Circle* somewhat different from that of Archimedes but still fundamentally based on the exhaustion method. (2) A determination of the value of π drawn from Proposition 3 of the same treatise but with further calculations similar to those found in the commentary of Eutocius. (3) Hero's theorem for the area of a triangle in terms of its sides (noted above), with the first demonstration of that theorem in Latin (the enunciation of this theorem had already appeared in the writings of the *agrimensores* and in Plato of Tivoli's translation of the *Liber embadorum* of Savasorda). (4) Theorems for the volume and surface area of a cone, again with demonstrations. (5) Theorems for the volume and surface area of a sphere with demonstrations of an Archimedean character. (6) A use of the formula for the area of a circle equivalent to $A = \pi r^2$ in addition to the more common Archimedean form, $A = 1/2\, cr$. Instead of the modern symbol π the authors used the expression "the quantity which when multiplied by the diameter produces the circumference." (7) The introduction into the West of the problem of finding two mean proportionals between two given lines. In this treatise we find two solutions: (*a*) one attributed by the Banū Mūsā to Menelaus and by Eutocius to Archytas, (*b*) the other presented by the Banū Mūsā as their own but similar to the solution attributed by Eutocius to Plato. (8) The first solution in Latin of the problem of the trisection of an angle. (9) A method of approximating cube roots to any desired limit.

The *Verba filiorum* was, then, rich fare for the geometers of the twelfth century. The tract was quite widely cited in the thirteenth and fourteenth cen-

turies. In the thirteenth, the eminent mathematicians Jordanus de Nemore and Leonardo Fibonacci made use of it. For example, the latter, in his *Practica geometrie,* excerpted both of the solutions of the mean proportionals problem given by the Banū Mūsā, while the former (or perhaps a continuator) in his *De triangulis* presented one of them together with an entirely different solution, namely, that one assigned by Eutocius to Philo of Byzantium. Similarly, Jordanus (or possibly the same continuator) extracted the solution of the trisection of an angle from the *Verba filiorum,* but in addition made the remarkably perspicacious suggestion that the *neusis* can be solved by the use of a proposition from Ibn al-Haytham's *Optics,* which solves a similar *neusis* by conic sections.

Some of the results and techniques of *On the Sphere and the Cylinder* also became known through a treatise entitled *De curvis superficiebus Archimenidis* and said to be by Johannes de Tinemue. This seems to have been translated from the Greek in the early thirteenth century or at least composed on the basis of a Greek tract. The *De curvis superficiebus* contained ten propositions with several corollaries and was concerned for the most part with the surfaces and volumes of cones, cylinders, and spheres. This was a very popular work and was often cited by later authors. Like Gerard of Cremona's translation of *On the Measurement of the Circle,* the *De curvis superficiebus* was emended by Latin authors, two original propositions being added to one version (represented by manuscript D of the *De curvis superficiebus*)[13] and three quite different propositions being added to another (represented by manuscript M of the *De curvis*).[14] In the first of the additions to the latter version, the Latin author applied the exhaustion method to a problem involving the surface of a segment of a sphere, showing that at least this author had made the method his own. And indeed the geometer Gerard of Brussels in his *De motu* of about the same time also used the Archimedean *reductio* procedure in a highly original manner.

In 1269, some decades after the appearance of the *De curvis superficiebus,* the next important step was taken in the passage of Archimedes to the West when much of the Byzantine corpus was translated from the Greek by the Flemish Dominican, William of Moerbeke. In this translation Moerbeke employed Greek manuscripts A and B which had passed to the pope's library in 1266 from the collection of the Norman kings of the Two Sicilies. Except for *The Sandreckoner* and Eutocius' *Commentary on the Measurement of the Circle,* all the works included in manuscripts A and B were rendered into Latin by William. Needless to say, *On the Method, The Cattle*

Problem, and the *Stomachion,* all absent from manuscripts A and B, were not among William's translations. Although William's translations are not without error (and indeed some of the errors are serious), the translations, on the whole, present the Archimedean works in an understandable way. We possess the original holograph of Moerbeke's translations (MS Vat. Ottob. lat. 1850). This manuscript was not widely copied. The translation of *On Spirals* was copied from it in the fourteenth century (MS Vat. Reg. lat. 1253, 14r–33r), and several works were copied from it in the fifteenth century in an Italian manuscript now at Madrid (Bibl. Nac. 9119), and one work (*On Floating Bodies*) was copied from it in the sixteenth century (MS Vat. Barb. lat. 304, 124r–141v, 160v–161v). But, in fact, the Moerbeke translations were utilized more than one would expect from the paucity of manuscripts. They were used by several Schoolmen at the University of Paris toward the middle of the fourteenth century. Chief among them was the astronomer and mathematician John of Meurs, who appears to have been the compositor of a hybrid tract in 1340 entitled *Circuli quadratura.* This tract consisted of fourteen propositions. The first thirteen were drawn from Moerbeke's translation of *On Spirals* and were just those propositions necessary to the proof of Proposition 18 of *On Spirals,* whose enunciation we have quoted above. The fourteenth proposition of the hybrid tract was Proposition 1 from Moerbeke's translation of *On the Measurement of the Circle.* Thus this author realized that by the use of Proposition 18 from *On Spirals,* he had achieved the necessary rectification of the circumference of a circle preparatory to the final quadrature of the circle accomplished in *On the Measurement of the Circle,* Proposition 1. Incidentally, the hybrid tract did not merely use the Moerbeke translations verbatim but also included considerable commentary. In fact, this medieval Latin tract was the first known commentary on Archimedes' *On Spirals.* That the commentary was at times quite perceptive is indicated by the fact that the author suggested that the *neusis* introduced by Archimedes in Proposition 7 of *On Spirals* could be solved by means of an *instrumentum conchoydeale.* The only place in which a medieval Latin commentator could have learned of such an instrument would have been in that section of the *Commentary on the Sphere and the Cylinder* where Eutocius describes Nicomedes' solution of the problem of finding two mean proportionals (Bk. II, Prop. 1). We have further evidence that John of Meurs knew of Eutocius' *Commentary* in the Moerbeke translation when he used sections from this commentary in his *De arte mensurandi* (Ch. VIII, Prop. 16), where three

of the solutions of the mean proportionals problem given by Eutocius are presented. Not only did John incorporate the whole hybrid tract *Circuli quadratura* into Chapter VIII of his *De arte mensurandi* (composed, it seems, shortly after 1343) but in Chapter X of the *De arte* he quoted verbatim many propositions from Moerbeke's translations of *On the Sphere and the Cylinder* and *On Conoids and Spheroids* (which latter he misapplied to problems concerning solids generated by the rotation of circular segments). Within the next decade or so after John of Meurs, Nicole Oresme, his colleague at the University of Paris, in his *De configurationibus qualitatum et motuum* (Part I, Ch. 21) revealed knowledge of *On Spirals,* at least in the form of the hybrid *Circuli quadratura.* Further, Oresme in his *Questiones super de celo et mundo,* quoted at length from Moerbeke's translation of *On Floating Bodies,* while Henry of Hesse, Oresme's junior contemporary at Paris, quoted briefly therefrom. (Before this time, the only knowledge of *On Floating Bodies* had come in a thirteenth-century treatise entitled *De ponderibus Archimenidis sive de incidentibus in humidum,* a Pseudo-Archimedean treatise prepared largely from Arabic sources, whose first proposition expressed the basic conclusion of the "principle of Archimedes": "The weight of any body in air exceeds its weight in water by the weight of a volume of water equal to its volume.") Incontrovertible evidence, then, shows that at the University of Paris in the mid-fourteenth century six of the nine Archimedean translations of William of Moerbeke were known and used: *On Spirals, On the Measurement of the Circle, On the Sphere and the Cylinder, On Conoids and Spheroids, On Floating Bodies,* and Eutocius' *Commentary on the Sphere and the Cylinder.* While no direct evidence exists of the use of the remaining three translations, there has been recently discovered in a manuscript written at Paris in the fourteenth century (BN lat. 7377B, 93v–94r) an Archimedean-type proof of the law of the lever that might have been inspired by Archimedes' *On the Equilibrium of Planes.* But other than this, the influence of Archimedes on medieval statics was entirely indirect. The anonymous *De canonio,* translated from the Greek in the early thirteenth century, and Thābit ibn Qurra's *Liber karastonis,* translated from the Arabic by Gerard of Cremona, passed on this indirect influence of Archimedes in three respects: (1) Both tracts illustrated the Archimedean type of geometrical demonstrations of statical theorems and the geometrical form implied in weightless beams and weights that were really only geometrical magnitudes. (2) They gave specific reference in geometrical language to the law of the lever (and in the *De canonio* the law of the lever is connected directly to Archimedes). (3) They indirectly reflected the centers-of-gravity doctrine so important to Archimedes, in that both treatises employed the practice of substituting for a material beam segment a weight equal in weight to the material segment but hung from the middle point of the weightless segment used to replace the material segment. Needless to say, these two tracts played an important role in stimulating the rather impressive statics associated with the name of Jordanus de Nemore.

In the fifteenth century, knowledge of Archimedes in Europe began to expand. A new Latin translation was made by James of Cremona in about 1450 by order of Pope Nicholas V. Since this translation was made exclusively from manuscript A, the translation failed to include *On Floating Bodies,* but it did include the two treatises in A omitted by Moerbeke, namely, *The Sandreckoner* and Eutocius' *Commentary on the Measurement of the Circle.* It appears that this new translation was made with an eye on Moerbeke's translations. Not long after its completion, a copy of the new translation was sent by the pope to Nicholas of Cusa, who made some use of it in his *De mathematicis complementis,* composed in 1453–1454. There are at least nine extant manuscripts of this translation, one of which was corrected by Regiomontanus and brought to Germany about 1468 (the Latin translation published with the *editio princeps* of the Greek text in 1544 was taken from this copy). Greek manuscript A itself was copied a number of times. Cardinal Bessarion had one copy prepared between 1449 and 1468 (MS E). Another (MS D) was made from A when it was in the possession of the well-known humanist George Valla. The fate of A and its various copies has been traced skillfully by J. L. Heiberg in his edition of Archimedes' *Opera.* The last known use of manuscript A occurred in 1544, after which time it seems to have disappeared. The first printed Archimedean materials were in fact merely Latin excerpts that appeared in George Valla's *De expetendis et fugiendis rebus opus* (Venice, 1501) and were based on his reading of manuscript A. But the earliest actual printed texts of Archimedes were the Moerbeke translations of *On the Measurement of the Circle* and *On the Quadrature of the Parabola (Tetragonismus, id est circuli quadratura etc.),* published from the Madrid manuscript by L. Gaurico (Venice, 1503). In 1543, also at Venice, N. Tartaglia republished the same two translations directly from Gaurico's work, and, in addition, from the same Madrid manuscript, the Moerbeke translations of *On the Equilibrium of Planes* and Book I of *On Floating Bodies* (leaving the erroneous impression that he had made these translations

from a Greek manuscript, which he had not since he merely repeated the texts of the Madrid manuscript with virtually all their errors). Incidentally, Curtius Trioianus published from the legacy of Tartaglia both books of *On Floating Bodies* in Moerbeke's translation (Venice, 1565). The key event, however, in the further spread of Archimedes was the aforementioned *editio princeps* of the Greek text with the accompanying Latin translation of James of Cremona at Basel in 1544. Since the Greek text rested ultimately on manuscript A, *On Floating Bodies* was not included. A further Latin translation of the Archimedean texts was published by the perceptive mathematician Federigo Commandino in Bologna in 1558, which the translator supplemented with a skillful mathematical emendation of Moerbeke's translation of *On Floating Bodies* (Bologna, 1565) but without any knowledge of the long lost Greek text. Already in the period 1534–1549, a paraphrase of Archimedean texts had been made by Francesco Maurolico. This was published in Palermo in 1685. One other Latin translation of the sixteenth century by Antonius de Albertis remains in manuscript only and appears to have exerted no influence on mathematics and science. After 1544 the publications on Archimedes and the use of his works began to multiply markedly. His works presented quadrature problems and propositions that mathematicians sought to solve and demonstrate not only with his methods, but also with a developing geometry of infinitesimals that was to anticipate in some respect the infinitesimal calculus of Newton and Leibniz. His hydrostatic conceptions were used to modify Aristotelian mechanics. Archimedes' influence on mechanics and mathematics can be seen in the works of such authors as Commandino, Guido Ubaldi del Monte, Benedetti, Simon Stevin, Luca Valerio, Kepler, Galileo, Cavalieri, Torricelli, and numerous others. For example, Galileo mentions Archimedes more than a hundred times, and the limited inertial doctrine used in his analysis of the parabolic path of a projectile is presented as an Archimedean-type abstraction. Archimedes began to appear in the vernacular languages. Tartaglia had already rendered into Italian Book I of *On Floating Bodies,* Book I of *On the Sphere and the Cylinder,* and the section on proportional means from Eutocius' *Commentary on the Sphere and the Cylinder.* Book I of *On the Equilibrium of Planes* was translated into French in 1565 by Pierre Forcadel. It was, however, not until 1670 that a more or less complete translation was made into German by J. C. Sturm on the basis of the influential Greek and Latin edition of David Rivault (Paris, 1615). Also notable for its influence was the new Latin edition of Isaac Barrow (London,

1675). Of the many editions prior to the modern edition of Heiberg, the most important was that of Joseph Torelli (Oxford, 1792). By this time, of course, Archimedes' works had been almost completely absorbed into European mathematics and had exerted their substantial and enduring influence on early modern science.

NOTES

1. Heath, *The Works of Archimedes,* pp. 91–93. Heath's close paraphrase has been used here and below because of its economy of expression. While he uses modern symbols and has reduced the general enunciations to statements concerning specific figures in some of the propositions quoted below, he nevertheless achieves a faithful representation of the spirit of the original text.
2. *Ibid.,* pp. 19–20.
3. *Ibid.,* pp. 251–252.
4. *Ibid.,* pp. 156–57.
5. *Ibid.,* pp. 1–2.
6. *Ibid.,* Suppl., pp. 18–22.
7. *Ibid.,* pp. 13–14.
8. Dijksterhuis, *Archimedes,* p. 373.
9. Clagett, *Archimedes in the Middle Ages,* pp. 667–668.
10. Schoy, *Die trigonometrischen Lehren,* pp. 82–83.
11. *Ibid.,* pp. 85–91.
12. Clagett, *op. cit.,* p. 27. The succeeding quotations from the various versions of *On the Measurement of the Circle* are also from this volume.
13. *Ibid.,* p. 520.
14. *Ibid.,* p. 530.

BIBLIOGRAPHY

I. ORIGINAL WORKS.

1. *The Greek Text and Modern Translations.* J. L. Heiberg, ed., *Archimedis opera omnia cum commentariis Eutocii,* 2nd ed., 3 vols. (Leipzig, 1910–1915). For the full titles of the various editions cited in the body of the article as well as others, see E. J. Dijksterhuis, *Archimedes* (Copenhagen, 1956), pp. 40–45, 417. Of recent translations and paraphrases, the following, in addition to Dijksterhuis' brilliant analytic summary, ought to be noted: T. L. Heath, *The Works of Archimedes,* edited in modern notation, with introductory chapters (Cambridge, 1897), which together with his *Supplement, The Method of Archimedes* (Cambridge, 1912) was reprinted by Dover Publications (New York, 1953); P. Ver Eecke, *Les Oeuvres complètes d'Archimède, suivies des commentaires d'Eutocius d'Ascalon,* 2nd ed., 2 vols. (Paris, 1960); I. N. Veselovsky, *Archimedes. Selections, Translations, Introduction, and Commentary* (in Russian), translation of the Arabic texts by B. A. Rosenfeld (Moscow, 1962). We can also mention briefly the German translations of A. Czwalina and the modern Greek translations of E. S. Stamates.

2. *The Arabic Archimedes* (the manuscripts cited are largely from Suter, "Die Mathematiker und Astronomen" [see Secondary Literature], and C. Brockelmann, *Geschichte der arabischen Literatur,* 5 vols., Vols. I–II [adapted to

Suppl. vols., Leiden, 1943–1949], Suppl. Vols. I–III [Leiden, 1937–1942]). *On the Sphere and the Cylinder* and *On the Measurement of the Circle;* both appear in Nāṣir al-Dīn al-Ṭūsī, *Majmūʿ al-Rasāʾil,* Vol. II (Hyderabad, 1940). Cf. MSS Berlin 5934; Florence Palat. 271 and 286; Paris 2467; Oxford, Bodl. Arabic 875, 879; India Office 743; and M. Clagett, *Archimedes in the Middle Ages,* I, 17, n. 8. The al-Ṭūsī edition also contains some commentary on Bk. II of *On the Sphere and the Cylinder. Book of the Elements of Geometry* (probably the same as *On Triangles,* mentioned in the *Fihrist*) and *On Touching Circles;* both appear in *Rasāʾil Ibn Qurra* (Hyderabad, 1947, given as 1948 on transliterated title page). *On the Division of the Circle into Seven Equal Parts* (only Props. 16–17 concern heptagon construction; Props. 1–13 appear to be the tract called *On the Properties of the Right Triangle;* Props. 14–15 are unrelated to either of other parts). MS Cairo A.-N.8 H.-N. 7805, item no. 15. German translation by C. Schoy, *Die trigonometrischen Lehren des persischen Astronomen Abu 'l-Raihân Muh. ibn Ahmad al-Bîrûnî* (Hannover, 1927), pp. 74–84. The text has been analyzed in modern fashion by J. Tropfke, "Die Siebeneckabhandlung des Archimedes," in *Osiris,* **1** (1936), 636–651. *On Heaviness and Lightness* (a fragment of *On Floating Bodies*); Arabic text by H. Zotenberg in *Journal asiatique;* Ser. 7, **13** (1879), 509–515, from MS Paris, BN Fonds suppl. arabe 952 bis. A German translation was made by E. Wiedemann in the *Sitzungsberichte der Physikalisch-medizinischen Sozietät in Erlangen,* **38** (1906), 152–162. For an English translation and critique, see M. Clagett, *The Science of Mechanics in the Middle Ages* (Madison, Wis., 1959, 2nd pr., 1961), pp. 52–55. *Lemmata (Liber assumptorum),* see the edition in al-Ṭūsī, *Majmūʿ al-Rasāʾil,* Vol. II (Hyderabad, 1940). MSS Oxford, Bodl. Arabic 879, 895, 939, 960; Leiden 982; Florence, Palat. 271 and 286; Cairo A.-N. 8 H.-N 7805. This work was first edited by S. Foster, *Miscellanea* (London, 1659), from a Latin translation of I. Gravius; Abraham Ecchellensis then retranslated it, the new translation being published in I. A. Borelli's edition of *Apollonii Pergaei Concicorum libri V, VI, VII* (Florence, 1661). Ecchellensis' translation was republished by Heiberg, *Opera,* II, 510–525. See also E. S. Stamates' effort to reconstruct the original Greek text in *Bulletin de la Societé Mathématique de Grèce,* new series, **6 II,** Fasc. 2 (1965), 265–297. *Stomachion,* a fragmentary part in Arabic with German translation in H. Suter, "Der Loculus Archimedius oder das Syntemachion des Archimedes," in *Abhandlungen zur Geschichte der Mathematik,* **9** (1899), 491–499. This is one of two fragments. The other is in Greek and is given by Heiberg, *Opera,* II, 416. Eutocius, *Commentary on the Sphere and the Cylinder,* a section of Bk. II. MSS Paris, BN arabe 2457, 44°; Bibl. Escor. 960; Istanbul, Fatīh Mosque Library Ar. 3414, 60v–66v; Oxford, Bodl. Arabic 875 and 895. Various tracts and commentaries *On the Sphere and the Cylinder,* Bk. II, in part paraphrased and translated by F. Woepcke, *L'Algebra d'Omar Alkhayâmmî* (Paris, 1851), pp. 91–116.

3. *The Medieval Latin Archimedes.* A complete edition and translation of the various Archimedean tracts arising

from the Arabic tradition have been given by M. Clagett, *Archimedes in the Middle Ages,* Vol. I (Madison, Wis., 1964). Vol. II will contain the complete text of Moerbeke's translations and other Archimedean materials from the late Middle Ages. Moerbeke's translation of *On Spirals* and brief parts of other of his translations have been published by Heiberg, "Neue Studien" (see below). See also M. Clagett, "A Medieval Archimedean-Type Proof of the Law of the Lever," in *Miscellanea André Combes,* II (Rome, 1967), 409–421. For the Pseudo-Archimedes, *De ponderibus* (*De incidentibus in humidum*), see E. A. Moody and M. Clagett, *The Medieval Science of Weights* (Madison, 1952; 2nd printing, 1960), pp. 35–53, 352–359.

II. SECONDARY LITERATURE. The best over-all analysis is in E. J. Dijksterhuis, *Archimedes* (Copenhagen, 1956), which also refers to the principal literature. The translations of Heath and Ver Eecke given above contain valuable evaluative and biographical materials. In addition, consult C. Boyer, *The Concepts of the Calculus* (New York, 1939; 2nd printing, 1949; Dover ed. 1959), particularly ch. 4 for the reaction of the mathematicians of the sixteenth and seventeenth centuries to Archimedes. M. Clagett, "Archimedes and Scholastic Geometry," in *Mélanges Alexandre Koyré,* Vol. I: *L'Aventure de la science* (Paris, 1964), 40–60; "The Use of the Moerbeke Translations of Archimedes in the Works of Johannes de Muris," in *Isis,* **43** (1952), 236–242 (the conclusions of this article will be significantly updated in M. Clagett, *Archimedes in the Middle Ages,* Vol. II); and "Johannes de Muris and the Problem of the Mean Proportionals," in *Medicine, Science and Culture, Historical Essays in Honor of Owsei Temkin,* L. G. Stevenson and R. P. Multhauf, eds. (Baltimore, 1968), 35–49. A. G. Drachmann, "Fragments from Archimedes in Heron's Mechanics," in *Centaurus,* **8** (1963), 91–145; "The Screw of Archimedes," in *Actes du VIIIe Congrés international d'Histoire des Sciences Florence-Milan 1956,* **3** (Vinci-Paris, 1958), 940–943; and "How Archimedes Expected to Move the Earth," in *Centaurus,* **5** (1958), 278–282. J. L. Heiberg, "Neue Studien zu Archimedes," in *Abhandlungen zur Geschichte der Mathematik,* **5** (1890), 1–84; and *Quaestiones Archimedeae* (Copenhagen, 1879). Most of the biographical references are given here by Heiberg. S. Heller, "Ein Fehler in einer Archimedes-Ausgabe, seine Entstehung und seine Folgen," in *Abhandlungen der Bayerischen Akademie der Wissenschaften. Mathematisch-naturwissenschaftliche Klasse,* new series, **63** (1954), 1–38. E. Rufini, *Il "Metodo" di Archimede e le origini dell'analisi infinitesimale nell'antichita* (Rome, 1926; new ed., Bologna, 1961). H. Suter, "Die Mathematiker und Astronomen der Araber und ihre Werke," in *Abhandlungen zur Geschichte der mathematischen Wissenschaften,* **10** (1892), *in toto;* "Das Mathematiker- Verzeichniss im Fihrist des Ibn Abī Jaʻkûb an-Nadîm," *ibid.,* **6** (1892), 1–87. B. L. Van der Waerden, *Erwachende Wissenschaft,* 2nd German ed. (Basel, 1966), pp. 344–381. See also the English translation, *Science Awakening,* 2nd ed. (Groningen, 1961), pp. 204–206, 208–228. E. Wiedemann, "Beiträge zur Geschichte der Naturwissenschaften III," in *Sitzungsberichte der Physikalisch-medizinischen Sozietät in Er-* langen, **37** (1905), 247–250, 257. A. P. Youschkevitch, "Remarques sur la méthode antique d'exhaustion," in *Mélanges Alexandre Koyré,* I: *L'Aventure de la science* (1964), 635–653.

MARSHALL CLAGETT

ARCHYTAS OF TARENTUM (*fl.* Tarentum [now Taranto], Italy, *ca.* 375 B.C.), *philosophy, mathematics, physics.*

After the Pythagoreans had been driven out of most of the cities of southern Italy by the Syracusan tyrant Dionysius the Elder at the beginning of the fourth century B.C., Tarentum remained their only important political center. Here Archytas played a leading role in the attempt to unite the Greek city-states against the non-Greek tribes and powers. After the death of Dionysius the Elder, he concluded, through the agency of Plato, an alliance with his son and successor, Dionysius the Younger.

Archytas made very important contributions to the theory of numbers, geometry, and the theory of music. Although extant ancient tradition credits him mainly with individual discoveries, it is clear that all of them were connected and that Archytas was deeply concerned with the foundations of the sciences and with their interconnection. Thus he affirmed that the art of calculation ($\lambda o \gamma \iota \sigma \tau \iota \kappa \acute{\eta}$) is the most fundamental science and makes its results even clearer than those of geometry. He also discussed mathematics as the foundation of astronomy.

A central point in Archytas' manifold endeavors was the theory of means ($\mu \varepsilon \sigma \acute{o} \tau \eta \tau \varepsilon s$) and proportions. He distinguished three basic means: the arithmetic mean of the form $a - b = b - c$ or $a + c = 2b$; the geometric mean of the form $a:b = b:c$ or $ac = b^2$; and the harmonic mean of the form $(a - b):(b - c) = a:c$. Archytas and later mathematicians subsequently added seven other means.

A proposition and proof that are important both for Archytas' theory of means and for his theory of music have been preserved in Latin translation in Boethius' *De musica.* The proposition states that there is no geometric mean between two numbers that are in "superparticular" ($\dot{\varepsilon} \pi \iota \mu \acute{o} \rho \iota o s$) ratio, i.e., in the ratio $(n + 1):n$. The proof given by Boethius is essentially identical with that given for the same proposition by Euclid in his *Sectio canonis* (Prop. 3). It presupposes several propositions of Euclid that appear in *Elements* VII as well as VIII, Prop. 8. Through a careful analysis of Books VII and VIII and their relation to the above proof, A. B. L. Van der Waerden has succeeded in making it appear very likely that many of the theorems in Euclid's *Elements* VII and their proofs existed before Archytas, but that a considerable part of the propositions and proofs of VIII were added by Archytas and his collaborators.

Archytas' most famous mathematical achievement was the solution of the "Delian" problem of the duplication of the cube. A generation before Archytas, Hippocrates of Chios had demonstrated that the problem can be reduced to the insertion of two mean proportionals between the side of the cube and its double length: If a is the side of the cube and $a:x = x:y = y:2a$, then x is the side of the doubled cube. The problem of the geometrical construction of this line segment was solved by Archytas through a most ingenious three-dimensional construction. In the figure below, everything, according to the custom of the ancients, is projected into a plane.

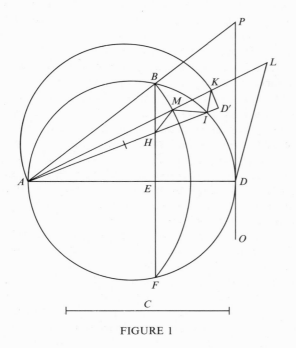

FIGURE 1

Let AD and C be the two line segments between which the two mean proportionals are to be constructed. Let a circle $ABDF$ be drawn with AD as diameter and $AB = C$ as a chord. Then let the extension of AB cut the line tangent to the circle at D at point P. Let BEF be drawn parallel to PDO. Next, imagine a semicylinder above the semicircle ABD (i.e., with ABD as its base) and above AD another semicircle located perpendicularly in the rectangle of the semicylinder (i.e., with AD as diameter in a plane perpendicular to plane $ABDF$). Let this semicircle be rotated around point A in the direction of B. Being rotated in this way, it will cut the surface of the semicylinder and will describe a curve.

If $\triangle APD$ is turned around the axis AD in the direction opposite to that of the semicircle, its side AP will describe the surface of a circular cone and in doing so will cut the aforementioned curve on the surface of the semicylinder at a point. At the same time, point B will describe a semicircle in the surface of the cone. Then, at the moment in which the aforementioned curves cut one another, let the position of the moving semicircle be determined by points AKD' and that of the moving triangle by points ALD, and let the point of intersection be called K. The semicircle described by B will then be BMF (namely, B at the moment of intersection of the curves being in M). Then drop a perpendicular from K to the plane of semicircle $ABDF$. It will fall on the circumference of the circle, since the cylinder is a right cylinder. Let it meet the circumference in I, and let the line drawn from I to A cut BF at H, and let line AL meet semicircle BMF in M (see above). Also let the connecting lines KD', MI, and MH be drawn.

Since each of the two semicircles AKD' and BMF is then perpendicular to the underlying plane ($ABDF$), their common intersection MH is also perpendicular to the plane of that circle, i.e., MH is perpendicular to BF. Hence the rectangle determined by BH, HF, and likewise that determined by AH, HI, is equal to the square on HM. Hence $\triangle AMI$ is similar to $\triangle HMI$ and AHM and $\angle AMI$ is a right angle. But $\angle D'KA$ is also a right angle. Hence $KD' \| MI$. Therefore $D'A:AK = KA:AI = AI:AM$ because of the similarity of the triangles. The four line segments $D'A$, AK, AI, and AM are therefore in continuous proportion. Thus, between the two given line segments AD and C (i.e., AB) two mean proportionals, AK and AI, have been found.

Tannery suspected and Van der Waerden, through an ingenious interpretation of *Epinomis* 990E, tried to show how the theory of means also served Archytas as a basis for his theory of music. Starting from the octave $1:2$ or $6:12$, one obtains the arithmetic mean 9 and the harmonic mean 8. The ratio $6:9 = 8:12$ is $2:3$ or, in musical terms, the fifth. The ratio $6:8 = 9:12$ is $3:4$ or, in musical terms, the fourth. Forming in like manner the arithmetic and harmonic means of the fifth, one obtains the ratios $4:5$ and $5:6$ or, in musical terms, the intervals of the major third and the minor third. Using the same procedure with the fourth, one obtains $6:7$, or the diminished minor third, and $7:8$, or an augmented whole tone. On these intervals Archytas built his three musical scales: the enharmonic, the chromatic, and the diatonic. The theory is also related to the theorem (mentioned above) that there is no geometric mean between two numbers in superparticular ratio. Since all the basic musical intervals are in that ratio, they can be sub-divided by means of the arithmetic and the harmonic means but not by the geometric mean.

Archytas also elaborated a physical theory of sound, which he expounded in the longest extant fragment of his works. He starts with the observation that arithmetic, geometry, astronomy, and the theory of music are all related, but then proceeds to draw conclusions from empirical observations that are not subjected to mathematical analysis within the fragment. The fundamental observation is that faster motion appears to produce higher sounds. Thus, the bull-roarers used at certain religious festivals produce a higher sound when swung around swiftly than when swung more slowly. There are other easy experiments that confirm this observation. For instance, when the holes of a flute that are nearest the mouth of the flutist are opened, a higher sound is produced than when the farther holes are opened. Archytas reasoned that the air pressure in the first case ought to be higher, and therefore the air motion should be faster than in the second case. This is true of the frequencies of the air impulses produced, but Archytas appears to have concluded that the higher sounds reach the ear of the listener more quickly than the lower ones. Thus, he can hardly have applied his arithmetical theory of music consistently to his theory of the production of sound, or he would almost certainly have discovered his error.

Archytas is also credited with the invention of a wooden dove that could fly.

BIBLIOGRAPHY

The surviving fragments of Archytas' work are in H. Diels and W. Kranz, *Fragmente der Vorsokratiker,* 6th ed. (Berlin, 1951). The following are most relevant to this article: 47A16, on the musical scales; 47A19, on the super-particular ratio (also in a Latin translation in Boethius' *De musica,* III, 11); 47B1, on the mathematical foundations of astronomy; 47B2, on the three basic means; Pappus, *Synagogê,* VIII, 13 (F. Hultsch, ed., I, 85 ff.), on other means; and 47B4, on the art of calculation. A three-dimensional drawing for the doubling of the cube is in Diels and Kranz, 6th ed., I, 426.

Writings related to Archytas or his work are T. L. Heath, *A History of Greek Mathematics,* I (Oxford, 1921), 215; P. Tannery, *Mémoires scientifiques,* III (Paris, 1915), 105; M. Timpanaro Cardini, *Pitagorici. Testimonianze e frammenti,* II (Florence, 1962), 226–384; and A. B. L. Van der Waerden, "Die Harmonielehre der Pythagoreer," in *Hermes,* **78** (1943), 184 ff.; *Mathematische Annalen,* **130** (1948), 127 ff.; and *Science Awakening* (Groningen, 1954), pp. 151, 153 f.

KURT VON FRITZ

ARDUINO (or **ARDUINI**), **GIOVANNI** (*b.* Caprino Veronese, Italy, 16 October 1714; *d.* Venice, Italy, 21 March 1795), *geology.*

Arduino was born of poor parents, and it was only through the interest of the Marchese Andrea Carlotti, who was impressed by the boy's intelligence and by his aptitude for the exact sciences, that he was able to complete a good literary and mathematical education at Verona. He did not, however, take a degree. Arduino spent much of his youth working in the mines of Chiusa di Bressanone (in the Upper Adige valley), and was soon able to establish himself as a mining expert.

Today Arduino is counted among the founders of geology: by applying Galilean methodology to investigations of the earth's structure and composition for the first time, he achieved results of lasting validity. He was, above all, a typical representative of the utilitarian rationalism characteristic of the eighteenth-century European mind. In Italy many governments turned to natural scientists for aid in solving the serious economic problems that resulted from a great increase in population. Scientists were employed to search for new or neglected resources, and to study and develop technological procedures that would be of economic advantage. In the Republic of Venice, of which Arduino was a citizen, the excellent reputation that he had earned as a scientist and technician, both as an independent mining expert and in the service of the city of Venice, led the Senate, in 1769, to entrust him with an important office concerned with the development of agriculture and industry throughout the republic.

The diversity of problems faced by Arduino in agriculture and industry is striking. He made each problem the subject of thorough study, most often accompanied by original experimental research, especially in chemistry and metallurgy. A few of his concerns were the reclamation of marshy lands, the fattening of cattle for slaughter, the construction of agricultural equipment for cultivating grain and rice, a chemical study of the ashes of marine plants to be used in glassmaking, and a metallurgical study of the best way of working iron to obtain the best possible castings. He sometimes had the collaboration of his brother Pietro (1728–1805), a botanist who was appointed to the first chair of agriculture at the University of Padua.

Arduino's lifelong passion, however, was mining. Following his early work in the mines of the Upper Adige valley, Arduino worked for an English copper and lead mining company in Montieri and Boccheggiano (Massa Marittima) in 1773 and for a mercury mining operation in Monte Amiata in 1775.

Even during his stay in Vicenza and in Venice, he did not miss an opportunity to visit and study mine sites; and in view of this interest, the Venetian Senate commissioned him to make a complete study of all the mines in the republic's territory.

Arduino's contribution to mining was not merely economic, for he was also receptive to the new discipline of geology. He used to say, "I have always loved to begin with facts, to observe them, to walk in the light of experiment and demonstration as much as possible, and to discuss the results." By observing the phenomena of nature without prejudice or consideration of the opinions of contemporary scientists, from John Woodward to William Whiston, he was able to identify four very distinct geological units of successively later periods in the Atesine Alps, the foothills of the Alps, the subalpine hills, and the plains of the Po. Discussing his observations, he established the bases for modern stratigraphic chronology: "From whatever I have been able to observe up to this time, the series of strata which form the visible crust of the earth appear to me classified in four general and successive orders. These four orders can be conceived to be four very large strata, as they really are, so that wherever they are exposed, they are disposed one above the other, always in the same way." He called these orders Primary, Secondary, Tertiary, and Quaternary, specifying that each was constituted of innumerable minor strata of different materials formed at different times under different conditions. He proposed a further subdivision only for the Primary order, distinguishing a lower part constituted of metamorphic rocks and an upper part of formerly sedimentary, calcareous, and arenaceous rocks. In consequence, he attributed to the Primary order the Paleozoic formations of the Atesine Alps; to the Secondary order, the Mesozoic prealpine formations from Lombardy to Venezia; and to the Tertiary order, the band of subalpine hills from Lombardy to Venezia and the Pliocene hills of Tuscany. In the Quaternary order he considered the alluvial deposits of the plain that stretches to the foot of the Alps.

Arduino's vision of paleontology was correspondingly clear. Not only did he understand that fossil species change according to variations in the age of the terrains in which they occur, but he also realized that in the Secondary order "unrefined and imperfect" species are found, while in the Tertiary order the species are "very perfect and wholly similar to those that are seen in the modern sea." He affirmed, as a result, that "as many ages have elapsed during the elevation of the Alps, as there are races of organic fossil bodies embedded within the strata." Arduino's investigations extended to magmatic rocks; he iden-

tified, among other things, the trachytic origin of the Euganean Hills and of the basaltic rocks in the area of Verona and Vicenza, rocks he linked to "ancient extinct volcanoes." He also realized the transformations that magmatic rocks can work upon preexistent sedimentary rocks. In these special researches, as in his general study of rocks and minerals, he utilized his skill as a chemist.

Arduino was one of the most brilliant precursors of actualism: "With the sole guidance of our practical knowledge of those physical agents which we see actually used in the continuous workings of nature, and of our knowledge of the respective effects induced by the same workings, we can with reasonable basis surmise what the forces were which acted even in the remotest times."

Arduino's fundamental ideas were diffused throughout Europe by means of his publications, his frequent letters to and conferences with Italian and foreign scholars, and, above all, the active interest of Ignaz de Born and Johann Jacob Ferber. De Born translated a collection of Arduino's writings into German, and Ferber fervently expounded Arduino's geological results in his well-known work on the natural history of Italy.

BIBLIOGRAPHY

I. ORIGINAL WORKS. Arduino's geological writings, of which there is no collected critical edition, include "Due lettere del Signor Giovanni Arduino sopra varie sue osservazioni naturali," in *Nuova raccolta d'opuscoli scientifici e filologici (dell' abate Calogerà)*, **6** (1760), 97, 133; *Raccolta di memorie chimico-mineralogiche, metallurgiche e orittografiche* (Venice, 1775), also translated into German by Ignaz de Born (Dresden, 1778); and "Effetti di antichissimi vulcani estinti . . . nei monti della villa di Chiampo, ed in altri luoghi del territorio di Vicenza e di quello di Verona," in *Nuovo giornale d'Italia*, **7** (1783), 163.

II. SECONDARY LITERATURE. There is no definitive biography, but see T. A. Catullo, *Elogio di Giovanni Arduino* (Padua, 1835), which has an incomplete bibliography of Arduino's works; G. B. Ronconi, *Giovanni Arduino e le miniere di Toscana* (Padua, 1865); and G. Stegagno, *Il veronese Giovanni Arduino e il suo contributo alla scienza geologica* (Verona, 1929), in which sketches and sections are reproduced from unpublished manuscripts that show Arduino to be a precursor of geological cartography.

FRANCESCO RODOLICO

ARETAEUS OF CAPPADOCIA (*fl. ca.* A.D. 50), *medicine.*

Aretaeus is known for his text on the causes, symptoms, and treatment of acute and chronic diseases.

The dates of this physician, who was rarely cited in antiquity, have long been a matter of dispute, but it should now be clear that Aretaeus belongs to the middle of the first century and that he was a contemporary of the famous pharmacologist Pedanius Dioscorides, who cites him once. Further, since Aretaeus probably knew Andromachos, Nero's personal physician (to whom Dioscorides dedicated his work), we may conclude that at some time he had resided in Rome. Nothing more is known about his life.

Aretaeus belonged to the so-called Pneumatic school of physicians, which had been founded in the first century B.C. by Athenaeus of Attalia, who had studied under the Stoic Posidonius. Since Aretaeus is the only one of the Pneumatic school whose work has come down to us intact, he is a valuable source in several respects: (1) One can trace in his work several specific influences of the Stoic-Posidonian ideas and influences in medicine (for instance, the idea of the soul's ability to predict). (2) Aretaeus' position on the physician's compassion for the patient, for instance, reveals that the Pneumatics took a position close to that of the early Christians, and thus forms an important link between medicine and early Christianity (which actually was not very affable to medicine). (3) Aretaeus reveals that the "orthodox" Pneumatic school of the first century led to a strong revival of the doctrine of Hippocrates as well as of the Ionic dialect within medical literature. Since Aretaeus also used Homeric words and modes of expression, he represents an important example of the Greek style of prose in imperial times, especially that of the so-called second sophistic.

BIBLIOGRAPHY

Aretaeus' text on acute and chronic diseases, the original title of which is unknown, is edited by C. Hude in *Corpus medicorum Graecorum,* 2nd ed., II (Berlin, 1958): for the physician's compassion, see p. 7, ll. 17 ff.; for the soul's mantic power, see p. 22, ll. 26 ff.

Dioscorides' reference to Aretaeus is *Pedanii Dioscuridis Anazarbei De materia medica,* M. Wellmann, ed., 2nd ed., III (Berlin, 1958), 298, l. 19. For the dating of Aretaeus' life and for the Stoic-Posidonic and Christian features of the Pneumatics and of Aretaeus, see F. Kudlien, "Untersuchungen zu Aretaios von Kappadokien," in *Abhandlungen der Akademie der Wissenschaften und Literatur in Mainz,* no. 11 (1963), ch. 1. See also "Pneumatische Ärzte," in Pauly-Wissowa, *Real-Encyclopädie der classischen Altertumswissenschaft,* supp. XI (in press).

FRIDOLF KUDLIEN

ARGAND, ÉMILE (*b.* Geneva, Switzerland, 6 January 1879; *d.* Neuchâtel, Switzerland, 14 September 1940), *geology.*

Argand's father was a clerk in government service; his mother, a remarkable woman, was from Morzine, Savoy. Mountain climbing was the favorite sport of the young people of Geneva, so Argand was familiar with the Alps long before he studied geology. His father apprenticed him to an architect, but his mother had other plans. She took him with her for long stays in Italy, France, and Greece, and encouraged him to read medicine. Argand began his studies in Geneva but soon transferred to Lausanne, where he met the young professor Maurice Lugeon and became interested in the problems of Alpine structure. He soon came to believe that these problems had been put into the world especially for him to solve, and he turned to the study of geology.

Argand had the talent to be a geologist but, as his friends remarked, he also could have been an architect, an artist, a linguist, a writer, or a businessman. He would have been outstanding in any of these professions. His extraordinary ability to think in three dimensions allowed him to visualize and to represent not only very complicated solids but also their movements and deformations. A gifted artist, he also could sketch these solids as seen from different angles. Argand had his own recognizable style, not only in his illustrations but also in his writing—and, as a result, in the kind of geology he developed. Argand's visual recall was uncommonly good and enabled him to sketch landscapes, maps, and stereograms from memory (and even portraits that were more or less caricatures). His students and colleagues used to compare the maps he drew on the blackboard during lectures with the atlas, and they were always astonished by his accuracy.

These gifts enabled Argand to solve some of the most complex problems of terrestrial architecture. It was also his good fortune to enter science at a crucial stage in the evolution of Alpine geology and at one of the best possible places. Lugeon, his teacher, not only had shown the existence of the Helvetic nappes but also was the first to analyze these structures over an extended area rather than a restricted cross section. He had studied the entire zone from the Lake of Geneva to the Rhine, clarifying and extending the new methods of structural interpretation used earlier by Marcel Bertrand, Hans Schardt, and Pierre Termier. These involved not only the recognition of the nappe folding but also the extension from the detailed geology of the simple parts to the complex structure on the regional scale. The work had to be extended to the interior of the Alps, but there the metamorphism and the paucity of fossils meant that the details of the stratigraphy would have to be worked out from the structure. In the outer zones, a well-developed stratigraphy had made the unraveling of the structure possible. To unravel the structure of the inner zone Argand had to develop geometric methods, for example, in proceeding from the Alpine surface to the missing structure that was the origin of the projection.

Several years of intensive mapping in the highest central part of the Pennine Alps resulted in the now classic map of the Dent Blanche massif and the memoir explaining his results (1908). A new world of forms was revealed by this work. Argand spoke of the strata deformed into *faisceaux* of families of cylindrical surfaces, of the deformation of these cylinders, of their ruin in depth and space by the processes of erosion, and of the concomitant sedimentation. Of this work, Ulrich Grubenmann said that it was the first time that the inversion of his metamorphic zones had been proved and used for structural explanation. Argand had shown that the top of the Matterhorn was in the Grubenmann katazone, or deepest zone of metamorphism, while the roots of the mountain, as revealed in the rock of the valley below, were in the shallow, or metamorphic, epizone. These geometric methods were the key that enabled Argand to unveil the whole of the Pennic zone, establishing the axial culminations and depressions (i.e., the deformation of the generatrices of the cylindrical nappe structures). He integrated consecutive series of vertical sections with surface geology in complex block diagrams and traced the architecture of the nappes from one sector to the next. His concept of grouping tectonic elements in preferred directions, inclinations, and orientations became a basic notion of structural geology and the foundation of many of the more advanced techniques of structural analysis.

In this way the "Pennic" type, a new type of deformation characteristic of the central zones of many other orogenic belts, was brought to light. Argand's methods of representation and the accompanying full chronological and dynamic interpretation soon became classic, and were adopted by the students and professors who made up a new generation of Alpine geologists. Unfortunately, the methods were not always applied with the caution of their author, who understood their limits. Some of the rigid applications of these heuristic principles were later attacked as "cylindrism" by the school of Grenoble, which nevertheless made use of the principles stated by Argand.

Having not only the keys for the solution of regional problems but also the necessary methods and

techniques, Argand extended his task and attempted a synthetic picture of the structure of the arc of the western Alps. The results were condensed in his famous four plates of 1911, with a brief commentary showing the relationships between the major lines and significant details. From regional problems Argand advanced to geology on the planetary scale. He knew by heart the fundamental five-volume work of Eduard Suess, *Das Antlitz der Erde,* and his linguistic skill allowed him to collect further information from many sources. He tried to synthesize this wealth of information as concretely as possible in a tectonic map of Eurasia conceived in a new style. In 1911 Argand had succeeded Hans Schardt as professor at Neuchâtel. Ordinarily systematic, almost to the point of compulsiveness, Argand, during the preparation of the map of Eurasia, worked in the midst of great disorder, driving himself and his assistants as much as thirty-two hours at a stretch, living on coffee and catching naps on an old sofa among the piles of books and papers. This map, although it exists only in the original manuscript, became famous, and in 1913 it received the Spendiaroff Prize. The map is preserved at the University of Neuchâtel, Switzerland.

Until then, Argand's research had been three-dimensional. In order to understand the genesis of the Alps, the dimension of time would have to be added. Lecturing to the Swiss Geological Society in 1915, Argand announced a new branch of research, kinematic analysis and synthesis, which he called embryotectonics. It was the sequential analysis of the evolving structure back through time to the original sedimentary terrain. His heuristic methods were intended to explain the succession of events leading to the present complex structures, and to connect the subsurface movements with the changing sedimentary landscapes of the successive former surfaces and with the emplacement of ophiolites. Argand's picture showed the importance of the sedimentology and stratigraphy of the western Alps and their place in a synthetic study. In this way he reconstructed what was then regarded as the typical evolution of a mountain chain. This "type biography" approach was later completed by a paper on the precursor phases and late phases of an orogenic segment (1920).

In 1915 Alfred Wegener published his fundamental paper containing his hypothesis of continental drift. Fascinated by the possibilities, Argand believed that continental drift offered a new motor for orogeny consistent with his evolutionary model. The Wegenerian hypothesis became the frame within which he created a new concept of Eurasian structural development. This work led to Argand's being chosen to deliver the inaugural address of the Brussels International Geological Congress in 1922. His revised tectonic map of Eurasia, *La tectonique de l'Asie,* was reproduced with text in 1924. This is not only a fundamental text of structural geology but also a work of art. One of the most important of the many new concepts introduced is the notion of basement folds. Contemporary models of the formation of mountain chains showed the upfolding of geosynclinal accumulations; against this simple pattern Argand set the concept of the warping and thrusting of old crystalline platforms without reactivation of the ancient structures and with the resulting sedimentary formations, drawing examples from Asia, Europe, and America. The paper had great influence in the French-speaking world, where Argand's vocabulary and manner of reasoning became a part of geological thinking.

In 1931 Argand was called upon to preside over the first congress for the study of the Precambrian and ancient mountain chains, convened by J. J. Sederholm.

Before World War II, Argand became interested in philosophy and linguistics, but this work was never published. He died suddenly, not long after the death of his mother.

BIBLIOGRAPHY

Argand's works are "Carte géologique du Massif de la Dent Blanche, 1:50.000," in *Matériaux pour la carte géologique de la Suisse,* n.s. **23** (1908), carte spéc. no. 52; "L'exploration géologique des Alpes pennines centrales," in *Bulletin de la Société vaudoise des sciences naturelles,* **45** (1909), 217–276; "Les nappes de recouvrement des Alpes pennines et leurs prolongements structuraux," in *Matériaux pour la carte géologique de la Suisse,* n.s. **31** (1911), 1–26; "Les nappes de recouvrement des Alpes Occidentales et les territoires environnents. Essai de carte structurale. 1:500.000," *ibid.,* n.s. **27** (1911), carte spéc. no. 64; "Sur l'arc des Alpes Occidentales," in *Eclogae geologicae Helvetiae,* **14** (1916), 145–191; "Plissements précurseurs et plissements tardifs des chaines de montagne," in *Actes de la Société helvétique des sciences naturelles,* sess. 101 (1920), 13–39; "La géologie des environs de Zermatt," *ibid.,* sess. 104 (1923), pt. 2, 96–110; "La tectonique de l'Asie," in *Comptes rendus de la XIIIᵉ Congrès international de géologie* (1924), 171–372; *Carte tectonique de l'Eurasie, 1922, 1:8.000.000. Réduction photographique à l'échelle 1:25.000.000* (Brussels, 1928); "La zone pennique," in *Guide géologique de la Suisse* (Basel, 1934), pp. 149–189; "Carte géologique du Grand Combin, 1:50.000," in *Matériaux pour la carte géologique de la Suisse* (1934), carte spéc. no. 93; "Feuille Saxon-Morcles, 1:25.000," in *Atlas géologique de la Suisse* (Bern, 1937), with Lugeon, Reinhard, Poldini, et al.; "Note explicative de la feuille 485, Saxon-Morcles avec annexes de la feuille 526 Martigny (feuille 1° de l'Atlas)," in *Atlas géologique de la Suisse,* pp. 25–53.

For a biography of Argand see Maurice Lugeon, "Emile Argand," in *Bulletin de la Société neuchâteloise des sciences naturelles,* **65** (1940), 25–53.

C. E. WEGMANN

ARGAND, JEAN ROBERT (*b.* Geneva, Switzerland, 18 July 1768; *d.* Paris, France, 13 August 1822), *mathematics.*

Biographical data on Argand are limited. It is known that he was the son of Jacques Argand and Èves Canac; that he was baptized on 22 July (a date given by some for his birth); that he had a son who lived in Paris and a daughter, Jeanne-Françoise-Dorothée-Marie-Élizabeth, who married Félix Bousquet and lived in Stuttgart.

Argand, a Parisian bookkeeper, apparently never belonged to any group of mathematical amateurs or dilettantes. His training and background are so little known that he has often been confused with a man to whom he probably was not even related, Aimé Argand, a physicist and chemist who invented the Argand lamp.

It is remarkable that Argand's single original contribution to mathematics, the invention and elaboration of a geometric representation of complex numbers and the operations upon them, was so timed and of such importance as to assure him of a place in the history of mathematics even among those who credit C. F. Gauss with what others call the Argand diagram.

Other circumstances make Argand's story unusual. His system was actually anticipated by Caspar Wessel, a Norwegian, in 1797, but Wessel's work was without significant influence because it remained essentially unknown until 1897. Argand's own work might have suffered the same fate, for it was privately printed in 1806 in a small edition that did not even have the author's name on the title page. He received proper credit for it through a peculiar chain of events and the honesty and generosity of J. F. Français, a professor at the École Impériale d'Artillerie et du Génie, who published a similar discussion in 1813.

Argand had shown his work to A. M. Legendre before its publication, and Legendre mentioned it in a letter to Français's brother. Français saw the letter among his dead brother's papers, and was so intrigued by the ideas in it that he developed them further and published them in J. D. Gergonne's journal *Annales de mathématiques.* At the end of his article Français mentioned the source of his inspiration and expressed the hope that the unknown "first author of these ideas" would make himself known and publish the work he had done on this project.

Argand responded to this invitation by submitting an article that was published in the same volume of the *Annales.* In it he recapitulated his original work (with a change in notation) and gave some additional applications. A key to his ideas may be presented by a description and analysis of Figures 1 and 2. Figure 1 accompanies his initial discussion of a geometric representation of $\sqrt{-1}$. His motivation for this can be traced back to John Wallis' *Treatise of Algebra* (1685). In it Wallis suggested that since $\sqrt{-1}$ is the mean proportional between $+1$ and -1, its geometric representation could be a line constructed as the mean proportional between two oppositely directed unit segments.

Argand began his book, *Essai sur une manière de représenter les quantités imaginaires dans les constructions géométriques,* with a brief discussion of models for generating negative numbers by repeated subtraction; one used weights removed from a pan of a beam balance, the other subtracted francs from a sum of money. From these examples he concluded that distance may be considered apart from direction, and that whether a negative quantity is considered real or "imaginary" depends upon the kind of quantity measured. This initial use of the word "imaginary" for a negative number is related to the mathematical-philosophical debates of the time as to whether negative numbers were numbers, or even existed. In general, Argand used "imaginary" for multiples of $\sqrt{-1}$, a practice introduced by Descartes and common today. He also used the term "absolute" for distance considered apart from direction.

Argand then suggested that "setting aside the ratio of absolute magnitude we consider the different possible relations of direction" and discussed the proportions $+1:+1::-1:-1$ and $+1:-1::-1:+1$. He noted that in them the means have the same or opposite signs, depending upon whether the signs of the extremes are alike or opposite. This led him to consider $1:x::x:-1$. In this proportion he said that x cannot be made equal to any quantity, positive or negative; but as an analogy with his original models he suggested that quantities which were imaginary when applied to "certain magnitudes" became real when the idea of direction was added to the idea of absolute number. Thus, in Figure 1, if KA taken as positive unity with its direction from K to A is written $\overline{KA}$ to distinguish it from the segment KA, which is an absolute distance, then negative unity will be $\overline{KI}$. The classical construction for the geometric mean would determine $\overline{KE}$ and $\overline{KN}$ on the unit circle with center at K. Argand did not mention the

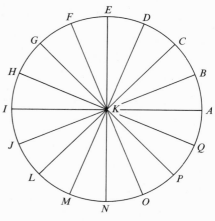

geometric construction, but merely stated that the condition of the proportion will be met by perpendiculars $\overline{KE}$ and $\overline{KN}$, which represent $\sqrt{-1}$ and $-\sqrt{-1}$, respectively. Analogously, Argand inserted $\overline{KC}$ and $\overline{KL}$ as the mean proportionals between $\overline{KA}$ and $\overline{KE}$ by bisecting angle AKE.

Argand's opening paragraphs included the first use of the word "absolute" in the sense of the absolute value of a positive, negative, or complex number; of the bar over a pair of letters to indicate what is today called a vector; and of the idea that $\overline{AK} = -\overline{KA}$. Later in the *Essai* Argand used the term "modulus" (*module*) for the absolute value or the length of a vector representing a complex number. In this Argand anticipated A. L. Cauchy, who is commonly given credit for originating the term.

Argand's notation in his original essay is of particular interest because it anticipated the more abstract and modern ideas, later expounded by W. R. Hamilton, of complex numbers as arbitrarily constructed new entities defined as ordered pairs of real numbers. This modern aspect of Argand's original work has not been generally recognized. One reason for this, no doubt, is that in later letters and journal articles he returned to the more standard $a + b\sqrt{-1}$ notation. In his book, however, Argand suggested omitting $\sqrt{-1}$, deeming it no more a factor of $a\sqrt{-1}$ than is $+1$ in $+a$. He wrote $\sim a$ and $+a$ for $a\sqrt{-1}$ and $-a\sqrt{-1}$, respectively. He then observed that both $(\sim a)^2$ and $(+a)^2$ were negative. This led him to the rule that if in a series of factors every curved line has a value of 1 and every straight line a value of 2—thus $\sim = 1$, $- = 2$, $+ = 3$, $+ = 4$—then the sign of the product of any series of factors can be determined by taking the residue modulo, 4, of the sum of the values of the symbols associated with the factors. Here he recognized the periodicity of the powers of the imaginary unit.

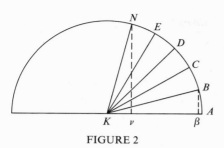

FIGURE 2

Argand generalized the insertion of geometric means between two given vectors to the insertion of any number of means, n, between the vectors $\overline{KA}$ and $\overline{KB}$ by dividing the angle between them by n. He noted that one could also find the means between $\overline{KA}$ and $\overline{KB}$ by beginning with the angles $AKB + 360°$, and $AKB + 720°$. This is a special case of de Moivre's theorem, as is more clearly and completely shown in Argand's explanation of Figure 2. In it AB, BC, $\cdots$ EN are n equal arcs. From the diagram Argand reasoned that $\overline{KN} = \overline{KB^n}$, $\overline{KN} = \overline{K\nu} + \overline{\nu N}$, and $\overline{KB} = \overline{K\beta} + \overline{\beta B}$; hence $\overline{K\nu} + \overline{\nu N} = (\overline{K\beta} + \overline{\beta B})^n$, which leads to $\cos na + \sqrt{-1}$ $\sin na = (\cos a + \sqrt{-1} \sin a)^n$.

This result was well known before Argand, as were the uses he made of it to derive infinite series for trigonometric and logarithmic functions. As noted earlier, we know nothing of Argand's education or contacts with other mathematicians prior to 1813. It seems highly probable, however, that he had direct or indirect contact with some of the results of Wallis, de Moivre, and Leonhard Euler. Nevertheless, the purely geometric-intuitive interpretation and reasoning leading to these results seem to have been original with Argand. This geometric viewpoint has continued to be fruitful up to the present day. Argand recognized the nonrigorous nature of his reasoning, but he defined his goals as clarifying thinking about imaginaries by setting up a new view of them and providing a new tool for research in geometry. He used complex numbers to derive several trigonometric identities, to prove Ptolemy's theorem, and to give a proof of the fundamental theorem of algebra.

Argand's work contrasts with Wessel's in that the latter's approach was more modern in its explicit use of definitions in setting up a correspondence between $a + b\sqrt{-1}$ and vectors referred to a rectangular coordinate system (which neither Wessel nor Argand ever explicitly mentioned or drew). Wessel stressed the consistency of his assumptions and derived results without regard for their intuitive validity. He did not present as many mathematical consequences as Argand did.

Just as it seems clear that Argand's work was entirely independent of Wessel's, so it also seems clear that it was independent of the algebraic approach published by Suremain de Missery in 1801. Argand refuted the suggestion that he knew of Buée's work published in the *Philosophical Transactions of the Royal Society* in 1806 by noting that since academic journals appear after the dates which they bear, and that his book was printed in the same year the journal was dated, he could not have known of Buée's work at the time he wrote the book. Buée's ideas were not as clear, extensive, or well developed as Argand's.

There are obvious connections between Argand's geometric ideas and the later work of Moebius, Bellavitis, Hermann Grassmann, and others, but in most cases it is as difficult to establish direct outgrowths of his work as it is to establish that he consciously drew on Wallis, de Moivre, or Euler.

Two of the most important mathematicians of the early nineteenth century, Cauchy and Hamilton, took care to note the relationship of Argand's work to some of their own major contributions, but claimed to have learned of his work only after doing their own. Gauss probably could have made a similar statement, but he never did. Cauchy mentioned Argand twice in his "Mémoire sur les quantités géométriques," which appeared in *Exercices d'analyse et de physique mathématique* (1847). He cited Argand as the originator of the geometric interpretation of imaginary quantities, which he suggested would give clarity, a new precision, and a greater generality to algebra than earlier theories of imaginary quantities had. He also cited Argand and A. M. Legendre as authors of proofs of what Gauss termed the "fundamental theorem of algebra." Argand's proof involved considering the modulus of

$$P(x) = a_0 x^n + a_1 x^{n-1} + \cdots + a_{n-1} x^1 + a_n$$

when $x = a + bi$. He noted that if $|P(x)| = 0$ the theorem was true, and argued geometrically that if $|P(x)| > 0$ one could find $x' = a' + b'i$ such that $|P(x')| < |P(x)|$. Servois objected that this only showed that $P(x)$ was asymptotic to 0 for some sequence of x's. Argand replied that such behavior was associated with hyperbolas having zeros at infinity, not with polynomials. Cauchy asserted that a proof proposed by Legendre reduced to Argand's but left much to be desired, while his own method for approximating roots of $P(x) = 0$ could be used to demonstrate their existence. Gauss had published a proof of this existence in his thesis (1799). Although the geometric representation of complex numbers was implicit in this thesis, Gauss did not actually publish a discussion of it until 1832 in his famous paper "Theoria residuorum biquadraticorum." Argand, however, was the first mathematician to assert that the fundamental theorem also held if the coefficients of $P(x)$ were complex.

Hamilton used lengthy footnotes in the first edition of his *Lectures on Quaternions* (1853) to assert the priority and quality of Argand's work, especially with respect to the "multiplication of lines." He traced the roots of his own development of the algebra of couples and of quaternions, however, to John Warren's *A Treatise on the Geometrical Representation of the Square Roots of Negative Quantities* (1828). This, like C. V. Mourrey's *La vraie théorie des quantités negatives et des quantités prétendues imaginaires* (1828), seems to have been free of any dependence on Argand's work.

Argand's later publications, all of which appeared in Gergonne's *Annales,* are elaborations of his book or comments on articles published by others. His first article determined equations for a curve that had previously been described in the *Annales* (**3**, 243). Argand went on to suggest an application of the curve to the construction of a thermometer shaped like a watch. His analysis of probable errors in such a mechanism showed familiarity with the mechanics of Laplace, as presented in *Exposition du système du monde.*

His fifth article in the *Annales,* defending his proof of the fundamental theorem of algebra, showed his familiarity with the works of Lagrange, Euler, and d'Alembert, especially their debates on whether all rational functions of $(a + bi)$ could be reduced to the form $A + Bi$ where a, b, A, and B are real. Argand, oddly enough, did not accept this theorem. He apparently was not familiar with Euler's earlier reduction of $\sqrt{-1}^{\sqrt{-1}}$, for he cited this as an example of an expression that could not be reduced to the form $A + Bi$.

His last article appeared in the volume of *Annales* dated 1815–1816 and dealt with a problem in combinations. In it Argand devised the notation (m,n) for the combinations of m things taken n at a time and the notation $Z(m,n)$ for the number of such combinations.

Argand was a man with an unknown background, a nonmathematical occupation, and an uncertain contact with the literature of his time who intuitively developed a critical idea for which the time was right. He exploited it himself. The quality and significance of his work were recognized by some of the geniuses of his time, but breakdowns in communication and the approximate simultaneity of similar developments by other workers force a historian to deny him full credit for the fruits of the concept on which he labored.

BIBLIOGRAPHY

I. ORIGINAL WORKS. There have been three editions of Argand's book (his first publication), *Essai sur une manière de représenter les quantités imaginaires dans les constructions géométriques.* The first edition (Paris, 1806) did not bear the name of the author; the second edition, subtitled *Précédé d'une préface par M. J. Hoüel et suivie d'une appendice contenant des extraits des Annales de Gergonne, relatifs à la question des imaginaires* (Paris, 1874), cites the author as "R. Argand" on the title page but identifies him as Jean-Robert Argand on page xv. The *Essai* was translated by Professor A. S. Hardy as *Imaginary Quantities: Their Geometrical Interpretation* (New York, 1881). Argand's eight later publications all appeared in Vols. **4**, **5**, and **6** (1813–1816) of J. D. Gergonne's journal *Annales de mathématiques pures et appliquées.* Hoüel lists them at the end of his preface to the second edition of the *Essai.*

II. SECONDARY LITERATURE. Data on Argand's life were included by Hoüel with the second edition of the *Essai.* Verification of the dates of his birth and death is given by H. Fehr in *Intermédiare des mathématiciens,* **9** (1902), 74. Niels Nielsen, *Géomètres français sous la Révolution* (Copenhagen, 1929), pp. 6–9, discusses Argand with reference to Wessel, Français, and others. William Rowan Hamilton gives a comparative analysis of contemporary work with complex numbers while praising Argand in *Lectures on Quaternions* (Dublin, 1853), pp. 31–34, 56, 57. Augustin Louis Cauchy's appraisal is found in "Mémoire sur les quantités géométriques," in *Exercices d'analyse et de physique mathématique,* IV (Paris, 1847), and in *Oeuvres,* 2nd series, XIV (Paris, 1938), 175–202. J. F. Français's development of Argand's ideas contained in a letter to his brother, "Nouveaux principes de géométrie de position, et interpretation géométrique des symboles imaginaires," is *Annales de mathématiques,* **4** (1813–1814), 61–71.

PHILLIP S. JONES

ARGELANDER, FRIEDRICH WILHELM AUGUST (*b.* Memel, Prussia, 22 March 1799; *d.* Bonn, Germany, 17 February 1875), *astronomy.*

Argelander's father, Johann Gottlieb Argelander, was a wealthy merchant from Finland; his mother, Dorothea Wilhelmine Grünlingen, was German. The boy grew up in the easternmost corner of Prussia, and the Napoleonic Wars brought him into close contact with the major political events of his day. After the defeat of Prussia in the campaign of 1806, Queen Louise and her sons fled from Berlin to Memel. The crown prince, who later became Friedrich Wilhelm IV, and Prince Friedrich lived in the Argelander home, and young Argelander formed a lasting friendship with both of them. After attending the secondary school in Elbing and the Collegium Fridericianum in Königsberg, Argelander entered the University of Königsberg in 1817 in order to study political economy and political science. At this time he attended the lectures of the astronomer Friedrich Wilhelm Bessel and took an active part in the calculating work of the observatory at Königsberg. When the results of this work were published, Bessel referred to Argelander as one of his "most outstanding students."

When he was twenty-one, Argelander was completely won over to astronomy by Bessel and was appointed an assistant in the observatory. He took part in a newly initiated project, designed to determine the exact positions of all the brighter stars of the northern sky between 15° southern declination and 45° northern declination; this was the first part of Bessel's projected survey of the entire northern sky. In 1822 Argelander earned his doctorate with a study of the older Greenwich observations (which were made with sextant and quadrant), *De observationibus astronomicis a Flamsteedio institutis,* and in the same year he earned his lectureship with a study entitled *Untersuchung über die Bahn des grossen Kometen von 1811* ("Investigation of the Orbit of the Great Comet of 1811"). In both these works he demonstrated his great proficiency in the critical evaluation of astronomical observations.

Bessel recommended him for the post of observer at the small, just rebuilt observatory in Åbo (now Turku), Finland. Thus Argelander, who had just turned twenty-four, went into the Russian civil service. Equipped with excellent instruments from the best German factories, so that the Åbo observatory could compete with Königsberg and Dorpat, Argelander made it famous as the northernmost station of the "three-point constellation" of east European observatories. Here he demonstrated his ability, later tested again and again, to achieve optimum results in spite of limited resources and an unfavorable climate. While Bessel continued to contribute to the knowledge of the positions of stars through observations of zones, Argelander dedicated his observatory to the study of the alteration of the positions in time—the "proper motions" of the fixed stars.

In 1718 Halley, by the comparison of older and more recent positions, had discovered that some brighter stars, such as Sirius, Arcturus, and Aldebaran, showed deviations that could be explained only through proper spatial motions and not through errors in observation. In 1760 Johann Tobias Mayer found that of eighty stars he investigated, fifteen or twenty showed proper motions of several arc-seconds in 100 years. Argelander devoted all his energies to this problem. In a few years he collected over 10,000 observations with the transit circle of several hundred stars that were suspected of proper motion. The catalog of 560 stars, which was based on these obser-

vations (1835), is incontestably the most exact of the contemporary catalogs.

Argelander was forced to abandon these observations in 1827 because of a fire that destroyed most of Åbo. Even if the observatory itself had been saved, a transfer of the entire university to Helsinki would still have been unavoidable. Argelander, who in 1828 was named full professor at the new university, was assigned the task of planning and building a new observatory. In 1832 he was finally able to move to Helsinki. Here his earlier work proved fruitful. The ingenious investigation *Über die eigene Bewegung des Sonnensystems, hergeleitet aus den eigenen Bewegungen der Sterne* ("Concerning the Peculiar Movement of the Solar System as Deduced From the Proper Motions of the Stars," 1837) is one of the few theoretical works in which Argelander found the basis of his observations conclusive enough to make certain deductions.

Through all his other works Argelander has become renowned as a master of practical investigations of fundamental importance. It would, however, be wrong to disregard his theoretical ability. His foresight and critical strength protected him from the danger of drawing premature and insufficiently proved conclusions from imperfect material. Lalande had already concluded from theoretical considerations that the sun, like the other fixed stars, has a progressive motion in space in addition to its rotation. All other bodies of the solar system, the planets and comets, participate in this movement; therefore the peculiar motion of the sun is only to be recognized as relative to the fixed stars outside the solar system. The motions of the fixed stars consist of the apparent perspectivic changes in position, which are caused by the motion of the sun, and of the real, progressive motions of the fixed stars through space. Only the most exact observations of a greater number of stars can allow the separation of these two aspects.

In 1783 Sir William Herschel had deduced, on the basis of the proper motions of only seven bright stars, that the apex of the movement of the sun was somewhat north of the star λ Herculis. A repetition of his calculations in 1805/1806 by the aid of a somewhat larger number of stars yielded data that did not essentially deviate. While Herschel himself had made no observations of his own for this purpose and had frequently encountered doubt and contradiction, Argelander saw in his observations an opportunity to derive anew the motion of the sun. He felt this would be worthwhile because of the progress both in the construction of instruments and in critical calculation methods that, as far as possible, freed observations from all accidental and systematic errors.

His result, based on no fewer than 390 proper motions, verified the accuracy of Herschel's pioneering work. The spatial movement of the sun has since then been proved beyond doubt.

It would have been obvious to a confirmed theorist that a further question should be asked: What is the law that governs the motion of the sun and the other stars through space? Are all bodies, Argelander asked, subject only to their mutual attractions, or do all of them obey the attractive force of a large central body? In other words, is the solar system only the smaller model of a larger, similarly constructed stellar system? Argelander did not address himself to this question; he did not indulge in idle speculation, as did other astronomers who claimed that now Sirius, or again the Pleiades, or even a central sun as yet unknown was the center of the realm of the stars. His merit lies much more in the recognition of the significance of the dynamics of the stellar system and in his provisions that enabled later astronomers to solve the problem. Everything he did in the next four decades served to increase the knowledge of the positions and proper motions of the stars, in the hope that someday a second Kepler might be successful in revealing the more complex laws of the orbits of the fixed stars. In November 1836 Argelander was appointed to the professorship of astronomy at the Prussian University of Bonn. He was also promised a new, richly fitted observatory, and his old friend the crown prince, who ascended the throne several years later, supported the project.

During his first years at Bonn, Argelander worked in an old bastion situated directly on the Rhine, where a provisional observatory was erected. Under these limitations Argelander again showed himself to be the ingenious improviser who, even with modest resources, could achieve lasting results. Although without measuring instruments, he created in these years one of his finest works, the *Uranometria nova* (1843). The main feature of this work was not the determination of exact positions, but the recording of all stars visible to the naked eye and a settlement of the nomenclature that had been used arbitrarily up to that time, as well as a demarcation of the constellations of the stars. At the same time, this atlas and the accompanying catalog fulfilled the task of a reliable representation of the magnitudes of the stars.

The exact observation of stellar magnitudes was not yet possible in Argelander's time because there was no suitable photometer. By means of the method of "estimation by steps," developed by Argelander, it was nevertheless possible, even without instruments, to obtain reliable magnitude data with an exactness of about one-third of a magnitude class. For this purpose the magnitudes were, by means of mutual comparison with neighboring stars of slightly different magnitudes, arranged in an arbitrary scale which could be gauged with the aid of stars of known magnitudes. This simple method, which is based on the ability of man's eyesight to perceive very slight differences in brightness, proved itself especially useful in the investigation of the changing brightness of variable stars, of which only eighteen were known at that time. By qualitatively determining the changing brightness of these stars, Argelander opened a completely new field of research which soon earned an important place in the working program of many astronomers; and, at his suggestion, it became of interest to many amateurs as well. It has to a considerable degree enriched our knowledge of the physical nature of the fixed stars. Argelander devoted himself to the continuous observation of these stars and inspired a similar zeal in his students. At the time of his death, the number of variable stars with known period of changing light had increased to almost 200.

When a five-foot transit instrument, the first larger instrument ordered for the new observatory, arrived from Ertel, it was immediately set up at the provisional observatory. With it Argelander extended the work begun by Bessel at Königsberg (which reached only to 45°) up to 80° northern declination. In more than 200 nights he measured the exact positions of 22,000 stars. The work was later continued on the same instrument at the new observatory to the south from 15° southern declination up to 31° southern declination with 17,000 additional stars. With this work, in conjunction with the Besselian zones, a first, although not wholly complete, inventory of the entire sky visible in the northern latitudes was made. This inventory included many faint stars which were invisible to the naked eye, but it was not completed to a limited magnitude, which is necessary to permit the investigation of certain questions of stellar statistics. Argelander stands out above all other astronomers of his century not only because of his perception of this important problem but also because he followed with all his energy the only practicable way to its solution. In order not to stretch this undertaking to an impossible extreme, he set the limit of completeness at stars of the ninth magnitude. His goal was a uniform registration of all stars up to this magnitude and the cataloging of their positions and magnitudes with an exactness sufficient for further identification.

From these considerations there arose the *Bonner Durchmusterung*, which has since provided the working basis for every observatory. It consists of a three-volume catalog of stars and a forty-plate atlas in which are recorded the positions (exactness $\pm0.1'$) and magnitudes ($\pm0.3^{M}$) of 324,198 stars between the northern celestial pole and 2° southern declination. The observations were made with a very small instrument, a so-called comet seeker with only a 7.8-centimeter aperture and a 63-centimeter focal distance with a ninefold magnification. The observations, which lasted over a period of 625 nights, from 1852 until 1859, extended for terms of five, six, seven, eight, and occasionally twelve hours, were mostly made by his assistants Eduard Schönfeld and Adalbert Krüger. The plan of observation, thought out to the smallest detail, comprised not only the tremendous number of individual observations, which exceeded a million, but also the extensive revisions of doubtful cases, which were carried out by Argelander himself on the meridian circle. In addition, it included the detailed calculations for the final catalog and for the plates of the atlas. Thus the results, despite the small circle of collaborators, were published after a few years and became the foundation for all future astronomical work.

The next step was the improvement of the preliminary determination of the positions of stars, utilizing the high development of the art of measurement, but it could no longer be the task of a single observatory. Therefore, in 1867 Argelander proposed to the Astronomische Gesellschaft that several observatories acting as a team undertake according to a uniform plan the observation of the most exact positions possible on meridian circles of all stars in the *Bonner Durchmusterung* up to the ninth magnitude. Argelander lived to see the project, in which seventeen observatories took part, set in motion in the 1870's.

Some idea of Argelander's renown as an astronomer may be gained from the fact that he was a member of the academies of St. Petersburg, London, Berlin, Stockholm, Paris, Vienna, Boston, and Brussels; of the Societas Fennica in Helsinki; of the Royal Astronomical Society of London; of the National Academy of Sciences of the United States; and a charter member of the Astronomische Gesellschaft, of which he was a member of the governing body from 1863 to 1871 and chairman from 1864 to 1867.

Argelander's achievement does not lie in substantial discoveries, but in the single-minded and systematic planning of his lifework and his unique resoluteness and skill in its execution. His main endeavor consisted in offering extensive and complete numerical data for the study of the construction of the heavens and the motions of the fixed stars in the stellar system. Without his work, which was con-

tinued at the Bonn Observatory, by Schönfeld and Küstner, the knowledge attained in our century about the structure of the universe would not have been imaginable.

BIBLIOGRAPHY

I. ORIGINAL WORKS. Argelander's writings include *De observationibus astronomicis a Flamsteedio institutis,* his dissertation (Königsberg, 1822); *Untersuchung über die Bahn des grossen Kometen von 1811* (Königsberg, 1822); *DLX stellarum fixarum positiones mediae ineunte anno 1830* (Helsinki, 1835); *Über die eigene Bewegung des Sonnensystems, hergeleitet aus den eigenen Bewegungen der Sterne* (St. Petersburg, 1837); *Uranometria nova* (Berlin, 1843), with seventeen charts and a catalog of stars; *Bonner Sternverzeichnis,* 3 vols. (Bonn, 1859–1862), Vols. III–V in the series Astronomische Beobachtungen auf der Königlichen Sternwarte zu Bonn; and *Atlas des nördlichen gestirnten Himmels für den Anfang des Jahres 1855* (Bonn, 1863), with forty charts.

II. SECONDARY LITERATURE. Works providing information about Argelander include B. Sticker, *Fr. W. Argelander und die Astronomie vor hundert Jahren* (Bonn, 1944); E. Schönfeld, obituary, in *Vierteljahrsschrift der Astronomische Gesellschaft,* **10** (1875), 150–178; articles on him in *Allgemeine deutsche Biographie,* Vol. XLVI; *Neue deutsche Biographie,* Vol. I; and *Westermanns Monatshefte,* **51** (1906), which concerns Argelander's family.

BERNHARD STICKER

ARGENVILLE, ANTOINE-JOSEPH DEZALLIER D' (*b.* Paris, France, 1 July 1680; *d.* Paris, 29 November 1765), *natural history, engraving, art history.*

D'Argenville was the son of Antoine and Marie Mariette Dezallier. His father owned the d'Argenville estate, near Bezons and Versailles, from which he took his name. After studying at the Collège du Plessis, he devoted himself to the fine arts under the direction of the engraver Bernard Picart, the painter Roger de Piles, and the architect Alexandre Le Blond. He also became interested in natural science. In 1709 his first work, *Traité sur la théorie et la pratique du jardinage,* was published. D'Argenville went to Italy in 1713, and upon his return in 1716 he purchased the post of secretary to the king; he was later named *maître des comptes* (2 July 1733) and counsellor to the king (1748). After settling in Paris, he soon acquired a deserved reputation as an expert collector of objects of art and curiosities of nature. Trips to Germany, Holland, and England (1728) made it possible for him to enrich both his knowledge and his collections.

Today d'Argenville is known particularly through his *Abrégé de la vie des plus fameux peintres* (1745–

1752), a mediocre work. He also produced *L'histoire naturelle éclaircie dans deux de ses parties principales, la lithologie et la conchyliologie* (1742). This work, illustrated with beautiful plates, was a great success. D'Argenville profited from the eighteenth century's infatuation with the natural sciences and, indeed, contributed to this vogue by publishing descriptions of the most notable exhibits of natural history in Paris and the provinces. His *L'histoire naturelle* was reissued in two volumes (1755, 1757), and there was also a third edition of *La conchyliologie* (1780).

In 1718 d'Argenville married Françoise-Thérèse Hémart; they had one son, Antoine-Nicolas. He became a member of the Société Royale des Sciences de Montpellier in 1740, of the Royal Society of London in 1750, and of the Académie de La Rochelle in 1758.

BIBLIOGRAPHY

I. ORIGINAL WORKS. D'Argenville's writings include *Traité sur la théorie et la pratique du jardinage* (Paris, 1709); *L'histoire naturelle éclaircie dans deux de ses parties principales, la lithologie et la conchyliologie* (Paris, 1742), reissued in 2 vols. (Paris, 1755–1757), and, for *La conchyliologie*, a 3rd ed., 2 vols. (Paris, 1780); and *Abrégé de la vie des plus fameux peintres,* 3 vols. (Paris, 1745–1752; 1762).

The Bibliothèque Nationale, Paris, Département des Manuscrits, has a catalog of d'Argenville's paintings, prints, and curiosities (n.a. 1564); corrections and additions to the *Abrégé de la vie des plus fameux peintres* (19.094); and letters (n.a. 4814). The Bibliothèque de l'Arsenal, Paris, has an autograph manuscript of the *Histoire générale des coquilles* (2807); and the Bibliothèque d'Avignon, two letters addressed to Esprit-Claude-François Calvet (2358, 3050). At the Royal Society of London are a letter to the Royal Society (MM. 3.85), and a copy and translation of another letter (L&P.II.160).

II. SECONDARY LITERATURE. Other writings on d'Argenville appear under his name in *Biographie universelle Michaud,* new ed., X (Paris, 1855), 598–599; *Dictionnaire de biographie française,* III (Paris, 1939), cols. 581–583; *Nouvelle biographie générale,* XIV (Paris, 1855), 10–11; see also de Ratte, "Éloge de M. Desallier d'Argenville," in d'Argenville's *La conchyliologie,* 3rd ed. (Paris, 1780), I, ix–xxiv.

YVES LAISSUS

ARGOLI, ANDREA (*b.* Tagliacozzo, Italy, 15 March 1570 [1568?]; *d.* Padua, Italy, 27 September 1657), *astrology, astronomy.*

Andrea was the son of Octavio Argoli, a lawyer, and Caterina Mati; his own son, Giovanni (*b.* 1609), achieved considerable celebrity as a precocious poet.

From 1622 to 1627 Argoli held the chair of mathematics at the Sapienza in Rome; evidence suggests that he lost this post because of his enthusiasm for astrology. In 1632 he became professor of mathematics in Padua, where he spent the remainder of his life. If the reports that he studied with Magini and taught Albrecht Wallenstein astrology are correct, then he must also have been in Padua earlier, around 1600.

Argoli's extensive astronomical ephemerides, based first on the *Prutenic Tables* (1620–1640) and later on his own tables (1630–1700), which were based on the observations of Tycho Brahe, gave a permanence to his reputation that his other writings would scarcely have achieved.

In his *Astronomicorum* (1629), Argoli proposed his own geocentric system of the world: the orbits of Mercury and Venus are centered on the sun but those of Mars, Jupiter, and Saturn are centered on the earth (in contradistinction to the Tychonic hypothesis). This scheme is essentially the same as that of Martianus Capella, with the addition of the rotation of the earth on its own axis. A communication to Galileo from F. Micanzio gives evidence that Argoli later planned a defense of Galileo's *Dialogi;* but if the work was ever completed, it no longer survives.

In his *Pandosion,* Argoli devotes chapter 41 to an accurate and succinct exposition of Harvey's doctrine of the circulation of the blood—without, however, mentioning Harvey's name. His principal astrological text, *De diebus criticis . . .,* which concerned astrology in general and astrological medicine in particular, has been described by Thorndike.

BIBLIOGRAPHY

I. ORIGINAL WORKS. Argoli's writings are *Problemata astronomica* (Rome, 1604); *Tabulae primi mobilis* (Rome, 1610; Padua, 1644, 1667); *Ephemerides . . . ab anno 1621 ad 1640 ex Prutenicis tabulis supputatae* (Rome, 1621; Venice, 1623); *Novae caelestium motuum ephemerides . . . et anno 1620 ad 1640* (Rome, 1629), which includes *Astronomicorum libri tres; Secundorum mobilium tabulae juxta Tychonis Brahe et novas e coelo deductas observationes* (Padua, 1634, 1650); *Ephemerides . . . juxta Tychonis Brahe hypotheses* (for 1630–1680, Venice–Padua, 1638; for 1631–1680, Padua, 1638, 1642)—the following editions, for 1641–1700, begin *Exactissimae coelestium motuum* and include the *Astronomicorum libri tres* (Padua, 1648, 1652; Lyons, 1659, 1677); *De diebus criticis et de aegrorum decubitu libri duo* (Padua, 1639, 1652); *Pandosion sphaericum* (Padua, 1644; 2nd ed., enl., 1653); *Ptolemaus parvus in genethliacis junctus Arabibus* (Padua–Lyons, 1652; Lyons, 1654, 1659, 1680); and *Brevis dissertatio de cometa 1652,*

1653 et aliqua de meteorologicis impressionibus (Padua, 1653).

II. SECONDARY LITERATURE. The most complete modern treatment is M. Gliozzi, in *Dizionario biografico degli italiani,* IV (Rome, 1964), 122–124. See also B. J. B. Delambre, *Histoire de l'astronomie moderne,* II (Paris, 1821), 514–517; R. P. Niceron, *Mémoires pour servir à l'histoire des hommes illustres,* XXXIX (Paris, 1738), 325–331; and Lynn Thorndike, *A History of Magic and Experimental Science,* VII (New York, 1958), 122–124.

OWEN GINGERICH

ARISTAEUS (*fl. ca.* 350–330 B.C.), *mathematics.*

Aristaeus lived after Menaechmus and was an older contemporary of Euclid. Nothing is known of his life, but he was definitely not the son-in-law of Pythagoras mentioned by Iamblichus. Pappus, whose *Collectio* (Book VII) is our chief source, calls him Aristaeus the Elder, so presumably there was a later mathematician with the same name.

None of Aristaeus' writings have been preserved. On the other hand, Pappus (some 650 years later) had in his possession Aristaeus' treatment of conic sections as loci, the *Five Books Concerning Solid Loci.* He mentions the work in his *Treasury of Analysis.* In another place, he speaks of the solid loci of Aristaeus as "standing in relation to conic sections."[1] For that reason, and because in a scholium there is mention of *Five Books of the Elements of Conic Sections,* some have concluded that Aristaeus wrote another work of this nature. According to Heiberg's investigations, this is untrue. Pappus also reports that Aristaeus introduced the terms "section of the acute-angled, right-angled, and obtuse-angled cone."

As for its contents, it can be determined from the passages by Pappus and Apollonius that the "locus with respect to three or four lines" was treated by Aristaeus.[2] Well-founded suppositions have been expressed concerning other loci treated by him, in connection with vergings ($\nu\epsilon\acute{\upsilon}\sigma\epsilon\iota\varsigma$) by means of conic sections, trisection of an angle with the aid of a hyperbola, and above all the focus-directrix property of conic sections; Pappus establishes them in a lemma to the lost *Surface Loci* of Euclid. Since Euclid evidently supposes that the principle necessary for an understanding of surface loci is well known, it could have originated with Aristaeus.

In any case, Aristaeus played a major part in the development of the conic section theory, which began with Menaechmus.[3] Zeuthen and Heath give a comprehensive presentation of his accomplishments. In 1645 Viviani undertook a revision of the *Solid Loci,* starting from the same general interpretation of the contents that was used later by Zeuthen.

Hypsicles (*ca.* 180 B.C.), the editor of Book XIV of Euclid's *Elements,* reports another work, *Concerning the Comparison of Five Regular Solids,* from which he quotes a proposition.[4] It is not certain whether Hypsicles had in mind here the author of the *Solid Loci.* One would suppose a younger Aristaeus; in that case, Euclid's dependence (in Book XIII) on Aristaeus, which has been maintained by Heath but has been denied with good reasons by Sachs, would not be a point of contention.

After Aristaeus, Euclid was the next to deal with conic sections; his work was rendered out-of-date by Apollonius and became superfluous. From a statement by Pappus one must assume that Euclid had no intention of developing further the treatment of conic sections as loci, but that he sought—as did Apollonius—to give a general, synthetic construction. The solution of the problem of the "locus with respect to three or four lines" must have been incomplete in Aristaeus' works, for the "proposition of powers" (prop. Euclid III, 36) extended to conics and the second branch of the hyperbola were still missing. Apollonius, who must have had the complete solution,[5] notes additionally that the problem could not be completely solved without the propositions he discovered. He does not give the solution, but in the third book Apollonius does prove the converse of the proposition.[6]

After Apollonius and Pappus became well known again during the Renaissance, the problem of loci again began to attract interest. It appears in letters from Golius to Mydorge (after 1629) and Descartes (1631), and in letters from Descartes to Mersenne (1632, 1634). Fermat gives (before 1637) a solution in the ancient manner; in a letter to him (4 August 1640), Roberval reports that he completely reconstructed the *Solid Loci.*[7] In Descartes's *Géométrie* (1637) the "locus with respect to three and four lines" forms the starting point for the new analytic treatment of conic sections. Descartes cites the pertinent passages in Pappus and, going beyond him, expands the problem to arbitrarily many straight lines. By means of this, he laid the foundation for a theory of the general properties of algebraic curves.

NOTES

1. $\sigma\upsilon\nu\epsilon\chi\hat{\eta}$ $\tau o\hat{\iota}\varsigma$ $\kappa\omega\nu\iota\kappa o\hat{\iota}\varsigma$ (Pappus VII, 672). Hultsch translates it freely as *supplementum conicorum doctrinae.*

2. The proposition is as follows: If from a given point arbitrarily directed lines *a, b, c* (or *a, b, c, d*) are drawn to meet at given angles three (or four) straight lines given in position, and then if $ac:b^2$ (or $ac:bd$) is a given value, then the point lies on a conic section. Cf. Pappus VII, 678.

3. Sarton (*Introduction,* I, 125) calls him the greatest mathematician of the second half of the fourth century.

4. "The same circle circumscribes both the pentagon of the dodecahedron and the triangle of the icosahedron when both are inscribed in the same sphere." (Euclid, Heiberg ed., V, 6 f.)

5. Descartes is of still another opinion. See also Zeuthen, *Lehre,* pp. 127 ff.

6. Heath, *Apollonius,* pp. cxxxviii ff. The proposition is this: For a point of a conic section the relationship given in note 2 holds true.

7. Tannery, "Note," pp. 46 ff. From Fermat only the solution for the locus of three straight lines survived.

BIBLIOGRAPHY

Aristaeus is also discussed in J. L. Coolidge, *A History of the Conic Sections and Quadric Surfaces* (Oxford, 1945, 1947), chs. 1 (para 2), 3, 5; P. ver Eecke, *Les coniques d'Apollonius de Perge* (Paris, 1932, 1959), pp. x, xvii, 2; and *Pappus d'Alexandrie,* I (Paris–Bruges, 1933), pp. lxxxix–ci; Euclid, *Elementa,* J. L. Heiberg, ed., V (Leipzig, 1888), 6 f.; T. L. Heath, *Apollonius of Perga* (Cambridge, 1896), pp. xxxviii, cxxxviii ff.; and *A History of Greek Mathematics,* I (Oxford, 1921), 143 f., 420; J. L. Heiberg, *Apollonii Pergaei quae Graece exstant,* I (Leipzig, 1891), 4; and *Geschichte der Mathematik und Naturwissenschaften im Altertum* (Leipzig, 1925, 1960), p. 13; F. Hultsch, trans., *Pappi Alexandrini Collectionis quae supersunt,* II (Berlin, 1877), 634, 636, 672 ff., 1004 ff.; Pauly-Wissowa, *Real-Encyclopädie,* supp. III (1918), 157 f.; E. Sachs, *Die fünf Platonischen Körper* (Berlin, 1917), pp. 107 ff.; G. Sarton, *Introduction to the History of Science,* I, 125; P. Tannery, "Note sur le problème de Pappus," in *Mémoires scientifiques,* 3 (1915), 42–50; V. Viviani, *De locis solidis secunda divinatio geometrica in quinque libros injuria temporum amissos Aristaei senioris geometrae* (Florence, 1673, 1701); and H. G. Zeuthen, *Die Lehre von den Kegelschnitten im Altertum,* R. von Fischer-Benzon, ed. (Copenhagen, 1886), repr. with foreword and index by J. E. Hofmann (Hildesheim, 1966), pp. 127 ff., 276, and *Geschichte der Mathematik im Altertum und Mittelalter* (Copenhagen, 1890), pp. 197 ff.

KURT VOGEL

ARISTARCHUS OF SAMOS (*ca.* 310–230 B.C.), *mathematics, astronomy.*

Aristarchus is celebrated as being the first man to have propounded a heliocentric theory, eighteen centuries before Copernicus. He was born on the island of Samos, close by Miletus, cradle of Ionian science and philosophy. Little is known of Aristarchus' subsequent habitation. He was a pupil of Strato of Lampsacos, third head of the Lyceum founded by Aristotle. It is more likely that he studied under Strato at Alexandria than at Athens after the latter's assumption of the headship of the Lyceum in 287 B.C. Aristarchus' approximate dates are determined by Ptolemy's record (*Syntaxis* 3.2) of his observation of the summer solstice in 280 B.C. and by Archimedes' account of his heliocentric theory in a treatise, *The Sand-Reckoner,* which Archimedes composed before 216 B.C. The sole surviving work of Aristarchus is the treatise *On the Sizes and Distances of the Sun and Moon.*

To his contemporaries Aristarchus was known as "the mathematician"; the epithet may merely have served to distinguish him from other men of the same name, although *On Sizes and Distances* is indeed the work of a highly competent mathematician. The Roman architect Vitruvius lists him with six other men of rare endowment who were expert in all branches of mathematics and who could apply their talents to practical purposes. Vitruvius also credits him with inventing the *skaphē,* a widely used sundial consisting of a hemispherical bowl with a needle erected vertically in the middle to cast shadows. Speculations as to why a reputable mathematician like Aristarchus should interest himself in the true physical orientation of the solar system thus appear to be idle. Some have pointed to the possible influence of Strato, who was known as "the physical philosopher." There is no evidence, however, to indicate that Aristarchus got his physical theories from Strato. A more likely assumption is that *On Sizes and Distances* gave him an appreciation of the relative sizes of the sun and earth and led him to propound a heliocentric system.

The beginnings of heliocentrism are traced to the early Pythagoreans, a religiophilosophical school that flourished in southern Italy in the fifth century B.C. Ancient tradition ascribed to Pythagoras (*ca.* 520 B.C.) the identification of the Morning Star and the Evening Star as the same body. Philolaus (*ca.* 440 B.C.) gave the earth, moon, sun, and planets an orbital motion about a central fire, which he called "the hearth of the universe." According to another tradition, it was Hicetas, a contemporary of Philolaus, who first gave a circular orbit to the earth. Hicetas was also credited with maintaining the earth's axial rotation and a stationary heavens. More reliable ancient authorities, however, associate the hypothesis of the earth's diurnal rotation with Heraclides of Pontus, a pupil of Plato, who is also explicitly credited with maintaining (*ca.* 340 B.C.) an epicyclic orbit of Venus—and presumably that of Mercury also—about the sun. Some Greek astronomer may have taken the next logical step toward developing a complete heliocentric hypothesis by proposing the theory advanced in modern times by Tycho Brahe, which placed the five visible planets in motion about the sun, and the sun, in turn, in motion about the earth. Several scholars have argued that such a step was indeed taken, the most notable being the Italian astronomer Schiaparelli, who ascribed the Tychonic system to Heraclides; but evidence of its existence in antiquity is lacking.

Ancient authorities are unanimous in attributing the heliocentric theory to Aristarchus. Archimedes, who lived shortly afterward, says that he published his views in a book or treatise in which the premises that he developed led to the conclusion that the universe is many times greater than the current conception of it. Archimedes, near the opening of *The Sand-Reckoner,* gives a summary statement of Aristarchus' argument:

> His hypotheses are that the fixed stars and the sun are stationary, that the earth is borne in a circular orbit about the sun, which lies in the middle of its orbit, and that the sphere of the fixed stars, having the same center as the sun, is so great in extent that the circle on which he supposes the earth to be borne has such a proportion to the distance of the fixed stars as the center of the sphere bears to its surface.

Plutarch (*ca.* A.D. 100) gives a similar brief account of Aristarchus' hypothesis, stating specifically that the earth revolves along the ecliptic and that it is at the same time rotating on its axis.

After reporting Aristarchus' views, Archimedes criticizes him for setting up a mathematically impossible proportion, pointing out that the center of the sphere has no magnitude and therefore cannot bear any ratio to the surface of the sphere. Archimedes intrudes the observation that the "universe," as it is commonly conceived of by astronomers, is a sphere whose radius extends from the center of the sun to the center of the earth. Accordingly, as a mathematician he imputes to the mathematician Aristarchus a proportion that he feels is implicit in his statement, namely, that the ratio that the earth bears to the universe, as it is commonly conceived, is equal to the ratio that the sphere in which the earth revolves, in Aristarchus' scheme, bears to the sphere of the fixed stars.

Modern scholars have generally supposed that Aristarchus did not intend to have his proportion interpreted as a mathematical statement, that instead he was using an expression conventional with Greek mathematical cosmographers—"having the relation of a point"—merely to indicate the minuteness of the earth's orbit and the vastness of the heavens. Sir Thomas Heath points to similar expressions in the works of Euclid, Geminus, Ptolemy, and Cleomedes, and in the second assumption of Aristarchus' extant treatise *On Sizes and Distances* (see below). Heath feels that Archimedes' interpretation was arbitrary and sophistical and that Aristarchus introduced the statement to account for the inability to observe

stellar parallax from an orbiting earth. Neugebauer defends the proportion that Archimedes ascribes to Aristarchus,

$$r : R_e = R_e : R_f,$$

as mathematically sound and providing finite dimensions for the sphere of the fixed stars: the earth's radius (r) is so small in comparison with the sun's distance (R_e) that no daily parallax of the sun is discernible for determining R_e; according to Aristarchus' hypothesis, the earth moves in an orbit whose radius is R_e and no annual parallax of the fixed stars is discernible.

Why did the Greeks, after evolving a heliocentric hypothesis in gradual steps over a period of two centuries, allow it to fall into neglect almost immediately? Only one man, Seleucus of Seleucia (*ca.* 150 B.C.), is known to have embraced Aristarchus' views. The common attitude of deploring the "abandonment" of the heliocentric theory as a "retrogressive step" appears to be unwarranted when it is realized that the theory, however bold and ingenious it is to be regarded, never attracted much attention in antiquity. Aristarchus' system was the culmination of speculations about the physical nature of the universe that began with the Ionian philosophers of the sixth century, and it belongs to an age that was passing away. The main course of development of Greek astronomy was mathematical, not physical, and the great achievements were still to come—the exacting demonstrations and calculations of Apollonius of Perga, Hipparchus, and Ptolemy. These were based upon a geocentric orientation.

To a mathematician the orientation is of no consequence; in fact it is more convenient to construct a system of epicycles and eccentrics to account for planetary motions from a geocentric orientation. A heliocentric hypothesis neatly explained some basic phenomena, such as the stations and retrogradations of superior planets; but a circular orbit for the earth, about a sun in the exact center, failed to account for precise anomalies, such as the inequality of the seasons. In explanation of this inequality, Hipparchus determined the eccentricity of the earth's position as 1/24 of the radius of the sun's circle and he fixed the line of absides in the direction of longitude 65° 30'. Ptolemy adopted Hipparchus' solar data without change, unaware that the sun's orbit describes a revolving eccentric, the shift being 32' in a century. The Arab astronomer al-Battānī (A.D. 858–929) discovered this shift. Epicyclic constructions had two advantages over eccentric constructions: they were applicable to inferior as well as superior planets and they palpably demonstrated planetary stations and retrograde motions. By the time of Apollonius it was understood that an equivalent eccentric system could be constructed for every epicyclic system. Henceforth, combinations of epicycles and eccentrics were introduced, all from a geocentric orientation. Aristarchus, too, had used a geocentric orientation in calculating the sizes and distances of the sun and moon.

It is not hard to account for the lack of interest in the heliocentric theory. The *Zeitgeist* of the new Hellenistic age was set and characterized by the abstruse erudition of the learned scholars and the precise researches of the astronomers, mathematicians, and anatomists working at the library and museum of Alexandria. Accurate instruments in use at Alexandria were giving astronomers a better appreciation of the vast distance of the sun. Putting the earth in orbit about the sun would lead to the expectation that some variation in the position of the fixed stars would be discernible at opposite seasons. Absence of displacement would presuppose a universe of vast proportions. The more precise the observations, the less inclined were the astronomers at Alexandria to accept an orbital motion of the earth. It is the opinion of Heath that Hipparchus (*ca.* 190–120 B.C.), usually regarded as the greatest of Greek astronomers, in adopting the geocentric orientation "sealed the fate of the heliocentric hypothesis for so many centuries."

The intellectual world at large was also disinclined to accept Aristarchus' orientation. Aristotle's doctrine of "natural places," which assigned to earth a position at the bottom or center among the elements comprising the universe, and his plausible "proofs" of a geocentric orientation, carried great weight in later antiquity, even with the mathematician Ptolemy. Religious minds were reluctant to relinquish the central position of man's abode. According to Plutarch, Cleanthes, the second head of the Stoic school (263–232 B.C.), thought that Aristarchus ought to be indicted on a charge of impiety for putting the earth in motion. Astrology, a respectable science in the eyes of many leading intellectuals, was enjoying an extraordinary vogue after its recent introduction. Its doctrines and findings were also based upon a geocentric orientation.

It is interesting to note in passing that Copernicus' disappointment at being anticipated by Aristarchus has recently come to light. Copernicus deliberately suppressed a statement acknowledging his awareness of Aristarchus' theory; the statement, deleted from the autograph copy of the *De revolutionibus,* appears in a footnote in the Thorn edition (1873) of that work. Elsewhere Copernicus tells of his search for classical

precedents for his novel ideas about the heavens and of his finding in Plutarch the views of Philolaus, Heraclides, and Ecphantus; but he omits mention of the clear statement about Aristarchus' theory that appears a few pages earlier. Lastly, Copernicus' almost certain acquaintance with Archimedes' *The Sand-Reckoner,* the work containing our best account of Aristarchus' theory, has recently been pointed out.

His accomplishments as an astronomer have tended to detract attention from Aristarchus' attainments as a mathematician. Flourishing a generation after Euclid and a generation before Archimedes, Aristarchus was capable of the same sort of rigorous and logical geometrical demonstrations that distinguished the work of those famous mathematicians. *On Sizes and Distances* marks the first attempt to determine astronomical distances and dimensions by mathematical deductions based upon a set of assumptions. His last assumption assigns a grossly excessive estimate to the apparent angular diameter of the moon (2°). We are told by Archimedes in *The Sand-Reckoner* that Aristarchus discovered the sun's apparent angular diameter to be 1/720 part of the zodiac circle (1/2°), a close and respectable estimate. Aristarchus uses a geocentric orientation in *On Sizes and Distances* and concludes that the sun's volume is over 300 times greater than the earth's volume. For these reasons it is generally assumed that the treatise was an early work, antedating his heliocentric hypothesis.

Aristarchus argues that at the precise moment of the moon's quadrature, when it is half-illuminated, angle *SME* is a right angle; angle *SEM* can be measured by observation; therefore it is possible to deduce angle *MSE* and to determine the ratio of the distance of the moon to the distance of the sun (Figure 1). Two obvious difficulties are involved in his procedures: the determination with any exactitude (1) of the time of the moon's dichotomy and (2) of the measurement of angle *SEM*. A slight inaccuracy in either case would lead to a grossly inaccurate result. Aristarchus assumes angle *SEM* to be 87°, when in actuality it is more than 89° 50′, and he derives a distance for the sun of 18 to 20 times greater than the moon's distance (actually nearly 400 times greater). His mathematical procedures are sound, but his observational data are so crude as to make it apparent that Aristarchus was interested here in mathematical demonstrations and not in physical realities.

Aristarchus' treatise begins with six assumptions:

(1) That the moon receives its light from the sun.

(2) That the earth has the relation of a point and center to the sphere of the moon.

(3) That when the moon appears to us to be exactly

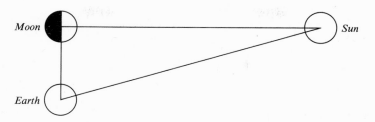

Figure 1

at the half the great circle dividing the light and dark portions of the moon is in line with the observer's eye.

(4) That when the moon appears to us to be at the half its distance from the sun is less than a quadrant by 1/30 part of a quadrant (87°).

(5) That the breadth of the earth's shadow (during eclipses) is that of two moons.

(6) That the moon subtends 1/15 part of a sign of the zodiac (2°).

He then states that he is in a position to prove three propositions:

(1) The distance of the sun from the earth is more than eighteen times but less than twenty times the moon's distance (from the earth); this is based on the assumption about the halved moon.

(2) The diameter of the sun has the same ratio to the diameter of the moon (i.e., assuming that the sun and moon have the same apparent angular diameter).

(3) The diameter of the sun has to the diameter of the earth a ratio greater than 19:3, but less than 43:6; this deduction follows from the ratio between the distances thus discovered, from the assumption about the shadow, and from the assumption that the moon subtends 1/15 part of a sign of the zodiac.

Then follow eighteen propositions containing the demonstrations. Heath has edited and translated the complete Greek text, together with Pappus' comments on the treatise, in his *Aristarchus of Samos* (pp. 352–414), and presents a summary account of the treatise in *A History of Greek Mathematics* (Vol. II).

Anticipating trigonometric methods that were to come, Aristarchus was the first to develop geometric procedures for approximating the sines of small angles. He deals with angles expressed as fractions of right angles and ratios of the sides of triangles, determining limits between which actual values lie. In Proposition 7, demonstrating that the distance of the sun is more than eighteen times but less than twenty times the distance of the moon, which would be expressed trigonometrically $1/18 > \sin 3° > 1/20$, he uses in his proof certain inequalities that he assumes to be known and accepted. These may be expressed

trigonometrically. If α and β are acute angles and $\alpha > \beta$, then

$$\tan\alpha/\tan\beta > \alpha/\beta > \sin\alpha/\sin\beta.$$

If Aristarchus had had a correct measurement of the angle *SEM*—89 5/6° instead of 87°—his result would have been nearly correct. A century later Hipparchus was able to obtain a very close approximation of the moon's distance, expressed in terms of earth radii, by measuring the earth's shadow during lunar eclipses; but an appreciation of the vast distance of the sun had to wait upon the development of modern precision instruments.

Other dimensions deduced by Aristarchus in his treatise, all of them grossly underestimated because of his poor observational data, are:

(Prop. 10) The sun has to the moon a ratio greater than 5,832:1 but less than 8,000:1.

(Prop. 11) The diameter of the moon is less than 2/45 but greater than 1/30 of the distance of the center of the moon from the observer.

(Prop. 16) The sun has to the earth a ratio greater than 6,859:27 but less than 79,507:216.

(Prop. 17) The diameter of the earth is to the diameter of the moon in a ratio greater than 108:43 but less than 60:19.

(Prop. 18) The earth is to the moon in a ratio greater than 1,259,712:79,507 but less than 216,000:6,859.

BIBLIOGRAPHY

Thomas W. Africa, "Copernicus' Relation to Aristarchus and Pythagoras," in *Isis*, **52** (1961), 403–409; Angus Armitage, *Copernicus, the Founder of Modern Astronomy* (London, 1938); John L. E. Dreyer, *A History of the Planetary Systems from Thales to Kepler* (Cambridge, England, 1906; repr., New York, 1953); Pierre Duhem, *Le système du monde*, Vols. I–II (Paris, 1954); Sir Thomas Heath, *Aristarchus of Samos* (Oxford, 1913) and *A History of Greek Mathematics*, 2 vols. (Oxford, 1921); Otto Neugebauer, "Archimedes and Aristarchus," in *Isis*, **39** (1942), 4–6; Giovanni V. Schiaparelli, "Origine del sistema planetario eliocentrico presso i Greci," in *Memorie del'Istituto lom-*

bardo di scienze e lettere, **18** (1898), fasc. 5; and William H. Stahl, "The Greek Heliocentric Theory and Its Abandonment," in *Transactions of the American Philological Association,* **77** (1945), 321–332.

WILLIAM H. STAHL

ARISTOTLE (*b.* Stagira in Chalcidice, 384 B.C.; *d.* Chalcis, 322 B.C.), *the most influential ancient exponent of the methodology and division of sciences; contributed to physics, physical astronomy, meteorology, psychology, biology.* The following article is in four parts: Method, Physics, and Cosmology; Natural History and Zoology; Anatomy and Physiology; Tradition and Influence.

Method, Physics, and Cosmology.

Aristotle's father served as personal physician to Amyntas II of Macedon, grandfather of Alexander the Great. Aristotle's interest in biology and in the use of dissection is sometimes traced to his father's profession, but any suggestion of a rigorous family training in medicine can be discounted. Both parents died while Aristotle was a boy, and his knowledge of human anatomy and physiology remained a notably weak spot in his biology. In 367, about the time of his seventeenth birthday, he came to Athens and became a member of Plato's Academy. Henceforth his career falls naturally into three periods. He remained with the Academy for twenty years. Then, when Plato died in 347, he left the city and stayed away for twelve years: his reason for going may have been professional, a dislike of philosophical tendencies represented in the Academy by Plato's nephew and successor, Speusippus, but more probably it was political, the new anti-Macedonian mood of the city. He returned in 335 when Athens had come under Macedonian rule, and had twelve more years of teaching and research there. This third period ended with the death of his pupil, Alexander the Great (323), and the revival of Macedon's enemies. Aristotle was faced with a charge of impiety and went again into voluntary exile. A few months later he died on his maternal estate in Chalcis.

His middle years away from Athens took him first to a court on the far side of the Aegean whose ruler, Hermeias, became his father-in-law; then (344) to the neighboring island Lesbos, probably at the suggestion of Theophrastus, a native of the island and henceforth a lifelong colleague; finally (342) back to Macedon as tutor of the young prince Alexander. After his return to Athens he lectured chiefly in the grounds of the Lyceum, a Gymnasium already popular with sophists and teachers. The Peripatetic school, as an institution comparable to the Academy, was probably not founded until after his death. But with some distinguished students and associates he collected a natural history museum and a library of maps and manuscripts (including his own essays and lecture notes), and organized a program of research which *inter alia* laid the foundation for all histories of Greek natural philosophy (see Theophrastus), mathematics and astronomy (see Eudemus), and medicine.

Recent discussion of his intellectual development has dwelt on the problem of distributing his works between and within the three periods of his career. But part of the stimulus to this inquiry was the supposed success with which Plato's dialogues had been put in chronological order, and the analogy with Plato is misleading. Everything that Aristotle polished for public reading in Plato's fashion has been lost, save for fragments and later reports. The writings that survive are a collection edited in the first century B.C. (see below, Aristotle: Tradition), allegedly from manuscripts long mislaid: a few items are spurious (among the scientific works *Mechanica, Problemata, De mundo, De plantis*), most are working documents produced in the course of Aristotle's teaching and research; and the notes and essays composing them have been arranged and amended not only by their author but also by his ancient editors and interpreters. Sometimes an editorial title covers a batch of writings on connected topics of which some seem to supersede others (thus *Physics* VII seems an unfinished attempt at the argument for a prime mover which is carried out independently in *Physics* VIII); sometimes the title represents an open file, a text annotated with unabsorbed objections (e.g., the *Topics*) or with later and even post-Aristotelian observations (e.g., the *Historia animalium*). On the other hand it cannot be assumed that inconsistencies are always chronological pointers. In *De caelo* I–II he argues for a fifth element in addition to the traditional four (fire, air, water, earth): unlike them, its natural motion is circular and it forms the divine and unchanging substance of the heavenly bodies. Yet in *De caelo* III–IV, as in the *Physics,* he discusses the elements without seeming to provide for any such fifth body, and these writings are accordingly sometimes thought to be earlier. But on another view of his methods (see below, on dialectic) it becomes more intelligible that he should try different and even discrepant approaches to a topic at the same time.

Such considerations do not make it impossible to reconstruct something of the course of his scientific thinking from the extant writings, together with what is known of his life. For instance it is sometimes said that his distinction between "essence" and "accident," or between defining and nondefining characteristics, must be rooted in the biological studies in which it plays an integral part. But the distinction is explored at greatest length in the *Topics,* a handbook of dialectical debate which dates substantially from his earlier years in the Academy, whereas the inquiries embodied in his biological works seem to come chiefly from his years abroad, since they refer relatively often to the Asiatic coast and Lesbos and seldom to southern Greece. So this piece of conceptual apparatus was not produced by the work in biology. On the contrary, it was modified by that work: when Aristotle tries to reduce the definition of a species to one distinguishing mark (e.g., *Metaphysics* VII 12, VIII 6) he is a dialectician, facing a problem whose ancestry includes Plato's theory of Forms, but when he rejects such definitions in favor of a cluster of differentiae (*De partibus animalium* I 2–3) he writes as a working biologist, armed with a set of questions about breathing and sleeping, movement and nourishment, birth and death.

The starting point in tracing his scientific progress must therefore be his years in the Academy. Indeed without this starting point it is not possible to understand either his pronouncements on scientific theory or, what is more important, the gap between his theory and his practice.

The Mathematical Model. The Academy that Aristotle joined in 367 was distinguished from other Athenian schools by two interests: mathematics (including astronomy and harmonic theory, to the extent that these could be made mathematically respectable), and dialectic, the Socratic examination of the assumptions made in reasoning—including the assumptions of mathematicians and cosmologists. Briefly, Plato regarded the first kind of studies as merely preparatory and ancillary to the second; Aristotle, in the account of scientific and philosophical method that probably dates from his Academic years, reversed the priorities (*Posterior Analytics* I; *Topics* I 1–2). It was the mathematics he encountered that impressed him as providing the model for any well-organized science. The work on axiomatization which was to culminate in Euclid's *Elements* was already far advanced, and for Aristotle the pattern of a science is an axiomatic system in which theorems are validly derived from basic principles, some proprietary to the science ("hypotheses" and "definitions," the second corresponding to Euclid's "definitions"), others having an application in more than one system ("axioms," corresponding to Euclid's "common notions"). The proof-theory which was characteristic of Greek mathematics (as against that of Babylon or Egypt) had developed in the attempt to show why various mathematical formulae worked in practice. Aristotle pitches

on this as the chief aim of any science: it must not merely record but explain, and in explaining it must, so far as the special field of inquiry allows, generalize. Thus mathematical proof becomes Aristotle's first paradigm of scientific explanation; by contrast, the dialectic that Plato ranked higher—the logical but free-ranging analysis of the beliefs and usage of "the many and the wise"—is allowed only to help in settling those basic principles of a science that cannot, without regress or circularity, be proved within the science itself. At any rate, this was the theory.

Aristotle duly adapts and enlarges the mathematical model to provide for the physical sciences. Mathematics, he holds, is itself a science (or rather a family of sciences) about the physical world, and not about a Platonic world of transcendent objects; but it abstracts from those characteristics of the world that are the special concern of physics—movement and change, and therewith time and location. So the nature and behavior of physical things will call for more sorts of explanation than mathematics recognizes. Faced with a man, or a tree, or a flame, one can ask what it is made of, its "matter"; what is its essential character or "form"; what external or internal agency produced it; and what the "end" or purpose of it is. The questions make good sense when applied to an artifact such as a statue, and Aristotle often introduces them by this analogy; but he holds that they can be extended to every kind of thing involved in regular natural change. The explanations they produce can be embodied in the formal proofs or even the basic definitions of a science (thus a lunar eclipse can be not merely accounted for, but defined, as the loss of light due to the interposition of the earth, and a biological species can be partly defined in terms of the purpose of some of its organs). Again, the regularities studied by physics may be unlike those of mathematics in an important respect: initially the *Posterior Analytics* depicts a science as deriving necessary conclusions from necessary premises, true in all cases (I ii and iv), but later (I xxx) the science is allowed to deal in generalizations that are true in most cases but not necessarily in all. Aristotle is adapting his model to make room for "a horse has four legs" as well as for "$2 \times 2 = 4$." How he regards the exceptions to such generalizations is not altogether clear. In his discussions of "luck" and "chance" in *Physics* II, and of "accident" elsewhere, he seems to hold that a lucky or chance or accidental event can always, under some description, be subsumed under a generalization expressing some regularity. His introduction to the *Meteorologica* is sometimes cited to show that in his view sublunary happenings are inherently irregular; but he probably means that, while the laws of sublunary physics are commonly (though not always) framed to allow of exceptions, these exceptions are not themselves inexplicable. The matter is complicated by his failure to maintain a sharp distinction between laws that provide a necessary (and even uniquely necessary), and those that provide a sufficient, condition of the situation to be explained.

But in two respects the influence of mathematics on Aristotle's theory of science is radical and unmodified. First, the drive to axiomatize mathematics and its branches was in fact a drive for autonomy: the premises of the science were to determine what questions fell within the mathematician's competence and, no less important, what did not. This consequence Aristotle accepts for every field of knowledge: a section of *Posterior Analytics* I xii is given up to the problem, what questions can be properly put to the practitioner of such-and-such a science; and in I vii, trading on the rule "one science to one genus," he denounces arguments that poach outside their own field—which try, for instance, to deduce geometrical conclusions from arithmetical premises. He recognizes arithmetical proofs in harmonics and geometrical proofs in mechanics, but treats them as exceptions. The same impulse leads him to map all systematic knowledge into its departments—theoretical, practical, and productive—and to divide the first into metaphysics (or, as he once calls it, "theology"), mathematics, and physics, these in turn being marked out in subdivisions.

This picture of the autonomous deductive system has had a large influence on the interpreters of Aristotle's scientific work; yet it plays a small part in his inquiries, just because it is not a model for inquiry at all but for subsequent exposition. This is the second major respect in which it reflects mathematical procedure. In nearly all the surviving productions of Greek mathematics, traces of the workshop have been deliberately removed: proofs are found for theorems that were certainly first reached by other routes. So Aristotle's theoretical picture of a science shows it in its shop window (or what he often calls its "didactic") form; but for the most part his inquiries are not at this stage of the business. This is a piece of good fortune for students of the subject, who have always lamented that no comparable record survives of presystematic research in mathematics proper (Archimedes' public letter to Eratosthenes—the *Ephodos,* or "Method"—is hardly such a record). As it is, Aristotle's model comes nearest to realization in the systematic astronomy of *De caelo* I–II (cf., e.g., I iii, "from what has been said, partly as premises and partly as things proved from these, it

follows . . ."), and in the proof of a prime mover in *Physics* VIII. But these constructions are built on the presystematic analyses of *Physics* I–VI, analyses that are expressly undertaken to provide physics with its basic assumptions (cf. I i) and to define its basic concepts, change and time and location, infinity and continuity (III i). *Ex hypothesi* the latter discussions, which from Aristotle's pupils Eudemus and Strato onward have given the chief stimulus to physicists and philosophers of science, cannot be internal to the science whose premises they seek to establish. Their methods and data need not and do not fit the theoretical straitjacket, and in fact they rely heavily on the dialectic that theoretically has no place in the finished science.

Dialectic and "Phenomena." Conventionally Aristotle has been contrasted with Plato as the committed empiricist, anxious to "save the phenomena" by basing his theories on observation of the physical world. First the phenomena, then the theory to explain them: this Baconian formula he recommends not only for physics (and specifically for astronomy and biology) but for ethics and generally for all arts and sciences. But "phenomena," like many of his key terms, is a word with different uses in different contexts. In biology and meteorology the phenomena are commonly observations made by himself or taken from other sources (fishermen, travelers, etc.), and similar observations are evidently presupposed by that part of his astronomy that relies on the schemes of concentric celestial spheres proposed by Eudoxus and Callippus. But in the *Physics* when he expounds the principles of the subject, and in many of the arguments in the *De caelo* and *De generatione et corruptione* by which he settles the nature and interaction of the elements, and turns Eudoxus' elegant abstractions into a cumbrous physical (and theological) construction, the data on which he draws are mostly of another kind. The phenomena he now wants to save—or to give logical reasons (rather than empirical evidence) for scrapping—are the common convictions and common linguistic usage of his contemporaries, supplemented by the views of other thinkers. They are what he always represents as the materials of dialectic.

Thus when Aristotle tries to harden the idea of location for use in science (*Physics* IV 1–5) he sets out from our settled practice of locating a thing by giving its physical surroundings, and in particular from established ways of talking about one thing taking another's place. It is to save these that he treats any location as a container, and defines the place of X as the innermost static boundary of the body surrounding X. His definition turns out to be circular:

moreover it carries the consequence that, since a point cannot lie within a boundary, it cannot strictly have (or be used to mark) a location. Yet we shall see later that his theories commit him to denying this.

Again, when he defines time as that aspect of change that enables it to be counted (*Physics* IV 10–14), what he wants to save and explain are the common ways of *telling* the time. This point, that he is neither inventing a new vocabulary nor assigning new theory-based uses to current words, must be borne in mind when one encounters such expressions as "force" and "average velocity" in versions of his dynamics. The word sometimes translated "force" (*dunamis*) is the common word for the "power" or "ability" of one thing to affect or be affected by another—to move or be moved, but also to heat or to soften or to be heated, and so forth. Aristotle makes it clear that this notion is what he is discussing in three celebrated passages (*Physics* VII 5, VIII 10, *De caelo* I 7) where later critics have discerned laws of proportionality connecting the force applied, the weight moved, and the time required for the force to move the weight a given distance. (Two of the texts do not mention weight at all.) A second term, *ischus*, sometimes rendered "force" in these contexts, is the common word for "strength," and it is this familiar notion that Aristotle is exploiting in the so-called laws of forced motion set out in *Physics* VII 5 and presupposed in VIII 10: he is relying on what a nontechnical audience would at once grant him concerning the comparative strengths of packhorses or (his example) gangs of shiphaulers. He says: let A be the strength required to move a weight B over a distance D in time T; then (1) A will move $1/2 B$ over $2D$ in T; (2) A will move $1/2 B$ over D in $1/2 T$; (3) $1/2 A$ will move $1/2 B$ over D in T; and (4) A will move B over $1/2 D$ in $1/2 T$; but (5) it does not follow that A will move some multiple of B over a proportionate fraction of D in T or indeed in any time, since it does not follow that A will be sufficient to move that multiple of B at all. The conjunction of (4) with the initial assumption shows that Aristotle takes the speed of motion in this case to be uniform; so commentators have naturally thought of A as a force whose continued application to B is just sufficient to overcome the opposing forces of gravity, friction, and the medium. In such circumstances propositions (3) and (4) will yield results equivalent to those of Newtonian dynamics. But then the circumstances described in (1) and (2) should yield not just the doubling of a uniform velocity which Aristotle supposes, but acceleration up to some appropriate terminal velocity. Others have proposed to treat A as prefiguring the later idea not of *force* but of *work*, or else *power*, if

these are defined in terms of the displacement of weight and not of force; and this has the advantage of leaving Aristotle discussing the case that is central to his dynamics—the carrying out of some finite task in a finite time—without importing the notion of action at an instant which, for reasons we shall see, he rejects. But Aristotle also assumes that, for a given type of agent, A is multiplied in direct ratio to the size or quantity of the agent; and to apply this to the work done would be, once more, to overlook the difference between conditions of uniform motion and of acceleration. The fact is that Aristotle is appealing to conventional ways of comparing the strength of haulers and beasts of burden, and for his purposes the acceleration periods involved with these are negligible. What matters is that we measure strength by the ability to perform certain finite tasks before fatigue sets in; hence, when Aristotle adduces these proportionalities in the *Physics*, he does so with a view to showing that the strength required for keeping the sky turning for all time would be immeasurable. Since such celestial revolutions do not in his view have to overcome any such resistance as that of gravity or a medium we are not entitled to read these notions into the formulae quoted. What then is the basis for these proportionalities? He does not quote empirical evidence in their support, and in their generalized form he could not do so; in the *Physics* and again in the *De caelo* he insists that they can be extended to cover "heating and any effect of one body on another," but the Greeks had no thermometer nor indeed any device (apart from the measurement of strings in harmonics) for translating qualitative differences into quantitative measurements. Nor on the other hand does he present them as technical definitions of the concepts they introduce. He simply comments in the *Physics* that the rules of proportion require them to be true (and it may be noticed that he does not frame any of them as a function of more than two variables: the proportion is always a simple relation between two of the terms, the others remaining constant). He depends on this appeal, together with conventional ways of comparing strengths, to give him the steps he needs toward his conclusion about the strength of a prime mover: it is no part of the dialectic of his argument to coin hypotheses that require elaborate discussion in their own right.

It is part of the history of dynamics that, from Aristotle's immediate successors onward, these formulae were taken out of context, debated and refined, and finally jettisoned for an incomparably more exact and powerful set of concepts which owed little to dialectic in Aristotle's sense. That he did not intend his proportionalities for such close scrutiny becomes even clearer when we turn to his so-called laws of natural motion. Aristotle's universe is finite, spherical, and geocentric: outside it there can be no body nor even, therefore, any location or vacuum or time (*De caelo* I 9); within it there can be no vacuum (*Physics* IV 6–9). Natural motion is the unimpeded movement of its elements: centripetal or "downward" in the case of earth (whose place is at the center) and of water (whose place is next to earth), centrifugal or "upward" in the case of fire and (next below fire) air. These are the sublunary elements, capable of changing into each other (*De generatione et corruptione* II) and possessed of "heaviness" or "lightness" according as their natural motion is down or up. Above them all is the element whose existence Aristotle can prove only by a priori argument: ether, the substance of the spheres that carry the heavenly bodies. The natural motions of the first four elements are rectilinear and terminate, unless they are blocked, in the part of the universe that is the element's natural place; the motion of the fifth is circular and cannot be blocked, and it never leaves its natural place. These motions of free fall, free ascent, and free revolution are Aristotle's paradigms of regular movement, against which other motions can be seen as departures due to special agency or to the presence of more than one element in the moving body. On several occasions he sketches some proportional connection between the variables that occur in his analysis of such natural motions; generally he confines himself to rectilinear (i.e., sublunary) movement, as, for example, in *Physics* IV 8, the text that provoked a celebrated exchange between Simplicio and Salviati in Galileo's *Dialoghi.* There he writes: "We see a given weight or body moving faster than another for two reasons: either because of a difference in the medium traversed (e.g., water as against earth, water as against air), or, other things being equal, because of the greater weight or lightness of the moving body." Later he specifies that the proviso "other things being equal" is meant to cover identity of shape. Under the first heading, that of differences in the medium, he remarks that the motion of the medium must be taken into account as well as its density relative to others; but he is content to assume a static medium and propound, as always, a simple proportion in which the moving object's velocity varies inversely with the density of the medium. Two comments are relevant. First, in this as in almost all comparable contexts, the "laws of natural motion" are dispensable from the argument. Here Aristotle uses his proportionality to rebut the possibility of motion in a vacuum: such motion would encounter a medium of nil density and hence would have infinite velocity, which is impossible. But this

is only one of several independent arguments for the same conclusion in the context. Next, the argument discounts acceleration (Aristotle does not consider the possibility of a body's speed in a vacuum remaining finite but increasing without limit, let alone that of its increasing to some finite terminal speed); yet he often insists that for the sublunary elements natural motion is always acceleration. (For this reason among others it is irrelevant to read his proportionalities of natural motion as an unwitting anticipation of Stokes's law.) But it was left to his successors during the next thousand years to quarrel over the way in which the ratios he formulated could be used to account for the steady acceleration he required in such natural motion; and where in the passage quoted he writes "we see," it was left to some nameless ancient scientist to make the experiment recorded by Philoponus and later by Galileo, of dropping different weights from the same height and noting that what we see does not answer to Aristotle's claim about their speed of descent. It was, to repeat, no part of the dialectic of his argument to give these proportionalities the rigor of scientific laws or present them as the record of exact observation.

On the other hand the existence of the natural motions themselves is basic to his cosmology. Plato had held that left to themselves, i.e., without divine governance, the four elements (he did not recognize a fifth) would move randomly in any direction: Aristotle denies this on behalf of the inherent regularity of the physical world. He makes the natural motions his "first hypotheses" in the *De caelo* and applies them over and again to the discussion of other problems. (The contrast between his carelessness over the proportionalities and the importance he attaches to the movements is sometimes read as showing that he wants to "eliminate mathematics from physics": but more on this later.)

This leads to a more general point which must be borne in mind in understanding his way of establishing physical theory. When he appeals to common views and usage in such contexts he is applying a favorite maxim, that in the search for explanations we must start from what is familiar or intelligible to us. (Once the science is set up, the deductions will proceed from principles "intelligible in themselves.") The same maxim governs his standard way of introducing concepts by extrapolating from some familiar, unpuzzling situation. Consider his distinction of "matter" and "form" in *Physics* I. He argues that any change implies a passage between two contrary attributes—from one to the other, or somewhere on a spectrum between the two—and that there must be a third thing to make this passage, a substrate which changes but survives the change. The situations to which he appeals are those from which this triadic analysis can be, so to speak, directly read off: a light object turning dark, an unmusical man becoming musical. But then the analysis is extended to cases progressively less amenable: he moves, via the detuning of an instrument and the shaping of a statue, to the birth of plants and animals and generally to the sort of situation that had exercised earlier thinkers—the emergence of a new individual, the apparent coming of something from nothing. (Not the emergence of a new *type:* Aristotle does not believe that new types emerge in nature, although he accepts the appearance of sports within or between existing types. In *Physics* II 8 he rejects a theory of evolution for putting the random occurrence of new types on the same footing with the reproduction of existing species, arguing that a theory that is not based on such regularities is not scientific physics.) *Ex nihilo nihil fit;* and even the emergence of a new individual must involve a substrate, "matter," which passes between two contrary conditions, the "privation" and the "form." But one effect of Aristotle's extrapolation is to force a major conflict between his theories and most contemporary and subsequent physics. In his view, the question "What are the essential attributes of matter?" must go unanswered. There is no general answer, for the distinction between form and matter reappears on many levels: what serves as matter to a higher form may itself be analyzed into form and matter, as a brick which is material for a house can itself be analyzed into a shape and the clay on which the shape is imposed. More important, there is no answer even when the analysis reaches the basic elements—earth, air, fire, and water. For these can be transformed into each other, and since no change can be intelligibly pictured as a mere succession of discrete objects these too must be transformations of some residual subject, but one that now *ex hypothesi* has no permanent qualitative or quantitative determinations in its own right. Thus Aristotle rejects all theories that explain physical change by the rearrangement of some basic stuff or stuffs endowed with fixed characteristics. Atomism in particular he rebuts at length, arguing that movement in a vacuum is impossible (we have seen one argument for this) and that the concept of an extended indivisible body is mathematically indefensible. But although matter is not required to identify itself by any permanent first-order characteristics, it does have important second-order properties. Physics studies the regularities in change, and for a given sort of thing at a given level it is the matter that determines what kinds of change are open to it. In some respects the idea has

more in common with the field theory that appears embryonically in the Stoics than with the crude atomism maintained by the Epicureans, but its chief influence was on metaphysics (especially Neoplatonism) rather than on scientific theory. By contrast, the correlative concept of *form,* the universal element in things that allows them to be known and classified and defined, remained powerful in science. Aristotle took it from Plato, but by way of a radical and very early critique of Plato's Ideas; for Aristotle the formal element is inseparable from the things classified, whereas Plato had promoted it to independent existence in a transcendent world contemplated by disembodied souls. For Aristotle the physical world is all; its members with their qualities and quantities and interrelations are the paradigms of reality and there are no disembodied souls.

The device of extrapolating from the familiar is evident again in his account of another of his four types of "cause," or explanation, viz. the "final," or teleological. In *Physics* II 8 he mentions some central examples of purposive activity—housebuilding, doctoring, writing—and then by stages moves on to discerning comparable purposiveness in the behavior of spiders and ants, the growth of roots and leaves, the arrangement of the teeth. Again the process is one of weakening or discarding some of the conditions inherent in the original situations: the idea of purposiveness sheds its connection with those of having a skill and thinking out steps to an end (although Aristotle hopes to have it both ways, by representing natural sports and monsters as *mistakes*). The resultant "immanent teleology" moved his follower Theophrastus to protest at its thinness and facility, but its effectiveness as a heuristic device, particularly in biology, is beyond dispute.

It is worth noting that this tendency of Aristotle's to set out from some familiar situation, or rather from the most familiar and unpuzzling ways of describing such a situation, is something more than the general inclination of scientists to depend on "explanatory paradigms." Such paradigms in later science (e.g., classical mechanics) have commonly been limiting cases not encountered in common observation or discourse; Aristotle's choice of the familiar is a matter of dialectical method, presystematic by contrast with the finished science, but subject to rules of discussion which he was the first to codify. This, and not (as we shall see) any attempt to extrude mathematics from physics, is what separates his extant work in the field from the most characteristic achievements of the last four centuries. It had large consequences for dynamics. In replying to Zeno's paradox of the flying arrow he concedes Zeno's claim that nothing can be said to be moving at an instant, and insists only that it cannot be said to be stationary either. What preoccupies him is the requirement, embedded in common discourse, that any movement must take a certain time to cover a certain distance (and, as a corollary, that any stability must take a certain time but cover no distance); so he discounts even those hints that common discourse might have afforded of the derivative idea of motion, and therefore of velocity, at an instant. He has of course no such notion of a mathematical limit as the analysis of such cases requires, but in any event this notion came later than the recognition of the cases. It is illuminating to contrast the treatment of motion in the *Mechanica,* a work which used to carry Aristotle's name but which must be at least a generation later. There (*Mechanica* 1) circular motion is resolved into two components, one tangential and one centripetal (contrast Aristotle's refusal to assimilate circular and rectilinear movements, notably in *Physics* VII 4). And the remarkable suggestion is made that the proportion between these components need not be maintained for any time at all, since otherwise the motion would be in a straight line. Earlier the idea had been introduced of a point having motion and velocity, an idea that we shall find Aristotle using although his dialectical analysis of movement and location disallows it; here that idea is supplemented by the concept of a point having a given motion or complex of motions at an instant and not for any period, however small. The *Mechanica* is generally agreed to be a constructive development of hints and suggestions in Aristotle's writings; but the methods and purposes evident in his own discussions of motion inhibit him from such novel constructions in dynamics.

It is quite another thing to say, as is often said, that Aristotle wants to debar physics from any substantial use of the abstract proofs and constructions available to him in contemporary mathematics. It is a common fallacy that, whereas Plato had tried to make physics mathematical and quantitative, Aristotle aimed at keeping it qualitative.

Mathematics and Physics. Plato had tried to construct the physical world of two-dimensional and apparently weightless triangles. When Aristotle argues against this in the *De caelo* (III 7) he observes: "The principles of perceptible things must be perceptible, of eternal things eternal, of perishable things perishable: in sum, the principles must be homogeneous with the subject-matter." These words, taken together with his prescriptions for the autonomy of sciences in the *Analytics,* are often quoted to show that any use of mathematical constructions in his physics must be adventitious or presystematic, dis-

pensable from the science proper. The province of physics is the class of natural bodies regarded as having weight (or "lightness," in the case of air and fire), heat, and color and an innate tendency to move in a certain way. But these are properties that mathematics expressly excludes from its purview (*Metaphysics* K 3).

In fact, however, the division of sciences is not so absolute. When Aristotle contrasts mathematics and physics in *Physics* II he remarks that astronomy, which is one of the "more physical of the mathematical sciences," must be part of physics, since it would be absurd to debar the physicist from discussing the geometrical properties of the heavenly bodies. The distinction is that the physicist must, as the mathematician does not, treat these properties as the attributes of physical bodies that they are; i.e., he must be prepared to explain the application of his model. Given this tie-line a good deal of mathematical abstraction is evidently permissible. Aristotle holds that only extended bodies can strictly be said to have a location (i.e., to lie within a static perimeter) or to move, but he is often prepared to discount the extension of bodies. Thus in *Physics* IV 11, where he shows an isomorphic correspondence between continua representing time, motion, and the path traversed by the moving body, he correlates the moving object with points in time and space and for this purpose calls it "a point—or stone, or any such thing." In *Physics* V 4, he similarly argues from the motion of an unextended object, although it is to be noticed that he does not here or anywhere ease the transition from moving bodies to moving points by importing the idea of a center of gravity, which was to play so large a part in Archimedes' *Equilibrium of Planes.* In his meteorology, explaining the shape of halos and rainbows, he treats the luminary as a point source of light. In the biological works he often recurs to the question of the number of points at which a given type of animal moves; these "points" are in fact the major joints, but in *De motu animalium* 1 he makes it clear that he has a geometrical model in mind and is careful to explain what supplementary assumptions are necessary to adapting this model to the actual situation it illustrates. In the cosmology of the *De caelo* he similarly makes use of unextended loci, in contrast to his formal account of any location as a perimeter enclosing a volume. Like Archimedes a century later, he represents the center of the universe as a point when he proves that the surface of water is spherical, and again when he argues that earth moves so as to make its own (geometrical) center ultimately coincide with that of the universe. His attempt in *De caelo* IV 3 to interpret this in terms of perimeter locations is correct by his own principles, but confused.

This readiness to import abstract mathematical arguments and constructions into his account of the physical world is one side of the coin whose other face is his insistence that any mathematics must be directly applicable to the world. Thus, after arguing (partly on dialectical grounds, partly from his hypothesis of natural movements and natural places) that the universe must be finite in size, he adds that this does not put the mathematicians out of business, since they do not need or use the notion of a line infinite in extension: what they require is only the possibility of producing a line n in any required ratio with a given line m, and however large the ratio n/m it can always be physically exemplified for a suitable interpretation of m. The explanation holds good for such lemmata as that applied in Eudoxus' method of exhaustion, but not of some proportionalities he himself adduces earlier in the same context or in *De caelo* I. (These proportionalities are indeed used in, but they are not the subject of, *reductio ad absurdum* arguments. In the *De caelo* Aristotle even assumes that an infinite rotating body would contain a point at an infinite distance from its center and consequently moving at infinite speed.) The same concern to make mathematics applicable to the physical world without postulating an actual infinite is evident in his treatment of the sequence of natural numbers. The infinity characteristic of the sequence, and generally of any countable series whose members can be correlated with the series of numbers, consists just in the possibility of specifying a successor to any member of the sequence: "the infinite is that of which, as it is counted or measured off, it is always possible to take some part outside that already taken." This is true not only of the number series but of the parts produced by dividing any magnitude in a constant ratio; and since all physical bodies are in principle so divisible, the number series is assured of a physical application without requiring the existence at any time of an actually infinite set of objects: all that is required is the possibility of following any division with a subdivision.

This positivistic approach is often evident in Aristotle's work (e.g., in his analysis of the location of A as the inner static boundary of the body surrounding A), and it is closely connected with his method of building explanations on the familiar case. But here too Aristotle moves beyond the familiar case when he argues that infinite divisibility is characteristic of bodies below the level of observation. His defense and exploration of such divisibility, as a defining characteristic of bodies and times and mo-

tions, is found in *Physics* VI, a book often saluted as his most original contribution to the analysis of the continuum. Yet it is worth noticing that in this book as in its two predecessors Aristotle's problems and the ideas he applies to their solution are over and again taken, with improvements, from the second part of Plato's *Parmenides*. The discussion is in that tradition of logical debate which Aristotle, like Plato, called "dialectic," and its problems are not those of accommodating theories to experimentally established facts (or vice versa) but logical puzzles generated by common discourse and conviction. (But then Aristotle thinks of common discourse and conviction as a repository of human experience.) So the argument illustrates Aristotle's anti-Platonic thesis that mathematics—represented again in this case by simple proportion theory—has standing as a science only to the extent that it can be directly applied to the description of physical phenomena. But the argument is no more framed as an advance in the mathematical theory itself than as a contribution to the observational data of physics.

Probably the best-known instance of an essentially mathematical construction incorporated into Aristotle's physics is the astronomical theory due to Eudoxus and improved by Callippus. In this theory the apparent motion of the "fixed stars" is represented by the rotation of one sphere about its diameter, while those of the sun, moon, and the five known planets are represented each by a different nest of concentric spheres. In such a nest the first sphere carries round a second whose poles are located on the first but with an axis inclined to that of the first; this second, rotating in turn about its poles, carries a third similarly connected to it, and so on in some cases to a fourth or (in Callippus' version) a fifth, the apparent motion of the heavenly body being the resultant motion of a point on the equator of the last sphere. To this set of abstract models, itself one of the five or six major advances in science, Aristotle makes additions of which the most important is the attempt to unify the separate nests of spheres into one connected physical system. To this end he intercalates reagent spheres designed to insulate the movement of each celestial body from the complex of motions propelling the body next above it. The only motion left uncanceled in this downward transmission is the rotation of the star sphere. It is generally agreed that Aristotle in *Metaphysics* XII 8 miscalculates the resulting number of agent and reagent spheres: he concludes that we need either fifty-five or forty-seven, the difference apparently representing one disagreement between the theories of Eudoxus and Callippus, but on the latest computation (that of Hanson) the figures should be sixty-six and forty-nine. The mistake had no effect on the progress of astronomy: within a century astronomers had turned to a theory involving epicycles, and Aristotle's physical structure of concentric nonoverlapping spheres was superseded. On the other hand his basic picture of the geocentric universe and its elements, once freed from the special constructions he borrowed and adapted from Eudoxus, retained its authority and can be seen again in the introductory chapters of Ptolemy's *Syntaxis*.

Conclusion. These arguments and theories in what came to be called the exact sciences are drawn principally from the *Posterior Analytics, Topics, Physics, De caelo* and *De generatione,* works that are generally accepted as early and of which the first four at least probably date substantially from Aristotle's years in the Academy or soon after. The influence of the Academy is strong on them. They are marked by a large respect for mathematics and particularly for the techniques and effects of axiomatizing that subject, but they do not pretend to any mathematical discoveries, and in this they are close in spirit to Plato's writings. Even the preoccupation with physical change, its varieties and regularities and causes, and the use of dialectic in analyzing these, is a position to which Plato had been approaching in his later years. Aristotle the meticulous empiricist, amassing biological data or compiling the constitutions of 158 Greek states, is not yet in evidence. In these works the analyses neither start from nor are closely controlled by fresh inspections of the physical world. Nor is he liable to think his analyses endangered by such inspections: if his account of motion shows that any "forced" or "unnatural" movement requires an agent of motion in constant touch with the moving body, the movement of a projectile can be explained by inventing a set of unseen agents to fill the gap—successive stages of the medium itself, supposed to be capable of transmitting movement even after the initial agency has ceased acting. In all the illustrative examples cited in these works there is nothing comparable to even the half-controlled experiments in atomistic physics and harmonics of the following centuries. His main concerns were the methodology of the sciences, which he was the first to separate adequately on grounds of field and method; and the meticulous derivation of the technical equipment of these sciences from the common language and assumptions of men about the world they live in. His influence on science stemmed from an incomparable cleverness and sensitiveness to counterarguments, rather than from any breakthrough comparable to those of Eudoxus or Archimedes.

BIBLIOGRAPHY

Aristotle is still quoted by reference to the page, column, and line of Vols. I, II of I. Bekker's Berlin Academy edition (1831–1870, recently repr.). The later texts published in the Oxford Classical Texts and in the Budé and Loeb series are generally reliable for the works quoted. The standard Oxford translation of the complete works with selected fragments occupies 12 volumes (1909–1952). The ancient commentaries are still among the best (*Commentaria in Aristotelem Graeca,* Berlin, 1882–1909). Of recent editions with commentaries pride of place goes to those by Sir David Ross of the *Metaphysics* (2nd ed., 1953), *Physics* (1936), *Analytics* (1949), *Parva naturalia* (1955), and *De anima* (1961). Others are T. Waitz, *Organon* (1844–1846); H. H. Joachim, *De generatione et corruptione* (1922).

Important modern works are W. Jaeger, *Aristotle* (2nd English ed., Oxford, 1948); W. D. Ross, *Aristotle* (4th ed., London, 1945). On the mathematics and physics, T. L. Heath, *Mathematics in Aristotle* (Oxford, 1949); P. Duhem, *Le système du monde,* I (Paris, 1913); H. Carteron, *La notion de force dans le système d'Aristote* (Paris, 1924); A. Mansion, *Introduction à la physique aristotélicienne* (2nd ed., Louvain–Paris, 1945); F. Solmsen, *Aristotle's System of the Physical World* (Ithaca, N.Y., 1960); W. Wieland, *Die aristotelische Physik* (Göttingen, 1962); I. Düring, *Aristoteles* (Heidelberg, 1966).

On the so-called laws of motion in Aristotle, I. Drabkin, *American Journal of Philology,* **59** (1938), pp. 60–84.

G. E. L. OWEN

ARISTOTLE: Natural History and Zoology.

It is not clear when Aristotle wrote his zoology, or how much of his natural history was his own work. This is unfortunate, for it might help us to interpret his philosophy if we knew whether he began theorizing in biology before or after his main philosophical formulations, and how many zoological specimens he himself collected and identified. Some believe that he began in youth, and that his theory of potentiality was directed originally at the problem of growth. Others (especially Jaeger) hold that his interest in factual research came late in life and that he turned to biology after founding the Lyceum. Most probably, however, it was in middle life, in the years 344–342 B.C., when he was living on Lesbos with Theophrastus; many of his data are reported from places in that area. This would imply that he wrote the zoology with his philosophical framework already established, and on the whole the internal evidence of the treatises bears this out. It follows that in order to understand his zoological theory, we must keep his philosophy in mind. Yet it may also be true that in thinking out his philosophy, he was conscious of biological problems in a general way.

The zoological treatises must represent many years' work, for they make up a fourth of the whole corpus, and both data and discussion are concisely presented. They owe little to Herodotus, Ctesias, Xenophon, or other extant literature; their possible debt to Democritus cannot be assessed, however, because his three zoological books are lost. Comparing the quality of Aristotle's data with previous writings, we must conclude that he sifted and rejected a great deal; even by modern standards of natural history his reports are cautious. The chief collection of data is the *Historia animalium*. Out of 560 species mentioned in all his zoology, 400 appear only in this work and only five are not included. The treatises, as we now have them, form a course of instruction in which the *Historia* is referred to as the descriptive textbook, intended to be studied first and then kept at hand. Internal evidence suggests, however, that it was in fact written after the others, and that most of it was not written by Aristotle himself. This implies that he wrote the theoretical treatises before the main collection of data. Not that the treatises lack supporting data, but most of the information was common knowledge, whereas the reports that read like new, firsthand observation are nearly all confined to the later parts of the *Historia*.

Biological data were normally quoted in cosmological arguments, not least in the Academy. The Academicians' interest was not so much in the animals for their own sake, but rather in using them as evidence for—and giving them a place within—a rational cosmology. There were two issues: to identify the formal groups of animals, and thus to classify them, and to explain their functioning as part of nature. Plato and Speusippus opposed the materialism of those like Democritus, whose lost books, entitled *Causes Concerning Animals*, were probably intended to explain biology in terms of atomism. Aristotle would have been familiar with these discussions since his youth, and his writings follow this essentially etiological approach. His earliest zoology is probably in the *De partibus animalium*, the *De incessu animalium*, and the *Parva naturalia* (all of which in their present form show signs of revision and editing), in which he sets out the "causes" of tissues and structures, and of such significant functions as locomotion, respiration, aging, and death. Here the a priori element in his theory appears strongly: for example, right is superior to left, and hence the right-hand side is the natural side to lead off with; organs properly exist in pairs, and hence the spleen (for which he found no function) exists as the partner of the liver. On the other hand, the teleological explanation, which is the main theme of

De partibus animalium, is argued in a mature fashion with evidential support. This scientific maturity is even clearer in the next great treatise, *De generatione animalium,* in which he applies his concepts of form and matter, actuality and potentiality, to the problems of reproduction, inheritance, and growth of such inessential characters as color. On the question of classification he remains tentative and critical, as we would expect of one who rejected Plato's theory of Forms. He often returns to the problem in both early and late writings, but states no clear position.

His teleology differs from others. He argues it in *De partibus* I on the same grounds as in *Physics* B, where he states more of his opponents' case. He makes it clear that the "natural philosophers" (Empedocles, Anaxagoras, Democritus) were combating a popular teleology which presented the gods as purposive powers intervening in nature, so that "rain falls in order to make the crops grow." Against it they had argued that the "necessity" of natural causes was sufficient to explain events and that the crops happened to grow because the rain happened to fall, the real cause being the automatic interactions of the hot, the cold, and the other elements. In reply, Plato had posited a world soul and a creative "Demiurge." Aristotle, however, does not invoke a supernatural agency (for the relation between the cosmos and the Unmoved Mover is different), nor does he present nature as a quasi-conscious entity capable of purpose: his personification of nature "who does nothing in vain" is no more than a rhetorical abbreviation for "each natural substance." Neither does he posit an extra factor in nature, as modern teleologists posit a *conatus* that is not reducible to physics.

The directiveness that Aristotle sees in nature is part of the natural interactions, so that the teleological explanation coexists with the causal explanation. But he bases the teleology not primarily on directiveness but on the existence of forms. To explain an organ, he says, we must first grasp the complete animal's form and functions, what it means to be that animal, its *ousia*. Our explanation will include both the "necessary" causes and the "end" toward which development tends. This is not the temporal end or a state of equilibrium between phases of activity; indeed, it may never be reached. It is the perfect condition of the whole animal, "for the sake of which" each part develops. Thus, Empedocles was wrong to suppose that the spine is vertebrated because it gets bent: on the contrary, vertebration is necessary to the animal's functioning, and was contained potentially in the parent's seed before the embryo's vertebrae were formed. He was also wrong to think that random necessity could be a primary cause, for it could not produce the general regularity of nature, let alone the absolute regularity of the stars. Necessity in nature is secondary, or, as Aristotle calls it, "hypothetical": on the hypothesis that an animal is coming into existence, certain materials must interact, but these materials do not of themselves produce the animal any more than bricks produce a house. As the house needs a builder and a plan, the animal needs a soul and a form—factors ignored by the materialists. But whereas builder and plan are separate, soul and form are identical. The final cause of the animal is the actualization of its form, and its primary efficient cause is its soul, which "uses" the necessary movements of the materials. Aristotle's teleology therefore rests upon his theory of substantial form. The definition of a substance is logically prior to the definition of its parts, and so the final cause is prior to the necessary cause. It is prior temporally as well as logically, for Aristotle believed that the world never began—so that hen has forever preceded egg.

Although he used Plato's language ("existence is prior to coming-into-existence" and necessity is "the concomitant cause"), Aristotle did not follow Plato in positing an overall teleology or in the dualism that the *Timaeus* set up between creator and material. The few passages where Aristotle seems to imply that some species exist for the sake of man, or act for the general good as opposed to their own, cannot be meant literally. What he probably meant was a balance of nature, in which species are interdependent. The final cause of each animal is its own complete state, and nothing more. And instead of Plato's dualism, Aristotle places finality within natural interactions, not as something imposed upon them.

Within sublunary nature there are continual fresh beginnings of movement for which there are no sufficient external causes. They may be stimulated from outside, but the source of the movements in plants and animals is their souls. Only in a general way is the Unmoved Mover the prime cause. As a final and formal cause it presents the perfection that lesser beings desire to imitate. It can therefore be argued, although it is never clearly stated by Aristotle, that nature's tendency toward actualization and the *orexis* within souls are ultimately oriented toward the Unmoved Mover's perfection. As an efficient cause, the Unmoved Mover promotes general growth and decay on earth because it elicits the sun's movements in the ecliptic, and these movements cause the alternation of summer and winter. These general causes, however, do not bring about the particular starts of motion in nature. Nor, again, are souls regarded as separable entities that inhabit bodies and direct them, as Plato thought and as Aristotle may once have

thought but later rejected. In his mature view, found in his biology as well as in the *Metaphysics* and *De anima,* the soul (except, possibly, for the intellect) is not an independent substance but is the form of the body. On the other hand, it is not merely a resultant form, as in the "harmonia" theory, which Aristotle refuted; rather, it is both form and source of action. In plants it causes growth and reproduction; in animals it also causes sensation (here he differs from Plato, who thought that plants had sensation); in man the soul has a third faculty, intellect, and this is its only faculty that is not the form of body and could therefore be separable.

The concept of soul as both form and efficient cause may reflect a trace of ancient hylozoism. In Aristotle's view, finality pervades nature. If there is a cosmos, this implies that the elements not only have simple motions but also combine with modified motions. Both the simple motions and their modifications are hypothetically necessary and are natural. An animal contains many motions, all natural, that by a natural coordination tend toward a specific pattern. Its soul is both the tendency and the pattern. In nonliving substances, which have no soul, the tendency to form complexes is in their nature. Aristotle accepts as his data both the observable materials and the observable forms and species; therefore the movement of nature is simultaneously necessitated and endlike.

According to the *Metaphysics,* the form toward which animals grow is their species: individual differences arise from matter and consequently are unknowable to science. In Aristotle's earlier zoology we cannot tell whether he maintains this strict view, but in *De generatione animalium* his theory of reproduction implies that individuals differ in form to some extent. He does not say so, but repeats the doctrine of *De generatione et corruptione* that sublunary beings, which cannot achieve eternity as individuals, instead achieve it as species by reproduction. Nevertheless, Aristotle's discussion is in fact about an individual's reproduction of another animal "like itself." He starts from the long-standing controversy about the origin of seed. Do both male and female contribute seed? From what part or parts of the body does it come, and what does it contain? He analyzes the problem in terms of form and matter. The male alone makes seed from his blood; it contains potentially the sensitive soul and the adult form, but actually it contains no bodily parts (here he ridicules preformism and pangenesis). The female contributes only material (the *catamenia*), whose form is nutritive soul. When the male's form has been imposed upon the female material, the somatic part of the seed is sloughed away: all that is transmitted is soul, the source of form and motion. If the fetus develops regularly, the father's form will be actualized; failing that, the mother's; failing that again, more distant ancestors successively, until eventually the form may be merely that of the species, or even just the genus *Animal* (that is, a monstrous birth).

This long and careful argument, which is supported by observed evidence, gives a brilliant impression of maturity and originality, and in several points goes beyond the biological arguments that we occasionally find in the philosophical works. Aristotle's view that the father's form is reproduced, as distinct from the species, can only mean that some individual differences are formal and apodictic. He also brings to scientific account other differences due to "necessity"—not only monstrous births but differences of coloration, voice, or sharpness of senses. Since he calls them "concomitants" arising from irregularities in the material, he may have regarded them as unpredictable, but they seem to be accountable after the event. He now argues not from the fixity of species but from the reproduction of forms. True, he does not contemplate the obsolescence or alteration of existing species (for he had no paleontology); but he does accept, within limits, the evidence for miscegenation's resulting in new forms. In fact, the emphasis on species becomes less, while the concept of necessity as hypothetical becomes more important and sophisticated than in the philosophical works, where necessity is either "simple" (axiomatic) or brute (material). The one exception among the biological works is the *Historia animalium,* from which the teleological explanation is absent. Although a discussion of causes is not to be expected here, nevertheless the account of characters and life histories involves some causal explanation; and it is noteworthy that this explanation is given only in material terms. No doubt this is because the *Historia* was mainly the work of Aristotle's successors, among whom Theophrastus ignores the final cause even in his *Causes of Plants.*

In explaining the "necessary" causes—the interaction of materials—Aristotle does not innovate so much as rationalize theories that were already current. He accepts from Plato's *Timaeus* the four elements—fire, air, water, and earth—that were common to the medical writers and can be traced back through Empedocles into popular tradition. But the tradition had confused two notions: the cosmic regions of fire, air, water, and earth, and the seasonal powers of hot, cold, wet, and dry. The two sets do not exactly match, as is obvious in the ambiguous reports of Empedocles. Aristotle systematizes them by means of a formula that survived through the Middle Ages, treating fire, air, water, and earth as combinations of hot, cold,

wet, and dry: fire is hot plus dry, air is hot plus wet, and so on. In his system hot, cold, wet, and dry are the primitive qualities of matter, but cannot exist in isolation. Fire, air, water, and earth are the simplest separable bodies, and are transformable into each other.

Like his predecessors, Aristotle regards the hot as the chief active power; its characteristic action is *pepsis* ("concoction"), which transforms food into blood and blood into flesh. By its opposite, the cold, he sometimes means merely the absence of hot, but more often a power in itself. The hot means more than temperature, which he calls "the hot according to touch." Another sort of hot is that possessed by pine wood, which is not hotter to the touch than other timber but contains more heat and therefore burns better. Animals have an innate heat upon which life depends. Their droppings still contain some of it, which generates flies. While the hot is the soul's chief agent in bringing about growth, cold is also needed to solidify things. Like the medical writers, Aristotle attaches importance to the due mingling (*krasis*) of hot and cold, which does not mean a point on a temperature scale but a mixture of two powers. He follows them in extending this notion to a general "right proportion" (*symmetria*) necessary for growth and health.

The other elements—the wet or watery, and the dry or earthy—are needed to provide the fluid and the solid parts of plants and animals. Whether Aristotle really intended a fifth element, *pneuma,* is debatable. The notion was current, and soon after him it became the chief element for the Pneumatic school of medicine and the Stoics. Aristotle had his own fifth substance in the outer heaven, the *aither,* and in *De generatione animalium* he compares it with the bodily *pneuma: pneuma* is the material of the animal seed, and conveys soul and the generative warmth, which he says is different from other heat. Yet he defines *pneuma* merely as warmed air, and since warmth has various powers for him, it is probable that he means no more. So he explains spontaneous generation by the presence of a warm soul-source in the materials.

The four elements combine to form the tissues, which Aristotle calls "made of like parts" (as flesh is divisible into flesh); and the tissues form the organs, which are "made of unlike parts" (hand is not divisible into hands). Taking this distinction from Plato, he uses it in finding homologies, but he makes only general statements about the processes. The hot concocts blood into flesh here, fat there, marrow or seed somewhere else; skin, hair, bone, nails, and horn all come from the earthy. He does not explain how. Medical literature of the time contains some practical investigations, such as the action of heat upon blood, and Aristotle occasionally refers to such evidence. In *Meteorologica* IV he goes further and analyzes the actions of hot and cold into evaporating, emulsifying, dissolving, condensing, and coagulating, and differentiates many types of earthy material. But this is a late work, and may not even be his. It seems, therefore, that in his biology Aristotle is content to take these theories in a general form from current tradition, although he is careful to rationalize them. For example, he will not allow Empedocles to say that spontaneous generation results from rottenness: new life comes not from disintegration but from concoction. The heart—not the brain, as many held—is the center of sensation and of the soul's motor impulses; as the first part to develop (observed in daily openings of a clutch of eggs), it is the source of the vital heat and innate *pneuma*. In it the blood is pneumatized and then flows out to nourish the tissues. (The distinction between arteries and veins is post-Aristotelian.) The lungs admit air to replenish the *pneuma* and to moderate the heat, an excess of which brings on senescence and death. Animals without lungs are cooled by the surrounding air or water: this suffices because they are "less perfect" and therefore cooler; also, their innate store of *pneuma* is sufficient.

Classification of animals remained a difficulty, and Aristotle suggested a solution by taking an animal's vital heat as an index of its superiority. Plato had proposed *diaeresis* (division), in which a major group is progressively divided by differentiae into genera and species. This method, used by Aristotle in his early logic and later by his successors, became the basis of Linnaean systematics. In his zoology, however, Aristotle criticizes it for splitting natural groups. He shows how groupings based on habitat and locomotion, and such characters as horns and rumination, cut across each other, while many animals belong to both sides of a formal division. He also criticizes the emphasis on morphology, which he holds subordinate to function. He prefers to start from the natural genus, as defined by multiple characters, then to arrange it with other types, not in a genus-species hierarchy but in a *scala naturae* ranging from man through less perfect animals down through plants to lifeless compounds. In this he emphasizes the continuity of nature and the many borderline or overlapping types, such as the seal, the bat, and the testaceans. The degree of vital heat is indicated by method of reproduction, state at birth, respiration, posture, and other signs. But he does not produce an actual scheme, nor does he finally reject genus-species classification. For practical purposes Aristotle discusses the animals by major groups: the "blooded" (i.e., red-blooded)—man, viviparous quadrupeds, oviparous quadrupeds, cetaceans, fishes, birds; and the "bloodless"—mollusks, crustaceans, testaceans, and insects. But he points out that even these groups exclude many types, such as snakes and sponges. In fact, before any classification could succeed, far more information was needed. He may have felt this, for the *Historia animalium* was begun as a comparative study of characters, arranged under the headings *parts, activities, lives, dispositions* (i.e., psychology). Major groups were to be compared by "analogy" (as wing to fin), while within a group each structure would vary by "the more and the less" (as wings are longer or shorter).

This project, however, was not carried through; instead, the treatise became a running collection of data. As new information came in and new significant characteristics were distinguished, they were inserted at convenient places, as if into a filing cabinet. Book I gives a program of the characters to be discussed, and by comparing this with the later books, we can see that many of those proposed are never mentioned again while many more new characters come to be recognized, so much so that the whole plan of the treatise is altered. The latest additions, which can be identified in all books from the second onward, consist of dossiers or even complete descriptions of single animals, no doubt awaiting breakdown under appropriate character headings. Thus the work eventually begins to approximate a descriptive zoology, and this is how it has been taken ever since. But in judging Aristotle as a natural historian, we should remember that we are judging him as something that he never set out to be. Although the classificatory intention of the *Historia animalium* came to nothing, it remained essentially an analysis of differentiae, the ways in which animals "are like to and different from each other," in the words of the introduction. The data about animals are put there to illustrate characteristic differences, and except in the late and unassimilated additions there is no description of an animal for its own sake. The statements about a given animal are spread through the nine books of the treatise, which is arranged not by animals but by characters. It has repeated signposts helping the reader to find his way among characters, but there are none to help him find animals, and there is no index. Some animals are cited frequently to illustrate but one point—for example, the mole's blindness: Aristotle obviously examined the mole, for he describes a dissection of its concealed eyes, which is of great interest; but this is all he tells us of the mole. In fact, like all his treatises, the *Historia animalium* is a theoretical study. It is not so much about animals as about *Animal*—and the various ways it is differentiated in nature.

Aristotle names about 500 "kinds" of animals. Some of these comprise several varieties, which his reports sometimes distinguish but sometimes confuse. Altogether, between 550 and 600 species can be distinguished, and of these as many as 200 are mentioned in connection with only one character. He includes some thirty from such distant places as Libya, Ethiopia, the Red Sea, and even India. A very few are taken from travelers' tales, especially from Herodotus and Ctesias, and of these some are fabulous—for example, the flying snake and the martichoras, or manticore (a monster, perhaps derived from a garbled account of the Indian tiger, which became a favorite of the Middle Ages), of which he plainly indicates his suspicion. But most were to be seen in Greece in menageries and shows—certainly the bear, monkeys and apes, elephant, camel, and lion. Aristotle gives much information about all of these, for the very reason that they exhibited interesting differences. Some information is evidently hearsay: for example, he reports that the lion has no cervical vertebrae, which shows that he never examined a dead lion. But his remarks about the lion's appearance and gait show equally that he observed it in life. He describes the elephant's leg joints in order to contradict a popular belief that it sleeps standing against a tree.

However, the great majority of Aristotle's reports concern animals native to Greece, its islands, and the Greek colonies in Asia Minor. It is incorrect to accuse him of showing more interest in exotics than in what was at his own doorstep. If we compare the variety of information given on each animal, we find not only that the nearest animals are the most fully reported but also that he covers most of what was available to him. Among mammals, of which he mentions some eighty, by far the most information is given about the horse, dog, sheep, ox, and pig; next comes a group including the goat, donkey, mule, hare, deer, elephant, bear, camel, seal, and dolphin. Of 180 birds mentioned, the best-reported are the domestic fowl, the pigeons, and the partridge, and there is a good deal on the sparrow, swallow, blackbird, crows, larks, eagles, hawks, quail, and stork. On the other hand, over 100 birds are mentioned only once or twice, as examples of differences in feeding or nesting, and so on. The information on marine animals is especially good, although out of 130 fishes only twenty are cited in connection with more than a very few characters. Among over eighty insects, he gives considerable information about the flies, ants, wasps, and cicadas, and three long, separate discussions of the honeybee;

there is a fair amount about the grasshoppers, gadflies, spiders, beetles, and chafers. It is true that he has relatively little on the gnats and mosquitoes, common though they were; but he reports their external structures, reproduction from larvae, feeding, and habitat—and there is, after all, little more that he could know, having no optical apparatus. Aristotle often complains that the smallness of some insects makes it impossible to discern their structures, especially the internal ones. Many features, in all groups of animals, are reported in a generalized form—"all two-winged insects have a proboscis and no rearward sting," "all fishes except selachians have gill covers"—so that if one is to assess what he knew about a given animal, these general statements have to be broken down and included. In some of them he generalizes further than the facts warrant, through faulty or deficient information.

The tests that Aristotle applies to reports are primarily observational checks, made either on the same type of animal or on "analogous" types. He shows himself well aware of the need for repeated observations, but he has not developed the refined technique of provoked and controlled observations that later (very much later) scientists learned to demand. Where observational checks are not available, he tests by inherent probability—that is, by reference to theory. The accusation that he relies on a priori argument, and not on observation, is not well founded; on the contrary, like most Greek philosophers, with the exception of Plato, he is overready to accept uncontrolled observation and to jump to large conclusions.

His chief sources of information are fishermen, farmers, stockbreeders, and hunters; to a lesser extent travelers, menageries, augurs, and drug manufacturers; and he owes a very little to such previous writers as Herodotus, Ctesias, Xenophon, Empedocles, and Democritus. There are many faulty reports that he corrects from observation. His favorite method is the counterinstance. He refutes a report that the viper does not slough its skin simply by describing an observation of the sloughing. The legend that the hyena has the genitalia of both sexes (which in fact it can appear to have externally) is refuted by inspection and dissection, and here he indicates that many specimens were examined. Fishermen said that all mullets are generated spontaneously, but he has examples of mullets with eggs and with sperm (although he allows that one kind of mullet is spontaneous).

Where such direct checks are not possible, he refers to analogous examples or to theory. He denies that the cuckoo is a metamorphosed hawk on the grounds that the hawk preys on the cuckoo, a thing never seen done by one bird to another of its own kind. Fishermen believed what Herodotus also said, that fishes are impregnated by swallowing the sperm; Aristotle denies this because there is no connection between stomach and uterus, and because fishes have been observed in coition—which, he remarks, is difficult to observe, and fishermen have missed it because they are not interested in acquiring knowledge. Here he has been misled by faulty observation that, unluckily, agreed with theory—a coincidence that accounts for many of the mistakes in his reports. He held that where there are separate male and female, there must be coition. He knew that the male fish sprinkles the eggs with sperm after spawning, but thought this an additional process of fertilization. Another famous example is the fishermen's report of hectocotylization—the extraordinary method by which a sperm-carrying tentacle is inserted into the female's mantle cavity and then completely detached from the male (eventually proved true): Aristotle denies that the tentacle assists reproduction, because it is not connected with the body and the spermatic channel—he was wrong because his theory could not accommodate what is, after all, a surprising fact. But in another context he makes it clear that theory must always yield to reliable observation: after his long discussion of the reproduction of bees he makes a statement that fairly represents his own practice (*De generatione animalium* 760b27):

> This, then, appears to be the method of reproduction of bees, according to theory together with the apparent facts. But the facts have not been satisfactorily ascertained, and if ever they are, then credence must be given to observation rather than to theory, and to theory only in so far as it agrees with what is observed.

Many of the reports, however, are from firsthand observation. He refers sometimes to "the dissections," evidently a collection of drawings and diagrams of internal organs; unfortunately nothing survives of them. Some of his data clearly come from deliberate dissection, while others come as clearly from casual observations in the kitchen or at augury. One of the best is a full-scale vivisection of a chameleon; and the internal organs of crabs, lobsters, cephalopods, and several fishes and birds are described from direct observation. Many of the exterior observations also presuppose a prolonged study. He speaks of lengthy investigations into the pairing of insects. He satisfies himself that birds produce wind eggs entirely in the absence of the cock. There are graphic accounts of courtship behavior, nest-building, and brood care. He records tests for sense perception in scallops, razor fish, and sponges. He watches the cuttlefish anchor

itself to a rock by its two long arms when it is stormy. The detailing of structures in some crustaceans and shellfishes vividly suggests that the author is looking at the animal as he dictates. The sea urchin's mouth parts are still known as "Aristotle's lantern" from his description, and his statement that its eggs are larger at the full moon has only recently been confirmed for the Red Sea urchin. He is able to assert that two kinds of *Serranidae* are "always female" (they are in fact hermaphrodite). All such data require deliberate and patient observation. How much Aristotle himself did is not known, but it is clear enough that he caused reports to be collected and screened with great care.

The first main heading in the *Historia animalium* is "Parts of the Body." Aristotle methodically lists the external and internal structures, noting the significant differences between animal types. Through drawing an analogy between legs and fins, he holds that fishes are moved primarily by their fins; this error creates difficulties for his theory of locomotion, whereby the blooded animals are moved by two or four points and the bloodless by more than four. He classifies the forms of uterus by position: rearward and ventral in the viviparous quadrupeds, forward and dorsal in the birds and oviparous quadrupeds, rearward and dorsal in the oviparous fishes, and "in both ways" in the ovoviviparous fishes—that is, extending from a forward dorsal to a rearward ventral position, because they first produce eggs and then hatch them within the uterus. There are various mistakes, mostly concerning man (where dissection was impossible) or the rarer animals. He is prone to accept them when they fall in with theory, thus accepting that men have more sutures in the skull than women (possibly based on an unlucky observation of a female skull with sutures effaced in pregnancy), for it fits his theory that men need more heat regulation in the brain. He reports that if one blows down the windpipe, the air reaches the heart: again a faulty observation that agreed with theory (that the *pneuma* in the heart is replenished from the lungs). His account of the heart's three intercommunicating chambers, disastrous for later anatomy, was due to wrong observation in a difficult field, but it fell conveniently into his theory of the blood system.

Nevertheless, Aristotle is aware how easily observations can mislead. For example, he remarks that those who believed the lungs to be devoid of blood were misled by observing dissected animals from which the blood had escaped. Much of what he says of the lion is mistaken, as is his statement that the crocodile moves the upper jaw: in these cases external appearances have not been tested by inspection of the dead body. Some could have been better tested—for example, his reports of the incidence of the gall bladder are unreliable, probably because he trusted the augurs. But the great majority of data in this section are accurate and shrewdly observed, especially the details of alimentary canal and reproductive organs, in which he took special theoretical interest.

Under "Lives and Activities" Aristotle compares differences in reproduction, feeding, migration, hibernation, and sloughing, and variations due to season, breeding, disease, age, and habitat. His theory of reproduction, applied to all groups of animals, is argued in *De generatione animalium;* the *Historia animalium* summarizes this and adds much more information about sexual behavior, breeding methods and seasons, gestation, incubation, and brood care. He distinguishes the viviparous quadrupeds theoretically by the degree of perfection in the young at birth, and he has many details of seal and dolphin as well as land animals. The next step down is to the ovoviviparous, such as the vipers, sharks, and dogfishes. In them he describes the egg's development and its movement rearward to the position where the young are released within the uterus; in one dogfish (*Mustelus laevis*) he notes the placentoid structure, like that of mammals, which was not rediscovered until comparatively modern times. He mistakenly generalizes that all cartilaginous fishes are ovoviviparous. He divides the ovipara into those that lay perfected eggs (birds and quadrupeds) and those whose eggs develop after laying, requiring what he took to be a second fertilizing by the male. He describes minutely the development of the eggs of birds, fishes, cephalopods, and others by opening eggs at intervals during the whole incubation period. He records many special cases: for example, the way that *Syngnathus acus* carries its eggs in a pouch, which then splits to release them (although he does not observe that it is the male which carries them). The lowest mode of reproduction in his scale of "perfectedness" is spontaneous generation, which he attributes to all testaceans, many insects, the eel, and a few fishes. He describes the spawn of whelks, but judges it to be a budding-off comparable with that of plants, not a mass of eggs; otherwise, testaceans originate from various mixtures of mud and rotting substances, the type of animal being determined by the mixture. He considers that insects (except for one butterfly) produce grubs, not eggs; although one speaks of spiders' or bees' eggs, and so on, he says that what at first looks like an egg is really a motionless larva, on the (mistaken) grounds that the subsequent animal is formed out of the whole of it. The grubs of spiders, bees, cicadas, and others develop into the parental type, but those of flies and beetles do not develop

further, and originate spontaneously from a variety of materials, which he lists. Gnats and mosquitoes do not even produce grubs, but themselves arise from grubs that are spontaneously generated. He describes many types of larval development through pupa to imago, including the change of the bloodworm into the gnat. His conclusion about the honeybee (which he says is a puzzle) is tentatively that the queen produces queens and workers, the workers produce the drones, and the drones produce nothing. His view here is not exactly parthenogenesis: he holds that bees contain both male and female principles, and therefore generate without coition.

The final section on "Characters," that is, animal psychology and intelligence, contains little imputation of motives: he records strictly the observed behavior. He compares animals in compatibility, rivalry, nesting and homemaking, and miscellaneous habits of defense and self-support. Among many, for example, he reports the nests made by the octopus and the wrasse, and the brood care by the male river catfish—recently rediscovered and named after him (*Parasilurus aristotelis*). He notes that the partridge makes two nests, on one of which the male sits; and his report that some partridges cackle and others whistle led to the discovery in 1962 that two populations (rock partridge and chukar) live side by side in Thrace. Among the honeybee's habits he seems to refer to the "dance language." The section is unfinished, and the treatise in its present form ends abruptly with a distinction between birds that take dust baths and those that take water baths.

The more complete descriptions, which have been inserted throughout the treatise and seem to be the latest additions, include those of the ape, chameleon, and wryneck, and extracts from Herodotus and Ctesias on the crocodile, hippopotamus, and martichoras. But most of the fabulous or unauthenticated reports are in a separate work called *Mirabilia,* where they were perhaps held awaiting corroboration: some of them—for example, the bison—are in both treatises. For entirely new animals, Aristotle no doubt required reliable eyewitnesses. But when it comes to details reported of known animals, which is the subject matter of most of his reports, his first point of reference is the adult living animal in its natural environment. His standard of judgment is function rather than morphology, as he makes clear in *De partibus animalium.* The "analogies" that he seeks, and from which he constantly argues, are not structural but functional; and, wherever possible, his identification of differentiae is based on function. Because this is his aim in the *Historia,* he picks out the significant details better, for instance, than does

Xenophon (whose excellent accounts of the hare and of horses provide the best contemporary comparison with Aristotle's reports). Its change of plan and lack of revision make the treatise seem incoherent and bewildering, but its comprehensiveness and acumen made it the outstanding descriptive zoology of ancient times, even though it was not intended to be primarily descriptive. It outlasted the work of such later encyclopedic compilers as Pliny, and combined with Aristotle's other zoological works it became—through the Arabic version translated into Latin by Michael Scot—the major ingredient in Albertus Magnus' *De animalibus,* which dominated the field until the sixteenth century.

BIBLIOGRAPHY

The standard text is Bekker's *Corpus Aristotelicum* with Latin trans. (Berlin, 1831–1870). There is also the text with English trans., intro., and brief notes in the Loeb Classical Library; see especially A. L. Peck's eds. of *De partibus animalium* (rev. 1955), *De generatione animalium* (rev. 1953), and *Historia animalium,* I (1965; remaining 2 vols. in press). *Parva naturalia* was ed. with full English commentary by W. D. Ross (Oxford, 1955). The Loeb and Ross eds. contain bibliographies of previous eds. and full accounts of the MSS.

There are also lesser works with zoological content included in the Bekker ed., but not all are by Aristotle—*De incessu animalium, De motu animalium, De spiritu, Mirabilia,* and *Problemata.* See also *The Works of Aristotle Translated Into English,* W. D. Ross, ed.: III, *De spiritu* (1931); V, *De incessu animalium* and *De motu animalium* (1912); VI, *Mirabilia* (1913); and VII, *Problemata* (1927).

D. M. BALME

ARISTOTLE: Anatomy and Physiology.

In his discussion of animals Aristotle gives great importance to the heart, the blood vessels, and the blood, making the possession of blood the basis for distinguishing one great class of animals, those with blood, from those without blood (roughly the vertebrates and invertebrates). In giving this fundamental position to the heart and blood Aristotle departs from the physiological ideas of the Hippocratic writers; in doing so he seems to have been influenced by the ideas of the Italo-Sicilian-Greek medical thinkers. The stopping of the heartbeat was a certain sign of death and thereafter the body rapidly cooled and became stiff and lifeless. In the developing chick Aristotle saw the beating heart as the first manifestation of life. From this beating heart he saw blood vessels grow out over the yolk, and within the skein

of blood vessels thus formed, the body of the young chick gradually emerged. Aristotle emphasized that the heart is the center and the origin of all the blood vessels. He considered that the blood was formed in the heart and passed out from it, because from the moment that the heart became visible it was seen to contain blood and as the network of blood vessels spread out from it, in the embryo chick, the blood accompanied them.

Since the heart, blood, and blood vessels were so fundamental to the bodies of animals Aristotle undertook to discuss them first in his *Historia animalium.* Possibly because of his belief in their fundamental importance he gave one of the earliest accurate descriptions of the blood vessels as a system extending throughout the body, but with its center in the heart. References to the blood vessels by Greek writers before Aristotle emphasized superficial veins, most easily visible in emaciated men, which might be used in bloodletting. Their accounts of the internal arrangement of the blood vessels were extremely vague and fragmentary. By his full and accurate account of the cardiovascular system Aristotle may be considered a founder of detailed anatomical study.

The basis for Aristotle's success in the dissection of the blood vessels was that instead of stunning the animal and bleeding it, in the manner of butchers, he first allowed it to starve to emaciation and then strangled it, thereby retaining in the dead animal all of the blood within the blood vessels. This treatment of the animal had, however, certain physiological consequences which were to influence the character of his observations. The animal killed by strangulation dies in a state of shock which produces a constriction of the small arteries and arterioles in the lungs, thereby cutting off the supply of blood to the left side of the heart. The left ventricle of the heart contracts to empty itself of blood and cannot be refilled. Moreover, the elastic muscle walls of the arterial system contract to squeeze the blood they contain through the capillaries into the veins. Almost all the blood in the body, therefore, accumulates in the venous system, leaving the left side of the heart and the arteries nearly empty. The right side of the heart, on the other hand, is enormously swollen and engorged with blood. When the heart relaxes in death the pressure of blood in the veins will keep open the right auriculoventricular aperture. The flaps of the tricuspid valve will be pressed back against the wall of the ventricle and will be relatively inconspicuous. As a result of these circumstances the right auricle and ventricle will appear as one large chamber continuous with the superior and inferior venae cavae. Instead of four cavities, the heart will appear to have only three, the largest of which will be the united right auricle and ventricle, while the two others will be the left ventricle and the left auricle. Thus to Aristotle the vena cava or "great blood vessel" appeared as a single continuous vessel that broadened in the heart "as a river that widens out in a lake" (*Historia animalium* 513b5, Thompson, trans.). The aorta he saw arising from the middle chamber of the heart and noted that it was more sinewy than the "great blood vessel."

Aristotle did not distinguish between arteries and veins and applied the same term, *phleps* (φλεψ), to both. Neither did he describe the heart valves. He saw the pulmonary artery extending from the "largest chamber on the right" (the right ventricle) upward toward the lung, and he described how in the lung the branches of the pulmonary artery are distributed throughout its flesh and everywhere lie alongside the branches of the tubes (bronchioles) that extend from the windpipe. He traced the main branches of both the venous and arterial systems and described the blood vessels, at least in outline, as a system coextensive with the body, having a shape "like a sketch of a manikin" (*ibid.,* 515a34–515b2).

Aristotle interpreted the pulsation of the heart as the result of a kind of boiling movement in the blood which caused it to press against the walls of the heart and to pour out into the blood vessels. The heart walls were thick in order to contain the innate heat generated in it and the heat of the heart produced respiration by causing the lungs to expand and cool air to rush in. The entering air cooled the lungs so that they again subsided and the air, warmed now by the heat taken up from the blood, was expired. Thus for Aristotle respiration served the purpose of cooling and moderating the heat of the blood and the heart.

Aristotle considered the brain to be cold and to exert a cooling influence on the body in opposition to the heating influence of the heart. Since he did not know of the existence of the nervous system as a system extending throughout the body in a manner similar to the blood vessels, he could not conceive of the brain as having the same kind of central role as the heart.

BIBLIOGRAPHY

See T. H. Huxley, "On Certain Errors Respecting the Heart Attributed to Aristotle," in *Nature,* **21** (1880), 1–5; William Ogle's note to 667b in his translation of Aristotle, *De partibus animalium* (Oxford, 1910); and Arthur Platt, "Aristotle on the Heart," in C. Singer, *Studies in the History and Method of Science,* 2 vols. (Oxford, 1921), II, 520–532.

LEONARD G. WILSON

ARISTOTLE: Tradition and Influence.

An account of the Aristotelian tradition would cover, without any interruption, the whole of the intellectual history of the Western world and, in recent times, of other areas as well. On the other hand, the influence of Aristotle's works and doctrines on the cultural developments of civilization is, in most fields, elusive and undefinable. Especially in the province of science—if we use "science" in the stricter, modern sense—it may be found that Aristotle's influence is very limited, or effective only in the sense that mistakes, eliciting opposition, criticism, and new solutions to old and new problems, are the starting point of scientific progress. Positive influence and starting points for positive developments are found, for the different sciences, much more frequently in the works of Euclid and Ptolemy; of Hippocrates and Galen; of Archimedes; of al-Fārābī, Ibn Sīnā (Avicenna), and Ibn Rushd (Averroës); possibly of Boethius; and, back through Boethius, of Nicomachus of Gerasa.

Still, there are two aspects in this progress that bear the Aristotelian imprint and justify an extensive account of the spread of Aristotle's works and of their study: the methodical aspect and the conceptual-linguistic aspect. These two cannot always be separated, but they must not be confused if Aristotle's influence is to be clearly seen and properly assessed. This section will, therefore, be devoted first and foremost to such an account. We shall then consider a set of concepts and words that became essential for the elaboration of scientific problems and, indeed, for making scientific discoveries clearly expressible and understandable in the technical and, at the same time, the common language. Some exemplification will be given of the methodical aspect, insofar as it can be traced back to Aristotle's influence, and of the actual contributions derived from his works, mainly by discussion, rejection, and positive substitution of anti-Aristotelian views. In this connection it must be recorded that a very limited amount of the literature that developed around the works of Aristotle in later antiquity, in the Middle Ages, and even into the eighteenth century has been properly edited, much less has been critically read, and only a minimal proportion of it has been examined from the point of view that interests us here.

The transmission and spread of Aristotle's works can best be followed by considering the different languages or groups of languages in which it took place: basic, of course, was the Greek tradition, from which all others sprang, directly or indirectly (fourth century B.C. to our times); most important and permanent in value was the Latin (fourth century A.D. to sixteenth and seventeenth centuries); very influential, especially through elaborations and translations into Latin, was the Semitic (first Syriac, then [and mainly] Arabic, finally Hebrew [fifth century A.D. to sixteenth century]); only occasionally effective in its own right and more valuable as a help in the rebirth of the study of Greek civilization was the tradition in German, Neo-Latin, English, and, more recently, many other modern languages (tenth century to our times); limited to very narrow cultural units was the Armenian and possibly the Georgian (*ca.* fifth century A.D. to tenth century and later).

The Transmission of Aristotle's Works in Greek. Compared with the impact of what constitutes the traditional Aristotelian corpus, typically represented by the Berlin Academy edition of 1835, the influence of the other works of Aristotle—preserved, if at all, in a number of more or less extensive fragments—can be considered negligible; we cannot pursue their tradition here. The corpus, based mainly, it seems, on lectures, preparations for lectures, accounts of lectures, and elaboration of collected material (*De animalibus*), must have begun to be organized in Aristotle's own time, by Aristotle himself and his pupils (Theophrastus, Eudemus, and others). The process continued in his school, with vicissitudes, for 250 years after his death. The quasi-final organization of Aristotle's available material seems to have been accomplished by Andronicus of Rhodes (*ca.* 70 B.C.). It may be assumed that from Andronicus' edition there derived, with minor changes and developments, the transmitted texts as we know them in Greek. From Andronicus to the middle of the sixth century, the spread of the corpus or parts of it is continuously testified by the activities in the several philosophical schools, whether mainly Peripatetic in character, or eclectic, or more purely Neoplatonic. Andronicus' pupil Boëthus of Sidon commented on Aristotle's works, making the *Physics* the basis of Aristotelian philosophy; a century after, Nicholas of Damascus expounded Aristotle's philosophy and wrote (in the mood of Aristotle's *De animalibus*) a *De plantis,* which came to be ascribed to Aristotle; and *ca.* A.D. 100, Ptolemy Chennos of Alexandria wrote a work on the life and works of Aristotle. In the second half of the second century A.D., Galen, famous for his medical work, was a critical popularizer of Aristotle's logic, physics, and metaphysics, and many other authors commented on this or that work.

The texts of Aristotle were, obviously, already popular over a wide area. When, *ca.* A.D. 200, Alexander of Aphrodisias became professor of philosophy in Athens, as a "second Aristotle," he commented upon a large proportion of the corpus and left in his works abundant evidence of the variety of readings

that had been infiltrating the nearly 300-year-old transmission of the basic edition. Although only minor fragments of papyri containing Aristotle's texts from the corpus and no manuscript older than the ninth century exist, the expanding study of the works in Athens, Constantinople, Alexandria, and Pergamum justifies the statement that many manuscripts were available in many centers. The sixth century adds new evidence, since, at least in the case of some logical works, we possess not only the quotations of many Greek commentators but also the literal translations into Latin, Syriac, and Armenian: these testify to the variety of the Greek tradition, a variety that continued and became more complicated in later centuries.

The ban on pagan schools in 529 led to a reduction, if not to a halt, in the production of Greek copies of the works of Aristotle until the revival of the late eighth and ninth centuries. Then really "critical" editions of some works, and transcriptions of many, if not all, started again. The University of Constantinople became a center of studies of some of these works; the old libraries still possessed among them at least one copy of each of the writings of Aristotle. And it is possible to surmise that in form (some of them were rich in scholia extracted from the old commentaries) they were like the manuscripts of the sixth or earlier centuries. The number of extant manuscripts of the ninth and tenth centuries is very small, and does not cover the whole corpus; but the stronger revival of the eleventh century was the beginning of the uninterrupted transcription and transmission of the more popular works. This gathered momentum, not only in Constantinople but also in the numerous centers where lay and theological schools were flourishing.

By the thirteenth and fourteenth centuries publication had expanded to such an extent that about 150 manuscripts from that period still survive. There are only a few exceptions to show that not all of Aristotle was dominating the higher philosophical studies, side by side with Plato: the *Politics,* unearthed perhaps in the eleventh century and turned into a fruitful career by the Latin translator William of Moerbeke, does not appear in our collections in any manuscript older than the thirteenth century. The *Poetics* appears in late manuscripts, except for one of the eleventh century and one of the thirteenth. But the bigger collections, especially of the logical works, are relatively numerous. A new impetus to the dissemination was given in the fifteenth century by the migration of scholars from the Greek world to Italy and by the interest in Greek studies in Florence, Venice, and other cities. In the fifteenth century the number of copies of the several parts of the corpus, including the rarest works, multiplied, and the way was prepared for the printed editions, from the Aldine of 1495–1498 to those of the seventeenth century. There was then about a century of interruption: Aristotle was "out" from most points of view. By the end of the eighteenth century the new interests of learning brought about the new wave of Greek editions of Aristotle—a process that is still in full swing.

The Transmission of Aristotle's Works in Latin. No evidence has come to light to show that any work by Aristotle or any extensive paraphrase was available in Latin before *ca.* A.D. 350. Cicero's claim that his *Topica* was based directly on Aristotle's work of the same title is false. His model was the work of a rhetorician, not of a logician, and bears only vague, occasional, accidental resemblances to what Aristotle wrote. The latinization of Aristotle took place through different channels: by far the most important was the direct translation from the Greek originals; second in importance was the translation of Greek paraphrases and commentaries; third, the translation of some of Aristotle's works from direct or indirect Arabic versions, whether alone or accompanied by Arabic commentaries; fourth, the versions of Arabic works based, in various measure, on Aristotelian texts; finally, some translations from the Hebrew renderings of Arabic versions, commentaries, and paraphrases. All this happened in the course of four identifiable stages, very different in length, between the middle of the fourth century and the end of the sixteenth: (*a*) the first stage probably lasted only a few years and involved a few individuals belonging to two groups working in Rome; (*b*) the second corresponds to a few years in the first quarter or first half of the sixth century, with Boethius as the only person concerned with this activity in Italy, and possibly some minor contributors in Constantinople; (*c*) the third stage covers about 150 years, from *ca.* 1130 to *ca.* 1280, when the work was carried out probably in Constantinople and certainly in Sicily, Italy, Spain, Greece, England, and France by at least a score of people of many nationalities and callings—by the end of this period the whole of the Aristotelian corpus as it has reached us in Greek, with very minor exceptions, could be read and studied in Latin; (*d*) the fourth stage extended from shortly after 1400 to *ca.* 1590. Only in the third stage did the Arabic tradition contribute directly to the Latin one; and only in the fourth did it do so through the Hebrew.

(*a*) The intellectual intercourse between Greek and Latin in the third and fourth centuries, of which the most striking example outside religion was the spread of the knowledge of Plotinus' doctrines, led to the need for Latin texts of some of the works considered basic by the Greeks. It was in this Neoplatonic atmosphere (tempered by Porphyry with more Aristotelianism than Plotinus had accepted, rather than discussed and criticized) that the African Marius Victorinus, a pagan converted to Christianity, popularized the contents of Porphyry's introduction to logic, the *Isagoge*; if we accept Cassiodorus' testimony, he also translated Aristotle's *Categories* and *De interpretatione*. He certainly included Aristotelian views in his *De definitionibus,* the only work by Victorinus that contains some Aristotle and that has reached us in full (only sections of his version of the *Isagoge* survive in one of Boethius' commentaries). The attraction exercised by Themistius' school in Constantinople led to another, possibly purer, wave of Aristotelianism among the pagan revivalists, so vividly depicted in Macrobius' *Saturnalia.* Vettius Agorius Praetextatus, one of their leaders, rendered into Latin Themistius' teaching on the *Analytics.* Agorius' work was probably lost very soon, and there was no Latin text of Themistius' work on the *Analytics* until the second half of the twelfth century. This was based on an Arabic translation of part of that work (which was not translated from the Greek before the end of the fifteenth century). But Themistius' teaching of the *Categories*—a detailed exposition with additions and modernizations—found its Latin popularizer in a member of the same circle (perhaps Albinus). It is from this work, later ascribed to St. Augustine, under the title of *Categoriae decem,* that the Latin Aristotelianism of the Middle Ages started its career, never since interrupted.

(*b*) The middle and late fourth-century Aristotelianism, and much else of the cultural life of that time, was a faded, but not a lost, memory when, in the first decade of the sixth century, Boethius married a descendant of one of the prominent intellectual families, Symmachus' daughter Rusticiana. He took up what remained of that tradition, and was encouraged by his father-in-law to renew it. Cultural relations with the Greeks were not as active around 505 as around 370, but Boethius managed to obtain some Greek books, among them a copy of the collection of Aristotle's logical texts with an ample selection of notes from the greater masters of the past (Alexander, Themistius, and, mainly, Porphyry). So he probably managed to achieve what he had planned, to translate as much of Aristotle as he could get hold of: at least, we still preserve, in more or less original form, his translations of the *Categories, De interpretatione, Prior Analytics, Topics,* and *Sophistici elenchi;* he also claims to have produced a now lost translation of the

Posterior Analytics. Since, by the fifth century, Aristotle's logical works were prefaced by Porphyry's *Isagoge*, Boethius also translated this text. He wrote that he intended to comment upon the works of Aristotle accessible to him; as it turned out, he commented on only the two shortest texts, the *Categories* and *De interpretatione*—or, better, he translated, adapted, and coordinated passages from Greek commentaries that he must have found on the margins of his Greek volume. The existence of a double recension for many sections of the *Categories, Prior Analytics,* and one short section of the *Topics;* the existence of a Latin version of a considerable collection of scholia to the *Prior Analytics* translated from the Greek and connected with one of the two recensions of this work; and a variety of evidence pointing to some editorial activity in Constantinople centering on Boethius' work in the first half of the sixth century suggest that Boethius' work as a translator in Italy had some continuation in the circle of Latin culture in Constantinople.

(*c*) The third stage is by far the most impressive, representing as it does a variety of interests, of cultural backgrounds, of centers of progressive attitude toward the renewal, on the basis of older traditions, of the intellectual life in Europe and, to a certain extent, also representing one further step in a continuity of Aristotelian studies, hardly interrupted from the first century B.C. to the thirteenth century A.D. It is here necessary to consider separately the translators from the Greek and those from the Arabic, as well as some of the centers and people connected with this transmission of Aristotle. First of all, it cannot be emphasized too strongly that Aristotle was latinized from the Greek much more than from the Arabic and, with very few exceptions, earlier from the Greek than from the Arabic. Although competent scholars have tried to make this fact known, the commonly held view of historians of ideas and of people in general is the wrong view: that the Latin Middle Ages owed their knowledge of Aristotle first and foremost to the translations from the Arabic.

(*c*-1) The Aristotelian revival of the ninth and the eleventh centuries in the higher schools of Constantinople—particularly the second revival, due to such people as Michael Psellus, Ioannes Italus, Eustratius of Nicaea, and Michael of Ephesus—brought its fruits to the Latin revival (or, better, discovery) in the twelfth and thirteenth centuries. In the second quarter of the twelfth century James (Iacobus), a cleric with philosophical, theological, and juridical interests who seems to describe himself as Venetian-Greek, was in Constantinople and in touch with the Aristotelian corpus. He translated, either in Constantinople itself, or possibly in Italy, at least the *Posterior Analytics,* the *Sophistici elenchi,* the *Physics,* the *De anima,* parts of the *Parva naturalia,* and the *Metaphysics.* Of the translation of the last work only Books I–III and the beginning of Book IV remain; of the translation of the *Elenchi* only fragments have been recovered, mainly in contaminated texts of Boethius' version. He also translated some Greek notes to the *Metaphysics,* a short introduction to the *Physics* (known, in much of the Latin tradition, as *De intelligentia Aristotelis*), and probably *Commentaries to the Posterior Analytics* and *Elenchi* ascribed to Alexander of Aphrodisias. Finally, he himself commented at least on the *Elenchi.* James's translations, in spite of their extreme literalness, reveal a considerable knowledge of the learned Greek language of his time and interests in a variety of fields. Conscious of his limitations, which seem to be more marked when the technical language of mathematics and some philosophical terminology in Latin are concerned, he transcribes some key words in Greek letters, occasionally attempting an approximate translation. Some of his versions remained the basis, directly and through revisions, of the knowledge and study of much of Aristotle until the fifteenth and sixteenth centuries.

In 1158 Henry, nicknamed Aristippus, a Norman dignitary of the church and court in Sicily, was on an embassy at Constantinople, from which he brought back several books. With its combination of a recent Arabic past, enlightened Norman rule, and refined cultural life, Sicily was, in its own right, one of the best training grounds for a man like Henry, interested in problems of human life and death (he translated Plato's *Phaedo* and *Meno*) and curious about the workings of nature (like Empedocles, he climbed Mt. Etna to observe the volcano firsthand). He, and others around him, were conscious of the scientific tradition of Sicily; books of mechanics, astronomy, optics, and geometry were available, and attracted people from as far as England. Henry contributed to this tradition with a translation of at least Book IV of the *Meteorologics.* With less pedantry than James, he varied his vocabulary more than a work of science could admit; still, his translation remained indispensable for about a century, and what may be called Aristotle's physical chemistry was known primarily through his text.

(*c*-2) At approximately the same time, and presumably drawing on the same Greek sources of Aristotelian studies, a number of scholars with quite a good knowledge of Greek produced either new versions of texts already translated—whether the older translations were known to them cannot always be established—and versions of works previously unknown in Latin. These scholars remain anonymous, with the possible exception of a certain John, who produced, after the Venetian James, another translation of the *Posterior Analytics;* a second scholar translated anew the *Topics* and the *Prior Analytics;* a third, the *De sensu;* a fourth, the short treatises *De somno* and *De insomniis;* a fifth, the *De generatione et corruptione* and the *Nicomachean Ethics* (of which only Book I ["Ethica nova"], Books II and III ["Ethica vetus"], and fragments of Books VII and VIII ["Ethica Borghesiana"] remain); a sixth, again after James, the *Physics* (only Book I ["Physica Vaticana"] remains) and the *Metaphysics* without Book XI (the first chapter is lost); and a seventh, probably the *Rhetoric.* Some of these translations had little or no success (*Prior* and *Posterior Analytics, Topics, Rhetoric, Physics*); the others, within the limits of their survival (*De generatione et corruptione, De sensu, De somno, De insomniis, Nicomachean Ethics, Metaphysics*), remained in use, in the original form or in revisions, for three or four centuries. They all testify to the vast interest in the recovery of Aristotle in the twelfth century.

(*c-3*) While Constantinople, possibly together with minor Greek centers, was giving the Aristotelian material to the Latin scholars, the intense cultural activity of the Arab world had spread to northwestern Africa and Spain, providing Latin scholarship, especially in the part of Spain freed from Arab domination, with a vast amount of scientific and philosophical material and the linguistic competence for this to be rendered into Latin. Leaving aside for the moment the spreading of Aristotelian ideas through works of Arabic writers, mention must be made of the one translator of Aristotelian work from the Arabic, the Italian Gerard of Cremona, active in Toledo from *ca.* 1150 to his death in 1187. Being a scientist, he translated from the Arabic what was accessible to him of the more scientific works of Aristotle: the *Posterior Analytics* (theory of science by induction and deduction), *Physics, De generatione et corruptione, De caelo,* and *Meteorologics* (most of Book IV of this was either not translated or was soon lost). He also translated Themistius' paraphrase of the *Posterior Analytics.* The two of these works that did not exist in translation from the Greek (*Meteorologics* I–III and *De caelo*) were often transcribed and not infrequently studied for about sixty years in these versions from the Arabic. The others were occasionally used as terms of comparison or as additional evidence where the texts from the Greek were considered basic. It should also be mentioned that Gerard translated, under the name of Aristotle, thirty-one propositions from Proclus' *Elements of Theology* accompanied by an Arabic commentary, which formed the text

(occasionally ascribed to Aristotle, more frequently left anonymous by the Latins) known under the title *Liber de causis.* Toward the end of the twelfth century, Alfred of Sareshel translated, again under the name of Aristotle (which attribution remained unchallenged for several centuries), Nicholas of Damascus' *De plantis.*

By the end of the twelfth century most of Aristotle had, therefore, found its way into Latin, but that does not mean that his works were soon widely accessible. To make them so, activity was still necessary in both transcription and translation. Some works had not yet been translated, and versions of others had been partly or completely lost; it was also realized that new versions made directly from the Greek would be necessary where only translations from the Arabic or inadequate versions from the Greek were available, and that revisions were necessary for almost every text; finally, it was felt that in order to achieve a more complete understanding of the words of Aristotle, translated by people whose knowledge of Greek was based mainly on the modernized, Byzantine usage, it was useful or necessary to give the reader of Latin access to many of the commentaries, Greek or Arabic, that linked the present with the past.

(*c-4*) The work done with these aims in view, on the basis of Greek texts, was carried out almost completely in the thirteenth century by two outstanding northerners: Robert Grosseteste, bishop of Lincoln and chancellor of Oxford University, and the Flemish Dominican William of Moerbeke, later archbishop of Corinth. A minor contribution came from a Sicilian, Bartholomew of Messina. Grosseteste, philosopher and theologian, linguist and scientist, politician and ecclesiastic, grew up at a time when it was already known how much Aristotle could help in the promotion of that Western European culture of which the foundations had been laid in the twelfth century. He was well aware of the contributions that the fading Greek renaissance could now offer, at least in books and teachers of the language. Grosseteste encouraged other Englishmen to go to Greece, southern Italy, and Sicily to collect books and men of learning. With their help, in the second quarter of the thirteenth century, he learned the language and, what concerns us here, thoroughly revised what remained of the older version of the *Nicomachean Ethics;* translated anew the major part of it, of which the older translation had been lost; and translated a large collection of commentaries on the several books of this work, some of them dating as far back as the third century, some as recent as the eleventh and twelfth. He also replaced with a translation from the Greek the *De caelo,* available until then only in a version from the

Arabic, and added the translation of at least part of the vast commentary by Simplicius on the same work. Finally, he translated as Aristotelian the short treatise *De lineis insecabilibus* ("On Lines Not Made of Points").

William of Moerbeke, also a philosopher, theologian, scientist, and ecclesiastic, but in these fields a lesser man than Grosseteste, traveled from the Low Countries to Italy, Greece, and Asia Minor, widening the scope of his discoveries and of his translations to include Neoplatonic philosophy, geometry, mechanics, and medicine. His activity as an Aristotelian translator was enormous and covered approximately the third quarter of the century. He was the first to translate from Greek into Latin the Aristotelian zoological encyclopedia, the *De animalibus,* and Books I–III of the *Meteorologics;* he can almost be considered the discoverer, for our civilization, of the *Politics;* he was the first to translate into Latin the *Poetics* and Book XI of the *Metaphysics;* he translated anew the *De caelo,* the *Rhetoric* (he probably did not know of the existence of the Greco-Latin translations of these two works), and Book IV of the *Meteorologics;* he accompanied his versions of Greek commentaries with new translations of the *Categories* and *De interpretatione;* and he revised, with different degrees of thoroughness but always having recourse to Greek texts, James's versions of *Posterior Analytics, Physics, De anima, De memoria* and other minor texts of the *Parva naturalia,* Boethius' version of the *Sophistici elenchi,* and the anonymous versions of the *De generatione et corruptione,* of Books I–X and XII–XIV of the *Metaphysics,* and of the *De sensu, De somno,* and *De insomniis.* He also translated the extensive commentaries by Simplicius on the *Categories* and (again, after Grosseteste) the *De caelo,* by Alexander of Aphrodisias on the *De sensu* and *Meteorologics,* by Themistius on the *De anima,* by Ammonius on the *De interpretatione,* and by Philoponus on one part of Book III of the *De anima.* With the possible exception of the *De coloribus* (one fragment seems to be translated by him), he avoided all the works wrongly ascribed to Aristotle.

In contrast, Bartholomew of Messina, working for King Manfred around 1260, specialized in the pseudepigrapha: *De mundo, Problemata, Magna moralia, Physionomia, De mirabilibus auscultationibus, De coloribus,* and *De principiis* (Theophrastus' *Metaphysics*). The only translation of a possibly genuine Aristotelian text made by Bartholomew is that of the *De Nilo.* To complete the picture of the translations from the Greek of "Aristotelian" works before the end of the thirteenth century (or possibly a little after), we should add a second translation of the *De mundo,*

by one of Grosseteste's collaborators, Nicholas of Sicily, two anonymous translations of the *Rhetorica ad Alexandrum,* and two partial translations of the *Economics.* Finally, an anonymous revision of Books I–II and part of Book III of James's translation of the *Metaphysics* was made around 1230, and an equally anonymous revision of the whole of Grosseteste's version of the *Nicomachean Ethics* was carried out probably between 1260 and 1270.

(*c*-5) The work of translating Aristotle or Aristotelian commentaries from the Arabic in the thirteenth century centered, again, mainly in Toledo and to a smaller extent in southern Italy. Most of this work was carried out by Michael Scot; other contributors were William of Luna and Hermann the German. Michael Scot was the first to make known to the Latins the *Books on Animals,* and it was his translation of most of the *Metaphysics* (parts of Books I and XII and the whole of Books XI, XIII, and XIV were not included), together with Averroës' *Great Commentary,* that provided many students of Aristotle with the bulk of this complex of Aristotelian texts: most of James's translation had probably been lost before anybody took any real interest in this work, and the anonymous Greco-Latin version (*Media*) made in the twelfth century emerged from some isolated repository *ca.* 1250. Under the title *Metaphysica nova,* Michael's version, isolated from Averroës' commentary, held its ground for about twenty years and was quite widely used for another twenty. The following translations must be ascribed to Michael Scot, some with certainty, some with great probability: the *De anima, Physics,* and *De caelo* with Averroës' *Great Commentary,* the *Middle Commentary* of the *De generatione et corruptione* and of Book IV of the *Meteorologics,* and Averroës' *Summaries* of the *Parva naturalia.*

William of Luna translated, in or near Naples, the *Middle Commentaries* to Porphyry's *Isagoge* and Aristotle's *Categories, De interpretatione,* and *Prior* and *Posterior Analytics.* Hermann the German translated Averroës' *Middle Commentaries* on the *Nicomachean Ethics, Rhetoric,* and *Poetics.* The last-mentioned was, in fact, the only source from which Latin readers acquired what knowledge they had—and that was mainly distorted—of Aristotle's *Poetics:* under the title *Poetria* (*Averrois* or *Aristotelis*) it was read quite widely; William of Moerbeke's translation from the Greek remained unknown until 1930, and the next translation from the Greek was not made until shortly before 1500.

By the end of the thirteenth century, the whole of the Aristotelian corpus as we know it, and as it has been known—if we except the relatively few fragments of early works—since the first century B.C., was available in Latin to practically everybody who cared to have access to it. The only exception consisted of the four books of the *Ethics* that are not common to the *Nicomachean Ethics* (which appears with the full complement of ten books) and to the *Eudemian Ethics* (which normally contains only the four that differ from those of the *Nicomachean*); only a small portion of this seems to have been translated, and is connected with passages of the *Magna moralia* in the so-called *De bona fortuna*. The general picture of the diffusion of Aristotle in these translations until the beginning of the sixteenth century is provided by the survival to our times of no fewer than 2,000 manuscripts containing from one to about twenty works, and by the fact that the most complete catalog of early printings (down to 1500) lists over 200 editions, without counting a large number of volumes that contain some of these translations with commentaries.

The detailed picture, when properly drawn, will show the difference in the popularity of the several works; but the difficulty in drawing such a picture derives from the fact that many works, especially minor ones, were transcribed as parts of general, mainly Aristotelian, collections without being actually taken into detailed account. Still, it may be significant that one of these collections, *Corpus Vetustius*—containing the *Physics, Meteorologics, De generatione et corruptione, De anima, Parva naturalia, De caelo,* and *Metaphysics* in the translations made before 1235—remains in slightly fewer than 100 manuscripts, all of the thirteenth (or very early fourteenth) century; a similar collection, including the same works in the new or revised translations in a more complete form (*Corpus recentius*) is preserved in about 200 manuscripts of the thirteenth, fourteenth, and fifteenth centuries. This shows that the more scientific of the works of Aristotle became indispensable in all centers of study and in private libraries. A statistical study of their provenance has not been made: it is, however, clear that France and England are most prominent in this respect for the *Corpus Vetustius;* and France, Italy, Germany, England, and Spain for the *Corpus recentius.*

If we consider the translations that most influenced Western culture and ascribe the authorship to those who produced them in the basic form, a quite accurate assessment of the individual abilities in transmitting Aristotle's works, and thus in shaping some of the philosophical, scientific, and common language of modern civilization, can be made. Their success in presenting formulations that, although not always carefully and strictly Aristotelian, have contributed

a basis for discussion and polemics, and have thus led, in the dialectic of history, to much progress, can be suggested by the following list:

(1) Boethius: *Categories, De interpretatione, Prior Analytics, Topics, Sophistici elenchi;*

(2) James the Venetian-Greek: *Posterior Analytics, De anima, Physics, De memoria* (perhaps *Metaphysics* I–III);

(3) Twelfth-century anonymous translators from the Greek: *Metaphysics* IV–X, XII–XIV (perhaps I–III), *De generatione et corruptione, Nicomachean Ethics* I–III, *De sensu, De somno, De insomniis;*

(4) Michael Scot: *Metaphysics* I–X, XII, *De animalibus;*

(5) Robert Grosseteste: *Nicomachean Ethics* IV–X;

(6) William of Moerbeke: *Meteorologics, Politics, Rhetoric, De animalibus, Metaphysics* XI, *De caelo.*

An important, if sometimes misleading, role in the Latin transmission of Aristotle must be ascribed to the translators of commentaries. All of them contributed to the transmission and improvement of the technique of interpretation, as developed in the Greek schools of the second through sixth centuries. From this point of view, the greatest influence was probably exercised by the commentaries adapted from the Greek by Boethius and those of Averroës, which are linked, through an almost continuous line of scholastic discipline, with the tradition of the Greek schools. From the point of view of the contributions to the actual critical understanding of Aristotle, probably the most important of Averroës' commentaries were those on the *Metaphysics, Physics,* and *De anima.*

(*d*) The last stage in the Latin transmission of Aristotle—if we disregard the occasional translations of the seventeenth to twentieth centuries—covers what is normally called the humanistic and Renaissance period. This is the period beginning with and following the reestablishment of a more intimate collaboration between Greeks and western European scholars, which extended and deepened the understanding of the "old" Greek through a wider knowledge of the history, literature, science, etc., of the ancient world and a much more accurate understanding of the language as it was understood in ancient times. Another aspect that was soon presented as typical of the new movement in translations was the purity and perspicuity of the Latin language (purity ought to have carried with it the elimination of technical words that were not yet technical in classical Latin); but a closer study of many translations shows that the standards of knowledge of the ancient Greek background and of the Greek language were not consistently higher than in the Middle Ages, and that the need for very literal translations and technical usages of a medieval or of a new kind could not be avoided. In fact, very many new versions of Aristotle are hardly distinguishable, in their essential features, from those of the twelfth and thirteenth centuries. And what there was of a new philosophy of language applied to translations—the philosophy of meanings of contexts as against the meanings of individual words—was not always conducive to a better understanding of the original.

A complete survey of new translations down to the last quarter of the sixteenth century is impossible here. Although some of the later versions may still have exercised some influence in their own right, it seems that greater influence was exercised by some of those of the fifteenth century. And it is questionable how much even the latter ousted the medieval translations, or substituted something of great importance for them. We shall confine ourselves to a quick survey of the new versions of the fifteenth century, which were due in almost equal measure to Greek scholars attracted to Italy and to the Italians whose Greek scholarship resulted from contact with them.

The first Italian translator was a pupil of Manuel Chrysoloras, Roberto de' Rossi, who in 1406 translated the *Posterior Analytics*. Probably the greatest and most influential translator at the beginning of this movement was Leonardo Bruni of Arezzo, translator of the *Nicomachean Ethics, Politics,* and *Economics* (1416–1438). Gianozzo Manetti added to new translations of the *Nicomachean Ethics* and *Magna moralia* the first version of the *Eudemian Ethics* (1455–1460), an effort soon followed by Gregorio of Città di Castello (or Tifernate). Giovanni Tortelli again translated (*ca.* 1450) the *Posterior Analytics;* and in the 1480's Ermolao Barbaro translated, if his statements are to be taken literally, the whole of the logical works, the *Physics,* and the *Rhetoric* (only some of his versions remain). Before 1498 Giorgio Valla produced new translations of the *De caelo, Magna moralia,* and *Poetics,* and Lorenzo Laurenziano one of the *De interpretatione.*

In the meantime, from the early 1450's, the Greeks who had entered into the heritage of Latin culture were competing, or leading the way, in translation. The greatest of all, as a man of culture, collector of books, theologian, ecclesiastic, and philosopher, was Iohannes Bessarion, who translated the *Metaphysics.* His vast collection of manuscripts, among them many Greek volumes of Aristotle, was the basis of the Library of St. Mark in Venice. The most productive were John Argyropulos, translator of the *Categories, De interpretatione, Posterior* (and part of the *Prior*) *Analytics, Physics, De anima, De caelo, Metaphysics,*

and *Nicomachean Ethics* (and the pseudo-Aristotelian *De mundo,* also translated shortly before by Rinucio Aretino), and George of Trebizond, translator of the *De animalibus, Physics, De caelo, De generatione et corruptione, De anima, Problemata,* and *Rhetoric.* Theodore of Gaza translated the *De animalibus* and *Problemata,* and Andronicus Callistus the *De generatione et corruptione.*

What had been done to a very limited extent in the fifteenth century was done on a large scale in the first half of the sixteenth, mainly by Italian scholars: the translation of Greek commentaries from the second to the fourteenth centuries. In this field the Renaissance obscured almost completely what had been done in the Middle Ages, something that, with a few exceptions, it failed utterly to do with the entrenched translations of Aristotle.

The Oriental Transmission of Aristotle's Works. The Greek philosophical schools of the fifth and sixth centuries were attended by people of the various nations surrounding the Mediterranean. Greek was the language of learning, but new languages were emerging to a high cultural level, especially as a consequence of the development of theology from the basic tenets and texts of the Christian faith. What had become necessary for the Greek-speaking theologian, a lay cultural basis, was necessary for the Syrian and for the Armenian. Apart from this, most probably, pure philosophical interest was spreading to other nations that were becoming proud of their nationhood. Thus, probably from the fifth century, and certainly from the sixth, Aristotelian texts started to be translated, and commentaries to be translated into, or originally written in, these languages.

The Armenian tradition, to some extent paralleled by or productive of a more limited Georgian tradition, has not been sufficiently investigated. Armenian culture continued in several parts of the world through the centuries—Armenia itself, India, Europe, and recently America—obviously depending on the culture of the surrounding nations but probably with some independence. A vast amount of unexplored manuscript material, stretching from the eighth century or earlier to the nineteenth century, is now concentrated in the National Library of Manuscripts in Yerevan, Armenian Soviet Socialist Republic. What is known in print is confined to translations of Porphyry's *Isagoge,* the *Categories* and *De interpretatione,* the apocryphal *De mundo,* and Helias' commentary to the *Categories.* A semimythical David the Unconquered (David Invictus) of the fourth or fifth century is mentioned as the author of some of these translations.

The Syriac tradition, more limited in time and space, apparently was richer both in translations of works of Aristotle and in original elaboration; apart from this, it formed the basis of a considerable proportion of the Arabic texts of Aristotle and, through them, of some of the Latin versions. The Nestorian Probus (Probha), of the fifth century, is considered the author of the surviving translations of *De interpretatione* and of *Prior Analytics* I.1–7, which may well belong to an eighth-century author. But there is no reason to doubt the ascription of translations and commentaries to Sergius of Theodosiopolis (Reshᶜayna). He was a student in Alexandria and later active in Monophysite ecclesiastical and political circles in Antioch and in Constantinople, where he died *ca.* 535. He translated into Syriac the *Categories* with the *Isagoge,* and the *De mundo* (all still preserved), and possibly an otherwise unknown work by Aristotle, *On the Soul.* Toward the end of the seventh century, the Jacobite Jacob of Edessa translated the *Categories;* shortly after, George, bishop of the Arabs (d. 724), produced a new version of this book, of the *De interpretatione,* and of the entire *Prior Analytics.* Probably the most influential Syriac translators were two Nestorians, Ḥunayn ibn Isḥāq (*d.* 876) and his son Isḥāq ibn Ḥunayn (*d.* 910 or 911). Ḥunayn translated into Syriac the *De interpretatione, De generatione et corruptione, Physics* II (with Alexander of Aphrodisias' commentary), *Metaphysics* XI, and parts of the *Prior* and *Posterior Analytics;* his son possibly finished the version of these last two works, and translated the *Topics* into Syriac. ᶜAbd al-Masih ibn Naᶜima and Abū Bishr Matta translated the *Sophistici elenchi.* Isḥāq and Abū Bishr Matta also are among the translators from Greek into Arabic. Other translations into Syriac, which cannot be assigned to a definite author, include the *Poetics* (probably by Isḥāq ibn Ḥunayn), the *De animalibus,* possibly the *Meteorologics,* and a number of Greek commentaries to Aristotelian works. Not the least important feature of these translations into Syriac is the fact that numerous Arabic versions were made from the Syriac, rather than from the Greek.

Arabic translations from Aristotle were made in the ninth and tenth centuries, some by Syriac scholars, among whom the most prominent was Isḥāq ibn Ḥunayn. They were done in the latter part of the ninth century and at the beginning of the tenth, when Baghdad had become the great center of Arabic culture under al-Mamun. Of the many translations listed in the old Arabic bibliographies we shall mention only those that still exist. Those made by Isḥāq ibn Ḥunayn, presumably directly from the Greek, are

Categories, De interpretatione, Physics, De anima, and *Metaphysics* II; by Yaḥyā ibn Abī-Manṣūr, Isa ben Zura, and ibn Naim, the *Sophistici elenchi* (Yaḥyā also translated part of *Metaphysics* XII); Abū ᶜUthman ad-Dimashki and Ibrahim ibn ᶜAbdallāh, the *Topics;* Abū Bishr Matta, the *Posterior Analytics* and the *Poetics* (perhaps both through the lost Syriac version by Isḥāq ibn Ḥunayn); Yaḥyā ibn al Bitriq, the *De caelo, Meteorologics,* and *De animalibus;* Astat (Eustathius), *Metaphysics* III–X; Theodorus (Abū Qurra [?]), the *Prior Analytics;* unknown translators, the *Rhetoric* and *Nicomachean Ethics* VII–X. Of the apocrypha, we have two translations of the *De mundo,* one of which was made by ᶜUsa ibn Ibrahim al-Nafisi from the Syriac of Sergius of Theodosiopolis (Reshᶜayna). Finally, it must be mentioned that it was in the Arab world that sections of Plotinus' work (or notes from his conversations) were edited under the title *Theology of Aristotle,* and thirty-one propositions from Proclus' *Elements of Theology* were commented upon and edited as Aristotle's *Book of Pure Goodness* (generally known under the title *De causis,* which it acquired in the Latin tradition).

Elaborations of Aristotle's Works. The transcriptions of the Greek texts, the translations into the several languages, and the multiplication of the copies of these translations were obviously only the first steps in the spread of Aristotle's pure or adulterated doctrines. The more permanent influence of those doctrines was established in the schools, through oral teaching, or on the margin of and outside the schools, through writings of different kinds at different levels. There would be, at the most elementary level, the division into chapters, possibly with short titles and very brief summaries; then occasional explanations of words and phrases in the margins or between the lines in the manuscripts of the actual Aristotelian texts (glosses or scholia), or more extensive summaries and explanations of points of particular interest at some moment or other in the history of thought.

At a higher level there would be systematic expositions or paraphrases, adhering closely to the original text but adapting the diction, the language, and the articulation of the arguments to the common scholastic pattern of this or that time, place, or school; then, expository commentaries, section by section, with or without introductory surveys and occasional recapitulations. The commentaries could aim at clarifying Aristotle's doctrine or adding doctrinal developments, criticisms, or digressions. The discussions would then take on an independent status: "questions about the *Physics,*" "questions about the *De anima,*" and so on. These would normally represent the most marked transition from the exposition of Aristotle's views—however critically they might be treated—to the original presentation of problems arising from this or that passage. Very often such *quaestiones* would not have more than an occasional, accidental connection with Aristotle: the titles of Aristotle's works would become like the headings of one or another of the main branches of philosophy, of the encyclopedia of knowledge, or of sciences. This soon led to the abandonment of the pretense of a connection with the "Philosopher's" works and doctrines or, in many cases, to the pretense of abandoning him and being original while remaining, in fact, under the strongest influence of what he had said.

Systematic works covering a wide province of philosophy, or even aiming at an exhaustive treatment of all its provinces, could take the form of a series of expositions or commentaries on the works of Aristotle, or organize the accumulated intellectual experience of the past and the original views of the author with great independence at many stages, but with explicit or implicit reference to Aristotle's corpus as it had been shaped into a whole—to a small extent by him and to a larger extent by his later followers.

Much of the philosophical literature from the first to the sixteenth centuries could be classified under headings corresponding to the ways in which Aristotle was explained, discussed, taken as a starting point for discussions, used as a model for great systematizations containing all kinds of details, or abandoned—either with or without criticism. In the Greek-speaking world, the vast commentaries by Alexander of Aphrodisias (third century) on the *Metaphysics,* the *Analytics, Topics,* and *Meteorologics;* those by Simplicius (sixth century) on the *Categories,* the *De caelo,* and the *Physics;* and those by John Philoponus (the Grammarian) on the *De anima* were among the most prominent examples of the developed, systematic, and critical commentaries of Aristotle's texts. They were matched in the Latin world of the sixth century by Boethius' commentaries on the *Categories* and *De interpretatione,* in the Arab world of the twelfth century by the "great" commentaries of Averroës, and in the Latin world of the twelfth and thirteenth centuries by those of Abailard, Robert Grosseteste, Aquinas, Giles of Rome, and many others. Themistius' paraphrases (fourth century) of the logical works and of the *De anima,* partly imitated or translated into Latin in his own time, had their counterparts in works by Syriac-, Armenian-, and Arabic-writing philosophers: al-Kindī in the ninth century, the Turk al-Fārābī in the tenth, the Persian Ibn Sīnā (Avicenna) in the eleventh, and Averroës in the

twelfth contributed in this way much-needed information on Aristotle to those who would not read his works, but would like to learn something of his doctrines through simplified Arabic texts. *Summae* or *summulae* of the *Elenchi,* of the *Physics,* and of other works appeared in Latin in the twelfth and thirteenth centuries, under such names as that of Grosseteste, or have remained anonymous. The collections of scholia of Greek manuscripts were continued by such genres as *glossae* and *notulae:* such collections on the *Categories,* written in the ninth century, and on the *Posterior Analytics,* the *De anima,* and the *Meteorologics,* written between the end of the twelfth and the middle of the thirteenth centuries, became in many cases almost standard texts accompanying the "authoritative" but difficult texts of the great master. At the level of philosophical systems we find the great philosophical encyclopedia of Avicenna (eleventh century), organized on the basis of the Aristotelian corpus but enriched by the philosophical experience of Aristotelians, Platonists, and other thinkers of many centuries, and above all by the grand philosophical imagination and penetration of its author. On the other hand, in the Latin world Albertus Magnus (thirteenth century), a man of inexhaustible curiosity, and with a frantic passion for communicating as much as he knew or thought he knew as quickly as possible, followed up his discoveries in the books of others with his own cogitations and developments, and presented his encyclopedia of knowledge almost exclusively as an exposition-cum-commentary of the works by Aristotle or those ascribed to him. What he had learned from others—he was one of the most learned men of his times, and much of his reading derived from the Arabic—finds its place in this general plan.

Quaestiones (ζητήσεις) are found in the Greek philosophical literature, and one might be tempted to include in this class much of Plotinus' *Enneads.* But it is when impatience with systematic explanatory commentary (mildly or only occasionally critical) leads to independent treatment of problems that the *quaestio* comes into its own—first, perhaps, as in Abailard, in the course of the commentary itself; then, in the second half of the thirteenth and much more in the fourteenth and fifteenth centuries, independently of the commentaries. It is in many of these collections of *quaestiones* that we find the minds of philosophers, impregnated with Aristotelian concepts and methods, searching more deeply the validity of accepted statements, presenting new points of view, and inserting in the flow of speculation new discoveries, new deductions from known principles, and corrected inferences from ambiguous formulations.

Aristotle's Influence on the Development of Civilization. The influence exercised by Aristotle's writings varied from work to work and often varied for the several sections of one and the same work. It would be relatively easy to select those short writings which, in spite of their inferior and confused nature or their incompleteness—the *Categories* and the *De interpretatione* from the first century B.C. to the sixteenth, and the *Poetics* from the early sixteenth to the nineteenth—penetrated more deeply and widely into the minds of intelligent people than did the more extensive, organized, and imaginative works, such as *De animalibus, De anima,* and the *Physics.* Moreover, one could possibly select a limited number of passages that left their permanent mark because they were repeatedly quoted, learned by heart, and applied, rightly or wrongly, as proverbs, slogans, and acquired "truths" are applied. Most of all, it is possible, and essential for our purpose, to select those concepts that became common property of the civilized mind, however much they may have been elaborated and, in the course of time, transformed. And if these concepts are not all originally Aristotelian, if they have found their way into the several fields of culture in more than one (the Aristotelian) way, it is our contention that pressure of continuous study and repetition and use of those concepts in Aristotelian contexts, in the ways sketched above, are responsible more than anything else for their becoming so indispensable and fruitful.

It is enough to try to deprive our language of a certain number of words in order to see how much we might have to change the whole structure of our ways of thinking, of expressing, even of inquiring. A conceptual and historico-linguistic analysis of a definition like "mass is the quantity of matter" would show us that whatever was and is understood by these words owes much to the fact that the concepts of "quantity" and of "matter" were for two millennia inculcated into the minds of men and into their languages, more than in any other way, through the agency of Aristotle's *Categories, Physics,* and *Metaphysics.* If "energy" means something when we read it in the formula $e = mc^2$, we may forget that this "linguistic" tool is the creation of Aristotle and that it traveled through the ages with all its appendages of truths, half-truths, and hypotheses, which affected its meaning in different ways through the centuries, stimulating thoughts, experiments, and interpretations of facts, because some bits of the *Metaphysics* and of the *Physics* were the *sine qua non* condition of men's "knowledge" of the world. And if "potential" has assumed so many uses—from social and military

contexts to electricity, dynamics, and what not—is it not because we have been trained to handle this term as an indispensable instrument to describe an infinite variety of situations that have something in common, as Aristotle repeated *ad nauseam,* when making "potency" (δύναμις) one of the basic concepts for the understanding of the structure of the world? We have used, misused, abused, eliminated, and reinstated the concepts of "substance" and "essence." "Relation" and "analogy," "form," "cause," "alteration of qualities," and "development from potentiality to actuality" are all terms that have not yet stopped serving their purpose. A writer of a detailed history of science would be hard put if he tried to avoid having recourse to Aristotle for his understanding of how things progressed in connection with them. At the very root of much of our most treasured scientific development lies the quantification of qualities; this started in the form of a general problem set by the distinction between two out of the ten "Aristotelian categories" in conjunction with Aristotle's theory of the coming into being of new "substances." It may be contended that, by his very distinction, Aristotle created difficulties and slowed progress. Perhaps there is something in that complaint; nevertheless, in this way he stimulated the search for truth and for formulations of more satisfactory hypotheses to fit, as he would say, τὰ φαινόμενα—to fit what we see.

His exemplification of continuous and discontinuous quantities in the *Categories* may elicit an indulgent smile from those who lack any historical sense; and it would be impertinent to skip over twenty-two and a half centuries and say that here we are, faced by the same problems that worried Aristotle, but with more sophistication: continuous waves or discontinuous quanta? But how did it happen that the problems came to be seen in this way, with this kind of alternative? No doubt Aristotle was not the only ancient sage who taught the concept of continuity to the millennia to come, but no text in which the distinction—and the problems it brought with it—appeared was learned by heart, discussed and commented upon, or became the text for examinations and testing as often and as unavoidably as the *Categories.* Do things happen by chance, or through a chain of causality? Can we determine how and why this happens—is it "essential" that it should happen or is it "accidental"? Much scientific progress was achieved by testing and countertesting, under *these,* Aristotelian, headings, what the world presents to our perception and to our mind.

Again: classification, coordination, and subordination have been and are instruments of clear thinking, of productive procedures, of severe testing of results. The terms "species" and "genus" may be outmoded in some fields, but the fashion is recent; the words have changed, yet the concepts have remained. And with them we find, not even outmoded, "property" and "difference." We have been conditioned by these distinctions, by these terms, because we come from Aristotelian stock.

It is, in conclusion, significant of Aristotle's impact on the development of culture, and particularly of science, that among the more essential elements in our vocabulary there should be the following terms, coming directly from his Greek (transliterated in the Latin or later translations) or from the Latin versions, or from texts where some of these terms had to be changed in order to preserve some equivalence of meaning when they proved ambiguous: (*a*) *category* (*class, group,* etc.) and the names of the four categories actually discussed in the *Categoriae*—*substance* (*essence*), *quantity, quality, relation;* (*b*) *universal* and *individual,* and the *quinque voces* (another title for Porphyry's *Isagoge,* which developed a passage of Aristotle's *Topics* and was studied as the introduction to his logic)—*genus, species, difference, property, accident* (in the sense of accidental feature); (*c*) *cause* and the names or equivalents applied to the four causes until quite recent times—*efficient, final, material,* and *formal;* (*d*) couples of correlative terms, like *matter-form* (structure), *potency-act* (energy), *substance-accident.*

Terms like "induction" and "deduction," "definition" and "demonstration" have certainly become entrenched in our language from many sources apart from Aristotle's *Analytics.* But again, the extent of their use, the general understanding of their meaning and implications, and the application in all fields of science of the methods of research and exposition that those terms summarize depend possibly more on the persistent study of Aristotle than on any other single source. All the wild anti-Aristotelianism of the seventeenth century would have been more moderate if people had realized then, as it had been realized, for instance, in the thirteenth century, how aware Aristotle was that experience, direct perception and knowledge of individual facts, is the very basis of scientific knowledge. The anti-Aristotelians were much more Aristotelian than they thought in some aspects of their methods; and that was because they had, unconsciously, absorbed Aristotle's teaching, which had seeped through from the higher level of philosophical discussion to the common attitude of people looking for truth.

It has become a truism that observation of facts was recognized as the necessary beginning of science through a revolutionary attitude which had as its pioneers such people as Roger Bacon and Robert Grosseteste. One wonders whether many realize that —because he thought Aristotle to be very often right on important matters—Aquinas insisted that a problem which, for him and his contemporaries, was of the utmost importance—the problem of the existence of God—could be solved only by starting from the observation of facts around us. If, as it happened, Aquinas was going to carry the day with his very awkward "five ways," he was also going to boost very widely the value of the basic principle on which so much depended in the development of science: observe first, collect facts, and draw your conclusions after. And it is in the course of the discussion of the *Posterior Analytics* that probably one of the main steps forward in the methodology of science was made by Grosseteste around 1230: probably not so much—as has been maintained—in passing from "experience" to "experiment" as in the discrimination of the contributory factors of a certain effect, in the search for the really effective causes, as against the circumstantial, accidental state of affairs.

One further example of the permanence of Aristotle's teaching is provided by his insistence on the old saying that nature does nothing in vain. The development from this principle of the wrongly called "Ockham's razor" is the result of a series of refinements; it may be possible (or has it already been done?) to see through which steps this principle of finality and economy of nature has established itself in all but the most independent or anarchic scientific minds.

Above all, probably, Aristotle's explicitly stated methodical doubt as a condition for the discovery of truth and his exhaustive accumulation of "difficulties" (ἀπορίαι) have trained generation after generation in the art of testing statements, of analyzing formulations, of trying to avoid sophistry. The picture of an Aristotelianism confined to teaching how to pile up syllogisms that either beg the question or, at best, make explicit what is already implicit in the premises is very far from the Aristotelianism of Aristotle, and hides most of what Aristotle has meant for the history of culture and science. It is through observation, ἀπορίαι, reasoned and cautious argument, that he thought our statements should fit the phenomena (φαινόμενα): no wonder that Aquinas himself was not troubled by the possibility that geocentrism might prove to be less "valid" than heliocentrism.

It is much more difficult to discover, isolate, and follow up the influence of Aristotle's writings on the advancement of science considered in the several fields and, what counts more, in the solution of particular problems. It is also difficult to locate exactly in time and space the several steps by which methods of inquiry, learned directly or indirectly at the Aristotelian school, have been successfully applied as Aristotelian. Out of the vast amount of evidence existing, only a small fraction has been studied. Influences have hardly ever been the result of isolated texts or of individual authors; the accumulation of interpretations, refinements, new contributions, and variations in the presentation of problems has continued for centuries, and the more striking turning points are those at which the influence has been *a contrario*. Whether it is Simplicius (sixth century) commenting on the *De caelo*, and thus contributing to the methical transformation of the study of the heavens, or William Harvey (eleven centuries later) taking as one of his basic texts for the study of the mechanics of the living body the *De motu animalium*, there is no doubt that we can rightly speak of Aristotle's influence on the advancement of astronomy and of physiology. But determining the exact point at which that influence can be located, in what precise sense it can be interpreted, and in what measure it can be calculated would require much more than a series of textual references.

It might be suggested that one precise point in history at which Aristotle's deductive theory in the *Posterior Analytics* contributed to the mathematization of nonmathematical sciences can be found in Robert Grosseteste's commentary on that work (*ca.* 1230). Aristotle had considered optics as a science dependent on mathematics (geometry), and in his discussion of two types of demonstration, the *demonstratio quia* and the more penetrating and valuable *demonstratio propter quid,* he had used optical phenomena to exemplify the general rule that it is the higher-level science (in those particular cases, obviously, mathematics) that holds the key to the *demonstratio propter quid.* For Grosseteste the whole of nature was fundamentally light, manifesting itself in different states. It could be argued, therefore, that Grosseteste would have inferred that Aristotle's examples revealed, more than he imagined, the mathematical structure of all natural (and supernatural) sciences. One can go further and, magnifying Grosseteste's influence, state that quantification in natural sciences has its roots in the *Posterior Analytics* as interpreted by Grosseteste in the frame of his metaphysics of light. This is the kind of fallacy that results from not realizing how difficult it is to discover and assess Aristotelian influences. Nothing has so far been

shown—although much has been said—to prove that statement.

Among the few fields in which many necessary inquiries have been made (through commentaries to Aristotle, *quaestiones* arising from the *Physics,* and independent treatises with an Aristotelian background) to show how (by appropriate or forced interpretation, by intelligent criticism or the process of development) modern science has to some extent come out of the study of Aristotle are those of the theories of rectilinear movement (constant velocity and acceleration), of "essential" transformations consequent to quantitatively different degrees of qualities, and of the nature and basic qualities of matter in connection with gravity. The temptation must, of course, be resisted to see Aristotle's influence wherever some connection can be established, whether *prima facie* or after detailed consideration of chains of quotations, repetitions, and slight transformations. But the pioneering studies of Pierre Duhem, the detailed analyses and historical reconstructions by Anneliese Maier, Nardi, Weisheipl; the attempts at wider historical systematizations by Thorndike, Sarton, and Crombie; and the contributions by many scholars of the last thirty years confirm more and more the view that the debt of scientists to the Aristotelian tradition is far greater than is generally accepted.

Setbacks in the Aristotelian Tradition. The progress in the spread of Aristotelian studies had its obstacles and setbacks, at different times in different spheres and for a variety of reasons. These ranged from purely philosophical opposition to purely theological convictions and prejudices, and to the interference of political and political-ecclesiastical powers with the free flow of speculation and debate. The story of the setbacks could be considered as diverse and rich as that of the actual progress; we shall mention only some of the most famous, or notorious, examples.

In 529 Justinian ordered the closing down of all philosophical schools in Athens; such people as Simplicius and Damascius became political-philosophical refugees in the "unfaithful" Persian kingdom. Greek Aristotelian studies then had over two centuries of almost total eclipse.

A similar attack on philosophy, at a very "Aristotelian" stage, was carried out in 1195 by Caliph Ya'ūb al-Manṣūr in southern Spain; one of the exiled victims was the great Averroës, who had, among other things, strongly defended philosophy against the religious mystical onslaught by al-Ghazali, the author of the *Destruction of Philosophers.* Whatever the reasons for the centuries-long eclipse of

Arabic philosophy, the blow of 1195 was certainly one of the most effective contributions to it.

Much has been made by the historians of philosophy, and particularly of science, of the Roman Church's hostility to Aristotelianism, as made manifest by the decrees of 1210, 1215, and 1231—also confirmed later—"prohibiting" the study of Aristotle's works on natural philosophy and then of those on metaphysics. The prohibitions, confined first to Paris and then to a few other places, and soon limited in scope (the works in question were to be examined by a committee of specialists and, where necessary, revised), turned out to be probably one of the most important factors in the most powerful and permanent expansion of Aristotelian studies in the whole of history. Interest was intensified, obstacles were avoided or disregarded, and witch-hunting did not succeed in doing much more than alerting philosophers and scholars to the danger of expressing Aristotle's views as their own views, and of describing developments based on Aristotle's works as *the* truth rather than as logically compelling inferences from authoritative statements.

The real setbacks to the spread of Aristotelian studies—not necessarily of the kind of Aristotelian influence sketched above—came in the seventeenth and eighteenth centuries, when progress in scientific and historical knowledge; the interplay of the new interests with a sterilized, scholastic "Aristotelianism"; a passion for grand philosophical systems; refined, systematic criticism of current beliefs; and the impact of new theological disputes filled the minds of thoughtful people with problems that either were not present in Aristotle's works or had now to be expressed in a differently articulated language.

BIBLIOGRAPHY

I. ORIGINAL WORKS. This section will be limited to the more essential references. The others will be found in works cited below under "Secondary Literature."

The tradition of the Greek texts of Aristotle is documented mainly in their critical editions; for these see the article on his "Life and Works." For the medieval Latin tradition see, above all, the *Corpus philosophorum medii aevi, Aristoteles Latinus* (Bruges–Paris, 1952–   ), of which the following vols. have appeared: I.1–5, *Categoriae,* L. Minio-Paluello, ed. (1961); I.6–7, *Supplementa Categoriarum* (Porphyry's *Isagoge* and Pseudo-Gilbertus' *Liber sex principiorum*), L. Minio-Paluello, ed. (1966); II.1–2, *De interpretatione,* L. Minio-Paluello, ed. (1965); III.1–4, *Analytica priora,* L. Minio-Paluello, ed. (1962); IV.1–4, *Analytica posteriora,* L. Minio-Paluello and B. G. Dod, eds. (1968); VII.2, *Physica* I ("Physica Vaticana"), A. Mansion, ed. (1957); XI.1–2, *De mundo,* 2nd ed., W. L. Lorimer *et al.,* eds. (1965); XVII.2.v, *De generatione animalium,* trans. Guillelmi, H. J. Drossaart Lulofs, ed. (1966); XXIX.1, *Politica* I–II.11, 1st vers. by William of Moerbeke, P. Michaud-Quantin, ed. (1961); and XXXIII, *Poetica,* 2nd ed., trans. Guillelmi, with Hermann the German's version of Averroës' *Poetria,* L. Minio-Paluello, ed. (1968). V.1–3, *Topica,* L. Minio-Paluello, ed., is to appear in 1969. Older eds. of most of the translations or revisions of the thirteenth century appeared from 1475 on. Among other more recent eds., the following should be recorded: *Politics,* in F. Susemihl's ed. of Greek text (Leipzig, 1872); *Rhetoric,* in L. Spengel's ed. of Greek text (Leipzig, 1867); *Metaphysica media,* in *Alberti Magni Opera omnia,* XVI, B. Geyer, ed. (Münster, 1960–   ); *Metaphysica,* trans. Iacobi ("Metaphysica Vetustissima"), in *Opera . . . Rogeri Baconi,* XI, R. Steele, ed. (Oxford, 1932).

The best ed. of the Armenian texts of the *Categoriae, De interpretatione,* and *De mundo* was produced by F. C. Conybeare in *Anecdota Oxoniensia,* Classical Series I.vi (Oxford, 1892). George's Syriac version of *Categoriae, De interpretatione,* and *Prior Analytics* was edited by G. Furlani in *Memorie dell'Accademia . . . dei Lincei,* Classe scienze morali, VI.5,i and iii, and VI.6.iii (Rome, 1933–1937). Most of the surviving Arabic translations of the Middle Ages were first edited or reedited by Abdurrahman Badawi in the collection Studii Islamici (then Islamica) (Cairo 1948–   ): these include all the works of logic, the *Rhetoric, Poetics, De anima, De caelo,* and *Meteorologics.* Of other eds. the following should be mentioned: *Metaphysics* (missing parts of Bks. I and XII, and the whole of Bks. XI and XIII–XIV), M. Bouyges, ed. (Beirut, 1938–1952); and *Poetics,* J. Tkatsch, ed. (Vienna, 1928–1932).

The extant Greek commentaries were edited by H. Diels and his collaborators in *Commentaria in Aristotelem Graeca* (Berlin, 1882–   ); the medieval Latin trans. are being published in the *Corpus Latinum commentariorum in Aristotelem Graecorum* (Louvain, 1957–   ), thus far consisting of I. *Themistius on De anima,* II. *Ammonius on De interpretatione,* III. *Philoponus on De anima,* and IV. *Alexander on De sensu*—all ed. by G. Verbeke.

The one major commentary by Averroës that is preserved in Arabic, on the *Metaphysics,* was published with the Aristotelian text by Bouyges (see above). Many of the Latin medieval trans. of the longer and shorter commentaries by Averroës were printed several times in the fifteenth and sixteenth centuries (1st ed., Venice, 1483); new trans. from the Hebrew of some of the same commentaries and of others (most importantly, the long commentary on *Posterior Analytics*) were published in the sixteenth century (first comprehensive ed., Venice, 1551–1561). Critical eds. of the medieval Latin and Hebrew trans. of Averroës' commentaries are being published in the *Corpus philosophorum medii aevi, Corpus commentariorum Averrois in Aristotelem,* the most important of which is Michael

Scot's trans. of the long commentary on *De anima,* in Vol. VI.1, F. Stuart Crawford, ed. (Cambridge, Mass., 1953).

II. SECONDARY LITERATURE. A list of Greek MSS of Aristotle's works and of those of his commentators, based mainly on printed catalogs, was ed. by A. Wartelle, *Inventaire des manuscrits grecs d'Aristote et de ses commentateurs* (Paris, 1963), and supplemented by D. Harlfinger and J. Wiesner in *Scriptorium,* **18,** no. 2 (1964), 238–257. A descriptive catalog of all the known MSS of Aristotle's works is being prepared by P. Moraux and his collaborators of the Aristotelian Archive at the University of Berlin. The best sources for knowledge of the printed tradition are still the general catalogs of the British Museum and of the Prussian libraries; for recent times, see also the catalog of the U.S. Library of Congress.

Nearly all the available basic information for the Latin tradition in the Middle Ages is collected in the three vols. of G. Lacombe, E. Franceschini, L. Minio-Paluello, *et al., Aristoteles Latinus, Codices:* I., Rome, 1939; II., Cambridge, 1955; *Supplem. Alt.,* Bruges, 1961. The bibliography that is in these vols. includes all the works of importance on the subject. Additional information on individual works will be found in the intros. to the eds. of texts in the *Aristoteles Latinus* series. Special mention should be made of E. Franceschini, "Roberto Grossatesta, vescovo di Lincoln, e le sue traduzioni latine," in *Atti della Reale Istituto Veneto,* **93,** no. 2 (1933–1934), 1–138; G. Grabmann, *Guglielmo di Moerbeke, il traduttore delle opere di Aristotele* (Rome, 1946); J. M. Millás Vallicrosa, *Las traducciones orientales en los manuscritos de la Biblioteca Catedral de Toledo* (Madrid, 1942); L. Minio-Paluello, "Iacobus Veneticus Grecus, Canonist and Translator of Aristotle" in *Traditio,* **8** (1952), 265–304; "Note sull'Aristotele Latino medievale," in *Rivista di filosofia neo-scolastica,* **42** ff. (1950 ff.). For the printed eds. of medieval Latin trans., see the *Gesamtkatalog der Wiegendrucke* and the library catalogs cited above.

For the humanistic and Renaissance trans. into Latin, see E. Garin, *Le traduzioni umanistiche di Aristotele nel secolo XV,* Vol. VIII in Accademia Fiorentina La Colombaria (Florence, 1951), and the *Gesamtkatalog* and the library catalogs.

For the study of Aristotle in the Middle Ages, M. Grabmann's *Mittelalterliches Geistesleben,* 3 vols. (Munich, 1926–1956), and his earlier *Geschichte der scholastischen Methode* (Freiburg im Breisgau, 1909–1911) are of fundamental importance. Among the many works of a more limited scope, see F. Van Steenberghen, *Siger de Brabant d'après ses oeuvres inédites, II: Siger dans l'histoire de l'Aristotélisme,* Vol. XII of Les Philosophes Belges (Louvain, 1942).

For the Armenian tradition, see Conybeare's ed. mentioned above; the catalogs of the more important collections of Armenian MSS (Vatican Library, British Museum, Bodleian Library, Bibliothèque Nationale); and G. W. Abgarian, *The Matenadaran* (Yerevan, 1962).

For the Syriac tradition, see A. Baumstark, *Geschichte der syrischen Literatur* (Bonn, 1922); and many articles by G. Furlani, listed in the bibliog. of his writings in *Rivista degli studi orientali,* **32** (1957).

For the Arabic tradition, see C. Brockelmann, *Geschichte der arabischen Literatur,* 2nd ed., 2 vols. (Leiden, 1943–1949) and 3 vols. of supps. (Leiden, 1937–1942); R. Walzer, "Arisṭūṭālīs," in *Encyclopaedia of Islam,* 2nd ed., I, 630–635; Abdurrahman Badawi, *Aristu ʿinda l-ʿArab* (Cairo, 1947); M. Steinschneider, "Die arabischen Uebersetzungen aus dem Griechischen," in *Zentralblatt für Bibliothekswesen,* **8** (1889) and **12** (1893), and "Die europäischen Uebersetzungen aus dem Arabischen bis Mitte des 17 Jahrhunderts," in *Sitzungsberichte der Kaiserliche Akademie der Wissenschaften,* philos.-hist. Klasse, **149,** no. 4, and **151,** no. 1.

For the Hebrew tradition, see M. Steinschneider, *Die hebräischen Uebersetzungen des Mittelalters und die Juden als Dolmetscher* (Berlin, 1893); and H. A. Wolfson, "Plan for the Publication of a *Corpus commentariorum Averrois in Aristotelem,*" in *Speculum* (1931), 412–427.

No comprehensive study of Aristotle's influence through the ages has ever been published. The standard histories of philosophy and science, general or specialized, contain much useful information, including bibliographies, e.g.: F. Ueberweg, *Geschichte der Philosophie,* 5 vols., 11th–13th eds. (Berlin, 1924–1928); E. Zeller, *Die Philosophie der Griechen,* 4th–7th eds. (1882–1920); I. Husik, *A History of Medieval Jewish Philosophy* (Philadelphia, 1916; 6th ed., 1946); G. Sarton, *Introduction to the History of Science,* 3 vols. (Baltimore, 1927–1948); Lynn Thorndike, *A History of Magic and Experimental Science,* 8 vols. (New York, 1923–1958); C. Singer, *Studies in the History and Method of Science* (Oxford, 1921); and A. C. Crombie, *Augustine to Galileo* (London, 1952).

Special problems, periods, or fields have been surveyed and analyzed in, e.g., P. Duhem, *Le système du monde,* 8 vols. (Paris, 1913–1916, 1954–1958), and *Études sur Léonard de Vinci* (Paris, 1906–1913); A. Maier, *Metaphysische Hintergründe der spätscholastischen Naturphilosophie* (Rome, 1951), *Zwei Grundprobleme der scholastischen Naturphilosophie,* 2nd ed. (Rome, 1951), *An der Grenze von Scholastik und Naturwissenschaft,* 2nd ed. (Rome, 1952), and *Zwischen Philosophie und Mechanik* (Rome, 1958); A. C. Crombie, *Robert Grosseteste and the Origins of Experimental Science* (Oxford, 1953); M. Clagett, *The Science of Mechanics in the Middle Ages* (Madison, Wis., 1959); and R. Lemay, *Abu Maʿshar and Latin Aristotelianism in the Twelfth Century* (Beirut, 1962).

L. MINIO-PALUELLO

ARISTOXENUS (*b.* Tarentum, *ca.* 375–360 B.C.; *d.* Athens [?]), *harmonic theory.*

Aristoxenus was a native of Tarentum, a Greek city in southern Italy. He flourished in the time of Alexander the Great (reigned 336–323), and can hardly have been born later than 360. His father's name was either Mnaseas or Spintharus; the latter was certainly his teacher, a musician whose wide acquaintance included Socrates, Epaminondas, and Archytas. Aristoxenus studied at Mantinea, an Arcadian city that had a strong conservative musical tradition, and later became a pupil of Aristotle in Athens. His position in the Lyceum was such that he hoped to become head of the school upon the death of Aristotle (322 B.C.); he is said to have vented his disappointment in malicious stories about his master. The date of his death is unknown, but the attribution to him of 453 published works (even if many were spurious) suggests a long life.

Of this vast production little has survived except for three books that have come down under the title *Harmonic Elements.* Modern scholars are agreed, however, that these represent two or more separate treatises. There is a substantial fragment of the second book of *Rhythmical Elements.* Aristoxenus' numerous other writings on music are all lost, except for quotations, but much of our scattered information on early Greek musical history must derive from him. He also wrote biographies (he was one of those who established this kind of writing as a tradition of the Peripatetic school); treatises on educational and political theory and on Pythagorean doctrine; miscellanies; and memoranda of various kinds.

It is proper, if paradoxical, that Aristoxenus should be included in a dictionary of scientific biography. It is proper because music under the form of "harmonics" or the theory of scales was an important branch of ancient science from the time of Plato onward, and because Aristoxenus was the most famous and influential musical theorist of antiquity. It is paradoxical because he turned his back upon the mathematical knowledge of his time to adopt and propagate a radically "unscientific" approach to the measurement of musical intervals.

When the Pythagorean oligarchs were expelled from Tarentum, Archytas, the celebrated mathematician and friend of Plato, remained in control of the new democracy and may still have been alive when Aristoxenus was born. From Archytas' pupils in Tarentum—or from the exiled Xenophilus in Athens—Aristoxenus must have become familiar with Pythagorean doctrine. The Pythagoreans recognized that musical intervals could be properly measured and expressed only as ratios (of string lengths or pipe lengths). Pythagoras himself is said to have discovered the ratios of the octave, fifth, and fourth; and the determination of the tone as difference between fifth and fourth must soon have followed. In each case the ratio is superparticular and incapable, without the aid of logarithms, of exact division in mathematical terms. Thus, "semitone" (Greek, *hemitonion*) is a

misnomer; when two tones were subtracted from the fourth, the Pythagoreans preferred to call the resulting interval "remainder" (*leimma*). The Pythagorean diatonic scale, consisting of tones (9:8) and *leimmata* (256:243), was known to Plato. Archytas worked out mathematical formulations for the diatonic, chromatic, and enharmonic scales upon a different basis.

Aristoxenus, however, turned his back upon the mathematical approach and stated that the ear was the sole criterion of musical phenomena. To the ear, he held, the tone was divisible into halves (and other fractions); the octave consisted of six tones, the fifth of three tones and a half, the fourth of two tones and a half, and so on. His conception of pitch was essentially linear; the gamut was a continuous line that could be divided into any required fractions, and these could be combined by simple arithmetic. It was for the cultivated ear to decide which intervals were "melodic," i.e., capable of taking their places in the system of scales.

The division of the octave into six equal tones and of the tone into two equal semitones recalls the modern system of "equal temperament," and it is held by some authorities that Aristoxenus envisaged such a system or sought to impose it upon the practice of music. If that were so, he might well have rejected a mathematics that was still incapable of expressing it. Equal temperament, however, was devised in modern times to solve a specific problem: how to tune keyboard instruments in such a way as to facilitate modulation between keys. No comparable problem presented itself to Greek musicians: although modulation was exploited to some extent by virtuosi of the late fifth century B.C. and after, there is no reason to suppose that it created a need for a radical reorganization of the system of intervals or that such could have been imposed upon the lyre players and pipe players of the time. Furthermore, such a "temperament" would distort all the intervals of the scale (except the octave) and, significantly, the fifths and fourths; but Aristoxenus always speaks as though his fifths and fourths were the true intervals naturally grasped by the ear and his tone the true difference between them. It seems more likely, then, that he took up a dogmatic position and turned a blind eye to facts that were inconsistent with it; this would be in keeping with the rather truculent tone he sometimes adopted.

Writers on harmonics, from Aristoxenus on, fall into two schools: his followers, who reproduced and simplified his doctrines in a number of extant handbooks, and the "Pythagoreans" such as Eratosthenes, Didymus the musician, and—notably—Ptolemy, who elaborated ratios for the intervals of the scale. It is perhaps doubtful whether any writer of the mathematical school prior to Ptolemy produced a comprehensive theory of scales in relation to practical music, and it may well have been the inadequacy and limited interests of the Pythagoreans that set Aristoxenus against this approach. Nor would it be fair to deny Aristoxenus' scientific merits because of his disregard of mathematics. He was not in vain a pupil of Aristotle, from whom he had learned inductive logic and the importance of clear definition; and what he attempted was, in the words of M. I. Henderson, "a descriptive anatomy of music." His arguments are closely reasoned, but, lacking his master's breadth and receptivity, he can be suspected of sacrificing musical realities to logical clarity.

The details of his system, which can be found in standard textbooks and musical encyclopedias, are not in themselves of primary interest to the historian of science. The quality of his thinking at its best can, however, be illustrated from his work on rhythm. Earlier writers had tended to discuss rhythm in terms of poetic meters, but, since rhythm also manifests itself in melody and in the dance, there was some confusion of thought and terminology. Aristoxenus drew a clear distinction between rhythm, which was an organized system of time units expressible in ratios, and the words, melodies, and bodily movements in which it was incorporated (*ta rhythmizomena*) and from which it could be abstracted. This was a much-needed piece of clarification worthy of Aristotle.

BIBLIOGRAPHY

I. ORIGINAL WORKS. Modern editions of Aristoxenus' works are *The Harmonics of Aristoxenus,* edited, with translation, notes, introduction, and index of words, by H. S. Macran (Oxford, 1902); and *Aristoxeni elementa harmonica,* Rosetta da Rios, ed. (Rome, 1954).

II. SECONDARY LITERATURE. Works dealing with Aristoxenus include Ingemar Düring, *Ptolemaios und Porphyrios über die Musik* (Göteborg, 1934), which contains, in German translation, Ptolemy's criticisms of Aristoxenus; C. von Jan, "Aristoxenos," in Pauly-Wissowa, *Real-Encyclopädie,* II (Stuttgart, 1895), 1057 ff.; L. Laloy, *Aristoxène de Tarente* (Paris, 1904), an outstanding work; F. Wehrli, *Die Schule des Aristoteles, Texte und Kommentar,* Vol. II, *Aristoxenos* (Basel, 1945), for the shorter fragments; and R. Westphal, *Aristoxenos von Tarent* (Leipzig, 1883–1893), which includes the fragment on rhythm.

R. P. WINNINGTON-INGRAM

ARISTYLLUS (*fl. ca.* 270 B.C.), *astronomy.*

We may infer when Aristyllus flourished from the information provided by Ptolemy and from the date of Hipparchus' observations.

He is mentioned by Plutarch in *De Pythiae oraculis* (402 F)—with Aristarchus, Timocharis, and Hipparchus—as an astronomer who wrote in prose. His name also occurs in two catalogs of commentators on Aratus; although two persons named Aristyllus are mentioned, the reference may be to one and the same person, as Maass maintains. Aristyllus' name also occurs in a catalog of astronomers who wrote about "the pole," i.e., about the polar stars. More important is the information we find in Ptolemy's *Syntaxis mathematica.* He mentions Aristyllus and Timocharis as two astronomers whose observations of the fixed stars (declinations and differences of longitude) were used by Hipparchus. The latter, partly because of the differences between his own observations and those made a hundred years earlier by Aristyllus and Timocharis, discovered the precession of the equinoxes and calculated the amount of retrogression of the equinoctial points. According to Ptolemy, the observations of Aristyllus were not very accurate.

BIBLIOGRAPHY

Aristyllus' observations are recorded in Ptolemy, *Syntaxis mathematica,* Heiberg ed., VII, 1 and 3. See also "Aristyllos," in Pauly-Wissowa, *Real-Encyclopädie der Altertumswissenschaft,* II, 1 (Stuttgart, 1895), cols. 1065–1066; and E. Maass, *Aratea* (Berlin, 1892), pp. 121, 123, 151.

L. TARÁN

ARKADIEV, VLADIMIR KONSTANTINOVICH (*b.* Moscow, Russia, 21 April 1884; *d.* Moscow, U.S.S.R., 1 December 1953), *physics.*

Arkadiev's father died when the boy was young, leaving him to be raised by his mother, who worked in a library. These circumstances disposed him to study from his earliest years. While still at the Gymnasium he became interested in physics; he met N. A. Umov—who at that time was a professor at Moscow University—and even tested his own apparatus in Umov's laboratory. Upon graduating from the Gymnasium in 1904, Arkadiev entered the Physics and Mathematics Faculty of Moscow University, where Umov and P. N. Lebedev lectured. In 1907, under Lebedev's direction, Arkadiev began an experimental study of the magnetic properties of ferromagnetic substances in high-frequency fields of which the wavelength was on the order of one centimeter. In 1908 he obtained new results—ferromagnetic properties of iron and nickel disappeared when the wavelength was on the order of three centimeters—a discovery for which Arkadiev was awarded the Society of Lovers of Natural Science Prize in 1908.

Arkadiev's work at Moscow University was interrupted in 1911 when many progressive professors and lecturers—including Lebedev, Umov, and Arkadiev himself—left the university to protest the arbitrariness of the administration of L. A. Kasso, the czarist minister of national education. Lebedev and his colleagues transferred to Shanyavsky Municipal University, which was privately run. After the October Revolution, Arkadiev returned to Moscow University, where he organized a large laboratory for electromagnetic research that he headed until his death. In 1927 he was chosen an associate member of the Academy of Sciences of the U.S.S.R.

The basic direction of Arkadiev's research was the development of his previous work on ferromagnetism. He was the first to determine experimentally the exact relationship between wavelength and the complex magnetic permeability of iron and nickel (1912). On the basis of his results, Arkadiev arrived at two important conclusions. First, he suggested that the magnetic parameters of a substance depend on the frequency of the field. Second, he proposed the introduction of an additional parameter—"permeance"—to calculate the influence of the lag between changes of magnetic induction and changes in the field, in connection with the field loss of energy during remagnetization. Thus he gave symmetric form to Maxwell's equations:

$$\nabla x\ H = \frac{\varepsilon}{c}\frac{\delta E}{\delta t} + 4\pi\delta E$$

$$-\nabla x\ E = \frac{\mu}{c}\frac{\delta H}{\delta t} + 4\pi\rho H.$$

Into this Arkadiev introduced the concept of complex magnetic permeability $\mu = \mu' - i\mu''$, where $\mu = 2\rho T$ (T is the period of the wave), by analogy to the concept of the complex dielectric constant, $\varepsilon = \varepsilon' - i\varepsilon''$, $\varepsilon = 2\delta T$.

In 1913, starting from the classic conceptions, Arkadiev was the first to indicate the possibility that natural oscillations of elementary magnets exist in ferromagnetic substances, resulting in the appearance of resonance; he confirmed this experimentally. Thus the honor of the discovery of ferromagnetic resonance (1913) belongs to him.

In 1922 Arkadiev proposed a generator of original construction that enabled A. A. Glagoleva-Arkadieva (his wife) to obtain the first electromagnetic spectra in the wavelength range of a few centimeters to 0.080 millimeters.

In 1934 Arkadiev developed a photographic plate sensitive to centimeter-length waves. Between 1934 and 1936 he thoroughly developed the theory of the behavior of ferromagnetic conductors in rapidly changing fields. In this work he introduced the concept of "magnetic viscosity," which proved to be exceedingly fruitful. He named the realm of these phenomena "magnetodynamics." In addition, he developed the theory of the magnetization and demagnetization of bodies with various shapes.

Among Arkadiev's other work was his 1913 study in which it was first proved that the diffraction of light can be observed on large objects as well as on small ones. He also was the first to construct a high-tension impulse generator, subsequently called a lightning generator (1925). Finally, in 1947 Arkadiev was the first to perfect a refined demonstration experiment—the levitation of a small permanent magnet above a superconducting dish.

BIBLIOGRAPHY

Arkadiev's writings are in his *Izbrannye trudy* ("Selected Works"; Moscow, 1961).

Articles on Arkadiev are N. N. Malov, "Vladimir Konstantinovitch Arkad'ev," in *Uspekhi fizicheskikh nauk* ("Successes of the Physical Sciences"), **52**, no. 3 (1954), 459–469; E. I. Miklashevskaja, "Kratkij ocherk nauchnoj i pedagogicheskoj dejatel'nosti V. K. Arkad'ev" ("Short Essay on the Scientific and Pedagogical Career of V. K. Arkadiev"), in *Izbrannye trudy,* pp. 11–16; and B. A. Vvedensky and N. N. Malov, "O nauchnom znachenii rabot V. K. Arkad'eva" ("On the Scientific Significance of V. K. Arkadiev's Work"), *ibid.,* pp. 5–10.

J. G. DORFMAN

ARKELL, WILLIAM JOSCELYN (*b.* Highworth, Wiltshire, England, 9 June 1904; *d.* Cambridge, England, 18 April 1958), *geology, paleontology.*

Arkell was the youngest of seven children of James Arkell, a partner in the family brewery at Kingsdown, Wiltshire, and of Laura Jane Rixon, daughter of a London solicitor. He married Ruby Lilian Percival of Boscombe, Hampshire, in 1929; they had three sons.

After a boarding-school education, he entered New College, Oxford, in 1922. He graduated in geology three years later and was awarded the Burdett-Coutts research scholarship. After appointment as a lecturer at New College in 1929, he was elected a senior research fellow of the college from 1933 to 1940.

Arkell became a principal in the Ministry of War Transport in 1941. In 1943 he contracted a serious chest illness, and for several years was unable to undertake strenuous activity. In 1947 he was elected a fellow of the Royal Society of London and became a senior research fellow at Trinity College, Cambridge. With improved health he was once more able to travel abroad, and his studies on the Jurassic ammonites and stratigraphy were intensified. In August 1956, Arkell suffered a stroke that left him severely paralyzed. Thereafter he was confined to his house, although he eventually managed, with the cooperation of Cambridge friends, to resume his writing.

Arkell received the Mary Clark Thompson Gold Medal of the National Academy of Sciences, Washington, in 1944; the Lyell Medal of the Geological Society of London in 1949; and the von Buch Medal of the German Geological Society in 1953. He was an honorary member or correspondent of the Linnean Society of Normandy; the Geological Societies of France, Germany, and Egypt; and the Paleontological Society of America.

Arkell's first research culminated in the publication of two works: "The Corallian Rocks of Oxford, Berkshire, and North Wiltshire" (1927) and "A Monograph of British Corallian Lamellibranchia." He had spent his youth among these rocks and so had come to know them well, but he also felt that these strata merited attention because in England they had been neglected, in comparison with the Middle and Lower Jurassic, where other workers had long been active. During the following years he extended his studies to other parts of the Jurassic, in "The Stratigraphical Distribution of the Cornbrash" (1928, 1932), and to the Continent, in "A Comparison Between the Jurassic Rocks of the Calvados Coast and Those of Southern England" (1930). Field study and museum visits in Europe greatly increased his knowledge of Jurassic rocks and their fossil fauna.

Early in his career Arkell conceived the plan of revising Albert Oppel's *Die Juraformation Englands, Frankreichs und des sudwestlichen Deutschlands* (1856–1858) and of extending its coverage throughout Europe and the rest of the world. Seen in this perspective, Arkell's book *The Jurassic System in Great Britain* (1933) was the first stage of a larger program. This work, published before he was thirty, is arranged in chapters under the traditional formation names. Arkell stated his difficulties in translating these "haphazard terms" into the systematized stage names that had evolved in Europe, and concluded that the problems involved in extended correlation were beyond solution by any one man.

Nevertheless, Arkell included a searching analysis of the means whereby the Jurassic rocks might be more precisely dated and correlated over wider areas. In particular he discussed the contribution of Alcide

d'Orbigny, whose concept of "stages"—a systematic classification based on a combination of paleontology and stratigraphy—Arkell later revived in Great Britain as the basis of Jurassic classification. He then dealt with Oppel's ideas aimed at providing a more detailed biostratigraphical time scale, with units that could be recognized independently of local lithological considerations. These "zones" were documented by guide fossils, which were characteristic of the beds they defined, and they enabled correlation planes to be established over considerable distances.

In the years following, Arkell made numerous contributions to the corpus of knowledge of Jurassic stratigraphy, and by detailed classification of the ammonites of the Middle and Upper Jurassic he gradually stabilized many stratigraphically significant zonal assemblages that had been in doubt or little known. Over a period of twenty years the Palaeontographical Society published his monographs on the Corallian (Upper Oxfordian) and Bathonian ammonites. In 1946 Arkell published a paper, "Standard of the European Jurassic," advocating a commission to formulate a code of rules for stratigraphical nomenclature analogous to that which had brought order into zoological terminology.

He himself put forward a draft code and showed how it could be applied to the European, including central Russian, Jurassic. Stages and zones were precisely defined, the latter being characterized by particular ammonite assemblages. Arkell further asserted that since the limits of usefulness of species are circumscribed by the ascertained facts of their distribution, there must be separate zonal tables for each faunal province. His proposals were widely accepted as a suitable framework and were applied by investigators into Jurassic stratigraphy in many countries.

In 1956 Arkell published *Jurassic Geology of the World*, designed as a guide to the Jurassic of particular areas and to each individual stage over the whole world. In it he brought together and reviewed critically the information dispersed throughout the enormous literature on the world's Jurassic stratigraphy; for the first time, a comprehensive picture began to emerge, forming the framework for further elaboration. By way of introduction, he set down his final judgment on the principles of stratigraphical classification, especially on the basic notion of the zone. Arkell used the concept of a zone as being any bed, stratum, or formation deposited in any part of the world that could be recognized to be of a particular age on the strength of the fossils it contained. For the Jurassic, the ammonites are most frequently used as the significant fauna. He also denied any necessity to construct a parallel terminology to express the time units to which the zones would correspond.

Whatever modifications may subsequently have emerged from theoretical or philosophical refinement of this definition of zone as a unit measure of strata defined by the special fauna as the time factor, and of stage as the grouping of zones capable of recognition over wide areas, Arkell's synthesis in *Jurassic Geology of the World* must stand as a unique contribution. By this work he brought about a vigorous revival of interest in the principles of stratigraphical classification, which has led to numerous proposals for a basic set of rules applicable to all geological systems and periods. In 1957 Arkell contributed the section on the Jurassic Ammonoidea to the *Treatise on Invertebrate Paleontology;* this section is to a large extent complementary to his *Jurassic Geology* and is in itself a major contribution to paleontology.

Other interests included the elucidation of structural and tectonic problems within the Jurassic. In 1936 Arkell published "Analysis of the Mesozoic and Cainozoic Folding in England," which was an important assessment of knowledge in this field. From 1926 to 1929, he and K. S. Sandford investigated the Pliocene and Pleistocene deposits of the Nile Valley and Red Sea coast of Egypt. The work was organized by the Oriental Institute of the University of Chicago, and four monographs were published under Sandford and Arkell's joint authorship.

BIBLIOGRAPHY

I. ORIGINAL WORKS. A complete list of Arkell's publications, amounting to more than 200 items, together with a memoir of his life and a portrait, is given in *Biographical Memoirs of Fellows of the Royal Society,* **4** (1958), 1–14. Details of those mentioned in the text are "The Corallian Rocks of Oxford, Berkshire, and North Wiltshire," in *Philosophical Transactions of the Royal Society,* **B216** (1927), 67–181; "A Monograph of British Corallian Lamellibranchia," in *Palaeontographical Society Monographs* (1929–1937); "A Comparison Between the Jurassic Rocks of the Calvados Coast and Those of Southern England," in *Proceedings of the Geologists' Association* (London), **41** (1930), 396–411; *The Jurassic System in Great Britain* (Oxford, 1933); "A Monograph on the Ammonites of the English Corallian Beds," in *Palaeontographical Society Monographs* (London, 1935–1948); "Analysis of the Mesozoic and Cainozoic Folding in England," in *Report of the 16th International Geological Congress,* **2** (Washington, D.C., 1936), 937–952; "Standard of the European Jurassic," in *Bulletin of the Geological Society of America,* **57** (1946), 1–34; "A Monograph of the English Bathonian Ammonites," in *Palaeontographical Society Monographs* (London,

1951–1958); and *Jurassic Geology of the World* (Edinburgh–London, 1956).

Works written with collaborators include the following: with J. A. Douglas, "The Stratigraphical Distribution of the Cornbrash. I. The South-western Area," in *Quarterly Journal of the Geological Society of London,* **84** (1928), 117–178; with K. S. Sandford: "Palaeolithic Man and the Nile-Faiyum Divide," in *Oriental Institute Publications* (Chicago), **10** (1929); "Palaeolithic Man and the Nile Valley in Nubia and Upper Egypt," *ibid.,* **17** (1933); "Paleolithic Man and the Nile Valley in Upper and Middle Egypt," *ibid.,* **18** (1934); "Paleolithic Man and the Nile Valley in Lower Egypt, With Some Notes Upon a Part of the Red Sea Littoral," *ibid.,* **46** (1939).

Arkell's library and manuscripts are deposited in the University Museum, Oxford, and his fossil collections are divided between Oxford and the Sedgwick Museum, Cambridge.

II. SECONDARY LITERATURE. See Alcide d'Orbigny, *Paléontologie française. Terrains jurassiques* (1842–1849); and Albert Oppel, *Die Juraformation Englands, Frankreichs und des sudwestlichen Deutschlands* (1856–1858).

J. M. EDMONDS

ARMSTRONG, EDWARD FRANKLAND (*b.* London, England, 5 September 1878; *d.* London, 14 December 1945), *chemistry.*

The eldest son of Henry Edward Armstrong, a fellow of the Royal Society, Edward went to Germany in 1898 for training in organic chemistry with Claisen and in physical chemistry with van't Hoff at the University of Berlin, where he received the Ph.D. in 1901. He conducted research with Emil Fischer, work that aroused his lifelong interest in carbohydrates. He returned to London to continue work on disaccharides, glucosides, and enzymes at Central Technical College, for which he received the first D.Sc. by research of the University of London.

In 1905 Armstrong entered the chemical industry but continued with his research; his monograph on carbohydrates—one of the first—appeared in 1910. He was intimately involved in the negotiations that resulted in the formation of Imperial Chemical Industries, Ltd., one of the largest industrial concerns in Great Britain. During World War I, he and associates solved a problem of great wartime importance—the large-scale catalytic production of acetic acid and acetone from ethyl alcohol. This was an important application of his extensive research on heterogeneous catalysis. During World War II, Armstrong served as scientific adviser to several important governmental agencies. At his untimely death he was a principal adviser to the British delegates and a delegate to the founding conference of UNESCO. He was instrumental in ensuring the inclusion of science in the programs of this organization.

From 1928 Armstrong was a consultant to the chemical industry. He was elected a fellow of the Royal Society of London and was active in its affairs.

BIBLIOGRAPHY

Among Armstrong's writings are *The Simple Carbohydrates and Glucosides* (London, 1910; 1912; 1919; 1924; 1935); a series of 13 papers, "Catalytic Actions at Solid Surfaces," in *Proceedings of the Royal Society* (1920–1925); a paper on heterogeneous catalysis, in *Proceedings of the Royal Society*, **97A** (1920), 259–264; *Chemistry in the 20th Century* (London, 1924); *The Glycosides* (London, 1931), written with his son Kenneth; "The Chemistry of the Carbohydrates and the Glycosides," in *Annual Review of Biochemistry*, **7** (1938), 51; and *Raw Materials From the Sea* (Leicester, 1944), written with W. MacKenzie Miall.

A discussion of Armstrong's career and of the significance of his research and of his lifework in industry and public service is in C. S. Gibson and T. P. Hildreth, "Edward Frankland Armstrong," in *Obituary Notices of Fellows of the Royal Society*, **5** (1948), 619. This includes references to nearly 100 publications.

CONRAD E. RONNEBERG

ARMSTRONG, EDWIN HOWARD (*b.* New York, N.Y., 18 December 1890; *d.* New York, 1 February 1954), *radio engineering.*

Armstrong's father, John Armstrong, was a publisher who became vice-president in charge of the American branch of Oxford University Press; his mother, Emily Smith, graduated from Hunter College and taught for ten years in New York public schools before her marriage in 1888. When Armstrong was twelve, the family moved to Yonkers, New York, where he attended high school and became interested in radiotelegraphy. He entered Columbia University at nineteen and studied electrical engineering under Michael Idvorsky Pupin, the inventor of the Pupin loading coil used in long-distance telegraphy and telephony, graduating in 1913.

While still an undergraduate, Armstrong made the first of his many inventions, one of four that proved to be particularly significant: the triode feedback (regenerative) circuit. That invention, and the negative-bias grid circuit invented by Frederick Löwenstein, ultimately led to wide utilization of the as yet little-exploited triode (invented in 1906 by Lee De Forest), but Armstrong became embroiled in patent litigation and received only modest royalties.

In 1917, after serving as an assistant at Columbia for some years, Armstrong became a U.S. Army

Signal Corps officer when the United States entered World War I. He was sent to France and while there developed his second important invention, the super-heterodyne circuit, an improvement on the heterodyne circuit that was invented in 1905 by Reginald Aubrey Fessenden. In the heterodyne circuit, the received signal is mixed with a locally generated signal to produce an audible "beat" note at a frequency equal to the difference between those of the two signals; Armstrong's method, which greatly improved the sensitivity and stability of radio receivers, extended the technique to much higher frequencies and shifted the beat note above the audible range.

Upon returning to America, Armstrong was once again beset by patent interference proceedings, although his personal fortunes took a turn for the better: he sold his feedback and superheterodyne patents to Westinghouse Electric & Manufacturing Company (retaining royalty-earning licensing rights for the use of amateurs); he resumed his position at Columbia University; and he married Marion Mac-Innis, secretary to David Sarnoff, then general manager of the Radio Corporation of America.

In 1921 Armstrong made his third important discovery, superregeneration—a method of overcoming the regenerative receiver's principal limitation, the tendency to burst into oscillations just as the point of maximum amplification was reached. RCA purchased the patent, but it did not yield the company much in royalties, since it was unsuited for broadcast receivers; it did not come into its own until special applications were developed many years later. However, RCA profited greatly from the "superhet," to which it had acquired the rights through a cross license with Westinghouse. Armstrong found himself a millionaire.

The next decade of his life was marred by the long battle with De Forest over the feedback patents. The case was taken to the U.S. Supreme Court but Armstrong lost on a legal technicality. Before that decision had been handed down, however, Armstrong had completed and patented his greatest invention, frequency modulation (FM). Once again he was beset by difficulties: the U.S. radio industry resisted the introduction of FM broadcasting, FM production was interrupted when the United States entered World War II, and the Federal Communications Commission dealt FM a stunning blow in 1945 when it relegated it to a new frequency band and put restrictions on transmitter power, thus making over fifty existing transmitters and half a million receivers obsolete. At the same time, FM came to be widely used in military and other mobile communications, radar, telemetering, and the audio portion of television; but widespread adoption of FM broadcasting came only after Armstrong's death. Exhausted by a five-year suit for patent infringement against RCA and almost destitute as his FM patents began to expire, Armstrong committed suicide in 1954.

He had received many honors, including the highest awards of the two U.S. electrical engineering societies, the American Institute of Electrical Engineers (Edison Medal, 1942) and the Institute of Radio Engineers (Medal of Honor, 1918, reaffirmed in 1934 when he tried to return it after losing the legal fight against De Forest); the Franklin Medal (1941); and, for his war work, the U.S. Medal for Merit (1945). No inventor contributed more profoundly to the art of electronic communication. Armstrong is one of the two dozen honored in the Pantheon of the International Telecommunications Union in Geneva.

BIBLIOGRAPHY

Armstrong received forty-two patents and wrote twenty-six papers; the papers are listed in his biography by Lawrence Lessing, *Man of High Fidelity* (Philadelphia, 1956). See also obituaries in *New York Times* (2 Feb. 1954), p. 27; and in *Proceedings of the Institute of Radio Engineers,* **42** (1954), 635.

CHARLES SÜSSKIND

ARMSTRONG, HENRY EDWARD (*b.* Lewisham, London, England, 6 May 1848; *d.* Lewisham, 13 July 1937), *chemistry, science education.*

Armstrong entered the Royal College of Chemistry, London, in 1865. Here he studied with A. W. Hofmann, then in his last year in Britain, and John Tyndal, whose lectures greatly impressed him. In his third year he started research under Sir Edward Frankland, at whose suggestion he went to Leipzig to study under Hermann Kolbe. He was awarded the Ph.D. in 1870 and returned to London in that year to start his lifelong career in research and teaching. Armstrong's first positions were largely "bread and butter" ones: teaching combined with research, often under primitive conditions. His first paper to the Chemical Society of London, "On the Formation of Sulpho-Acids," was submitted in 1870. In 1884 he became professor of chemistry at the then new Central Institution, South Kensington, which merged with the Imperial College of Science and Technology in 1907. He retired from teaching in 1911.

Armstrong had a very vigorous mind and independent spirit, which, coupled with great breadth of interests and personal drive, enabled him to assume leadership in the development of technological chemistry in Great Britain. He became a fellow of the Royal Society of London when only twenty-eight, and he served the Chemical Society of London as secretary, president, and vice-president. He had an extraordinary impact on his contemporaries, his accomplishments and influence being such that between 1890 and 1935 he was regarded as the doyen of British chemists. Armstrong's mission was to advance chemistry in order to improve society, and he carried it out with the fervor of a prophet. His published papers, many written with students, totaled more than 250. He did pioneer work on the structure of benzene, devising the centric formula independently of Baeyer, and his work with W. P. Wynne on the structure and reactions of naphthalene helped establish the dye industry. Many of his papers were concerned with the quinonoid theory for the color of organic compounds, the reactions of camphor and terpenes, and the mechanism of enzyme reactions.

Armstrong's views were often prophetic. He was among the first to base instruction and writing in chemistry upon Mendeleev's periodic table, and he early emphasized that molecules must have spatial configurations that determine crystal structures. His researches in crystallography were significant and antedated X-ray diffraction methods.

The vigor of Armstrong's advocacy of unorthodox views at times caused intense controversy and often made enemies. On the basis of the unique properties of water and the hypothetical structure of water molecules, he castigated and ridiculed the theories of Arrhenius, van't Hoff, and Ostwald because they ignored the solvent and complex character of water. He believed that the process of solution of electrolytes had to consider and include the unique properties of water. Thus, his ideas and researches were an important step toward the present concepts of ion complexes and ion atmospheres in aqueous solutions of electrolytes.

He was the first to devise curricula to relate chemistry and engineering, and he came to be regarded as the father of chemical engineering. Armstrong helped organize the Education Section of the British Association for the Advancement of Science and served as its president in 1902. He vigorously opposed the didactic method of teaching and championed the view that the best method of teaching science was experimental. Appointed to the Committee on Management for Rothamsted Experiment Station at Harpenden, Armstrong served the rest of his life as member, vice-chairman, or chairman of this committee. Here his guidance and vision in the application of chemistry and scientific procedures to the problems of agriculture did much to advance this basic economic activity.

In 1877 Armstrong married Frances Louisa Lavers of Plumstead, Kent, who bore him four sons and three daughters. His eldest son, Edward Frankland, achieved prominence as an industrial chemist.

During his long career Armstrong's zeal and pioneering spirit brought him acknowledged leadership in many areas of organic research, in science and technical education, and in agriculture. But in the minds of his colleagues his chief contribution to chemistry was the teaching and inspiration of his many distinguished pupils.

BIBLIOGRAPHY

I. Original Works. Armstrong's most important books are *The Teaching of the Scientific Method and Other Papers on Education* (London, 1903, 1925) and *The Art and Principles of Chemistry* (London, 1927). His first paper to the Chemical Society was "On the Formation of Sulpho-Acids," in *Journal of the Chemical Society of London* (1871), p. 173.

II. Secondary Literature. J. Vargas Eyre, *Henry Edward Armstrong 1848–1937* (London, 1958), a biography by a former colleague and intimate, gives titles and journal sources for many of Armstrong's papers on benzene, naphthalene, crystallography, enzymes, and electrolytes. Many of these papers were influential. For example, his sixty papers on laws of substitution in naphthalene materially helped to establish naphthalene chemistry and the dye industry. A long and very detailed obituary notice is "Henry Edward Armstrong," in *Journal of the Chemical Society of London* (1940), p. 1418.

Conrad E. Ronneberg

ARNALD OF VILLANOVA (*b.* Aragon, Spain, *ca.* 1240; *d.* at sea off Genoa, Italy, 6 September 1311), *medical sciences.*

The family of Arnald of Villanova may originally have been Provençal, but he himself was Catalan by birth, probably from Valencia. We have no information about his parents (except that they may have been converted Jews) and little about his professional education. It is certain only that he was a student at Montpellier *ca.* 1260; the ascription to him of training under John Casamicciola at the University of Naples between 1267 and 1276 rests on the doubtful authenticity of the *Breviarium practice* traditionally included among his works. By 1281 Arnald had become physician to Peter III of Aragon, and he subsequently served Peter's son and heir, Alfonso III, in the same capacity. The death of the latter in 1291

and the succession of his brother as James II brought Arnald further into prominence.

By 1291 Arnald had taken up residence in Montpellier as a medical master at its newly chartered *studium generale,* but he was repeatedly called back to Spain during the next several years for professional consultations. Moreover, he seems to have been able to win considerable support from the royal family for his developing religious views. While Arnald's teaching and writings at Montpellier were of the first importance in establishing the content of scholastic medicine there, his own commitment to medicine was gradually being replaced by a concern for theological matters. He studied for six months with the Montpellier Dominicans, but he seems to have been most strongly influenced by the Joachimite Peter John Olivi and the spiritual-Franciscans, a group of rigorists within that order. By 1299 Arnald had completed a number of mystical, prophetic works—notably the *De adventu antichristi* (begun in 1288), which announced that the world would end and the Antichrist appear in 1378 and insisted upon the need for a drastic reform of the Church. When in 1299 Arnald was sent by James II on a diplomatic mission to Philip IV of France, he took the opportunity to explain his beliefs to the Parisian theologians. The *De adventu* was condemned, however, and Arnald was spared imprisonment only through the intervention of Philip's minister, William of Nogaret.

Arnald spent the next five years traveling between Provence and Rome. He continued to write while defending himself against his critics in the Church. Two popes, Boniface VIII and Benedict XI, were willing to tolerate him as a physician but were not receptive to his theology. With the accession in 1305 of Clement V, Arnald's friend for some time, he finally had both papal and royal patronage and was repeatedly given the opportunity to express his views, in which his concern for Church reform soon became predominant over his interest in eschatology. Then, in 1309, before a large assembly at Avignon, Arnald made statements that called James II's orthodoxy into question, thereby losing the king's favor. Thereafter Arnald attached himself to James's younger brother, Frederick I of Trinacria, a much more willing instrument for Arnald's plans for the reform of Christian society. He died while on a mission for Frederick.

In his medical practice Arnald seems to have been remarkable only for his success. There are many striking testimonies to his abilities, two of which are James II's demand that Arnald come from Montpellier to attend the queen's second pregnancy (1297) and Boniface VIII's delight at his relief from the stone (1301). From the various regimens and practical guides composed for such patients—for example, the *Regimen sanitatis* written for James II in 1307, and the *Parabole medicationis* dedicated to Philip IV (1300)—it is clear that his methods continued to be those in which he had been trained at Montpellier. His diagnostic and therapeutic principles appear quite conservative, with none of the dependence on uroscopy or extreme polypharmacy that marks the work of some of his colleagues. As a practicing physician, Arnald was evidently committed to experience rather than to theory or to authority.

Yet Arnald was also the principal figure in Montpellier's fusion of the Western empirical tradition with the systematic medical philosophy of the Greeks and Arabs. He was well placed for this role. Living in Valencia shortly after its reconquest by James I, it was natural for him to learn Arabic, and at the Aragonese court in the 1280's he translated, from Arabic into Latin, Avicenna's *De viribus cordis,* which subsequently proved immensely popular, and Galen's *De rigore;* he also translated a work on drugs by Albuzale and one on regimen by Avenzoar. There is very little in the choice of these texts to suggest any interest in the natural-philosophical aspects of medicine, but Arnald's stay at Montpellier seems to have deepened his medical as well as his theological interests. One indication of this is the unusual number of different Hippocratic and Galenic works on which he is known to have lectured. The classical authors had been commented upon by earlier masters at Montpellier, notably Cardinalis, but apparently not so extensively; they had preferred to pursue the more purely empirical methods of such moderns as Gilbert the Englishman and Walter Agilon. By the fourteenth century, however, Arnald's approach had become more widespread. The program of the university was unsettled in the 1290's, and Arnald certainly encouraged its subsequent Scholasticism by his example; moreover, it was his advice that shaped the papal bull of 8 September 1309, which regularized medical education at Montpellier, defining a set of fifteen Greek and Arab texts as the basis for future study at the school.

Arnald himself went beyond commentary to try to develop a coherent, systematic science of medicine on the Galenic foundations. It is possible to trace the development of his ideas in a continuous series of works datable to Montpellier and the 1290's, bound together by cross-references and a remarkably consistent interest in the philosophical aspects of medicine. In the earlier works (e.g., the *De intentione medicorum*) he is primarily concerned to defend pragmatically the presence of a rational element in medicine. Against his colleagues, Arnald holds that the physician can and should draw on theory insofar as it is meaningful to his practice; he requires simply that it save the medical phenomena, not that it be absolutely, philosophically true. Arnald repeatedly makes an analogy with the astronomers' epicycles.

Gradually, however, Arnald became more preoccupied with problems of philosophy apart from any practical applications, and the later Montpellier treatises are highly technical discussions of sophisticated medical theory. They most often treat the *complexio* (the set of sensible qualities, principally hot and cold, that characterizes a man's state of health), which provides Arnald with a basis for both medical practice and theory. In the *Aphorismi de gradibus* he develops this qualitative medicine most fully: drawing on material from al-Kindī and Averroës, he establishes a mathematical pharmacy upon the empirical law that qualitative intensity increases arithmetically with a geometric increase in the ratio of the opposing forces that produce it. For medicinal qualities, the law would have the form (in modern terms) intensity $= \log_2$ hot/cold. The *Aphorismi* continued in use at Montpellier for over fifty years, and may have provided the stimulus for Bradwardine's Law, the Merton College dynamic rule that, in local motion, velocity $\sim \log_n$ force/resistance. But this success was exceptional. For the most part, Arnald's writings—even his final synthesis of medical theory, the *Speculum medicine*—were too elaborate and too abstract to have any vogue among professional physicians.

Arnald's unusual attention to philosophical medicine coincided with the development of his theological position, and one concern may well have inspired the other. Certainly he should not be understood as a simple rationalist in medical matters. Although Boniface VIII once told him, "Occupy yourself with medicine and not with theology and we will honor you," Arnald did not find it easy to make such a distinction, for to him the two disciplines were continually overlapping in subject matter. The outstanding instance of this is his *De esu carnium* (1304), a defense of the Carthusians' abstension from meat, which gave equal weight to citations from Hippocrates and from St. Paul. More profoundly, his epistemology shows the same blurred dualism, for it is the mystical element in Arnald's thought that restricts his rationalism. He believes that while all physical events may be natural and ordered, their causes are not all easily and directly accessible to the understanding and men wise in these more occult matters will prove to have been guided by chance—or, like himself, by divine illumination. This is the spirit behind his scientific writings on astrology and oneiromancy, as well as his prophetic works; it is also the rationale behind his acceptance of medical intuition as a tool complementary to reason, which was quite in agreement with the view of his more orthodox colleagues that medicine is an art as much as (or more than) a science. The scholastic writings by themselves do not make plain this complexity of his scientific thought, the coexistence in it of rationalism and mysticism.

Arnald's heterodoxy made a great impression upon the fourteenth and fifteenth centuries, and during that period his name became associated with a number of alchemical texts. Some of these, notably the *Flos florum* and the *Rosarius philosophorum,* were until recently accepted as genuine. At present the authenticity of all appears doubtful, the more so because Arnald himself considered alchemists "ignorant" and "foolish." More recently the empirical element in Arnald's medicine has been emphasized by critics, who cite the *Breviarium practice* in support. But the authenticity of this work is dubious as well. From internal evidence, it seems that it must have been written in the first years of the fourteenth century, at just the time when Arnald was deeply concerned with medical theory and theology, and there is no hint of these subjects in the *Breviarium.* The most famous of the medical writings once attributed to him, the *Commentum super regimen sanitatis Salernitanum,* is now also thought to be apocryphal.

BIBLIOGRAPHY

I. ORIGINAL WORKS. Virtually all of Arnald's Latin medical works were collected in various sixteenth-century editions of his *Opera* (Lyons, 1504, 1509, 1520, 1532; Venice, 1505, 1527; Basel, 1585). In general, the later editions are the more complete, although the collection entitled *Praxis medicinalis* (Lyons, 1586) omits his discussions of medical theory. None of these works has been published in a modern edition, but one not printed earlier, *De conservatione visus,* was published by P. Pansier in *Collectio ophtalmologica veterum auctorum,* I (Paris, 1903), 1–25.

Arnald's translations from the Arabic are not included in his *Opera.* His versions of Aristotle and Galen were included with other writings of the same authors in editions of the fifteenth and sixteenth centuries; his translation of the *De medicinis simplicibus* attributed to Albuzale or Albumasar (MSS Paris, Univ. 128, 165–168; Erfurt, Amplon. F. 237, 63–66; Q. 395, 138–160) and the translation of the *De regimine sanitatis* of Avenzoar less certainly ascribed to him (MS Oxford, Corpus Christi 177, 261–265v; cf. MS Paris, Univ. 131, 54v–59v [among others], where it is attributed to Profatius) have not been published. He has also been credited with two translations that are demonstrably not by him: Costa ben Luca's *De physicis ligaturis* (which exists in a twelfth-century manuscript, MS

Brit. Mus. Add. 22719, fol. 200v) and al-Kindī's treatise *De gradibus* (for which Arnald's own *Aphorismi de gradibus* were mistaken).

A good bibliographical guide to the printed and manuscript sources is Juan Antonio Paniagua Arellano, "La obra médica de Arnau de Vilanova. Estudio 1°: Introducción y fuentes," in *Estudios y notas sobre Arnau de Vilanova* (Madrid, 1962), pp. 1–51, reprinted from *Archivo iberoamericano de historia de la medicina y antropología médica,* **11** (1959), 351–402.

A satisfactory bibliography of Arnald's theological writings, indicating those that have been published in whole or in part, will be found in Joaquín Carreras y Artau, "Les obres teológiques d'Arnau de Vilanova," in *Analecta sacra Tarraconensia,* **12** (1936), 217–231, although this is by now somewhat incomplete. The article by Paniagua cited above lists a number of more recent editions. It might also be mentioned that MSS Vat. Borg. 205 and Vat. Lat. 3824 are collections of Arnald's theological writings made at his own direction, in 1302 and 1305, respectively; the former manuscript may be annotated in Arnald's hand (see Anneliese Maier, "Handschriftliches zu Arnaldus de Villanova und Petrus Johannis Olivi," in *Analecta sacra Tarraconensia,* **21** [1948], 53–74).

Arnald's Catalan writings have been edited by Miguel Batllori as *Obres catalanes* (Barcelona, 1947) in two volumes, the first of which contains religious texts and the second, medical texts.

II. SECONDARY LITERATURE. The Arnaldian literature up to 1947 is thoroughly covered in the bibliographies of the volumes edited by Batllori, cited above; of this early material, Paul Diepgen's articles go most deeply into Arnald's scientific work. Since then a few other important studies of Arnald's science and medicine have appeared: Michael McVaugh, "Arnald of Villanova and Bradwardine's Law," in *Isis,* **58** (1967), 56–64. Juan Antonio Paniagua Arellano, "La patología general en la obra de Arnaldo de Vilanova," in *Archivos iberoamericanos de historia de la medicina,* **1** (1948), 49–119; Jacques Payen, "*Flos florum* et *Semita semite,* deux traités d'alchimie attribués à Arnaud de Villeneuve," in *Revue d'histoire des sciences,* **12** (1959), 288–300; René Verrier, *Études sur Arnaud de Villeneuve,* 2 vols. (Leiden, 1947–1949). The many biographical and theological studies that have appeared since 1947 can best be found by following up the references given in Miguel Batllori, "Dos nous escrits espirituals d'Arnau de Vilanova," in *Analecta sacra Tarraconensia,* **28** (1955), 45–70; or in Joaquín Carreras y Artau, *Relaciones de Arnau de Vilanova con los reyes de la casa de Aragón* (Barcelona, 1955).

MICHAEL MCVAUGH

ARNAULD, ANTOINE (*b.* Paris, France, 1612; *d.* Brussels, Belgium, 6 August 1694), *mathematics, linguistics.*

Arnauld was the youngest of the twenty children

of Antoine Arnauld, a lawyer who defended the University of Paris against the Jesuits in 1594. He was ordained a priest and received the doctorate in theology in 1641, and entered the Sorbonne in 1643, after the death of Richelieu. In 1656 he was expelled from the Sorbonne for his Jansenist views, and spent a good part of the rest of his life in more or less violent theological dispute. He died in self-imposed exile.

Although in many of his nontheological writings Arnauld is identified with the Port-Royal school, his voluminous correspondence—with Descartes and Leibniz, among others—bears witness to his own influence and acumen. His philosophical contributions are to be found in his objections to Descartes's *Méditations,* in his dispute with Malebranche, and in the *Port-Royal Logic,* which he wrote with Pierre Nicole. The latter, a text developed from Descartes's *Regulae,* elaborates the theory of "clear and distinct" ideas and gives the first account of Pascal's *Méthode.* It had an enormous influence as a textbook until comparatively recent times.

The profound influence of the *Regulae* is shown in both the *Logic* and the *Port-Royal Grammar,* where it is assumed that linguistic and mental processes are virtually identical, that language is thus to be studied in its "inner" and "outer" aspects. This point of view underlies the project for a universal grammar and the notion of the "transparency" of language: mental processes are common to all human beings, although there are many languages. The *Grammar* and the *Logic* are based on a common analysis of signs that has brought the Port-Royal school to the attention of modern linguistic theorists, who see in it an anticipation of their own point of view.

The *Élémens* (1667) undertakes a reworking and reordering of the Euclidean theorems in the light of the contemporary literature (in which he was widely read) and Pascal's influence. It bases its claim to originality and influence on the new order in which the theorems, many of them adapted from contemporary sources, are arranged. As mathematics, it is characterized by the mastery of the contemporary literature and by its clear and fresh exposition; its virtues are pedagogical. It is interesting to compare Arnauld's order of theorems with such recent ones as that of Hilbert and Forder, whose aims are quite different. If Arnauld's pedagogical concerns are insufficiently appreciated, it may be because the role of what are properly pedagogical concerns in the habits and "methods" of modern science is insufficiently understood: its preoccupation with clarity and procedure, with formal exercises and notation, and the use of these as instruments of research.

BIBLIOGRAPHY

I. ORIGINAL WORKS. Arnauld's writings include *Grammaire générale et raisonnée* (Port-Royal Grammar; Paris, 1660); *La logique ou l'art de penser* (Port-Royal Logic; Paris, 1662), crit. ed. by P. Clair and F. Girbal (Paris, 1965); and *Nouveaux élémens de géométrie* (Paris, 1667). Collections of his work are *Oeuvres,* 45 vols. (Lausanne, 1775–1783); and *Oeuvres philosophiques,* J. Simon and C. Jourdain, eds. (Paris, 1893).

II. SECONDARY LITERATURE. Works on Arnauld are K. Bopp, "Arnauld als Mathematiker," in *Abhandlundgen zur Geschichte der mathematischen Wissenschaften,* **14** (1902), and "Drei Untersuchungen zur Geschichte der Mathematik," in *Schriften der Strassburger wissenschaftlichen Gesellschaft in Heidelberg,* no. 10 (1929), pt. 2, 5–18; H. L. Brekle, "Semiotik und linguistische Semantik in Port-Royal," in *Indogermanische Forschungen,* **69** (1964), 103–121; Noam Chomsky, *Cartesian Linguistics* (Cambridge, Mass., 1966); J. Coolidge, *The Mathematics of Great Amateurs* (Oxford, 1949); Leibniz, "Remarques sur les nouveaux Élémens de Géométrie Antoine Arnaulds," in *Die Leibniz-Handschriften zu Hannover,* E. Bodemann, ed., I (Hannover, 1895), no. 21, 287; and H. Scholz, "Pascals Forderungen an die mathematische Methode," in *Festschrift Andreas Speiser* (1945).

HENRY NATHAN

ARNOLD, HAROLD DE FOREST (*b.* Woodstock, Connecticut, 3 September 1883; *d.* Summit, New Jersey, 10 July 1933), *electronics.*

Arnold received bachelor's and master's degrees from Wesleyan University in Connecticut and the doctorate from the University of Chicago (1911), where he studied physics under Robert Andrews Millikan. When the Bell System needed someone to develop repeaters for its projected transcontinental line, Millikan recommended Arnold, who thus became one of the scientists who later laid the foundation of the Bell Telephone Laboratories. Arnold first developed a mercury-arc repeater, but the device saw only limited use before his attention turned to the triode, which had been invented six years earlier by Lee de Forest (no kin). Its operation was still not entirely understood; the inventor himself did not appreciate the need for the highest attainable vacuum. Arnold was among the first to recognize the importance of high vacuum, and quickly developed designs that utilized reliable triodes and thus made long-distance telephony possible for the first time.

After World War I, part of which he spent as a captain in the U.S. Army Signal Corps, Arnold returned to research work for Bell and made a number of important contributions to the development of new magnetic alloys used in sound reproduction and to electroacoustics generally. He was named the first director of research when the Bell Telephone Laboratories were formed in 1925, a post he occupied until his death. He helped to lead that organization to its preeminent position among the industrial laboratories of the world.

BIBLIOGRAPHY

A biography containing extensive quotations from Arnold's writings on the organization of research appears in *Bell Laboratories Record*, **11** (1933), 351–359. See also his obituary in *New York Times* (11 July 1933), p. 17.

CHARLES SÜSSKIND

AROMATARI, GIUSEPPE DEGLI (*b.* Assisi, Italy, 25 March 1587; *d.* Venice, Italy, 16 July 1660), *embryology.*

Aromatari was the son of Favorino Aromatari and Filogenia Paolucci. He was brought up by his paternal uncle, Renier Aromatari, a learned and wealthy physician. He studied philosophy and medicine in Perugia, Montpellier, and Padua, where he attended Fabricius' lectures. After graduating M.D. in 1605, Aromatari remained at Padua until 1610 when he settled at Venice to practice medicine. His fame soon caused him to be requested as personal physician by King James I of England and by Pope Urban VIII; but Aromatari declined. He died of a stone in the urinary bladder and was buried in the Church of Saint Luke in Venice.

Aromatari was famous as a man of letters as well as a physician. From 1609 until 1613, he was involved in a literary debate with the poet Alessandro Tassoni over the work of Petrarch. At an advanced age, he wrote and published an anthology of passages from the classics. Aromatari is remembered today, however, for his hypothesis of the preformation of the germ. He also investigated the so-called permeability of the interventricular septum of the heart; but on this subject no writing exists.

In 1625 Aromatari published at Venice his famous *Epistola de generatione plantarum ex seminibus* ("Letter on the Generation of Plants from Seeds"). Addressed to a friend, Bartholomeo Nanti, the work was only four pages long, but it immediately made Aromatari famous. It was reprinted in 1626 at Frankfurt; and it was included by Richter in his *Epistolae selectae* in 1662, and by Junge in *Opuscula botanico-physica* in 1747.

Aromatari affirmed that the seeds of plants are composed of two parts: a smaller part, the germ, which contains, in miniature, all parts of the future plant; and a larger part, which is destined as nourishment for the germ and therefore comparable to the yolk of an egg. He was also explicit on two other fundamental points: he denied, absolutely, the spontaneous generation of all living species (animal and vegetable) and postulated that each living kind is born from the seed (plants) or the egg (animals) of the same kind.

In the beginning of the seventeenth century, animal generation was studied in Padua; it is possible that Aromatari was induced to study the problems of generation by reading the works of Volcher Coiter or Ulisse Aldrovandi on generation.

Aromatari was unaware of the sexuality of plants, demonstrated in 1694 by Rudolph Camerarius. Aromatari thought that a single plant, as a hermaphrodite, produced both the *ova* (seeds) and the *semen prolificum* (pollen). However, on the precise problem of embryogenesis, he first advanced the hypothesis of the preformation of the germ: "In the aforesaid seeds, the plant exists already made . . . the plant arises from the seed, but it is not generated in the seed; we think that likely the chick is sketched in the egg, before it is brooded by the hen." Aromatari's priority on the doctrine of the preformation of the germ was acknowledged by William Harvey in his *De generatione animalium.*

Aromatari's hypothesis of germinal preformation became the new idea of the seventeenth century, and was developed later in the famous works of Marcello Malpighi, Jan Swammerdam, and Charles Bonnet, the greatest theorists of preformation in animal generation. Therefore, Aromatari's *Epistola* marks the origin of an idea of great importance in the history of embryology.

BIBLIOGRAPHY

I. ORIGINAL WORKS. Works by Aromatari include *Disputatio de rabie contagiosa, cui praeposita est epistola de generatione plantarum ex seminibus, qua detegitur in vocatis seminibus plantas contineri vere confirmatas, ut dicunt, actu* (Venice, 1625) and *Autori del bel parlare* (Venice, 1643).

II. SECONDARY LITERATURE. Works relating to Aromatari include *Memorie di Giuseppe Aromatari letterato medico e naturalista, pubblicate per cura dell'Accademia Properziana del Subasio* (Assisi, 1887), which contains a portrait engraved on copper, a bibliography, and the complete text of the *Epistola de generatione plantarum*; these bibliographical notes, collected by Leonello Leonelli, were extracted from the paper *Vita dell'Eccellentissimo Gioseffe degli Aromatari* (Venice, 1661), written by Father Giovanni Battista De Fabris; W. Harvey, Exercitatio XI, "Ovum esse primordium commune omnibus animalibus, ut et semina plantarum omnium . . . Ita olim mihi, Venetiis cum essem, Aromatarius, Medicus clarissimus, ostendit," of *De generatione animalium* (London, 1651); R. Herrlinger, *Volcher Coiter* (Nuremberg, 1952), p. 72; J. Rostand, *La formation de l'être: histoire des idées sur la génération* (Paris, 1930), p. 50; and *Esquisse d'une histoire de la biologie* (Paris, 1945), p. 24.

PIETRO FRANCESCHINI

ARONHOLD, SIEGFRIED HEINRICH (*b.* Angerburg, Germany [now Węgorzewo, Poland], 16 July 1819; *d.* Berlin, Germany, 13 March 1884), *mathematics.*

Aronhold attended the Angerburg elementary school and the Gymnasium in Rastenburg (now Kętrzyn, Poland). Following the death of his father, his mother moved to Königsberg, where the boy attended a Gymnasium. He graduated in 1841 and then studied mathematics and natural sciences at the University of Königsberg from 1841 to 1845. Among his teachers were Bessel, Jacobi, Richelot, Hesse, and Franz Neumann. When Jacobi went to Berlin, Aronhold followed him and continued his studies under Dirichlet, Steiner, Gustav Magnus, and Dove. He did not take the state examinations, but in 1851 the University of Königsberg awarded him the *Doctor honoris causa* for his treatise "Über ein neues algebraisches Prinzip" and other studies.

From 1852 to 1854 Aronhold taught at the Artillery and Engineers' School in Berlin and, from 1851, at the Royal Academy of Architecture in Berlin, where he was appointed professor in 1863. In 1860 he joined the Royal Academy for Arts and Crafts, where, when Weierstrass became ill in 1862, he took over the entire teaching schedule. He was appointed professor in 1864. In 1869 Aronhold became a corresponding member of the Academy of Sciences in Göttingen. He was considered an enthusiastic and inspiring teacher, and was held in high esteem everywhere.

Aronhold was particularly attracted by the theory of invariants, which was then the center of mathematical interest, and was the first German to do research in this area. The theory of invariants is not, however, connected with Aronhold alone—others who worked on it were Sylvester, Cayley, and Hesse—but he developed a special method that proved to be extremely successful. In 1863 he collected his ideas in a treatise entitled "Über eine fundamentale Begründung der Invariantentheorie."

In this treatise, Aronhold offers solid proof of his theory, which he had welded into an organic entity. His method refers to functions that remain unchanged under linear substitutions. He stresses the importance of the logical development of a few basic principles so that the reader may find his way through other papers. Aronhold establishes his theory in general and does not derive any specific equations. He derives the concept of invariants from the concept of equivalency for the general linear theory of invariants. Special difficulties arise, of course, if not only general but also special cases are to be considered. His efforts to obtain equations independent of substitution coefficients led to linear partial differential equations of the first order, which also have linear coefficients. These equations, which are characteristic for the theory of invariants, are known as Aronhold's differential equations.

With these equations "Aronhold's process" can be carried out. This process permits the derivation of additional concomitants from one given concomitant. Aronhold investigates the characteristics of these partial differential equations and expands the theory to include the transformation of a system of homogeneous functions, furnishes laws for simultaneous invariants, and investigates contravariants (relevant forms), covariants, functional invariants, and divariants (intermediate forms).

Aronhold stresses that he arrived at his principles as early as 1851, citing his doctoral dissertation and the treatise "Theorie der homogenen Funktionen dritten Grades . . ." (1858). Since the subsequent theory and terminology did not yet exist, he claimed priority.

Before Aronhold developed his theory, he had worked on plane curves. The problem of the nine points of inflection of the third-order plane curve, which had been discovered by Plücker, was brought to completion by Hesse and Aronhold. Aronhold explicitly established the required fourth-degree equation and formulated a theorem on plane curves of the fourth order. Seven straight lines in a plane always determine one, and only one, algebraic curve of the fourth order, in that they are part of their double tangents and that among them there are no three lines whose six tangential points lie on a conic section.

BIBLIOGRAPHY

I. ORIGINAL WORKS. Aronhold's writings are "Zur Theorie der homogenen Funktionen dritten Grades von drei Variabeln," in *Journal für die reine und angewandte Mathematik* (Crelle), **39** (1849); "Bemerkungen über die Auflösung der biquadratischen Gleichung," *ibid.,* **52** (1856), trans. into French as "Remarque sur la résolution des équations biquadratiques," in *Nouvelles annales de mathématiques,* **17** (1858); "Theorie der homogenen Funktionen dritten Grades von drei Veränderlichen," in *Journal für die reine und angewandte Mathematik* (Crelle), **55** (1858); "Algebraische Reduktion des Integrals ∫F(x,y) dx, wo F(x,y) eine beliebige rationale Funktion von x,y bedeutet und zwischen diesen Grössen eine Gleichung dritten Grades von der allgemeinsten Form besteht, auf die Grundform der elliptischen Transzendenten," in *Berliner Monatsberichte* (1861); "Form der Kurve, wonach die Rippe eines T-Konsols zu formen ist," in *Verhandlung der Polytechnischen Gesellschaft* (Berlin), **22** (1861); "Über eine neue algebraische Behandlungsweise der Integrale irrationaler Differentiale von der Form Π (x,y) dx, in welcher Π (x,y) eine beliebige rationale Funktion ist, und zwischen x und y eine allgemeine Gleichung zweiter Ordnung besteht," in *Journal für die reine und angewandte Mathematik* (Crelle), **61** (1862); "Über eine fundamentale Begründung der Invariantentheorie," *ibid.,* **62** (1863); "Über den gegenseitigen Zusammenhang der 28 Doppeltangenten einer allgemeinen Kurve vierten Grades," in *Berliner Monatsberichte* (1864); "Neuer und direkter Beweis eines Fundamentaltheorems der Invariantentheorie," in *Journal für die reine und angewandte Mathematik* (Crelle), **69** (1868); and "Grundzüge der kinetischen Geometrie," in *Verhandlungen des Vereins für Gewerbefleiss,* **52** (1872).

II. SECONDARY LITERATURE. More detailed information on mathematics in Berlin can be found in E. Lampe, *Die reine Mathematik in den Jahren 1884–1899 nebst Aktenstücken zum Leben von Siegfried Aronhold* (Berlin, 1899), pp. 5 ff. For the theory of invariants, see Weitzenböck, *Invariantentheorie* (Groningen, 1923); *Enzyklopädie der mathematische Wissenschaften,* I, pt. 1 (Leipzig, 1898), 323 ff.; Felix Klein, *Vorlesungen über die Entwicklung der Mathematik im 19. Jahrhunderts* (Berlin, 1926–1927), I, 157, 166, 305; II, 161, 195; and Enrico Pascal, *Repertorium der höheren Analysis,* 2nd ed. (Leipzig–Berlin, 1910), ch. 5, pp. 358–420.

HERBERT OETTEL

AROUET, FRANÇOIS-MARIE. See **Voltaire.**

ARREST, HEINRICH LOUIS D' (*b.* Berlin, Germany, 13 August 1822; *d.* Copenhagen, Denmark, 14 June 1875), *astronomy.*

A diligent investigator of comets, asteroids, and nebulae, d'Arrest is known today chiefly for his role in the discovery of the planet Neptune, and for the periodic comet that bears his name—this comet, which he discovered in 1851, was last seen in October 1963 and is significant because its orbit is gradually getting larger through the action of some nongravitational force.

D'Arrest, whose father was an accountant of Huguenot descent, attended the Collège Français in

Berlin before entering the University of Berlin in 1839. He was a promising graduate student, with half a dozen publications and a medal from the King of Denmark (for discovering the comet 1845 I), when Johann Gottfried Galle got permission from Johann Franz Encke, director of the Berlin Observatory, to look for the trans-Uranian planet predicted by Urbain Leverrier. D'Arrest volunteered to help, and suggested the star chart to use: Hora XXI of the *Berliner Akademische Sternkarten,* completed by Carl Bremiker but not yet published. The search was successful that same night (23 September 1846), owing in large part to the excellence of the chart, but in making the initial announcement Encke mentioned only his staff member Galle and himself; it was not until 1877 that Galle set the record straight.

In 1848 d'Arrest was elected a foreign associate of the Royal Astronomical Society of London and chosen to fill a new post at the Leipzig observatory, where he worked under August Ferdinand Möbius—whose daughter he subsequently married. He received his Ph.D. degree from the University of Leipzig in 1850, and in 1851 published his first book, *Ueber das System der kleinerer Planeten zwischen Mars und Jupiter,* a study of the thirteen asteroids then known. His interest in comets and asteroids continued, as shown by his discovery of two more comets (1851 II, mentioned above, and 1857 I) and of the asteroid (76) Freia in 1862, but now d'Arrest began the studies of nebulae for which he received the Gold Medal of the Royal Astronomical Society in 1875.

Although many nebulae had already been observed, notably by William Herschel and his son John, their nature and particularly their distances were still unknown. To improve the situation d'Arrest made, and published in 1857, accurate measurements of the positions and appearances of two hundred and sixty-nine selected nebulous objects; after he became, in 1858, professor in the University of Copenhagen and director of its new observatory, he extended these observations to 1,942 nebulae, published as *Siderum nebulosorum observationes Hafniensis 1861–1867,* but gave up this approach when he realized that even those nebulae bright enough to be detected by his eleven-inch telescope were too numerous for any one man to observe in a lifetime.

Just before his untimely death d'Arrest began spectroscopic observations, following the lead of Sir William Huggins, and was the first to point out, in 1873, that the gaseous nebulae (those with bright line spectra) were preferentially located near the plane of the Milky Way and therefore probably relatively nearby objects in our own galaxy.

BIBLIOGRAPHY

I. ORIGINAL WORKS. D'Arrest's discovery of comet 1845 I was announced in the "Cometen-Circular" of the *Astronomische Nachrichten,* **22** (1845), cols. 343–344, and the orbit he calculated for it was published in a letter to the editor written by Encke, *ibid.,* **23** (1846), cols. 81–82. His early publications included three letters to the editor, on Colla's comet of June 1845: *ibid.,* cols. 231–234, 275–278, and 349–352; "Bestimmung der Elemente der Astraea, mit Rücksicht auf die Störungen aus der ganzen Reihe der Beobachtungen," *ibid.,* **24** (1846), cols. 277–288; "Elemente und Ephemeride der Astraea. 1846–47," *ibid.,* cols. 349–358; and "Ueber die Bahn des vom Dr. Peters entdeckten Cometen," *ibid.,* cols. 387–390.

During his stay in Leipzig d'Arrest's publications included: "Neue Verbesserung der Elemente der Hygiea-Bahn," in *Berichte über die Verhandlungen der königlich sächsischen Gesellschaft der Wissenschaften,* **2** (1850), 1–9; "Nachricht von der Entdeckung und den ersten Beobachtungen des Planeten Victoria, des Cometen von Bond und des dreizehnten Hauptplaneten," *ibid.,* 105–108; "Über die Gruppirung der periodischen Cometen," *ibid.,* **3** (1851), 31–38; the discovery of comet 1851 II [comet d'Arrest] in the "Cometen-Circular" of *Astronomische Nachrichten,* **32** (1851), cols. 327–328, with further observations of it in cols. 341–342; *Ueber das System der kleineren Planeten zwischen Mars und Jupiter* (Leipzig, 1851); "Resultate aus Beobachtungen der Nebelflecken und Sternhaufen. Erste Reihe," in *Abhandlungen der mathematisch-physischen Classe der königlich sächsischen Gesellschaft der Wissenschaften,* **3** (1857), 293–377, with errata on 378; and his discovery of comet 1857 I, announced in the "Cometen-Circular" of *Astronomische Nachrichten,* **45** (1857), cols. 223–224, with more observations in cols. 253–254 and 365–368.

While in Copenhagen d'Arrest's works included the discovery of asteroid (76) Freia, announced in *Astronomische Nachrichten,* **59** (1863), cols. 16–17, with further observations and orbital elements in cols. 77–78 and 91–92; *Siderum nebulosorum observationes Havnienses institutae in secula universitatis per tubum sedecimpedalem Merzianum, ab anno 1861 ad annum 1867* (Copenhagen, 1867); "Om Beskaffenheden og Ubbyttet af de spektral analytiske Undersogelser indenfor Solsystemet, sete i forbindelse med Kometernes Udviklingshistorie," in *Forhandlingerne ved de Skandinaviske Naturforskeres* (1873), 145–161; and a letter to the editor concerning the location of gaseous nebulae, in *Astronomische Nachrichten,* **80** (1873), cols. 189–190.

There is a list of 127 papers by d'Arrest in the Royal Society of London's *Catalogue of Scientific Papers*: I (London, 1867), 101–103; VII (London, 1877), 49–50; IX (London, 1891), 72; and XII (London, 1902), 24. A number of additional items can be found among the more than 400 entries under d'Arrest's name in the cumulative indices to *Astronomische Nachrichten*: **21–40** (Hamburg, 1856), 123–128; **41–60** (Hamburg, 1866), 122–124; and **61–80** (Leipzig, 1875), 80–81.

II. SECONDARY WORKS. An address delivered by the president of the Royal Astronomical Society, John Couch Adams, when d'Arrest received—*in absentia*—that society's Gold Medal, was printed in *Monthly Notices of the Royal Astronomical Society,* **35** (1875), 265–276, and gives a contemporary evaluation of his accomplishments. For further details on his life, see the biographical memoir by John Louis Emil Dreyer in *Vierteljahrsschrift der Astronomischen Gesellschaft,* **11** (1876), 1–14 and an unsigned obituary in *Monthly Notices of the Royal Astronomical Society,* **36** (1876), 155–158.

The discovery of the planet Neptune was announced by Encke, in a letter to the editor dated 26 Sept. 1846, that appeared in *Astronomische Nachrichten,* **25** (1847), cols. 49–52. The first printed mention of d'Arrest's contribution was in Dreyer's memoir (see above); Galle's first public acknowledgment of the part played by d'Arrest in this discovery was "Ein Nachtrag zu den in Band 25 und dem Ergänzungshefte von 1849 der Astr. Nachrichten enthaltenen Berichten über die erste Auffindungen des Planeten Neptun," in *Astronomische Nachrichten,* **89** (1877), cols. 349–352. In his "Historical Note Concerning the Discovery of Neptune," published in *Copernicus,* **2** (1882), 63–64, Dreyer called attention to this paper by Galle, remarking upon the fact that neither Encke nor Galle had previously seen fit to give proper credit to d'Arrest. Galle agreed to the justice of this rebuke in "Ueber die erste Auffindung der Planeten Neptun," *ibid.,* 96–97.

SALLY H. DIEKE

ARRHENIUS, SVANTE AUGUST (*b.* Vik, Sweden, 19 February 1859; *d.* Stockholm, Sweden, 2 October 1927), *chemistry, physics.*

Svante August Arrhenius, one of the founders of modern physical chemistry, came from a Swedish farming family. His father, Svante Gustav Arrhenius, was a surveyor and later a supervisor of the University of Uppsala. He also was employed as overseer on the ancient estate of Vik (Wijk), on Lake Målar near Uppsala. In 1855 he married Carolina Christina Thunberg; Svante August was their second son. By the beginning of 1860, the father's position had improved enough so that the family moved to Uppsala, where he could devote full time to his university position.

After attending the Cathedral School in Uppsala, Arrhenius entered the University of Uppsala at the age of seventeen. He studied mathematics, chemistry, and physics, and passed the candidate's examination in 1878. Arrhenius chose physics as the principal subject for his doctoral study, but he was not satisfied with his chief instructor, Tobias Robert Thalén. Although Thalén was an eminent and competent experimental physicist and lecturer, he was interested only in spectral analysis. Arrhenius went to Stockholm in 1881 with the intention of working under Erik Edlund, physicist of the Swedish Academy of Sciences. The results of his first independent research, entitled "The Disappearance of Galvanic Polarization in a Polarization Vessel, the Plates of Which Are Connected by Means of a Metallic Conductor," was published in 1883. During the winter of 1882–1883 Arrhenius determined the conductivity of electrolytes; this resulted in his doctoral dissertation (1884), in which he discussed the electrolytic theory of dissociation. He presented it to the University of Uppsala and defended it in May 1884, but his dissertation was awarded only a fourth class (*non sine laude approbatur,* "approved not without praise") and his defense a third (*cum laude approbatur,* "approved with praise"). According to the then prevailing custom, this was not sufficient to qualify him for a docentship, which was a bitter disappointment to Arrhenius.

The chemist Sven Otto Pettersson, professor of chemistry at the Technical High School of Stockholm, reviewed Arrhenius' dissertation in the journal *Nordisk Revy* and praised it very highly, however: "The faculty have awarded the mark *non sine laude* to this thesis. This is a very cautious but very unfortunate choice. It is possible to make serious mistakes from pure cautiousness. There are chapters in Arrhenius' thesis which alone are worth more or less all the faculty can offer in the way of marks."[1] Pettersson referred here to the discovery of the connection between conductivity and speed of reaction. Per Theodor Cleve, speaking to Ostwald during the latter's visit to Uppsala, remarked, "But it is nonsense to accept with Arrhenius that in a solution of potassium-chloride chlorine and potassium are separated from each other," and in his speech honoring Arrhenius at the Nobel banquet in 1903 he said: "These new theories also suffered from the misfortune that nobody really knew where to place them. Chemists would not recognize them as chemistry; nor physicists as physics. They have in fact built a bridge between the two."

Arrhenius sent copies of his thesis to a number of prominent scientists: Rudolf Clausius in Bonn, Lothar Meyer in Tübingen, Wilhelm Ostwald in Riga, and Jacobus Henricus van't Hoff in Amsterdam. Ostwald, a physical chemist and professor at the Polytechnikum in Riga, was deeply impressed by the paper. He visited Arrhenius in Uppsala in August 1884, and offered him a docentship in Riga. Thanks to this, Arrhenius was appointed lecturer in physical chemistry at the University of Uppsala in November of that year. The English physicist Oliver Lodge was also impressed by Arrhenius' paper, and wrote an abstract and critical analysis of it for the *Reports of the British Association for the Advancement of Science* in 1886.

Through the influence of Edlund, Arrhenius re-ceived a travel grant from the Swedish Academy of Sciences which made it possible for him to work in the laboratories of Ostwald in Riga (later in Leipzig), Kohlrausch in Würzburg, Ludwig Boltzmann in Graz, and van't Hoff in Amsterdam. During these *Wanderjahre* (1886–1890), he further developed the theory of electrolytic dissociation. Arrhenius' theory was, however, slowly accepted at first, but because of neglect rather than active opposition. It was the enthusiasm and influence of Ostwald and van't Hoff that helped to make it widely known. In 1887 Arrhenius met Walther Nernst in Kohlrausch's laboratory. There, too, he carried out an important investigation on the action of light on the electrolytic conductivity of the silver salts of the halogens. In 1891 Arrhenius received an invitation from the University of Giessen, but he preferred the post of lecturer at the Technical High School in Stockholm, where he was appointed professor of physics in 1895 and was rector from 1896 to 1905. After refusing an offer from the University of Berlin, he became director of the physical chemistry department of the newly founded Nobel Institute in Stockholm, a post which he held until his death.

One of Arrhenius' first honors was election as honorary member of the Deutsche Elektrochemische Gesellschaft in 1895. In 1901 he was appointed to the Swedish Academy of Sciences, over strong opposition. The following year he received the Davy Medal from the Royal Society of London, and in 1903 he won the Nobel Prize for chemistry "in recognition of the extraordinary services he has rendered to the advancement of chemistry by his theory of electrolytic dissociation." Arrhenius was elected an honorary member of the Deutsche Chemische Gesellschaft in 1905; he became a foreign member of the Royal Society of London six years later. During his visit to the United States in 1911, Arrhenius was awarded the first Willard Gibbs Medal. In 1914 he received the Faraday Medal.

Arrhenius was married twice: in 1894 to his best pupil and assistant, Sofia Rudbeck, and in 1905 to Maria Johansson. By the first marriage he had one son, Olof, and by the second, a son, Sven, and two daughters, Ester and Anna-Lisa.

Arrhenius' aim, during his study of the conductivity of electrolytic solutions at Edlund's laboratory, was to find a method for determining the molecular weight of dissolved nonvolatile compounds by measuring electric conductivity. Soon he recognized that the state of the electrolyte was the matter of primary importance. Arrhenius completed his experimental work in the spring of 1883 and submitted a long memoir (in French) to the Swedish Academy of Sciences on 6

June 1883, with the results of his experiments and the conclusions he deduced from them. The memoir was published in 1884 under the title "Recherches sur la conductibilité galvanique des électrolytes." The first part ("La conductibilité des solutions aqueuses extrèmement diluées" and "Recherches sur la conductibilité galvanique des électrolytes") contains his findings on the conductivity of many extremely dilute solutions. Instead of measuring the conductivities with the exact alternating-current method, which Kohlrausch had introduced in 1876, Arrhenius used a "depolarizer," devised by Edlund in 1875, which corresponded roughly to a hand-driven rotating commutator.

In the first part of his memoir, Arrhenius gave an account of his experimental work: He measured the resistance of many salts, acids, and bases at various dilutions to 0.0005 normal (and sometimes to even lower concentrations), and gave his results so as to show in what ratio the resistance of an electrolyte solution is increased when the dilution is doubled. It is true that Heinrich Lenz and Kohlrausch had made similar measurements, but they did not use such great dilutions. Like Kohlrausch, Arrhenius found that for very dilute solutions the specific conductivity of a salt solution is in many cases nearly proportional to the concentration (thesis 1) when the conditions are identical. The conductivity of a dilute solution of two or more salts is always equal to the sum of the conductivities that solutions of each of the salts would have at the same concentration (thesis 2). Furthermore, the conductivity of a solution equals the sum of the conductivities of salt and solvent (thesis 3).

If these three laws are not observed, it must be because of chemical action between the substances in the solution (theses 4 and 5). The electrical resistance of an electrolytic solution rises with increasing viscosity (thesis 7), complexity of the ions (thesis 8), and the molecular weight of the solvent (thesis 9). Thesis 9 is an example of a proposition that is not correct. In addition to the viscosity of the solvent, its dielectric constant, not the molecular weight, is significant. Arrhenius worked, however, with a limited number of solvents (water, several alcohols, ether) for which the dielectric constant decreases approximately as the molecular weight rises. Arrhenius summarized Part I of his memoir as follows:

> In the first six sections of the present work we have described a new method of measuring the resistance of electrolytic solutions. In this method we made use of rapidly alternating currents, produced by a depolarizer constructed for the purpose by M. Edlund. We have tried to show the use of this method, and to make clear the practical advantages which it possesses.

The main importance of Arrhenius' memoir, however, does not lie in the experimental measurements or in the thirteen detailed deductions of Part I, but in his development of general ideas. These contain the germ of the theory of electrolytic dissociation (which received its definitive statement only three years later).

In Part II ("Théorie chimique des électrolytes"), Arrhenius gave a theoretical treatment of his experimental work, which he based on the hypothesis of the British chemist Alexander William Williamson and the German physicist Rudolf Clausius. In his famous article "Theory of Aetherification," Williamson suggested that in a chemical system a molecule continually exchanges radicals or atoms with other molecules, so that there is a state of dynamic equilibrium between atoms and molecules. Thus, in hydrochloric acid "each atom of hydrogen does not remain quietly in juxtaposition with the atom of chlorine with which it first united, but, on the contrary, is constantly changing places with other atoms of hydrogen, or, what is the same thing, changing chlorine." Williamson, however, did not assume that the radicals or atoms were electrically charged. Clausius advanced the hypothesis that a small fraction of a dissolved salt is dissociated into ions even when no current is passing through the solution. He did not state or calculate how much of the salt is thus affected.

Arrhenius stated that the dissolved molecules of an electrolyte are partly "active," partly "inactive": "The aqueous solution of any hydrate [by *hydrates* Arrhenius always meant hydrogen compounds like acids and bases] is composed, in addition to the water, of two parts, one active, electrolytic, the other inactive, non-electrolytic. These three substances, viz. water, active hydrate, and inactive hydrate, are in chemical equilibrium, so that on dilution the active part increases and the inactive part diminishes" (thesis 15). Arrhenius gave no precise account of the nature of the active and inactive parts, however; he only indicated what they might be. He extended his hypothesis to other dissolved electrolytes (salts) and defined the "coefficient of activity of an electrolyte" (corresponding to our notion of degree of electrolytic ionization) as "the number expressing the ratio of the number of ions actually contained in the electrolyte to the number of ions it would contain if the electrolyte were completely transformed into simple electrolytic molecules." In 1890 Arrhenius said that he chose the name "activity coefficient" instead of "degree of electrolytic dissociation" on grounds of prudence![2]

After thesis 16 we find a number of chemical applications. Arrhenius asserted that "the strength of an acid is the higher, the greater its activity coefficient. The same holds for bases." The dissociation becomes complete at infinite dilution of the solution (thesis 31); and in solutions of salts of weak acids, strong acids displace the weak acids (thesis 34). From a chemical point of view, thesis 23 is important: "When the relative amounts of ions A, B, C, and D are given, the final result is independent of their original form of combination, whether AB and CD, or AD and BC." The principle of the calculation of the degree of hydrolyzation by means of the law of mass action is given in thesis 29: "Every salt, dissolved in water, is partly dissociated in acid and base. The amount of the decomposition products is greater the weaker the acid and the base and the greater the amount of water."

In the last thesis (56), Arrhenius clearly stated the constancy of the heat of neutralization of a strong acid with a strong base: "The heat of neutralisation, set free by the transformation of a perfectly active base, and perfectly active acid, into water and simple salt, is only the heat of activity of the water," where "heat of activity" is the heat used in transforming a body from the inactive to the active state. Arrhenius ended his memoir with a long summary, which begins as follows:

> In the present part of this work we have first shown the probability that electrolytes can assume two different forms, one active, the other inactive, such that the active part is always, under the same exterior circumstances (temperature and dilution), a certain fraction of the total quantity of the electrolyte. The active part conducts electricity, and is in reality the electrolyte, not so the inactive part.[3]

Although Arrhenius discussed electrolytic dissociation in his memoir of 1884, he nowhere used the word "dissociation," nor is there any explicit identification of the "active part" of the electrolyte with free ions in the solution. It is not so surprising that the acceptance of his theory was slow at first, above all because it had to overcome preconceived ideas that oppositely charged ions could not exist separately in solution. The influence and enthusiasm of Ostwald and van't Hoff were consequently needed to make it widely known and accepted.

The next step toward a definite and clear electrolytic dissociation theory came from a famous memoir of van't Hoff, "The Role of Osmotic Pressure in the Analogy Between Solutions and Gases" (1887). Van't Hoff recognized in this memoir an analogy between dilute solutions and gases: "The pressure which a gas exerts at a given temperature, if a definite number of molecules is contained in a definite volume, is equal to the osmotic pressure which is produced by most substances under the same conditions, if they are dissolved in any given liquid." He showed that it was

possible to write for solutions an equation $PV = iRT$, analogous to the gas equation, where P is the osmotic pressure instead of the gaseous pressure, R the gas constant, V the volume, T the absolute temperature, and i a coefficient that is sometimes equal to unity but for the salts is greater than unity. Thus, van't Hoff concluded that the law was valid only for the "great majority of substances," but he could not explain the fact that solutions of salts, acids, and bases possess greater osmotic pressure, higher vapor tension, and greater depression of the freezing point than the results calculated from Raoult's experiments. Van't Hoff made no attempt to explain this exception, but Arrhenius identified the number of ions in solution with the value of i. In a letter to van't Hoff, dated 30 March 1887, Arrhenius wrote: "Your paper has cleared up for me to a remarkable degree the constitution of solutions. . . . Since . . . electrolytes decompose into their ions, the coefficient i must lie between unity and the number of ions." He continued with a statement of the theory of electrolytic dissociation in a clear and definite form: "In all probability all electrolytes are completely dissociated at the most extreme dilution."

In 1887 Arrhenius published a much revised, extended, and consolidated version of his theory of electrolytic dissociation in its quantitative formulation under the title "Ueber die Dissociation der im Wasser gelösten Stoffe." He wrote:

> In a previous communication . . . I have designated those molecules whose ions have independent motion, active molecules, and those whose ions are bound together, inactive molecules. I have also maintained it probable that at the most extreme dilution all the inactive molecules of an electrolyte are converted into active molecules. On this assumption I will base the calculations now to be carried out. The ratio of the number of active molecules to the total number of molecules, active and inactive, I have called the activity coefficient. The activity coefficient of an electrolyte at infinite dilution is therefore taken as unity. At smaller dilutions it is less than unity. . . .[4]

Arrhenius calculated the degree of electrolytic dissociation quantitatively as the ratio of the actual molecular conductivity of the solution and the limiting value to which the molecular conductivity of the same solution approaches with increasing dilution. He then gave the relationship between van't Hoff's constant i and the degree of ionization or activity coefficient α in the form $i = 1 + (k - 1)\alpha$, where k is the number of ions into which the molecule of the electrolyte dissociates. He compared the values of i calculated from Raoult's freezing-point data of solutions in water with the values obtained from the molecular conductivity for twelve nonconductors, fifteen bases, twenty-three acids, and forty salts, and found a very satisfactory agreement. He concluded that van't Hoff's law holds good, not merely for the majority but for all substances, including electrolytes in aqueous solution. "Every electrolyte in aqueous solution consists in part of molecules electrolytically and chemically active and in part of inactive molecules, which, however, on dilution change into active molecules, so that at infinite solution only active molecules are present."[5] With this publication, the full statement of the theory of electrolytic dissociation was given, and soon received substantial confirmation.

Among Arrhenius' most important contributions to this theory are his publications on isohydric solutions, solutions of two acids that can be mixed without any change in the degree of dissociation (1888); the relation between osmotic pressure and lowering of vapor tension (1889); the heat of dissociation of electrolytes and the influence of temperature on the degree of dissociation (1889); the condition of equilibrium between electrolytes (1889); the determination of electrolytic dissociation of salts through solubility experiments (1892); the hydrolysis of salts and weak acids and weak bases (1894); and the alteration of the strength of weak bases by the addition of salts (1899).

A problem that had always held Arrhenius' attention was the abnormality of strong electrolytes that do not follow Ostwald's law of dilution, which can be obtained by applying the law of mass action to the equilibrium between the dissociated and undissociated parts of an electrolyte. Arrhenius stated clearly that the law of mass action is not applicable to strong electrolytes, even when they are very diluted. A theory for the modern treatment of strong electrolytes was given by the Danish chemist Niels Bjerrum, by the Dutch-American scholar Peter Joseph Debye, and by the German Erich Hückel, who based their treatment on electrical interactions between the ions in solution.

Among the other physical-chemical works of Arrhenius, his important theoretical contribution, "Ueber die Reaktionsgeschwindigkeit bei der Inversion von Rohrzucker durch Säuren" (1889) must be mentioned. In this publication, Arrhenius studied the influence of an increase in temperature on the reaction velocity. Using the equilibrium equation deduced by van't Hoff in 1884, which gives mathematically the relation between the velocity coefficient and the temperature, Arrhenius realized that the study of the temperature coefficients of reaction velocity is important from the point of view of the general mechanism of chemical change. From the observation that the reaction velocity shows an abnormal increase of 10 to 15 per cent for one degree in temperature, Arrhenius supposed that active cane sugar molecules are formed;

these activated molecules (with much greater than average energy) are more susceptible to reaction. In a reaction system there are only a certain number of "active" molecules that can undergo reaction. This idea that molecules require a certain critical energy in order to react, as well as the concept of activation energy, is of great significance in modern chemistry.

During the last twenty-five years of his life, Arrhenius' interests were diverted to other fields of science, especially to the physics and chemistry of cosmic and meteorological phenomena. His contribution to these subjects consists mostly in the application of the laws of theoretical chemistry to existing astronomical, geophysical, and geological observations. Besides a short treatise on ball lightning (1883) and a publication on the influence of the rays of the sun on the electric phenomena of the earth's atmosphere (1888), Arrhenius and the meteorologist Nils Ekholm investigated the influence of the moon on the electric state of the atmosphere, on the aurora, and on thunderstorms (1887). Arrhenius supposed in the 1888 article that electric charges originate from ionization of the air by ultraviolet rays.

In 1896 he published a long memoir "On the Influence of Carbonic Acid in the Air Upon the Temperature of the Ground," in which he developed a theory for the explanation of the glacial periods and other great climatic changes, based on the ability of carbon dioxide to absorb the infrared radiation emitted from the earth's surface. Although the theory was based on thorough calculations, it won no recognition from geologists. In 1898 Arrhenius wrote a remarkable paper on the action of cosmic influence on physiological processes.

"Zur Physik des Vulkanismus," published in 1901, was also based on physical-chemical facts. Although at normal temperature, water is an acid about a hundred times weaker than silicic acid, increasing ionic dissociation with increased temperature would at a few hundred degrees make water a stronger acid than silicic acid. Arrhenius calculated by extrapolation that water at 1000°C. is eighty times, and at 2000°C. 300 times, stronger than silicic acid. In the magma, water penetrates at a temperature of between 1000°C. and 2000°C., and decomposes silicates. The magma expands, its volume increases, and it penetrates into the fissures of volcanoes. When the rising magma is cooled, the reverse process takes place, water is liberated, and under low pressure violent explosions occur, leading to volcanic eruptions. However, the hypothetical reaction between the molten silicate and water was not tenable, and Arrhenius' theory was soon forgotten.

In 1903 Arrhenius published his *Lehrbuch der kosmischen Physik,* the first textbook on cosmic physics. His work on the cosmic effects of the pressure of light rays attracted deserved attention in professional circles. With the aid of very light mirrors in a vacuum, the Russian physicist Pëtr Nikolajevich Lebedev and the American physicists Ernest Fox Nichols and Gordon Ferrie Hull proved in 1901 that a ray of light that meets material particles exerts a pressure on them, as James Clerk Maxwell had predicted in his electromagnetic theory of light. Arrhenius applied the radiation pressure to various phenomena even before its experimental confirmation. He calculated that we might expect streams of minute particles to be shot out from the sun in all directions. Arrhenius explained phenomena of the solar corona, comets, the aurora, and the zodiacal light by these charged particles, many of which, he said, would be electrically charged by ionization in the gaseous atmosphere of the sun. In 1905 he applied this concept to the problem of the origin of life by assuming that living seeds, spores, and so forth could be transported from interstellar space by the pressure of light (panspermic theory). Since Arrhenius' basic idea of the universe was its infinity in time, he did not have any need for a hypothesis involving a singular event like the creation of life. His concept that there was no beginning and no end of the universe follows from his inability to resolve by any other means the paradox in the application of the first and second laws of thermodynamics to the universe. According to Clausius, the energy of the world is constant and the entropy approaches a maximum, so that the universe is tending to what he called the *Wärmetod* ("heat death") through exhaustion of all sources of heat and motion. Now, if the universe were assumed to have a finite lifetime, the creation of energy at some time would be required—and this is contrary to the first law of thermodynamics. On the other hand, if the universe were assumed to have existed for an infinite time, according to the second law of thermodynamics, the maximum entropy would have been achieved. To solve the paradox, Arrhenius assumed that it is possible that there are galaxies in the universe where processes take place with decreasing entropy. His last paper (1927) was on thermophilic bacteria and the radiation pressure of the sun. In it he stated that on earth there are thermophilic bacteria that exist in volcanic areas at temperatures between 40°C. and 80°C. The temperature of the surface of the planet Venus is 50°C., and Arrhenius thought that it was possible that these bacteria are transported from Venus to earth by radiation pressure. Of course, he did not know of the existence of cosmic radiation, which makes it physically impossible for unprotected living things to survive transportation through interplanetary space.

In addition to his cosmic researches, Arrhenius was concerned with the theory of immunity, an interest that resulted in two textbooks: *Immunochemistry* (1907) and *Quantitative Laws in Biological Chemistry* (1915). After working during the summer of 1902 in the Frankfurt laboratory of the German bacteriologist Paul Ehrlich, Arrhenius and the Danish bacteriologist Thorvald Madsen (later founder and director of the Danish State Serum Institute at Copenhagen) published a paper on physical chemistry applied to toxins and antitoxins (1902). Against Ehrlich, who in his "side-chain theory" regarded the mutual relationship of toxins and antitoxins as a phenomenon of chemical neutralization, Arrhenius postulated a chemical equilibrium between toxin and antitoxin which follows the ordinary mass action law. The immunological phenomenon of antitoxin action was linked to the interaction of a weak acid and a weak base.

Besides the textbooks on immunochemistry and cosmic physics mentioned above, Arrhenius wrote a number of scientific books: *Lärobok i teoretisk elektrokemi* (1900), *Theorien der Chemie* (1906), and *Theories of Solution* (the Silliman Lectures of 1911, published in 1912). Arrhenius devoted most of his later years to popularizing science. His books and articles had a simple but always scientific approach, and were immediate worldwide successes. They were translated into several languages and appeared in numerous editions. Among these are *Världnarnas utveckling* (1906), *Människan inför världsgåtan* (1907), *Das Schicksal der Planeten* (1911), and *Stjärnornas Öden* (1915). His *Kemien och det moderna livet* (1919) contains a popular scientific treatment of the significance and the problems of technical chemistry. These books give a good idea of Arrhenius' aptitude for scientific speculation, a penchant also exhibited in his original ideas in cosmic physics, meteorology, immunology, and in his greatest contribution to chemistry, the theory of electrolytic dissociation.

NOTES

1. *Nordisk revy* (15 December 1884); *cf. Svensk kemisk tidskrift* (1903), 208.
2. *Svensk kemisk tidskrift* (1890), 9.
3. *Bihang till K. Svenska Vet.-Akad. Handlingar,* **8,** no. 14 (1884), 87.
4. *Zeitschrift für phys. Chemie,* **1** (1887), 632.
5. *Ibid.,* p. 637.

BIBLIOGRAPHY

For a bibliography of Arrhenius' works and writings, see E. H. Riesenfeld, *Svante Arrhenius* (Leipzig, 1931), pp.

93–110. In the bibliography given below, the following abbreviations are used: *Bihang* (*Bihang till kungliga vetenskapsakademiens handlingar*); *Öfversigt* (*Öfversigt af kungliga vetenskapsakademiens för handlingar*); *Meddelanden* (*Meddelanden från kungliga vetenskapsakademiens Nobelinstitut*); *Z. phys. Chem.* (*Zeitschrift für physikalische Chemie*).

I. ORIGINAL WORKS. Articles that are autobiographical or deal with the history of the theory of electrolytic dissociation are "The Development of the Theory of Electrolytic Dissociation," in *Les prix Nobel en 1903* (Stockholm, 1905); *Proceedings of the Royal Institute,* **17,** pt. 3 (1906); and *Nobel Lectures Chemistry 1901–1921* (Amsterdam-New York-London, 1966), pp. 45–58; "Electrolytic Dissociation," in *Journal of the American Chemical Society,* **34** (1912), 353–364; "Aus der Sturm- und Drangzeit der Lösungstheorien," in *Chemisch weekblad,* **10** (1913), 584–599; "The Theory of Electrolytic Dissociation," in *Lectures Delivered Before the Chemical Society* (London, 1928), pp. 237–249.

Articles by Arrhenius concerning the theory of electrolytic dissociation are "Recherches sur la conductibilité galvanique des électrolytes," in *Bihang,* **8,** no. 13 (1884) and no. 14 (1884), translated as *Untersuchungen über die galvanische Leitfähigkeit der Elektrolyte,* in Ostwald's *Klassiker der exakten Wissenschaften,* no. 160 (Leipzig, 1907); "Ueber die Dissociation der im Wasser gelösten Stoffe," in *Z. phys. Chem.,* **1** (1887), 631–648, expanded from two papers published in *Öfversigt* (1887), pp. 405–414, 561–575, and translated in the Alembic Club Reprints, no. 19 (Edinburgh, 1929); "Theorie der isohydrischen Lösungen," in *Öfversigt* (1888), pp. 233–247, and *Z. phys. Chem.,* **2** (1888), 284–295; "Einfache Ableitung der Beziehung zwischen osmotischem Druck und Erniedrigung der Dampfspannung," in *Z. phys. Chem.,* **3** (1889), 115–119; "Ueber die Dissociationswärme und den Einfluss der Temperatur auf den Dissociationsgrad der Elektrolyte," *ibid.,* **4** (1889), 96–116; "Ueber die Gleichgewichtsverhältnisse zwischen Elektrolyten," in *Öfversigt* (1889), pp. 619–645, and *Z. phys. Chem.,* **5** (1890), 1–22; "Ueber die Bestimmung der elektrolytischen Dissociation von Salzen mittelst Löslichkeitsversuchen," in *Öfversigt* (1892), pp. 481–494, and *Z. phys. Chem.,* **11** (1893), 391–402; "Ueber die Hydrolyse von Salzen schwacher Säuren und schwacher Basen," in *Z. phys. Chem.,* **13** (1894), 407–411; "Ueber die Aenderung der Stärke schwacher Säuren durch Salzzusatz," *ibid.,* **31** (1899), 197–229; "Zur Berechungsweise des Dissociationsgrades starker Elektrolyte," *ibid.,* **36** (1901), 28–40.

Articles on other physical-chemical subjects are "Ueber die Einwirkung des Lichtes auf das elektrische Leitungsvermögen der Haloïdsalze des Silbers," in *Zeitschrift der Wiener Akademie der Wissenschaft,* **96** (1887), 831–837; "Ueber die Reaktionsgeschwindigkeit bei der Inversion von Rohrzucker durch Säuren," in *Z. phys. Chem.,* **4** (1889), 226–248; and "Zur Theorie der chemischen Reaktionsgeschwindigkeit," in *Bihang,* **24,** no. 2 (1898), and *Z. phys. Chem.,* **28** (1899), 317–335.

Articles about meteorology and cosmic physics are "Ueber den Einfluss der Sonnenstrahlen auf die elektrischen Erscheinungen in der Erdatmosphäre," in *Meteorologische Zeitschrift,* **5** (1888), 297–304, 348–360; "Ueber den Einfluss des atmosphärischen Kohlensäuregehalts auf die Temperatur der Erdoberfläche," in *Bihang,* **22,** no. 1 (1896), 102 ff., excerpted in *Philosophical Magazine,* **41** (1896), 237–276; "Die Einwirkung kosmischer Einflüsse auf die physiologischen Verhältnisse," in *Skandinavisches Archiv für Physiologie,* **8** (1898), 367–426; "Zur Physik des Vulkanismus," in *Geologiska föreningens i Stockholm förhandlingar,* **22,** no. 5 (1901), 26 ff.; "Ueber die Wärmeabsorption durch Kohlensäure," in *Öfversigt* (1901), pp. 25–58, and *Drudes Annalen,* **4** (1901), 689–705; "Lifvets utbredning genon världsrymden," in *Nordisk tidskrift* (1905), pp. 189–200, and *The Monist* (1905), pp. 161 ff.; "Die vermutliche Ursache der Klimaschwankungen," in *Meddelanden,* **1,** no. 2 (1906); "Physikalisch-chemische Gesetzmässigkeiten bei den kosmisch-chemischen Vorgängen," in *Zeitschrift für Elektrochemie,* **28** (1922), 405–411; and "Die thermophilen Bakterien und der Strahlungsdruck der Sonne," in *Z. phys. Chem.,* **130** (1927), 516–519.

An article on serum therapy is "Anwendung der physikalischen Chemie auf das Studium der Toxine und Antitoxine," in *Festskrift v. inv. af Stat. Serum-Inst.* (Copenhagen, 1902), and *Z. phys. Chem.,* **44** (1903), 7–62, written with Thorvald Madsen.

Books by Arrhenius are *Lärobok i teoretisk elektrokemi* (Stockholm, 1900), translated as *Text-Book on Theoretical Electrochemistry* (London-New York, 1902); *Lehrbuch der kosmischen Physik,* 2 vols. (Leipzig, 1903); *Theorien der Chemie* (Leipzig, 1906), translated as *Theories of Chemistry* (London-New York, 1907); *Immunochemistry* (New York, 1907); *Theories of Solution* (London-New Haven, Conn., 1912); and *Quantitative Laws in Biological Chemistry* (New York-London, 1915).

II. SECONDARY LITERATURE. Works on Arrhenius include W. Ostwald, "Svante August Arrhenius," in *Z. phys. Chem.,* **69** (1909), v–xx; J. Walker, "Arrhenius Memorial Lecture," in *Journal of the Chemical Society* (1928), pp. 1380–1401; W. Palmaer, "Arrhenius," in G. Bugge, *Buch der grossen Chemiker* (Weinheim, 1929), II, 443–462, translated and abridged by R. E. Oesper in E. Farber, ed., *Great Chemists* (New York, 1961), pp. 1093–1109; E. H. Riesenfeld, "Svante Arrhenius," in *Berichte der Deutschen Chemischen Gesellschaft,* **63** (1930), 1–40, and *Svante Arrhenius* (Leipzig, 1931); and A. Olander, O. Arrhenius, A. L. Arrhenius-Wold, and G. O. S. Arrhenius, in *Svante Arrhenius till 100-arsminnet av hans födelse* (Stockholm, 1959).

H. A. M. SNELDERS

ARSONVAL, ARSÈNE D' (*b.* Chateau de la Borie, St. Germain-les-Belles, La Porcherie, France, 8 June 1851; *d.* Chateau de la Borie, 31 December 1940), *biophysics.*

The d'Arsonval family was part of France's ancient nobility, having held land and wealth in Limoges for centuries. D'Arsonval studied classics at the Lycée Impérial de Limoges and later at the Collège Ste.-Barbe. By the time he received a baccalaureate degree from the Université de Poitiers (1869), d'Arsonval had decided upon a career in medicine. He was the fourth generation to make this decision. His studies began at Limoges, but after the war of 1870 he continued them in Paris. A chance social encounter with Claude Bernard at the Salon de Lachard altered the course of the young physician's career. Drawn to Bernard's lectures, d'Arsonval on one occasion was able to correct the faulty wiring in Bernard's equipment, permitting the completion of a classroom demonstration. Thereafter d'Arsonval became Bernard's *préparateur* from 1873 to 1878. After Bernard's death he assisted C. Brown-Séquard, eventually replacing him at the Collège de France. With Paul Bert's assistance as Minister of Public Education, the Collège de France was able to establish a laboratory for biophysics at rue St.-Jacques in 1882. D'Arsonval directed the laboratory until 1910, when he moved to the new laboratory at Nogent-sur-Marne, erected with funds raised by public subscription. He directed this laboratory until his retirement in 1931.

Bernard's influence led d'Arsonval formally to give up a medical career for a life of physiological research. His thesis (1876) was on pulmonary elasticity and circulation. The young scientist adopted Bernard's organismic philosophy, adding little to it but a belief that electrical potential was one of the physicochemical characteristics of cells.[1] D'Arsonval believed life was vital but completely deterministic. The primary manifestation of life was the conversion of various forms of energy for work. As Bernard's assistant, d'Arsonval's first projects were on animal heat and body temperature.

In 1882 d'Arsonval was awarded the Prix Montyon of the Académie des Sciences for his ingenious apparatus for studying these problems. His double-chambered calorimeter was remarkably accurate and based upon a new approach. He maintained a constant temperature within its inner chamber by circulating ice water through tubes surrounding the inner chamber. The temperature and quantity of water exchanged was a measure of the heat produced. The constant interior temperature increased the accuracy of gas volume measurements and insured more constant rates of breathing. He also devised thermoelectric needles which allowed Bernard to measure simultaneously the temperature of tissue and blood in adjacent vessels. In 1894 d'Arsonval invented a simplified but less accurate calorimeter for hospital tests.

While assisting Brown-Séquard, d'Arsonval became involved in the former's famous experiments on endocrine extracts. D'Arsonval took personal charge of preparing the extracts and sterilizing them by immersion in high-pressure carbon dioxide atmospheres.[2] Their investigations of the therapeutic properties of animal extracts revealed clues to the later controversial hormone theory of wound healing. They found that testicular extracts from guinea pigs had definite antiseptic properties.[3]

D'Arsonval's most outstanding scientific contributions involved the biological and technological applications of electricity. His early studies dealt with the electrical properties of muscle contraction. He recognized that Bell's new invention, the telephone, provided a perfect device for detecting the current in muscle tissue. Telephones operate on extremely feeble currents similar to animal electricity. Galvanometers then in use drew too much current for sensitive tests. D'Arsonval used a frog muscle to join the mouthpiece of a phone and an induction coil with the receiving portion, which completed the circuit of a functional telephone. This interest in muscle current led to a series of practical inventions in the early 1880's. They included nonpolarizable silver chloride electrodes for biological research, refinement of carbon-rod microphones, and the invention with Marey of myographic equipment. D'Arsonval, in cooperation with Deprez, invented the mobile circuit galvanometer in 1882.[4]

Muscle contraction continued to interest him, especially Ranvier's histological studies of striated muscle and L. Hermann's discovery that a negative potential reading characterized the point of direct excitation of a muscle and was followed by a positive variation throughout the body of the muscle. D'Arsonval's own research on contraction led to the same conclusions about the negative activation potential. Using his highly sensitive galvanometer, d'Arsonval found a feeble positive current during normal rest or tonus, which vanished during the act of direct excitation. Experiments showed that the electrical changes were surface phenomena of approximately the same strength as is needed to induce contraction in a muscle adjacent to an excited nerve or muscle. E. DuBois-Reymond explained the negative action potential by assuming a basic bipolarity in muscles. D'Arsonval believed the contractile elements were Ranvier's disks and that the surface production of electrical charge had a physical explanation. Lippmann had shown that a globule of mercury in acidified water produced a measurable current flow when mechanically deformed. D'Arsonval reversed the argument, stating that every current causes a physical deformation. He theorized that a positive stimulus should cause elongation and a negative variation should cause contraction; he built a model to test his concept. A thin rubber tube was filled with porous plugs impregnated with mercury surrounded by acidified water. When subjected to electrical charges the model acted exactly according to d'Arsonval's predictions.[5] Later studies of the electrical organs of the torpedo fish substantiated his suggestions, which were highly plausible in the absence of an alternate chemical theory.

D'Arsonval also found that high voltage shocks did not always lead to sudden or inevitable death. Artificial respiration could frequently revive victims of accidental electric shock.[6] Gradually d'Arsonval's interests shifted from pure biological research to technological problems. For example, as an aside to his calorimetric work, d'Arsonval designed the first electrically controlled constant temperature incubator for embryological and bacterial research.[7] The d'Arsonval incubator was used well into the twentieth century. He was consulted frequently by E. Marey, and he aided Ferrie in constructing the first triode.[8] D'Arsonval became known as the foremost authority on laboratory apparatus, especially in regard to electrical equipment.

In later years d'Arsonval became increasingly involved in the application of electricity to industry, a role which he clearly enjoyed and fostered. He was instrumental in founding national (1881) and international (1897) societies for electrical science, a government supported laboratory for electrical research (1888), the École Supérieure d'Électricité (1894), an international society for cryogenic studies (1908), and La Compagnie Générale d'Électro-Céramique (1923), to name only a few. He worked with Georges Claude on industrial methods for the liquefaction of gases (1902), was consulted on high energy electrical transmission equipment, served as government science consultant during World War I, and was a constant promoter of the automobile and airplane.

His contribution to medicine, now overshadowed by the antibiotic era, created a minor revolution in clinical therapeutics. D'Arsonval literally founded the paramedical field of physiotherapy. In 1918 he was elected president of the Institute for Actinology. H. Herz, a physicist, built the first high frequency oscillator, and shortly thereafter d'Arsonval used it to experiment upon the effects of high frequency (500,000–1,500,000 c.p.s.), low voltage alternating current on animals. This led him in 1891 to report that no sensory or motor responses were evoked by high frequency currents. As Herz had noted earlier, the only effect was the production of heat.[9] The heating effect could be applied to muscle aches, spasms, tetanus, tumors, arthritis, and circulatory and gynecological problems. D'Arsonval correlated the frequency with expected temperatures for a given period of time.

The first high frequency heat therapy unit was established under d'Arsonval's direction at the Hôtel-Dieu Hospital in 1895. Indeed, electrotherapy was called *d'Arsonvalization* until the broader term *diathermy* came into use after 1920. The applications of high frequency treatment were highly successful. D'Arsonval helped to develop apparatus for electrocoagulation which was widely used for surgical excisions and tumor treatments.[10] High energy procedures were favored because these wavelengths were antibacterial. By 1910 methods of physiotherapy utilizing high frequency waves, X rays, and radium had become a professional discipline.

D'Arsonval's international reputation was closely associated with physiotherapy and industrial applications of electricity. He was an active member of societies for electrotherapy, physics, electronics, civil engineering, electroceramics, and soldering, in addition to being a member of the Society of Biologists, the Academy of Medicine (1888), and the Academy of Sciences (1894). In 1933 the Ministry of Education held an official jubilee for d'Arsonval at the Sorbonne. He was created knight of the Legion of Honor in 1884 and received the Grand Cross in 1931.

NOTES

1. *Lumière électrique,* **7** (1882), 302.
2. *Bulletin de l'Académie de médicine.* Paris, 3rd ser., **27** (1892), 250–261.
3. *Comptes rendus des séances de la Société de biologie.* Paris, 9th ser., **3** (1891), 235, 248–250; O. Glasser, *Medical Physics* (1947), pp. 1582–1583.
4. *Comptes rendus de l'Académie des sciences,* **94** (1882), 1347–1350.
5. *Archives de Physiologie,* 5th ser., **1** (1889), 246–252, 460–472; Chauvois (1937), 160–161.
6. *Comptes rendus de l'Académie des sciences,* **104** (1887), 978–981.
7. *Archives de physiologie,* 5th ser., **2** (1890), 83–86.
8. Chauvois (1937), p. 377.
9. Glasser, p. 414.
10. Chauvois (1937), pp. 270–271, 359.

BIBLIOGRAPHY

I. ORIGINAL WORKS. A bibliography of d'Arsonval's works is *L'oeuvre scientifique du Prof. A. d'Arsonval,* compiled by the Institut d'Actinologie (Paris, 1933). D'Arsonval's technological work may be best approached through his *Traité de physique biologique,* 2 vols. (Paris, 1903); "Nouveaux appareils destinés aux recherches d'électrophysiologie," in *Archives de physiologie,* 5th ser., **1** (1889), 423–437, and "Appareils a température fixe pour embryologie et cultures microbiennes," *ibid.,* **2** (1890), 83–88.

The following articles are only a few of the hundreds of articles written by d'Arsonval: "Les nouvelles applications et les perfectionnements du téléphone," in *Revue scientifique,* **1** (1879), 200–212; "Les sciences physiques en biologie," in *Lumière électrique,* **6** (1882), 174–177, 329–331, 394–395, 415–416, 512–513, 546–547; **7** (1882), 43–45, 64–65, 222–224, 302–303, 352–353, 421–422, 495–497, 519–522, 543–544, 567–570, 595–598; "Recherches sur le téléphone," in *Comptes rendus de l'Académie des sciences,* **95** (1882), 290–292; "Nouvelle méthode calorimétrique applicable a l'homme," in *Comptes rendus de la Société de biologie,* 8th ser., **1** (1884), 651–654; "La mort par l'électricité dans l'industrie . . . Moyens préservateurs," in *Comptes rendus de l'Académie des sciences,* **104** (1887), 978–981; "Relations entre la forme de l'excitation électrique et la réaction néuro-musculaire," in *Archives de physiologie,* **1** (1889), 246–252; "Recherches d'électro-physiologie," *ibid.,* 460–472; **2** (1890), 156–167; "De l'injection des extraits liquides provenant des différent tissus de l'organisme . . .," in *Comptes rendus de la Société de biologie,* 9th ser., **4** (1891), 248–250, or *Bulletin de l'Académie de médecine,* 3rd ser. (1892), pp. 250–261. "Galvanomètre apériodique," written with Deprez, is in *Comptes rendus de l'Académie des sciences,* **94** (1882), 1347–1350. Some of d'Arsonval's letters may be found in L. Delhome, *De Claude Bernard et une correspondance Brown-Séquard-d'Arsonval* (Paris, 1939).

II. SECONDARY LITERATURE. Useful but not always reliable are two works by Louis Chauvois, *D'Arsonval, soixante-cinq ans à travers la science* (Paris, 1937) and *D'Arsonval; une vie, une époque 1851–1940* (Paris, 1945). Other useful articles are J. Belot, "Jubilé du professeur d'Arsonval," in *La presse médicale,* **41,** no. 44 (1933), 899–901, and "D'Arsonval (1851–1940)," in *Journal de radiologie et d'électrologie,* **24** (1941), 49–60; G. Blech, "D'Arsonval's Service to Surgery," in *Archives of Physical Therapy,* **13** (1932), 775–779; G. Bourguignon, "Professor d'Arsonval," *ibid.,* 717–726; H. Bordier, "L'Oeuvre scientifique de d'Arsonval," in *Paris médical,* **88** (1933), v–viii; and Otto Glasser, ed., *Medical Physics* (Chicago, 1947).

CHARLES A. CULOTTA

ARTEDI, PETER (*b.* Anundsjö, Angermanland, Sweden, 27 February/10 March 1705; *d.* Amsterdam, the Netherlands, 27 September 1735), *biology.*

Artedi was the son of a curate, Olaus Arctaedius, and his second wife, Helena Sidenia, the daughter of a court chaplain. In September 1716 the father was appointed to the living of Nordmaling, on the Gulf of Bothnia. Artedi had early shown a strong interest in animals, especially fishes; and that same autumn he was sent to school at Hernösand, where he did well, using out-of-school hours for dissecting fishes

and collecting plants. As soon as he could read Latin, he greedily devoured the writings of the medieval alchemists. With the highest certificate he matriculated at Uppsala University on 30 October 1724 as Petrus Arctelius Angerm., but he used the signature Petrus Arctaedius Angermannus; some years later he assumed the variant Artedi.

Although he was expected to succeed his father (and grandfather) as a clergyman, Artedi devoted his time to chemistry and natural history in the medical faculty, where only Lars Roberg and Olof Rudbeck were interested in natural sciences. Both were old: Roberg, the anatomist, had practically stopped teaching, and lectured privately on the *Problemata* of Aristotle in the light of the principles of Descartes; Rudbeck was engaged in philological investigations and not until 1727 did he start a two-year course on the birds of Sweden. As Linnaeus, who arrived in Uppsala in 1728, wrote, "No one ever heard or saw any anatomy, nor chemistry or botany." Absent, because of the death of his father, when Linnaeus arrived, Artedi returned about March 1729 and their lifelong friendship began. They compared notes and at last divided their interests, Artedi studying fishes, amphibians, mammals, minerals, alchemy, and, in botany, the *Umbelliferae.* Linnaeus describes Artedi as lofty of stature and spare of figure, with long black hair and a face that reminded him of John Ray's: humble-minded, cautious, firm, mature, a man of Old World honor and faith.

In September 1734 Artedi, with the financial aid of his brothers-in-law, set sail for England. He stayed there for nearly a year, studying collections and writing on the literature and taxonomy of fishes, amphibians, and mammals (*Trichozoologia*), and on mineralogy. Returning through Leiden, where he hoped to qualify for the doctor's degree in medicine, Artedi unexpectedly met Linnaeus. He told Linnaeus of the excellent opportunities he had had in England for studying ichthyology and of the kind help of the president of the Royal Society, Sir Hans Sloane. Since Artedi was short of money, Linnaeus introduced him to the chemist Albert Seba of Amsterdam, a well-known collector. Seba entrusted Artedi with the study of the fishes for the third part of his *Thesaurus.* Artedi hired a room in Amsterdam and Linnaeus lived at "Hartekamp," the estate of his Maecenas, George Clifford. The two friends met only once more to discuss Artedi's scientific manuscripts. One evening, returning from a convivial evening with Seba and some friends, Artedi lost his way in the darkness and drowned in one of Amsterdam's many canals.

Thanks to Linnaeus, Artedi's manuscripts were

saved and, according to a vow they had made concerning their scientific papers, Linnaeus published, without altering anything, *Petri Artedi sueci, medici, ichthyologia sive opera omnia de piscibus* (1738). This taxonomically most important work assured Artedi the honor of being the father of the science of ichthyology. It contains an analytical review of the literature and a philosophical dissertation on a natural classification, proving that he and Linnaeus agreed on the principles that were to govern the new systematics. Artedi applied these to the system of fishes and résuméd their synonyms from older literature. In the last section he describes the seventy-two species of fishes he dissected and examined alive, an important comparative anatomy of fishes.

Artedi was the first to settle definitely the notion of genus in zoology; the distinction between species and variety; and the classification into classes, orders, and maniples (families). Most of the descriptions of the fishes in Part III of Seba's *Thesaurus* were prepared by Artedi. Artedi's classification of the *Umbelliferae* was incorporated in the first edition of Linnaeus' *Systema naturae* (1735). In 1905 a manuscript of 1729 on the plants near Nordmaling was published in Uppsala to commemorate the two-hundredth anniversary of Artedi's birth.

BIBLIOGRAPHY

I. ORIGINAL WORKS. Artedi's writings include *Petri Artedi sueci, medici, ichthyologia sive opera omnia de piscibus* (Leiden, 1738), which contains a biography by Linnaeus and was reprinted with an introduction by A. C. Wheeler as No. 15 of Hist. Nat. Class. (Weinheim, 1962); and "Kort förteckning på de träen, buskar åg örter såmm wäxa sponté wid Nordmalings prästebord" ("List of Trees, Bushes and Plants That Are Indigenous in the Glebe-Lands in Nordmaling and the Villages Lying in Its Immediate Vicinity"), in *Yearbook of the Swedish Academy of Science* (Uppsala, 1905).

II. SECONDARY LITERATURE. Works on Artedi are H. Engel, "Some Artedi Documents in the Amsterdam Archives," in *Svenska linnésällskapets årsskrift,* **33–34** (1950–1951), 51–66; E. Lönnberg, "Petrus Artedi, a Bicentenary Memoir," in *Yearbook of the Swedish Academy of Science* (Uppsala, 1905), also translated into English by W. E. Harlock; "Linne og Artedi," in *Svenska linnésällskapets årsskrift,* **2** (1919), 30–43; and "Artedi," in *Svensk Biografisk Lexikon,* II (1920); D. Merriman, "A Rare Manuscript Adding to Our Knowledge of the Work of Peter Artedi," in *Copeia,* **2** (1941), 65–69; and O. Nybelin, "Tvenne opublicerade Artedi manuscript," in *Svenska linnésällskapets årsskrift,* **17** (1934), 35–90.

H. ENGEL

ARTIN, EMIL (*b.* Vienna, Austria, 3 March 1898; *d.* Hamburg, Germany, 20 December 1962), *mathematics.*

Artin was the son of the art dealer Emil Artin and the opera singer Emma Laura-Artin. He grew up in Reichenberg, Bohemia (now Liberec, Czechoslovakia), where he passed his school certificate examination in 1916. After one semester at the University of Vienna he was called to military service. In January 1919 he resumed his studies at the University of Leipzig, where he worked primarily with Gustav Herglotz, and in June 1921 he was awarded the Ph.D.

Following this, he spent one year at the University of Göttingen, and then went to the University of Hamburg, where he was appointed lecturer in 1923, extraordinary professor in 1925, and ordinary professor in 1926. He lectured on mathematics, mechanics, and the theory of relativity. In 1929 he married Natalie Jasny. Eight years later they and their two children emigrated to the United States, where their third child was born. Artin taught for a year at the University of Notre Dame, then from 1938 to 1946 at Indiana University in Bloomington, and from 1946 to 1958 at Princeton. He returned to the University of Hamburg in 1958, and taught there until his death. He was divorced in 1959. His avocations were astronomy and biology; he was also a connoisseur of old music and played the flute, the harpsichord, and the . clavichord.

In 1962, on the three-hundredth anniversary of the death of Blaise Pascal, the University of Clermont-Ferrand, France, conferred an honorary doctorate upon Artin.

In 1921, in his thesis, Artin applied the arithmetical and analytical theory of quadratic number fields over the field of rational numbers to study the quadratic extensions of the field of rational functions of one variable over finite constant fields. For the zeta function of these fields he formulated the analogue of the Riemann hypothesis about the zeros of the classical zeta function. In 1934 Helmut Hasse proved this hypothesis of Artin's for function fields of genus 1, and in 1948 André Weil proved the analogue of the Riemann hypothesis for the general case.

In 1923 Artin began the investigations that occupied him for the rest of his life. He assigned to each algebraic number field k a new type of L-series. The functions

$$L(s,\chi) = \Sigma\chi(n)(Nn)^{-s}$$

—generalizations of the Dirichlet L-series—in which χ is the character of a certain ideal class group and n traverses certain ideals of k were already known.

These functions play an important role in Teiji Takagi's investigations (1920) of Abelian fields K over k. Artin started his L-series from a random Galois field K over k with the Galois group G; he utilized representations of the Frobenius character χ by matrices. Further, he made use of the fact that, according to Frobenius, to each unbranched prime ideal, p, in K, a class of conjugated substitutions σ from G, having the character value $\chi(\sigma)$, can be assigned in a certain manner. Artin made $\chi(p^h) = \chi(\sigma^h)$ and formulated $\chi(p^h)$ for prime ideals p branched in K; he also defined his L-series by the formula

$$\log L(s,\chi,K/k) = \sum_{p,h} h^{-1}\chi(p^h)(Np^h)^{-s}.$$

Artin assumed, and in 1923 proved for special cases, the identity of his L-series formed of simple character and the functions $L(s,\chi)$ for Abelian groups, if at the same time χ were regarded as a certain ideal class character. The proof of this assumption led him to the general law of reciprocity, a phrase he coined. Artin proved this in 1927, using a method developed by Nikolai Chebotaryov (1924). This law includes all previously known laws of reciprocity, going back to Gauss's. It has become the main theorem of class field theory.

With the aid of the theorem, Artin traced Hilbert's assumption, according to which each ideal of a field becomes a principal ideal of its absolute class field, to a theory on groups that had been proved in 1930 by Philip Furtwaengler.

Artin had often pointed to a supposition of Furtwaengler's according to which a series k_i ($i = 1,2, \ldots$) is necessarily infinite if k_{i+1} is an absolute class field over k_i. This was disproved in 1964 by I. R. Safarevic and E. S. Gold.

In 1923 Artin derived a functional equation for his L-series that was completed in 1947 by Richard Brauer. Since then it has been found that the Artin L-series define functions that are meromorphic in the whole plane. Artin's conjecture—that these are integral if χ is not the main character—still remains unproved.

Artin had a major role in the further development of the class field theory, and he stated his results in *Class Field Theory,* written with John T. Tate (1961).

In 1926 Artin achieved a major advance in abstract algebra (as it was then called) in collaboration with Otto Schreier. They succeeded in treating real algebra in an abstract manner by defining a field as real—today we say formal-real—if in it -1 is not representable as a sum of square numbers. They defined a field as real-closed if the field itself was real but none of the algebraic extensions were. They then demonstrated that a real-closed field could be ordered in one exact manner and that in it typical laws of algebra, as it had been known until then, were valid.

With the help of the theory of formal-real fields, Artin in 1927 solved the Hilbert problem of definite functions. This problem, expressed by Hilbert in 1900 in his Paris lecture "Mathematical Problems," is related to the solution of geometrical constructions with ruler and measuring standard, an instrument that permits the marking off of a single defined distance.

In his work on hypercomplex numbers in 1927, Artin expanded the theory of algebras of associative rings, established in 1908 by J. H. Maclagan Wedderburn, in which the double-chain law for right ideals is assumed; in 1944 he postulated rings with minimum conditions for right ideals (Artin rings). In 1927 he further presented a new foundation for, and extension of, the arithmetic of semisimple algebras over the field of rational numbers. The analytical theory of these systems was treated by his student Käte Hey, in her thesis in 1927.

Artin contributed to the study of nodes in three-dimensional space with his theory of braids in 1925. His definition of a braid as a tissue made up of fibers comes from topology, but the method of treatment belongs to group theory.

Artin's scientific achievements are only partially set forth in his papers and textbooks and in the drafts of his lectures, which often contained new insights. They are also to be seen in his influence on many mathematicians of his period, especially his Ph.D. candidates (eleven in Hamburg, two in Bloomington, eighteen in Princeton). His assistance is acknowledged in several works of other mathematicians. His influence on the work of Nicholas Bourbaki is obvious.

BIBLIOGRAPHY

I. ORIGINAL WORKS. Artin's works are in *The Collected Papers of Emil Artin,* Serge Lang and John T. Tate, eds. (Reading, Mass., 1965), and in the books and lecture notes that are listed there, including "Einführung in die Theorie der Gammafunktion" (1931); "Galois Theory" (1942); "Rings With Minimum Condition," written with C. J. Nesbitt and R. M. Thrall (1944); *Geometric Algebra* (1957); and *Class Field Theory,* written with J. T. Tate (1961). Missing from the list is "Vorlesungen über algebraische Topologie," a mathematical seminar given with Hel Braun at the University of Hamburg (1964).

II. SECONDARY LITERATURE. Works on Artin are R. Brauer, "Emil Artin," in *Bulletin of the American Mathematical Society,* **73** (1967), 27–43; H. Cartan, "Emil Artin," in *Abhandlungen aus dem Mathematischen Seminar der Hamburgischen Universität,* **28** (1965), 1–6; C. Chevalley, "Emil Artin," in *Bulletin de la Société mathematique de France,* **92** (1964), 1–10; B. Schoeneberg, "Emil Artin zum Gedächtnis," in *Mathematisch-physikalische Semesterberichte,* **10** (1963), 1–10; and H. Zassenhaus, "Emil Artin and His Work," in *Notre Dame Journal of Formal Logic,* **5** (1964), 1–9, which contains a list of Artin's doctoral candidates.

BRUNO SCHOENEBERG

ĀRYABHAṬA I (*b.* A.D. 476).

Āryabhaṭa I clearly states his connection with Kusumapura (Pāṭaliputra, modern Patna in Bihar), which had been the imperial capital of the Guptas for much of the fourth and fifth centuries. The assertion of Nīlakaṇṭha Somasutvan (*b.* 1443) that Āryabhaṭa was born in the Aśmakajanapada (this presumably refers to the Nizamabad district of Andhra Pradesh) is probably the result of a confusion with his predecessor, Bhāskara I, as commentator on the *Āryabhaṭīya.* Āryabhaṭa I wrote two works: the *Āryabhaṭīya* in 499 (see Essay V), and another, lost treatise in which he expounded the *ārddharātrika* system (see Essay VI).

The *Āryabhaṭīya* consists of three parts and a brief introduction: *Daśagītikā,* introduction with parameters (ten verses); *Gaṇitapāda,* mathematics (thirty-three verses); *Kālakriyāpāda,* the reckoning of time and the planetary models (twenty-five verses); *Golapāda,* on the sphere, including eclipses (fifty verses). It was translated into Arabic in about 800 under the title *Zīj al-Arjabhar,* and it is to this translation that all the quotations in al-Bīrūnī refer, including those that led Kaye to conclude—mistakenly—that the *Gaṇitapāda* was not written by Āryabhaṭa I.

The *Āryabhaṭīya* has been commented on many times, especially by scholars of south India, where it was particularly studied. The names of those commentators who are known are as follows:

1. Prabhākara (*ca.* 525). His commentary is lost.

2. Bhāskara I (629). His *Bhāṣya* is being edited by K. S. Śukla of Lucknow.

3. Someśvara (*fl.* 1040). His *Vāsanābhāṣya* is preserved in two manuscripts in the Bombay University Library.

4. Sūryadeva Yajvan of Kerala (*b.* 1191). There are many manuscripts of his *Bhaṭaprakāśa,* in south India.

5. Parameśvara (*fl.* 1400–1450). His *Bhaṭadīpikā,* based on Sūryadeva's *Bhaṭaprakāśa,* was published by H. Kern (see below).

6. Nīlakaṇṭha Somasutvan (*b.* 1443). His *Bhāṣya* is published in *Trivandrum Sanskrit Series* (see below).

7. Yallaya (*fl.* 1482). His *Vyākhyāna* is based on Sūryadeva's *Bhaṭaprakāśa;* there is one manuscript of it in Madras and another among the Mackenzie manuscripts in the India Office Library.

8. Raghunātha (*fl.* 1590). His *Vyākhyā* is dealt with by K. Madhava Krishna Sarma, "The *Āryabhaṭīyavyākhyā* of Raghunātharāja—A Rare and Hitherto Unknown Work," in *Brahmavidyā,* **6** (1942), 217–227.

9. Kodaṇḍarāma of the Koṭikalapūḍikula, a resident of Bobbili in the Godāvarī district of Andhra Pradesh (*fl.* 1854). Besides an *Āryabhaṭatantragaṇita,* he wrote a Telugu commentary on the *Āryabhaṭīya* entitled *Sudhātaraṅga;* it was edited by V. Lakshmi Narayana Sastri, in *Madras Government Oriental Series,* **139** (Madras, 1956).

10. Bhūtiviṣṇu. There is apparently only one manuscript (in Berlin) and its apograph (in Washington, D.C.) of his commentary (*Bhāsya*) on the *Daśagītikā.*

11. Ghaṭīgopa. There are two manuscripts of his *Vyākhyā* in Trivandrum.

12. Virūpākṣa Sūri. There is a manuscript of his Telugu commentary in Mysore.

There also exists a Marāṭhī translation of the *Āryabhaṭīya* in a manuscript at Bombay.

There are several editions of the *Āryabhaṭīya.* That by H. Kern (Leiden, 1874) is accompanied by the commentary of Parameśvara. Kern's text and commentary were reprinted and translated into Hindi by Udaya Nārāyana Singh (Madhurapur, Etawah, 1906). A new edition of the text, with the commentary of Nīlakaṇṭha Somasutvan (who does not include the *Daśagītikā*), was published in three volumes: Vols. I and II by K. Sāmbaśiva Śāstrī and Vol. III by Suranad Kunjan Pillai, in *Trivandrum Sanskrit Series,* **101, 110,** and **185** (Trivandrum, 1930, 1931, 1957). The text has also been published accompanied by two new commentaries, one in Sanskrit and one in Hindi, by Baladeva Mishra (Patna, 1966). The *Gaṇitapāda* was translated into French by Léon Rodet, in *Journal Asiatique,* **7,** no. 13 (1879), 393–434; and into English by G. R. Kaye, in *Journal of the Asiatic Society of Bengal,* **4** (1908), 111–141. Complete English translations have been made by Baidyanath Rath Sastri (Chicago, 1925; unpub.); P. C. Sengupta, *Journal of the Department of Letters of Calcutta University,* **16** (1927), 1–56; and W. E. Clark (Chicago, 1930).

BIBLIOGRAPHY

It is intended here to include references only to those books and articles that are primarily concerned with Āryabhata I and his works; the many other papers and volumes that mention and/or discuss him can be found listed in David Pingree, *Census of the Exact Sciences in India.* Listed chronologically, the references are F.-E. Hall, "On the Ārya-siddhānta," in *Journal of the American Oriental Society,* **6** (1860), 556–559, with an "Additional Note on Āryabhaṭṭa and his Writings" by the Committee of Publication (essentially W. D. Whitney), *ibid.,* 560–564; H. Kern, "On Some Fragments of Āryabhaṭa," in *Journal of the Royal Asiatic Society,* **20** (1863), 371–387; repr. in Kern's *Vespreide Geschriften,* I (The Hague, 1913), 31–46; Bhāu Dājī, "Brief Notes on the Age and Authenticity of the Works of Āryabhaṭa, Varāhamihira, Brahmagupta, Bhaṭṭotpala, and Bhāskarāchārya," in *Journal of the Royal Asiatic Society* (1865), pp. 392–418 (Āryabhaṭa only pp. 392–406, 413–414); L. Rodet, "Sur la véritable signification de la notation numérique inventée par Āryabhaṭa," in *Journal Asiatique,* ser. 7, **16** (1880), 440–485; Sudhākara Dvivedin, *Gaṇakataraṅgiṇī* (Benares, 1933; repr. from *The Pandit,* **14** [1892]), 2–7; Ś. B. Dīkṣita, *Bhāratīya Jyotiḥśāstra* (Poona, 1931; repr. of Poona ed., 1896), pp. 190–210; G. Thibaut, *Astronomie, Astrologie und Mathematik, Grundriss der indo-arischen Philologie und Altertumskunde,* III, pt. 9, (Strasbourg, 1899), 54–55; T. R. Pillai, *Ārybhaṭa or the Newton of Indian Astronomy* (Madras, 1905—not seen—reviewed in *Indian Thought* [1907], pp. 213–216); G. R. Kaye, "Two Āryabhaṭas," in *Bibliotheca mathematica,* **10** (1910), 289–292; J. F. Fleet, "Āryabhaṭa's System of Expressing Numbers," in *Journal of the Royal Asiatic Society* (1911), pp. 109–126; N. K. Mazumdar, "Āryyabhatta's Rule in Relation to Indeterminate Equations of the First Degree," in *Bulletin of the Calcutta Mathematical Society,* **3** (1911/1912), 11–19; J. F. Fleet, "Tables for Finding the Mean Place of Saturn," in *Journal of the Royal Asiatic Society* (1915), pp. 741–756; P. C. Sengupta, "Āryabhaṭa's Method of Determining the Mean Motions of Planets," in *Bulletin of the Calcutta Mathematical Society,* **12** (1920/1921), 183–188.

See also R. Sewell, "The First Arya Siddhanta," in *Epigraphia Indica,* **16** (1921/1922), 100–144, and **17** (1923–1924), 17–104; A. A. Krishnaswami Ayyangar, "The Mathematics of Āryabhaṭa," in *Quarterly Journal of the Mythic Society,* **16** (1926), 158–179; B. Datta, "Two Āryabhaṭas of al-Biruni," in *Bulletin of the Calcutta Mathematical Society,* **17** (1926), 59–74; S. K. Ganguly, "Was Āryabhaṭa Indebted to the Greeks for His Alphabetical System of Expressing Numbers?," *ibid.,* 195–202, and "Notes on Āryabhaṭa," in *Journal of the Bihar and Orissa Research Society,* **12** (1926), 78–91; B. Datta, "Āryabhaṭa, the Author of the *Gaṇita,*" in *Bulletin of the Calcutta Mathematical Society,* **18** (1927), 5–18; S. K. Ganguly, "The Elder Āryabhaṭa and the Modern Arithmetical Notation," in *American Mathematical Monthly,* **34** (1927), 409–415; P. C. Sengupta, "Āryabhaṭa, the Father of Indian Epicyclic Astronomy," in *Journal of the Department of Letters of Calcutta University,* **18** (1929), 1–56; S. K. Ganguly, "The Elder Āryabhaṭa's Value of π," in *American Mathematical Monthly,* **37** (1930), 16–29; P. C. Sengupta, "Āryabhaṭa's Lost Work," in *Bulletin of the Calcutta Mathematical Society,* **22** (1930), 115–120; B. Datta, "Elder Āryabhaṭa's Rule for the Solution of Indeterminate Equations of the

First Degree," *ibid.,* **24** (1932), 19–36; P. K. Gode, "Appayadīkṣita's Criticism of Āryabhaṭa's Theory of the Diurnal Motion of the Earth (*Bhūbhramavāda*)," in *Annals of the Bhandarkar Oriental Research Institute,* **19** (1938), 93–95, repr. in Gode's *Studies in Indian Literary History,* II, *Singhi Jain Series,* **38** (Bombay, 1954), 49–52; S. N. Sen, "Āryabhaṭa's Mathematics," in *Bulletin of the National Institute of Sciences of India,* **21** (1963), 297–319; Satya Prakash, *Founders of Sciences in Ancient India* (New Delhi, 1965), pp. 419–449.

DAVID PINGREE

ĀRYABHAṬA II (*fl.* between *ca.* A.D. 950 and 1100).

Of the personality of Āryabhaṭa II, the author of the *Mahāsiddhānta* (or *Āryasiddhānta*), virtually nothing is known. His date can be established only by his alleged dependence on Śrīdhara, who wrote after Mahāvīra (*fl.* 850) and before Abhayadeva Sūri (*fl.* 1050); and by his being referred to by Bhāskara II (*b.* 1114). He must be dated, then, between *ca.* 950 and 1100. Kaye's strange theories about the two Āryabhaṭas, which would have placed Āryabhaṭa II before al-Bīrūnī (963–after 1048), have been refuted by Datta. Nothing further can be said of Āryabhaṭa II; manuscripts of his work are found in Mahārāṣṭra, Gujarat, and Bengal.

The *Mahāsiddhānta* (see Essay VII) consists of eighteen chapters:

1. On the mean longitudes of the planets.

2. On the mean longitudes of the planets according to the (otherwise unknown) *Parāśarasiddhānta.*

3. On the true longitudes of the planets.

4. On the three problems relating to diurnal motion.

5. On lunar eclipses.

6. On solar eclipses.

7. On the projection of eclipses and on the lunar crescent.

8–9. On the heliacal risings and settings of the planets.

10. On the conjunctions of the planets.

11. On the conjunctions of the planets with the stars.

12. On the *pātas* of the sun and moon.

Chapters 13–18 form a separate section entitled *Golādhyāya* ("On the Sphere").

13. Questions on arithmetic, geography, and the mean longitudes of the planets.

14–15. On arithmetic and geometry.

16. On geography.

17. Shortcuts to finding the mean longitudes of the planets.

18. On algebra.

The *Mahāsiddhānta* was edited, with his own Sanskrit commentary, by MM. Sudhākara Dvivedin, in *Benares Sanskrit Series* **148–150** (Benares, 1910).

BIBLIOGRAPHY

Works dealing with Āryabhaṭa II, listed chronologically, are F. Hall, "On the Ārya-Siddhānta," in *Journal of the American Oriental Society,* **6** (1860), 556–559; G. R. Kaye, "Two Āryabhaṭas," in *Bibliotheca mathematica,* **10** (1910), 289–292; J. F. Fleet, "The Katapayadi Notation of the Second Arya-Siddhanta," in *Journal of the Royal Asiatic Society* (1912), 459–462; B. Datta, "Two Āryabhaṭas of al-Biruni," in *Bulletin of the Calcutta Mathematical Society,* **17** (1926), 59–74, and "Āryabhaṭa, the Author of the *Gaṇita,*" ibid., **18** (1927), 5–18; Ś. B. Dīkṣita, *Bhāratīya Jyotiḥśāstra* (Poona, 1931; repr. from Poona, 1896), pp. 230–234.

DAVID PINGREE

ARZACHEL. See **al-Zarqālī.**

ASADA GŌRYŪ (*b.* Kizuki, Bungo Province, Japan, 10 March 1734; *d.* Osaka, Japan, 25 June 1799), *astronomy.*

Asada was instrumental in turning Japanese astronomy and calendrical science away from the traditional Chinese style and toward Western models. His given name was Yasuaki, but he is better known by his pen name, Gōryū. He was the fourth son of Ayabe Yasumasa, a Confucian scholar-administrator of the Kizuki fief government.

Asada taught himself medicine and astronomy. Because Japanese books written on the basis of the Chinese *Shou-shih* calendrical system (promulgated in 1281) were abundant and popular in his youth, his first steps in the study of astronomy must have been to read some of these works. He may also have had direct access to some Chinese writings of the seventeenth- and early eighteenth-century Jesuit missionaries.

Asada placed great weight upon empirical verification, and every time he came across a new theory, he determined its value by observation. The earliest record of an observation by him is that of a lunar eclipse in 1757.

A year before the current official ephemeris caused a crisis of confidence in the official techniques by miscalculating a solar eclipse in 1763, Asada had already pointed out the systematic error and had shown the results of his calculations to his friends. When the day arrived, the eclipse coincided exactly with his calculations. It is apparent that his capacity as a student of astronomy was far superior to that

of the official astronomers of the shogunate. Because the position of official astronomer was hereditary, it often happened that the incumbent lacked the ability required to produce a sound revision of the calendar. Such untalented officials did no more than concentrate on preserving their sinecures. Within this hereditary bureaucracy conservatism naturally prevailed, and the spirit of free inquiry was stifled; innovations were dangerous. But in the eighteenth century astronomical knowledge was diffused by various means to private scholars, who then openly criticized the failure of the official ephemeris. Asada was most prominent among those amateur astronomers.

Asada was financially dependent upon his father until 1767; the freedom from money worries left him free to devote himself to the study of astronomy and medicine. In that year, however, he was appointed a physician of the fief government, and since he was ever on the move accompanying his feudal lord to Edo (Tokyo) or Osaka, he found it impossible to pursue his favorite study. He repeatedly implored his lord to excuse him from service, but in vain. He made up his mind at last to desert his fief and in 1772 went to Osaka, where he resumed the study of astronomy, making his living by practicing medicine. It was during his residence in Osaka that he changed his surname from Ayabe to Asada, because normal relations with his fief could no longer be openly maintained.

Osaka was the right choice for his residence, for the city was the focus of nationwide commercial activities; and the wealthy Osaka merchants, whose financial power often surpassed that of the fief governments, could afford expensive imported books and could support instrument-making and astronomical observation. Such was the case of the wealthy merchant Hazama Shigetomi (1756–1816), one of Asada's most able pupils.

Asada and his school introduced modern instruments and observational methods into Japan. Traditional fieldwork was limited largely to solstitial observations of gnomon shadows, eclipses, and occultations. It was customary to make regular observations during the few years preceding an anticipated calendar reform; beyond this, only occasional checks were made. Earlier astronomers had done little more than make minor amendments to the *Shou-shih* calendar.

Long before, the shogun Tokugawa Yoshimune (1684–1751) had intended to carry out observations with new instruments, but even at the time of the *Hōryaku* calendar reform in 1755, astronomers employed instruments of the traditional Chinese type, such as the gnomon. Japanese observations up to this period had been much inferior to those of Kou Shou-ching in thirteenth-century China; the data could be used only to check a calendar, not to make significant improvements.

Now the Asada school began to gather more reliable data. Asada himself initiated techniques for precise observation. He ground lenses and made a telescope, which he used to observe the movements of Jupiter's satellites. Hazama showed the greatest talent of his time for inventing and improving instruments; expending his wealth freely, he also sponsored the training of talented instrument-makers and conducted systematic observations with the assistance of his employees.

Only a few of Asada's treatises exist. One of them, *Jikkenroku* ("Records Based on Observations," 1786), gives the essentials of his calendar; taking the winter solstice of 1781 as the temporal origin and Osaka as the standard station, he gives the fundamental constants and his method for determining the positions of the sun and the moon, and calculating solar and lunar eclipses. He adopted the method described in the first volume of the Chinese *Li-hsiang k'ao-ch'eng* ("Compendium of Calendrical Science," 1713)—essentially Tychonian in content—which was his chief means of studying Western astronomy. The constants employed for calculation were mostly new ones that Asada had worked out from his own data.

In the spring of 1793 he made a considerable correction in the constant for the distance between the sun and the earth, and corrected other constants affected by it. That the corrected constant is almost identical with that given in the partly Keplerian sequel to the *Li-hsiang k'ao-ch'eng* (*hou p'ien,* compiled in 1737) shows that Asada had access to the sequel about this time, when he came across the theory of the elliptic orbit and became aware of the gross error in the constant for the distance of the sun given in the first volume. It seems, remarkably enough, that Asada retained the old theory concerning the mode of the motions of the sun and the moon while he made radical corrections in the important constants, evidently for the purpose of testing their adaptability. From the time that Asada obtained the sequel to the *Li-hsiang k'ao-ch'eng,* through the efforts of Hazama, he and his best pupils occupied themselves with studying the theory of the elliptic orbit.

The sequel employs Kepler's first and second laws without reference to the heliocentric system. Dynamics, as an approach, is absent, and the name of Newton is associated only with observational data, most of which are J. D. Cassini's. The arrangement of the treatise is to a great extent that dictated by traditional Chinese calendar-making practice. Within this framework it was unnecessary to relate Kepler's laws to heliocentric coordinates. Lack of interest in planetary motion in traditional calendar-making seems to have made adoption of the third law unnecessary.

Asada's pupils attributed two major innovations to him—cyclic variation of astronomical parameters and independent discovery of Kepler's third law.

He mistakenly claimed the discovery of the Antarctic continent by means of lunar eclipse observations. After repeated observations of the shadow of the earth projected on the surface of the moon, Asada came to believe that the parts of the shadow corresponding to the South Pole and the Asian continent are somewhat more upthrust than the other parts of the shadow, and identified part of the shadow outline with the Antarctic continent, which appeared on a world map newly imported from the West.

Asada, after settling down in Osaka, was busily engaged for twenty years in making observations and in educating his pupils. Consequently, his influence increased and led to the formation of an important school of calendrical scientists. For this reason, when the shogunate proposed to revise the current Japanese calendar by use of the new theories of Western astronomy and found that its own official astronomers were not equal to the task, it turned to him. Instead of accepting the appointment himself, Asada recommended his best pupils, Takahashi Yoshitoki (1764–1804) and Hazama. Takahashi, since he belonged to the Samurai class (although he was only a minor official), was appointed an official astronomer; Hazama became a consultant or assistant.

When Asada deserted his fief and hid in Osaka, his feudal lord, to whom his whereabouts was known, was generous enough not to charge him with the crime of desertion, and even permitted him to communicate with his relatives at home, because he was eager for him to succeed in his pursuit of learning. This made it possible for Asada to receive a gift of some money each year from his eldest brother and thus to study astronomy without being destitute. Asada was so grateful to his former master for this that when he became a well-known scholar and was offered a high position by other feudal lords—and even by the shogunate—he always refused, saying that he could not turn his back on his former lord.

In Asada's later years a limited number of Japanese pioneers, the *rangakusha* (scholars of Dutch learning), undertook the prodigious and almost completely unaided labor of translating Dutch scientific works into Japanese. In the 1770's a notable expansion of the study of the Dutch language and of science led to a movement for the translation of Dutch scientific works—or retranslation of Dutch translations of European works. This task was begun by two groups, the official interpreters at Nagasaki, who alone were authorized access to foreign books, and the physicians of Edo.

The interpreters concentrated on introducing the core of genuine Western science—particularly of elementary astronomy, navigation, and geography—but this material did not have much interest for practical astronomers, except when directly applicable to traditional calendar-making. Men like Asada wanted observational data and astronomical constants. For this reason the writings of the Jesuit missionaries in China, although cosmologically obsolete, were much more useful to him. He himself had found no time to learn the Dutch language.

In studying medicine, as in studying astronomy, Asada collected and read the very best literature. He also dissected dogs and cats, and thus became acquainted with internal organs. From Asada's expounding of Western-style astronomy, some people conclude that his medical art was copied from some Dutch school of medicine. This is entirely wrong. At the time that Asada taught himself there were a few Japanese physicians who taught a type of very elementary Western-style surgery, but there was no proper literature for students. As for the European style of internal treatment, no one in Japan knew about it, and naturally there was nothing written on it. Asada could have had no access to what knowledge was available. Thus, his style of medicine was not Western, but the positivistic and clinical *koihō* (ancient medical learning) school that flourished during the mid-eighteenth century in Japan.

In Osaka, Asada practiced medicine, but it was only a means to make his living. All his energy had been devoted to the study of astronomy, but now his research was temporarily completed. When, in addition, Takahashi and Hazama, on whom his mantle had fallen, accomplished the task of revising the official calendar in 1797 and Asada himself was rewarded by the shogunate, he could say, "I have found men who will develop my astronomy. I have henceforth to devote myself to the study of medicine."

His health failed about the beginning of 1798 and he suffered a stroke, of which he died in the summer of the following year.

In praise of Asada, his distinguished pupil Takahashi stated in his *Zōshū shōchō hō* ("Variations of Astronomical Parameters," rev. and enl., 1798):

> Laboring over Chinese and Western works, Asada Gōryū at Osaka discovered the *shōchō* law. Although Western astronomy is most advanced, we have not heard of its mentioning this law, known only in our country. Therefore I have said that although we are unable to boast about our achievements in comparison with those

of the Westerners, my country should be proud of this man and his discovery.

This is perhaps the only notable originality to be found in the entire history of Japanese astronomy; it therefore merits critical examination.

In adopting the idea of *shōchō* (*hsiao-ch'ang* in Chinese, the secular diminution of tropical-year length), astronomers at the time of the *Shou-shih* and *Jōkyō* (promulgated in 1685) calendars were required only to account for the ancient records and modern data of Chinese solstitial observations by a single formula. While it is true that neither the Jesuits nor the Chinese had incorporated the concept of *hsiao-ch'ang* into their calendars during the Ming and Ch'ing periods, the Jesuit compilation *Ch'ung-chen li-shu* ("Ch'ung-chen Reign Period Treatise on Calendrical Science," 1635) pointed out three possible causes of variation in tropical-year length: (1) rotation of the center of the solar orbit in reference to the earth (perhaps referring to the progressive motion of the solar perigee); (2) variation of the eccentricity of the solar orbit; (3) variable precession (trepidation). Numerical values were not given, however, because such a minute parameter was not determinable within a single lifetime.

Classical Western data, such as those listed in the *Almagest* of Ptolemy, became available to Asada through the Jesuit treatises. He dared endeavor to synthesize Western and Chinese astronomy and to give a numerical explanation, by means of a single principle, of all the observational data available to him—old and new, Eastern and Western.

It seems that Asada did not fully comprehend the epicyclic system, based on that of Tycho Brahe, which appeared in the Jesuit works. In Western astronomy, only observed data and numerical parameters interested him. These he could utilize for his purely traditional approach, that of obtaining an algebraic representation that corresponded as closely as possible to the observed phenomena.

Copernicus appears in the *Ch'ung-chen li'shu,* not as an advocate of heliocentrism but as an observational astronomer and the inventor of the eighth sphere of trepidation. He is said in that work to have believed that the ancient tropical year was longer than that of the Middle Ages, which in turn was shorter than the contemporary constant. Asada, perhaps struck by this passage, formulated a modified conception in which the length of the ancient tropical year tended to decrease until it reached a minimum in the Middle Ages and to grow longer afterward, varying in a precession cycle of 25,400 years. The minimum was not associated with the solar perigee, but was arbitrarily chosen in order to fit the recorded data. He also presumed that the only perpetual constant was the length of the anomalistic (sidereal) year. Other basic parameters, such as the length of the synodic, nodical, and anomalistic months, were assumed to be subject to variation in a precession cycle. This idea seems to have originated in the Chinese *T'ung-t'ien* calendar (1199) of the Sung period. In the West, the first systematic study of the variation of basic astronomical parameters was carried out by Laplace on the basis of the perturbation theory. Although superficially similar, Asada's approach was by no means comparable with Laplace's well-founded theoretical considerations.

Although the mathematical derivation is quite complicated, the length of the tropical year, T, in Asada's formula is essentially expressed in terms of the equations

$$T = 365.250469717756 - 1.038645 \times 10^{-5}t,$$

where t is years elapsed since the epoch of 720 B.C. (this equation is valid up to A.D. 133), and

$$T = 365.2416204385 + 0.0435370 \times 10^{-5}t,$$

where t is years elapsed since the epoch of A.D. 133 (this equation is valid up to A.D. 11981).

These two equations together cover only half of the precession cycle since 720 B.C. In the other half of the cycle, t is expressed in the dotted line of Figure 1. Applying this formula to historical observations, we see in Figure 2 the extent to which it reconciles the data. After A.D. 133, the year of the epoch, the formulas of Simon Newcomb, Asada, and the *Shou-shih* calendar roughly coincide. Before the epoch, Asada's formula appears as a parabola of deep curvature, which comprehends the Greek observations as well as the ancient Chinese records. It is apparent

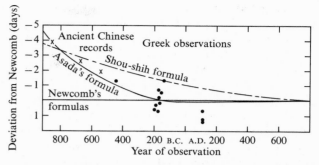

The X-axis represents the calculated value following Newcomb's formula. Each observation is plotted with the indication of the amount of deviation from calculation in the Y-axis direction (negative values represent times earlier than the calculated date, and positive later).

FIGURE 2

that what Asada really intended to do was account for the newly acquired Western data. His basic goal, that of "saving the ancient records" by numerical manipulation, differs not at all from that of the traditional approach. His consideration of the precession cycle was theoretical decoration.

In spite of resistance from the conservative hereditary official astronomers, Asada's pupils finally succeeded in applying Asada's variation term to the *Kansei* calendar promulgated in 1798. In the same year, Takahashi wrote the *Zōshū shōchō hō* in order to provide a theoretical foundation for his teacher's method. Takahashi had attained a mastery of the theory of spherical geometry and epicycles. Furthermore, rejecting the authority of Tycho, he revived the old idea of trepidation as contained in the *Ch'ung-chen li-shu,* in which trepidation was somewhat vaguely mentioned in order to contrast it with Tycho's more accurate view. Unlike Alphonsine trepidation, which had a 7,000-year cycle, however, Takahashi's cycle of trepidation had the same period as the cycle of precession.

The falsity of Asada's variation concept soon became apparent. In the 1830's it was realized that observations did not agree with the *Kansei* calendar; removal of Asada's variation factors gave better agreement. Asada's idea was doomed. In the next calendar reform, that of *Tenpo* (1843), it was entirely neglected.

During the Tokugawa period (seventeenth to early nineteenth centuries) Japanese astronomers were continually preoccupied by the contrast between Chinese and Western astronomy. While they generally followed Chinese astronomy in the first half of the period, Western astronomy became dominant during the latter half. During the period of transition there appeared mental attitudes like those of Asada,

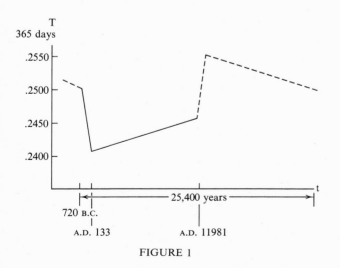

FIGURE 1

who tended to syncretize and synthesize Chinese and Western astronomy. His originality proved to be rather anachronistic, however, in view of the rapid contemporary development of Western astronomy.

His pupils claimed for Asada the honor of having independently discovered the relationship between the distances of planets from the sun and the periods of their revolution (in other words, Kepler's third law), although he did not publish it. Ōtani Ryōkichi maintained, however, that the law was first known in Japan in 1800, after Asada's death, when his pupils obtained the Dutch translation of J. J. L. de Lalande's *Astronomie*. Kepler's third law had, as a matter of fact, been described in the *Tenmon kanki* ("Astronomical Collection," 1782), one of Shizuki Tadao's draft translations of the Dutch version of John Keill's *Introductiones ad veram astronomiam*. One suspects that Asada somehow had the chance to become acquainted with Shizuki's works.

There is another possible interpretation. Prior to Asada's time, Chinese and Japanese observations of planetary motions were infrequent and imprecise. Even if neither the Keplerian planetary theory nor adequate observational data were available to him, he was fully acquainted with the first two volumes of the *Li-hsiang k'ao-ch'eng*, in which values for the relative sizes of planetary orbits are mentioned. These are close to the modern values, as they are calculated by trigonometry in the post-Copernican fashion. Thus, Asada might have tried a blind search for some numerical relationship between these values and the planets' revolution periods, and finally reached Kepler's third law independently.

Asada was not geometry-oriented, as were Western astronomers, but he was accustomed to the traditional algebraic approach and was fascinated by numerical manipulation. It would have been impossible for him to recognize the potential importance of Kepler's third law, which led to the discovery of Newton's inverse-square law and the establishment of modern mechanics.

Although Asada missed the meaning of his alleged discovery, it is interesting that his pupils believed that Asada had suggested a crude analogy between a balance and the solar system in a pseudomechanistic interpretation of Kepler's third law. Hazama elaborated it in his own fashion, as follows:

If we express a weight in a balance as the area of a square, the side of which is x, the relationship between arm length a and weight x^2 is $ax^2 = $ constant. A similar relationship holds between length l and frequency v of a pendulum: $lv^2 = $ constant.

The radius of planetary orbit r seems to correspond to balance arm length a, which in turn corresponds to pendulum length l. The velocity of the planet v is taken to correspond to the frequency of the pendulum v. An analogous relationship between r and v thus should hold in the planetary domain: $rv^2 = $ constant. Substituting $2r/T$ ($T = $ period of revolution) for v in the above equation, $r^3/T^2 = $ constant is obtained. In this way, we arrive at Kepler's third law.

The argument is, of course, quite misleading, but at a time when modern mechanics was not well understood, this crude analogy between planetary motion and simple mechanical laws gave an explanation satisfactory to Hazama's contemporaries.

BIBLIOGRAPHY

I. ORIGINAL WORKS. Asada has left unusually few works. Almost all of his ideas appear in his pupils' writings and compilations. Notable among his own works are *Jichūhō* ("The Method of the Jichū Calendar" [1786]), MS preserved in Mukyūkai Library; *Shōchō hō* ("Variation of Astronomical Parameters" [1788]), MS preserved in Tohoku University Library; *Gekkei o motte nisshoku o osu hō* ("A Method to Predict Solar Eclipses by Means of Observing the Moon's Shadow" [n.d.]), MS preserved in the Sonkeikaku Library; *Gosei kyochi no kihō* ("Remarkable Law of Planetary Distance" [n.d.]), MS preserved in the Sonkeikaku Library; and Takahashi Yoshitoki, *Zōshū shōchō hō* ("Variation of Astronomical Parameters," enl. and rev. [1798]), MS preserved in the Tokyo Astronomical Observatory.

II. SECONDARY LITERATURE. Works on Asada in English are Shigeru Nakayama, "Cyclic Variation of Astronomical Parameters and the Revival of Trepidation in Japan," in *Japanese Studies in the History of Science*, no. 3 (1964), 68–80, and *Outline History of Japanese Astronomy* (Cambridge, Mass., in press); and Ryōkichi Ōtani, *Tadataka Inō* (Tokyo, 1932).

A work on Asada in Japanese is Nishimura Tachū (one of Asada's four major pupils), "Asada sensei gyōjōki" ("Achievements of Master Asada") in Nomura Jun *et al.*, eds., *Nishimura Tachū jiseki* ("Achievements of Nishimura Tachū" [Toyama, 1934]). Watanabe Toshio is now preparing a comprehensive biography of Asada.

SHIGERU NAKAYAMA

ASCLEPIADES (*b*. Prusa, Bithynia, *ca*. 130 B.C.; *d*. Rome, *ca*. 40 B.C.), *medicine*.

Trained originally as a philosopher and orator, Asclepiades achieved fame as a physician in Rome. He had a large practice and wealthy patients, and was befriended by Cicero, Crassus, and other influential Romans. At the height of his fame he was invited to become the personal physician of Mithridates Eupator, king of Pontus, but he declined and remained in Rome until his death. His forceful personality, his clinical successes, and the simplicity of his therapeutic counsels aided in the acceptance of his doctrines and did much to overcome the Roman prejudice against Greek medicine. None of his many writings has survived intact.

Asclepiades rejected the teachings of Hippocrates and other advocates of humoralism in favor of his own original system of solidism. Thoroughly and consistently materialistic, his doctrines derived partially from Epicurean atomism and partially from the now lost, quasi-atomistic teachings of Heracleides Ponticus. The most important ideas derived from his predecessors were a theory of knowledge based upon sensory appearances alone and the rejection of teleology. These, plus his atomism, provided the philosophical basis of his medical theories. All diseases, Asclepiades held, resulted from an abnormal arrangement of the atoms relative to the "pores" that constituted the physical basis of the human body. Since he also denied the healing power of nature, it followed that diseases could be cured by human intervention. His therapy was simple but effective, and capable of innumerable modifications, depending upon the patient's condition and his purse. He relied principally upon diet, exercise, massage, and baths, avoiding, whenever possible, powerful drugs and surgery. The purpose of therapy was to restore the atomic constituents of the human body to their normal state of unimpeded movement. By means of a controlled regimen, he claimed that he was capable of achieving the goal of a good physician—*curare tuto, celeriter et jucunde* ("to cure safely, swiftly, and pleasantly").

Despite the rigid outlines of his mechanistic system, Asclepiades wisely was not always consistent in his adherence to it or in its practical application. His writings on the pulse show the influence of Stoic pneumatic theory. He recognized a limited role for enemas, surgery, bloodletting, and cupping; but he was violently opposed to the study of anatomy. For this reason, and perhaps because of his extravagant claims of success, he was much maligned and criticized for charlatanry. His influence in antiquity, however, was great, and he is often cited by Caelius Aurelianus, Celsus, and Galen. The philosophical and theoretical foundations of the methodist school can, in part, be traced back to Asclepiades' pupil, Themison of Laodicea.

Among the several hundred fragments that survive (many are in Wellmann), the following titles of his writings are recorded: "On Acute Diseases," "On the Preservation of Health," "Common Aids," "Practices," "To Geminius on Hygiene," "On Enemas," "On Periodic Fevers," "On Baldness," "On Pestilence," "On Dropsy," "On the Use of Wine," "On the Elements," "Definitions," "On Respiration and the Pulse," "On Ulcers," and commentaries on the *Aphorisms* and *In the Surgery*, both attributed to Hippocrates.

BIBLIOGRAPHY

Works dealing with Asclepiades are E. Gurlt, *Geschichte der Chirurgie und ihrer Ausübung*, I (Berlin, 1898), 329–330; W. A. Heidel, "The ἄναρμοι ὄγκοι of Heraclides and Asclepiades," in *Transactions of the American Philological Association*, **40** (1909), 5–21; T. Meyer-Steineg, *Das medizinische System der Methodiker* (Jena, 1916), pp. 5–18; and Max Wellmann, "Asklepiades aus Prusa" ["Asklepiades 39"], in Pauly-Wissowa, *Real-Encyclopädie der classischen Altertumswissenschaft*, and "Asklepiades aus Bithynien von einem herrschenden Vorurteil befreit," in *Neue Jahrbücher für das klassische Altertum*, **21** (1908), 684–703, the best modern study.

JERRY STANNARD

ASELLI, GASPARE (*b.* Cremona, Italy, 1581; *d.* Milan, Italy, 9 September 1625), *anatomy*.

A descendant of an ancient patrician family, Aselli revealed a marked propensity for the natural sciences early in his schooling. He studied medicine at the University of Pavia, where he soon distinguished himself among his fellow students. His teacher of anatomy was Giambattista Carcano-Leone, a pupil of Fallopio and author of *De cordis vasorum in foetu unione* (1574).

Later Aselli moved to Milan, where he gained recognition in his profession. Since his scientific preparation was essentially in anatomy, he distinguished himself in his practice of surgery. He was appointed first surgeon of the Spanish army in Italy from 1612 to 1620. In Milan he had the opportunity to continue his anatomical researches, which won him honorary citizenship of that city and an outstanding position in the history of anatomy. He died at the age of forty-four from an acute and malignant fever.

Aselli's scientific activity occurred during the first decades of the seventeenth century, in an atmosphere that was particularly sympathetic to anatomical studies, especially in northern Italy. At the end of the sixteenth century the study of descriptive human anatomy had made considerable progress. The early decades of the seventeenth century felt the effects of the baroque attitude toward science and the influences of the new mechanical concepts of Galileo. Anatomy, which had been essentially static in the sixteenth century, now assumed a dynamic character. It was enlivened by a new consideration of physiology.

Aselli discovered the chylous vessels, although it would perhaps be more correct to refer to his work as a rediscovery rather than a discovery. According to information that has come down to us from Galen, Herophilus, and Erasistratus, both Hippocrates and Aristotle had with considerable clarity already pointed to the existence of the so-called absorbent vessels. Nevertheless, not even Eustachi and Fallopio, who in the sixteenth century had noted and described the thoracic duct in the horse and the deep lymphatics in the liver, respectively, had succeeded in clarifying the functional significance of these vessels.

On 23 July 1622, during a vivisection performed on a dog that had recently been fed, Aselli, in the course of removing the intestinal tangle to reveal the abdominal fasciae of the diaphragm, noticed numerous white filaments ramified throughout the entire mesentery and along the peritoneal surface of the intestine. The most obvious interpretation was that these filaments were nerves. The incision of one of the larger of these "nerves" released a whitish humor similar to milk. Therefore, Aselli interpreted these formations as a multitude of small vessels, proposing to call them "aut lacteas, sive albas venas." The vivisection had been performed at the request of four of his friends, among whom were Senator Settala and Quirino Cnogler, to demonstrate the recurrent nerves and the movements of the diaphragm.

Immediately following his discovery, Aselli began a systematic study of the significance of these vascular structures. He recognized the chronological relationship that existed between their turgidity and the animal's last meal. His experimental findings enabled Aselli to observe the chylous vessels in different species of animals. The results of these investigations were collected in *De lactibus sive Lacteis venis quarto vasorum mesaraicorum genere novo invento Gasparis Asellii Cremonensis anatomici Ticinensis dissertatio* (1627), which is divided into thirty-five chapters that are followed by an index and preceded by four charts with accompanying commentaries and a portrait of the author. Besides their intrinsic scientific value, the importance of the charts lies in the new technique used in composing them: they were the first anatomical illustrations to appear in color. Aselli used color because he felt that several tints were needed in order to distinguish the various types of vessels more clearly.

Aselli traced the course of the chylous vessels to the mesenteric glands and probably confused them with the lymphatics of the liver; therefore he did not follow their course to the thoracic duct. (His discovery occurred four years before the publication of Harvey's *De motu cordis,* and so the Galenic concept of the liver as the center of the venous system still appeared

valid.) Harvey himself believed that the absorption of the chyle took place through the mesenteric veins and that the liver generated the blood. With the discovery of the thoracic duct in the dog by Jean Pecquet in 1651, the old Galenic error, according to which the vessels of the intestine carried the chyle to the liver, was corrected. In addition to noting and describing the valvular apparatus of the chylous vessels, Aselli attempted to interpret their functional significance in health and in disease.

BIBLIOGRAPHY

I. ORIGINAL WORKS. Aselli's only published work is *De lactibus sive Lacteis venis quarto vasorum mesaraicorum genere novo invento Gasparis Asellii Cremonensis anatomici Ticinensis dissertatio* (Milan, 1627; Basel, 1628; Leiden, 1640; Amsterdam, 1645), which was issued at the insistence of his friends Senator Settala and Alessandro Tadino.

Two earlier works by Aselli, *De venenis* and *Observationes chirurgicae,* are presumed lost. Two series of manuscripts are extant: the more important is preserved in the Archives of the Civic Museum of Pavia. In addition to other lectures and charts, it contains the full text of the lectures on the chylous vessels that Aselli delivered in 1625. The other series concerns the *Observationes chirurgicae;* formerly in the possession of the noble Belgioioso family, it was turned over in 1920 to the Trivulziana Library of Milan.

II. SECONDARY LITERATURE. Writings on Aselli are F. Argelati, *Biblioteca scriptorum Mediolan* (Milan, 1755), II, 2058; H. Boruttau, "Geschichte der Physiologie . . . ," in Theodor Puschmann's *Handbuch der Geschichte der Medizin,* II (Jena, 1903), 335–336; C. A. Calderini, *Storia della letteratura e delle arti in Italia* (Milan, 1836), II, 379; P. Capparoni, *Profili bio-bibliografici di medici e naturalisti celebri italiani dal sec. XV al sec. XVIII* (Rome, 1928), II, 70–72; B. Corte, *Notizie istoriche intorno a' Medici Scrittori Milanesi* (Milan, 1718), p. 176; V. Ducceschi, "I manoscritti di Gaspare Aselli," in *Archivio di storia della scienza,* **3** (1922), 125–134; J. F. Fulton, "The Early History of the Lymphatics," in *Bulletin of the Hennepin County Medical Society,* **9** (1938), 5; J. I. Mangeti, *Bibliotheca scriptorum medicorum* (Geneva, 1731), I, 185; G. Mazzucchelli, *Gli scrittori d'Italia* (Brescia, 1753), I, part 2, 1159–1160; L. Premuda, *Storia dell'iconografia anatomica* (Milan, 1957), pp. 163–164; R. von Töply, "Geschichte der Anatomie," in Puschmann's *Handbuch* (*supra*), pp. 215–216; and G. Zoia, *Cenno sulla vita di Gaspare Aselli anatomico del secolo XVII* (Pavia, 1875).

LORIS PREMUDA

ASHMOLE, ELIAS (*b.* Lichfield, England, 23 May 1617; *d.* London, 18 [or 19] May 1692), *natural philosophy.*

Elias Ashmole was the only child of Simon Ashmole, a Lichfield saddler, and Anne Ashmole (née Bowyer). In keeping with the family's humble social position, Elias was educated at Lichfield Grammar School, in the expectation that he would enter a craft. Through the intervention of James Pagit, a relative of the Bowyer family, he settled in London, however, and there obtained legal training. He established a law practice in 1638 but practiced only sporadically, for he was involved in the Royalist faction during the first part (from 1641 to 1646) of the Civil War. A fortunate marriage then provided him with independent means that reduced his reliance on the income from his law practice.

In 1660 Ashmole's loyalty to the crown was rewarded by Charles II, who granted him the offices of comptroller of the excise and Windsor herald. He was successful in both offices; the former provided a large income, and he devoted his intellectual energies to the latter. He contributed greatly to the revival of English heraldry and in the course of his work gained an encyclopedic knowledge of its history and complex rules.

His chambers at the Middle Temple and South Lambeth house were used to display substantial and famous antiquarian collections. Ashmole's office at the College of Arms brought him considerable social prestige, and he became well known in court circles. In religious and political matters he was excessively conservative and orthodox. His closest friends, however, were drawn from the eccentric and varied class who shared his obsession with alchemy and astrology. These interests showed no diminution in his later life, despite his association with the Royal Society, whose view of nature undoubtedly did not accord with his own.

Ashmole married three times but had no children. His first wife was Eleanor Manwaring; the second was a rich widow, Lady Mary Manwaring (née Forster); the third was Elizabeth Dugdale, daughter of Sir William Dugdale, Ashmole's friend and a prominent antiquarian.

Ashmole's scientific outlook was deeply influenced by the mathematicians and astrologers with whom he associated during the Civil War. Both factions in the war made use of astrology, which became a fashionable and respectable scientific pursuit; its influence affected various disciplines from mathematics to medicine. While serving in the Oxford garrison in 1645, Ashmole became acquainted with the Royalist astrologers George Wharton and Sir John Heydon. After retiring from the conflict in 1646, he formed his most significant and lasting astrological friendship, with the Parliamentarian astrologer William Lilly, who had greatly contributed to the revival of astrology in England. Ashmole's first published writings were two short translations of astrological works included in Lilly's *Worlds Catastrophe* (1647).

From astrology, Ashmole gradually extended his interests to botany, medicine, and stenography. Inevitably, alchemy attracted him, and he became the eager pupil of William Backhouse of Swallowfield, Berkshire. Alchemy appealed to Ashmole's mystical and antiquarian instincts. As a practical and contemplative study, it appeared to offer the key to the secrets of nature; its antiquarian aspect lay in the collection and publication of the rare and often corrupt texts that formed the basis for its theory. Ashmole aspired to publish the "choicest flowers" of alchemical literature, and his first book, the *Fasciculus chemicus* (1650), was a modest translation of works by Arthur Dee and Jean d'Espagnet. By this time he had embarked upon a more ambitious enterprise—the restoration of English astrology. He hoped to produce a comprehensive collection of English verse and prose alchemical works, drawn from manuscript sources. This project had an auspicious beginning with the publication of the *Theatrum chemicum Brittanicum* (1652), a collection of verse alchemical works that displayed Ashmole's industry, erudition, and editorial skill. The *Prolegomena* indicate familiarity and agreement with the leading themes of Hermetic philosophy.

After the publication of this work, Ashmole's alchemical activities diminished. The only other English alchemical work he published was *The Way to Bliss* (1658). Ashmole saw no incompatibility between the occult sciences that he favored and the experimental natural philosophy that was becoming a dominant influence among his contemporaries. He regarded them as complementary means of discovering the fundamental principles of natural philosophy. Consequently, he was mildly interested in experimental science, became a founding fellow of the Royal Society in 1660, and made significant bequests to the society's museum.

Ashmole's other scientific activities diminished considerably after 1660, as he concentrated on the duties connected with his crown appointments. His major intellectual energies were increasingly absorbed by the compilation of the history of the Order of the Garter, begun in 1655 and completed in 1672. This book has become a major reference work on many aspects of heraldry. At the same time he continued collecting books, manuscripts, and archaeological and scientific "rarities." This was not an uncommon avocation among the gentry of Restoration England, but Ashmole exceeded others in his zeal for collection and in his desire to replace ephemeral personal "cabinets" with permanent public museums.

In 1675 he offered his collections to Oxford University, on the condition that suitable housing was provided for it. The university gladly complied, and the elegant museum, designed by Thomas Wood, was opened in 1683. This was the first English public museum, and Ashmole actively supervised its affairs. He added to the collections and persuaded other collectors, notably the zoologist Martin Lister, to make donations. His protégé, Robert Plot, who shared his patron's alchemical interests, was appointed keeper of the museum and first professor of chemistry. The museum was equipped with a laboratory that became the focus for scientific activities at Oxford. Thus, paradoxically, Ashmole created the institutional basis for the growing tradition of experimental science while himself representing the declining magical and astrological outlook.

BIBLIOGRAPHY

I. ORIGINAL WORKS. Ashmole's works include *Fasciculus chemicus: Or, Chymical Collections. Expressing the Ingress, Progress, and Egress, of the Secret Hermetick Science, out of the Choicest and Most Famous Authors* (London, 1650), written under the name of James Hasolle and presenting translations of Arthur Dee's *Fasciculus chemicus* (1629) and Jean d'Espagnet's *Arcanum hermeticae philosophiae* (1623); *Theatrum chemicum Britannicum. Containing Severall Poeticall Pieces of Our Famous English Philosophers, Who Have Written the Hermetique Mysteries in their owne Ancient Language* (London, 1652), reprinted with an introduction by A. G. Debus as No. 39 in the series *Sources of Science* (New York, 1967); *The Way to Bliss. In Three Books* (London, 1658); *Sol in Ascendente: Or, The Glorious Appearance Of Charles the Second, Upon The Horizon of London* (London, 1660), an anonymously published poem celebrating the Restoration; *A Catalogue of the Peers of the Kingdome of England* (London, 1661); *A Brief Narrative of His Majestie's Solemn Coronation* (London, 1662); "The Worlds Catastrophe, or the Miraculous Changes, and Alterations, . . . in several Kingdoms, and Commonwealths of Europe . . . ," translated from Franciscus Spina's *De mundi catastrophe* (1625), and "A Prophecie of Ambrose Merlin . . . ," from Geoffrey of Monmouth's *Historia regum Britanniae*, in William Lilly's *The Worlds Catastrophe, Or, Europes many Mutations untill 1666* (London, 1647); and *The Institution, Laws & Ceremonies of the Most Noble Order of the Garter* (London, 1672).

II. SECONDARY LITERATURE. More information on Ashmole and his work can be found in Mea Allen, *The Tradescants* (London, 1964), pp. 200–207; Thomas Birch, *History of the Royal Society*, 4 vols. (London, 1756/7), I, 4,8; J. Campbell, in *Biographia Britannica*, 2nd ed. (London, 1778), I, 293–307; J. Ferguson, *Bibliotheca chemica*, 2 vols. (Glasgow, 1906), II, 52–53; C. H. Josten, *Elias Ashmole (1617–1692). His Autobiographical and Historical Notes, His Correspondence, and Other Contemporary Sources Relating to His Life and Work*, 5 vols. (Oxford, 1966), the most comprehensive work on Ashmole, superseding the partial editions of the *Diary* by C. Burnan (1774) and R. T. Gunther (1927), and "William Backhouse of Swallowfield," in *Ambix*, **4** (1949), 1–33; R. Rawlinson, "Some Memoires of the Life of Elias Ashmole," prefixed to *The Antiquities of Berkshire* (London, 1719), which is incorrectly attributed to Ashmole; Taylor E. Sherwood, "Alchemical Papers of Dr. Robert Plot," in *Ambix*, **4** (1949), 61–79; and A. Wood, *Athenae Oxonienses*, P. Bliss, ed., 4 vols. (London, 1817), III, 354–364.

CHARLES WEBSTER

ASSALTI, PIETRO (*b.* Acquaviva Picena, Italy, 23 June 1680; *d.* Rome, Italy, 29 April 1728), *medicine.*

A descendant of a family who had held public office in the small town of Fermo in the fifteenth and sixteenth centuries, Assalti received his early education, which included Latin, in Acquaviva Picena. At fifteen he went to Fermo, where he studied Greek, Hebrew, Syriac, and Arabic. Four years later, following his father's wishes, he went to Rome to study law; he continued, however, to show increasing interest in languages and natural history. Assalti soon earned a reputation as a scholar and was chosen by Pope Clement XI to be one of the "writers" of the Vatican Library, where he had the means to broaden the scope of his learning.

In 1709 Assalti was appointed professor of botany at the University of Rome, succeeding Giovanni Battista Trionfetti; his teaching of the natural sciences led to his appointment as professor of anatomy in 1719 and, two years later, of theoretical medicine, with a stipend of 234 *scudi.*

Assalti collected the works of Lancisi and published them in two volumes (1718), and he was almost certainly the author of the scholarly and elegant annotations to Michele Mercati's *Metallotheca* (1717). His letter to Morgagni regarding Lancisi was published as a preface to Lancisi's *De motu cordis et aneurysmatibus* (1728). Also worthy of mention is his unpublished "Oratio de incrementis anatomicae in hoc saeculo XVIII," which, among other topics, deals with the function of the spleen.

In *De incrementis anatomie* Lorenz Heister writes most enthusiastically of Assalti, and the anatomist G. B. Bianchi (1681–1761) describes him as "eximium Medicum virum longe doctissimum, et in linguis eruditis peritissimum."

BIBLIOGRAPHY

I. ORIGINAL WORKS. Assalti collected and edited Lancisi's work as *Opera omnia in duos tomos distributa*, 2 vols. (Geneva, 1718). The year before, his annotations to Michele Mercati's *Metallotheca* (Rome, 1717) had appeared. He was also responsible for the preface to Lancisi's *De motu cordis et aneurysmatibus* (Rome, 1728).

II. SECONDARY LITERATURE. Works on Assalti are A. Bacchini, *Vita ed opere di G. M. Lancisi* (Rome, 1920), p. 32; Biblioteca Comunale di Fermo, MSS 8/3, in *Notizie raccolte da Rodolfo Emiliani sulla famiglia Assalti e su Pietro Assalti;* V. Curia, *L'Università degli Studi di Fermo* (Ancona, 1880), p. 71; G. Natalucci, *Medici insigni italiani antichi e contemporanei nati nelle Marche* (Falerona, 1934), pp. 49–50; G. Panelli, *Memorie degli uomini illustri e chiari in medicina del Piceno*, II (Ascoli, 1767), 364–383; A. Pazzini, *La storia della Facoltà Medica di Roma*, II (Rome, 1961), 458–459; S. de Renzi, *Storie della medicina in Italia*, IV (Naples, 1846), 53; and F. Vecchietti, *Biblioteca Picena o sia Notizie storiche delle opere e degli scrittori Piceni*, I (Osimo, 1790), 228–232.

LORIS PREMUDA

ASTBURY, WILLIAM THOMAS (*b.* Longton [now part of Stoke-on-Trent], England, 25 February 1898; *d.* Leeds, England, 4 June 1961), *X-ray crystallography, molecular biology.*

Astbury was brought up in the pottery town of Longton. He read chemistry at Cambridge and began research under Sir William Bragg at University College, London, in 1921, moving with him to the Royal Institution in 1923. In 1928 Astbury was appointed lecturer in textile physics at the University of Leeds, then reader, and finally professor of biomolecular structure.

In London, Astbury worked on the structure of tartaric acids, measured diffraction intensities photometrically, and, with Kathleen Lonsdale, produced the first tables of space groups. His assignment at Leeds was the structure of natural and synthetic fibers, especially wool. In 1930 he discovered that two diffraction patterns can be produced from the same wool fiber by exposing it to the X-ray beam when relaxed and when under tension. On the meridian the relaxed fiber showed a prominent spot at 5.1 A., and the stretched fiber a spot at 3.4 A. Astbury concluded that the long polypeptide chains which make up the keratin fiber are folded into a series of hexagons resembling diketopiperazines in structure, and are spaced 5.1 A. apart. When the wool fiber is stretched, these hexagon folds are pulled out into long chains in which the residue repeat is at 3.4 A. He noted the similarity of this stretched, or beta, form of keratin to silk, and proposed for both a two-dimensional grid structure, the cross-links between the polypeptide chains being through salt linkages and sulfur bridges.

Henceforth, Astbury's work was dominated by this theory of the reversible transformation of keratin. In 1940 Hans Neurath showed that the amino acid side chains could not be accommodated in his structures, so in 1941 Astbury, with Florence Bell, modified them; but when the alpha helix and pleated sheets were proposed by Linus Pauling in 1951, Astbury's models were discarded.

In 1937 Astbury and Florence Bell took the first good X-ray pictures of sodium thymonucleate and discovered the strong meridional spot at 3.4 A. In 1946 Astbury assigned this spot to the eighth layer line, and Mansel M. Davies built a single-chain "pile of plates" model with a chemical repeat at 27 A. From model-building, Davies recognized that the planes of sugar and purine or pyrimidine must be at right angles and that the most likely phosphate ester linkages are between C3 and C5.

Although Astbury's structures for proteins were all wrong in detail, they represent the first attempt at molecular models in which specific cross-linkages hold the polypeptide chains in a characteristic conformation. His suggestion of the folding and unfolding of these chains as the basis of extensibility of fibrous proteins and of the denaturation process of globular proteins was correct in essence. Nowhere did he utilize helical models, but his picture of DNA as a dense molecule with the bases stacked one above another 3.4 A. apart was the first step toward the elucidation of its structure.

As a pioneer, Astbury was bound to see his work superseded, but by his enthusiasm and mastery of the art of lecturing he drew others into the then young field of molecular biology. He provided the stimulus to the more detailed and reliable work of his successors.

BIBLIOGRAPHY

I. ORIGINAL WORKS. Astbury wrote over 100 papers and two books. J. D. Bernal has published an almost complete bibliography in his Royal Society memoir on Astbury (see below). Astbury's most important papers are the three he published under the title "The X-ray Studies of the Structure of Hair, Wool, and Related Fibres," in *Philosophical Transactions of the Royal Society*, **230A** (1931), 75–101; **232A** (1933), 333–394; and *Proceedings of the Royal Society*, **150A** (1935), 533–551. His best papers on nucleic acids are "X-ray Studies of Nucleic Acids," in *Symposium of the*

Society for Experimental Biology, **1** (1947), 66–76; and "Protein and Virus Studies in Relation to the Problem of the Gene," in *Proceedings of the 7th. International Congress of Genetics* [held at Edinburgh in 1939] (Cambridge, 1941), pp. 49–51. Biographical information will be found in "The Fundamentals of Fibre Research: A Physicist's Story," in *Journal of the Textile Institute,* **51** (1960), 515–526. His two books are *Fundamentals of Fibre Structure* (London, 1933); and *Textile Fibres Under the X-Rays* (London, 1940).

II. SECONDARY LITERATURE. The most detailed biography is J. D. Bernal's, in *Biographical Memoirs of Fellows of the Royal Society,* **9** (1963), 1–35, with bibliography and portrait. For obituary notices see K. Lonsdale, in *Chemistry and Industry* (1961), 1174–1175; and I. MacArthur, in *Nature,* **191** (1961), 331–332.

ROBERT OLBY

ASTON, FRANCIS WILLIAM (*b.* Harbonne, Birmingham, England, 1 September 1877; *d.* Cambridge, England, 20 November 1945), *experimental chemistry, physics.*

Aston was the second son of William Aston, a metal merchant and farmer, and Fanny Charlotte Hollis, the daughter of a Birmingham gunmaker. After primary education at Harbonne vicarage school, Aston spent four years at Malvern College. In 1893 he entered Mason's College, Birmingham, where he studied for the London intermediate science examination with the chemists W. A. Tilden and P. F. Frankland and the physicist J. H. Poynting. In 1898 he obtained a Forster Scholarship to work with Frankland on the stereochemistry of dipyromucyltartaric acid esters. Simultaneously he took a course in fermentation chemistry, and from 1900 to 1903 he earned a living as a brewery chemist at Wolverhampton. He returned to Birmingham University (formed from Mason's College in 1900) from 1903 to 1908 as a physics research student with Poynting, and after a world tour in 1909 he spent a term at Birmingham as an assistant lecturer. From 1910 to 1919 Aston worked with J. J. Thomson at the Cavendish Laboratory, Cambridge, and the Royal Institution, London; first as a personal assistant, then from 1913 as a Clerk Maxwell Scholar. This period was interrupted by the war, during which Aston returned to chemistry as a technical assistant at the Royal Aircraft Establishment, Farnborough. In 1919 he was elected a fellow of Trinity College, Cambridge, where he spent the remainder of his life.

Conservative in politics and of no decided religious views, Aston was an animal lover, a keen traveler, a varied and skilled sportsman, a technically brilliant photographer, and an accomplished amateur musician. Like most of J. J. Thomson's associates, he acquired an interest in finance, and in consequence of skilled investment he was able to leave a large estate to Trinity College and several scientific beneficiaries. Aston was a bachelor, a poor teacher and lecturer, and a lone worker who detested the thought of experimental collaboration. (Only six out of 143 papers were collaborative.) He recognized his own fallibility as a theorist, and frequently sought the aid of such mathematical physicists as F. A. Lindemann (Lord Cherwell), R. H. Fowler, and W. W. Sawyer. Aston received the Nobel Prize for chemistry in 1922. He held several honorary degrees, and was elected to, and received medals from, many scientific institutions. From 1936 to 1945 he was chairman of the Committee on Atoms of the International Union of Chemistry.

Although Aston liked to recall that his first two publications were on organic chemistry, these two papers broke no new ground although they did exhibit his talent for devising ingenious apparatus. The appearance of Thomson's *Conduction of Electricity Through Gases* in 1903 opened up, for Aston the chemist, the physicist's world of cathode rays, positive rays, and X rays. Already an expert glassblower, and trained by Frankland in "extreme care and meticulous accuracy," he began to work under Poynting on the variable structure of the phenomena observed during gaseous conduction at low pressures. He was particularly interested in the variation, with pressure and current, of the length of the dark space between the cathode and the negative glow named after W. C. Crookes. By making special Geissler discharge tubes with movable aluminum cathodes, Aston was able to obtain a sufficiently well-bounded Crookes space to demonstrate that its length was proportional to $1/P + 1/\sqrt{C}$, where P is the pressure and C is the current. In 1908, while using hydrogen and helium, he detected a new "primary cathode dark space," about a millimeter thick and directly adjoining the cathode. This phenomenon now bears Aston's name. Research on the relationship between the Crookes dark space and current, voltage, pressure, and electrode nature and design continued intermittently until 1923. Aston then abandoned it in order to devote all his attention to isotopes.

When Aston became Thomson's assistant in 1910, he was given the task of improving the apparatus in which a beam of positively charged particles (positive rays), which emerged through a perforated cathode in a discharge tube, were deflected by perpendicularly arranged electric and magnetic fields into sharp, visible parabolas of constant e/m (charge over mass). Aston produced an improved spherical discharge tube, finely engineered cathode slits, an improved pump, a coil for detecting vacuum leaks, and an ingenious camera for photographing the parabolas. In 1912 he thought this apparatus for positive ray analysis gave a rigorous proof that all the individual molecules of any given substance had the same mass. This Daltonian belief was rudely shattered in the same year when Thomson obtained two parabolas, of mass 20 and 22, for neon. There were two obvious possibilities: if neon had a true atomic weight of 20 (instead of 20.2), then either mass 22 was an unknown hydride, NeH_2, or a new element, meta-neon. Thomson investigated the first possibility and left Aston to check the unlikely alternative.

Aston, who was sympathetic toward F. Soddy's contemporary ideas on radioactive isotopes, tried to separate the meta-neon by fractional distillation, and later by diffusion. He invented a quartz microbalance, which was sensitive to 10^{-9} gram, to measure the density of the minute heavier fraction. The partial separation of a new element, with the same properties as neon, was announced in 1913; Thomson, however, remained doubtful. During the war Aston had time to think over the problem and to debate the possibility of the existence of natural isotopes with the skeptical F. A. Lindemann.

In 1919, to test the neon isotope hypothesis, Aston built a positive ray spectrograph, or mass spectrograph, with a resolving power of 1 in 100 and an accuracy of 1 part in 10^3. The design was based upon an optical analogy. Just as white light can be analyzed into an optical spectrum by a prism, so an electric field will disperse a beam of heterogeneous positive rays. By arranging a magnetic field to deflect the dispersed rays in the opposite direction, but in the same plane, rays of uniform mass can be focused into a mass spectrum on a photographic plate, irrespective of their velocities. This was a great advance on Thomson's apparatus, where the arrangement of the fields produced parabolas that were dependent on the velocities of the positive rays. Aston adopted several methods to calculate the masses of the particles, including comparison with a calibration curve of reference lines of known masses. In the case of neon, the intensities of the 20 and 22 mass lines implied a relative abundance of about 10:1, enough to produce an average mass of 20.2, the known atomic weight of neon. Neon was isotopic.

Two larger mass spectrographs were built. The second (1927) had five times more resolving power and an accuracy of 1 in 10^4; the third (1935) had a resolving power of 1 in 2000 and a claimed accuracy of 1 in 10^5. The latter instrument proved difficult to adjust, and World War II intervened before any significant work could be done with it. By then, however, Aston's instruments had been surpassed by the mass spectrometers developed by A. J. Dempster (1918), K. T. Bainbridge (1932), and A. O. Nier (1937).

Aston's personal motto, "Make more, more, and yet more measurements," led him to analyze successfully all but three of the nonradioactive elements in the periodic table. But since the mass spectrograph was unsuitable for detecting minute amounts of isotopes, he missed finding those of oxygen and hydrogen. In 1930 Aston showed how his instrument could be used photometrically to determine and correct chemical atomic weights. Here much depended on his brilliant development of photographic plates that were highly sensitive to positive ions.

In December 1919 Aston announced the "whole-number rule" that atomic masses were integral on the scale O^{16} (a notation introduced by Aston in 1920). Fractional atomic weights were merely "fortuitous statistical effects due to the relative quantities of the isotopic constituents," and the elements were to be defined physically by their atomic numbers, rather than in terms of isotopic mixtures. Prout's hypothesis (1816), that all elements were built up from atoms of a common substance, appeared to be vindicated at last.

Aston's work, therefore, provided important insights into the structure of the atom and the evolution of the elements. At first, only hydrogen appeared to violate the whole-number rule. Aston explained this seeming violation as due to the "loss" of mass within this atom by binding energy; mass was additive only when nuclear charges were relatively distant from one another. This concept of "packing" had been proposed on theoretical grounds by W. D. Harkins (1915), and derived ultimately from J. C. G. Marignac (1860). However, it soon became clear that all elements deviated slightly from whole numbers. In 1927, with his second machine, Aston measured and codified the deviations in terms of the "packing fraction" (the positive or negative deviation of an atomic mass from an integer divided by its mass number). By plotting these fractions against mass numbers, Aston obtained a simple curve which gave valuable information on nuclear abundance and stability.

Aston's achievements were kept continually before the scientific public by revised editions of his excellent book *Isotopes* (1922). This included observations on the abundance and distribution of isotopes and a clear forecast of the power and dangers of harnessed atomic energy.

BIBLIOGRAPHY

I. Original Works. A full list of Aston's papers can be found in Hevesy (see below); to it should be added "The Mass-spectra of the Elements (Part II)," in *The London, Edinburgh and Dublin Philosophical Magazine,* **40** (1920),

628–636; reports of the Committee on Atoms of the International Union of Chemistry (Paris, 1936–1941); and the obituary of J. J. Thomson, in *The Times* (London, 4 Sept. 1940).

The most important papers are "Experiments on the Length of the Cathode Dark Space," in *Proceedings of the Royal Society of London,* **79A** (1907), 80–95; "Experiments on a New Cathode Dark Space," *ibid.,* **80A** (1908), 45–49; "Sir J. J. Thomson's New Method of Chemical Analysis," in *Science Progress,* **7** (1912), 48–65; "A New Elementary Constituent of the Atmosphere," in *British Association for the Advancement of Science Reports,* **82** (1913), 403; "A Micro-balance for Determining Densities," in *Proceedings of the Royal Society of London,* **89A** (1914), 439–446; "A Positive Ray Spectrograph," in *The London, Edinburgh and Dublin Philosophical Magazine,* **38** (1919), 707–714; "The Possibility of Separating Isotopes," *ibid.,* **37** (1919), 523–534, written with F. A. Lindemann; "Problems of the Mass-spectrograph," *ibid.,* **43** (1922), 514–528, written with R. H. Fowler; "Photographic Plates for the Detection of Mass Rays," in *Proceedings of the Cambridge Philosophical Society,* **22** (1923–1925), 548–554; "A New Mass-spectrograph," in *Proceedings of the Royal Society of London,* **115A** (1927), 487–514, a Bakerian lecture; "The Photometry of Mass-spectra," *ibid.,* **126A** (1930), 511–525; and "A Second-order Focusing Mass-spectrograph," *ibid.,* **163A** (1937), 391–404.

Also of interest are his Nobel lecture, "Mass-spectra and Isotopes," in *Nobel Lectures in Chemistry (1922–1941)* (Amsterdam-London-New York, 1966); and "Forty Years of the Atomic Theory," in J. Needham and W. Pagel, eds., *Background to Modern Science* (Cambridge, 1938).

Aston's books are *Isotopes* (London, 1922; 2nd ed., 1924); and *Mass-spectra and Isotopes* (London, 1933; 2nd ed., 1942), on which he was assisted by C. P. Snow.

A few of Aston's original instruments are displayed in various museums: a quartz microbalance, 1913 (Science Museum, London); fragments from the neon diffusion apparatus, 1913 (Cavendish Laboratory Museum, Cambridge); the first mass spectrograph, 1919 (Science Museum, London); the third mass spectrograph, 1935 (Cavendish Laboratory Museum). The mass spectrograph of 1927 appears to have been broken up.

II. SECONDARY LITERATURE. Works concerning Aston include N. Feather, "F. W. Aston," in *Dictionary of National Biography (1941–1950)* (Oxford, 1959), pp. 24–26; G. C. de Hevesy, "F. W. Aston," in *Obituary Notices of Fellows of the Royal Society,* **5** (1945–1948), 635–651, which includes a photograph and a bibliography; F. M. Green, "The Chudleigh Mess," in *R. A. E. News* (Jan. 1958), pp. 4–7, available only at Farnborough; G. P. Thomson, "F. W. Aston," in *Nature,* **157** (1946), 290–292, and *J. J. Thomson and the Cavendish Laboratory* (London, 1964), pp. 93, 136; J. J. Thomson, *Rays of Positive Electricity* (London, 1913), passim; and *Who Was Who (1941–1950)* (London, 1952), p. 38, which includes a complete list of honors.

W. H. BROCK

ASTRUC, JEAN (*b.* Sauve, Gard, France, 19 March 1684; *d.* Paris, France, 5 May 1766), *medicine.*

Astruc was the son of a Protestant clergyman who probably had Jewish ancestors who chose to renounce their religion rather than leave France. After receiving a doctorate in medicine at Montpellier in 1703, he temporarily occupied Pierre Chirac's chair of medicine in 1706. He passed the competitive examination of the Faculty of Medicine of Toulouse in 1711, and then returned to Montpellier to occupy the chair of medicine of Jacques Chastelain from 1716 to 1728, at which time he became general physician to the duke of Orléans. In 1720 he received a pension from the king and in the following year was named inspector general of the mineral waters of Languedoc. In 1729 Astruc became the chief physician of Augustus II of Poland, and he was named municipal magistrate of Toulouse in 1730. In that same year he became the king's counsellor and physician, and in 1751 he occupied E. F. Geoffroy's chair of pharmacy at the Collège Royal.

In 1743 Astruc was elected regent doctor of the Faculty of Medicine of Paris, the first time that this exceptional honor was awarded to a doctor from a provincial medical school—despite the fact that the statutes of the university forbade it. This honor was followed by a second one, that of having his bust placed in the amphitheater of the Faculty. These honors were a recompense for his constant fight against his two enemies, the surgeons and the *variolisateurs* (users of a primitive form of vaccination against variola), as well as for his assiduous attendance at meetings. He died after twenty-three years in Paris, years made painful by a tumor of the bladder that Georges de la Faye, a member of the Académie de Chirurgie, perforated with a metal probe in order to overcome chronic retention of urine.

Astruc was a born teacher, extremely methodical and clear in his instruction. In a series of courses lasting six years he covered all phases of medicine: anatomy, physiology, psychology, gerontology, pathology, therapy, venereology, gynecology, neurology, and pediatrics. Even in American libraries there are manuscript copies of these carefully prepared and highly appreciated courses; during Astruc's lifetime some of them were used for editions printed without his knowledge in England, Switzerland, and Holland. His works were translated into English and German and were widely known in Europe. An iatrochemist and iatrophysicist, Astruc had no personal doctrine. His philosophy, influenced by Descartes and Malebranche, was only mildly opposed to the cold reason of Locke. His place in the history of medicine was somewhat behind Haller, Morgagni, and Boerhaave, rather than ahead of them.

Although a mediocre practitioner, Astruc was a scientist of note, a solitary and erudite scholar who often worked through the winter nights until three in the morning, without a fire in the library. Among his several thousand volumes were many works on theology, history, geography, and literature. He called this his "militant life." Around 1730 Astruc began to frequent the mansion of Mme. de Tencin, who was a patient. The famous hostess was helpful in arranging the marriage of Astruc's daughter to Daubin de Silhouette and also remembered him in her will. For some time Astruc, Bernard de Fontenelle, Pierre Marivaux, Jean de Mairan, the Marquis Victor de Mirabeau, Claude de Boze, and Charles Duclos were considered the seven sages of Mme. de Tencin's salon.

In his *Traité sur les maladies des femmes* (1761) Astruc described septicemia caused by uterine infections and puerperal fever, ovarian cysts, tubal pregnancies, abdominal pregnancies, and lithopedions, of which he reported four cases. He advised operating on extrauterine pregnancies, and the use of Caesarean sections only in emergencies.

In 1743 Astruc compared the transformation of an impression or sensation into a motor discharge to a ray of light reflected on a surface; he called it *reflex*. He thus had an intuition of reflex action, which was described in 1833 by Marshall Hall.

Astruc's best-known work is his treatise on venereology, *De morbis venereis*, the fourth French edition of which (1773–1774) contains "Dissertation sur l'origine, la dénomination, la nature et la curation des maladies vénériennes à la Chine," in which for the first time Chinese medical terminology was reproduced in an Occidental work in correctly printed Chinese characters.

His family background led Astruc to consider the exegesis of the Old Testament as one of the elements of his personal inner life. This work appeared as *Conjectures sur la Genèse* (1753), in which the different names of God (Elohim or Jehovah) gave him the key to dating various parts of the Bible. Both Catholic and Protestant theologians frowned on these discoveries, for they were incapable of appreciating Astruc's quick mind, his constructive criticism, and his remarkable philological knowledge. Now, after more than two centuries of discussion of these ideas, often minute and often passionate, historical criticism always comes back to them. It still cannot be proved that the thesis is true, but Astruc's conception is in line with our present knowledge and, according to

Lods, gives the best account of the formation of Jewish historiography. Sir William Osler judged the *Conjectures* worthy of inclusion in his *Bibliotheca prima* as a remarkable example of scientific criticism.

BIBLIOGRAPHY

I. ORIGINAL WORKS. The complete bibliography of Astruc's works has been drawn up by Janet Doe (see below). The principal items are *De motus fermentativi causa* (Montpellier, 1702); *Responsio critica animadversionibus F. R. Vieussens in tractatum de causa motus fermentativi* (Montpellier, 1702); *Dissertatio physico medica de motu musculari* (Montpellier, 1710); *Mémoire sur la cause de la digestion des aliments* (Montpellier, 1711); *Traité de la cause de la digestion . . .* (Toulouse, 1714); *Epistolae Joannès Astruc quibus respondetur epistolari dissertationi Thomae Boerü, de concoctione* (Toulouse, 1715); *Dissertatio de ani fistula* (Montpellier, 1718); *De sensatione* (Montpellier, 1719); *Dissertatio medica de hydrophobia* (Montpellier, 1720); *Quaestio medica de naturali et praeternaturali judicii exercitio* (Montpellier, 1720); *De phantasia et imaginatione* (Montpellier, 1723); *Cinq lettres contre les chirurgiens* (Paris, ca. 1731); *De morbis venereis libri sex* (Paris, 1736, 1738, 1740), translated into French by Augustin Jault with notes by Antoine Louis (Paris, 1743; 4th ed., 1773–1774); *Mémoires pour servir à l'histoire naturelle de la province du Languedoc* (Paris, 1737); *An sympathia partium a certa nervorum positura in interno sensorio* (Paris, 1743); *Conjectures sur les mémoires originaux . . . de la Genèse* (Paris, 1753); *Traité sur l'immatérialité et l'immortalité de l'âme* (Paris, 1755); *Doutes sur l'inoculation de la petite vérole, proposés à la Faculté de Médecine de Paris* (Paris, 1756); *Traité des tumeurs et des ulcères* (Paris, 1759); *Traité sur les maladies des femmes* (Paris, 1761; 1765); *L'art d'accoucher* (Paris, 1766, 1771); and *Mémoire pour servir ici l'histoire de la Faculté de Médecine de Montpellier* (Paris, 1767).

II. SECONDARY LITERATURE. Writings on Astruc are P. Astruc, "Une bibliothèque médicale au XVIIIème siècle," in *Progrès médicale,* **2** (1934), 94–95; Louis Barbillion, "Un ancien syphiligraphe," in *Paris médical,* **52** (1924), 196–198; C. S. Butler, "Hero Worship and the Propagation of Fallacies," in *Annals of Internal Medicine,* **5** (1932), 1033–1038; Georges Canguilhem, *La formation du concept de réflexe au XVIIème et XVIIIème siècles* (Paris, 1955), which includes Hall's description; F. Chaussier and N. P. Adelon, "Astruc," in *Biographie universelle ancienne et moderne* (Paris, 1811), pp. 486–487; A. Chéreau, "Astruc," in *Dictionnaire encyclopédique des sciences médicales,* VII (Paris, 1867), 31–34; Paul Delauney, *Le monde médical parisien au XVIIIème siècle* (Paris, 1935), *passim;* J. E. Dézeimeris, Claude Ollivier, and J. Raige-Delorme, *Dictionnaire historique de la médecine ancienne et moderne,* I (Paris, 1828), 200–203; Janet Doe, "Jean Astruc (1684–1766), a Biographical and Bibliographical Study," in *Journal of the*

History of Medicine, **20** (Apr. 1960), 184–197; Charles Fiessinger, "La thérapeutique de Jean Astruc," in *Thérapeutique des vieux maîtres* (Paris, 1897), pp. 226–232; Fischer, *De senio eiusque gradibus* (Erfurt, 1754); Pierre Huard and Ming Wong, "Montpellier et la médecine chinoise," in *Montpelliensis Hippocrates,* no. 2 (Dec. 1958), pp. 13–20; "Antonio Nunes Ribeiro Sanchès," in *Société Française de l'Histoire de la Médecine,* spec. no. 4 (13 Jan. 1962) pp. 96–103; and "J. Astruc Scholar and Biblical Critic," in *Journal of the American Medical Association,* **92** (1965), 249 ff.; A. M. Lautour, "Astruc," in *Dictionnaire de biographie française* (Paris, 1939); A. C. Lorry, "Éloge de J. Astruc," in *Mémoires pour servir à l'histoire de la Faculté de Médecine de Montpellier* (Paris, 1767), pp. xxxiii–li; A. Lods, *Jean Astruc et la critique biblique au XVIIIème siècle* (Strasbourg–Paris, 1924); P. M. Masson, *Madame de Tencin* (Paris, 1909); R. O. Moreau, "L'oeuvre d'Astruc dans son traité de maladies des femmes," thesis (Univ. of Paris, 1930); Sir William Osler, "Jean Astruc and the Higher Criticism," in *Canadian Medical Association Journal,* **2** (1912), 151–152; E. Ritter, "Jean Astruc, auteur des *Conjectures sur la Genèse,*" in *Bulletin de l'histoire du protestantisme français,* **15** (1916), 274–287; John Ruhrah, "J. Astruc the Pediatrician," in *American Journal of Diseases of Children,* **39** (1930), 403–408; F. M. Scapin, "L'inchiesta di Giovanni Astruc sulla sifilide cinese," in *Acta medicae historiae Patavina,* **3** (1956), 57–61; Sir A. Simpson, "Jean Astruc and his *Conjectures,*" in *Edinburgh Medical Journal,* **14** (1915), 461–475, and *Proceedings of the Royal Society of Medicine,* no. 8 (1914/15), 59–71; and F. D. Zeman, "Jean Astruc on Old Age," in *Journal of the History of Medicine,* **20** (1965), 52–57.

PIERRE HUARD

ATHENAEUS OF ATTALIA (*b.* Attalia in Pamphylia [?] [now Antalya, Turkey]), *medicine.*

Athenaeus was a physician who practiced in Rome, apparently during the reign of Claudius I. Biographical details are lacking, but it is known that he founded the Pneumatic school of medicine. His successors in the school included his pupil Agathinos and Herodotus, Magnus, and Archigenes, who flourished during the reign of Trajan.

The name of Athenaeus' school came from a new term, *pneuma* ("breath" or "spirit"), that he introduced into medical theory from Stoic philosophy. Chrysippus, the third head of the Stoic school, had defined soul as "a spirit [pneuma] innate in us, continuously penetrating the whole body." Athenaeus taught that the body was composed, ultimately, of the traditional four qualities—hot, cold, wet, dry—but that these were held together and governed by pneuma, which permeated the entire body. Although it owed something to Aristotle's view of pneuma as associated with semen in generation, the Stoic doctrine was more

general—and, indeed, cosmic in extent. Athenaeus, accepting the materialism of the Stoics, could identify with pneuma the ruling part of the soul (*hegemonikon*), which for Aristotle was immaterial. Athenaeus is often linked with Aristotle in Galen's criticism of previous teachings. Following Aristotle and Chrysippus, Athenaeus located the *hegemonikon* in the heart, and from this belief he drew certain conclusions about the medical treatment of mental illness. He explained disease in general as a pathological affection of the pneuma caused by the putrefaction or rotting of pneuma.

The doctrine of the proper mixture of the qualities or the humors composed of them was a staple of ancient medical tradition. The Pneumatic school felt the need of a governing spirit to maintain a proper temperament of the components of the physical body. Athenaeus, according to Galen, considered hot and cold as efficient causes and wet and dry as material ones, but apparently he was not able to conceive of them as operating on their own. Galen also asserts that Athenaeus was not clear as to whether the four qualities were potencies or bodies.

Athenaeus was an original thinker who enriched medical theory with a consistent philosophical position. He was also a teacher, as his founding of a school proves. He is known to have written a comprehensive treatise on medicine that ran to at least thirty books. He treated in detail the principal branches of medicine: physiology, pathology, embryology, therapeutics, and dietetics, as well as the medical aspects of meteorology and geography.

Practically all of our information about Athenaeus comes from Galen, who cites him frequently and seems to have accepted some of his teachings, and from Oribasius, who was the physician of Julian the Apostate and who was known to his contemporaries as the second Galen. Galen cites Athenaeus in many of his writings. The diverse subjects of the citations testify to the breadth of Athenaeus' knowledge. Galen, in general, states the opinion of Athenaeus relevant to the point he is discussing and tries either to refute it or to interpret it in the light of his own beliefs. Whether Galen agrees with Athenaeus or not, he treats him with obvious respect. Oribasius' extensive quotations from Athenaeus show us the latter's care and thoroughness in handling a subject as well as giving us some of the content of his teaching.

BIBLIOGRAPHY

Some idea of Athenaeus' works and views may be found in Galen, *Claudii Galeni opera omnia,* C. Kühn, ed., 20 vols. (Leipzig, 1821–1833), Index; and Oribasius, *Oribasii collectionum reliquiae,* J. Raeder, ed. (Leipzig–Berlin, 1928–   ), and *Medici Graeci varia opuscula,* CH. F. Matthai, ed. (Moscow, 1908).

Modern accounts are Pauly-Wissowa, eds., *Realencyclopädie der classischen Altertumswissenschaft;* and M. Wellman, *Die pneumatische Schule* (Berlin, 1895).

JOHN S. KIEFFER

ATWATER, WILBUR OLIN (*b.* Johnsburg, New York, 3 May 1844; *d.* Middletown, Connecticut, 22 September 1907), *agricultural chemistry, physiology, scientific administration.*

The son of William Warren Atwater, a Methodist clergyman, and Eliza Barnes Atwater, Wilbur Atwater studied for two years at the University of Vermont and received his bachelor's degree at Wesleyan College in 1865. Interested in both agriculture and chemistry, he then went for postgraduate work to Yale University's Sheffield Scientific School, where he studied under the chemist Samuel W. Johnson, a Leipzig graduate and America's leading authority on agricultural chemistry. Atwater earned his doctorate in 1869, with a thesis on the analysis of the composition of several varieties of American maize. He then spent two years at Leipzig and Berlin. After brief teaching periods at the University of Tennessee and Maine State College, in 1873 he was appointed professor of chemistry at Wesleyan, a position he held until his death.

In 1875 the Connecticut legislature—with the encouragement and financial aid of agricultural editor Orange Judd—established America's first agricultural experiment station, patterned largely after German stations, institutions admired by both Johnson and Atwater. The establishment of the station was a goal to which Johnson had been dedicated since the mid-1850's. From 1875 until 1877, the station was at Middletown and under Atwater's direction. In 1877 it moved to New Haven and the guidance of Johnson. Like most of his contemporary agricultural chemists, Atwater became increasingly involved in fertilizer investigation and testing, using this work partly as a means of gaining agricultural support for scientific research generally. (In the course of it he was able to demonstrate independently the role of leguminous plants in the fixation of atmospheric nitrogen.) Even after the directorship of the Connecticut station had passed into Johnson's hands, Atwater continued to organize fertilizer experiments and to write regularly for farm readers on the application of science to agriculture.

In 1887, with the passage of the Hatch Act, a measure providing federal funds for the establishment of an agricultural experiment station in each state, Atwater was appointed chief of the Office of Experiment Stations, established within the U.S. Department of Agriculture to oversee and coordinate the work of the state experiment stations. Although he occupied this post for only two years—during which he continued his academic duties at Wesleyan—Atwater exerted a decisive influence on administrative policy in regard to the stations. His basic policies were elaborated and implemented through the next quarter century by his successor, A. C. True, a Wesleyan classicist who depended heavily on Atwater's advice. The influence of True and Atwater upon the development of agricultural research in the United States was both positive and surprisingly pervasive, extending to many aspects of basic biological investigation.

In 1887 Atwater also visited Europe, where at Munich he became deeply interested in the calorimetric work of Carl Voit and Max Rubner. On his return to Wesleyan, Atwater sought the aid of E. B. Rosa, his physicist colleague, in the design and construction of what came to be called the Atwater-Rosa calorimeter. Begun in 1892, the calorimeter was in operation by 1897 (preliminary studies had appeared in 1896). Atwater was concerned not only with metabolism as a problem in physiology, but also with the use of his new techniques for the determination of improved dietary standards for the working class, standards that might prescribe a diet providing optimum food value at lowest cost. An adroit manipulator of political and business support, Atwater was able to demonstrate the value of such nutritional investigations to the Committee on Agriculture of the House of Representatives, which in 1894 began to support nutrition research (a program directed by Atwater until his death). Graham Lusk, Francis Benedict, and H. P. Armsby were among the other American students of metabolism who used Atwater's calorimetric techniques.

By the first decade of the twentieth century, calorimetric work had become an extremely popular, almost fashionable field, with broad implications for public policy and popular health education. It is ironic that the total impact of Atwater's nutrition work was somewhat clouded: his emphasis on caloric values—in the absence of knowledge of vitamin and amino acid requirements—led to recommendations that the working class purchase carbohydrates and avoid such "luxuries" as green vegetables. Vigorous though Atwater's scientific work was, his greatest contribution to the development of science in the United States was organizational and administrative—especially his efforts to establish scientific standards for experiment station research. Indeed, his forcefulness in such matters provided an occasional source of disquietude to certain of his colleagues and his career was marked at times by friction with contemporaries.

BIBLIOGRAPHY

The basic source for Atwater's life is his extensive collection of papers and correspondence, including documents recording his tenure as first director of the Office of Experiment Stations. The papers are in the possession of the University Archives, Wesleyan University, Middletown, Conn.; microfilm copies are available at Cornell University and the University of Pennsylvania. There is no full-length biography of Atwater, but for sketches of his life see Benjamin Harrow, "Wilbur Olin Atwater," in *Dictionary of American Biography;* Leonard A. Maynard, "Wilbur O. Atwater—A Biographical Sketch (May 3, 1844–September 22, 1907)," in *Journal of Nutrition,* **78** (1962), 3–9. For useful studies placing Atwater's work, both administrative and scientific, in perspective see Graham Lusk, *The Elements of the Science of Nutrition,* 2nd ed. (Philadelphia-London, 1909); E. V. McCollum, *A History of Nutrition* (Boston, 1957); and A. C. True, *A History of Agricultural Experimentation and Research in the United States, 1607–1925,* U.S. Department of Agriculture, Misc. Pub. No. 251 (Washington, D.C., 1937).

CHARLES E. ROSENBERG

ATWOOD, GEORGE (*b.* England, 1745; *d.* London, England, July 1807), *mathematics, physics.*

Atwood attended Westminster School and was awarded a scholarship to Trinity College, Cambridge, at the age of nineteen. He graduated with a B.A. in 1769, received his M.A. in 1772, then became a fellow and tutor at his college. His lectures were well attended and well received because of their delivery and their experimental demonstrations. These experiments, published in 1776, the year he was elected a fellow of the Royal Society, consisted of simple demonstrations to illustrate electricity, optics, and mechanics.

Among his admirers was William Pitt, who in 1784 gave Atwood an office in the treasury, at £500 a year, so that, according to an obituary in the *Gentleman's Magazine,* he could "devote a large portion of his time to financial calculation" in which he was apparently employed "to the great advantage of revenue." His only published work in this connection was *A Review of the Statutes* . . . (1801), in which he analyzed the cost of bread. The price that the baker could charge for a loaf of bread was governed by statute and was determined by the cost of grain plus an allowance for profit. Central to the problem was how much grain was required to make a loaf of bread. Atwood's work,

an attempt to rationalize the standards, was based on computation as well as on the results of experiments carried out by Sir George Young in 1773.

The work for which Atwood is best known and which bears his name—Atwood's machine—is described in *A Treatise on the Rectilinear Motion* . . . (1784), which is essentially a textbook on Newtonian mechanics. Atwood's machine was designed to demonstrate the laws of uniformly accelerated motion due to gravity and was constructed with pulleys, so that a weight suspended from one of the pulleys descends more slowly than a body falling freely in air but still accelerates uniformly.

Most of Atwood's other published work consisted of the mathematical analysis of practical problems. In "A General Theory for the Mensuration . . ." (1781), he derived equations for use in connection with Hadley's quadrant; and in "The Construction and Analysis . . ." (1796) and "A Disquisition on the Stability of Ships" (1798), he extended the theories of Euler, Bougier, and others to account for the stability of floating bodies with large angles of roll. For "The Construction and Analysis . . ." he was awarded the Copley Medal of the Royal Society. His work on arches, *A Dissertation on the Construction and Properties of Arches* (1801), based on the assumption that the material of an arch is perfectly hard and rigid and that the only critical forces are those relating to the wedging action of the individual arch units, is now totally superseded. It was published with a supplement containing Atwood's questions about the proposed new London Bridge over the Thames, which was to be of iron.

BIBLIOGRAPHY

Atwood's works are *A Description of the Experiments Intended to Illustrate a Course of Lectures on the Principles of Natural Philosophy* (London, 1776); "A General Theory for the Mensuration of the Angle Subtended by Two Objects, of Which One Is Observed by Rays After Two Reflections From Plane Surfaces, and the Other by Rays Coming Directly to the Spectator's Eye," in *Philosophical Transactions of the Royal Society,* **71,** part 2 (1781), 395–434; *An Analysis of a Course of Lectures on the Principles of Natural Philosophy* (Cambridge, 1784), a revised version of *A Description of the Experiments* . . . ; *A Treatise on the Rectilinear Motion and Rotation of Bodies With a Description of Original Experiments Relative to the Subject* (Cambridge, 1784); "Investigations Founded on the Theory of Motion for Determining the Times of Vibration of Watch Balances," in *Philosophical Transactions,* **84** (1794), 119–168; "The Construction and Analysis of Geometrical Propositions Determining the Positions Assumed by Homogeneal

Bodies Which Float Freely, and at Rest, on the Fluid's Surface; Also Determining the Stability of Ships and of Other Floating Bodies," *ibid.*, **86** (1796), 46–130; "A Disquisition on the Stability of Ships," *ibid.*, **88** (1798), 201–310; *A Dissertation on the Construction and Properties of Arches* (London, 1801); and *Review of the Statutes and Ordinances of Assize Which Have Been Established in England From the Fourth Year of King John, 1202 to the Thirty-seventh of His Present Majesty* (London, 1801).

ERIC M. COLE

AUBERT DUPETIT-THOUARS, L. M. See **Dupetit-Thouars, L. M. Aubert.**

AUBUISSON DE VOISINS, JEAN-FRANÇOIS D' (*b.* Toulouse, France, 19 April 1769; *d.* Toulouse, 20 August 1841), *mining, geology, hydraulics.*

Son of a squire, Jean-François d'Aubuisson de Voisins, and of Jeanne-Françoise Dassié, d'Aubuisson entered the Benedictine College of Sorèze in 1779. In 1786, having won prizes in infinitesimal calculus, physics, and natural history, he was admitted to the Artillery School in Metz. D'Aubuisson was commissioned a second lieutenant on 1 January 1791 and spent the next six years in military service in Spain.

After the Treaty of Campo Formio, d'Aubuisson retired to Freiberg, where he taught mathematics. His civilian vocation was determined by Werner's courses in mineralogy, geology, and mining, which he attended at the Bergakademie in 1800–1801, and field trips to Saxon mines. In 1802 he published the translation of a work by Werner, which he enriched with personal annotation. In the same year d'Aubuisson also published *Des mines de Freiberg en Saxe et de leur exploitation.*

Returning to France in 1802, d'Aubuisson attempted to enter the mining administration, although since 1795 it had been reserved for highly qualified graduates of the École Polytechnique who had spent two years at the École des Mines. He had an old Sorèze colleague, Antoine-François Andréossy, intervene for him. On Andréossy's very first recommendation to the minister of the interior, d'Aubuisson was appointed to the mining administration on 20 January 1803 as assistant to Tonnelier, the curator of the mineralogical collections and library.

Like Werner, d'Aubuisson attributed the formation of the Saxon basalts to precipitates from the primeval sea. Since volcanists, as a result of the observations made in Auvergne by Guettard and Desmarest, regarded the basalts as the product of volcanic eruptions, d'Aubuisson decided to study the question by spending the summer of 1803 in Auvergne. He returned a convert to volcanism.

Andréossy again aided d'Aubuisson by proposing to the minister of the interior that d'Aubuisson would be of greater service if he were appointed a mining engineer. In March 1807 d'Aubuisson became mining engineer for the departments of Doire and Sesia, in the Piedmont, now part of Italy. He was promoted to chief engineer, second class, in March 1811 and was appointed chief of the mineralogical district of Toulouse less than two months later. There he served for more than thirty years in an administrative post covering the entire Pyrenees region.

In 1819 d'Aubuisson published *Traité de géognosie, ou Exposé des connaissances actuelles sur la constitution physique et minérale du globe terrestre,* the first competent treatment of general geology published in France. As a result of this book, on 5 February 1821 the Académie des Sciences named him correspondent for the Mineralogical Section, replacing the Abbé Palassou, whose death had been erroneously announced. When the mistake was discovered, the Academy decided that d'Aubuisson should retain his title.

Publications by English, German, and French authors soon considerably enlarged the scope of geology, and d'Aubuisson undertook a second edition of his *Traité.* The first volume appeared in 1828. Pressed for time, he entrusted the task of publishing the subsequent volumes to Amédée Burat, the first professor of geology at the École Centrale; Volume II appeared in 1834 and Volume III in 1835.

During the latter part of his career d'Aubuisson was compelled gradually to abandon his geological studies in order to attend to the major tasks that resulted from his living in Toulouse. He had to devote a great deal of time to the "miners' mine" of Rancié (Ariège), which he administered for thirty years. Intelligent, tenacious, self-assertive, and industrious, he was the prototype of the technical civil servant in a young state. Against the changes of the political regime, he symbolized the continuity of viewpoint of this state, working untiringly for the adaptation of the miners' mine to the new economic situation. His work led to a pamphlet entitled *Observations sur les mines et les mineurs de Rancié, et sur l'administration de ces mines* (1818).

Aided by the engineer Marrot, in July 1825 d'Aubuisson found that in an airshaft the resistance to passage of the air is directly proportional to the length of the pipe and the square of the speed of the air flow, and inversely proportional to the diameter. He published these findings in two articles in the *Annales des mines* in 1828. These results served as the starting point for Théophile Guibal's establishment of the temperature constant of a mine. D'Aubuisson also found that the volumes of two gases streaming from equal openings and under the same pressure are inversely proportional to the square roots of their densities. A further accomplishment was the establishment of a simple formula that made it possible to use cast-iron water pipes with walls half as thick as those previously used.

The nature of the technical problems he dealt with as municipal councillor induced d'Aubuisson to publish *Traité du mouvement de l'eau dans les tuyaux de conduite* (1827) and "Histoire de l'établissement des fontaines à Toulouse" (1830). His professional activities had caused him to reflect on many problems of hydraulics, and he summarized his experiments and thoughts on these problems in *Traité d'hydraulique à l'usage des ingénieurs* (1834).

On 2 August 1828, d'Aubuisson was appointed chief engineer, first class. Since he preferred to remain at Toulouse, he refused a transfer to Paris and thus lost all chance of rising to the rank of inspector general.

BIBLIOGRAPHY

I. ORIGINAL WORKS. D'Aubuisson's writings include *Des mines de Freiberg en Saxe et de leur exploitation,* 3 vols. (Leipzig, 1802); *Nouvelle théorie de la formation des filons. Application de cette théorie à l'exploitation des mines, particulièrement de celles de Freiberg* (Freiberg, 1802), his trans. of Werner's *Neue Theorie von der Entstenung der Gänge; Observations sur les mines et les mineurs de Rancié, et sur l'administration de ces mines* (Toulouse, 1818); *Traité de géognosie, ou Exposé des connaissances actuelles sur la constitution physique et minérale du globe terrestre,* 2 vols. (Paris, 1819), 2nd ed., completed by Burat, 3 vols. (Paris, 1828–1835); *Considérations sur l'autorité royale en France depuis la Restauration et sur les administrations locales* (Paris, 1825); *Traité du mouvement de l'eau dans les tuyaux de conduite* (Paris, 1827; 2nd ed., 1836); "Expériences sur la résistance que l'air éprouve dans des tuyaux de conduite, faites aux mines de Rancié, en 1825," in *Annales des mines,* 2nd ser., **3** (1828), 367–486; "Expériences sur la trompe du ventilateur des mines de Rancié, suivies de quelques observations sur les trompes en général," *ibid.,* **4** (1828), 211–244; "Histoire de l'établissement des fontaines à Toulouse," in *Mémoires de l'Académie royale des sciences, inscriptions et belles-lettres de Toulouse* (1823–1827), **2,** pt. 1 (1830), 159–400; *Traité d'hydraulique à l'usage des ingénieurs* (Paris, 1834; 2nd ed., 1840, 1846; 3rd ed., 1858); and *Tables à l'usage des ingénieurs et des physiciens. Tables de logarithmes* (Paris, 1842).

D'Aubuisson's many articles in the *Journal des mines* are listed in P.-X. Leschevin's *Table analytique des matières* (Paris, 1813), which covers the first 28 vols., and in A.-C.-L. Peltier's work of the same title (Paris, 1821), which covers the last 10 vols. (the name is spelled Daubuisson in the two works). The articles in the *Annales des mines* (the title of the *Journal* after 1815) are listed in the indexes for the

1st and 2nd ser. (Paris, 1831) under "D'Aubuisson" and in the index for the 3rd ser. (Paris, 1847) under "Aubuisson (d')."

II. SECONDARY LITERATURE. Works on d'Aubuisson are E. Brassinne, "Éloge de M. d'Aubuisson de Voisins," in *Mémoires de l'Académie royale des sciences, inscriptions et belles-lettres de Toulouse,* 3rd ser., **1** (1845), 265–284; and René Garmy, *La "mine aux mineurs" de Rancié 1789–1848* (Paris, 1943), pp. 117–133. Original materials may be found in Archives Nationales, Paris, F14.2712[2], and the Archives de la Guerre at Vincennes, in the dossier "D'Aubuisson de Voisins."

ARTHUR BIREMBAUT

AUDOUIN, JEAN VICTOR (*b.* Paris, France, 27 April 1797; *d.* Paris, 9 November 1841), *zoology.*

Audouin was the second child of Victor Joseph Audouin, a notary, and Jeanne Marie Pierrette Enée. He began his studies at Rheims in 1807, and continued them at Paris in 1809 and at Lucca from 1812 to 1814; in Lucca he stayed with a relative who was an official in the household of Princess Elisa Baciocchi. He then returned to Paris and attended the Lycée Louis-le-Grand. Later Audouin began to study law, but he soon abandoned it for medicine, pharmacy, and the natural sciences. In 1816 he met the mineralogist Alexandre Brongniart, who hired him as his secretary and had a notable influence on Audouin's scientific career. In the same year Audouin published his first entomological work, and in 1820 he read his important paper, "Recherches anatomiques sur le thorax des animaux articulés et celui des insectes en particulier," before the Académie des Sciences. This report won him the praise of Cuvier and was printed in 1824. He and other naturalists founded the Société d'Histoire Naturelle de Paris in 1822, and in 1824 he began publication of the *Annales des sciences naturelles,* an important scientific periodical still in existence. His collaborators on the journal were Adolphe Brongniart and Jean-Baptiste Dumas, both of whom later became his brothers-in-law. In 1825 he became assistant to Lamarck and Latreille at the Museum of Natural History in Paris; and the following year he was asked to finish the work of Savigny (then incapacitated by serious eye trouble) on the invertebrates collected during the Egyptian expedition of 1798–1799.

The same year, 1826, Audouin and Henri Milne Edwards began a course of anatomical, physiological, and biological research on the marine invertebrates of the Breton and Norman coast. These were pioneer studies of this type in France. It was also in 1826 that Audouin presented his doctoral thesis on the chemical, pharmaceutical, and medical natural history of the cantharides. On 6 December 1827, he married Mathilde Brongniart, who became his collaborator because of her talent as a draftsman; in 1827 and 1828 he and Milne Edwards published the results of their anatomical and physiological research on crustacea. In 1830 he replaced Latreille as assistant naturalist at the Natural History Museum. He and Milne Edwards then published, in 1832, the first volume of their *Recherches pour servir à l'histoire naturelle du littoral de la France.* This work initiated the bionomic classification of coastal marine invertebrates. Also in 1832, Audouin and other entomologists founded the Société Entomologique de France, and in 1833 he succeeded Latreille as professor of zoology (in the chair dealing with crustacea, arachnids, and insects) at the Natural History Museum. From 1834 on, he specialized in agricultural entomology, and in 1836–1837 he confirmed the observations of Agostino Bassi concerning the muscardine of the silkworm (*Beauveria bassiana*). On 5 February 1838, Audouin was elected a member of the Académie des Sciences (Section d'Économie Rurale). He died after a short illness, and his *Histoire naturelle des insectes nuisibles à la vigne* was finished by his collaborator, Émile Blanchard, and his friend Henri Milne Edwards, in 1842.

Audouin's work is both that of a scrupulously careful morphologist and anatomist of Cuvier's school, and that of a biologist who has left behind important observations on the physiology of crustacea as well as on the ethology of various insects harmful to cultivated plants. This last phase of his research marks Audouin's work as the precursor of modern applied entomology.

BIBLIOGRAPHY

I. ORIGINAL WORKS. Audouin's published works include "Recherches anatomiques sur le thorax des animaux articulés et celui des insectes en particulier," in *Annales des sciences naturelles,* **1** (1824), 97–135, 416–432; "Recherches pour servir à l'histoire naturelle des Cantharides," *ibid.,* **9** (1826), 31–61; "Recherches anatomiques et physiologiques sur la circulation dans les crustacés," written with Henri Milne Edwards, *ibid.,* **11** (1827), 283–314, 352–393; "Recherches anatomiques sur le système nerveux des crustacés," written with Henri Milne Edwards, *ibid.,* **14** (1828), 77–102; *Recherches pour servir à l'histoire naturelle du littoral de la France ou Recueil de mémoires sur l'anatomie, la physiologie, la classification et les moeurs des animaux de nos côtes,* written with Henri Milne Edwards, 2 vols. (Paris, 1832–1834); "Recherches anatomiques et physiologiques sur la maladie contagieuse qui attaque les vers à soie, et qu'on désigne sous le nom de muscardine," in *Annales des sciences naturelles (zoologie),* 8th series, **2** (1837), 229–245; "Nouvelles expériences sur la nature de la maladie contagieuse qui attaque les vers à soie et qu'on désigne sous le nom de muscardine," *ibid.,* 257–270; and *Histoire des insectes nuisibles à la vigne et particulièrement de la pyrale* (Paris, 1842), completed by Émile Blanchard and Henri Milne Edwards.

Numerous manuscripts, drawings, and letters of Audouin's are in the Archives de la Famille Audouin, Archives de l'Académie des Sciences, Bibliothèque de l'Institut, Bibliothèque du Muséum National d'Histoire Naturelle, and Archives de la Société Entomologique de France—all in Paris; and the Wellcome Historical Medical Library and the Library of the British Museum of Natural History—both in London.

II. SECONDARY LITERATURE. More on Audouin and his work can be found in M. Duponchel, "Notice sur la vie et les travaux de Jean-Victor Audouin," in *Annales de la Société Entomologique de France,* **11** (1842), 95–164; H. Milne Edwards, *Notice sur la vie et les travaux de Victor Audouin* (Paris, 1850); and Jean Théodoridès, "Jean-Victor Audouin, Journal d'un étudiant en médecine et en sciences à Paris sous la Restauration (1817–1818)," texte inédit, in *Histoire de la médecine,* **9** (Nov. 1958), 4–63; *ibid.* (Dec. 1958), 5–56; **10** (Jan. 1959), 5–48; "La Rhénanie en 1835 vue par un naturaliste français," unpublished letters, in *Sudhoffs Archiv,* **43** (1959), 233–253; and "Les débuts de la biologie marine en France: Jean-Victor Audouin et Henri Milne Edwards, 1826–1829," in *Actes du 1er Congrès International d'Histoire de l'Océanographie (Monaco, 1966),* 1968.

JEAN THÉODORIDÈS

AUDUBON, JOHN JAMES (*b.* Les Cayes, Santo Domingo [now Haiti], 26 April 1785; *d.* New York, N.Y., 27 January 1851), *ornithology.*

Audubon's father was Jean Audubon, a French sea captain and planter of moderate substance in Santo Domingo; his mother was a Mlle. Jeanne(?) Rabin(e?), who died soon after his birth. In 1791, he and a half sister were sent to Nantes, where their father had already arrived, to join him and Mme. Audubon (Anne Moynet), who graciously accepted the children of her husband's island sojourn. They were formally adopted in 1794, the boy as Jean Jacques Fougère Audubon.

Audubon's youth at Nantes and Coüeron, where he received a minimal elementary education, was comfortable and unexceptional. In 1803 he was sent to a farm, owned by his father, in eastern Pennsylvania and entrusted to the care of good friends. There his boyhood interest in birds—especially in drawing them—was intensified. In 1808 he married Lucy Bakewell, daughter of a prosperous neighbor, and moved to the new settlement of Louisville, Kentucky, where Audubon was to share in running a store.

Audubon had no formal training in natural history, having had only a brief acquaintance (upon revisiting France in 1805) with the obscure naturalist Charles d'Orbigny and a period in New York as a taxidermist under the many-faceted Samuel L. Mitchell (later founder of the Lyceum of Natural History). As an artist he was equally untutored (a persistent legend that he had briefly studied under Jacques Louis David seems to lack foundation). Marginally literate, Audubon had only hunting skill, undisciplined curiosity, great latent artistic power, and unfailing energy. He worked hard on his bird drawings, however, and developed a useful method of mounting dead birds on wires as an aid to delineation—a technique invaluable in a day without binoculars or cameras.

Between 1808 and 1819 Audubon failed as merchant and miller in both Louisville and Henderson, Kentucky, but in these formative years he ranged widely, from Pittsburgh as far west as Ste. Genevieve (now in Missouri). The country, if not untouched, was mostly unspoiled wilderness teeming with birds as little known to science as to him. He hunted and drew, sporadically at first, innocent of such patchy and uncertain knowledge as the few extant, relevant books would have given him. In common with not a few better-educated naturalists of the time, Audubon lacked formal method. He merely sought birds new to him, and shot and painted them, sometimes repeatedly, often substituting improved efforts for old.

Audubon briefly met the distinguished ornithologist Alexander Wilson at Louisville in 1810, and saw the first two (of nine) volumes of the artist–author's pioneer *American Ornithology* (he later implied, perhaps correctly, that his own drawings were, even at that time, better than Wilson's). Perhaps the idea of publication first entered his mind on this occasion, yet not until 1820, after going bankrupt, did Audubon set out by flatboat for Louisiana, with the single goal of enriching his portfolio of bird pictures. He would support himself precariously as itinerant artist and tutor, leaving much of the burden of supporting herself and their two sons to Lucy.

For the first time Audubon began a regular journal, some of which is extant. The journal of 1820 (the original of which survives) is a disorderly, semiliterate document. Like all the rest—the later ones are more articulate—it combines daily events, impressions of people and countryside, and random notes on birds encountered. These journals are valuable to ornithologists as checks on the formal texts that followed. Often more informative than the latter, they are nevertheless marked by lack of detail, imprecision,

and not infrequent discrepancies. Audubon never kept a full, orderly record of his observations on birds, and in formal writing he obviously relied as often on memory as on the sketchy notes he kept.

In 1821–1824, chiefly in Louisiana and Mississippi, Audubon came into his full powers as a gifted painter of birds and master of design. There would be many more pictures, but he would never improve upon the best of those years. Neither, although he would acquire a modicum of worldliness and a veneer of zoological sophistication, would his working methods and descriptive skills be basically changed. Whatever Audubon in essence was to be, he was by 1824.

In that year Audubon sought publication of his work in Philadelphia and New York. This failing, he traveled to England in 1826. There, finding support, subscribers, and skilled engravers, he brought out the 435 huge, aquatint copperplates of *The Birds of America,* in many parts, over the next twelve years.

The dramatic impact of his ambitious, complex pictures and a romantic image as "the American woodsman" secured Audubon entry into a scientific community much preoccupied with little-known lands. He met the leaders of society and science and was elected to the leading organizations, including the Royal Society of London. Among his friends were the gifted ornithologist William Swainson, from whom he learned some niceties of technical ornithology, and the orderly, brilliant Scottish naturalist-anatomist William MacGillivray. The text for Audubon's pictures, separately produced at Edinburgh, emerged as the five-volume *Ornithological Biography.* MacGillivray edited this for grammatical form, and he also contributed extensive anatomical descriptions to the later volumes.

Audubon's remaining efforts were devoted to the hopeless task of including all the birds of North America in his work. To this end he made increasing efforts to obtain notes and specimens from others and to cull the growing literature. Thus, much more than the early ones, the last volumes of his work have an element of compilation. He returned several times from his publishing labors in Scotland and England for more fieldwork, visiting the Middle Atlantic states in 1829, the Southeast as far as the Florida keys in 1831–1832, part of Labrador in 1833, and as far southwest as Galveston, Texas, in 1837. After his final return to the United States in 1839, Audubon journeyed up the Missouri River to Fort Union (the site of which is now in North Dakota) in 1843, obtaining birds treated in a supplement to the small American edition of his *Birds,* as well as some of the mammals discussed in his *Viviparous Quadrupeds,* which he wrote with John Bachman. In this, his last major effort, he was considerably assisted by his sons Victor and John.

Much, if not most, of Audubon's singularly enduring fame, which tends to cloud scientific and popular thought alike, rests on his much-debated but obviously significant efforts as an artist. (The relevancy of his established artistic stature to his scientific contribution is critical and difficult to assess, but can scarcely be ignored.) The illustration of new and little-known animals, as part of their zoological descriptions, was a characteristic and important part of eighteenth- and nineteenth-century natural history. Certainly Audubon kindled wide and enduring interest in this aspect of zoology—more, indeed, than would have been necessary for the strictly scientific appreciation of the subjects; his birds were portrayed with a flair, a concern for the living, acting animal in a suggested environment that was undreamed of before, and with a vigorous sense of drama, color, and design rarely equaled since. He had few significant predecessors and no debts in this area (only Thomas Bewick had earlier drawn—in simple woodcuts—birds as authentic). That Audubon's pictures contained innumerable technical errors seems to be comprehended only by specialists. The facial expressions and bodily attitudes of his birds are often strikingly human, rather than avian, but this is natural enough, considering his emotional nature and lack of optical equipment; paradoxically, this kind of error may have much to do with his enduring popularity with the general public.

Other than his art—aside from the inevitable accumulation of general knowledge of the kinds, habits, and distribution of birds—Audubon produced little that was new. Even the grand scale of his work had been anticipated by Mark Catesby a century earlier and by François Levaillant a generation earlier. Essentially, he built on Wilson's descriptive–anecdotal model (name the bird; say something general of its ways, habits, and haunts; and flesh out the account with a story or two of encounters with it in nature), as he states in the introduction to Volume V of the Biography. He went beyond Wilson in scope because he lived longer and had greater vigor; in point-for-point comparison, he tends to come off second best—where Wilson is dry and factual, even acerbic (but not artless), Audubon is grandiose, often irrelevant, romantic at best and florid at worst. His work, nevertheless, was the most informative available to American ornithologists between that of Alexander Wilson (as supplemented 1825–1833 by C. L. Bonaparte) and the beginning of Spencer Fullerton Baird's vast in-fluence around 1860. He influenced such American successors as Baird, Elliott Coues, and Robert Ridgway, however, more by kindling interest than by procedural example.

Although he possessed a good eye for specific differences and inevitably discovered a number of new forms, Audubon was not basically a systematist; the classification of his Synopsis (1839), which ordered the randomly discussed birds of the Biography, is routine. As a theoretician he fared little better, being distinctly inferior to Gilbert White, who wrote half a century earlier and without pretension (see Audubon's curiously labored and undistinguished discussion of why birds do not need to migrate, in Biography, V, 442–445).

That Audubon possessed an original mind is shown, however, by a penchant (unfortunately little exploited) for experiment. As a young man in Pennsylvania he marked some phoebes with colored thread and recovered individuals after a year, thus anticipating bird banding by more than half a century. With Bachman in 1832, he conducted experiments designed to test the ability of the turkey vulture to locate its food by smell. The ingenious experiments lacked adequate controls and produced erroneous (though long credited) results.

In assessing Audubon, whose firm grip on the popular imagination has scarcely lessened since 1826, we must as historians of science seriously ask who would remember him if he had not been an artist of great imagination and flair. Not only does Audubon's artistic stature seem to dwarf his scientific stature, but the latter would probably be still less had he not been a painter expected to provide text for his paintings. The chances seem to be very good that had he not been an artist, he would be an unlikely candidate for a dictionary of scientific biography, if remembered to science at all.

BIBLIOGRAPHY

I. ORIGINAL WORKS. Nearly all the paintings for The Birds of America are at the New-York Historical Society, and have been reproduced by modern methods in The Original Water-color Paintings by John James Audubon for The Birds of America (New York, 1966). Miscellaneous additional paintings are cited by biographers listed below.

Audubon's books are The Birds of America, 435 aquatint copperplate engravings, 4 vols. without text (Edinburgh–London, 1827–1838); Ornithological Biography, 5 vols. (Edinburgh, 1831–1839); Synopsis of the Birds of North America (Edinburgh, 1839); The Birds of America, 7 vols. (New York–Philadelphia, 1840–1844), which combines the text of *Ornithological Biography* with inferior, much reduced, and sometimes altered copies of the plates of the 1st ed. of *The Birds of America;* and *Viviparous Quadrupeds of North America,* 3 vols. plates (New York, 1845–1848) and 3 vols. text (New York, 1846–1854), subsequent eds. (to at least 1865) combine text and reduced plates (plates by J. J. and J. W. Audubon; text by J. J. Audubon and John Bachman).

Audubon's comparatively few short articles in periodical literature are cited by biographers listed below.

The Life and Adventures of John James Audubon, written by Charles Coffin Adams from materials provided by Mrs. Audubon, Robert Buchanan, ed. (London, 1868), and its variant text, *The Life of John James Audubon,* Lucy Audubon, ed. (New York, 1869), contain the sole (but doubtless considerably modified) surviving record of Audubon's trip to Ste. Genevieve in 1810–1811 (pp. 25–33 in the 1868 version; 1869 version not seen) and other matter; Maria R. Audubon's *Audubon and His Journals,* E. Coues, ed. (New York, 1897), presents the only surviving version of the Labrador, Missouri River, and European journals. There is also a painstaking transcript of the extant *Journal of John James Audubon Made During His Trip to New Orleans in 1820–21* (Boston, 1929).

II. SECONDARY LITERATURE. The biographies cited below all contain extensive bibliographies that collectively provide detailed collations of Audubon's major works, elucidate the complexities of later editions and imprints, and give access to all but the most recent literature on the subject.

Lesser biographies and much miscellany are cited in F. H. Herrick's *Audubon the Naturalist,* 2nd ed., rev. (New York, 1938), still the basic and most extensive source but now outdated in some particulars by Ford; in S. C. Arthur's *Audubon, an Intimate Life of the American Woodsman* (New Orleans, 1937), which includes some sources not cited elsewhere; and in A. Ford's *John James Audubon* (Norman, Okla., 1964), which contains extensive new information on his parentage and early life in France. The popular *John James Audubon* by A. B. Adams (New York, 1966) contains some new sources and insights.

Searching appraisal of Audubon as an ornithologist may be found in the historical introduction to A. Newton's *A Dictionary of Birds* (London, 1896), p. 24; in E. Stresemann's preeminent *Die Entwicklung der Ornithologie* (Berlin, 1951), pp. 407–409; and in W. E. C. Todd's exhaustive *Birds of the Labrador Peninsula* (Toronto–Pittsburgh, 1963), pp. 731–732, 742, a detailed evaluation of his work in Labrador. An extensive critique of Audubon as a bird painter is given in R. M. Mengel's "How Good Are Audubon's Bird Pictures in the Light of Modern Ornithology?," in *Scientific American,* **216,** no. 5 (1967), 155–159.

ROBERT M. MENGEL

AUENBRUGGER, JOSEPH LEOPOLD (*b.* Graz, Austria, 19 November 1722; *d.* Vienna, Austria, 18 May 1809), *medicine.*

The son of a wealthy innkeeper, Auenbrugger received his medical education at the University of Vienna, where Gerard van Swieten had, through a series of reforms, made the Faculty of Medicine the leading one in Europe. Soon Auenbrugger came under van Swieten's influence; the extent of this influence is shown by his dedication to van Swieten of a work suggesting camphor as a treatment for a special form of mania (*Experimentum nascens de remedio specifico sub signo specifico in mania virorum,* 1776). He graduated on 18 November 1752.

From 1751 to 1758 Auenbrugger worked as assistant physician at the Spanish Hospital, but did not receive a salary until 1755. Because of his work in the hospital, Empress Maria Theresa in 1757 ordered the Faculty of Medicine to admit him as a member without charging him any fees. From 1758 to 1762 he was chief physician at the Spanish Hospital, obtaining experience in the diagnosis of chest diseases. After leaving the Spanish Hospital, Auenbrugger was a prominent practitioner in Vienna. For his medical achievements he was ennobled in 1784 by Emperor Joseph II.

Auenbrugger is considered the founder of chest percussion. He was undoubtedly aided in developing this diagnostic technique by his musical knowledge (he wrote the libretto for a comic opera by Antonio Salieri), which enabled him to perceive differences in tone when the chest was tapped. For seven years he had observed the changes in tone caused by diseases of the lungs or the heart in patients at the Spanish Hospital, checking and controlling his findings by dissections of corpses and by experiments. In the *Inventum novum* (1761) he presented his findings. If one taps with the fingertips on a healthy chest wall, one will perceive a sound like that of a drum. Diseases in the chest cavity change the normal tone of the tapping to a *sonus altior* (high or tympanitic sound), a *sonus obscurior* (indistinct sound), or a *sonus carnis percussae* (dull sound). Auenbrugger's method permitted the determination of disease-caused changes in the lungs and heart of a live patient and thus gave a new, dependable foundation to the diagnosis of chest diseases. Even with the development of X rays, this method still has diagnostic value.

In the first few years after its publication the *Inventum novum* was reviewed in several journals, the first mention probably being that of Oliver Goldsmith in the London *Public Ledger* (27 August 1761). In 1762 Albrecht von Haller drew attention to "this important work" in his lengthy review in the *Göttingische Anzeigen von gelehrten Sachen.* More influential than these positive references, however, was the opinion of Rudolf August Vogel, who could not find anything new in the *Inventum novum;* rather, he claimed to recognize in it only the *succussio Hippocratis.* Van Swieten and Anton de Haen, the chief of the Vienna Clinic, never mentioned Auenbrugger's percussion, not even when discussing diseases of the chest, but Maximilian Stoll, de Haen's successor, described it in his publications and systematically taught it at the bedside. The spread of Auenbrugger's technique was interrupted by Stoll's premature death; his successors Jacob Reinlein and Johann Peter Frank did nothing to carry on his work.

Nevertheless, chest percussion was used as a diagnostic tool before 1800. Heinrich Callisen, a surgeon in Copenhagen, reported several observations obtained by percussion in his *System der Wundarzneikunst* (1788); and the Parisian surgeon Raphael Bienvenu Sabatier used it to advantage for the diagnosis of empyema. Percussion was practiced and taught at several German universities, including Halle, Wittenberg, Würzburg, and Rostock. About 1797 Jean-Nicolas Corvisart learned of chest percussion by reading Stoll. He investigated the method for several years and soon taught it to his students. In his classic book on heart diseases, *Essai sur les maladies et les lésions organiques du coeur* (1806), he based numerous diagnoses on percussion. Since there was only Rozière de la Chassagne's inadequate translation of the *Inventum novum* (1770), Corvisart published a new one in 1808, enriching it with a large number of his own observations and thus ending any question of the applicability of the new method.

BIBLIOGRAPHY

I. ORIGINAL WORKS. Auenbrugger's major work was *Inventum novum ex percussione thoracis humani ut signo abstrusos interni pectoris morbos detegendi* (Vienna, 1761, 1763, 1775). French translations were made by Rozière de la Chassagne, in *Manuel des pulmoniques* (Paris, 1770), and by Jean-Nicolas Corvisart (Paris, 1808). An English translation by John Forbes, in *Original Cases With Dissections and Observations . . . Selected from Auenbrugger, Corvisart, Laennec and Others* (London, 1824), was reprinted in F. A. Willius and T. E. Keys, *Cardiac Classics* (St. Louis, Mo., 1941), pp. 193–213, and in C. N. B. Camac, *Classics of Medicine and Surgery* (New York, 1959), pp. 120–147; it also appears, with an introduction by Henry E. Sigerist, in *Bulletin of the Institute of the History of Medicine*, **4** (1936), 373–403. A facsimile of the Latin text, together with the French, English, and German translations and a biographical sketch, has been published by Max Neuburger (Vienna–Leipzig, 1922). Auenbrugger also wrote *Von der stillen Wuth oder dem Triebe zum Selbstmorde als einer wirklichen Krankheit, mit Original-Beobachtungen und Anmerkungen* (Dessau, 1783) and the libretto for Salieri's *Der Rauchfangkehrer* (Vienna, 1781).

II. SECONDARY LITERATURE. Writings on Auenbrugger or his work are P. James Bishop, "A List of Papers, etc., on Leopold Auenbrugger (1722–1809) and the History of Percussion," in *Medical History*, **5** (1961), 192–196, a bibliography listing all important works pertinent to the subject with short critical remarks that facilitate orientation; H. L. Blumgart, "Leopold Auenbrugger. His 'Inventum novum'—1761," in *Circulation*, **24** (1961), 1–4; C. Costa, "Sobre la vicisitud creadora—Auenbrugger y Morgagni frente a frente," in *Anales chilenos de historia de la medicina*, **5** (1963), 63–223; Charles Coury, "Auenbrugger, Corvisart et les origines de la percussion," in *J. N. Corvisart, Nouvelle méthode pour reconnaître les maladies internes de la poitrine par la percussion de cette cavité, par Auenbrugger* (Paris, 1968), pp. 109–160; M. Jantsch, "200 Jahre 'Inventum novum,' " in *Wiener medizinische Wochenschrift*, **111** (1961), 199–202; R. G. Rate, "Leopold Auenbrugger and the 'Inventum novum,' " in *Journal of the Kansas Medical Society*, **67** (1966), 30–33; and J. J. Smith, "The 'Inventum novum' of Joseph Leopold Auenbrugger," in *Bulletin of the New York Academy of Medicine*, **38** (1962), 691–701.

JOHANNES STEUDEL

AUGUSTINE OF HIPPO, SAINT, also known as **Aurelius Augustinus** (*b.* Tagaste, North Africa, 13 November 354; *d.* Hippo, North Africa, 28 August 430), *theology, philosophy.*

Augustine was the son of Patricius, a minor official in the Roman province of Numidia, and his Christian wife, Monica. A thorough education in the classics of Roman rhetoric and philosophy led to his becoming at the age of twenty-one a teacher of rhetoric in nearby Carthage. For a time he was greatly attracted by the Manichaean religious doctrines, then at the height of their popularity in Africa, but their promise of a true "science of all things" proved illusory, and he turned to Stoic, Pythagorean, and Aristotelian sources for a surer light. His enormous success as a teacher led him to think of a wider field for his talents, and in 383 he embarked for Rome. After a year there, he was appointed to a professorship of rhetoric in Milan. The influence of Ambrose, bishop of Milan, led him to realize that the Manichaean objections to the Christian Scriptures were based on a simplistic, literalist mode of interpretation of the Bible. This realization and the reading of Plotinus and Porphyry led him to reject Manichaeism and begin the formulation of a highly personal Neoplatonism. His final step to Christianity was brought about by a dramatic conversion experience, centered around the letters of St. Paul. At this point, he gave up his teaching career, and with a group of friends retired to a monastic life of seclusion and study.

After his baptism in 387, he decided to return to Africa. There he began a prodigious writing career which led to almost one hundred books and countless treatises in sermon or letter form. In 395, he was consecrated bishop of Hippo, one of the major centers of Christian influence in North Africa, and was forced to forsake his monastic retirement for a life of constant travel and demanding pastoral duties. Despite this, he somehow found time for a stream of powerful polemics against those who seemed to him to threaten the doctrinal structure of Christianity; he opposed Donatists, Pelagians, and Arians in turn. In addition, he wrote such great creative works as *The City of God, On the Trinity,* and his incomparable *Confessions.* But the Empire was crumbling around him, and as he lay dying in 430, the Vandal armies had crossed the Strait of Gibraltar, and Roman Africa (once the most prosperous and fertile province of the Empire) lay in ruins. The Church of Africa, which Augustine had done so much to shape, was wiped out within a few years of his death.

But Augustine's influence had not been confined to the administration of the affairs of the church in North Africa. His was unquestionably the most powerful mind the Christian church had known until then, perhaps the most creative it has ever known. The success of his efforts to isolate and define the heretical elements in the work of Pelagius, Arius, and a legion of others gave to Roman Christianity a self-understanding, a methodology, a philosophical power and scope it had never before possessed. The categories in which the medieval church thought of man, of the world, of God, were largely those developed by Augustine. His metaphysics resembled those of Neoplatonism, but with *creation* replacing *emanation* as the focal concept. But what shaped his thought was not primarily the categorial systems of the Greek and Roman philosophers; rather, it was the overwhelming experience of sin and of conversion he had known in his own life. To an extent not to be seen again until the rise of existentialism in our own day, he built his philosophy around the certainties and realities of a profound inner experience. The experience was first and foremost one of weakness: naturally weak both in understanding and in will, man needs the help of God if he is to accomplish anything of value. Augustine's theory of knowledge is built around the notion of a Divine illumination which is integral to any genuine human act of understanding, and his theory of will centers on the idea of grace, that is, the aid God freely gives man to strengthen his will in pursuit of the good. The universe (and man

with it) is thus dependent on God in two significantly different ways: first in its being, because God, the Creator, is responsible for all that it is; second, in its activity, because it does not have within it a sufficiency of power to bring it to the goals that God designated for it and so He has to intervene to help it to completion.

Few men have influenced human thought as Augustine did Western religion and philosophy. But does he have any claim to notice in the history of natural science? At first sight it might not seem so. In the sixteen enormous volumes of his collected works, there is not a single treatise on what would be called today a "scientific" topic. Yet, in point of fact, Augustine's work can be seen as marking the second crucial stage in the development of the peculiar matrix of thought and value within which natural science, as we know it, emerged in the West. Greek philosophers had already made the bold and hitherto unthinkable claim that the universe can be grasped in a "true knowledge," a "science," of purely human making, and Greek geometers had produced an impressive ideal of what such a science might aspire to. But after an unparalleled burst of creative activity, Greek science had just as rapidly declined, until by the period of Roman dominance in the first century A.D. it had become little more than a memory. At that point, Christianity made its first appearance and rapidly swept through the Empire. Its message was primarily a religious one, but gradually this message was seen to have far-reaching philosophical consequences.

The major one—and Augustine was the first to draw it clearly—was that if all that is depends totally on God for its being, then it must be good through and through: "Everything which You made was good, and there is nothing at all which You did not make. . . . Each thing by itself is good, and the sum of them all is very good."[1] There is nothing independent of God, therefore, no positive principle of evil on which all the defects of the world can be blamed. At one stroke, the dualism of Manichaeism and of Oriental religions was rejected. The universe is henceforth to be regarded in the Christian West as the work of an intelligent Creator, itself therefore both intelligible and good. Christian faith thus began to point the way, dimly at first, to the possibility of a science of nature of the sort that the Greeks had dreamed of, but a science whose pursuit could now be construed in religious terms, something the Greeks had never succeeded in doing. A second consequence of Christian belief, one that equally permeated Augustine's thinking, would take even longer for Christian thinkers to explore, namely that human history has a meaning, a direction, a beginning, and an end. The way was thus opened to developmental thinking, to an understanding of things in terms of their origins and of the steps that have led to their present state. A shift away from the cyclic concept of time that dominated Greek and Oriental ways of thinking about the world had begun.

Augustine stands, therefore, at a fateful parting of the ways between West and East, one whose importance was often overlooked by early historians of science because it lay at a deeper level of thought than they were wont to regard as relevant. Yet it was at this deeper level that really crucial changes were occurring over the next millennium, so that by the seventeenth century the West was prepared in both attitude and motivation for a giant new effort of understanding.

Augustine's influence on the growth of the approach to nature and the knowledge of nature that science would one day demand cannot be represented as in all respects a positive one, however. There was a tension in his attitude toward the project of a "science of Nature," a tension deriving from many sources. He thought of the universe as a "sign" of God, and elaborated one of the most detailed treatments of the notion of "sign" before Peirce's work on signs in our own day. As a sign, the world should somehow be transparent; we should see God through it. It ought not become an object of interest entirely in its own right; if our gaze terminates at the sign instead of what the sign points to, it has failed to function as a sign for us. We have not really understood it, and our reputed knowledge is vain curiosity instead of true science. The knowledge of nature can never be a proper end in itself, then, unless "I proceed by occasion thereof to praise Thee."[2] Even though the universe is eminently worthy of study as the handiwork of God and the domain in which we can best come to grasp His power and wisdom, such study is always to be subordinate, a means to a knowledge of something other than the universe itself.

Some of Augustine's suspicion of science derived, however, from a much more specific cause. One of the features of Manichaeism that had most attracted him as a young man was its claim to a special knowledge of past and future, the former through an elaborate mythology of the origins of the cosmos and the latter through astrology. He rapidly came to see through both of these claims; in an incisive critique of astrology,[3] he points to instances of people born at the same hour of the same day whose subsequent fate is altogether different. What particularly irked him about the "rash promises of a scientific knowl-

edge" made by the Manichaean astrologers was the denial of human freedom implicit in such claims, and their use of "creatures of God" (the stars) to turn men away from God. His comments on astronomy, by far the most developed science of his day, are always tinged by the current misuse of astronomy on the part of astrologers: "I do not care to know the courses of the stars, nor does my soul ever demand an answer from a departed spirit, for I detest all such sacrilegious superstitions."[4] The sciences with which he was most familiar, instead of fulfilling their function of revealing the Creator in His creation, tended instead, it seemed, to satisfy men's lower instincts. He felt constrained to warn his readers of the dangers inherent in their pursuit: "Some men dive toward the discovery of secrets in Nature, whereof the knowledge, though not beyond our ken, doth profit nothing, yet men desire to know it for the sake of knowing. From this perverse desire of knowledge also it groweth that men enquire into things by magical arts."[5] Faith brought men to God and thus to the fullest satisfaction of their natures as free intelligent creatures. If a question of priorities arose, faith had therefore to rank before knowledge, although in principle the two ought to work together. "A faithful man . . . although he knows not the circles of the Great Bear is much better than another who can weigh out the elements and number the stars and measure the skies, if withal he neglects Thee, O Lord, who disposest of all things in number, weight and measure."[6]

Augustine's theory of knowledge dominated all discussions of scientific method for almost a millennium, until challenged by Aristotelian doctrines in the schools of Paris and Oxford in the mid-thirteenth century. Since all human knowledge (he asserted) needed the help of an intellectual illumination from God, the knowledge in which this illumination showed itself most clearly would obviously have to be the supreme type of knowledge. This pointed immediately to the revealed word of God in the Bible, and to its systematic explication in theology. When Augustine asserted that theology is the "queen of the sciences," this was no arbitrary claim on his part; it was a logical and quite inevitable consequence of his theory of knowledge. The Greek philosophers had seen something suprahuman in man's power of insight, the power by which men recognize eternal truths. These truths so far transcend the realm of sense and of the mutable in which man himself lives and moves that they can be grasped only with the aid of a power that equally transcends the normal material and human order. The notion of the Bible as the "revealed word of God" gave the Christian a warrant and model for such a theory of knowledge, a warrant that carried even more conviction than did the geometrical analogies of the Platonists.

Because the primary instance of Divine illumination is the Bible, and because all human sciences have to depend ultimately on a Divine illumination (rather than upon automatic modes of deduction or of empirical generalization), it follows that the word of the Bible carries immensely more weight than any claim of human science ever could. "That which is supported by Divine authority ought to be preferred over that which is conjectured by human infirmity."[7] Augustine favored the literal interpretation of Scripture, except where there was internal evidence that it was intended to be taken metaphorically or where the passage, literally taken, conflicted with a strictly demonstrated conclusion of a human science. In this literal emphasis, he differed from other Scriptural scholars of his day, especially those of the Eastern church who favored a more allegorical approach. His influence swung the Latin church heavily toward a "literalist" theory of inspiration, the view most in keeping with Augustine's overall theory of knowledge.

Augustine himself did not hesitate to depart from the literal interpretation of Scripture when he felt that scientific orthodoxy excluded the possibility of such an interpretation. The problem that preoccupied him by far the most in this regard was that of cosmic origins, about which the Neoplatonists had had much to say. The idea of a series of discrete creations spread over six days was absolutely unacceptable from the Neoplatonic point of view. It is interesting to note that Augustine assumed without further question that this conflict legitimized a partly metaphorical interpretation of the disputed *Hexaemeron,* the account of creation given in the first three chapters of Genesis. His commentary on this narrative, the *De Genesi ad litteram,* clearly gave him much trouble in the writing. It appeared in different versions, and the final one was written and rewritten over fourteen years. His purpose in writing it was to resolve what he clearly took to be the major dispute between Scripture and the science of his day.

He argued that the days mentioned in the Creation story have to be understood as lengthy periods of time, not as days in the strict sense. This was plausible enough, but he went much further than this. Instead of innumerable successive acts of creation, God implanted in the primal nebulous (*nebulosa*) matter the seminal potentialities (or *rationes seminales,* as the Neoplatonists called them) from which all the species of the world we know would successively develop in the order described in Genesis. There was very little internal evidence in support of this ingenious mode

of interpretation and the detailed theory of origins based on it; despite appearances, therefore, the warrant of the theory was really nothing more than its original philosophicoscientific one. But then methodological distinctions of this sort were not part of the Augustinian theory of knowledge to begin with.

Despite the liberties Augustine took in this particular instance, he much more often showed himself unexpectedly literalist, even when a metaphorical reading of Scripture would have seemed the obvious one to adopt. In one passage he discusses the Biblical phrase, "the waters above the firmament," the implications of which appeared to run counter to the contemporary belief that the "natural" place of water is below that of air. After an ingenious speculation about "waters" here perhaps meaning water vapor, he concludes: "In whatever manner the waters may be (above the firmament of air), and of whatsoever kind they may be, that they *are* there we cannot doubt. The authority of Scripture is far greater than the strength of man's reasoning."[8]

The influence of Augustine was thus a dangerously ambiguous one in this regard. Although in his view the knowledge of nature is worth attaining, it can apparently be discovered in the phrases of Scripture, as well as in the elaborations of science. And if a conflict should arise between a literal reading of the Bible and some finding of science, the former must take precedence unless and until the latter has been demonstrated beyond all possibility of error, in which case the theologian will have grounds for assuming that a metaphorical interpretation is the proper one. The potential for conflict in such a theory of interpretation is sufficiently obvious today, but it was more than a millennium before scientific claims would depart sufficiently from the commonsense Hebrew world view for the problem to become a disruptive one. It was no accident that both Galileo and his opponents called upon Augustine when the question arose whether the Copernican doctrine was invalidated by the frequent Scriptural mentions of the sun's motion.

Three Augustinian doctrines are worth noting because of the part they played in the early history of the natural sciences. The first of these is the doctrine of *rationes seminales,* which has already been mentioned and which has often been said to prefigure the theory of an evolutionary origin of species. The *De Genesi ad litteram* became the definitive work in the Middle Ages on origins and greatly encouraged developmental ways of understanding cosmic history, despite the counter influence of Aristotle in the later medieval period. But the Augustinian theory of *rationes seminales* was a developmental and not in any genuine sense an evolutionary view. Augustine believed in the fixity of species as strongly as did any of his Neoplatonist precursors. He did not suppose that one species could give rise to another; his theory was in no sense intended to suggest that every present species developed from a chain of earlier different species, back to the primal chaos of first matter. Rather, he held that God had implanted within this matter the germ of each separate species that would later develop; at some later appropriate moment, each germ would be activated, and the adult species would appear. The germs were not, therefore, earlier species, themselves destined to be replaced by the new species descending from them (as evolutionary theories hold); they were invisibly small seeds, each one carrying within it the potentiality for only one species. Furthermore, the activation of the seeds in some cases (as in the case of man's origin) required a further Divine intervention; the potentialities were not sufficient of themselves to bring about the new species unaided. Thus it was not a true theory of evolution. Yet it cannot be denied that it was a lot closer to evolutionary modes of thought than were the major cosmologies of Greek origin.

A second characteristically Augustinian emphasis had a more direct effect on the direction taken by earlier medieval science. Augustine made much of a passing Biblical phrase about God's having formed the universe "in number, weight and measure" in order to reinforce the mathematicism of Plato with an additional Biblical sanction. "These three things, measure, form, and order . . . are as it were generic good things to be found in all that God has created. . . . Where the three are present in a high degree, there are great goods. Where they are absent, there is no goodness."[9] Being, goodness, and mathematical intelligibility are one in the world God created. The Forms of Plato become for Augustine Ideas in the mind of God, and he is more sanguine than is Plato about the success of the Demiurge-Creator in incarnating them in matter. Since mathematical truths come closest to the immutability characteristic of God, mathematical ideas provide the most appropriate patterns for the Creator. Augustine emphasized, even more than Plato did, the preeminence of mathematics in the constructing of a science of nature. This assurance about the type of concept appropriate to physics came to be taken for granted during the long period of dominance of Augustinian theology, so that even when Aristotelian natural science was rediscovered in the mid-thirteenth century, the old reluctance about the use of mathematics in physics had almost vanished, and the new mechanics of Merton and Paris was a nascent mathematical physics.

A final feature of Augustine's thought that laid its impress upon medieval science was his basic metaphor of illumination, the principal causal mode relating God and man.[10] It was clearly all-important to understand the nature of illumination, since this would lead to a grasp of causal action generally. Such was quite explicitly the motivation that led to the extraordinary developments in mathematical and experimental optics in the thirteenth century, for instance to the work of Grosseteste and Theodoric of Fribourg on reflection and refraction.

When the third, and decisive, stage in the development of natural science occurred in the seventeenth century, Augustine was not one of those (like Archimedes and Aristotle) with whose views the pioneers of the new science would have to reckon directly. He is not quoted by them, nor would they have been likely to be aware of what they owed him. His contributions lay far beneath the surface; they were of the sort that once made are later taken for granted, so obvious do they seem. But when one tries to grasp what it was that came about in western Europe in the centuries between Grosseteste and Newton, the specific new theories of the workings of nature are less relevant than are the underlying slow changes in attitude toward nature, man, and God that made the search for such theories seem worth making and suggested the general lines along which the search would take place. In this more fundamental development, Augustine played a not inconsiderable role.

NOTES

1. *Confessions*, Bk. VII, ch. 12.
2. *Ibid.*, Bk. X, ch. 35. See also Bk. V, ch. 3.
3. *Ibid.*, Bk. VII.
4. *Ibid.*, Bk. X, ch. 35.
5. *Ibid.*, Bk. X, ch. 35.
6. *Ibid.*, Bk. V, ch. 4.
7. *De Genesi ad litteram*, Bk. II, ch. 9.
8. *Ibid.*, Bk. II, ch. 5.
9. *De natura boni*, Bk. I, ch. 3.
10. A. C. Crombie, *Augustine to Galileo* (London, 1952), pp. 71–80.

BIBLIOGRAPHY

Augustine's works fill sixteen vols. of Migne's standard *Patrologia Latina* collection (Vols. 32–47). There is an enormous amount of secondary literature, but Augustine's role in the history of science is scarcely mentioned in it. See, however, H. Pope, "St. Augustine and the World of Nature," ch. 6 of his *Saint Augustine of Hippo* (London, 1937); and F. van der Meer, *Augustine, the Bishop* (London, 1961), ch. 4. For a good general treatment of Augustine's work and a useful bibliography, see E. Portalié, *A Guide to the Thought of St. Augustine* (New York, 1960).

ERNAN McMULLIN

AUSTEN, RALPH A. C. See **Godwin-Austen, Ralph A. C.**

AUSTIN, LOUIS WINSLOW (*b.* Orwell, Vermont, 30 October 1867; *d.* Washington, D.C., 27 June 1932), *radio physics.*

Austin graduated from Middlebury College in Vermont in 1889 and received the doctorate from the University of Strasbourg in 1893. He served as a member of the physics faculty of the University of Wisconsin from 1893 to 1901, and then returned to Germany for research work at Charlottenburg. In 1904 he entered U.S. government service in the Bureau of Standards and began a series of researches on radio transmission that made him world famous. The scope of his research was considerably enhanced by the establishment of a naval radiotelegraphic laboratory at the Bureau of Standards in 1908. This arrangement continued until 1923, when the laboratory and two others were merged into the radio division of a new unit (at the Navy Department), the Naval Research Laboratory.

Austin was in charge throughout this period, and thus had many opportunities for long-range transmission experiments. The most important was a test made in 1910, when U.S. cruisers en route to and from Liberia maintained radio contact with America and helped Austin and his collaborator Louis Cohen (1876–1948) to establish the Austin-Cohen formula, a semiempirical method for predicting the strength of radio signals at remote locations. The formula remained in use for many years and played an important role in the design and manufacture of improved apparatus. (Prior to World War I, the U.S. Navy had so much difficulty in making American firms meet its specifications that it began to design and manufacture its own radio receivers.)

In 1923 Austin resumed his work for the Bureau of Standards proper and became head of its laboratory for special radio transmission research. He contributed significantly to the understanding of the sources of radio atmospheric disturbances ("static"), a field in which he remained fruitfully active until his death.

As the doyen of U.S. government radio scientists, Austin exerted considerable influence and leadership in the development of radio engineering. He was one of the first members of the Institute of Radio Engineers (he joined on 22 January 1913), and one of the

few with a doctorate; he served as IRE's third president in 1914 and in 1927 received its Medal of Honor. Just before his death, Austin was unanimously nominated for the presidency of the International Radio Scientific Union (URSI), of whose U.S. national committee he had served as president.

BIBLIOGRAPHY

A list of Austin's major publications appears in Poggendorff, *Biographisch-literarisches Handwörterbuch,* Vols. V and VI. An obituary by Lyman J. Briggs is in *Science,* **76** (1932), 137. For Austin's contributions to marine radio communications, see L. S. Howeth, *History of Communications-Electronics in the U.S. Navy* (Washington, D.C., 1963).

CHARLES SÜSSKIND

AUTOLYCUS OF PITANE (*fl. ca.* 300 B.C.), *astronomy, geometry.*

Autolycus came from Pitane in the Aeolis, Asia Minor, and was an instructor of Arcesilaus, also of Pitane, who founded the so-called Middle Academy. It is reported by Diogenes Laertius (4.29) that Arcesilaus accompanied his master on a journey to Sardis.

Autolycus was a successor to Eudoxus in the study of spherical astronomy, but was active somewhat later than the successors of the Cnidian, Callippus, and Polemarchus. It appears that he attempted to defend the Eudoxian system of concentric rotating spheres against critics, notably Aristotherus, the teacher of the astronomer-poet Aratus. The critics had pointed out that Venus and Mars seem brighter in the course of their retrograde arcs and that eclipses of the sun are sometimes annular and sometimes total, so that not all heavenly bodies remain at fixed distances from the earth. Autolycus acknowledged the difficulty in his discussion with Aristotherus and, inevitably, was unable to account for the variations by means of the Eudoxian system.

The two treatises of Autolycus, *On the Moving Sphere* and *On Risings and Settings,* are among the earliest works in Greek astronomy to survive in their entirety. *On the Moving Sphere* is almost certainly earlier than Euclid's *Phaenomena,* which seems to make use of it (*Sphere,* Ch. 11, may be compared with *Phaenomena* 7). Pappus tells us it was one of the works forming the "Little Astronomy"—the "Small Collection," in contrast with the "Great Collection" of Ptolemy.

Both Euclid and Autolycus make use of an elementary textbook, now lost, on the sphere, from which they take several propositions without proof, because the proofs were already known. In *On the Moving Sphere*, a sphere is considered to move about an axis extending from pole to pole. Four classes of circular sections through the sphere are assumed: (1) great circles passing through the poles; (2) the equator and other, smaller, circles that are sections of the sphere formed by planes at right angles to the axis—these are the "parallel circles"; (3) great circles oblique to the axis of the sphere. The motion of points on the circles is then considered with respect to (4) the section formed by a fixed plane through the center of the sphere. A circle of class (3) is the ecliptic or zodiac circle, and (4) is equivalent to the horizon circle, which defines the visible and invisible parts of the sphere. In Euclid the great circle (4) has already become a technical term, "horizon," separating the hemisphere above the earth; Autolycus' treatment is more abstract and less overtly astronomical.

On Risings and Settings is strictly astronomical and consists of two complementary treatises or "books." True and apparent morning and evening risings and settings of stars are distinguished. Autolycus assumes that the celestial sphere completes one revolution during a day and a night; that the sun moves in a direction opposite to the diurnal rotation and traverses the ecliptic in one year; that by day the stars are not visible above the horizon owing to the light of the sun; and that a star above the horizon is visible only if the sun is 15° or more below the horizon measured along the zodiac (i.e., half a zodiacal sign or more).

The theorems are closely interrelated. Autolycus explains, for example, that the rising of a star is visible only between the visible morning rising and the visible evening rising, a period of less than half a year; similarly, he shows that the setting of a star is visible only in the interval from the visible morning setting to the visible evening setting, again a period of less than half a year. Another theorem states that the time from visible morning rising to visible morning setting is more than, equal to, or less than half a year if the star is north of, on, or south of the ecliptic, respectively.

Autolycus' works were popular handbooks and were translated into Arabic, Latin, and Hebrew.

BIBLIOGRAPHY

In addition to works cited in the text, see J. Mogenet, *Autolycus de Pitane* (Louvain, 1950); and O. Schmidt, "Some Critical Remarks About Autolycus' 'On Risings and Settings,'" in *Transactions of Den 11te Skandinaviske Matematikerkongress i Trondheim* (Oslo, 1952), pp. 202–209. See also the Mogenet edition of the Latin translation by Gerard of Cremona of *De sphaera mota*, in *Archives internationales d'histoire des sciences*, **5** (1948), pp. 139–164; and T. L. Heath, *Aristarchus of Samos* (Oxford, 1913), pp. 221–223.

G. L. HUXLEY

AUVERGNE, WILLIAM OF. See **William of Auvergne.**

AUWERS, ARTHUR JULIUS GEORG FRIEDRICH VON (*b.* Göttingen, Germany, 12 September 1838; *d.* Lichterfelde bei Berlin, Germany, 24 January 1915), *astronomy.*

The son of Gottfried Daniel Auwers, the riding master of Göttingen University, Auwers attended the gymnasia in Göttingen and Schulpforta from 1847 to 1857. He made a great number of observations and calculations of planets, comets, and variable stars as early as 1857–1859, his first years at Göttingen University. During his term as assistant at Königsberg (1859–1862) he made heliometric observations of double stars, which led him to his dissertation *Untersuchungen über veränderliche Eigenbewegungen* (1862). Bessel's assumption that certain changes in the proper motions of the stars Sirius and Procyon are based on the presence of invisible companion stars had opened a new field in celestial mechanics. Auwers was able to derive the orbits for both Sirius and Procyon as weakly eccentric ellipses, corresponding to the motion of the visible principal stars around the center of gravity of the double star system in forty or fifty years, respectively. A few years later it became possible also to observe their very faint companions by optical means.

Auwers then spent four years with Hansen at the Gotha observatory, for the most part determining parallaxes of the fixed stars. On Hansen's recommendation, in 1866 Auwers was appointed astronomer of the Berlin Academy, where he displayed great scientific and organizational ability during the next five decades. In 1878 the Academy appointed him as its permanent secretary, a position he held until his death. He was elected secretary of the Astronomical Society (founded in 1865) at its first meeting, and from 1881 to 1889 he was its president. Later he was awarded the Ordre pour le Mérite, grade of chancellor, and in 1912 was elevated to the hereditary nobility.

Auwers' lifework was the meticulous observation and calculation necessary to draw up star catalogs with highly accurate positions of stars. Since this required exact knowledge of the proper motions of the fixed stars, he also made new reductions of previous observations. Therefore, from 1865 to 1883 he undertook the laborious task of making a completely new reduction of Bradley's Greenwich observations, the oldest measurements of tolerable precision. The result was the publication of three volumes of Bradley's observations (1882–1903), the basis of all modern star positions and proper motions.

Auwers participated in the Zonenunternehmen der Astronomischen Gesellschaft, a project which had as its aim the observation and cataloging of all stars in the *Bonner Durchmusterung* up to the ninth magnitude. He not only observed the half of the zone for which Berlin was responsible but also took over the secretaryship of the zone commission appointed by the Astronomical Society to coordinate this task and to perform the final reduction. He also demonstrated his great organizational talents when he was in charge of the German expeditions that observed the transits of Venus in 1874 and 1882 in order to determine the sun's parallaxes. On the first expedition Auwers observed in Luxor, and on the second one in Punta Arenas, Chile. He published the results of both expeditions in six volumes (1887–1898).

In 1889 the opposition of the minor planet Victoria gave Auwers the opportunity to undertake the determination of the sun's parallax once again. He made the complete reduction of the meridian observations done in this connection by twenty-two other observatories, and obtained a surprisingly good determination of the sun's distance, considering the relatively great distance of the planet from the earth.

His incomparable experience and his remarkable endurance enabled Auwers to establish extremely accurate fundamental catalogs of positions of selected bright stars that had been observed for hundreds of years. These efforts led to the *Neue Fundamentalcatalog der Astronomischen Gesellschaft,* the foundation of all present precise measurements. Here his talent for the detection and elimination of systematic errors in observations was brought to the fore. Auwers also initiated the *Geschichte des Fixsternhimmels,* an extensive reduction and listing of all meridian observations of fixed stars from 1743 to 1900. Thus he must be considered the one who completed Bessel's epoch of classical astronomy in the second half of the nineteenth century. His participation in the founding of the astrophysical observatory in Potsdam bears witness also to his receptivity to the new science of astrophysics.

BIBLIOGRAPHY

I. ORIGINAL WORKS. Auwers' writings include *Untersuchungen über veränderliche Eigenbewegungen,* 2 vols. (Königsberg, 1862; Leipzig, 1868); *Bericht über die Beobachtung des Venusdurchgangs 1874 in Luxor* (Berlin, 1878); *Fundamentalcatalog für die Zonenbeobachtungen am nördlichen Himmel* (Leipzig, 1879); *Neue Reduktion der Bradleyschen Beobachtungen 1750 bis 1762,* 3 vols. (St. Petersburg, 1882–1903); *Die Venusdurchgänge 1874 und 1882,* 6 vols. (Berlin, 1887–1898); *Fundamentalcatalog für die Zonenbeobachtungen am südlichen Himmel* (Kiel, 1897); *Bearbeitung der Bradleyschen Beobachtungen an der Greenwicher Sternwarte* (Leipzig, 1912–1914); and many other works.

II. SECONDARY LITERATURE. Articles on Auwers are in *Neue deutsche Biographie,* I, 462; *The Observatory,* **38** (1915), 177–181; Poggendorff, Vols. III, IV, V; and *Vierteljahrschrift der Astronomischen Gesellschaft,* **53** (1918), 15–23.

BERNHARD STICKER

AUWERS, KARL FRIEDRICH VON (*b.* Gotha, Germany, 16 September 1863; *d.* Marburg, Germany, 3 May 1939), *chemistry.*

Auwers was a master organic chemist who investigated problems in structural theory for more than fifty years. He was a student of A. W. von Hofmann at Berlin, an assistant to Victor Meyer at Göttingen and Heidelberg, and then director of the chemical institute at the University of Marburg. On joining Victor Meyer, he became involved in stereochemical studies. In 1888 Auwers and Meyer substituted the name "stereochemistry" for van't Hoff's "chemistry in space." At this time the concept of geometrical isomerism had not been extended to structures other than those involving carbon atoms. Auwers and Meyer found that there were three isomeric forms of benzildioxime

$$C_6H_5-\underset{\underset{OH}{|}}{\overset{||}{C}}-\underset{\underset{OH}{|}}{\overset{||}{C}}-C_6H_5$$

and proposed, contrary to van't Hoff's principle of the free rotation of single bonds, that the isomerism resulted from the restricted rotation about the singly bound carbon atoms. Arthur Hantzsch and Alfred Werner elaborated the presently accepted theory in 1890 by extending geometric isomerism from double-bonded carbon atoms to double-bonded carbon and nitrogen atoms. Auwers and Meyer themselves aided in the confirmation of the Hantzsch and Werner theory.

Auwers' studies on isomerism led him into a lifelong investigation of stereochemical problems. He mastered the difficult art of assigning configuration to stereoisomers, establishing the configuration of the crotonic acids as well as many other geometric isomers. Auwers also investigated the spectrochemistry of organic compounds, the relation of physical properties to molecular structure, and molecular rearrangements, the most outstanding result of these studies being the determination of the keto-enol proportions in many tautomeric mixtures.

BIBLIOGRAPHY

Auwers was a prolific organic chemist, publishing over 500 papers in German journals from 1884 to 1938. A bibliography of his periodical publications, with a biographical notice by Hans J. Meerwein, is in *Berichte der Deutschen chemischen Gesellschaft*, **72** (1939), 111–121. His only book is *Die Entwicklung der Stereochemie* (Heidelberg, 1890). Among his important early papers with Victor Meyer on the stereochemistry of oxime compounds are "Untersuchungen über die zweite van't Hoffsche Hypothese," in *Berichte . . .*, **21** (1888), 784–817; "Weitere Untersuchungen über die Isomerie der Benzildioxime," *ibid.*, 3510–3529; and "Über die isomeren Oxime unsymmetrischer Ketone und die Konfiguration des Hydroxylamins," *ibid.*, **23** (1890), 2403–2409. His unraveling of the spatial configuration of the crotonic acids is found in "Über die Konfiguration der Crotonsäuren," in *Berichte . . .*, **56** (1923), 715–791, written with H. Wissebach. Among the many important papers on the relation between physical properties and chemical constitution are "Zur Spektrochemie und Konstitutionsbestimmung tautomerer Verbindungen," in *Annalen der Chemie*, no. 415 (1918), 169–232; "Über Beziehungen zwischen Konstitution und physikalischen Eigenschaften hydroaromatischer Stoffe," *ibid.*, no. 420 (1920), 84–111; and "Zur Bestimmung der Konfiguration raumisomerer Äthylenderivate," in *Zeitschrift für physikalische Chemie*, **143** (1929), 1–20, written with L. Harres.

ALBERT B. COSTA

AUZOUT, ADRIEN (*b*. Rouen, France, 28 January 1622; *d*. Rome, Italy, 23 May 1691), *astronomy, physics, mathematics.*

Auzout approached science with instruments rather than with mathematics. In the fall of 1647 he designed an ingenious experiment—creating one vacuum inside another—in order to prove that the weight of a column of air pressing on a barometer causes the mercury to rise inside. Auzout did not neglect mathematics, however; he criticized the treatise of François-Xavier Anyscom on the quadrature of the circle and prepared a treatise of reasons and proportions. By 1660 his career centered on astronomical instruments. He made a significant contribution to the final development of the micrometer and to the replacement of open sights by telescopic sights.

Not until after Christiaan Huygens discovered that there exists a special point (the focus) inside the Keplerian telescope, which has only convex lenses, could there be a breakthrough leading to the micrometer and to radically superior instruments. (Well before Huygens, William Gascoigne, after discovering the focal point, invented the micrometer and telescopic sights, but his inventions remained unknown to Continental astronomers until 1667.) Since an object can be superimposed on the image without distortion at the focus, precise measurements of the size of the image can be made. To do this, Huygens fashioned a crude micrometer. Cornelio Malvasia's lattice of fine wires was for Auzout, and probably Jean Picard, who worked with him, the jumping-off point for the perfection of the micrometer. They were dissatisfied with the accuracy of the lattice because images never covered exactly an integral number of squares, so they modified it. Two parallel hairs were separated by a distance variable according to the size of the image; one hair was fixed to a mobile chassis that was displaced at first by hand and later by a precision screw. By the summer of 1666 Auzout and Picard were making systematic observations with fully developed micrometers.

Soon after Huygens' discovery, Eustachio Divini and Robert Hooke replaced open sights with telescopic sights, and during the period 1667–1671 Auzout, Picard, and Gilles Personne de Roberval developed the systematic use of telescopic sights. An incomplete concept of focus caused the delay between discovery and systematic use, for Auzout, reasoning by analogy with open sights, suggested at the end of 1667 that each hair in the crosshairs be placed in a separate plane so that a line of sight might be assured. Unfortunately, after Auzout withdrew from the Académie des Sciences in 1668, he drifted into obscurity.

BIBLIOGRAPHY

I. ORIGINAL WORKS. A complete bibliography of Auzout's work is in R. M. McKeon (see below), pp. 314–324; the claims to priority in development of the micrometer of Auzout, Picard, and Pierre Petit are discussed on pp. 63–68. Most of Auzout's published works are reprinted in the *Mémoires de l'Académie Royale des Sciences, depuis 1666 jusqu'à 1699* (Paris, 1729), **6**, 537–540; **7**, Part 1, 1–130; **10**, 451–462. The major part of his correspondence is published in E. Caillemer, *Lettres de divers savants à l'Abbé Claude Nicaise* (Lyons, 1885), pp. 201–226; Christiaan Huygens, *Oeuvres*, 22 vols. (La Haye, 1888–1950), IV, 481–482; V, *passim;* VII, 372–373 (two letters are incorrectly attributed to Auzout in VI, 142–143, 580); H. Oldenberg, *Correspondence*, A. Rupert Hall and Marie Boas, eds. and trans. (Madison, Wis., 1965–); S. J. Rigaud and S. P. Rigaud, *Correspondence of Scientific Men* of the Seventeenth Century (Oxford, 1841), I, 206–210. The manuscript copies of Auzout's letters to Abbé Charles that were in the possession of the Ginori-Venturi family of Florence—called *Épreuves* in McKeon, p. 228, n.1—were listed in the spring 1966 catalog of Alain Brieux, Paris, and were sold. (The editors of Huygens' *Oeuvres* identify Abbé Charles as Charles de Bryas [IV, 72, n.4], but Abbé Charles's horoscope, which relates that he was born at Avignon in March 1604 and formerly was employed by Cardinal Mazarin [Bibliothèque Nationale, MSS fonds français, 13028, fol. 323], rules out their identification.)

II. SECONDARY LITERATURE. Writings on Auzout or his work are Harcourt Brown, *Scientific Organizations in Seventeenth Century France (1620–1680)* (Baltimore, 1934); C. Irson, *Nouvelle méthode pour apprendre facilement les principes et la pureté de la langue française* (Paris, 1660), pp. 317–318; and Robert M. McKeon, "Établissement de l'astronomie de précision et oeuvre d'Adrien Auzout," unpublished dissertation (University of Paris, 1965); "Le récit d'Auzout au sujet des expériences sur le vide," in *Acts of XI International Congress of the History of Science* (Warsaw, 1965), Sec. III; and "Auzout," in *Encyclopaedia universalis,* in preparation.

ROBERT M. McKEON

AVEBURY, BARON. See **Lubbock, John.**

AVEMPACE. See **Ibn Bājja.**

AVENARE. See **Ibn Ezra.**

AVERROËS. See **Ibn Rushd.**

AVERY, OSWALD T. (*b.* Halifax, Nova Scotia, Canada, 21 October 1877; *d.* Nashville, Tennessee, 20 February 1955), *biology.*

Avery began his career as a physician. His father, a Canadian clergyman, had moved his family to New York in 1887, and Avery spent the next sixty-one years of his life there. He attended Colgate University, graduating A.B. in 1900, and received his medical degree from the Columbia University College of Physicians and Surgeons in 1904. He worked for a short time in the field of clinical medicine and then joined the Hoagland Laboratory in Brooklyn, New York, as a researcher and lecturer in bacteriology and immunology (his lectures at Hoagland won him the appellation "The Professor," by which he was known throughout his career). In 1913 he became a member of the staff of the Rockefeller Institute Hospital, where he remained until 1948.

At the time that Avery came to the hospital, an investigation of lobar pneumonia was in progress, and he joined with A. Dochez in work on the immunological classification of the pneumococcus bacterium.

This research led to the announcement, in 1917, that the pneumococcus produced an immunologically specific soluble chemical substance during growth in a culture medium.[1] Dochez and Avery further established that the substance was not a disintegration product of cell mortality but a true product of its metabolic processes, and that the substance was also present in the serum and urine of animals and men suffering from lobar pneumonia.

Beginning in 1922, Avery and his colleagues studied the chemical nature of these "soluble specific substances," which Avery believed were closely related to the immunological specificity of bacteria. They were soon shown to be polysaccharides derived from the capsular envelopes of the bacteria and to be specific to each pneumococcal type. By relating differences in bacterial specificity to these chemical differences in the capsular substances produced, Avery was able to explain in chemical terms many of the anomalies of immunological specificities. He showed that immunology could be analyzed biochemically, in terms of specific cellular components rather than the entire cellular complex, and thus contributed to the development of the study of immunochemistry.

Because of his concern with the extracellular substances of the pneumococcus, Avery began work in 1932 on a phenomenon first reported by F. Griffith in 1928. Griffith had observed that heat-killed virulent pneumococci could convert a nonvirulent strain to a disease-producer *in vivo.* Later investigations showed that this change in immunological specificity could be brought about *in vitro,* and that the alteration was permanent. Avery set out to isolate and analyze the active factor in the transformation, and his conclusions were reported in a well-known 1944 paper.[2]

A culture of an unencapsulated, and therefore nonvirulent, variant (designated *R*) of Type II pneumococcus, when exposed to an extract derived from encapsulated, virulent (*S*) Type III pneumococcus, was found to be converted to a Type III *S* culture. The isolated transforming material, upon examination, tested strongly positively for desoxyribonucleic acid (DNA) by the diphenylamine reaction. Elementary analysis revealed close resemblances in element ratios between the transforming substance and sodium desoxyribonucleate. Transforming ability was not inhibited by protein-destroying and ribonucleate-destroying enzymes, but only by those enzyme-containing preparations also capable of depolymerizing DNA. Treatment with desoxyribonucleodepolymerase also produced complete inactivation, at all temperatures up to the point of inactivation of the enzyme. Serologically it was found that transforming activity increased with increasing purity while the purified substance itself exhibited little or no immunological reactivity. On the basis of these and other tests, Avery and his collaborators concluded that the active fraction consisted principally, if not solely, of a highly polymerized form of desoxyribonucleic acid.

Avery thus showed that, in one instance at least, DNA was the active causative factor in an inherited variation in bacterial cells. The experiments showed that the preparations most active in bringing about transformation were those purest and most protein-free, thereby effectively casting doubt on the widespread and commonly accepted belief that proteins were the mediators of biological specificity and cellular inheritance. It was to a great extent through this work that the stage was set for the rapidly ensuing elaboration of the structure, function, and importance of DNA. Avery himself speculated about the mechanism of specificity determination and pointed out that "There is as yet relatively little known of the possible effect that subtle differences in molecular configuration may exert on the biological specificity of these substances,"[3] a situation that was well on the way to being remedied within ten years with the development of the Watson-Crick model for the DNA molecule.

NOTES

1. *J. Exp. Med.,* **26** (1917), 477–493; *Proc. Soc. Exp. Biol. Med.,* **14** (1917), 126–127.
2. *J. Exp. Med.,* **79** (1944), 137–158.
3. *Ibid.,* p. 153.

BIBLIOGRAPHY

I. ORIGINAL WORKS. Avery's major early work, on the immunological specificity of the pneumococcus involved in lobar pneumonia, is to be found in his two 1917 papers with A. Dochez, "The Elaboration of Specific Soluble Substance by Pneumococcus During Growth," in *Journal of Experimental Medicine,* **26** (1917), 477–493, also published in the *Transactions of the Association of American Physicians,* **32** (1917), 281–298, and "Soluble Substance of Pneumococcus Origin in the Blood and Urine During Lobar Pneumonia," in *Proceedings of the Society for Experimental Biology and Medicine,* **14** (1917), 126–127. The majority of his work on the chemical nature of the soluble specific substance appeared in a series of papers with M. Heidelberger: "Soluble Specific Substance of Pneumococcus," in *Journal of Experimental Medicine,* **38** (1923), 73–79; "The Specific Soluble Substance of Pneumococcus," in *Proceedings of the Society for Experimental Biology and Medicine,* **20** (1923), 434–435; and "The Soluble Specific Substance of Pneumococcus," in *Journal of Experimental Medicine,* **40** (1924), 301–316. The one paper for which Avery is best known reported his work with MacLeod and McCarty, "Studies on the Chemical Nature of the Substance Inducing Transformation of Pneumococcal Types. Induction of Transformation by a Desoxyribonucleic Acid Fraction Isolated from Pneumococcus Type III," in *Journal of Experimental Medicine,* **79** (1944), 137–158.

II. SECONDARY LITERATURE. Complete bibliographies of Avery's work can be found appended to two major biographical sketches written by former colleagues: R. J. Dubos, in *Biographical Memoirs of Fellows of the Royal Society,* **2** (1956), 35–48; and A. R. Dochez, in *National Academy of Sciences, Biographical Memoirs,* **32** (1958), 32–49.

ALAN S. KAY

AVICENNA. See Ibn Sīnā.

AVOGADRO, AMEDEO (*b.* Turin, Italy, 9 August 1776; *d.* Turin, 9 July 1856), *physics, chemistry.*

He was the son of Count Filippo Avogadro and Anna Maria Vercellone. His father was a distinguished lawyer and higher civil servant who had become a senator of Piedmont in 1768 and had been appointed advocate general to the senate of Vittorio Amedeo III in 1777. His subsequent important administrative work led to his being chosen under the French rule of 1799 to reorganize the senate, of which he was made president. Amedeo Avogadro received his first education at home but went to the grammar school in Turin for his secondary education. Coming from a family well established as ecclesiastical lawyers (the name *Avogadro* itself probably being a corruption of *Advocarii*), Avogadro was guided toward a legal career and in 1792 he became a bachelor of jurisprudence. In 1796 he gained his doctorate in ecclesiastical law and began to practice law. In 1801 he was appointed secretary to the prefecture of the department of Eridano. Avogadro also showed interest in natural philosophy, and in 1800 he began to study privately mathematics and physics. Probably he was particularly impressed by the recent discoveries of his compatriot Alessandro Volta, since the first scientific research undertaken by Avogadro (jointly with his brother Felice) was on electricity in 1803.

In 1806 he was appointed demonstrator at the college attached to the Academy of Turin, and on 7 October 1809 he became professor of natural philosophy at the College of Vercelli. In 1820 when the first chair of mathematical physics (*fisica sublime*) in Italy was established at Turin with a salary of 600 lire, Avogadro was appointed. The political changes of 1821 led to the suppression of this chair, which Avogadro lost in July 1822. In 1823 he was given the purely honorary title of professor emeritus by way of compensation. When the chair was reestablished in 1832 it was first given to Cauchy. At the end of 1833 Cauchy went to Prague, and on 28 November 1834 Avogadro was reappointed. He held this position until his retirement in 1850.

In 1787 Avogadro succeeded to his father's title. He married Felicita Mazzé and they had six children. Avogadro was described in the *Gazzetta Piemontese* after his death as "religious but not a bigot."

Avogadro led an industrious life. His modesty was one of the factors contributing to his comparative obscurity, particularly outside Italy. Unlike his great contemporaries Gay-Lussac and Davy, he worked in isolation. Only toward the end of his life do we find letters exchanged with leading men of science in other countries. Avogadro's isolation cannot be attributed to language difficulties. He wrote good French, understood English and German, and kept abreast of all developments in physics and chemistry.

On 5 July 1804 Avogadro was elected a corresponding member of the Academy of Sciences of Turin, and on 21 November 1819 he became a full member of the Academy. His name is conspicuously absent from the foreign membership of the Paris Academy of Sciences and the Royal Society of London. Avogadro was a member of a government commission on statistics and served as president of a commission on weights and measures. In this latter capacity he was largely responsible for the introduction of the metric system in Piedmont. After 1848 Avogadro served on a commission on public instruction.

Avogadro is known principally for Avogadro's hypothesis, which provided a much-needed key to the problems of nineteenth-century chemistry by distinguishing between atoms and molecules. Dalton had considered the possibility that equal volumes of all gases might contain the same number of atoms but had rejected it. The source of Avogadro's inspiration was not however Dalton but Gay-Lussac, whose law of combining volumes of gases was published in 1809. In Avogadro's classic memoir of 1811 he wrote:

> M. Gay-Lussac has shown in an interesting memoir . . . that gases always unite in a very simple proportion by volume, and that when the result of the union is a gas, its volume also is very simply related to those of its components. But the quantitative proportions of substances in compounds seem only to depend on the relative number of molecules which combine, and on the number of composite molecules which result. It must then be admitted that very simple relations also exist between the volumes of gaseous substances and the numbers of simple or compound molecules which form them. The first hypothesis to present itself in this connection, and apparently even the only admissible one,

is the supposition that *the number of integral molecules in any gas is always the same for equal volumes, or always proportional to the volumes.* . . . The hypothesis we have just proposed is based on that simplicity of relation between the volumes of gases on combination, which would appear to be otherwise inexplicable.[1]

Avogadro, therefore, modestly presented his hypothesis as no more than an extension of Gay-Lussac's law.

From Avogadro's hypothesis there immediately follows the inference that the relative weights of the molecules of any two gases are the same as the ratios of the densities of these gases under the same conditions of temperature and pressure. Molecular weights could thus be determined directly. The hypothesis also enabled the chemist to deduce atomic weights without recourse to Dalton's arbitrary rule of simplicity. The molecular weight of water would be calculated in the following way:

$$\frac{\text{Weight of molecule of oxygen}}{\text{Weight of molecule of hydrogen}}$$
$$= \frac{\text{Density of oxygen}}{\text{Density of hydrogen}} = \frac{1.10359}{0.07321} = \frac{15.074}{1}.$$

As water is produced by the combination of two volumes of hydrogen with one of oxygen, this would give for the weight of two molecules of water vapor: $15 + 2 = 17$. The weight of one molecule would therefore be 8.5 (or, more accurately, 8.537). This agreed well with the known density of water vapor referred to the hydrogen standard. It should be noted that Avogadro's molecular weights are values based on the comparison with the weight of a molecule of hydrogen rather than an atom of hydrogen. The molecular weights given in Avogadro's paper of 1811 are therefore half the modern values. However expressed, they were a vast improvement on Dalton's values.

The superiority of Avogadro's method of deriving the molecular weights of compounds over that of Dalton is seen not only with water but with many other compounds. Where the values given by Avogadro were of the same order as those given by Dalton, the Italian pointed out that this resulted from the canceling out of errors. Avogadro was, however, completely fair in his criticism of Dalton, and at the end of his memoir he modestly concluded that his hypothesis was "at bottom merely Dalton's system furnished with a new means of precision from the connection we have found between it and the general fact established by Gay-Lussac."

It is necessary to comment on Avogadro's use of

the term *molecule*. Although it has been suggested that he used the term inconsistently, a close examination of his memoir enables us to distinguish four uses of the term: *molécule* ("molecule"), a general term denoting either what today would be called an atom or a molecule; *molécule intégrante* ("integral molecule"), corresponding to the present-day usage of molecule, particularly in relation to compounds; *molécule constituante* ("constituent molecule"), denoting a molecule of an element; and *molécule élémentaire* ("elementary molecule"), denoting an atom of an element. Although Avogadro deserves credit for his application of these expressions, he did not invent them. The terms *partie intégrante, molécule primitive intégrante,* and *partie constituante* are to be found in Macquer's *Dictionnaire de chimie* of 1766 (article on "Agrégation"); and the terms *integrant, constituent,* and *elementary* molecules are to be found in Fourcroy's textbook of 1800.

Avogadro had a solution to the problem that arose when the hypothesis of equal volumes was applied to compound substances. Gay-Lussac had shown that (above 100°C.) the volume of water vapor was twice the volume of oxygen used to form it. This was possible only if the molecule of oxygen was divided between the molecules of hydrogen. Dalton had seen this difficulty and, as it was to him inconceivable that the particles of oxygen could be subdivided, he had rejected the basic hypothesis that Avogadro was now defending. Avogadro overcame the difficulty by postulating compound molecules. This is the second and most important part of Avogadro's hypothesis. It may be regarded as his second hypothesis; and, unlike the first, it seems completely original. Avogadro wrote: "We suppose . . . that the constituent molecules of any simple gas whatever . . . are not formed of a solitary elementary molecule, but are made up of a certain number of these molecules united by attraction to form a single one." Compound molecules of gases must therefore be composed of two or more atoms. Avogadro implies that there are always an even number of atoms in the molecule of a gas. For nitrogen, oxygen, and hydrogen it is two, "but it is possible that in other cases, the division might be into four, eight, etc." Avogadro is not at his clearest in this part of the memoir, but clarity is achieved when he gives an example: "Thus, for example, the integral molecule of water will be composed of a half-molecule of oxygen with one molecule, or, what is the same thing, two half-molecules, of hydrogen."

Avogadro's reasoning about the divisibility of the integrant molecule raises the question of atomicity. Gases for Avogadro were usually diatomic, but certain substances could be tetratomic in the vapor state, as

indeed phosphorus is. In later memoirs he allowed for the possibility of monatomic molecules, as, for example, in gold. In his work there is implicit the idea of equivalence, e.g., that one atom of oxygen is equivalent to two atoms of hydrogen, which in turn is equivalent to two atoms of chlorine. The concept of valency, was, however, not developed until the time of Frankland (1852).

In a second memoir, which he sent in January 1814 for publication in Lamétherie's *Journal de physique,* Avogadro developed his earlier ideas. He began by pointing out that no alternative explanation had been offered to the one published by him three years previously to account for Gay-Lussac's law of combining volumes of gases. He suggested that his hypothesis could be used to correct the theory of definite proportions, which he now saw as "the basis of all modern chemistry and the source of its future progress." It was therefore important "to establish by facts, or in default, by probable conjectures, the densities which the gases of different substances would have at a common pressure and temperature." The recent experimental work of Gay-Lussac, Davy, Berzelius, and others now gave Avogadro scope to apply his principle to a greater number of substances. In 1811 Avogadro had been able to give the modern formulas (in words) for water vapor, nitric oxide, nitrous oxide, ammonia, carbon monoxide, and hydrogen chloride. In 1814 he was able to give the correct formulas for several compounds of carbon and sulfur, including carbon dioxide, carbon disulfide, sulfur dioxide, and hydrogen sulfide. Falling back on analogy when experimental evidence was lacking, he reasoned correctly that silica was SiO_2 by comparison with CO_2. He also extended his earlier treatment of metals in the hypothetical gaseous state. He gave molecular weights for (using modern symbols) Hg, Fe, Mn, Ag, Au, Pb, Cu, Sn, Sb, As, K, Na, Ca, Mg, Ba, Al, and Si, based on analyses of the compounds of these elements. His mention of "gaz métalliques" may have done more harm than good to the reception of his hypothesis.

In 1821 Avogadro was able to state the correct formulas of several other compounds including those of phosphorus and the oxides of nitrogen. After deducing the formulas of such inorganic compounds from combining volumes, densities, or merely by analogy, he turned to organic chemistry. He gave the correct empirical formula for turpentine, $C:H = 1.6:1$, (in the symbols of Berzelius $C_{10}H_{16}$) and the correct molecular formulas for alcohol (C_2H_6O) and ether ($C_4H_{10}O$). Berzelius did not arrive at the correct formulas for alcohol and ether until 1828. Berzelius, however, who had developed a theory deriving from

345

both Dalton and Gay-Lussac, took little account of Avogadro.

Avogadro's claim to the hypothesis that is named after him rests on more than his mere statement of it. We have seen that Dalton earlier considered a similar hypothesis but rejected it. Ampère in 1814 independently arrived at a similar conclusion, and later Dumas (1827), Prout (1834), and others formulated the same hypothesis. To Avogadro alone, however, belongs the distinction of applying his hypothesis to the whole field of chemistry.

Ampère's ideas on the constitution of molecules were published in 1814 in the form of a letter to Berthollet. He stated that it was only after writing his memoir that he had "heard that M. Avogadro had used the same idea." Ampère was not primarily concerned with providing an explanation of Gay-Lussac's law. He was interested in the structure of crystals and introduced geometrical considerations which led him to suppose that molecules of, for example, hydrogen, oxygen, and nitrogen each contained four atoms, whereas Avogadro had already shown correctly that these gases contained two atoms per molecule. Despite the inferiority in many respects of Ampère's memoir to that of Avogadro and its clear lack of priority, Avogadro's hypothesis was usually attributed to Ampère until the Italian Cannizzaro called the attention of chemists to the publication of his fellow countryman. Certainly by being published in the *Annales de chimie* Ampère's paper had the greatest possible publicity, and Ampère himself became famous throughout the scientific world after his work on electromagnetism in the 1820's.

In view of the lack of interest shown by chemists in Avogadro's hypothesis, it is all the more noteworthy that he himself continually drew attention to the significance of his ideas. If Avogadro was not heard, therefore, it was not because he had made an isolated pronouncement. He repeated it in a memoir published in 1816 and 1817; and again in two different memoirs published in 1818 and 1819 in Italian publications, he drew attention to his earlier work. The 1819 memoir was later translated into French and the relevant passage reads:

> In considering the matter theoretically and supposing in conformity with what I have established elsewhere (*Journal de Phys. de La Metherie,* July 1811 and February 1814) that in gases reduced to the same temperature and pressure the distances between the centers of the integrant molecules is constant for all gases, so that the density of a gas is proportional to the mass of its molecules. . . .[2]

Even more important was Avogadro's long memoir of 1821: "Nouvelles considerations sur . . . la déter-

mination des masses des molécules des corps." This was published in the memoirs of the Turin Academy of Science, but a summary was published in France in 1826 in the *Bulletin . . . de Ferussac,* and this extract contains a reassertion of Avogadro's hypothesis with the claim that its introduction would do much to simplify and generalize chemistry. Avogadro insisted in this memoir on the necessity of correlating the data obtained by Gay-Lussac on the combining volumes of gases with the theory of fixed proportions—a problem that had been considered only superficially by Berzelius.

From the above it is clear that Avogadro stated his new hypothesis repeatedly over the period 1811–1821. It is true that the later memoirs were particularly long, and only the most relevant parts are included here. More important for the reception of Avogadro's work, however, is that these later memoirs were published in Italy, then at the periphery of the scientific world. When these memoirs were translated into French they appeared not in the influential *Annales de chimie et de physique* but in the comparatively obscure and second-rate *Bulletin . . . de Ferussac.* As regards translation into other languages, not more than three of Avogadro's papers were translated into English and not more than two into German, and the memoirs chosen are not those that we should today regard as significant. Reports on Avogadro's later work were, however, included in Berzelius' *Jahresberichte* from 1832 onward. Some part of the blame for the lack of attention given to Avogadro's hypothesis by his contemporaries must attach to the editors of the influential British, French, and German scientific periodicals.

One of the most remarkable features of Avogadro's hypothesis was the way in which it was neglected by the vast majority of chemists for half a century after its initial publication. The following are some of the reasons for this delay:

(1) It was not clearly enough expressed, particularly in the 1811 memoir. Avogadro did not coin a new term for the "solitary elementary molecules" nor did he use the term *atom.* In any case there was general looseness in the use of the terms *atom* and *molecule,* and they were often used synonymously. It would not have been clear to everyone in the early nineteenth century that Avogadro's hypothesis was quite different from that of Berzelius. Berzelius had substituted atom for volume in cases of combining gases and had ended with the logical contradiction of half an atom. Avogadro overcame this difficulty by introducing a polyatomic molecule, but this concept was quite novel.

(2) Avogadro did not support his hypothesis with any impressive accumulation of experimental results.

He never acquired, nor did he deserve, a reputation for accurate experimental work. Thus, for Regnault, for example, Avogadro was not a brilliant theoretician but merely a careless experimenter.

(3) From the beginning Avogadro applied his hypothesis to solid elements. When experimental evidence was not available, he relied only on analogy. He was correct in considering oxygen and hydrogen as diatomic, but he had little justification in coming to a similar conclusion in the cases of carbon and sulfur. His speculative treatment of metals in the vapor state in his second paper of 1814 cannot have helped his cause. He was, therefore, overly ambitious in extending his hypothesis. (Yet Berzelius too used a "volume theory" not restricted to the gaseous state, and his work did not suffer any eclipse because of this.) There were only a comparatively small number of well-defined substances that existed in the gaseous state and to which Avogadro's hypothesis could be applied. Only with Gerhardt was its full relevance to organic substances appreciated.

(4) The half century after the publication of Avogadro's hypothesis was a time when most attention was paid to organic chemistry, where the primary need was for analysis and classification. Organic analysis was based on weights, not volumes.

(5) Avogadro's idea of a diatomic molecule conflicted with the dominant dualistic outlook of Berzelius. According to the principles of electrochemistry, two atoms of the same element would have similar charges and therefore repel rather than attract each other.

(6) Avogadro, a modest and obscure physicist on the wrong side of the Alps, remained intellectually isolated from the mainstream of chemistry.

Despite the failure of chemists to appreciate the full significance of Avogadro's hypothesis, he could claim in 1845 that his statement that the mean distances between the molecules of all gases were the same under the same conditions of temperature and pressure and the consequence that the molecular weight was proportional to the density was generally accepted by physicists and chemists either explicitly or implicitly.

What was ignored, however, was the use of the hypothesis to determine atomic weights. It was Cannizzaro who, in a paper published in 1858 but not made widely known until 1860 at the Karlsruhe Congress, showed how the application of Avogadro's hypothesis would solve many of the major problems of chemistry. In particular he clarified the relation between atom and molecule which Avogadro had not made explicit. Gerhardt and Laurent had applied the hypothesis with some success to organic chemistry.

Cannizzaro performed a roughly complementary task in systematizing inorganic chemistry on the basis of Avogadro's hypothesis. He determined the molecular weights of many inorganic substances and hence the atomic weights. For the first time there began to exist among chemists substantial agreement on atomic weights. Cannizzaro had been able to make use of techniques unknown in Avogadro's time for the determination of the molecular weights of solid elements, including sulfur, phosphorus, and mercury.

Avogadro's first two memoirs to be published, in 1806 and 1807, were on electricity. He considered the state of a nonconductor placed between two oppositely charged elementary layers. If there was air between two charged bodies, it would become charged. In the later terminology of Faraday the claim could be made that Avogadro had some conception of the polarization of dielectrics. In 1842 Avogadro himself claimed that some of Faraday's treatment of condensers was to be found in his own earlier work. At the end of the same memoir Avogadro suggested that the capacity of a condenser was independent of the gas between the plates and that there would be the same process of induction even in a vacuum—a phenomenon later verified by James Clerk Maxwell.

Avogadro's 1822 memoir "Sur la construction d'un voltimètre multiplicateur" was given publicity by Oersted. Avogadro's "multiplier" was one of the most sensitive instruments of the time, and by using it he found that when certain pairs of metals are plunged into concentrated nitric acid the direction of the electric current is momentarily reversed. This happens for the pairs of metals: Pb/Bi, Pb/Sn, Fe/Bi, Co/Sb. This phenomenon had actually been observed in the case of Pb/Sn by Pfaff in 1808, but it was sometimes referred to as "Avogadro's reversal." Avogadro used a succession of pairs of metals with an electrolyte to establish the order Pt, Au, Ag, Hg, As, Sb, Co, Ni, Cu, Bi, Fe, Sn, Pb, Zn, a list that showed several differences from the order found by Volta using a condenser.

Avogadro published his first article dealing only with chemistry in 1809. This memoir, on acids and alkalies, is interesting for several reasons. In the first place it illustrates his abiding concern with chemical affinity and incidentally the great influence exerted on him by Berthollet. Second, in the opening paragraph, which criticizes the oxygen theory of acidity, it illustrates his radical approach to post-Lavoisier chemistry. He postulated a relative scale of acidity in which oxygen and sulfur were placed toward the acid end of the scale, neutral substances in the middle, and hydrogen at the alkali end. A significant feature of this scale was that it was continuous. Avogadro would not allow any absolute distinctions. He was not, for example, prepared to agree with Berzelius that oxygen was absolutely electronegative. Davy, in 1807, had suggested a connection between acidity and alkalinity and electricity; Avogadro developed this idea. Another feature of Avogadro's interests found in this memoir is the subject of nomenclature. He was to give more detailed attention to this in the 1840's.

Avogadro might claim to share with Berthollet the honor of having been one of the founders of physical chemistry in the early nineteenth century. Certainly he saw no boundary between physics and chemistry and made constant use of a mathematical approach. This is exemplified by his various studies on heat; his thermal studies of gases provided a useful approach to physical chemistry. In 1813 Delaroche and Bérard suggested that there was a simple relationship between the specific heat of a compound gas and its chemical composition. Particles of a gas were then envisaged as surrounded by an "atmosphere" of caloric. But the amount of caloric between particles of a gas governed the mutual attraction between its particles. Avogadro thus saw a means of relating chemical affinity to specific heat. Assuming that $(specific heat)^m$ is the attractive power of each molecule and that these attractive powers are additive, Avogadro obtained a number of equations from which m was found to be rather less or rather greater than 2. Taking the deviation from $m = 2$ to be due to experimental error (Avogadro never claimed any high degree of accuracy in his experimental work), he derived the general formula:

$$c^2 = p_1 c_1{}^2 + p_2 c_2{}^2 + \text{etc.,}$$

where c, c_1, c_2, etc. are the specific heats at constant volume of the compound gas and its constituents, respectively, and p_1, p_2, etc. are numbers of molecules of the components taking part in the reaction.

In 1822 Avogadro considered himself justified in making the generalization that the specific heats at constant volume of gases were proportional to the square root of the attractive power of their molecules for caloric. In 1824 he made further progress toward an evaluation of a "true affinity for heat," to which he could assign a numerical value. This value was obtained by taking the square of the specific heat determined by experiment and dividing by the density of the gas, which by Avogadro's hypothesis was proportional to its molecular weight. He thus obtained a series of values ranging from oxygen = 0.8595 to hydrogen = 10.2672. This confirmed his conjecture that oxygen and substances similar to it had the least affinity for heat. He concluded triumphantly that the order so obtained, representing the affinity for heat, coincided with the order in the electrochemical series. He obtained further confirmation by comparing his results with those obtained by Biot and Arago for the relationship between affinity for heat and the refractive indices of gases. Avogadro concluded with a table of twenty-nine substances, headed by acids and terminating with bases. By dividing each affinity for heat by that of oxygen, he obtained a series of what he called "affinity numbers" (*nombres affinitaires*), and in his next memoir he attempted to determine further affinity numbers.

By 1828 he doubted the validity of much of his earlier work on assigning numerical values to affinities, and he therefore reverted to a purely chemical method, developing Berthollet's idea of combining proportions as a measure of affinity. At the end of his life Avogadro claimed that he had succeeded in deriving affinity numbers from atomic volumes and "by a method independent of all chemical considerations"[3]— reminding us of his predominantly physical attitude. By trying to derive chemical information from nonchemical sources, however, he contributed to a situation in which his work lay outside the sphere of interest of contemporary chemists.

In 1819 Dulong and Petit announced that there was a simple relationship between specific heats and atomic weights. Although they suggested that their law might be extended to compounds, it was F. E. Neumann who, in 1831, first applied the law practically to solid compounds. Avogadro, who began his research in this field in 1833, investigated both liquids and solids.

He decided that the formula of a compound in the liquid or solid state could not be the same as that in the gaseous state. He therefore introduced the arbitrary division of molecules and considered, for example, that a molecule of water or ice contained only a quarter as many atoms as one of steam. Thus since H_2O represented steam, water would have been $HO_{1/2}$. (Actually Avogadro says a compound of "1/4 *atom* of hydrogen and 1/4 *atom* of oxygen," but if we interpret "atom" as "molecule" and consider these to be diatomic this would have been the resultant formula.) Mercuric oxide was considered to be 1/2 atom of metal + 1/4 atom of oxygen; aluminum oxide was considered to be 1/2 atom of metal + 3/8 atom of oxygen; ferric oxide was considered to be 1/4 atom of metal + 3/16 atom of oxygen. By such arbitrary division he was able to fit a fairly wide selection of solid compounds into a "law" that he devised to relate specific heat to molecular weight. His 1838 memoir on this subject probably shows Avogadro at his very worst. Fractional atoms were introduced in the most irresponsible way although they were related to the supposed specific heats. The latter soon proved to be inaccurate. Because the memoir was published so long after the first announcement of Avogadro's hypothesis, it was not mentioned earlier as one of the reasons for the rejection of the hypothesis by his contemporaries. Yet the publication of the memoir can only have weakened Avogadro's scientific reputation.

The inaccuracies of the values obtained by Avogadro for specific heats were later criticized by Regnault. We are reminded by such criticism of the opposite poles represented by such men of science as Avogadro and Regnault—the one intuitive, speculative, and theoretical and the other empirical, precise, and practical. Avogadro's research on the vapor pressure of mercury cannot stand comparison for accuracy with Regnault's later work, yet Avogadro deserves credit for being the first to make this determination over the temperature range 100°C.-360°C.

Toward the end of his life Avogadro devoted a total of four memoirs to the subject of atomic volumes. In the first (1843) he pointed out the connection with his classic memoir of 1811—the mean distance between the molecules of all gases is the same under the same conditions of temperature and pressure. In 1824 he had read to the Turin Academy a memoir in which he had pointed out that the atomic volumes (i.e., the volume occupied by the molecule together with its surrounding caloric) of all substances in the liquid or solid state would be the same if it were not for certain factors and in particular the different affinities of bodies for caloric. But the latter factor was directly related to the electronegativity of the element. Comparing the densities of the elements with their atomic weights, he now concluded that the distances between the molecules of solids and liquids, and consequently their volumes, were greater, and hence their densities compared with their atomic weights were less as the body became more electropositive. Alternatively expressed, the atomic volume (atomic weight/density) is greater for the more electropositive elements, and this is now accepted.

Avogadro's work on atomic volumes differs from that of his contemporaries in his insistence on its connection with the position of elements in the electrochemical series. Also his "atomic" volumes were really molecular volumes. In this later work he was as isolated as he had been in his earlier speculations. By his habit of consistently giving references to his own earlier work Avogadro established the lineage of his research with any corresponding priority claim, but the practice had the disadvantage of revealing him as a solitary worker perhaps born a generation too soon.

NOTES

1. Alembic Club Reprint, No. 4, pp. 28–30 (the italics are the author's).
2. *Bulletin . . . de Ferussac*, **5** (1826), 39.
3. *Annales de chimie et de physique*, **29** (1850), 248.

BIBLIOGRAPHY

I. ORIGINAL WORKS. Articles by Avogadro include "Considérations sur l'état dans lequel doit se trouver une couche d'un corps non-conducteur de l'électricité, lorsqu'elle est interposée entre deux surfaces douées d'électricités de différente espèce," in *Journal de physique*, **63** (1806), 450–462; "Second mémoire sur l'électricité," in *Journal de physique*, **65** (1807), 130–145; "Idées sur l'acidité et l'alcalinité," in *Journal de physique*, **69** (1809), 142–148; "Essai d'une manière de déterminer les masses relatives des molécules élémentaires des corps, et les proportions selon lesquelles elles entrent dans ces combinaisons," in *Journal de physique*, **73** (1811), 58–76; "Réflexions sur la théorie électro-chimique de M. Berzelius," in *Annales de chimie*, **87** (1813), 286–292; "Mémoire sur les masses relatives des corps simples, ou densités présumées de leurs gaz, &c.," in *Journal de physique*, **78** (1814), 131–156; "Memoria sul calore specifico de' gaz composti paragonato a quello de' loro gaz componenti," in *Biblioteca italiana*, **4** (1816), 478–491; **5** (1817), 73–87; "Osservazioni sulla legge di dilatazione dell'acqua pel calore," in *Giornale di fisica*, **1** (1818), 351–377; "Sopra la relazione che esiste tra i calori specifici e i poteri refringenti delle sostanze gazose" [1817], in *Memorie di matematica e di fisica*, **18** (1818), 154–173; "Sulla determinazione delle quantità di calorico che si sviluppano nelle combinazioni per mezzo de' poteri refringenti" [1817], *ibid.*, pp. 174–182; "Osservazioni sulla forza elastica del vapor acqueo a diverse temperature," in *Giornale di fisica*, **2** (1819), 187–199; "Memoria sulle leggi della dilatazione de' diversi liquidi pel calore," *ibid.*, pp. 416–427; "Memoria sopra lo stabilimento d'una relazione tra le densità e dilatabilità de' liquidi e la densità dei vapori che essi formano," *ibid.*, pp. 443–456; "Memoria sulla legge della dilatazione del mercurio dal calore," *ibid.*, **3** (1820), 24–38; "Nouvelles considérations sur la théorie des proportions déterminées dans les combinaisons, et sur la détermination des masses des molécules des corps," in *Memorie della Reale Accademia delle scienze*, **26** (1821), 1–162; "Sur la manière de ramener les composés organiques aux lois ordinaires des proportions déterminées, *ibid.*, pp. 440–506; "Nuove considerazioni sull' affinità dei corpi pel calorico, calcolate per mezzo de' loro calori specifici" [1822], in *Memorie di matematica e di fisica*, **19** (1823), 83–137; "Sur la construction d'un voltimètre multiplicateur" [1822], in *Memorie della Reale Accademia delle scienze*, **27** (1823), 43–82; "Sur l'affinité des corps pour le calorique, et sur les rapports d'affinité qui en résultent entre eux:-1er Mém." [1823], *ibid.*, **28** (1824), 1–122; **29** (1825), 79–162; "Osservazioni sopra un articolo del Bollettino delle Scienze del sig. B. di Ferussac relativo alle Memorie sull' affinità dei corpi pel calorico, e sui rapporti d'affinità che ne risultano tra oro," in *Giornale di fisica,* **8** (1825), 432–438; "Mémoire sur la densité des corps solides et liquides, comparée avec la grosseur de leurs molécules et avec leurs nombres affinitaires" [1824], in *Memorie della Reale Accademia della scienze,* **30** (1826), 80–154; **31** (1827), 1–94; "Comparaison des observations de M. Dulong sur les pouvoirs réfringens des corps gazeux, avec les formules de relation entre ces pouvoirs et les affinités pour le calorique" [1826], *ibid.,* **33** (1829), 49–112; "Sur la loi de la force élastique de l'air par rapport à sa densité dans le cas de compression sans perte de calorique" [1828], *ibid.,* pp. 237–274; "Sur les pouvoirs neutralisants des différents corps simples, déduits de leurs proportions en poids dans les composés neutres qui en sont formés," *ibid.,* **34** (1830), 146–216; "Mémoire sur les chaleurs spécifiques des corps solides et liquides," in *Annales de chimie et de physique,* **55** (1833), 80–111; "Sur la force élastique de la vapeur du mercure à différentes températures" [1831], **49** (1832), 369–392; "Nouvelles recherches sur la chaleur spécifique des corps solides et liquides," *ibid.,* **57** (1834), 113–148; "Fisica de' corpi ponderabili, ossia trattato della costituzione generale de' corpi," in *Giornale Arcadio di Scienze,* **79** (1839), 104–107; "Diversi gradi della facoltà elettronegativa ed elettropositiva dei corpi semplice," in *Reunione degli scienziati italiana atti* (1840), 64–65; "Note sur la chaleur spécifique des différents corps, principalement à l'état gazeux," in *Bibliothèque universelle,* **29** (1840), 142–152; "Note sur la nature de la charge électrique," in *Archives de l'électricité,* **2** (1842), 102–110; "Saggio di teoria matematica della distribuzione della elettricità sulla superficie dei corpi conduttori nell'ipotesi della azione induttiva esercitata dalla medesima sui corpi circostanti, per mezzo delle particelle dell'aria frapposta" [1842], in *Memorie di matematica e di fisica,* **23** (1844), 156–184; "Proposizione di un nuovo sistema di nomenclatura chimica" [1843], *ibid.,* pp. 260–304; "Mémoire sur les volumes atomiques, et sur leur relation avec le rang que les corps occupent dans la série électro-chimique" [1843], in *Memorie della Reale Accademia delle scienze,* **8** (1846), 129–194; "Mémoire sur les volumes atomiques des corps composés" [1845], *ibid.,* pp. 293–532; "Note sur la nécessité de distinguer les molécules intégrantes des corps de leurs équivalents chimiques dans la détermination de leurs volumes atomiques," in *Archives des sciences physiques et naturelles,* **11** (1849), 285–298; "Sopra un sistema di nomenclatura chimica" [1847], in *Memorie di matematica e di fisica,* **24** (1850), 166–211; "Troisième mémoire sur les volumes atomiques. Détermination des nombres affinitaires des différents corps élémentaires par la seule considération de leur volume atomique et de celui de leurs composés" [1849], in *Memorie della Reale Accademia delle scienze,* **11** (1851), 231–318; "Quatrième mémoire sur les volumes atomiques. Détermination des volumes atomiques des corps liquides à leur température d'ébullition" [1850], *ibid.,* **12** (1852), 39–120; "Mémoire sur les conséquences qu'on peut déduire des expériences de M. Regnault sur la loi de compressibilité des gaz" [1851], *ibid.,* **13** (1853), 171–242.

In addition Avogadro wrote the major treatise: *Fisica de' corpi ponderabili ossia trattato della costituzione generale de' corpi,* 4 vols. (Turin, 1837–1841).

II. SECONDARY LITERATURE. V. Cappelletti and A. Alippi, "Avogadro," in *Dizionario biografico degli Italiani,* IV (Rome, 1962), 689–707; N. C. Coley, "The Physico-Chemical Studies of Amedeo Avogaɗro," in *Annals of Science,* **20** (1964), 195–210; I. Guareschi, "Amedeo Avogadro e la sua opera scientifica. Discorso storico-critico," in *Opere scelte di Amedeo Avogadro pubblicata dalla R. Accademia delle scienze di Torino* (Turin, 1911), 1–140; A. N. Meldrum, *Avogadro and Dalton. The Standing in Chemistry of Their Hypotheses* (Edinburgh, 1904); L. K. Nash, "The Atomic Molecular Theory," Case 4 of *Harvard Case Histories in Experimental Science,* J. B. Conant, ed., Vol. I (Cambridge, Mass., 1957); J. R. Partington, *A History of Chemistry,* Vol. IV (London, 1964).

M. P. CROSLAND

IBN AL-ʿAWWĀM ABŪ ZAKARIYYĀ YAḤYĀ IBN MUḤAMMAD (*fl.* Spain, second half of the twelfth century; nothing more is known of his life), *agronomy.*

Ibn Khaldūn mentions Ibn al-ʿAwwām in his *Muqaddima* as the author of a treatise on agriculture, the *Kitāb al-filāḥa,* which was, according to him, a summary of the *Nabatean Agriculture* of Ibn Waḥshiyya. The work of Ibn al-ʿAwwām, published in Spanish at the beginning of the nineteenth century, consists of thirty-five chapters, of which thirty are devoted to agronomy and the rest to related matters. It deals with 585 plants and more than fifty fruit trees, and is generally limited to a repetition of the doctrines of his predecessors, although there are a few observations, made by Ibn al-ʿAwwām in the Aljarafe of Seville, that are introduced by the term *lī.*

Among the classical writers he mentions Democritus, the Pseudo Aristotle, Theophrastus, Vergil, Varro, and especially Columella (the format of the *Kitāb al-filāḥa* is similar to that of the *De re rustica*). The Oriental Arabs are represented by Abū Ḥanīfa al-Dīnawarī (the tenth-century botanist who wrote the *Kitāb al-nabāt*) and the *Nabatean Agriculture.* The most extensive quotations, however, are from the Hispano-Arab agriculturists, among them Albucasis, possibly the author of a *Mukhtaṣar kitāb al-filāḥa;* the Sevillian Abū ʿUmar ibn Ḥajjāj (d. ca. 1073), author of the *Muqniʿ;* Ibn Baṣṣāl, a Toledan who was the director of the botanical garden of al-Maʾmūn and later that of al-Muʿtamid, as well as author of the *al-Qaṣd waʾl-bayān;* Abūʾl-Khayr al-Shajjār of Seville; and Abū ʿAbd Allāh Muḥammad al-Tijnarī, author of the *Zahr al-bustān wa-nuzhat al-adhhān.* Most of the works of these authors were known, until very recently, only through the quotations of Ibn al-ʿAwwām.

The *Kitāb al-filāḥa* is an excellent manual that was designed to increase the value of land through the education of the farmer. Therefore the Spanish governments of the Enlightenment, advised by Pedro Campomanes (1723–1802), incited the Arabists of the period to publish its translation.

BIBLIOGRAPHY

The first Spanish edition of the *Kitāb al-filāḥa* was prepared by José Antonio Banqueri, a canon from Tortosa who was a disciple of Casiri: *Libro de agricultura, su autor el doctor excelente Abu Zacaria . . .*, 2 vols. (Madrid, 1802). There is also a résumé of this translation by D. C. Boutelou, 2 vols. (Madrid, 1878), and a translation into French by J. J. Clément Mullet (Paris, 1864–1867) that is not definitive. Interesting observations about the text have been made by J. J. Clément Mullet, in *Journal asiatique,* **1** (1860), 449–454; E. M. Chehabi, in *Revue de l'Académie arabe,* **11** (1931), 193 ff.; and C. C. Moncada, "Sul taglio della vita di'Ibn al-ʿAwwām," in *Actes du VIIIᵉ Congrès des orientalistes* (Stockholm, 1889), Sec. I, 215 ff.

There are no Arabic sources for Ibn al-ʿAwwām's life, except for the quotation by Ibn Khaldūn in his *Muqaddima,* trans. de Slane, III (Paris, 1863–1868), 165. For the manuscripts, consult Ziriklī, *Aʿlām,* IX (1954–1959), 208; Brockelmann, *Geschichte der arabischen Litteratur,* I (Weimar, 1898), 494, and Supp. I (Leiden, 1937), 903; and George Sarton, *Introduction to the History of Science,* II, 424.

JUAN VERNET

AZARA, FÉLIX DE (*b.* Barbuñales, Huesca, Spain, 18 May 1742; *d.* Huesca, 20 October 1821), *mathematics, geography, natural history.*

Azara was the third son of Alejandro de Azara y Loscertales and María de Perera. At the University of Huesca he studied philosophy, arts, and law from 1757 to 1761 and in 1764 became an infantry cadet. The following year he continued his mathematical training in Barcelona, and by 1769, as a second lieutenant, he was assisting in the hydrographic surveys being carried out near Madrid; afterward he taught mathematics in the army until 1774. During the assault on Argel in 1775 he received a serious chest wound.

In 1781 Azara received a commission to establish the frontier between Brazil and the neighboring Spanish colonies. Upon his arrival in Montevideo, Uruguay, he was appointed captain of a frigate by the Spanish viceroy, who then sent him to Rio Grande and later to Asunción, Paraguay; this was the area Azara was to explore as both a geographer and a naturalist for thirteen years. Félix de Azara never married but, according to Walckenaer, while on his travels he was fond of female company, particularly that of mulattoes.

Between 1784 and 1796 Azara prepared at least fifteen maps of the Brazilian frontier; the Paraná, Pequeri, and Paraguay rivers; and the territory of Mato Grosso, Uruguay, Paraguay, and Buenos Aires. During those years he filled several diaries with accounts of travels in Paraguay and the Buenos Aires viceroyalty, the geography of Paraguay and the Río de la Plata, and the natural history of the birds and quadrupeds in those areas, relying on direct observation because he was practically without books or reference collections.

Azara returned to Spain in 1801, but soon afterward he moved to Paris, where his brother José Nicolás—a man greatly admired by Napoleon—was the Spanish ambassador. He was welcomed by the French naturalists because his *Essais sur l'histoire naturelle des quadrupèdes . . . du Paraguay* had just appeared, but on the death of José Nicolás in 1804 he returned to Madrid. Azara, with his liberal ideas, declined an appointment as viceroy of Mexico, and after 1808 during the Napoleonic War in Spain he was torn between his political and patriotic beliefs. Azara retired to Barbuñales and, as mayor of Huesca, ended his days there.

Azara enlarged natural history by discovering a large number of new species. He also visualized great biological concepts expanded by Cuvier and Darwin, both of whom quoted and accepted his views; for instance, on the variation undergone by horses under domestication.

BIBLIOGRAPHY

I. ORIGINAL WORKS. Azara's first published work was *Essais sur l'histoire naturelle des quadrupèdes de la province du Paraguay,* M. L. E. Moreau de Saint Méry, trans. (Paris, 1801), which shortly afterward was much improved and corrected (Madrid, 1802). Other works by Azara are *Apuntamientos para la historia natural de los pájaros del Paraguay y Río de la Plata* (Madrid, 1802); *Voyages dans l'Amérique méridionale,* C. A. Walckenaer, trans. (Paris, 1809), with notes by Cuvier; *Descripción e historia del Paraguay y del Río de la Plata* (Madrid, 1847); and *Memorias sobre el estado rural del Río de la Plata en 1801 . . .* (Madrid, 1847), published by his nephew Agustín de Azara. Several other works have subsequently appeared in Madrid and Buenos Aires.

II. SECONDARY LITERATURE. Both Moreau de Saint Méry's translation of the *Essais* (1801) and C. E. Walckenaer's translation of the *Voyages* give details of Azara's life. An excellent bibliographical survey, including the manuscript material in Madrid, Rome, Rio de Janeiro, and Buenos Aires, is Luis M. de Torres, "Noticias biográficas de D. Félix de Azara y exámen general de su obra," in *Anales de la Sociedad científica argentina,* **108** (1929), 177–190. The biography of Azara and a discussion of his role as a precursor of Darwin's ideas on the origin of species and the hypothesis of successive creations is E. Álvarez López, *Félix de Azara* (Madrid, 1935).

FRANCISCO GUERRA

BAADE, WILHELM HEINRICH WALTER (*b.* Schröttinghausen, Westphalia, Germany, 24 March 1893; *d.* Bad Salzuflen, Westphalia, Germany, 25 June 1960), *astronomy.*

Baade's father, Konrad, was a schoolteacher; he and his wife, Charlotte Wulfhorst, were Protestants and planned a career in theology for their son. But at the Friedrichs-Gymnasium in Herford, which he attended from 1903 to 1912, Baade decided that astronomy appealed to him more than the church: his choice resulted in a lifetime devoted to telescopic observations that have seldom been equaled, either in technical skill or in theoretical significance.

From the Gymnasium, Baade went briefly to the University of Münster, transferring to Göttingen in the Easter term of 1913. There he remained as a student throughout World War I, gaining competence in the observatory under Leopold Ambronn and serving for three years as assistant to the famous mathematician Felix Klein. Because of his congenitally dislocated hip, Baade was exempt from active military service, but beginning in 1917 had to spend eight hours a day on war work, in an installation for testing airplane models.

Shortly after passing his doctoral examination in July 1919, Baade became scientific assistant to Richard Schorr, director of the University of Hamburg's observatory at Bergedorf, located about ten miles southeast of the city. His main interest was in astrophysical problems—as shown by his dissertation, written under Johannes Hartmann, on the spectroscopic binary star β Lyrae (1921)—but his job required him to confirm the positions of many comets and asteroids. This he did conscientiously, soon dis-

covering a comet of his own (1923) and providing an explanation for the shape of comets' tails, published in 1927 with the first of a series of distinguished collaborators—the theoretical physicist Wolfgang Pauli, who was then a *Privatdozent* at Hamburg. Baade also discovered two remarkable asteroids (1925, 1949): (944) Hidalgo, which recedes farther from the sun than any other asteroid, and (1566) Icarus, noted for its close approaches both to the sun and to the earth, having passed within 4,000,000 miles of us as recently as 14 June 1968.

A meeting with Harlow Shapley in 1920 aroused Baade's interest in globular star clusters and the pulsating variables they contain. Despite the relatively small size of his telescope, Baade began observing them and in 1926 suggested a way to prove that the radiating surface of such variable stars actually rises and falls. That same year a Rockefeller fellowship enabled him to realize his dream of visiting the big telescopes in California.

Returning to Bergedorf in 1927, Baade was promoted to observer, but got no action on his plea that their 39-inch telescope be moved to a more favorable site. He turned down a job offered him at Jena, because it provided even less in the way of good observing facilities, and became a *Privatdozent* at Hamburg in 1928. The following year he married Johanna Bohlmann and went to the Philippine Islands to observe a total solar eclipse on 9 May. Clouds covered the sun during the crucial time, but the long sea voyage served to cement his friendship with the Estonian Bernard Voldemar Schmidt, who at Baade's urging designed the optical system used in the Schmidt wide-angle telescopes.

The year 1931 brought Baade an invitation to join the staff at Mt. Wilson Observatory near Pasadena, California; he accepted immediately, resigning his position at Hamburg and moving to the clearer skies and larger instruments in California as to the Promised Land. When his friend Rudolf Minkowski was forced to resign his professorship at Hamburg in 1933, Baade helped him to emigrate, thus enabling the two men to continue in California an already productive collaboration.

Now that Baade had realized his dream of working with the best telescopes in the world, he made the most of it. With Minkowski he continued spectroscopic work begun in Germany (1937), and with Edwin Powell Hubble he studied distant galaxies (1938). His work with Fritz Zwicky on supernovae (1938) led to papers on the Crab Nebula (1942) and on Nova Ophiuchi 1604 (1943).

When the United States entered World War II, Baade was classified as an enemy alien, but this favored rather than hampered his astronomical career: with many astronomers engaged in war work, and the lights of Los Angeles dimmed to protect coastal shipping, Baade had increased access to the telescopes and the added advantage of darker skies. Under these favorable circumstances he was able to photograph stars in the hitherto unresolved inner portions of the Andromeda galaxy, M31, and in both of its satellite galaxies, M32 and NGC205 (1944). This achievement was both technically difficult— thought, indeed, to be unattainable with the 100-inch telescope he used—and theoretically significant, because the brightest stars in the nucleus of M31 turned out to be red—not blue, as in the surrounding spiral arms. Baade realized he was dealing with two different stellar populations, which he called Type I (found in dusty regions, brightest stars blue) and Type II (found in dust-free regions, brightest stars red).

At a ceremony dedicating the 200-inch Palomar telescope on 1 July 1948, Baade outlined the ways he thought this great new instrument should be used to explore the universe. He suggested that since distance measurements depend critically on a reliable standard sequence of stellar magnitudes, the first thing to do was to replace the North Polar Sequence with a better one based on photoelectric techniques. His concern with distance criteria soon had spectacular results in another way, when he looked for cluster-type variables in the Andromeda galaxy. At the accepted distance of 750,000 light-years, these stars should have appeared in photographs taken with the 200-inch telescope; when they did not, Baade reasoned correctly that the galaxy was more distant than had previously been thought. Announced in 1952 at the Rome meeting of the International Astronomical Union, this conclusion cleared up several inconsistencies, but also essentially doubled the size of the universe. At a symposium on stellar evolution held during that same meeting, Baade presented color-magnitude diagrams for star clusters that his young collaborators Halton C. Arp, William A. Baum, and Allan R. Sandage had just completed, in support of his theory that Type I stars are younger—on a cosmological time scale—than Type II stars. This was an oversimplification, as suggested by Boris V. Kukarkin during the ensuing discussion, but it represented a major step toward today's understanding of the life cycles of stars.

Baade left his mark on yet another aspect of astronomy when he identified, in photographs he had taken with the 200-inch telescope, several objects first detected by radiotelescopes (1954). One of them, the radio source Cygnus A, had a twinned appearance: Baade correctly placed it far outside our galaxy— which seemed unbelievable—but his conclusion, based on theoretical work done in 1950 with Lyman Spitzer, Jr., that it represented two galaxies in collision, has not stood the test of time. In a final contribution to the understanding of objects later called quasars, Baade showed that a jet issuing from the galaxy M87 emitted strongly polarized light (1956).

Upon his retirement in 1958 Baade gave a series of lectures at Harvard University (published as *Evolution of Stars and Galaxies*), and then spent six months in Australia, where he used the 74-inch telescope at Mt. Stromlo near Canberra, before returning to Göttingen as Gauss professor. An operation on his hip and six months' convalescence in bed preceded his death from respiratory failure. Much of his work remained unpublished—in some cases because he was dissatisfied with it, in others because he preferred active research to the tedious job of writing about it—but of what did appear, the British astronomer Fred Hoyle has commented: "Almost every one of Baade's papers turned out to have far-reaching consequences."

Considering his accomplishments, Baade received few honors during his lifetime. He was awarded the Gold Medal of the Royal Astronomical Society in 1954, for his observational work on galactic and extragalactic objects, and in 1955 received the Bruce Medal of the Astronomical Society of the Pacific. He was a member of the American Philosophical Society, and of scientific academies in Amsterdam, Göttingen, Lund, Munich, and Mainz.

BIBLIOGRAPHY

I. ORIGINAL WORKS. Baade's dissertation, "Bahnbestimmung des spektroskopischen Doppelsterns β Lyrae nach Spectrogrammen von Prof. Hartmann," was presented at Göttingen 3 Aug. 1921. Works cited above are "Über die Möglichkeit, die Pulsationstheorie der δ Cephei-Veränderlichen zu prüfen," in *Astronomische Nachrichten,* **228** (1926), 359–362; "Über den auf die Teilchen in den Kometenschweifen ausgeübten Strahlungsdruck," in *Die Naturwissenschaften,* **15** (1927), 49–51, written with W. Pauli, Jr.; "The Trapezium Cluster of the Orion Nebula" and "Spectrophotometric Investigations of Some O- and B-type Stars Connected With the Orion Nebula," in *Astrophysical Journal,* **86** (1937), 119–122 and 123–135, both written with R. Minkowski; "The New Stellar Systems in Sculptor and Fornax," in *Publications of the Astronomical Society of the Pacific,* **51** (1938), 40–44, written with E. Hubble; "Photographic Light Curves of the Two Supernovae in IC4182 and NGC1003," in *Astrophysical Journal,* **88** (1938), 411–421, written with F. Zwicky; "The Crab Nebula," *ibid.,* **96** (1942), 188–198; "Nova Ophiuchi of 1604 as a Supernova," *ibid.,* **97** (1943), 119–127; "The Resolution of Messier 32, NGC205, and the Central Region of the Andromeda Nebula," *ibid.*, **100** (1944), 137–146; "A Program of Extragalactic Research for the 200-inch Hale Telescope," in *Publications of the Astronomical Society of the Pacific,* **60** (1948), 230–234; "Stellar Populations and Collisions of Galaxies," in *Astrophysical Journal,* **113** (1950), 413–418, written with L. Spitzer, Jr.; "Basic Facts on Stellar Evolution," in *Transactions of the International Astronomical Union VIII* (Cambridge, 1954), pp. 682–688 (discussion on pp. 688–689); "Identification of the Radio Sources in Cassiopeia, Cygnus A, and Puppis A," and "On the Identification of Radio Sources," in *Astrophysical Journal,* **119** (1954), 206–214, and 215–231, both written with R. Minkowski; "Polarization in the Jet of Messier 87," *ibid.*, **123** (1956), 550–551; and *Evolution of Stars and Galaxies* (Cambridge, Mass., 1963), ed. by Cecilia Payne-Gaposhkin from tape recordings of Baade's lectures at Harvard in 1958.

A list that includes seventy-three papers by Baade and ninety short communications is appended to Heckmann's obituary notice (see below); references to Baade's book (mentioned above) and several other contributions to symposia can be found in Poggendorff, VIIb (1967), 166. Baade's notebooks and other unpublished material are divided between the Mt. Wilson–Palomar Observatories and the Leiden Observatory.

II. SECONDARY LITERATURE. The citation delivered by John Jackson when Baade received (*in absentia*) the Gold Medal of the Royal Astronomical Society was printed in *Monthly Notices of the Royal Astronomical Society* (London), **114** (1954), 370–383; the one by Olin Chaddock Wilson that accompanied the Bruce Medal appeared in *Publications of the Astronomical Society of the Pacific,* **67** (1955), 57–61, and includes a portrait. Obituary notices on Baade include those by Fred Hoyle, in *Nature,* **187** (1960), 1075; Erich Schoenberg, in *Bayerische Akademie der Wissenschaften. Jahrbuch 1960,* pp. 177–181, plus a portrait facing p. 184; Otto Hermann Leopold Heckmann, in *Mitteilungen der Astronomischen Gesellschaft* [Hamburg] *1960* (1961), 5–11, with portrait and list of publications; Allan R. Sandage, in *Quarterly Journal of the Royal Astronomical Society,* **2** (1961), 118–121; and Halton C. Arp, in *Journal of the Royal Astronomical Society of Canada,* **55** (1961), 113–116.

The role Baade played in the early days of quasar research is described in Ivor Robinson, Alfred Schild, and E. L. Schücking, eds., *Quasi-Stellar Sources and Gravitational Collapse* (Chicago, 1965), pp. xi–xiv; and an essay on Baade's life and works by a longtime associate, Robert S. Richardson, constitutes ch. 16 (pp. 260–294) of Richardson's *The Star Lovers* (New York, 1967).

Further accounts of Baade's work are Fred Hoyle, "Report of the Meeting of Commission 28," in *Transactions of the International Astronomical Union VIII* (Cambridge, 1954), pp. 397–399; Hermann Kobold, "Komet 1922c (Baade)," in *Astronomische Nachrichten,* **217** (1923), cols. 175–176, and "Mitteilung über einen von W. Baade entdekten neuen Himmelskorper" [Planet 1924TD, later named Hidalgo], *ibid.*, **223** (1925), cols. 23–24; and R. S.

Richardson, "A New Asteroid With Smallest Known Distance" [Icarus], in *Publications of the Astronomical Society of the Pacific,* **61** (1949), 162–165.

SALLY H. DIEKE

BABBAGE, CHARLES (*b.* Teignmouth, England, 26 December 1792; *d.* London, England, 18 October 1871), *mathematics, computer logic, computer technology.*

Babbage's parents were affluent. As a child, privately educated, he exhibited unusually sharp curiosity as to the how and why of everything around him. Entering Cambridge University in 1810, he soon found that he knew more than his teachers, and came to the conclusion that English mathematics was lagging behind European standards. In a famous alliance with George Peacock and John Herschel, he began campaigning for a revitalization of mathematics teaching. To this end the trio translated S. F. Lacroix's *Differential and Integral Calculus* and touted the superiority of Leibniz's differential notation over Newton's (then widely regarded in England as sacrosanct).

After graduation, Babbage plunged into a variety of activities and wrote notable papers on the theory of functions and on various topics in applied mathematics. He inquired into the organization and usefulness of learned societies, criticizing the unprogressive ones (among which he included the Royal Society) and helping found new ones—in particular the Astronomical Society (1820), the British Association (1831), and the Statistical Society of London (1834). He became a fellow of the Royal Society in 1816, and in 1827 was elected Lucasian professor of mathematics at Cambridge. He had not sought this prestigious chair (he described his election as "an instance of forgiveness unparalleled in history") and, although he held it for twelve years, never functioned as professor. This is a little surprising, in that the position could have been used to further the pedagogic reforms he advocated. But Babbage was becoming absorbed, if not obsessed, by problems of the mechanization of computation. He was to wrestle with these for decades, and they were partly responsible for transforming the lively, sociable young man into an embittered and crotchety old one, fighting all and sundry, even the London street musicians, whose activities, he figured, had ruined a quarter of his working potential.

Babbage had a forward-looking view of science as an essential part of both culture and industrial civilization, and he was among the first to argue that national government has an obligation to support scientific activities, to help promising inventors, and even to give men of science a hand in public affairs.

Few eminent scientists have had such diversified interests as Babbage. A listing of them would include cryptanalysis, probability, geophysics, astronomy, altimetry, ophthalmoscopy, statistical linguistics, meteorology, actuarial science, lighthouse technology, and the use of tree rings as historic climatic records. Two deserve special mention: the devising of a notation that not only simplified the making and reading of engineering drawings but also helped a good designer simplify his "circuits"; and his insightful writings on mass production and the principles of what we now know as operational research (he applied them to pin manufacture, the post office, and the printing trade).

Computational aids began to haunt Babbage's mind the day he realized that existing mathematical tables were peppered with errors whose complete eradication was all but infeasible. As a creature of his era—the machine-power revolution—he asked himself, at first only half in earnest, why a table of, say, sines could not be produced by steam. Then he went on to reflect that maybe it could. He was at the time enthusiastic about the application of the method of differences to tablemaking, and was indeed using it to compile logarithms. (His finished table of eight-figure logarithms for the first 108,000 natural numbers is among the best ever made.) While still engaged in this work, Babbage turned to the planning of a machine that would not only calculate functions but also print out the results.

To understand his line of thought, we must take a close look at the method of differences—a topic in what later became known as the calculus of finite differences. The basic consideration is of a polynomial $f(x)$ of degree n evaluated for a sequence of equidistant values of x. Let h be this constant increment. We next take the corresponding increments in $f(x)$ itself, calling these the *first* differences; then we consider the differences between consecutive first differences, calling these the *second* differences. And so forth. An obvious recursive definition of the rth difference for a particular value of x, say x_i, is

$$\Delta^r f(x_i) = \Delta^{r-1} f(x_i + h) - \Delta^{r-1} f(x_i),$$

and it is not difficult to show that, specifically,

$$\Delta^r f(x_i) = \sum_{m=0}^{r} (-1)^m \binom{r}{m} f[x_i + (r - m)h].$$

As r increases, the differences become smaller and more nearly uniform, and at $r = n$ the differences are constant (so that at $r = n + 1$, all differences are

zero). A simple example—one that Babbage himself was fond of using—is provided by letting the function be the squares of the natural numbers. Here $n = 2$, and we have

x	1	2	3	4	5	6	$\cdots$
$f(x)$	1	4	9	16	25	36	$\cdots$
Δ^1		3	5	7	9	11	$\cdots$
Δ^2			2	2	2	2	$\cdots$

Two propositions follow. The first, perhaps not obvious but easily demonstrated, is that the schema can be extended to most nonrational functions (such as logarithms), provided that we take the differences far enough. (This is linked to the fact that the calculus of finite differences becomes, in the limit, the familiar infinitesimal calculus.) The second, originated by Babbage, is that the inverse of the schema is readily adaptable to mechanization. In other words, a machine can be designed (and it will be only slightly more sophisticated than an automobile odometer or an office numbering machine) that, given appropriate initial values and nth constant differences, will accumulate values of any polynomial, or indeed of almost any function. (For nonrational functions the procedure will be an approximation conditioned by the choice of r and h and the accuracy required, and will need monitoring at regular checkpoints across the table.)

This is what Babbage set out—and failed—to do. As the work progressed, he was constantly thinking up new ideas for streamlining the mechanism, and these in turn encouraged him to enlarge its capacity. In the end his precepts ruined his practice. The target he set was a machine that would handle twenty-decimal numbers and sixth-order differences, plus a printout device. When he died, his unfinished "Difference Engine Number One" had been a museum piece for years (in the museum of King's College, at Somerset House, London, from 1842 to 1862, and subsequently in the Science Museum, London—where it still is). What is more revealing and ironic is that, during his own lifetime, a Swedish engineer named Georg Scheutz, working from a magazine account of Babbage's project, built a machine of modest capacity (eight-decimal numbers, fourth-order differences, and a printout) that really worked. It was used for many years in the Dudley Observatory, Albany, New York.

Aside from technicalities, two factors militated against the production of the difference engine. One was cost (even a generous government subsidy would not cover the bills), and the other was the inventor's espousal of an even more grandiose project—the

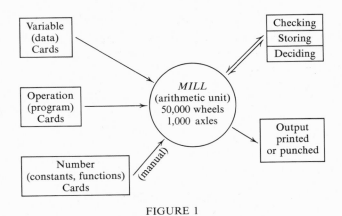

FIGURE 1

construction of what he called an analytical engine.

Babbage's move onto this new path was inspired by his study of Jacquard's punched cards for weaving machinery, for he quickly saw the possibility of using such cards to code quantities and operations in an automatic computing system. His notion was to have sprung feeler wires that would actuate levers when card holes allowed them access. On this basis he drew up plans for a machine of almost unbelievable versatility and mathematical power. A simplified flow diagram of the engine is shown in the accompanying figure. The heart of the machine, the mill, was to consist of 1,000 columns of geared wheels, allowing up to that many fifty-decimal-digit numbers to be subjected to one or another of the four primary arithmetic operations. Especially remarkable was the incorporation of decision-making units of the logical type used in today's machines.

Although the analytical engine uncannily foreshadowed modern equipment, an important difference obtains: it was decimal, not binary. Babbage, not having to manipulate electronics, could not have been expected to think binarily. However, his having to use wheels meant that his system was not "purely" digital, in the modern sense.

All who understood the plans expressed unbounded admiration for the analytical engine and its conceiver. But material support was not forthcoming, and it remained a paper project. After Babbage's death his son, H. P. Babbage, sorted the mass of blueprints and workshop instructions, and, in collaboration with others, built a small analytical "mill" and printer. It may be seen today in the Science Museum, London.

BIBLIOGRAPHY

I. ORIGINAL WORKS. Babbage appended a list of eighty of his publications to his autobiographical *Passages From the Life of a Philosopher* (London, 1864), and it is repro-duced in P. and E. Morrison's *Charles Babbage and His Calculating Engines* (New York, 1961). It is a poor list, with reprinted papers and excerpts separately itemized. Apart from translations and the autobiography and a few small and minor works, the only books of substance that Babbage published were *Reflections on the Decline of Science in England* (London, 1830); *Economy of Manufactures and Machinery* (London, 1832); and *The Exposition of 1851* (London, 1851). His logarithms deserve special mention: they were originally published in stereotype as *Table of the Logarithms of the Natural Numbers From 1 to 108,000* (London, 1827), with a valuable introduction dealing with the layout and typography of mathematical tables. A few years later he published *Specimen of Logarithmic Tables* (London, 1831), a 21-volume, single-copy edition of just two of the original pages printed in a great variety of colored inks on an even greater variety of colored papers, in order "to ascertain by experiment the tints of the paper and colors of the inks least fatiguing to the eye." In the same "experiment" about thirty-five copies of the complete table were printed on "thick drawing paper of various tints." In 1834 regular colored-paper editions were published in German at Vienna and in Hungarian at Budapest, by C. Nagy. Babbage's formal scientific articles number about forty. The first publication dealing with his main subject is "A Note Respecting the Application of Machinery to the Calculation of Mathematical Tables," in *Memoirs of the Astronomical Society,* **1** (1822), 309; the last is chs. 5–8 of his entertaining autobiography (see above).

II. SECONDARY LITERATURE. Practically all the significant material is either reproduced or indexed in the Morrisons' book, the only one entirely devoted to Babbage (see above). The symposium *Faster Than Thought* (London, 1953) has a first chapter (by the editor, B. V. Bowden) that is largely concerned with Babbage. Both of these books carry reprints of a translation and annotation of an article on the analytical engine written by the Italian military engineer L. F. Menabrea (Geneva, 1842). The translator was Lady Lovelace, Lord Byron's mathematically gifted daughter, and her detailed annotations (especially a sketch of how Bernoulli numbers could be computed by the engine) are excellent. It is in the course of this commentary that she finely remarks that "the Analytical Engine *weaves algebraic patterns,* just as the Jacquard-loom weaves flowers and leaves." The sectional catalog *Mathematics, I. Calculating Machines and Instruments,* The Science Museum (London, 1926), contains much useful illustrated information about Babbage's engines, as well as about allied machines, such as the Scheutz difference engine.

NORMAN T. GRIDGEMAN

BABCOCK, STEPHEN MOULTON (*b.* Bridgewater, New York, 22 October 1843; *d.* Madison, Wisconsin, 1 July 1931), *agricultural chemistry.*

Babcock, the son of Pelig and Mary Scott Babcock, received the B.A. from Tufts College in 1866. His engineering studies at Rensselaer Polytechnic Institute were cut short when he had to manage the family farm after his father's death. However, he was soon taking chemistry courses at Cornell University, and in 1875 was made an instructor in the subject. In 1877 Babcock began graduate studies at the University of Göttingen under Hans Hübner, receiving the Ph.D. in 1879. He resumed his instructorship at Cornell in 1881 but left in 1882 to become chief chemist at the New York Agricultural Experiment Station in Geneva. He moved to an equivalent position at the Wisconsin Agricultural Experiment Station in 1888 and was also appointed professor of agricultural chemistry at the University of Wisconsin. Both positions were held until his retirement as emeritus professor in 1913. He married May Crandall in 1896.

Babcock is best known for his test for butterfat in milk, introduced in 1890. By using sulfuric acid to release the fat from its normal suspension and centrifuging and diluting, it was possible to measure directly the percentage of fat by observing it in the neck of a specially designed test bottle. The simplicity of the test permitted its use by persons without scientific training. Its use altered the economics of dairying and stimulated growth of the dairy industry.

With the bacteriologist Harry L. Russell, Babcock developed the process for cold curing of cheese in 1900. The great improvement in the quality of cheese led to wide acceptance of the process in the dairy industry.

Babcock's most important contribution arose from his skepticism regarding the biological equivalency of chemically similar feeds from different crops. In 1907 four of his younger associates—E. B. Hart, E. V. McCollum, H. Steenbock, and G. Humphrey—began a cattle-feeding experiment using chemically equivalent rations, each derived from a different plant. The experiment not only confirmed Babcock's skepticism but led to studies that helped develop the vitamin concept.

Babcock also studied metabolic water in insects and, in his later years, sought to investigate the structure of matter and its relation to energy.

BIBLIOGRAPHY

I. ORIGINAL WORKS. Babcock had an aversion to writing and published very little. Most of his work is described in bulletins and annual reports of the New York and Wisconsin Agricultural Experiment Stations. The fat test was originally published as "A New Method for the Estimation of Fat in Milk, Especially Adapted to Creameries and Cheese Factories," in *Bulletin of the University of Wisconsin Experiment Station,* no. 24 (July 1890). The studies with H. L. Russell on cold curing of cheese appeared in *Bulletin,* no. 94 (1902). Research Bulletin no. 22 (1912) is entitled *Metabolic Water: Its Production and Role in Vital Phenomena.* The single-grain feeding experiments, under the authorship of E. B. Hart, E. V. McCollum, H. Steenbock, and G. Humphrey, are reported in Research Bulletin no. 17 (1911).

Babcock's unpublished papers are held by the State Historical Society of Wisconsin.

II. SECONDARY LITERATURE. Paul de Kruif has a perceptive biographical sketch of Babcock in *Hunger Fighters* (New York, 1928), ch. 9; and Aaron J. Ihde has a short sketch in Eduard Farber, ed., *Famous Chemists* (New York, 1961), pp. 808–813, with a bibliography of other biographical sketches on pp. 828–829. The history of the fat test is described by J. L. Sammis, *The Story of the Babcock Test,* Circular 172, Extension Services of the College of Agriculture, University of Wisconsin (Madison, 1924).

AARON J. IHDE

BABINET, JACQUES (*b.* Lusignan, France, 5 March 1794; *d.* Paris, France, 21 October 1872), *physics, meteorology.*

Jacques Babinet was a French physicist who did important work in the theory of diffraction, meteorological optics, and optical instrumentation. His parents—Jean Babinet, the mayor of Lusignan, and Marie-Anne Félicité Bonneau du Chesne, daughter of a lieutenant-general—hoped that he would become a magistrate and gave him a strong literary education. Jacques preferred science, however, and entered the École Polytechnique in 1812. After graduation he held professorships at Fontenay-le-Comte and Poitiers. In 1820 he became professor of physics at the Collège Louis-le-Grand in Paris. Babinet was elected a member of the physics section of the Académie des Sciences in 1840 and a year later he was appointed librarian at the Bureau of Longitudes. He married Adelaide Laugier, by whom he had two sons.

An early proponent of the wave theory of light which had recently been perfected by Fresnel and Young, Babinet devoted much of his research to extending its applications. His first published paper on optics, "Sur les couleurs des réseaux," dealt with Fraunhofer's discovery that white light viewed through a wire grating produces a series of continuous spectra. Babinet derived the formula that relates the deviation of rays of a given color to the ratio of their wavelength divided by the sum of the diameter of the wires plus the distance between any two wires. He also showed that diffraction experiments could yield an improved measure of wavelengths and presented a table of new values.

Babinet realized that the grating was only one of a number of means of producing diffraction effects, so he extended his theoretical work to include other systems. The result was a concept known today as Babinet's principle: "If parallel rays fall normally on a diffraction system formed from a large number of openings . . . the diffraction phenomena will remain identically the same if the transparent parts become opaque, and reciprocally."

This theoretical work was accompanied by experimental investigations of several unexplained optical phenomena in mineralogy and meteorology. Here Babinet showed his talent as an inventor. Finding Malus' goniometer (a device for measuring angles of refraction) too cumbersome for his experiment on minerals, he constructed a portable one, which was considerably easier to use and was capable of making measurements that previously required separate instruments. To aid in his study of polarization he invented the Babinet compensator, which could produce or analyze arbitrarily polarized light.

Babinet's interests in physics transcended laboratory work and included all phenomena in nature. Thus, the study of meteorology, particularly meteorological optics, occupied much of his career. He began his work in this field with an investigation of interference phenomena produced in the atmosphere: rainbows and "coronas," or colored rings surrounding the sun or moon under certain weather conditions. Later work included modifications of the theory of atmospheric refraction and a study of polarization of skylight, especially the mysterious existence of neutral or unpolarized points in the sky.

While engaged in this original research, Babinet also achieved considerable fame as a popularizer of science, explaining natural phenomena to the layman in public courses and in articles in popular journals. In these exercises, whose subjects ranged over geology, mineralogy, astronomy, and meteorology, Babinet exhibited his rare ability to reduce complex phenomena to an easily comprehensible level.

BIBLIOGRAPHY

I. ORIGINAL WORKS. Among Babinet's works are "Sur les couleurs des réseaux," in *Annales de chimie*, **60** (1829), 166–176; "Mémoires d'optique météorologique," in Académie des Sciences, *Comptes rendus*, **4** (1837), 638–648; "Sur les caractères optiques des minéraux," *ibid.*, 758–766; "Sur la réfraction terrestre," *ibid.*, **52** (1861), 394–395, 417–425, 529–535. A study of polarization of skylight, especially the mysterious existence of neutral or unpolarized points in the sky, may be found in Académie des Sciences, *Comptes rendus*, **11** (1840), 618–620; **20** (1845), 801–804; **23** (1846), 233–235. Many of Babinet's treatises on science for the layman were collected in a volume entitled *Études et expériences sur les sciences d'observation* (Paris, 1855).

II. SECONDARY LITERATURE. Biographical material on Babinet is found in the following sources: *Revue des cours scientifiques de la France et de l'étranger*, **3** (1872), 409–410; L. Figuier, *L'année scientifique*, **16** (1872), 533; the speech by Becquerel at Babinet's funeral; E. Beauchat-Filleau, *Dictionnaire historique et généalogique de Poitou*, 2nd ed., I (Poitiers, 1891), 120, especially for family background. A complete bibliography of Babinet's original papers is given in the *Royal Society Catalogue of Scientific Papers*, I, 134–136 and VII, 72. Other publications are listed in J. C. Poggendorff's *Biographisch-literarisches Handwörterbuch . . .*, I (Leipzig, 1863; repr. Amsterdam, 1965), 82.

EUGENE FRANKEL

BABINGTON, CHARLES CARDALE (*b.* Ludlow, England, 23 November 1808; *d.* Cambridge, England, 22 July 1895), *botany*.

The only child of Joseph Babington and Catherine Whitter, Charles married Anna Maria Walker in 1866. His father, a physician, was a keen amateur botanist and doubtless influenced his son's inclination to natural history.

After a succession of private schools and a brief interlude at Charterhouse, Babington entered St. John's College, Cambridge, in 1826, graduating B.A. in 1830 and receiving the M.A. in 1833. In his first year at Cambridge he established an enduring friendship with J. S. Henslow, professor of botany, whose enthusiasm confirmed Babington's lifelong devotion to botany. Completely involved in the natural history activities of Cambridge for more than forty years, Babington was a leading member of the Ray Club, which developed into the Ray Society (founded 1844); and a number of its publications, such as *Memorials of John Ray* and *Correspondence of John Ray*, owed much to his help. A man of wide intellectual interests, he was a founding member of the Entomological Society in Cambridge and the Cambridge Antiquarian Society.

Babington's first work, *Flora Bathoniensis* (1834), with critical notes and references to Continental floras, adumbrated the direction of his future taxonomic work. Two visits to the Channel Islands, in 1837 and 1838, resulted in his *Primitiae florae Sarnicae* (1839). The Napoleonic Wars had isolated the British Isles from botanical research in the rest of Europe, where the natural system of plant classification was generally accepted, and therefore Linnaeus' artificial arrangement was perpetuated in such standard English works as J. E. Smith's *English Botany* and the earlier editions of W. J. Hooker's *British Flora*. Consequently, it was difficult for English botanists to identify the new plants published in Continental floras, a defect remedied by Babington in successive editions of his *Manual of British Botany.* Considered to be his *magnum opus,* it made its first appearance in 1843 and, with the exception of the fifth edition of Hooker's *British Flora,* was the first complete guide to British plants arranged according to a natural system. Accurate and clear in its descriptions, meticulous in its assignment of genera and species, the *Manual* soon established itself as an indispensable field companion.

Babington differed from many of his contemporaries in insisting upon a more critical delimitation of species; this was well demonstrated in his *British Rubi* (1869), which described in impressive detail some forty-five species.

On the death of his friend Henslow in 1861, Babington was elected to the chair of botany at Cambridge, which he held until his death. He was an indifferent and infrequent lecturer; his interests were mainly in research, and during his professorship many additions were made to the Cambridge Herbarium, the most notable being John Lindley's collection. His own collection of nearly 55,000 sheets was bequeathed to Cambridge, together with his library. At the time of his death Babington was the senior fellow of the Linnean Society, having been elected in 1830; in 1851 he was elected a fellow of the Royal Society.

BIBLIOGRAPHY

I. ORIGINAL WORKS. Babington's writings include *Flora Bathoniensis* (Bath, 1834); *Primitiae florae Sarnicae* (London, 1839); *Manual of British Botany* (London, 1843; 8th ed., 1881); *Synopsis of British Rubi* (London, 1846); *Flora of Cambridgeshire* (London, 1860); and *British Rubi* (London, 1869).

II. SECONDARY LITERATURE. A. M. Babington, ed., *Memorials, Journal and Botanical Correspondence of Charles Cardale Babington* (Cambridge, 1897), contains reprinted obituaries and reminiscences of Babington and a bibliography of his periodical articles. Obituaries include James Britten, in *Journal of Botany,* **33** (1895), 257–266; and J. E. B. Mayor, in *Cambridge Chronicle* (30 Aug. 1895), p. 4.

R. G. C. DESMOND

BABINGTON, WILLIAM (*b.* Port Glenone, Antrim, Northern Ireland, 21 May 1756; *d.* London, England, 29 April 1833), *mineralogy, geology.*

After apprenticeship to a medical practitioner in Londonderry, Northern Ireland, and completion of his medical training at Guy's Hospital, London, Babington was appointed assistant surgeon at Haslar Naval Hospital, Portsmouth, in 1777. He became apothecary (1781), assistant physician (1795), and full physician (1802) at Guy's Hospital, where he also lectured on chemistry. In 1795 he was awarded an M.D. by Aberdeen University. The following year he qualified as licentiate of the College of Physicians, London, and was created fellow of the college by "special grace" in 1827. Also in 1796 he commenced private practice, and was so successful that in 1811 he resigned from Guy's Hospital. Although prominent as a practicing physician for the rest of his life, Babington made no conspicuous contribution to medical science. He was elected a fellow of the Royal Society in 1805.

Babington's interest in mineralogy arose through the purchase of a cabinet of minerals—the collection of minerals was at that time a fashionable pursuit. His study of these minerals, to which he applied his knowledge of chemistry, led to the publication of his *Systematic Arrangement of Minerals* (1795). In 1799 he published a greatly enlarged *New System of Mineralogy.* He classified minerals by the Linnaean system into orders, genera, and species, the main subdivisions being based on chemical composition; crystal form was used only to establish subdivisions. This constituted an advance on the then widely used Wernerian system, which was based principally on external characters.

Babington was a member of the British Mineralogical Society, which was formed in 1799 to carry out analyses of British minerals. Some of the members of the society, including Babington and a few others with scientific inclinations, founded the Geological Society of London on 13 November 1807. As an influential member, Babington played an important part in establishing the new society on a firm basis and in promoting mineralogical and geological science in general. He served as president from 1822 to 1824.

BIBLIOGRAPHY

I. ORIGINAL WORKS. Works by Babington are *A Syllabus of a Course of Lectures Read at Guy's Hospital on Chemistry* (London, 1789); *A Systematic Arrangement of Minerals, Founded on the Joint Consideration of Their Chemical, Physical, and External Characters, &c.* (London, 1795, 2nd ed. 1796); and *A New System of Mineralogy in the Form of a Catalogue, &c.* (London, 1799).

II. SECONDARY LITERATURE. See G. B. Greenough, "President's Anniversary Address, for 1834," in *Proceedings of the Geological Society of London,* **2** (1838), 42–44; W. Munk, *The Roll of the Royal College of Physicians,* II (London, 1878), 451; S. Wilks and G. T. Bettany, *A Biographical History of Guy's Hospital* (London, 1892), pp.

199–204; and H. B. Woodward, *The History of the Geological Society of London* (London, 1907), pp. 6–11.

V. A. EYLES

BACCELLI, GUIDO (*b.* Rome, Italy, 25 November 1830; *d.* Rome, 10 January 1916), *clinical medicine.*

Baccelli, the son of Antonio Baccelli and Adelaide Leonori, studied in Rome. He graduated surgeon (1852) and physician (1853) from the Roman School of Medicine; he was appointed director of the Medical Clinic of Rome in 1863, and remained in that chair until his death. Of wealthy family, Baccelli had a youthful interest in politics, and from 1870 was active in public life. In 1875 he was elected a deputy of the Italian parliament. Loyal to the house of Savoy, Baccelli was always staunchly liberal in his political beliefs. He was Minister of Public Education three times (1881, 1893, 1898) and Minister of Agriculture, Commerce, and Industry (1901). In Rome, he advocated the repair of the Capitol, the Pantheon, and the Palatine, and conceived the beautiful Archeological Walk; he also founded the Gallery of Modern Art and promoted the draining of the Pontine Marshes. On the national level, Baccelli restored the autonomy of the Italian universities and reformed the system of primary education. He promoted agriculture, resolutely supported the idea of an armed nation, and used his political power to advance the cause of public health through legislation setting up programs to eliminate malaria and pellagra. In 1893, in collaboration with the noted surgeon Francesco Durante, he founded the widely read medical weekly *Il policlinico.* Baccelli's greatest achievement, however, was the founding of the Policlinico Umberto I, a medical center which was opened in Rome on 9 April 1906. A fascinating orator, Baccelli presided at the first congress of the Italian Society of Internal Medicine (Rome, 1888), and the Eleventh International Congress of Medicine (Rome, 1894).

Baccelli's medical writings covered a variety of subjects. From 1863 to 1877 he studied heart diseases and pleural diseases, and in 1876 illustrated Gaucher's disease. From 1866 to 1894 he studied malarial infection, demonstrating that such infection acts upon the erythrocytes.

Baccelli appreciated traditional therapeutics, but he was also one of the first supporters of oxygen therapy (1870). However, his major merit was "to have opened the way of the veins to the heroic drugs," as he wrote. The first introduction of drugs into the veins of a living animal (1656, in a dog) was performed in Oxford by Sir Christopher Wren; previously, in the sixteenth century, Alessandro Massaria, teacher of practical medicine at Padua University, had proposed the same operation in man. But these facts were practically unknown when, in 1890, Baccelli first injected quinine chlorhydrate into a vein of a woman, thereby saving her from death by pernicious malaria. In 1906 Baccelli also announced positive results from the intravenous injection of strophantine in the treatment of grave heart failure.

Baccelli gave great impetus to the modern study of medicine, but he also acknowledged the importance of the ancient masters; in 1907, he was elected chairman of the committee that drafted the constitution of the Italian Society of the History of Medicine.

BIBLIOGRAPHY

I. ORIGINAL WORKS. Baccelli's works include *Ascoltazione e percussione nella Scuola Romana* (Rome, 1857); *Patologia del cuore e dell'aorta,* 3 vols. (Rome, 1863–1866); *La pettiroloquia afonetica e la diplofonia* (Rome, 1864); *Il plessimetro lineare della Scuola Clinica di Roma* (Rome, 1866); *De primitivo splenis carcinomate* (Rome, 1876); *Sulla trasmissione dei suoni attraverso i liquidi endopleurici di differente natura* (Rome, 1877); "Le iniezioni endovenose di sali di chinino nella infezione malarica," in *La riforma medica,* 6 (1890), 14–16; *L'infezione malarica. Studi di Guido Baccelli 1866–1894 raccolti dal Dott. Zeri* (Rome, 1894); "I discorsi inaugurali pronunciati dal Baccelli ai Congressi Nazionali di Medicina Interna," in *La clinica medica italiana,* 45 (1906), 317–338; *La via delle vene aperta ai medicamenti eroici* (Rome, 1907).

II. SECONDARY LITERATURE. Works relating to Baccelli include "Numero speciale in occasione delle onoranze a Guido Baccelli," in *Il policlinico,* 14 (8 April 1906); A. Baccelli, *Guido Baccelli. Ricordi* (Naples, 1931); L. Belloni, *Da Asclepio ad Esculapio* (Milan, 1959); A. Castiglioni, *Storia della Medicina,* II (Milan, 1948), 699–700; M. Di Segni, "Il contributo italiano alle origini della trasfusione del sangue e della iniezione di medicamenti nelle vene," in *Bollettino dell'Istituto Storico Italiano dell'Arte Sanitaria,* 10 (1930), 66–90 and 179–199; G. Gorrini, *Guido Baccelli. La vita, l'opera, il pensiero* (Turin, 1916), which contains a portrait of Baccelli and a complete inventory of his medical works; E. Maragliano, "Guido Baccelli clinico," in *Il policlinico,* 23 (1916), 217–262; A. Pazzini, *La storia della Facoltà Medica di Roma,* 2 vols. (Rome, 1961); and G. Sanarelli, "Guido Baccelli uomo politico e medico sociale," in *Il policlinico,* 23 (1916), 263–280.

PIETRO FRANCESCHINI

BACH, ALEKSEI NIKOLAEVICH (*b.* Zolotonosha [now in Ukrainian S.S.R.], Russia, 17 March 1857; *d.* Moscow, U.S.S.R., 13 May 1946), *biochemistry, physical chemistry.*

Bach's father, a technician in a distillery, stimulated his son's interest in science. During his years in a

Gymnasium in Kiev (1867–1875), Bach, under the influence of the ideas of the writer and revolutionary Dmitrii Ivanovich Pisarev, decided to dedicate himself to the natural sciences and to their dissemination for the good of society. In 1875 he enrolled in the natural science section of the Department of Physics and Mathematics of Kiev University, where he specialized in chemistry. In 1878 he was expelled from the university and exiled to Belozersk for three years for participating in student political activities. Allowed to resume his studies at the university in 1882, Bach devoted even more energy than before to the political struggle, and soon became one of the leaders of the Kiev branch of the Narodnaja Volja ("People's Will") party. Inspired by revolutionary propaganda, Bach wrote the pamphlet "Tsar'-golod" ("Tsar-hunger"; 1883), one of the first statements of Marxist economic theory to be published in Russian. (Before 1917 this pamphlet had sold 100,000 copies, including translations into the languages of several Russian peoples.) In 1883, fearing arrest, Bach went into hiding; the utter defeat of the Narodnaja Volja by the tsarist government forced him to flee to France in 1885.

From 1885 to 1894 Bach lived in Paris, where he collaborated on the journal *Moniteur scientifique,* a collaboration that enabled him to establish close contact with French scientific circles. As a result, Paul Schützenberger invited him in 1890 to work in his laboratory at the Collège de France. There Bach completed his first investigations of the chemical mechanism of the assimilation of carbon by plants, the results of which Schützenberger regularly reported to the Paris Academy of Sciences. In the same year Bach married Aleksandra Aleksandrovna Cherven-Vodali, a teacher who had later become a pediatrician. In 1891 Bach traveled to the United States at the behest of the Brussels Society of Maltose, in order to introduce an improved method of fermentation into Chicago's distilleries.

Bach moved to Switzerland in 1894, residing there until he returned to Russia in 1917. In the laboratory that he built in his home in Geneva, Bach conducted his investigations into slow oxidation and biological oxidation, investigations culminating in the peroxide theory of oxidation and the theory of biological oxidation.

In 1916 Bach was elected chairman of the Société de Physique et d'Histoire Naturelle de Genève, and in the following year he was awarded the doctorate *honoris causa* by Lausanne University.

After the February 1917 revolution Bach returned to his homeland. In Moscow he met Maxim Gorky, at whose request he wrote a series of articles that were later published as *Istorija narodnogo khozjajstva* ("The History of the National Economy"). Bach renewed his scientific research in the spring of 1918 in Moscow, first at Blumenthal's chemical and bacteriological institute and later at the chemical laboratory of the chemical industry section of the Higher Soviet National Economy. He was made director of this laboratory upon the recommendation of Lev Yakovlevich Karpov, a renowned chemist and prominent Communist and statesman. Owing to a significant degree to Bach's efforts, the laboratory became a major scientific center and, in 1922, was renamed the L. Y. Karpov Institute of Physics and Chemistry. Many prominent chemists, including Aleksandr Ivanovich Oparin, began their scientific careers there under Bach's guidance. At this institute—as well as at the National Commissariat of Health's Biochemistry Institute, which was founded in 1920 on Bach's recommendation—wide-ranging investigations of oxidation and the problems of biological catalysis, as well as many applied studies into the biochemical methods of processing raw material, were carried out.

In 1927 Bach was chosen a member of the Central Executive Committee of the U.S.S.R. and was awarded the Lenin Prize. The following year the All-Union Association of Scientists and Technicians was organized at his urging. He was chosen a member of the Academy of Sciences of the U.S.S.R. in 1929, and in 1935 he and Oparin organized the Institute of Biochemistry, with Bach as director, within the Academy of Sciences. This institute became the coordinating center of Soviet biochemistry. Bach participated in the preparation of the scientific publications *Zhurnal fizicheskoj khimii* ("Journal of Physical Chemistry"), *Acta physicochimica URSS,* and *Biokhimija* ("Biochemistry") and of the *Bol'shaja sovetskaja èntsiklopedija* ("Great Soviet Encyclopedia") and the *Bol'shaja meditsinskaja èntsiklopedija* ("Great Medical Encyclopedia"). In 1939 Bach was chosen the first academician-secretary of the newly created chemical sciences section of the Academy of Sciences. From 1932 until his death, he was the permanent president of the Dmitrii Ivanovich Mendeleev All-Union Chemical Society.

During World War II Bach organized the research of the evacuated institutes of the Academy of Sciences. In 1942–1943, in Frunze, Kirghiz S.S.R., he directed the study of the exploitational possibilities of local biological raw materials. Bach was awarded the State Prize for his work in biochemistry in 1941 and, in 1945, the title Hero of Socialist Labor—the highest distinction for civilians in the U.S.S.R.—was conferred upon him. In 1943 Bach was chosen an honorary member of the Imperial Society of the Chemical Industry (London) and of the American Chemical Society. Annual memorial "Bach readings" on the fundamental questions of biochemistry are held in the Soviet Union on his birthday.

Bach's most important works are studies of carbon assimilation by plants and of slow oxidation and biological oxidation. These investigations are the basis of his works on enzymology (oxidizing and hydrolytic enzymes) and on technical biochemistry (the regulating principles of industrial biochemical processes). Research into the assimilation of carbonic acid preceded the development of the theory of slow oxidation: Bach proposed that in plants carbonic acid decomposes into H_2CO_3, and not $CO_2 + H_2O$; that this process is completed in several stages; and that during this process hydrogen peroxide and peroxides of organic compounds must be formed as intermediary products. On this basis he formed the conclusion that the oxygen formed during photosynthesis is the oxygen of water, and not of carbonic acid, as would follow from the hypotheses concerning the assimilation of carbonic acid proposed by Adolph von Baeyer and E. Erlenmeyer.

The supposition of the existence of conjugate oxidation-reduction reactions and of the formation of intermediary peroxides during the assimilation of carbonic acid led Bach to deal with biological oxidation. Inasmuch as there was no satisfactory general theory of oxidation, he first developed one. His work on slow oxidation, and later on biological oxidation, continued the development of the idea concerning the necessary activation of oxygen in the process of oxidation that had been stated in 1845 by Christian Friedrich Schönbein. "O roli perekisej v protsessakh medlennogo okislenija" ("On the Role of Peroxides in the Process of Slow Oxidation") stated the foundations of a new theory of slowly proceeding oxidation processes and was published in the *Zhurnal Russkago fiziko-khimicheskago obshchestva* in 1897. This paper was presented to the Paris Academy of Sciences by Schützenberger in 1897 and published in the *Comptes rendus* the same year. Almost simultaneously there appeared, in the *Berichte der Deutschen chemischen Gesellschaft,* an article by Karl Engler and Wilhelm Wild, "Die sogennante Activirung des Oxygens und über Superoxydbildung," which developed a theory analogous to Bach's and independent of it. The theory of slow oxidation was later named the Bach-Engler peroxide theory of oxidation.

At the heart of the peroxide theory lies the notion that the energy necessary for the activation of oxygen is introduced by the oxidized substance itself. Before Bach, the activation process was considered either the result of the break-up of an oxygen molecule into separate atoms, as was envisaged by Rudolph Clausius, Felix Hoppe-Seyler, and Jacobus van't Hoff, or the result of the severance of only one bond in the oxygen molecule and the formation of hydrogen peroxide, as Moritz Traube proposed. Bach significantly widened the limits of Traube's hypothesis, thus formulating a new theory of slow oxidation.

(1) In slow combustion processes the oxygen molecule $O=O$ partially dissociates under the influence of the free energy of the substance being oxidized and enters into the reaction in the form $-O-O-$.

(2) All substances capable of being oxidized, independent of their chemical nature, annex such $-O-O-$ groups, initially forming a peroxide, either

$$R'-O-O-R'' \text{ or } R\diagup_{\diagdown}^{O}_{O}.$$

(3) Peroxides formed in such a manner contain half of the annexed oxygen in a weakly bonded, "active" state, and therefore easily lose this to other substances.

Thus, slow oxidation can be represented schematically as a two-stage process:

(1) $A + O_2 = AO_2$

(2) $AO_2 + A = 2AO$.

Having advanced a correct presentation of the influence of the oxidized substance on oxygen, Bach could not explain the nature of this influence. An explanation became possible only after the development of the theory of free organic radicals. It was subsequently demonstrated that during oxidation the free valence of such a radical influences the oxygen molecule. With this correction, Bach's views are at the base of the modern chain theory of oxidation processes.

Bach subsequently extended the peroxide theory to processes of biological oxidation, focusing attention on the following facts: oxidation processes in organisms proceed with great intensity; the organic substances that serve as food or enter into the composition of the body are practically indifferent to free oxygen; and the oxygen that is separated from the blood's oxyhemoglobin is found in a passive state. According to Bach, these facts attested to the existence in organisms of the sources—biological catalysts—of the activation of oxygen: enzymes (whose existence was considered far from indisputable at the time) and unsaturated organic compounds. In order successfully to apply the peroxide theory in the explanation of biological oxidation, it was necessary to prove not only the presence of peroxides in living cells but also the existence of mechanisms that would defend the cell from their harmful influence. Bach's most important work on biological oxidation during the Geneva period of his career was specifically directed to the solution of these problems. In 1902, with R. Chodat, he investigated the action of hydrogen peroxide on a cell, a new reaction for the assay of hydrogen peroxide in green plants (the system potassium bichromate-aniline-oxalic acid) that he had proposed. During the next two years he investigated the formation of peroxides in plants. According to the peroxide theory of biological oxidation proposed by Bach in 1904, the oxidation of biological substances proceeds according to the following schema:

$$A + O_2 \xrightarrow{\text{oxygenase}} AO_2$$

$$AO_2 + B \xrightarrow{\text{peroxidase}} AO + BO \quad \text{or} \quad A + BO_2.$$

The proposition that at the base of these processes are two consecutively coordinated enzymatic reactions is the most important statement in such an interpretation of biological oxidation. Such an approach was altogether new in the description of metabolic chemical processes. The representation introduced by Bach made note of new means for elucidating the general order of chemical processes in organisms. Although the peroxide mechanism has been confirmed only for the action of lipoxydase, and although it has been found that the more important oxidation-reduction processes are achieved with the aid of mechanisms other than peroxide mechanisms, Bach's theory played a positive role in the development of the concepts involved in biological oxidation by stimulating Otto Warburg's successful search for the enzymatic mechanisms of oxidation. Experimental investigations of the conditions under which many oxidation processes are achieved enabled Bach to draw conclusions that were subsequently used in various industrial processes.

Bach carried out fundamental investigations in industrial biochemistry after his return to the Soviet Union. These were inspired by work on the reconstruction and development of the Soviet food industry in the 1920's and 1930's. Many recommendations for the improvement of the baking of bread and for the drying and preservation of grain and flour were worked out with Bach's help. Original investigations aimed at the creation of new methods for the processing of tea, wine, tobacco, and raw-vitamin materials (tea leaves, pine needles, etc.) were carried out. The methods of industrial biochemistry developed by Bach are widely used in many countries.

BIBLIOGRAPHY

I. ORIGINAL WORKS. Articles by Bach are "O roli perekisej v protsessakh medlennogo okislenija" ("On the Role of Peroxides in the Process of Slow Oxidation"), in *Zhurnal Russkago fiziko-khimicheskago obshchestva*, **29**, no. 2 (1897), 375; "Untersuchungen über die Rolle der Peroxyde in der Chemie der lebenden Zelle. I. Ueber das Verhalten der lebenden Zelle gegen Hydroperoxyde," in *Berichte der Deutschen chemischen Gesellschaft*, **35** (1902), 1275, with R. Chodat; and "Khimizm dykhatel'nykh protsessov" ("The Chemical Mechanism of Respiratory Processes"), in *Zhurnal Russkago fiziko-khimicheskago obshchestva*, **44**, no. 2 (1912), 1–74. His *Sobranie trudov po khimii i biokhimii* ("A Collection of Works on Chemistry and Biochemistry"; Moscow, 1950), A. I. Oparin and A. N. Frumkin, eds., includes a detailed bibliography of his works.

II. SECONDARY LITERATURE. Works on Bach are *Aleksei Nikolaevich Bach,* in the series Materialy k bibliografii uchenykh SSSR ("Materials Toward the Bibliography of Scientists of the U.S.S.R."), A. N. Nesmejanov, ed. (Moscow-Leningrad, 1946); L. A. Bach and A. I. Oparin, *Aleksei Nikolaevich Bach. Biograficheskij ocherk* ("Aleksei Nikolaevich Bach. Biographical Essay"; Moscow, 1957); B. E. Bykhovsky, *Razvitie biologii v SSSR* ("The Development of Biology in the U.S.S.R."; Moscow, 1957); J. I. Gerassimov, ed., *Razvitie fizicheskoj khimii v SSSR* ("The Development of Physical Chemistry in the U.S.S.R."; Moscow, 1967); L. A. Orbeli, ed., *Trudy soveshchanija, posvjashchennoogo 50-letiju perekisnoj teorii medlennogo okislenija i roli Bacha v razvitii otechestvennoj biokhimii* ("Works of the Conference Dedicated to the Fiftieth Anniversary of the Peroxide Theory of Slow Oxidation and to Bach's Role in the Development of National Biochemistry"; Moscow-Leningrad, 1946); and "Trudy konferentsii, posvjashchennoj 40-letiju perekisnoj teorii Bacha-Englera" ("Works of the Conference Dedicated to the Fortieth Anniversary of the Bach-Engler Peroxide Theory"), in M. B. Neyman, ed., *Problemy kinetiki i kataliza* ("Problems of Kinetics and Catalysis"), IV (1940).

ALEKSEI NIKOLAEVICH SHAMIN

BACHE, ALEXANDER DALLAS (*b.* Philadelphia, Pennsylvania, 19 July 1806; *d.* Newport, Rhode Island, 17 February 1867), *physics.*

Bache was a great-grandson of Benjamin Franklin and related to leading families of Philadelphia, facts not insignificant in his future career. After graduating from West Point at the head of his class in 1825, he served for two years in the Corps of Engineers before accepting a professorship of natural philosophy and chemistry at the University of Pennsylvania, a position he held until his resignation in 1836 to organize Girard College. Upon returning from a two-year sojourn in Europe (1836–1838), where he studied primary and secondary education, Bache wrote a report on his findings for Girard College that exerted considerable influence on the development of education in the United States, by proposing adoption, in American high schools, of features from the German Gymnasium and the French *lycée* (1839). He put his views into practice by organizing Central High School of Philadelphia. In 1842 Bache returned to the University of Pennsylvania, but left for Washington at the end of 1843 to succeed F. R. Hassler as head of the Coast Survey, a position he held for the rest of his life.

In Philadelphia, Bache's scientific career followed many of the conventional paths for that period. He dabbled in chemical analysis and experimented on the effects of color on the radiation and absorption of heat. Like many of his contemporaries, he tried his hand at electromagnetism and astronomy, but with no particular success, his dispute with Denison Olmsted on meteoric showers being a notably poor showing. He was, however, outstanding in assuming leading roles in the affairs of both the American Philosophical Society and the Franklin Institute.

At the latter he directed a significant investigation of the explosion of steam boilers for the federal government (*Journal of the Franklin Institute,* **17,** 1836). Not only was this notable for experimental virtuosity; it was also one of the first deliberate uses of science by the government for the solution of a practical problem. It also established a pattern for Bache's subsequent career and a precedent for the later development of federal policy toward science and technology.

Increasingly during the Philadelphia period, Bache became involved in studies of the physics of the earth, particularly terrestrial magnetism and meteorology. After returning from Europe, where he had made observations of declination and inclination for comparison with American readings, he attempted to establish an American system that would fit into Sir Edward Sabine's world network of magnetic observatories. All that resulted, however, was an observatory at Girard College, the first of its kind in the United States. Perhaps the most interesting work in this vein was Bache's unsuccessful attempt with Humphrey Lloyd to determine longitude by simultaneous magnetic observations (*Proceedings, Royal Irish Academy,* **1,** 1839).

When Bache assumed direction of the Coast Survey, it was a small, insecurely established body with high scientific standards. In less than two decades it became entrenched, the largest employer of physical scientists in the United States, and active in many scientific fields. First-order triangulation was expanded along the Atlantic, Gulf, and Pacific coasts. Under Bache's direction, Sears Walker and W. C. Bond developed the use of telegraphy in the determination of longitude. Bache and the Survey supported astronomical research, including study of the solar eclipses of 26 May 1854 and 18 July 1860. Survey vessels amassed the most extensive series of observations of

the Gulf Stream up to that time. Continuing and broadening Hassler's tidal observations, Bache became embroiled in a dispute with Whewell in 1851, when the Survey's findings deviated from the latter's theory. Using deflections on tide staffs on the Pacific Coast, Bache studied waves from an earthquake in Japan (*American Journal of Science,* **21,** 1855), work that foreshadowed the Survey's later work in seismology. Bache also succeeded Hassler as head of the Office of Weights and Measures, the predecessor of the National Bureau of Standards. During all this time, while he was successfully administering a large research program, Bache was able to spend several months in the field with a survey party and to continue doing his own investigations.

Bache is clearly one of the founders of the scientific community in the United States. His administration of the Coast Survey established a model for large-scale scientific organization that was followed either implicitly or explicitly by later groups. Bache and his close friend Joseph Henry established many of the patterns of interaction of science and the federal government. Perhaps most significant of all was the way pure science, in Bache's scheme of things, became the necessary antecedent and companion of applied science, rather than purely a philosophical endeavor. Around him gathered a small, changing group of followers, the *Lazzaroni,* or scientific beggars. Bache clearly had their admiration, but what they specifically wanted is hazy in many respects. The group included nonscientists; some of the scientists, such as Dana and Henry, later split with Bache. The *Lazzaroni* wanted to form a true professional scientific community to reform higher education so that more young people would be interested in science, and to find administrative means of increasing governmental support of science. It was Bache's misfortune that his warm admirers in Cambridge—including Louis Agassiz, B. A. Gould, and Benjamin Peirce—lacked his diplomatic talents, thus embroiling the *Lazzaroni* "program" in irrelevant personal squabbles.

The culmination of Bache's influence and of the outlook he represented came during the Civil War. Because of his knowledge of the coasts, in 1861 he served with the informal Commission on Conference planning the naval campaign against the Confederacy. As vice-president of the U.S. Sanitary Commission, Bache became involved in a notable medical and welfare program. A member of the Permanent Commission in 1863–1864, Bache advised the navy on technical matters. Linked to the Permanent Commission was the formation of the National Academy of Sciences in 1863, with Bache as its first president. The Academy was the concrete culmination of the attitudes he enunciated in his 1851 presidential address to the American Association for the Advancement of Science.

Bache was incapacited by a stroke early in the summer of 1864. After Bache's death, Henry kept the Academy alive largely because his friend had left his estate to it. The Bache Fund was a small but important source of support for research in the United States before 1900. The Michelson-Morley experiment, for example, was conducted with its aid.

BIBLIOGRAPHY

I. ORIGINAL WORKS. Joseph Henry's memoir of Bache in *Biographical Memoirs of the National Academy of Sciences,* I (1869), has a usable bibliography of Bache's writings. The best single source of information on his career is the *Annual Reports of the U.S. Coast Survey* (1844–1866). For his pre-Washington experiences, see *Journal of the Franklin Institute* and *Transactions of the American Philosophical Society.*

An extensive body of manuscripts from Bache's tenure as head of the Coast Survey is preserved in the U.S. National Archives. They are described in Nathan Reingold, *Records of the Coast and Geodetic Survey* (Washington, D.C., 1958), Preliminary Inventory No. 105 of the National Archives. A discussion of their significance is in Reingold's "Research Possibilities in the U.S. Coast and Geodetic Survey Records," in *Archives internationales d'histoire des sciences,* **11** (Oct.-Dec. 1958), 337–346. These records include a considerable amount of private correspondence. Substantial portions of Bache's private papers are also found in the Rhees Collection of the Huntington Library in San Marino, Calif., the Smithsonian Archives, and the Library of Congress. Other Bache letters are in the American Philosophical Society, the Franklin Institute, and the Benjamin Peirce Papers at Harvard. For hostile comments on Bache's work by a scientific amateur, see the John Warner Papers at the American Philosophical Society. For hostile comments of a professional scientist, see the letters of C. H. F. Peters in the Harvard Observatory records.

II. SECONDARY LITERATURE. The most recent biography of Bache, M. M. Odgers, *Alexander Dallas Bache, Scientist and Educator, 1806–1867* (Philadelphia, 1947) is a slight advance over the necrologies published by friends shortly after Bache's death. It suffers, however, from the absence of work in many of the major manuscript sources and a nearly total lack of insight into or knowledge of Bache's scientific environment. *Proceedings of the American Philosophical Society,* **84,** no. 2 (1941), "Commemoration of the Life and Work of Alexander Dallas Bache and Symposium on Geomagnetism," is still quite useful for an introduction to Bache's career. Two recent publications discuss the steam boiler investigations: John G. Burke, "Bursting Boilers and the Federal Power," in *Technology and Culture,* **7** (Winter 1966), 1–23; and Bruce Sinclair, *Early Research at the Franklin Institute, the Investigation Into the Causes of*

Steam Boiler Explosions, 1830–1837 (Philadelphia, 1966). For Bache's career in more general frames of reference, see Nathan Reingold, *Science in Nineteenth Century America, a Documentary History* (New York, 1964), pp. 127–161, 200–225; and A. H. Dupree, *Science in the Federal Government . . .* (Cambridge, Mass., 1957), pp. 216–232, 316–336. The activities of the *Lazzaroni* are treated in E. Lurie, *Louis Agassiz, a Life in Science* (Chicago, 1960), pp. 166–211, 303–350; and A. H. Dupree, *Asa Gray* (Cambridge, Mass., 1959).

NATHAN REINGOLD

BACHELARD, GASTON (*b*. Bar-sur-Aube, France, 27 June 1884; *d*. Paris, France, 16 October 1962), *philosophy of science, epistemology.*

Bachelard became a philosopher late in life. He had previously taught physics and chemistry in the *collège* of his native city. His knowledge of physics later enabled him to determine the epistemological change brought about by modern science and, particularly, to gauge the growing distance between it and classical physics, which had suddenly become only relative.

As early as 1928, in the *Essai sur la connaissance approchée,* Bachelard penetrated to the heart of the new mathematical physics and began to simplify its methods of measuring (calculus of errors), experimenting, and generalizing. A complementary study, *Étude sur l'évolution d'un problème de physique* (1928), was designed to show how thermodynamics was both established by and liberated from its early, very poor intuitions (such as that a metal bar heated at one end will become longer). His study of conductibility in anisotropic media, and the mathematical theory of Poisson and Fourier, facilitated the integration of thermodynamics with mechanics, especially since heat was not linked to an isolated molecule but was determined within a rather large volume (the quantitative view).

As early as 1930 Bachelard's work branched out in several directions. One was pedagogical, concerned with how to arouse the mind and modernize it so that it could participate in the formulation of scientific concepts. This led to *La formation de l'esprit scientifique* (1938), in which Bachelard examines mental resistances and prejudices anthropologically and methodologically, in order to expose them. His original objective was to apply Freud's psychoanalytic method to epistemology and to science itself, and to draw up a highly systematic list of complexes that paralyze intelligence.

Bachelard's work was also historical: he became the historian of scientific changes. He did not give a chronological description of the evolutionary stages of thought as it grappled with reality, but clarified its tensions and expressed its breakdowns. These tensions and breakdowns occurred because modern physics attacked what had previously been considered basic principles.

A vast prescientific or, as it were, prehistoric universe underlies the period of concentrated scientific discovery—the revolution that substituted the surrationalism of the twentieth century for the rationalism of the nineteenth. If this rationalism conditions our view of the science of the eighteenth and, *a fortiori,* the preceding centuries, it by no means invalidates it. Bachelard used earlier, naive physics as a subject for a new study of elemental psychology. Alchemy represented for him the projection of the soul's desires, the magic lantern that enlarged dreams. From this belief came his celebrated analyses of the classical four elements and of dreams, space, time, and imagination.

Bachelard was never satisfied merely to point out obstructive archaisms. He went further, introducing the reader to the most abstract categories of contemporary science. From generalities, he moved on to make specialized analyses on the point, the corpuscle, movement, space, and the simultaneous. Bachelard also simplified the dialectic contained in apparatus that embodied a theory: the Wilson cloud chamber, the spectroscope, and the particle accelerator. "Phenomenotechnology" replaced instruments based on calculating systems; probabilism replaced realism; the discursive replaced the intuitive.

Bachelard attempted to renew the traditional questions of philosophy and physical reality. He sought to base metaphysics upon the new physics and to resume the work of Descartes, Newton, and Leibniz.

All these avenues of endeavor cut across each other. With Bachelard the past became the poetry of the world; classical science, a basis for exploration and enlargement; and modern science, a phenomenon that must constantly be reviewed.

BIBLIOGRAPHY

I. ORIGINAL WORKS. Bachelard's writings are *Essai sur la connaissance approchée* (Paris, 1928); *Étude sur l'évolution d'un problème de physique: La propagation thermique dans les solides* (Paris, 1928); *La valeur inductive de la relativité* (Paris, 1929); *Le pluralisme cohérent de la chimie moderne* (Paris, 1932); *Le nouvel esprit scientifique* (Paris, 1934); *Les intuitions atomistiques* (Paris, 1935); *L'intuition de l'instant* (Paris, 1935); *La dialectique de la durée* (Paris, 1936); *L'expérience de l'espace dans la physique contemporaine* (Paris, 1937); *La formation de l'esprit scientifique. Contribution à une psychanalyse de la connaissance objective* (Paris, 1938); *La psychanalyse du feu* (Paris, 1938); *La philosophie du non* (Paris, 1940); *Lautréamont* (Paris, 1940); *L'eau et les rêves. Essai sur l'imagination de la matière* (Paris, 1942); *L'air et les songes. Essai sur l'imagination du mouvement* (Paris, 1943); *La terre et les rêveries de la volonté. Essai sur l'imagination des forces* (Paris, 1948); *La terre et les rêveries du repos. Essai sur l'imagination de l'intimité* (Paris, 1948); *Le rationalisme appliqué* (Paris, 1949); *L'activité rationaliste de la physique contemporaine* (Paris, 1951); *Le materialisme rationnel* (Paris, 1953); *La poétique de l'espace* (Paris, 1957); *La flamme d'une chandelle* (Paris, 1961); and *La poétique de la rêverie* (Paris, 1961).

II. SECONDARY LITERATURE. Three essential studies on Bachelard's epistemology are in Vrin, ed., *Problèmes d'histoire et de philosophie des sciences* (Paris, 1968); Georges Canguilhem, "L'histoire des sciences dans l'oeuvre epistémologique de Gaston Bachelard," originally in *Annales de l'Université de Paris* (1963); "Gaston Bachelard et les philosophes," originally in *Sciences* (March 1963); and "Dialectique et philosophie du non chez Gaston Bachelard," originally in *Revue internationale de philosophie* (1963).

See also François Dagognet, *Gaston Bachelard* (Paris, 1965); *Hommage à Gaston Bachelard* (Paris, 1957), consisting mainly of articles by Georges Canguilhem and Jean Hyppolite; Jean Hyppolite, "L'épistémologie de Gaston Bachelard," in *Revue d'histoire des sciences* (January 1964); R. Martin, "Dialectique et esprit scientifique chez Gaston Bachelard," in *Les études philosophiques* (October 1963); and Pierre Quillet, *Bachelard* (Paris, 1964).

F. DAGOGNET

BACHELIER, LOUIS (*b.* Le Havre, France, 11 March 1870; *d.* Saint-Servan-sur-Mer, Ille-et-Villaine, France, 28 April 1946), *mathematics.*

Bachelier obtained the bachelor of sciences degree in 1898, and two years later he defended his doctoral dissertation on the theory of speculation. Encouraged by Henri Poincaré, he published three memoirs on probability: "Théorie mathématique des jeux" (1901), "Probabilités à plusieurs variables" (1910), and "Probabilités cinématiques et dynamiques" (1913). After being named lecturer at Besançon in 1919, he taught at Dijon and Rennes before returning to Besançon as professor from 1927 to 1937, when he retired.

Under the name "théorie de la spéculation" Bachelier introduced continuity into problems of probability. Making time the variable, he considered the movements of probabilities and chains of probabilities, then applied these ideas to the fluctuations of market rates and to the propagation of light and radiance. The relation between haphazard movement and diffusion was the first attempt at a mathematical theory of Brownian movement, a classic theory known today as the Einstein–Wiener theory; Wiener's rigorous study was made in 1928. Bachelier was the first to examine the stochastic methods of the Markovian type, on which A. N. Kolmogorov's theory is based.

Yet lack of clarity and precision, certain considerations of doubtful interest, and some errors in definition explain why, in spite of their originality, his studies exerted no real scientific influence.

Bachelier participated in the diffusion of probabilistic thought through his articles "La périodicité du hasard" and "Quelques curiosités paradoxales du calcul des probabilités" and the book *Le jeu, la chance et le hasard.*

BIBLIOGRAPHY

Bachelier's writings include "Théorie de la spéculation," in *Annales de l'École normale supérieure,* 3rd ser., **17** (1900), 21–86; "Théorie mathématique des jeux," *ibid.,* **18** (1901), 143–210; "Théorie des probabilités continues," in *Journal de mathématiques pures et appliquées,* 6th ser., **2,** pt. 3 (1906), 259–327; "Probabilités à plusieurs variables," in *Annales de l'École normale supérieure,* 3rd ser., **27** (1910), 340–360; "Mouvement d'un point ou d'un système soumis à l'action de forces dépendant du hasard," in *Comptes rendus de l'Académie des sciences,* **151** (1910), 852–855; *Calcul des probabilités* (Paris, 1912); "Probabilités cinématiques et dynamiques," in *Annales de l'École normale supérieure,* 3rd ser., **30** (1913), 77–119; *Le jeu, la chance et le hasard* (Paris, 1924); *Les lois du grand nombre du calcul des probabilités* (Paris, 1937); *La spéculation et le calcul des probabilités* (Paris, 1938); and *Les nouvelles méthodes du calcul des probabilités* (Paris, 1939).

LUCIENNE FÉLIX

BACHET DE MÉZIRIAC, CLAUDE-GASPAR

(*b.* Bourg-en-Bresse, France, 9 October 1581; *d.* Bourg-en-Bresse, 26 February 1638), *mathematics.*

One of the ablest men of the seventeenth century, Bachet came from an ancient and noble family. His grandfather, Pierre Bachet, seigneur de Meyzériat, was counselor to King Henry II. His father was the honorable Jean Bachet, appeals judge of Bresse and counselor to the duke of Savoy; his mother was the noblewoman Marie de Chavanes. Orphaned at the age of six, the precocious Claude-Gaspar received his early education in a house of the Jesuit order that belonged to the duchy of Savoy. Presumably he studied in Padua as a young man, and he may have taught in a Jesuit school in Milan or Como. Bachet also spent a few years in Paris and in Rome, where, with his friend Claude Vaugelas, he composed a great deal of Italian verse. He was a prolific reader of poetry, history, commentary, scholarship, and mathematics.

In his fortieth year Bachet married Philiberte de Chabeu, by whom he had seven children. He suffered greatly from rheumatism and gout; when the Académie Française was founded in 1634, he was too ill to attend the inaugural ceremony. He was made a member of the Académie in the following year. His early literary works, humanist in outlook, consisted of poems in Latin, French, and Italian. Between 1614 and 1628 he published a Latin epistle from the Virgin Mary to her Son, canticles, brief sacred and profane Latin poems, translations of psalms, and a metrical translation of seven of Ovid's *Epistulae heroïdum.* He also published an anthology of French poetry, *Délices,* and the *Epistles of Ovid* (1626); the latter assured his reputation as a mythologist.

Bachet claims our attention today, however, chiefly for his contributions to the theory of numbers and to the field of mathematical recreations, in which he was one of the earliest pioneers. The two mathematical works for which he is remembered are his first edition of the Greek text of Diophantus of Alexandria's *Arithmetica,* accompanied by prolix commentary in Latin (1621), and his *Problemes plaisans et delectables qui se font par les nombres* (1612).

Diophantus had anticipated the advent of algebra and the theory of numbers. His work, which was known to the Arabs, was not appreciated until it was rediscovered in Europe during the latter part of the sixteenth century. Prior to Bachet's translation, only a few scholars had written on the work of Diophantus: Maximus Planudes, who gave an incomplete commentary on the first two books of the *Arithmetica* (*ca.* 1300); Raphael Bombelli, who embodied all of the problems of the first four books in his *Algebra* (1572); Wilhelm Holzmann, better known as Xylander, who gave a complete Latin translation (1575); and Simon Stevin, who gave a French translation of the first four books (1585). Bachet's translation, *Diophanti Alexandrini Arithmeticorum libri sex,* was based largely on the writings of Bombelli and Xylander, particularly the latter, although he admitted this with reluctance. Indeed, it is the opinion of T. L. Heath that although Bachet generally has been regarded as the only writer to interpret the contributions of Diophantus effectively, perhaps as much—if not more—of the credit is due to Xylander.

It is noteworthy that Bachet struggled with this work while suffering from a severe fever. He asserted that he corrected many errors in Xylander's version; filled in numerous omissions, such as proofs of porisms and abstruse theorems that Diophantus merely mentioned; and clarified much of the exposition. He apparently added few original contributions to number theory or Diophantine analysis, however, except for a generalization of the solution of the system $ax + v = u^2$, $cx + d = w^2$. Yet despite its imperfections, Bachet's work is commendable for being the first and only edition of the Greek text of Diophantus. It was subsequently reprinted, with the addition of Fermat's notes, in 1670; and while Fermat's notes are significant, the Greek text is inferior to that of the first edition.

Bachet's penchant for arithmetical rather than geometric problems is also obvious in the contents of his *Problemes plaisans et delectables*. These problems fall into several readily recognizable categories. The most elementary are those mildly amusing but mathematically unimportant parlor tricks of finding a number selected by someone, provided the results of certain operations performed on the number are revealed. Variations include problems involving two or three numbers, or two persons; problems depending upon the scale of notation; and tricks with a series of numbered objects, such as watch-dial puzzles and card tricks—many of these have appeared ever since in most collections of mathematical recreations. Somewhat more sophisticated is the famous problem of the Christians and the Turks, which had previously been solved by Tartaglia. (In a storm, a ship carrying fifteen Christians and fifteen Turks as passengers could be saved only by throwing half the passengers into the sea. The passengers were to be placed in a circle, and every ninth man, beginning at a certain point, was to be cast overboard. How should they be arranged so that all the Christians would be saved? Answer: CCCCTTTTTCCTCCCTCTTCCTTTCTTCCT.)

Of greater mathematical significance was Bachet's problem of the weights: to determine the least number of weights that would make possible the weighing of any integral number of pounds from one pound to forty pounds, inclusive. Bachet gave two solutions: the series of weights 1, 2, 4, 8, 16, 32; and the series 1, 3, 9, 27—depending upon whether the weights may be placed in only one scale pan or in each of the two scale pans. Last, there is the celebrated prototype of ferrying problems or difficult crossings, the problem of the three jealous husbands and their wives who wish to cross a river in a boat that can hold no more than two persons, in such a manner as never to leave a woman in the company of a man unless her husband is also present. Eleven crossings are required, but Bachet gave a solution that asserts "Il faut qu'ils passent en six fois en cette sorte." The analogous problem with four married couples cannot be solved; Bachet stated this fact without proof. It should also be noted that Bachet gave a method for constructing magic squares which is essentially that of Moschopulous (*ca.* 1300), although Bachet appears to have discovered it independently.

BIBLIOGRAPHY

I. ORIGINAL WORKS. Bachet's translation of Diophantus' *Arithmetica* is *Diophanti Alexandrini Arithmeticorum libri sex, et de numeris multangulis liber unus. Nunc primum Graecè et Latinè editi, atque absolutissimis commentariis illustrati* (Paris, 1621); it was reprinted with the subtitle *Cum commentariis C. G. Bacheti V. C. & observationibus D. P. de Fermat senatoris Tolosani accessit doctrinae analyticae inventum novum, collectum ex variis D. de Fermat epistolis* (Toulouse, 1670). His other major work is *Problemes plaisans et delectables, qui se font par les nombres; Partie recueillis de diuers autheurs, & inuentez de nouueau auec leur demonstration. Tres-utiles pour toutes sorte de personnes curieuses, qui se seruent d'arithmetique* (Lyons, 1612). It was reprinted in several editions: *2ᵉ édition, revue, corrigée, et augmentée de plusieurs propositions, et de plusieurs problems, par le meme autheur* (Lyons, 1624; reprinted 1876); *3ᵉ édition, revue, simplifiée, et augmentée par A. Labosne* (Paris, 1874; abridged version, 1905); and *Cinquième édition, revue, simplifiée et augmentée par A. Labosne. Nouveau tirage augmenté d'un avant-propos par J. Itard* (Paris, 1959), a paperback edition.

II. SECONDARY LITERATURE. Works dealing with Bachet are W. W. R. Ball and H. S. M. Coxeter, *Mathematical Recreations and Essays* (London, 1942), pp. 2–18, 28, 30, 33, 50, 116, 313, 316; Pierre Bayle, *Dictionnaire historique et critique* (Amsterdam, 1734), pp. 553–556; Moritz Cantor, *Vorlesungen über die Geschichte der Mathematik* (Leipzig, 1913), II, 767–780; C.-G. Collet and Jean Itard, "Un mathématicien humaniste: Claude-Gaspar Bachet de Méziriac (1581–1638)," in *Revue d'histoire des sciences*, **1** (1947), 26–50; and T. L. Heath, *Diophantos of Alexandria; A Study in the History of Greek Algebra* (Cambridge, 1885), pp. 49–54.

WILLIAM SCHAAF

BACHMANN, AUGUSTUS QUIRINUS, also known as **Augustus Quirinus Rivinus** (*b.* Leipzig, Germany, 9 December 1652; *d.* Leipzig, 30 December 1723), *botany.*

Bachmann was a son of the physician Andreas Bachmann (1600–1656), professor of poetry and then of physiology in the University of Leipzig. The father had already adopted the latinized form of his family name, and the son consistently used it. Young Rivinus studied humanities and medicine in Leipzig but took his degree at the then flourishing University of Helmstedt in 1676. He settled in his native town as a medical practitioner and became a lecturer in medicine in the University of Leipzig in 1677. He was appointed to the chair of physiology and botany in 1691; became professor of pathology in 1701; and was made professor of therapeutics and dean perpetual in 1719. His last years were clouded by failing vision and urolithiasis, and he died of what was

Rivinus' System of Plant Classification (1690)

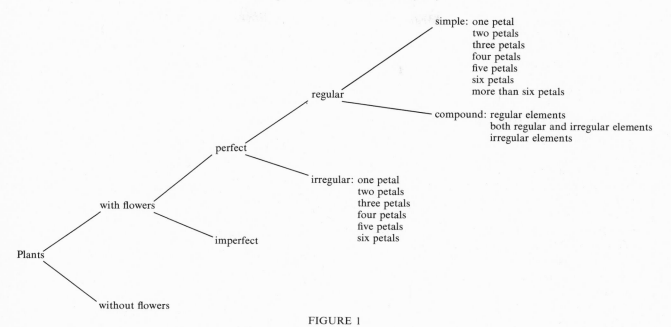

FIGURE 1

diagnosed as a pleurisy. Rivinus was married four times and had one son, Johannes Augustus Rivinus (1692–1725), who also became a physician.

Rivinus wrote many medical dissertations, among them *De dyspepsia* (1678), in which he describes the excretory ducts of the sublingual salivary glands. He also tried to remove from the *materia medica* of his time such squalid substances as feces and urine, as well as all superstitious, counterfeit, or otherwise useless drugs.

Rivinus' main scientific interest, however, was botany, particularly botanical taxonomy. In 1690 he published *Introductio generalis in rem herbariam,* with 125 tables of "plants with irregular flowers of one petal" (*Labiatae* and others). Atlases of "irregular" flowers of four petals (mostly *Leguminosae,* 121 tables) and of five petals (mostly *Umbelliferae,* 139 tables) followed in 1691 and in 1699, respectively. Rivinus published these tables at his own expense; and it is therefore no wonder that he could not afford to bring out the last volume he had prepared, which dealt with "irregular" flowers of six petals (orchids). He anticipated Tournefort and Linnaeus in devising an artificial system of plant classification. His system comprised eighteen classes (*ordines*) based on the number of petals of a flower and on its regularity or irregularity.

Rivinus' standards of regularity were extremely high. For instance, he included all the *Umbelliferae* in the class of *irregulares pentapetalae* because they have not only one style exactly in the center of the flower but also two eccentric ones. His attempt to base classification on a single part of a plant led Rivinus into a controversy with the famous English naturalist John Ray, who held the sound view that the whole plant must be considered.

Since he emphasized the need for short plant names of no more than two words, Rivinus was a pioneer of modern binomial nomenclature.

BIBLIOGRAPHY

I. ORIGINAL WORKS. Among Rivinus' works are *De dyspepsia* (Leipzig, 1678); *Introductio generalis in rem herbariam* and *Ordo plantarum, quae sunt flore irregulari monopetalo* (Leipzig, 1690), *Introductio* also published separately (Leipzig, 1696, 1720); *Ordo plantarum, quae sunt flore irregulari tetrapetalo* (Leipzig, 1691); *Epistola botanica ad Johannem Raium* (Leipzig, 1694; repr. London, 1696, with Ray's answer); *Ordo plantarum quae sunt flore irregulari pentapetalo* (Leipzig, 1699); and *De medicamentorum officinalium censura* (Leipzig, 1701, 1707), repr. with forty-six other papers in *Dissertationes medicae, diversis temporibus habitae, nunc vero in unum fasciculum collectae* (Leipzig, 1710).

Universal-Lexicon (see below) gives a complete list of Rivinus' writings, and Jourdan (see below) lists his more important medical publications.

II. SECONDARY LITERATURE. Articles on Rivinus are L.-M. Dupetit-Thouars, in *Biographie universelle ancienne et moderne,* new ed., XXXVI (*ca.* 1860), 90–94, which gives a very careful account of Rivinus' botanical work; A. von Haller, in *Bibliotheca botanica,* I (Zurich, 1771), 551, para.

651; C. G. Jöcher, in *Allgemeines Gelehrten-Lexicon,* III (Leipzig, 1751; repr. Hildesheim, 1961); A.-J.-L. Jourdan, in *Dictionnaire des sciences médicales—Biographie médicale,* VIII (1825); and Zedler's *Universal-Lexicon,* XXXI (Leipzig-Halle, 1742). See also C. Rabl, *Geschichte der Anatomie an der Universität Leipzig* (Leipzig, 1909).

HULDRYCH M. KOELBING

BACHMANN, PAUL GUSTAV HEINRICH (*b.* Berlin, Germany, 22 June 1837; *d.* Weimar, Germany, 31 March 1920), *mathematics.*

Bachmann's father was pastor at the Jacobi Kirche, and from his home the young Paul inherited a pious Lutheran view of life, coupled with modesty and a great interest in music. During his early years in the Gymnasium he had some trouble with his mathematical studies, but his talent was discovered by the excellent teacher Karl Schellbach. After a stay in Switzerland for his health, presumably to recover from tuberculosis, Bachmann studied mathematics at the University of Berlin until he transferred to Göttingen in 1856 to attend Dirichlet's lectures. Here he became a close friend of Dedekind, who was a fellow student.

From 1856 on, Bachmann's interests were centered almost exclusively upon number theory. He completed his studies in Berlin, where in 1862 he received his doctorate under the guidance of Ernst Kummer for a thesis on group theory. Two years later he completed his habilitation in Breslau with a paper on complex units, a subject inspired by Dirichlet. After some years as extraordinary professor in Breslau, Bachmann was appointed to a professorship in Münster.

Around 1890 Bachmann divorced his wife and resigned his professorship. With his second wife he settled in Weimar, where he combined his mathematical writing with composing, playing the piano, and serving as music critic for various newspapers. His main project, however, was a complete survey of the state of number theory, *Zahlentheorie. Versuch einer Gesamtdarstellung dieser Wissenschaft in ihren Hauptteilen* (1892–1923). It includes not only a review of known results but also an evaluation of the various methods of proof and approach, labors for which his close association with Dirichlet, Kummer, Dedekind, and Hensel made him ideally suited.

BIBLIOGRAPHY

Bachmann's writings are *Vorlesungen über die Natur der Irrationalzahlen* (Leipzig, 1892); *Zahlentheorie. Versuch einer Gesamtdarstellung dieser Wissenschaft in ihren Haupt-*

teilen, 5 vols. (Leipzig, 1892–1923); *Niedere Zahlentheorie,* 2 vols. (Leipzig, 1902–1910); and *Das Fermat-Problem in seiner bisherigan Entwicklung* (Leipzig, 1919), which has stimulated much research in this field.

OYSTEIN ORE

BACK, ERNST E. A. (*b.* Freiburg im Breisgau, Germany, 21 October 1881; *d.* Munich, Germany, 20 July 1959), *physics.*

Back, a scion of an old Alsatian family, entered the University of Strasbourg in 1902. There and at Berlin and Munich he studied law for four years. After passing his first state examination he served as a law clerk from 1906 to 1908. In 1908 Back abandoned the law and began to study experimental physics in Friedrich Paschen's institute at the University of Tübingen, which specialized in atomic spectroscopy. After completing his doctoral dissertation, *Zur Prestonschen Regel* (accepted February 1913, published 1921), Back stayed on at Tübingen as Paschen's assistant until the outbreak of World War I.

Preston's rule—that the magnetic splittings (Zeeman effects) of the lines in a given series (e.g., triplet diffuse series, doublet sharp series, and so forth) are identical—suffered many apparent exceptions. Clarification required better—above all, sharper—spectrographs, and Back's entire scientific career was devoted to meeting this need. His most important technical innovations were in the design and fabrication of the light source, because this was the component of the apparatus chiefly responsible for the failure of Zeeman-effect spectrographs to match the quality of those made in the absence of a magnetic field. By the late 1920's Back's unique vacuum arc, packed into the four millimeters between the pole pieces of Tübingen's electromagnet, included extraordinarily elaborate features: the electrode containing the element to be investigated was advanced (through a vacuum seal) by clockwork, while the other electrode, oscillated (also through a vacuum seal) by a motor, intermittently struck and extinguished the arc precisely on the axis of the field.

Although Back was able to rule out a number of apparent exceptions to Preston's rule, others were confirmed. The latter were usually very narrow or unresolved doublets or triplets showing "normal" Lorentz triplets in a magnetic field rather than the anticipated superposition of the anomalous splittings of the individual lines. It was Paschen who saw the solution to the difficulty: in sufficiently strong magnetic fields the several splitting patterns characteristic of the different types of series are transformed into the normal triplet (the Paschen-Back effect, 1912).

During the following years this effect was regarded by leading theorists as both one of the most important problems in atomic physics and one of the most promising sources of information on the subject of atomic structure.

A lieutenant in the reserve, Back was employed in the service corps (*Train*) on the Western Front from the outbreak of World War I until 1918. In 1918 he became head (*Leiter*) of the physical laboratory of Veifa-Werke, a manufacturer of electrical and X-ray equipment in Frankfurt am Main. Yet Back never abandoned his interest in the Zeeman effect, and in the spring of 1920 he returned to Tübingen as an assistant in Paschen's institute. There Back accumulated spectrographs of unparalleled quality, including the Zeeman effects of elements in whose spectra Miguel Catalán (working at the University of London) and Hilda Gieseler (working at Tübingen) were then discovering the existence of higher multiplicities (quartets, quintets, and so forth). When Alfred Landé arrived in Tübingen in October 1922, Back made this data available to him. Six months later, in consecutive articles in the *Zeitschrift für Physik*, Landé published the well-known formula expressing the "*g* factors" for all multiplicities as a function of the quantum numbers of the stationary state of the atom, and Back published the data upon which it was based.

In the spring of 1923 Back became *Privatdozent* at Tübingen. An appointment as extraordinary professor at the Landwirtschaftliche Hochschule in Hohenheim in 1926 (ordinary professor in 1929) provided financial security, but his scientific work was still carried on in the Tübingen institute. There, in the fall of 1926, he showed Samuel Goudsmit photographs of the bismuth spectrum that he had made over the years. Together they effected an analysis of the hyperfine structure of several lines, interpreting it as the result of the interaction of the total electronic angular momentum with an angular momentum that they attributed to the bismuth nucleus. Back's spectrographs (1927) fixed this nuclear angular momentum at $9/2 \cdot h/2\pi$. They thus provided the first firm evidence of a counterexample to an almost inescapable inference from the contemporary assumption that nuclei consisted of protons and electrons—namely, that a nucleus of even atomic number must have integral angular momentum (in units of $h/2\pi$).

In 1936 Back became professor at Tübingen; he retired in 1948. After the acceptance of electron spin (1926) the Zeeman effect lost most of its intrinsic importance, and in the 1930's other techniques vied with spectroscopy in determinations of angular momenta and magnetic moments. Moreover, after 1930 Back lacked the perceptive collaborators who had previously kept his very special talents directed toward significant problems in atomic physics.

BIBLIOGRAPHY

I. Original Works. A bibliography of Back's works is in J. C. Poggendorff, *Biographisch-literarisches Handwörterbuch zur Geschichte der exakten Naturwissenschaften* (Leipzig, 1926–1962), V, 47–48; VI, 100–101; VIIA, pt. 1, 74. Some twenty-five letters to Sommerfeld, Landé, and Goudsmit are listed in T. S. Kuhn, *et al., Sources for History of Quantum Physics. An Inventory and Report* (Philadelphia, 1967), p. 13.

II. Secondary Literature. For the Paschen-Back effect, see J. B. Spencer, "An Historical Investigation of the Zeeman Effect (1896–1913)," Ph.D. dissertation (University of Wisconsin, 1964). Back's work in the early 1920's is discussed in P. Forman, "Environment and Practice of Atomic Physics in Weimar Germany," Ph.D. dissertation (University of California, Berkeley, 1967), ch. 3; the later 1920's, in S. A. Goudsmit, "Pauli and Nuclear Spin," in *Physics Today* (June 1961), pp. 18–21. The author of the present article is preparing a fuller account of Back's work and career.

Paul Forman

BACKLUND, JÖNS OSKAR (*b.* Långhem, Sweden, 28 April 1846; *d.* Pulkovo, Russia, 29 August 1916), *astronomy.*

The main object of Backlund's research was comet 1786 I, known as Encke's comet or (in the U.S.S.R.) comet Encke-Backlund. Despite its forty-eight observed returns to perihelion between 1786 and 1967, this comet still puzzles astronomers: Backlund was the third man, following Johann Franz Encke and Friedrich Emil von Asten, to devote a major portion of his life to studying it, and the first to show that the long-term acceleration in its motion is subject to irregular changes, attributable to nongravitational forces.

Born in poverty, Backlund left school at an early age but nevertheless managed to prepare himself for entrance to the University of Uppsala, where he received a Ph.D. in 1875. After three years at the observatory of Dorpat, he went to Pulkovo Observatory, located about ten miles south of Petrograd (now Leningrad), to work under Otto von Struve. In 1886 he left Pulkovo for the Imperial Academy of Sciences of Petrograd, to which he had been elected in 1883, but returned in 1895 to serve for the rest of his life as director at Pulkovo. He also traveled throughout Europe and the United States to attend scientific meetings. He received worldwide recognition for his work on Encke's comet, including the award in 1909 of the Gold Medal of the Royal Astronomical Society.

Although Backlund favored Encke's idea that the comet's accelerated motion was due to a thin interplanetary medium, he nevertheless wanted to make sure no gravitational accelerations had been overlooked. He therefore decided to recalculate all planetary perturbations since 1819, the year Encke first obtained an orbit for the comet. By 1886 Backlund had got the financial backing necessary to carry out this tremendous task and had hired a number of people as computers.

The results, published between 1892 and 1898, were impressive, but the comet continued to depart from predictions based upon them in a way that Backlund was unable to explain, although he considered two different possibilities: first, a patchy stream of meteoroids lying along the inner part of the comet's orbit, then electrical forces related to the sunspot cycle. Until the advent of electronic computers the efforts of later workers served mainly to confirm Backlund's suspicion that no single explanation would suffice. Current thinking tends toward the idea, first suggested in 1836 by Friedrich Wilhelm Bessel, that loss of mass by the comet itself is responsible.

BIBLIOGRAPHY

I. ORIGINAL WORKS. Backlund's first paper on Encke's comet was written with A. Bonnsdorf and appeared as "Allmänna störingar, som af jorden förorsakas i Enckeska Kometens rörelse i en viss del af dess bana," in *Bihang till Kongliga Svenska Vetenskaps-Akademiens Handlingar,* 4th series, **3**, no. 16 (1876), 39 pp.; another early work on the subject was "Ueber die Berechnung der allgemeinen Jupiterstörung des Encke'schen Cometen," in *Vierteljahrsschrift der Astronomischen Gesellschaft* (Leipzig), **12** (1877), 313–323. His recalculation of the perturbations affecting Encke's comet between 1819 and 1891 was published in six parts in *Mémoires de l'Académie Impériale des Sciences de Saint-Pétersbourg* under the general title "Calculs et Recherches sur la Comète d'Encke": 7th series, **38**, no. 8 (1892); 7th series, **41**, nos. 3, 7 (1893); 7th series, **42**, nos. 7, 8 (1894); 8th series, **6**, no. 13 (1898). Three papers by Backlund summarize his attempts to reconcile the observed motion of Encke's comet with theory: "Sur la Masse de la Planète Mercure et sur l'Accélération du Mouvement Moyen de la Comète d'Encke," in *Bulletin astronomique* (Paris), **11** (1894), 473–485; "Vergleichung der Theorie des Encke'schen Cometen mit den Beobachtungen 1894–95," in *Mémoires de l'Académie Impériale des Sciences de Saint-Pétersbourg*, 8th series, **16**, no. 3 (1904); and "Encke's Comet, 1895–1908," in *Monthly Notices of the Royal Astronomical Society* (London), **70** (1910), 429–442.

Approximately fifty other papers that Backlund wrote between 1874 and 1900 are listed in the Royal Society of London's *Catalogue of Scientific Papers,* IX (London, 1891), 93, and XIII (Cambridge, 1914), 228–229. After 1900 he wrote about thirty more, mainly for various publications of the Pulkovo Observatory and of the St. Petersburg Academy. His last paper, "On Chandler's Period in the Latitude Variation," appeared posthumously in *Monthly Notices of the Royal Astronomical Society* (London), **77** (1917), 2–6.

II. SECONDARY LITERATURE. Further details about Backlund's life can be found in an obituary notice, signed H. H. T. [Herbert Hall Taylor], in *Proceedings of the Royal Society* (London), **94A** (1918), xx–xxiv. The citation delivered by Hugh Frank Newall when Backlund received the Gold Medal of the Royal Astronomical Society provides an assessment of Backlund's work by one of his contemporaries; it appeared in *Monthly Notices of the Royal Astronomical Society* (London), **69** (1909), 324–331. A retrospective evaluation, pointing out the shortcomings of Backlund's methods, appeared in a paper by S. G. Makover and N. A. Bokhan, of the Leningrad Institute of Theoretical Astronomy, entitled "The Motion of Comet Encke-Backlund during 1898–1911 and a New Determination of the Mass of Mercury," in *Soviet Physics-Doklady,* **5** (1961), 923–925.

For other recent material on Encke's comet, see: K. Wurm, "Die Kometen," in *Handbuch der Physik*, Vol. 52, ed. S. Flügge (Berlin, 1959), p. 476; F. L. Whipple, "On the Structure of the Cometary Nucleus," chap. 19 of *The Moon, Meteorites and Comets,* ed. B. M. Middlehurst and G. P. Kuiper (Chicago, 1963), pp. 648 and 659; and B. G. Marsden, "Comets and Nongravitational Forces," in *Astronomical Journal,* **73** (1968), 367–379.

SALLY H. DIEKE

BACON, FRANCIS (*b.* London, England, 22 January 1561; *d.* London, 9 April 1626), *philosophy of science.*

Bacon was the son of Sir Nicholas Bacon, lord keeper of the great seal, and Ann, daughter of Sir Anthony Cooke. He was educated at Trinity College, Cambridge, from 1573 to 1575, when he entered Gray's Inn; he became a barrister in 1582. Bacon's life was spent in court circles, in politics, and in the law; in religion he adhered to the middle road of the Church of England, neither authoritarian nor sectarian. In 1606 he married Alice Barnham. He was knighted on the accession of James I in 1603, became lord chancellor in 1618, and was made viscount St. Albans in 1621. Bacon was dismissed from the chancellorship in 1621 after being convicted of bribery, a strain under which his health broke down. He then lived in retirement near St. Albans, devoting his remaining years to natural philosophy.

Bacon's writings in history, law, politics, and morals are extensive; but his place in the history of science rests chiefly upon his natural philosophy, his philosophy of scientific method, his projects for the practical organization of science, and the influence of all these upon the science of the later seventeenth century. During and immediately following his lifetime his principal publications in these areas were *The Advancement of Learning* (1605), expanded and latinized as *De augmentis scientiarum* (1623); *De sapientia veterum* (1609); *Novum organum* (1620); and *Sylva sylvarum* and *New Atlantis* (1627). Many of his shorter works, some of them fragmentary and published posthumously, are of equal scientific and philosophical interest.

Although Bacon was a contemporary of William Gilbert, Galileo, Johannes Kepler, and William Harvey, he was curiously isolated from the scientific developments with which they were associated. His knowledge of and contribution to the natural sciences were almost entirely literary; and, indeed, it has been shown that much of the empirical material collected in his "histories" is not the result of his own firsthand observation, but is taken directly from literary sources. Furthermore, most of Bacon's comments on both his scientific contemporaries and his philosophical predecessors are critical. For example, he never accepted the Copernican "hypothesis," attacking both Ptolemy and Copernicus for producing mere "calculations and predictions" instead of "philosophy . . . what is found in nature herself, and is actually and really true."[1] On similar grounds he attacked the theory of "perspective" as not providing a proper theory of the nature of light because it never went further than geometry. Mathematics was, he thought, to be used as a tool in natural philosophy, not as an end, and he had no pretensions to mathematical learning. He was not unsympathetic to Gilbert's magnetic philosophy, but he criticized him for leaping too quickly to a single unifying principle without due regard for experiment.

Bacon's closest associations with contemporary science were with atomism and with the Renaissance tradition of natural magic. His views on atomism underwent considerable change during the period of his philosophical writings, from a sympathetic discussion of Democritus in *De sapientia veterum* and *De principiis atque originibus*,[2] to outright rejection of "the doctrine of atoms, which implies the hypothesis of a vacuum and that of the unchangeableness of matter (both false assumptions)" in *Novum organum*.[3] There were both philosophical and scientific reasons for this change of mind. Even in his earlier works, Bacon posed the fundamental dilemma of atomism: either

the atom is endowed with some of the qualities that are familiar to sense, such as "matter, form, dimension, place, resistance, appetite . . .,"[4] in which case it is difficult to justify taking these qualities rather than any other sensible qualities as primary; or the atom is wholly different from bodies apprehended by the senses, in which case it is difficult to see how we come to know anything about them. On the other hand, empirical phenomena of cohesion and continuity are impossible to understand in terms of inert atoms alone; and the existence of spirituous substances, even in space void of air, seems to cast doubt upon the existence of the absolute void demanded by atomism.

In any case, Bacon was never an orthodox atomist, for as early as *De sapientia veterum* he insisted that the atom has active powers other than mere impenetrability—it has "desire," "appetite," and "force that constitutes and fashions all things out of matter."[5] In *Novum organum* these qualities are ascribed to bodies in general. All bodies have powers to produce change in themselves and in other bodies; they have "perceptions" that, although distinct from the "sensations" of animals, nevertheless enable them to respond to other bodies, as iron does in the neighborhood of a magnet. That virtues seem thus to emanate from bodies through space is an argument for suspecting that there may be incorporeal substances: "Everything tangible that we are acquainted with contains an invisible and intangible spirit, which it wraps and clothes as with a garment." It "gives them [bodies] shape, produces limbs, assimilates, digests, ejects, organises and the like." It "feeds upon" tangible parts and "turns them into spirit."[6]

Commentators have seen in this dualism of tangible, inert matter and active, intangible spirits a legacy of Renaissance animism, and have tended to apologize for it as being out of harmony with Bacon's other, more progressive views. Indeed, in seventeenth-century writings and later, Bacon was most often listed with the revivers of the Democritan philosophy, in company with those to whom his "active spirits" might be an embarrassment. It would be a mistake, however, to suppose that Bacon necessarily thought of his view on spirits as opposed to a mechanical theory of nature. There are many passages in which he objects to his predecessors' purely verbal ontologies of spirits and describes his own view as essentially unitary: "this spirit, whereof I am speaking, is not a virtue, nor an energy, nor an actuality, nor any such idle matter, but a body thin and indivisible, and yet having place and dimension, and real . . . a rarefied body, akin to air, though greatly differing from it."[7] Both in the description of heat as a species of motion in *Novum organum* and in the discussion of transmission of light and sound in *Sylva sylvarum,*[8] Bacon showed his sympathy with explanations in terms of mechanical analogues.

Bacon's natural philosophy is indecisive, and also a good deal more subtle than that of his corpuscularian successors. It is not surprising, therefore, that it did not lead to any detailed theoretical developments (as did, for example, Descartes's) and had, in fact, little direct influence. It can be argued, however, that, unlike Descartes, Bacon was not attempting to reach theoretical conclusions but, rather, to lay the necessary foundations for his inductive method. To that method we now turn.

Bacon's method is foreshadowed in the early *Valerius terminus* (1603), but was not developed until the last few years of his life. *De augmentis scientiarum* and *Novum organum* are the first and second parts of his projected *Great Instauration,* and the applications of the method that were to have constituted four further parts reached only a fragmentary stage in the *Histories,* most of which were published posthumously.

In *De augmentis scientiarum,* which is concerned primarily with the classification of philosophy and the sciences, Bacon develops his influential view of the relation between science and theology. He distinguishes in traditional fashion between knowledge by divine revelation and knowledge by the senses, and divides the latter into natural theology, natural philosophy, and the sciences of man. Natural philosophy is independent of theology; but in a sense its end is also knowledge of God, for it seeks the "footprints of the Creator imprinted on his creatures."[9] Indeed, Bacon sees both speculative and practical science as religious duties, the first for the understanding of creation and the second for the practice of charity to men. We should not read back into Bacon's separation of science and theology any implication that theology is depreciated or superseded by science. Such a view was hardly influential until the Enlightenment, whereas seventeenth-century natural philosophers generally followed Bacon in claiming a religious function for their investigations; this was undoubtedly one important factor in the public success of the scientific movement.

Having placed his project within the complete framework of knowledge in true Aristotelian fashion, Bacon proceeds to demolish all previous pretensions to natural philosophy. His aim is to lay the foundations of science entirely anew, neither leaping to unproved general principles in the manner of the ancient philosophers nor heaping up unrelated facts in the manner of the "empirics" (among whom he

counts contemporary alchemists and natural magicians). "Histories," or collections of data, are to be drawn up systematically and used to raise an ordered system of axioms that will eventually embrace all the phenomena of nature. Many commentators, in the seventeenth century and later, have been misled, by the apparently unorganized collections of facts that fill Bacon's works, into supposing that his method was a merely empirical one, with no concern for theoretical interpretation. Such an impression is easily dispelled, however, by a closer reading of the text of *Novum organum.* We shall follow his account of the method in that work.

The first step in making true inductions is, as in a religious initiation, a purging of the intellect of the "idols" that, in man's natural fallen state, obstruct his unprejudiced understanding of the world. Bacon holds that we must consciously divest our minds of prejudices caused by excessive anthropomorphism (the "idols of the tribe"), by the particular interests of each individual (the "idols of the cave"), by the deceptions of words (the "idols of the market place"), and by received philosophical systems (the "idols of the theater").[10] Only in this way can the mind become a *tabula abrasa* on which true notions can be inscribed by nature itself. The consequences of the Fall for the intellect will then be erased, and man will be able to return to his God-given state of dominion over creation.

The aim of scientific investigation is to discover the "forms of simple natures." What Bacon means by a "form" is best gathered from his example concerning the form of heat (which is the only application of his method that he works out in any detail): "The Form of a thing is the very thing itself, and the thing differs from the form no otherwise than as the apparent differs from the real, or the external from the internal, or the thing in reference to man from the thing in reference to the universe." Hence, when the "form or true definition of heat" is defined as *Heat is a motion, expansive, restrained, and acting in its strife upon the smaller parts of bodies,* Bacon means "Heat itself, or the *quid ipsum* of Heat, is Motion and nothing else."[11] Thus, the form is not to be understood in a Platonic or Aristotelian sense but, rather, as what was later called an "explanation" or "reduction" of a secondary quality (heat) to a function of primary bodies and qualities (matter in motion). In order to discover what primary qualities are relevant to the form, Bacon prescribes his Tables of Presence, Absence, and Comparison: "[the form] is always present when the nature is present. . . . absent when the nature is absent" and "always decrease[s] when the nature in question decreases, and . . . always increase[s] when the nature in question increases."[12]

Therefore, we are to draw up a Table of Instances that all agree in the simple nature, heat—such as rays of the sun, flame, and boiling liquids—and then to look for other natures that are copresent with heat and therefore are candidates for its form. To ensure that as many irrelevant natures as possible are eliminated at this stage, these instances should be as unlike each other as possible except in the nature of heat. Second, a Table of Absence should be drawn up, in which as far as possible each instance in the Table of Presence should be matched by an instance similar to it in all respects *except* heat, such as rays of the moon and stars, phosphorescence, and cool liquids. This is the method of *exclusion* by negative instances, which will at once test a putative form drawn from the Table of Presence; if it is not the true form, it will not be absent in otherwise similar instances when heat is absent. The tables are the precursors of Mill's "Joint Method of Agreement and Difference," and clearly are more adequate than the method of induction by simple enumeration of positive instances, with which Bacon has so often been wrongly identified. Construction of the tables demands not a passive observation of nature, but an active search for appropriate instances; and it therefore encourages artificial experiment. Nature, Bacon says, must be "put to the question."[13]

Inference of the form from the tables is, however, only the beginning of the method. Bacon speaks often of raising a "ladder of axioms" by means of the forms, until we have constructed the complete system of natural philosophy that unifies all forms and natures. The conception seems to be something like an Aristotelian classification into genus, species, and differentia, in which every nature has its place. It also has some affinity with the later conception of a theoretical structure that yields observation statements by successive deductions from theoretical premises. But it would be misleading to press these parallels too closely, for the essence of Bacon's ascent to the axioms is that it is the result of a number of inductive inferences whose conclusions are infallible if they have been properly drawn from properly contrived Tables of Instances. The axioms are emphatically not the result of a leap to postulated premises from which observations may be deduced, for this is not an infallible method and gives no guarantee that the axioms arrived at are unique, let alone true. This deductive method is, in fact, what Bacon calls the method of "anticipation of nature," which, he thinks, may be useful in designing appropriate Tables of Instances, but is to be avoided in inductive inference proper.

Bacon is not unaware that the infallibility of his method depends crucially on there being only a finite number of simple natures and on our ability to enumerate all those present in any given instance. His faith that nature is indeed finite in the required respects seems to rest upon his natural philosophy. Although he rejected atomism, he retained the belief that the primary qualities are few in number and regarded the inductive method as the means to discover which qualities they are. Forms are the "alphabet of nature"[14] that suffice to produce the great variety of nature from a small stock of primary qualities, just as the letters of the alphabet can generate a vast literature. The whole investigation is further complicated, as Bacon also sees, by the fact that some natures are "hidden" and cannot be taken account of in the tables unless we employ "aids to the senses" to bring them within reach of sensation. Much of the later part of *Novum organum* is taken up with this problem, which leads Bacon to commend not only instruments such as the telescope, but also "fit and apposite experiments" that bring hidden and subtle processes to light.[15]

Complementary to Bacon's ascent to axioms is his insistence on subsequent descent to works. The aim is not merely passive understanding of nature, but also practical application of that understanding to the improvement of man's condition; Bacon holds that each of these aspects of his method is sterile without the other. Furthermore, he claims to have given in his method a means whereby anyone who follows the rules can do science—he has "levelled men's wits."[16] Thus, with proper organization and financial support, it should be possible to complete the edifice of science in a few years and to gather all the practical fruit that it promised for the good of men. Such a vision inspired Bacon as early as 1592, when he described in a letter to Cecil his "vast contemplative ends . . . I hope I should bring in industrious observations, grounded conclusions, and profitable inventions and discoveries."[17] Throughout his life he used his status and influence in a succession of frustrated attempts to obtain the Crown's support for this enterprise. In 1605 it was advertised in *The Advancement of Learning*—the only work Bacon ever published in English. His unfinished account of the ideal scientific society was published posthumously in *New Atlantis,* which ranks among the best-known and most delightful Utopian writings in the world and has been perhaps the most influential.

New Atlantis contains a description of the island of Bensalem, on which there is a cooperative college of science called Salomon's House. Bacon's account of it begins with a concise expression of his whole vision of science: "The End of our Foundation is the knowledge of Causes, and secret motions of things; and the enlarging of the bounds of Human Empire, to the effecting of all things possible."[18] The house is essentially a religious community, having "certain hymns and services, which we say daily, of laud and thanks to God."[19] It contains all kinds of laboratories and instruments for the pursuit of science, and is organized on the principle of a division of labor among those who perform experiments and collect information from various sources; those who determine the significance of the information and experiments, and direct and perform new and more penetrating experiments; and the "Interpreters," who "raise the former discoveries by experiments into greater observations, axioms, and aphorisms."[20] It is noticeable that while there are said to be thirty-three men assigned to the experimental parts of this task, only three are assigned to interpretation—a proportion that seems to reflect neither the status Bacon gives to the raising of axioms in his explicit accounts of method, nor the ease with which he thought this part of the task would be completed. Unfortunately, however, it does reflect the way Bacon's ideas were subsequently understood.

Bacon's immense prestige and influence in later seventeenth-century science does not rest upon positive achievements in either experiment or theory but, rather, upon his vision of science expressed in *Novum organum* and *New Atlantis,* and in particular upon his fundamental optimism about the possibilities for its rapid development. Now that the true method had been described, he thought all that was required was the purgation of the intellect to make a fit instrument for the method, and the human and financial resources to carry it out. When patronage and manpower for the organization of science were eventually forthcoming in the form of the Royal Society, its *Philosophical Transactions* was soon full of just the sort of "histories" Bacon had prescribed. His program for the raising of axioms, however, was taken less seriously than his strictures against "anticipations" and hypotheses, so that the weight of his influence was toward empiricism rather than toward theoretical system-building. At the time this did provide a useful corrective to Cartesianism, as can even be seen in Newton's insistence on the inductive "ascent" to the law of gravitation, in contrast with the merely imagined hypotheses of Descartes. But although most leading members of the Royal Society took every opportunity to proclaim themselves Bacon's loyal disciples, they tacitly adopted a more tolerant attitude toward hypotheses than his; and subsequent theoretical developments took place in spite of, rather than

as examples of, his elaboration of method. His successors in this area should be sought among the inductive logicians, beginning with Hume and Mill, and not among the scientists.

NOTES

1. *Descriptio globi intellectus* (1612), in *Works,* III, 734; V, 511.
2. Probably written before 1620, published 1653.
3. *Novum organum,* in *Works,* I, 234; IV, 126.
4. *De principiis atque originibus,* in *Works,* III, 111; V, 492.
5. *De sapientia veterum,* in *Works,* VI, 655, 729.
6. *Novum organum,* I, 310; IV, 195.
7. *Historia vitae et mortis* (1623), in *Works,* II, 213; V, 321.
8. *Sylva sylvarum,* in *Works,* II, 429 ff.
9. *De augmentis scientiarum,* in *Works,* I, 544; IV, 341. Also *Novum organum,* I, 145; IV, 33.
10. *Novum organum,* I, 169; IV, 58 ff.
11. *Ibid.,* I, 248, 262, 266; IV, 137, 150, 154.
12. *Ibid.,* I, 230, 248; IV, 121, 137.
13. *Ibid.,* I, 403; IV, 263.
14. *Abecedarium naturae,* in *Works,* II, 85; V, 208.
15. *Novum organum,* I, 168; IV, 58.
16. *Ibid.,* I, 217; IV, 109.
17. *Letters and Life,* I, 109.
18. *New Atlantis,* in *Works,* III, 156.
19. *Ibid.,* III, 166.
20. *Ibid.,* III, 165.

BIBLIOGRAPHY

I. ORIGINAL WORKS. The standard edition of Bacon's works is *The Works of Francis Bacon,* J. Spedding, R. L. Ellis, and D. D. Heath, eds., 7 vols. (London, 1857–1859), which contains valuable prefaces and notes. The philosophical and scientific works are in Vols. I–III and VI, with English translations in Vols. IV and V. Also of value is *The Letters and Life of Francis Bacon, Including All His Occasional Works,* J. Spedding, ed., 7 vols. (London, 1861–1874). All page references in the Notes are to these editions. I have modified some of the translations. For further original works and secondary literature, see R. Gibson, *Francis Bacon: A Bibliography of His Works and of Baconiana to the Year 1750* (Oxford, 1950). A useful edition of an individual work with notes, introduction, and bibliography is *Novum organum,* Thomas Fowler, ed. (2nd ed., Oxford, 1889).

II. SECONDARY LITERATURE. There are many biographies, and their quality varies greatly. The most valuable recent examples are F. H. Anderson, *Francis Bacon, His Career and His Thought* (Los Angeles, 1962); J. G. Crowther, *Francis Bacon* (London, 1960); and B. Farrington, *Francis Bacon; Philosopher of Industrial Science* (London, 1961). The last two interpret Bacon mainly as a "philosopher of works."

The literature on Bacon's philosophy and science is enormous, and there is no attempt at completeness here. The recent books and articles listed give references to further material whose absence from this list does not imply any value judgment: B. Farrington, *The Philosophy of*

Francis Bacon, an Essay on Its Development From 1603 to 1609 With New Translations of Fundamental Texts (Liverpool, 1964)—neither the commentary nor the newly translated texts throw much additional light on Bacon's scientific ideas during this period; Kuno Fischer, *Francis Bacon of Verulam, Realistic Philosophy and Its Age,* John Oxenford, trans. (London, 1857), which is still a useful analysis of Bacon's method but, like most nineteenth-century works (except those of Ellis and Spedding), underestimates the significance of Bacon's doctrine of spirits; Thomas Fowler, *Bacon* (London–New York, 1881), which deals with Bacon's philosophy and scientific method and their influence; W. Frost, *Bacon und die Naturphilosophie* (Munich, 1927); Mary B. Hesse, "Francis Bacon," in D. J. O'Connor, ed., *A Critical History of Western Philosophy* (New York, 1964), pp. 141–152; C. W. Lemmi, *The Classic Deities in Bacon* (Baltimore, 1933), not always accurate on Bacon's science; A. Levi, *Il pensiero di F. Bacone considerato in relazione con le filosofie della natura de Rinascimento e col razionalismo cartesiano* (Turin, 1925), one of the first detailed accounts of Bacon's relation to his immediate predecessors; G. H. Nadel, "History as Psychology in Francis Bacon's Theory of History," in *History and Theory,* **5** (1966), 275–287; M. Primack, "Outline of a Reinterpretation of Francis Bacon's Philosophy," in *Journal of the History of Philosophy,* **5** (1967), 123–132; P. Rossi, *Francesco Bacone, dalla magia alla scienza* (Bari, 1957; English trans. by S. Rabinovitch, London, 1968), which interprets Bacon's science as being heavily indebted to the natural magic tradition and his logic as indebted to Ramist rhetoric; P. M. Schuhl, *La pensée de lord Bacon* (Paris, 1949); and K. R. Wallace, *Francis Bacon on Communication and Rhetoric* (Chapel Hill, N.C., 1943).

Recent general works with extensive references to Bacon are R. M. Blake, C. J. Ducasse, and E. H. Madden, *Theories of Scientific Method: The Renaissance Through the Nineteenth Century* (Seattle, Wash., 1960), ch. 3; C. Hill, *Intellectual Origins of the English Revolution* (Oxford, 1965), esp. ch. 3; R. H. Kargon, *Atomism in England From Hariot to Newton* (Oxford, 1966), which contains a good bibliography of recent scholarly articles on Bacon, pp. 150–153; R. McRae, *The Problem of the Unity of the Sciences: Bacon to Kant* (Toronto, 1961); and Margery Purver, *The Royal Society: Concept and Creation* (Cambridge, Mass., 1967), esp. ch. 2.

MARY HESSE

BACON, ROGER (*b.* England, *ca.* 1219; *d. ca.* 1292), *natural philosophy, optics, calendar reform.*

Apart from some brief references in various chronicles, the only materials for Roger Bacon's biography are his own writings. The date 1214 for his birth was calculated by Charles, followed by Little, from his statements in the *Opus tertium* (1267) that it was forty years since he had learned the alphabet and that for all but two of these he had been "in studio."[1] Taking this to refer to the years since he entered the

university—the usual age was then about thirteen—they concluded that in 1267 Bacon was fifty-three and thus was born in 1214. But Crowley has argued that his statements more probably refer to his earliest education, beginning about the age of seven or eight, which would place his birth about 1219 or 1220. Of his family the only good evidence comes again from Bacon himself. He wrote in the *Opus tertium* that they had been impoverished as a result of their support of Henry III against the baronial party, and therefore could not respond to his appeal for funds for his work in 1266.[2]

After early instruction in Latin classics, among which the works of Seneca and Cicero left a deep impression, Bacon seems to have acquired an interest in natural philosophy and mathematics at Oxford, where lectures were given from the first decade of the thirteenth century on the "new" logic (especially *Sophistici Elenchi* and *Posterior Analytics*) and *libri naturales* of Aristotle as well as on the mathematical *quadrivium.* He took his M.A. either at Oxford or at Paris, probably about 1240. Probably between 1241 and 1246 he lectured in the Faculty of Arts at Paris on various parts of the Aristotelian corpus, including the *Physics* and *Metaphysics,* and the pseudo-Aristotelian *De vegetabilibus* (or *De plantis*) and the *De causis,* coincident with the Aristotelian revival there. In arguing later, in his *Compendium studii philosophie,* for the necessity of knowledge of languages,[3] he was to use an incident in which his Spanish students laughed at him for mistaking a Spanish word for an Arabic word while he was lecturing on *De vegetabilibus.* He was in Paris at the same time as Albertus Magnus, Alexander of Hales (*d.* 1245),[4] and William of Auvergne (*d.* 1249).[5]

The radical intellectual change following Bacon's introduction to Robert Grosseteste (*ca.* 1168–1253) and his friend Adam Marsh on his return to Oxford about 1247 is indicated by a famous passage in the *Opus tertium:*

> For, during the twenty years in which I have laboured specially in the study of wisdom, after disregarding the common way of thinking [*neglecto sensu vulgi*], I have put down more than two thousand pounds for secret books and various experiments [*experientie*], and languages and instruments and tables and other things; as well as for searching out the friendships of the wise, and for instructing assistants in languages, in figures, in numbers, and tables and instruments and many other things.[6]

Grosseteste's influence is evident in Bacon's particular borrowings, especially in his optical writings, but above all in the devotion of the rest of his life to the promotion of languages and of mathematics, optics (*perspectiva*), and *scientia experimentalis* as the essential sciences.

He was in Paris again in 1251, where he says in the *Opus maius*[7] that he saw the leader of the Pastoreaux rebels. This story and some later works place him there for long periods as a Franciscan. He entered the Franciscan order about 1257 and, soon afterward, he also entered a period of distrust and suspicion—probably arising from the decree of the chapter of Narbonne, presided over by Bonaventure as master general in 1260, which prohibited the publication of works outside the order without prior approval. Bonaventure had no time for studies not directly related to theology, and on two important questions, astrology and alchemy, he was diametrically opposed to Bacon. He held that only things dependent solely on the motions of the heavenly bodies, such as eclipses of the sun and moon and sometimes the weather, could be foretold with certainty. Bacon agreed with the accepted view that predictions of human affairs could establish neither certainty nor necessity over the free actions of individuals, but he held that nevertheless astrology could throw light on the future by discovering general tendencies in the influence of the stars, acting through the body, on human dispositions, as well as on nature at large. In alchemy Bonaventure was also skeptical about converting base metals into gold and silver, which Bacon thought possible.

Whatever the particular reasons for Bacon's troubles within the order, he felt it necessary to make certain proposals to a clerk attached to Cardinal Guy de Foulques; as a result, the cardinal, soon to be elected Pope Clement IV (February 1265), asked him for a copy of his philosophical writings. The request was repeated in the form of a papal mandate of 22 June 1266.[8] Bacon eventually replied with his three famous works, *Opus maius, Opus minus,* and *Opus tertium,* the last two prefaced with explanatory *epistole* in which he set out his proposals for the reform of learning and the welfare of the Church. It is reasonable to suppose that after twenty years of preparation he composed these *scripture preambule* to an unwritten *Scriptum principale* between the receipt of the papal mandate and the end of 1267. In that year he sent to the pope, by his pupil John, the *Opus maius* with some supplements, including *De speciebus et virtutibus agentium* in two versions[9] and *De scientia perspectiva,*[10] followed (before the pope died in November 1268) by the *Opus minus* and *Opus tertium* as résumés, corrections, and additions to it. The pope left no recorded opinion of Bacon's proposals.

Perhaps at this time Bacon wrote his *Communia*

naturalium and *Communia mathematica,* mature expressions of many of his theories. These were followed in 1271 or 1272 by the *Compendium studii philosophie,* of which only the first part on languages remains and in which he abused all classes of society, and particularly the Franciscan and Dominican orders for their educational practices. Sometime between 1277 and 1279 he was condemned and imprisoned in Paris by his order for an undetermined period and for obscure reasons possibly related to the censure, which included heretical Averroist propositions, by the bishop of Paris, Stephen Tempier, in 1277. The last known date in his troubled life is 1292, when he wrote the *Compendium studii theologii.*[11]

Scientific Thought. The *Opus maius* and accompanying works sent to the pope by Bacon as a *persuasio* contain the essence of his conception of natural philosophy and consequential proposals for educational reform. He identified four chief obstacles to the grasping of truth: frail and unsuitable authority, long custom, uninstructed popular opinion, and the concealment of one's own ignorance in a display of apparent wisdom. There was only one wisdom, given to us by the authority of the Holy Scriptures; but this, as he explained in an interesting history of philosophy, had to be developed by reason, and reason on its part was insecure if not confirmed by experience. There were two kinds of experience, one obtained through interior mystical inspiration and the other through the exterior senses, aided by instruments and made precise by mathematics.[12] Natural science would lead through knowledge of the nature and properties of things to knowledge of their Creator, the whole of knowledge forming a unity in the service and under the guidance of theology. The necessary sciences for this program were languages, mathematics, optics, *scientia experimentalis,* and alchemy, followed by metaphysics and moral philosophy.

Bacon leaves no doubt that he regarded himself as having struck a highly personal attitude to most of the intellectual matters with which he dealt, but his writings are not as unusual as the legends growing about him might suggest. They have, on the whole, the virtues rather than the vices of Scholasticism, which at its best involved the sifting of evidence and the balancing of authority against authority. Bacon was conscious of the dangers of reliance on authority: Rashdall draws attention to the irony of his argument against authority consisting chiefly of a series of citations. Most of the content of his writings was derived from Latin translations of Greek and Arabic authors. He insisted on the need for accurate translations. When it was that he learned Greek himself is not certain, but his Greek grammar may be placed after 1267, since in it he corrected a philological mistake in the *Opus tertium*. He also wrote a Hebrew grammar to help in the understanding of Scripture.

One of the most interesting and attractive aspects of Bacon is his awareness of the small place of Christendom in a world largely occupied by unbelievers, "and there is no one to show them the truth."[13] He recommended that Christians study and distinguish different beliefs and try to discover common ground in monotheism with Judaism and Islam, and he insisted that the truth must be shown not by force but by argument and example. The resistance of conquered peoples to forcible conversion, such as practiced by the Teutonic knights, was "against violation, not to the arguments of a better sect."[14] Hence the need to understand philosophy not only in itself but "considering how it is useful to the Church of God and is useful and necessary for directing the republic of the faithful, and how far it is effective for the conversion of infidels; and how those who cannot be converted may be kept in check no less by the works of wisdom than the labour of war."[15] Science would strengthen the defenses of Christendom both against the external threat of Islam and the Tartars and against the methods of "fascination" that he believed had been used in the Children's Crusade and the revolt of the Pastoreaux, and would be used by the Antichrist.

Bacon's mathematics included, on the one hand, astronomy and astrology (discussed later) and, on the other, a geometrical theory of physical causation related to his optics. His assertions that "in the things of the world, as regards their efficient and generating causes, nothing can be known without the power of geometry" and that "it is necessary to verify the matter of the world by demonstrations set forth in geometrical lines"[16] came straight from Grosseteste's theory of *multiplicatio specierum,* or propagation of power (of which light and heat were examples), and his account of the "common corporeity" that gave form and dimensions to all material substances. "Every multiplication is either according to lines, or angles, or figures."[17] This theory provided the efficient cause of every occurrence in the universe, in the celestial and terrestrial regions, in matter and the senses, and in animate and inanimate things. In thus trying to reduce different phenomena to the same terms, Grosseteste and Bacon showed a sound physical insight even though their technical performance remained for the most part weak. These conceptions made optics the fundamental physical science, and it is in his treatment of this subject that Bacon appears most effective. Besides Grosseteste his main optical sources were Euclid, Ptolemy, al-Kindī, and Ibn

al-Haytham (Alhazen). He followed Grosseteste in emphasizing the use of lenses not only for burning but for magnification, to aid natural vision. He seems to have made an original advance by giving constructions, based on those of Ptolemy for plane surfaces and of Ibn al-Haytham for convex refracting surfaces, providing eight rules (*canones*) classifying the properties of convex and concave spherical surfaces with the eye in various relationships to the refracting media. He wrote:

> If a man looks at letters and other minute objects through the medium of a crystal or of glass or of some other transparent body placed upon the letters, and this is the smaller part of a sphere whose convexity is towards the eye, and the eye is in the air, he will see the letters much better and they will appear larger to him. For in accordance with the truth of the fifth rule [Fig. 1] about a spherical medium beneath which is the object or on this side of its centre, and whose convexity is towards the eye, everything agrees towards magnification [*ad magnitudinem*], because the angle is larger under which it is seen, and the image is larger, and the position of the image is nearer, because the object is between the eye and the centre. And therefore this instrument is useful for the aged and for those with weak eyes. For they can see a letter, no matter how small, at sufficient magnitude.[18]

According to the fifth rule,[19] if the rays leaving the object, *AB,* and refracted at the convex surface of the lens meet at the eye, *E,* placed at their focus, a magnified image, *MN,* will be seen at the intersections of the diameters passing from the center of curvature, *C,* through *AB* to this surface and the projections of the rays entering the eye. As he did not seem to envisage the use of combinations of lenses, Bacon got no further than Grosseteste in speculating about magnifications such that "from an incredible distance we may read the minutest letters and may number the particles of dust and sand, because of the magnitude of the angle under which we may see them."[20]

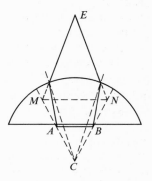

FIGURE 1

But he did make an important contribution to the history of physiological optics in the West by his exposition of Ibn al-Haytham's account of the eye as an image-forming device, basing his ocular anatomy on Ḥunayn ibn Isḥāq and Ibn Sīnā. In doing so, he seems to have introduced a new concept of laws of nature (a term found in Lucretius and numerous other authors more widely read, such as St. Basil) by his reference to the "laws of reflection and refraction" as *leges communes nature.*[21] His meaning is clarified by his discussion elsewhere of a *lex nature universalis*[22] requiring the continuity of bodies and thus giving a positive explanation, in place of the negative *horror vacui,* which he rejected, of such phenomena as water remaining in a clepsydra so long as its upper opening remained closed—an explanation comparable to one found in Adelard of Bath's *Natural Questions.* Universal nature constituted from these common laws, including those *de multiplicatione specierum,* was superimposed on the system of particular natures making up the Aristotelian universe—not yet the seventeenth-century concept but perhaps a step toward it.

"Having laid down the roots of the wisdom of the Latins as regards languages and mathematics and perspective," Bacon began Part VI of the *Opus maius,* "I wish now to unfold the roots on the part of *scientia experimentalis,* because without experience [*experientia*] nothing can be known sufficiently."[23] This science, "wholly unknown to the general run of students," had "three great prerogatives with respect to the other sciences."[24] The first was to certify the conclusions of deductive reasoning in existing speculative sciences, including mathematics. As an example he gave an investigation of the shape and colors of the rainbow involving both theoretical reasoning and the collection of instances of related phenomena in order to discover their common cause. The second prerogative was to add to existing sciences new knowledge that they could not discover by deduction. Examples were the discovery of the properties of the magnet, the prolonging of human life by observing what plants produced this effect naturally in animals, and the purification of gold beyond the present achievements of alchemy. The third prerogative was to investigate the secrets of nature outside the bounds of existing sciences, opening up knowledge of the past and future and the possibility of marvelous inventions, such as ever-burning lamps and explosive powders.

It is clear that Bacon's *scientia experimentalis* was not exactly what this term might now suggest, but belonged equally to "natural magic" aimed at producing astonishing as well as practically useful effects by harnessing the hidden powers of nature. His approach had been profoundly influenced by the pseudo-Aristotelian *Secretum secretorum,* of which he had produced an annotated edition variously dated between 1243 and sometime before 1257, but he also insisted that his new science would expose the frauds of magicians by revealing the natural causes of effects. The "dominus experimentorum" of the *Opus tertium,*[25] who may have been Pierre de Maricourt, the pioneer investigator of magnetism, is praised for understanding all these essential characteristics. In the *Opus minus,*[26] Bacon described possibly original experiments of his own with a lodestone held above and below a floating magnet, and argued that it was not the Nautical (Pole) Star that caused its orientation, or simply the north part of the heavens, but all four parts equally. It was in this work, and in the *Opus tertium,*[27] that he inserted his main discussion of alchemy, including the conversion of base metals into gold and silver. There is a further discussion in the *Communia naturalium,*[28] together with sketches of the sciences of medicine and agriculture. In the *Communia mathematica*[29] and the *Epistola de secretis operibus artis et naturae et de nullitate magiae,*[30] he described more wonderful machines for flying, lifting weights, and driving carriages, ships, and submarines, and so on, which he believed had been made in antiquity and could be made again.

Despite his occasional references to them, Bacon in his accredited writings deals with neither instruments nor mathematical tables in any but a superficial way. For this reason it is hard to measure his stature by comparison with that of his contemporaries whom we should call astronomers and mathematicians. We are not encouraged to set great store by the stories that while in Paris he constructed astronomical tables and supplied the new masters with geometrical problems that none of their audiences could solve.[31] His mathematics and astronomy were in fact almost wholly derivative, and he was not always a good judge of competence, preferring, for instance, al-Biṭrūjī to Ptolemy.

Bacon is often held to have achieved a deep and novel insight in regard to the role of mathematics in science, an insight that to the modern mind is almost platitudinous. In this connection it is easy to forget the large numbers of astronomers of antiquity and the Middle Ages for whom mathematics was an essential part of the science, and the smaller numbers of natural philosophers who had made use of simpler mathematical techniques than those of astronomy. It is more to the point to notice that Bacon argued for the usefulness of mathematics in almost every realm of academic activity. Part IV of the *Opus maius* is devoted to the usefulness of mathematics (1) in human affairs (this section was published separately as the *Specula mathematica*); (2) in divine affairs, such as chronology, the fixing of feasts, natural phenomena, arithmetic, and music; (3) in ecclesiastical affairs, such as the certification of faith and the emendation of the calendar; and (4) in affairs of state, under which heading are included geography and astrology. When Bacon sang the praises of mathematics, "the first of the sciences," "the door and key of the sciences," "the alphabet of philosophy," it has to be remembered that he used the word in an unusually wide sense. Bacon seemed to fear that mathematics would be dismissed as one of the blacker arts, as when arithmetic was applied to geomancy. He sought "per vias mathematice verificare omnia que in naturalibus scientias sunt necessaria"; and yet in the last resort, experience was still necessary, and in a sense supreme.[32]

So loud and long were Bacon's praises of mathematics that it is hard to avoid the conclusion that his love of the subject was unrequited. He could compose his *De communibus mathematice* and mention, in geometry, nothing beyond definitions, axioms, and methods. Apart from mathematically trivial results in such practical contexts as engineering, optics, astronomy, and the like, his works apparently contain not a single proof, not a single theorem; and we must take on trust the story of the difficult problems he devised for the young Paris masters. As for his analytical skills and his views on the citation of authority, rather than try to resolve the geometrical paradox of the doctrine of atomism—that it can make the hypotenuse and side of a square commensurable—he preferred simply to dismiss it as being contrary to Euclid.

The standard discussion of ratios in Euclid, Book V, did not include a numerical treatment of the subject, for which the standard medieval authority was the *Arithmetica* of Boethius. There the different species of ratio are tediously listed and subdivided, and the absence of a similar logical division of ratio in Euclid was complained of by Bacon in *Communia mathematica*.[33] He was not to carry out the program at which he might seem to have hinted, and not until Bradwardine's *Geometria speculativa* did the Schoolmen make any progress toward a numerical description of irrational ratios, except perhaps in some halting attempts to elucidate Proposition III of Archimedes' *De mensura circuli.*

As for the relation of logic to mathematics, Bacon inverted, in a sense, the logistic thesis of our own century: without mathematics, for instance, the categories were unintelligible.[34] Mathematics alone gave

absolute certainty. Bacon was unusual in that he generally named his sources, citing such authors as Theodosius, Euclid, Ptolemy, Boethius, al-Fārābī, and—among modern writers—Jordanus de Nemore (*De triangulis* and *Arithmetica*) and Adelard. Despite his criticism of Jordanus, by any reckoning a better mathematician than Bacon, he had praise for "the only two perfect mathematicians" (of his time), John of London and Pierre de Maricourt. He also condescended to praise Campanus of Novara and a "Master Nicholas," teacher of Amauri, son of Simon de Montfort. In the last analysis, almost everything Bacon wrote under the title of mathematics is best regarded as being at a metaphysical level. His view that in mathematics we have perfect demonstration reinforced his theory of natural action. His philosophy of science, however, was inherently empiricist: rational argument may cause us to dismiss a question, but it neither gives us proof nor removes doubt.

It was held in the *Opus maius* that a more accurate knowledge of the latitudes and longitudes of places was needed for (1) knowledge of mankind and the natural world; (2) facilitation of the spiritual government of the world—missionaries, for example, would be saved from danger and from much wasted labor; (3) knowledge of the whereabouts of the ten tribes and even of the Antichrist. His geography was nevertheless a compilation of works on descriptive geography (in which he gave, as it were, an extended verbal map of the world) by such writers as Ptolemy and al-Farghānī, supplemented by the reports of Franciscan travelers, especially to the East.

In the *Opus maius*[35] he stated the possibility of voyaging from Spain to India. The passage was inserted, without reference to its source, in the *Imago mundi*[36] of Cardinal Pierre d'Ailly (*d.* 1420). Humboldt argued that this passage, quoted by Columbus in a letter of 1498 to Ferdinand and Isabella, was more important in the discovery of America than the Toscanelli letters. Thorndike suggests that Columbus probably did not read the vital work until his return from the first voyage of 1492.[37] It is immaterial, as Thorndike points out, whether Bacon was merely optimistically citing Aristotle, Seneca, Nero, and Pliny on the distance of Spain from India. In fact Bacon argued as cogently from such longitudes and latitudes as were available in the Toledan tables as he did from classical authors.

For the radius of the earth Bacon took a figure of 3,245 miles (al-Farghānī). He stated that the earth's surface was less than three-quarters water. In both cases he selected good figures from a great many authoritative but bad ones. It is clear, nevertheless, from his repetition of the method of determining the size of the earth—a method he took from al-Farghānī—that he had no appreciation whatsoever of the practical difficulties it involved.

Bacon appears to have sent a map to the pope with his *Opus maius*. Although it is now lost, from the description he gave it appears to have included the better-known towns of the world plotted by their latitudes and longitudes as found in many contemporaneous lists.[38] We have no knowledge of the projection adopted, but the description is compatible with the use of a rectangular coordinate system.

Bacon used the words "astronomia" and "astrologia" in a typically ambiguous manner, but there is no doubt that he believed in the reasonableness of what we would call astrology. In the *Opus tertium* he spoke of astrology as the most important part of mathematics, dividing it into a speculative, or theoretical, part, presumably of the sort included in Sacrobosco's *Sphere,* and a practical part, "que dicitur astronomia,"[39] concerned with the design of instruments and tables.[40] A remark in the *Opus maius,*[41] written in 1267, confirms a similar remark made four years later by Robertus Anglicus,[42] to the effect that conscious efforts were being made to drive what amounts to a clock (in Bacon's example the spherical astrolabe was to be driven) at a constant rate. This seems to confirm approximately the *terminus ante quem non* previously determined for the mechanical clock.

On many occasions Bacon emphasized at length that the two sorts of "astrology" were essential if man was to learn of the celestial influences on which terrestrial happenings depended. By reference to Ptolemy, Haly, Ibn Sīnā, Abū Maʿshar, Messahala, and others, he showed that the best astrologers had not held that the influence of the stars subjugated the human will, and that the Fathers who objected to astrology on these grounds had never denied that astrology could throw light on future events. It was possible to predict human behavior statistically but not with certainty in individual cases. Astrology might strengthen faith in the stability of the Church and foretell the fall of Islam and the coming of the Antichrist; and all these things "ut auctores docent et experiencia certificat."[43] On occasion he likened astrological influence to the influence of a magnet over iron.

In his main works Bacon did not discuss the technicalities of astronomy or astrology, but in both of the works ascribed to him with the title *De diebus creticis*[44] the standard medical astrology of the time is rehearsed. These works are not merely compilations of older authorities. Although technically they are in no sense new, they have a rational cast and even include the testimony of medical men of the time.

The first of these two works is interesting because it incorporates the whole of the *De impressione aeris* attributed to Grosseteste and printed among his works by Baur. Little[45] suggests that Grosseteste (*d.* 1253) collaborated with Bacon. Internal evidence suggests a date of composition of about 1249. Some planetary positions quoted for that year are sufficiently inaccurate to suggest that the work was written before 1249 rather than after, and that the author was by no means as skilled as the best astronomers of the time.

The *Speculum astronomie,* of doubtful authorship (see below), is inconsistent with certain of Bacon's accredited writings. It is essentially a criticism of Stephen Tempier's decree of 1277 attacking 219 errors, several involving a belief in astrology. As already seen, Bacon's prison sentence was probably related to the bishop's decrees.

Bacon's astronomical influence was slight in all respects, although through Paul of Middelburg he is said to have influenced Copernicus.[46] His writings on the calendar were frequently cited.[47] Theologians treated the calendar with a respect it did not deserve, regarding it as a product of astronomy, while astronomers would have treated it with more disdain had they been detached enough to perceive it in a historical context. Here Bacon's skepticism was useful, and whatever the depth of his astronomical knowledge, he wrote on calendar reform with as much insight as anyone before Regiomontanus—Nicholas of Cusa notwithstanding. In discussing the errors of the Julian calendar, he asserted that the length of the Julian year (365 ¼ days) was in excess of the truth by about one day in 130 years, later changing this to one day in 125 years. The length of the (tropical) year implied was better than Ptolemy's, and indeed better than that accepted in the Alphonsine tables compiled a few years after the *Opus maius.* (The correct figure for Bacon's time was one day in a little over 129 years.) The Alphonsine tables imply that the Julian error is one day in about 134 years. There is no reason whatsoever to suppose, as many have done following Augustus De Morgan, that Bacon's data were his own. Thābit ibn Qurra made the length of the year shorter than the Julian year by almost exactly one day in 130 years, and according to a curious passage in the *Communia naturalium,* Thābit was "maximus Christianorum astronomus." In the *Computus,* however, Thābit is grouped with al-Battānī and others who are said to have argued for one day in 106 years, while Asophus (ʿAbd al-Raḥmān ibn ʿUmar al-Sūfī) appears to have been the most probable source of influence, with his one day in 131 years.[48]

As a means of reforming the calendar, Bacon seems finally to have recommended the removal of one day in 125 years (cf. the Gregorian method of ignoring three leap years in four centuries), and in connection with Easter, since the nineteen-year cycle is in error, the astronomical calculation of the feast; otherwise a lunisolar year like that of the eastern nations should be adopted. (Grosseteste had previously made this proposal.) He tempered this rash suggestion with the pious qualification that if an astronomical calculation of Easter was to be adopted, Hebrew astronomical tables should be used. His proposals may be compared with the much less radical ones of Nicholas of Cusa, who in his *Reparatio calendarii* (pre 1437?) merely suggested a temporary patching up of the calendar, eliminating a number of days to alter the equinox suitably (Gregorian reform, supervised by Clavius, took the same superfluous step) and changing the "golden number" so as to make the ecclesiastical moon correspond for a time with reality. These solutions were inferior to Bacon's, including fewer safeguards against a future state of affairs in which Church usage and the ordinances of the Fathers might differ appreciably. It is worth noting that Stöffler proposed to omit one day in 134 years (an obviously Alphonsine parameter), while Pierre d'Ailly followed Bacon explicitly in advocating a lunisolar cycle. Again, in connection with a proposal for calendar reform in England, we find that in 1582 John Dee commended Bacon to Queen Elizabeth as one who had "instructed and admonished" the "Romane Bishopp," who was now "contented to follow so neare the footsteps of veritye."[49] Judging by the speed of English legislation in the matter of calendar reform, it seems that Bacon was a little less than five centuries ahead of most of his countrymen.

Little wrote in 1914, "The extant manuscripts of Bacon's works show that the 'Doctor mirabilis never wanted admirers,'"[50] and cited as evidence the existence of twenty-seven manuscripts of the *Perspectiva*[51] alone, dating from the thirteenth to the seventeenth centuries. Apart from his proposals for the calendar it was on Bacon's optics that most scientific value was placed, by his contemporary Witelo as well as by Francesco Maurolico, John Dee, Leonard Digges, Hobbes, and the first editors of his works. At the same time his accounts of alchemy and natural magic gave him more dubious fame, varying from the sixteenth to the nineteenth centuries with current popular prejudices.

NOTES

1. *Opus tertium,* Brewer ed., p. 65.
2. *Ibid.,* p. 16.
3. *Compendium studii philosophie,* Brewer ed., pp. 467–468.
4. *Opus minus,* Brewer ed., p. 325; *Opus tertium,* Brewer ed., p. 30; *Compendium studii philosophie,* p. 425.

5. *Opus tertium,* Brewer ed., pp. 74–75.
6. *Ibid.,* p. 59.
7. *Opus maius* (1266–1267), Bridges ed., I, 401.
8. Brewer, p. 1.
9. Cf. *Opus maius,* Bridges ed., pt. IV, dist. ii–iv; and *De multiplicatione specierum,* Bridges ed.
10. Cf. *Opus maius,* pt. V.
11. Rashdall, pp. 3, 34.
12. *Opus maius,* VI, 1.
13. *Ibid.,* Bridges ed., III, 122.
14. *Ibid.,* II, 377.
15. *Opus tertium,* Brewer ed., pp. 3–4.
16. *Opus maius,* Bridges ed., I, 143–144.
17. *Ibid.,* p. 112.
18. *Ibid.,* V.iii.ii.4 (Bridges ed., II, 157).
19. Figure 1 is redrawn and relettered from *Opus maius,* V.iii.ii.3, British Museum MS Royal 7.f.viii, 13th cent., f. 93r.
20. *Ibid.,* Bridges ed., II, 165.
21. *Opus tertium,* Duhem ed., pp. 78, 90; *Opus maius,* Bridges ed., II, 49.
22. *Ibid.,* I, 151; *De multiplicatione specierum, ibid.,* II, 453; *Communia naturalium,* Steele ed., fasc. 3, pp. 220, 224.
23. *Opus maius,* Bridges ed., II, 167.
24. *Ibid.,* p. 172.
25. Brewer ed., pp. 46–47.
26. *Ibid.,* pp. 383–384.
27. Little ed., pp. 80–89.
28. Steele ed., fasc. 2, pp. 6–8.
29. Steele ed., fasc. 16, pp. 42–44.
30. Brewer ed., p. 533.
31. *Opus tertium,* Brewer ed., pp. 7, 36, 38.
32. See, e.g., *Opus maius,* Bridges ed., II, 172–173.
33. Steele ed., fasc. 16, p. 80.
34. *Opus maius,* Bridges ed., I, 102; cf. *Communia mathematica,* Steele ed., fasc. 16, p. 16.
35. Bridges ed., I, 290 ff.
36. *Imago mundi* was first published at Louvain in 1480 or 1487.
37. *A History of Magic and Experimental Science,* II, 645.
38. Bridges ed., I, 300.
39. Cf. *Communia mathematica,* Steele ed., fasc. 16, p. 49.
40. Brewer ed., p. 106. Since in ch. XII of the same work he seems to have used the word "tables" to refer primarily to almanacs, i.e., ephemerides, and to have spoken of instruments only as a means of verifying tables, it is probable that here he meant to refer only to the astrolabe and the equatorium.
41. Bridges ed., II, 202–203.
42. See L. Thorndike, *The Sphere of Sacrobosco and Its Commentators* (Chicago, 1949), p. 72.
43. *Opus maius,* I, 385.
44. Steele ed., fasc. 9, appendices ii and iii, ed. Little.
45. Little, *ibid.,* p. xxx.
46. Bridges ed., I, xxxiii, 292.
47. See bibliography. Note that the same passage occurs, word for word, in *Opus tertium,* Brewer ed., pp. 271–292; and in *Opus maius,* Bridges ed., I, 281. Notice, however, that the *Computus,* written 1263–1265, does not contain any passage from either of these works, and that it acknowledges Arabic, rather than paying lip service to Hebrew, sources.
48. Steele ed., fasc. 6, pp. 12–18.
49. Corpus Christi College, Oxford, MS C. 254, f. 161r.
50. Pp. 30–31.
51. *Opus maius,* pt. V.

BIBLIOGRAPHY

I. ORIGINAL WORKS. A number of Baconian problems must remain unsolved until there is a complete critical edition of his works: see the bibliography by Little in *Roger Bacon: Essays* (Oxford, 1914), pp. 375–426; compare

G. Sarton, *Introduction to the History of Science,* II (Baltimore, 1931), 963–967; and L. Thorndike and P. Kibre, *A Catalogue of Incipits of Mediaeval Scientific Writings in Latin* (2nd ed., Cambridge, Mass., 1963).

The earliest of Bacon's authentic works to be printed was the *Epistola de secretis operibus artis et naturae* (*De mirabili potestate artis et naturae*) (Paris, 1542; Basel, 1593); in the *Opera,* J. Dee, ed. (Hamburg, 1618); in French (Lyons, 1557; Paris, 1612, 1629); in English (London, 1597, 1659); in German (Eisleben, 1608); and other eds. After this appeared the *De retardandis senectutis accidentibus et de sensibus conservandis* (Oxford, 1590; in English, London, 1683); and *Specula mathematica* (part of *Opus maius* IV); *in qua De specierum multiplicatione earumdemque in inferioribus virtute agitur* and *Perspectiva* (*Opus maius* V), both ed. J. Combach (Frankfurt, 1614). There were other early eds. of the doubtful *Speculum alchemiae* (Nuremburg, 1541; in French, 1557; English, 1597; German, 1608; with later reissues) and the collection *De arte chymiae scripta* (Frankfurt, 1603, 1620).

The 1st ed. of the *Opus maius* was by S. Jebb (London, 1733), followed by an improved ed. (Venice, 1750), both including only pts. I–VI. Pt. VII was included in the new ed. by J. H. Bridges, 2 vols. (Oxford, 1897), with a supp. vol. (III) of revisions and additional notes (London, 1900). This ed. was trans. into English by R. B. Burke (Philadelphia, 1928). Pt. VII of the actual MS sent to the pope has been ed. by E. Massa, *Rogeri Baconi Moralis philosophia* (Zurich, 1953). The eds. of Jebb and Bridges (Vols. II and III, pp. 183–185) both include *De multiplicatione specierum,* a separate treatise forming part of a larger work; a further section of this has been ed. with a discussion of its date and associations by F. M. Delorme, "Le prologue de Roger Bacon à son traité De influentiis agentium," in *Antionianum,* **18** (1943), 81–90.

The 1st eds. of the *Opus minus* and the *Opus tertium,* together with the *Compendium studii philosophie* and a new ed. of the *Epistola de secretis operibus,* were by J. S. Brewer in *Fr. Rogeri Bacon Opera quaedam hactenus inedita* (London, 1859). Further sections of the first two works have been ed. by F. A. Gasquet, "An Unpublished Fragment of Roger Bacon," in *The English Historical Review,* **12** (1897), 494–517, a prefatory letter and other parts of *Opus minus;* P. Duhem, *Un fragment inédit de l'Opus tertium de Roger Bacon* (Quaracchi, 1909), on optics, astronomy, and alchemy; and A. G. Little, *Part of the Opus tertium of Roger Bacon,* British Society of Franciscan Studies, IV (Aberdeen, 1912). The last two items include Bacon's *De enigmatibus alkimie.* For further parts of the *Opus minus,* including discussions of alchemy, still unpublished, see A. Pelzer, "Une source inconnue de Roger Bacon, Alfred de Sareshel, commentateur des Météorologiques d'Aristote," in *Archivium Franciscanum historicum,* **12** (1919), 44–67.

Other works have been ed. by E. Nolan and S. A. Hirsch, *The Greek Grammar of Roger Bacon, and a Fragment of His Hebrew Grammar* (Cambridge, 1902); H. Rashdall, *Fratris Rogeri Baconi Compendium studii theologii,* British Society of Franciscan Studies, III (Aberdeen, 1911); S. H. Thomson, "An Unnoticed Treatise of Roger Bacon on

Time and Motion," in *Isis,* **27** (1937), 219–224; and in *Opera hactenus inedita Rogeri Baconi,* R. Steele, ed. (unless otherwise stated), 16 fasc. (Oxford, 1905–1940): (1) *Metaphysica: De viciis contractis in studio theologie* (1905); (2–4) *Communia naturalium* (1905–1913); (5) *Secretum secretorum cum glossis et notulis* (1920); (6) *Computus* (1926); (7) *Questiones supra undecimum prime philosophie Aristotelis* (*Metaphysica,* XII) (1926); (8) *Questiones supra libros quatuor physicorum Aristotelis,* F. M. Delorme, ed. (1928); (9) *De retardatione accidentium senectutis cum aliis opusculis de rebus medicinalibus,* A. G. Little and E. Withington, eds. (1928); (10) *Questiones supra libros prime philosophie Aristotelis* (*Metaphysica,* I, II, V–X) (1930); (11) *Questiones altere supra libros prime philosophie Aristotelis* (*Metaphysica,* I–IV), *Questiones supra de plantis* (1932); (12) *Questiones supra librum de causis* (1935); (13) *Questiones supra libros octo physicorum Aristotelis,* F. M. Delorme, ed. (1935); (14) *Liber de sensu et sensato, Summa de sophismatibus et distinctionibus* (1937); (15) *Summa grammatica, Sumule dialectices* (1940); and (16) *Communia mathematica* (1940). The *Chronica XXIV generalium ordinis minorum* (*ca.* 1370) was pub. in *Analecta Franciscana,* **3** (1897).

II. SECONDARY LITERATURE. The best critical study of Bacon's life is T. Crowley, *Roger Bacon: The Problem of the Soul in His Philosophical Commentaries* (Louvain–Dublin, 1950). The pioneering study by E. Charles, *Roger Bacon: Sa vie, ses ouvrages, ses doctrines d'après des textes inédits* (Paris, 1861), is now mostly of historical interest. Essential general studies are A. G. Little, ed., *Roger Bacon: Essays Contributed by Various Writers* (Oxford, 1914), especially contributions by Little (life and works); L. Baur (Grosseteste's influence); Hirsch (philology); E. Wiedemann, S. Vogl, and E. Würschmidt (optics); Duhem (vacuum); M. M. P. Muir (alchemy); E. Withington (medicine); and J. E. Sandys (English literature); Little, *Franciscan Letters, Papers and Documents* (Manchester, 1943); L. Thorndike, *A History of Magic and Experimental Science,* II (New York, 1929), 616–691; S. C. Easton, *Roger Bacon and His Search for a Universal Science* (Oxford, 1952), with bibliography; and F. Alessio, *Mito e scienza in Ruggero Bacone* (Milan, 1967).

Studies of particular aspects are E. Schlund, "Petrus Peregrinus von Maricourt: Sein Leben und seine Schriften," in *Archivum Fransiscanum historicum,* **4** (1911), 445–449, 636–643; L. Baur, "Die philosophischen Werke des Robert Grosseteste," in *Beiträge zur Geschichte der Philosophie des Mittelalters,* **9** (1912), 52–63; and "Die Philosophie des Robert Grosseteste," *ibid.,* **18** (1917), 92–120; P. Duhem, *Le système du monde* (Paris, 1916–1958), III, 260–277, 411–442; V, 375–411; VIII, 121–168; A. Birkenmajer, "Études sur Witelo, i–iv," in *Bulletin international de l'Académie polonaise des sciences et des lettres,* Classe d'histoire et de philosophie (1920), 354–360; and "Robert Grosseteste and Richard Fournival," in *Mediaevalia et humanistica,* **5** (1948), 36–41; R. Carton, *L'expérience physique chez Roger Bacon, L'expérience mystique de l'illumination intérieure chez Roger Bacon, La synthèse doctrinale de Roger Bacon,* nos. 2, 3, 5 in the series

Études de philosophie médiévale (Paris, 1924); C. B. Vandewalle, *Roger Bacon dans l'histoire de la philologie* (Paris, 1929); G. Meyer, "En quel sens peut-on parler de 'méthode scientifique' de Roger Bacon," in *Bulletin de littérature ecclésiastique* (Toulouse), **53** (1952), 3–25, 77–98; A. C. Crombie, *Robert Grosseteste and the Origins of Experimental Science 1100–1700,* 3rd imp. (Oxford, 1969), pp. 41, 139–162, 204–207, 213–218, 278–281, with bibliography; and "The Mechanistic Hypothesis and the Scientific Study of Vision," in *Proceedings of the Royal Microscopical Society,* **2** (1967), 20–30, 43–45; M. Schramm, "Aristotelianism: Basis and Obstacle to Scientific Progress in the Middle Ages," in *History of Science,* **2** (1963), 104–108; and A. Pacchi, "Ruggero Bacone e Roberto Grossatesta in un inedito hobbesiano del 1634," in *Rivista critica di storia della filosofia,* **20** (1965), 499–502.

A. C. CROMBIE
J. D. NORTH

BADĪᶜ AL-ZAMĀN AL-JAZARĪ. See **al-Jazarī.**

BAEKELAND, LEO HENDRIK (*b.* Ghent, Belgium, 14 November 1863; *d.* Beacon, New York, 23 February 1944), *chemistry.*

Baekeland graduated with honors from the Municipal Technical School of Ghent in 1880, received the degree of Doctor of Natural Science from the University of Ghent in 1884, and stayed on to serve as professor of chemistry and physics at the Government Normal School of Science. In 1887 he received first prize in the chemistry division of a competition among the graduates of the four Belgian universities. Baekeland's travels took him to the United States in 1889, and he settled there, first as an employee of a photographic firm and then as the head of his own company, which manufactured a photographic paper he named Velox. This was a "gaslight paper" like that invented by Josef M. Eder for making, developing, and handling prints from negatives by artificial light. Baekeland perfected the process and sold it in 1899. He then became a consultant in electrochemistry and obtained patents on dissolving salt in spent electrolytes and on making more durable diaphragms from asbestos cloth treated with gummy iron hydroxides.

In 1905 Baekeland began his third enterprise, which he developed with great success and pursued until his death: the manufacture of condensation products from phenol and formaldehyde. This condensation had first been described in 1872 by Adolf von Baeyer. In a lecture before the American Chemical Society on 8 February 1909, Baekeland surveyed the previous attempts at industrial utilization of the reaction, which resulted in slow processes and brittle products; then he continued: ". . . by the use of small amounts of bases, I have succeeded in preparing a solid initial condensation product, the properties of which sim-

plify enormously all molding operations. . . ." He distinguished three stages of reaction, with a soluble intermediate product. Manufacture of Bakelite resins started in 1907; by 1930, the Bakelite Corporation occupied a 128-acre plant at Bound Brook, New Jersey.

In 1914, Baekeland received the first Chandler Medal. During World War I, he was active in the National Research Council. He was elected president of the American Chemical Society in 1924 and received many other honors.

BIBLIOGRAPHY

Baekeland's writings include "The Synthesis, Constitution, and Uses of Bakelite," in *Industrial and Engineering Chemistry,* **1** (1909), 149–161; and "Some Aspects of Industrial Chemistry," in *Science,* **40** (1914), 179–198.

Further information on Baekeland and his work can be found in Helmut and Alison Gernsheim, *The History of Photography From the Earliest Use of the Camera Obscura in the 11th Century up to 1914* (London, 1955), pp. 284 ff.; see also J. Gillis, *Leo Hendrik Baekeland* (Brussels, 1965).

EDUARD FARBER

BAER, KARL ERNST VON (*b.* Piep, near Jerwen, Estonia, 28 February 1792; *d.* Dorpat, Estonia [now Tartu, Estonian S.S.R.], 28 November 1876), *biology, anthropology, geography.*

During the earlier years of his professional life, Baer concentrated his principal efforts on what is now known as embryology. He is known to Western biologists for his discovery of the mammalian egg in 1826 and for his treatise *Ueber die Entwickelungsgeschichte der Thiere, Beobachtung und Reflexion* (1828, 1837), the publication of which provided a basis for the systematic study of animal development. Baer was a professor in Germany when he carried out his embryological investigations. When he was about forty-two years old, he left Germany for Russia; there, during the remaining years of his long, active life, he devoted his attention primarily to anthropology, both physical and ethnographic, to geography, and, to a lesser degree, to archaeology. But this gives only a bare indication of how widely and how philosophically his mind ranged through nature.

Baer, whose complete style was Karl Ernst Ritter von Baer, Edler von Huthorn, was descended from an originally Prussian family. One of his ancestors, Andreas Baer, emigrated from Westphalia to Reval, Livonia, in the mid-sixteenth century; a collateral descendant of Andreas bought an estate in Estonia during the mid-seventeenth century and was made a member of the nobility. Karl's father, Magnus Johann von Baer, was an Estonian landholder whose estate, Piep, was modest in size. He had been trained in law and, after Karl's birth, served a term as a district official (*Landrat*) and as an official of the Estonian knighthood, in which the family had gained membership during the late eighteenth century.

Magnus Johann von Baer married his first cousin Juliane Louise von Baer. Karl was one of ten children, of whom three were sons. His parents, because of the large size of the family, entrusted Karl during his early years to his father's brother Karl and his wife, Baroness Ernestine von Canne, from Coburg, who lived on a neighboring estate and were childless. Here Karl acquired the love of plants that later drew his interest to botany and natural history. He returned to his own family when he was seven. His first formal instruction was from tutors at home; then, from 1807 to 1810, he attended a cathedral school for members of the nobility in Reval.

Baer's uncle Karl had enjoyed a military life and hoped that his nephew would follow a similar career, as did the boy's father. When Karl decided to enter a university instead, his father encouraged him to go to Germany, but he insisted on entering the University of Dorpat, opened six years earlier. He matriculated in August 1810 as a medical student, perhaps to prepare himself for a career in natural science. He later said that he did not know why he decided to take a medical degree.

Dorpat was a small university, and a provincial one. Baer was interested, however, in his work in botany, physics, and physiology. The professor of physiology was Karl Friedrich Burdach, who later exerted further influence on Baer's career. Baer received the M.D. at Dorpat in September 1814. He was dissatisfied with his medical training, however, and continued his studies in Berlin and Vienna in 1814–1815 and in Berlin during the winter semester 1816–1817.

Baer went to Würzburg in 1815 to further his medical studies, but as an indirect result of his interest in botany he met Ignaz Döllinger, one of the great teachers of the nineteenth century. During the academic year 1815–1816 he studied comparative anatomy with Döllinger, an experience that was critical for his later career. At that time Döllinger tried to persuade him to study the development of the chick by improved methods, studying the blastoderm removed from the yolk, but Baer was not willing to spend the time or money that would have been necessary. He was instrumental, however, in bringing to Würzburg Christian Heinrich Pander, whom he had known in Dorpat and Berlin, and Pander began the study.

In August 1817, Baer went to Königsberg as prosector in anatomy at the invitation of Burdach, who was professor there. In 1819 he became extraordinary professor of anatomy, and in 1826 ordinary professor of zoology. At various times during his years at Königsberg he taught zoology, anatomy, and anthropology. Baer founded a zoological museum, acted several times as director of the botanical gardens, and served terms as dean of the medical faculty and as rector of the university. He married Auguste von Medem of Königsberg on 1 January 1820. They had five sons and a daughter; the first son died in childhood; the second, Karl, who was interested in natural history, died of typhus at the age of twenty-one while a student at the University of Dorpat.

Most of Baer's contributions to embryology were made between 1819 and 1834, when he was in Königsberg. He made a number of specific discoveries in vertebrate morphogenesis relating to the development of particular organs or organ systems. These alone would have sufficed to warrant his inclusion among major contributors to embryology. He was the first to discover and describe the notochord. He was among the first to recognize that the neural folds represent the rudiment of the central nervous system and that they form a tube, although he did not understand the precise mechanism by which the folds form the substance of brain and spinal cord. He was the first to describe and name the five primary brain vesicles. He made considerable advances in the understanding of the development and function of the extraembryonic membranes (chorion, amnion, allantois) in the chick and the mammal. Incidentally, he was responsible for the introduction of the term "spermatozoa" for what were then known as animalcules in the seminal fluid (but he thought them parasites).

Baer's greatest contributions to embryology were of far wider general significance. In 1826 he discovered the egg of the mammal in the ovary, bringing to completion a search begun at least as early as the seventeenth century. William Harvey had unsuccessfully attempted to find eggs of the deer in the uterus; others, after Harvey's time, had mistaken ovarian follicles for mammalian eggs. Baer first found the true egg in Burdach's house dog, a bitch sacrificed for the investigation; subsequently he found eggs in a number of other mammals. Thus he concluded that "every animal which springs from the coition of male and female is developed from an ovum, and none from a simple formative liquid" (*De ovi mammalium et hominis genesi,* O'Malley trans., p. 149). This was a unifying doctrine whose importance cannot be over-emphasized.

Equally important were Baer's careful descriptions and thoughtful interpretations of the whole course of vertebrate development. He had been in Würzburg in 1815–1816 when his friend Pander had first analyzed the development of the chick in terms of germ layers, and he had participated in that work. In Königsberg, Baer continued the work begun by Pander, extending the observations and generalizing their meaning. Some of his ideas were first published in contributions to Volumes I and II (1826, 1827) of Burdach's *Die Physiologie als Erfahrungswissenschaft.* The first volume of Baer's own treatise was published in 1828, the second volume (unfinished) in 1837; part of what was lacking in Volume II was published posthumously in 1888. *Entwickelungsgeschichte* was the key word in his title and his thought; his great contribution rested on his ability to envisage the organism as a historical entity, as a being that undergoes observable change during its life. He described the development of vertebrates from conception to hatching or birth. Baer observed the formation of the germ layers and described the way in which they formed various organs by tubulation, and he knew this to be more or less similar in all vertebrates. Even more important, he emphasized that development is epigenetic, that it proceeds from the apparently homogeneous to the strikingly heterogeneous, from the general to the special. The old idea, long disputed, that embryonic parts might be preformed in the egg was no longer tenable after Baer's work.

In discussing his view that development proceeds from the general to the special, Baer emphasized that embryos resemble each other more than adults do, and he strongly opposed the opinion previously expressed by Johann Friedrich Meckel that embryos resemble adults of other species. As part of the heritage of German *Naturphilosophie* in which he had been trained, Baer had a great interest in symmetry. His embryological observations led him to believe that there are four fundamental animal types that differ from each other according to their symmetry: the peripheral or radial, the segmental, the massive, and the double symmetrical (vertebrate). These types were very similar to the four *embranchements* described at approximately the same time by Cuvier. Baer held some belief in limited transformationism, the idea that one kind of animal species might during the course of history be transformed into another, but when Darwin's *Origin of Species* was published (1859) Baer could not agree that all organisms could

have evolved from a single or a few progenitors. Unfortunately, Baer's valid objections to Meckel's interpretations were ignored by Darwin's immediate followers, who made the recapitulation doctrine a key to evolution theory. But when the new analytical and experimental approach to the study of development began to be followed in the late nineteenth century, the new pathways led out not from the ideas of the recapitulationists, but from those of Baer.

Although Baer reached the peak of his career as an embryologist when at Königsberg, he was restless, and for reasons not yet fully understood, he was unwilling to remain there. He was elected a corresponding member of the Academy of Sciences in St. Petersburg in 1826, and in 1828 he refused an invitation to work at the academy, even though his friend Pander was already there as academician. Baer spent several months in St. Petersburg in 1829–1830, but found conditions for work less favorable than in Königsberg. Nonetheless, when his elder brother Louis, who had been managing the estate at Piep, died in 1834, Baer moved with his wife and children to St. Petersburg. His wish to retain the Piep estate for his family and broken health resulting from overwork may have been factors contributing to a move that had not seemed desirable earlier. Baer entered the academy as a full member in zoology in December 1834, and remained there for the rest of his working life. He performed many duties, his first appointment being as librarian for the foreign division. In 1846 Baer became academician for comparative anatomy and physiology, and from 1846 to 1852 he served as ordinary professor in those fields at the Medico-Chirurgical Academy in St. Petersburg. He retired from active membership in the Academy of Sciences in 1862 but continued work as an honorary member until 1867. He then returned to Dorpat, where he resided until his death.

When he became academician for comparative anatomy and physiology, Baer took charge of the academy's anatomical museum, a decision related to his long-standing interest in anthropology. His doctoral dissertation (1814), on diseases endemic among Estonians, was ethnographically inclined. He first lectured on anthropology as early as the winter of his first year in Königsberg (1817–1818), to students of all faculties, not only of medicine. One volume of these lectures was published in 1824; a second, although promised, did not appear.

In the 1820's, while he was still in Königsberg, Baer had contemplated a trip to Lapland and Novaya Zemlya. After becoming an academician in St. Petersburg, he was able to satisfy his desire for travel. In 1837 he headed an expedition to Novaya Zemlya under the auspices of the academy and was the first naturalist to collect specimens there. During more than twenty-five years he made a number of scientific expeditions, traveling widely: to Lapland, to the North Cape, to the Caspian Sea and the Caucasus, to the Sea of Azov, to Kazan, and to other far parts of Russia, as well as on the Continent and in England. Baer made a number of important discoveries in natural history and geology, and contributed, beginning in 1845, to the founding of the Russian Geographical Society. From 1839 he was coeditor of and contributor to the important *Beiträge zur Kenntniss des Russischen Reiches und der angränzender Länder Asiens.* His travels also increased his already considerable interest in ethnography.

Baer classified man into six categories, ranked according to the degree of primitiveness. His interpretations of some peoples as more primitive than others were similar to those of his contemporaries and immediate predecessors; he did not bring to this area of investigation the same vision that he had carried into embryology. Nonetheless, at least one of his contributions to modern anthropology was truly effective. After he became academician for comparative anatomy and physiology, one of his primary accomplishments, perhaps growing out of his earlier museum experience in Königsberg, was the establishment at the academy of a craniological collection. Attempts to classify skulls were based on measurements, and Baer thought it desirable that methods of cranial measurement be standardized. To this end, he called together a group of craniologists in Göttingen in 1861. The measurements were not standardized, but the meeting led to the founding of the German Anthropological Society and of the German *Archiv für Anthropologie.*

Baer's scientific and intellectual interests reached beyond the areas already enumerated. He did some work in entomology and was instrumental in the establishment of the Russian Entomological Society, of which he was the first president in 1860. He was deeply interested in pisciculture and in the Russian fisheries. He wrote on the origin of the tin found in ancient bronze, on the routes of Odysseus' voyages, and on the whereabouts of biblical Ophir.

Among his other abilities Baer had particular talents that distinguished him socially. He had great wit, which endeared him to those who knew him, and he was very loyal to his friends. One friend in particular may be singled out. In the winter of 1839–1840 Baer made the acquaintance of the Grand Duchess Helen Pavlovna, the former Princess Frederika Charlotte Marie of Württemberg. The wife of Grand Duke

Michael Pavlovitch, youngest brother of Czar Alexander I, she was an enlightened and intelligent patron of the arts and the sciences; Baer instructed her two daughters in natural history and enjoyed her friendship for many years.

Baer was a patriotic Russian, as is clear from the zeal with which he carried out his duties for the academy and from his evident interest in Russian geography and ethnography. But he was also an expressed enthusiast of Prussia. His true political views remain obscure, for some were expressed cryptically and others, we are told by his biographer Stieda, were probably eliminated from his publications by the censors.

As for his writing, Baer began more than he completed. The second volume of his great *Entwickelungsgeschichte* was never finished; he neglected even to read the proofs when the publisher decided to bring it out unfinished. He began, but failed to complete, other writings; he never completely described his collections from Novaya Zemlya. Nonetheless, he was a prolific lecturer and author. The second edition of Stieda's biography enumerates approximately 300 of his publications, and the list is incomplete.

Baer was not only an accomplisher but also a thinker, and the range and profundity of his thought are reflected in many of his writings. He was particularly interested in problems related to teleology; he lectured and wrote on living creatures and life as related to the wider cosmos. Baer saw nature as a whole, not merely as did the *Naturphilosophen,* who constructed elaborate ideas about natural schemes, but as an observer and discoverer who with his eyes as well as his mind searched deep into many of nature's realms.

Baer received many honors during his lifetime. An island in the Russian North was named for him; and in 1864 the Estonian Knights held a celebration for him on the golden jubilee of his doctorate. They also published his autobiography, which was especially prepared for that event. In 1872, Volume 5 of the *Archiv für Anthropologie* was dedicated to him. Baer was elected a member of the Royal Society of London and of the Paris Academy. He was awarded the Copley Medal by the Royal Society and also received a medal from the Paris Academy. Alexander von Humboldt personally brought him the medal from Paris, much to Baer's delight. Baer once wrote of Humboldt that he was "versatile, yet always accurate as an observer, deep and far-seeing as a thinker, exalted as a seer" (*Reden,* I, 296). He might well have been speaking of himself.

BIBLIOGRAPHY

The most important sources of information about Baer's life and writings are his autobiography and an authoritative biography by Ludwig Stieda. Both contain extensive classified and annotated lists of publications by Baer.

I. ORIGINAL WORKS. Baer's writings include *De ovi mammalium et hominis genesi epistola* (Leipzig, 1827); German trans., B. Ottow, ed., *Ueber die Bilding des Eies der Säugetiere und des Menschen* (Leipzig, 1927); facsimile of Latin ed. in George Sarton, "The Discovery of the Mammalian Egg and the Foundation of Modern Embryology," in *Isis,* **16** (1931), 315–[378]; English trans. by Charles Donald O'Malley, *ibid.,* **47** (1956), 117–153; *Ueber die Entwickelungsgeschichte der Thiere. Beobachtung und Reflexion,* 2 vols. (Königsberg, 1828, 1837), Vol. III, L. Stieda, ed. (Königsberg, 1888); *Reden gehalten in wissenschaftlichen Versammlungen und kleinere Aufsätze vermischten Inhalts,* 3 vols. (St. Petersburg, 1864–1876); and *Nachrichten über Leben und Schriften des Geheimrathes Dr. Karl Ernst von Baer, mitgetheilt von ihm selbst. Veröffentlicht bei Gelegenheit seines fünfzigjährigen Doctor-Jubiläums, am 29. August 1864, von der Ritterschaft Ehstlands* (St. Petersburg, 1865), privately distributed ed. of 400 copies; trade eds. appeared under same title (St. Petersburg, 1866; 2nd ed., Brunswick, 1886).

II. SECONDARY LITERATURE. Works on Baer include B. Ottow, "K. E. von Baer als Kraniologe und die Anthropologen-Versammlung 1861 in Göttingen," in *Sudhoffs Archiv für Geschichte der Medizin und der Naturwissenschaften,* **50** (1966), 43–68; and L. Stieda, *Karl Ernst von Baer. Eine biographische Skizze* (Brunswick, 1878, 1886).

JANE OPPENHEIMER

BAEYER, ADOLF JOHANN FRIEDRICH WILHELM VON (*b.* Berlin, Germany, 31 October 1835; *d.* Starnberg, Oberbayern, Germany, 20 August 1917), *chemistry.*

Adolf von Baeyer was the eldest of the five children of Johann Jacob Baeyer and Eugenie Hitzig. His father, a lieutenant general in the Prussian army, took part in the government project to measure degrees of latitude and longitude directed by the astronomer W. F. Bessel. He subsequently participated in a general European measurement program and published these results, as well as other investigations on the shape of the earth. Baeyer's mother was the daughter of Julius Eduard Hitzig, a criminal judge. Her uncle, the art historian Franz Kugler, and her grandfather made Baeyer's first home on Friedrichstrasse a center for Berlin literary life by attracting E. T. A. Hoffman and others for weekly evenings of conversation. Baeyer's mother was Jewish but had been converted to the Evangelical faith and had been confirmed by Schleiermacher. Baeyer was of the same faith as his parents.

Baeyer's early education at the Friedrich-Wilhelms Gymnasium and at the University of Berlin under P. G. Dirichlet and G. Magnus emphasized mathematics and physics. In 1856, after a year's military service, he decided to study experimental chemistry with R. Bunsen in Heidelberg, where the emphasis was on applied physical chemistry. Dissatisfied with this approach, Baeyer in 1858 entered Kekulé's private laboratory in Heidelberg. Since he was pleased with Kekulé's tuition in organic chemistry, Baeyer followed him to Ghent and remained there until 1860, taking time out only in 1858 to receive his doctoral degree from Berlin for work on arsenic methyl chloride. After leaving Ghent, Baeyer returned to Berlin and held various teaching positions at the technical institute and the military academy. He married Lida, daughter of Emil Bendemann, in 1868; the couple had three children: Eugenie, Hans, and Otto. In 1872 Baeyer was appointed ordinary professor of chemistry at the new imperial university at Strasbourg. Three years later he moved to Munich as successor to Justus von Liebig.

Baeyer's contributions to science were widely recognized during his lifetime. He received the Liebig Medal of the Berlin Chemists Congress, the Royal Society's Davy Medal, and in 1905 the Nobel Prize for his work on dyes and hydroaromatic compounds. Among the many scientific societies to which he belonged were the Berlin Academy of Sciences and the German Chemical Association.

Most of Baeyer's scientific interests grew out of work he began at the technical institute in Berlin. His early work, in which he followed the lead of Liebig and Wöhler, centered on the derivatives of uric acid. He prepared various derivatives, including barbiturates. From his uric acid studies Baeyer turned to another physiological problem, that of assimilation in green plants. He thought that the ease with which a water molecule could be eliminated from a carbon atom with two hydroxyl groups would explain the formation of sugars in plants. Baeyer also saw that a study of condensation reactions where water was eliminated might be used to probe the structure of complicated organic molecules. He and his students conducted a series of investigations on condensation reactions of aldehydes and phenols which led to the discovery of phenolphthalein and other members of the phthalein group. Baeyer developed the dyestuffs gallein and coerulein from this class of compounds.

Connected with his work on phthaleins was his work with phthalic acid, which led Baeyer to investigate the structure of benzene. He started with mellitic acid, which he showed was a benzene derivative rather than an alkyne, as he had first believed. He then investigated the carboxylic acids of benzene and found one new tricarboxylic and two new tetracarboxylic acids. From the reduced forms of these acids, prepared by heating them with zinc dust—a method he had previously introduced—he tried to elucidate the structure of benzene. Failure to find cis-trans isomers led him to reject Kekulé's double-bond model and Ladenberg's prism model and to adopt his own model of benzene, in which one valence bond from each carbon was directed inward. But in 1892 he produced cis-trans derivatives of benzene, which made him reject any one theory of benzene structure.

Baeyer's best-known research, on indigo, was begun in 1865 and followed up earlier work on phthalein dyes. In 1841 Laurent had investigated indigo and had obtained isatin by oxidation. Baeyer reversed Laurent's process, and in 1870 he and Emmerling produced indigo by treatment of isatin with phosphorous trichloride, followed by reduction. In 1878, by synthesizing isatin from phenylacetic acid, Baeyer demonstrated the possibility of a complete synthesis of indigo. However, neither the exact process nor the structure of indigo was yet known. Baeyer had worked on isatin in 1865–1866 and had produced a series of related compounds, dioxindole and oxindole, with successively less oxygen. It occurred to him that this series bore a similarity to the alloxan series he had developed with uric acid. Consequently, he predicted and found a final member of the series, which he named indole, containing no oxygen. He found the structure of indole, the kernel of the indigo molecule, through work with pyrrole. To determine the structural formula of indigo, Baeyer examined the linkage of the two indole kernels. He prepared indigo from several other reagents, and finally in 1883 he showed, through a synthesis from o-dinitrodiphenyldiacetylene, the exact location of the link, and thus the exact structural formula.

Naturally the German dye industry was interested in the synthesis of indigo, and spent large sums on research to discover a practical process. Baeyer declined to take an active part in eliminating commercial difficulties, and the resulting ill feeling on the part of the dye industry caused him to discontinue further work on dyestuffs and to turn his attention elsewhere. He began an investigation of the polyacetylenes and prepared a number of highly explosive compounds. The properties of these compounds focused his attention on the resistance of double and triple carbon bonds. From these considerations he developed his strain theory, in which the stability of a ring structure is related to the amount of bending necessary to form a closed ring.

A final area of extensive research for Baeyer was that of oxonium compounds. In the course of his work on terpenes Baeyer had used peroxide compounds and had suggested that hydrogen peroxide had the formula HO · HO. Certain phthalein salts, derivatives of pyrone, also had unusual oxygen linkages. At first Baeyer opposed the idea of J. N. Collie and T. Tickle that the oxygen in these compounds becomes quadrivalent and basic, but work with the peroxides and perchloric acid convinced him of the weak basic properties of oxygen, and he called such compounds of oxygen "oxonium compounds."

Baeyer's chemical research was in many ways an extension of Kekulé's work on the tetravalency of carbon. He used this framework to elucidate the structure of compound after compound. His work on indigo indicated that he was not interested merely in synthesis, but also believed that understanding a compound required knowing its exact structure. Baeyer's work on the stability of ring structures showed his concern with the direction of valence bonds and the extent to which the direction can be changed. With the idea that valence bonds can be strained and with his criticism of existing benzene formulas, Baeyer went beyond Kekulé's earlier picture. His final unwillingness to assign a definite structure to benzene, his work on stable and unstable isomers of isatin and indoxyl, which he called lactim and lactam forms, as well as that on phloroglucinol, pointed up difficulties in determining exact structure, which were later resolved with the concept of tautomerism.

Baeyer's approach to chemistry, however, was different from that of Kekulé. Baeyer had little interest in theoretical statements and attacked most problems empirically. His work on benzene, he explained, was only an experimental investigation and not an attempt to prove a particular hypothesis. He was a master at test-tube analysis, and eschewed complicated apparatus.

Most of Baeyer's investigations of compounds grew out of his early work on uric acid derivatives, which Liebig had also investigated. He was instrumental in setting up a chemical laboratory at Munich in 1877 and thus was a successor of Liebig in several senses. As a teacher, Baeyer's strength lay in the laboratory rather than in the lecture hall. He gathered about him a large group of students and assistants, among whom were C. Lieberman, C. Graebe, V. and R. Meyer, and E. and O. Fischer. The enormous number of articles by Baeyer himself, those written with his students, and those written by his students indicates both the scope of the activities in his laboratory and the cooperative nature of the research. Baeyer filled out and extended existing theory by the vast amount of his empirical research, stimulated the chemical dye industry through his work on indigo, and laid the foundation for subsequent work in biochemistry through his investigation of complex ring structures.

BIBLIOGRAPHY

I. ORIGINAL WORKS. Baeyer's works are collected in *Gesammelte Werke* (Brunswick, 1905). Also of interest are unpublished letters to H. Caro, which are in the library of the Deutsches Museum, Munich.

II. SECONDARY LITERATURE. Works on Baeyer include Günther Bugge, "Adolf v. Baeyer," in *Prometheus,* **29** (1917), 1–5; W. Dieckmann, O. Dimroth, F. Friedländer, C. Harries, P. Karrer, R. Meyer, W. Schlenk, H. Wieland, and R. Willstätter, *Die Naturwissenschaften,* Sonderheft zum 80 Geburtstag von Adolf v. Baeyer, **44** (29 Oct. 1915); J. Gillis, "Lettres d'Adolf Baeyer à son ami Jean Servais Stas," in *Mémoires de l'Académie royale de Belgique. Classe des sciences,* **32** (1960), 1–45; J. Partington, "Adolf von Baeyer," in *Nature,* **136** (1935), 669; H. Rupe, *Adolf von Baeyer als Lehrer und Forscher* (Stuttgart, 1932); Karl Schmorl, *Adolf von Baeyer* (Stuttgart, 1952); Richard Willstätter, "Adolf von Baeyer," in *Das Buch der grossen Chemiker,* ed. Günther Bugge (Weinheim, 1955).

RUTH ANNE GIENAPP

AL-BAGHDĀDĪ. See **Ibn Ṭāhir.**

BAGLIVI, GEORGIUS (*b.* Republic of Dubrovnik [now a part of Yugoslavia], 8 September 1668; *d.* Rome, Italy, 15 June 1707), *biology.*

Baglivi's family name was Armeno, which probably indicates that his father was of Armenian origin. His parents were Blasius Armeno and Anna de Lupis, respectable but poor merchants who both died in 1670; Georgius and his younger brother Jacobus were educated first by their uncle and then in the Jesuit College of Dubrovnik. At the age of fifteen, Georgius left his native town and went to southern Italy, where he and his brother were adopted by Pietro Angelo Baglivi, a physician in Lecce. At college Georgius received very good classical training and was imbued with Peripatetic philosophy. He began medical practice with his foster father. After completing his medical studies in Naples and receiving the M.D. degree— probably at Salerno in 1688—Baglivi attended Bellini's lectures at Pisa; worked in hospitals in Padua, Venice, Florence, Bologna, and other Italian cities; traveled to Dalmatia; and finally decided to settle in

Bologna as a pupil and assistant of Marcello Malpighi in 1691.

In his student days Baglivi had been attracted by physiological experiments and by postmortem examinations. Therefore, in 1685 he began to experiment with the infusion of various substances into the jugular veins of dogs and to observe the life habits of tarantulas. From 1689 to 1691, he dissected such various animals as lions, tortoises, snakes, and deer, and made morphological and physiological discoveries, studied the function of *dura mater* by experiments on dogs and observations on wounded men, performed many autopsies, and experimented with toxic drugs. At the same time he served as a physician in many hospitals. In this way he became aware of a curious discrepancy between clinical practice and newly developing biological research. In his opinion, physicians were slaves to systems and hypotheses. Under Malpighi's direction Baglivi experimented on dogs (performing resection of the pneumogastric nerve, infusion of drugs in the veins and spinal canal, and so forth) and on frogs (experiments concerning circulation of blood) and continued his anatomical research, perfecting it by microscopic observations. He studied the fine structure of muscles and of the brain's membranous envelopes.

Accepting a position as the pope's archiater, Malpighi moved from Bologna to Rome, and in 1692 invited Baglivi to join him and to live in his house as a kind of scientific secretary. They collaborated closely until Malpighi's death in 1694. Baglivi performed an autopsy on his master's corpse and gave a very good description of his last illness, cerebral apoplexy. Introduced to the papal court, the friend of such influential scientists as Lancisi, Bellini, Redi, Tozzi, and Trionfetti, and praised as a highly competent practitioner, the young man was destined for a brilliant career. He became the pope's second physician in 1695 and in the following year was elected professor of anatomy at the Sapienza in Rome. In connection with this election, Baglivi published and dedicated to his protector, Innocent XII, a book entitled *De praxi medica* (1696). It was a lucid program of what medicine should be in the future, an attack against the medico-philosophical systems, and a claim for the Hippocratic principles of sound clinical observation. With the exception of some fine general statements in an aphoristic form and a small number of fairly good clinical descriptions (e.g., of typhoid fever and of cardiac decompensation), this book offers little to a modern reader; its style is somewhat baroque, and its factual medical content is often doubtful. In any case, Baglivi's treatise is representative of a stream of thought opposed to philosophical generalizations in medical practice. Baglivi became a member of the Royal Society in 1697, the Academia Naturae Curiosorum and the Arcadia in 1699, and the Accademia dei Fisiocritici in 1700.

The new pope, Clement XI, confirmed Baglivi in his position at court, and even named him professor of theoretical medicine at the Sapienza in 1701. Baglivi's research was now concentrated upon the microscopic structure of muscle fibers and the physical and physiological properties of saliva, bile, and blood. His lectures and anatomical demonstrations, as well as his medical consultations, acquired a very high reputation all over Europe.

His philosophical conception of life phenomena makes Baglivi a member of the iatrophysical school, a defender of biomechanicism. Strongly influenced by Santorio, he wrote a commentary to the latter's *De medicina statica*. Accepting Harvey's theory, Baglivi hoped to complete it with his own theory of fluid circulation in nerves propelled by contractions of the *dura mater*. He was able to distinguish between the smooth and striated muscles; and he discovered the histological distinction between two categories of fibers, which he called *fibrae motrices seu musculares* (with parallel fiber bundles) and *fibrae membranaceae* (with bundles running in various directions). He believed that all physiological and pathological processes should be explained by the living properties of *fibrae*. Baglivi gave new life to the ancient doctrine of the methodists that life and health are determined by the physical balance of the active solids (fibers) and the more passive fluids of the body. His fundamental research concerning the fibers made him one of the most important students of muscle physiology before Albrecht von Haller. Baglivi denied the possibility of spontaneous generation of intestinal parasites, described paralytic phenomena after infusion of certain substances into the spinal canal, and predicted the rise of specific chemotherapy. A strange conflict in his writings is his acceptance of biomechanistic doctrine as a guide for research work and his rejection of all speculative theoretical background in actual medical practice. He said that the iatromathematic physician must forget his theories when he appears at the bedside.

BIBLIOGRAPHY

I. ORIGINAL WORKS. Among Baglivi's writings are *De praxi medica ad priscam observandi rationem revocanda* (Rome, 1696), trans. as *The Practice of Physick* (London, 1704); *De fibra motrice, et morbosa, nec non de experimentis, ac morbis salivae, bilis et sanguinis* (Perugia, 1700); *Speci-*

men quatuor librorum de fibra motrice et morbosa (Rome, 1702); *Canones de medicina solidorum ad rectum statices usum* (Rome, 1704); *Opera omnia medico-practica et anatomica* (Lyons, 1704; new enlarged ed., 1710); and *Opera omnia medico-practica et anatomica*, C. G. Kuhn, ed., 2 vols. (Leipzig, 1827–1828). For a complete list of Baglivi's published works, see M. D. Grmek, *Hrvatska medicinska bibliografija*, I, pt. 1 (Zagreb, 1955), 32–34.

The main collections of Baglivi's papers and letters are in the National Library, Florence; the Waller Collection, Uppsala; and the Osler Collection, McGill University, Montreal.

II. SECONDARY LITERATURE. More information on Baglivi and his work can be found in E. Bastholm, *History of Muscle Physiology* (Copenhagen, 1950), pp. 178–189; A. Castiglioni, "Di un illustre medico raguseo del secolo decimosettimo," in *Rivista di storia critica delle scienze mediche e naturali*, **12** (1921), 1–11; P. Fabre, *Un médecin italien de la fin du XVII siècle: Georges Baglivi* (Paris, 1896); M. D. Grmek, "Osservazioni sulla vita, opera ed importanza storica di Giorgio Baglivi," in *Atti del XIV Congresso Internazionale di Storia della Medicina*, I (Rome, 1954), p. 423, and "Životni put dubrovačkog liječnika Gjure Baglivija," in *Liječnički vjesnik*, **79** (1957), 599–624; J. Jiménez Girona, *La Medicina de Baglivi* (Madrid, 1955); L. Münster, "Nuovi contributi alla biografia di Giorgio Baglivi," in *Archivio storico Pugliese*, **3**, nos. 1–2 (1950); M. Salomon, *Giorgio Baglivi und seine Zeit* (Berlin, 1889); F. Scalzi, *Giorgio Baglivi, altre notizie biografiche* (Rome, 1889); and F. Stenn, "Giorgio Baglivi," in *Annals of Medical History*, 3rd ser., **3** (1941), 183–194.

M. D. GRMEK

BAIER, JOHANN JACOB (*b.* Jena, Germany, 14 June 1677; *d.* Altdorf, Bavaria, 11 July 1735), *medicine, geology, paleontology.*

Baier was the son of Johann Wilhelm Baier, professor of Protestant theology at the University of Jena, and Anna Katharina Musaeus. After private tutoring he matriculated in 1693 at the University of Jena, where he dutifully studied philosophy, classical languages, mathematics, medicine, and natural science. During 1699 and 1700 he traveled in northern Germany and in the Baltic Sea provinces to Riga and Dorpat, enriching his knowledge by conversations with other scholars and by examining collections and visiting libraries. In 1700 he finished his studies and was awarded the degrees of M.A., Ph.D., and M.D. After another educational trip, to visit mining facilities in the Hartz Mountains and university towns in northern Germany, he settled in 1701 as a practicing physician in Nuremberg.

In 1703, during the War of the Spanish Succession, Baier was director of a field hospital for the soldiers of the Nuremberg contingent. The following year he was awarded a professorship at the medical faculty of the University of Altdorf in Nuremberg, which he held until his death. He was twice elected rector of the University. In 1708 he became a member of the Leopoldina (Academy of Natural Scientists) and in 1730 was chosen its president.

Baier's scientific fame today does not rest on his medical investigations, but on his studies of minerals and fossils. At that time the natural sciences could be pursued only within the framework of medicine: oryctography, comprising geology and paleontology, was at the very beginning of its development. Baier's *Oryctographia norica* (1708) was a new, systematic presentation based on his own studies. The work contributed much to disproving the idea that fossils were a mere sport of nature. By means of exact descriptions and good illustrations he laid the foundations for the investigation of Jurassic fauna and of scientific paleontology in general. Instead of theory, he clearly presented what could be observed. He believed that the earth had been created in one act and that the Deluge was the only great change since the Creation. His exact foundation work, however, helped to prepare the ground for the next generation to determine historically the geological structure of mountains and to transform oryctography into geology.

BIBLIOGRAPHY

I. ORIGINAL WORKS. Baier's most important publications (a complete list comprises about forty titles) are *Dissertatio de ambra* (Jena, 1698); *Dissertatio de necessaria salinae inspectione ad conservandum et restaurandum sanitatem* (Halle-Magdeburg, 1698); *Dissertatio de capillis* (Jena, 1700); *Oryctographia norica sive rerum fossilium et ad minerale regnum pertinentium in territorio norimbergensi eiusque vicinia observatarum succincta descriptio* (Nuremberg, 1708); *Wahrhaffte und gründliche Beschreibung der Nürnbergischen Universitätsstadt Altdorf samt dero fürnehmsten Denkwürdigkeiten kürtzlich entworfen und mit accuraten Kupferstichen gezieret* ("Real and True Description of the Nuremberg University Town Altdorf With Its Most Noble Places of Interest Recently Designed and Adorned With Accurate Copper Engravings," Altdorf, 1714); *Horti medici Academia Altorfina historia, curiose conquisita* (Altdorf, 1727); *Orationum varii argumenti, variis occasionibus in Academia Altorfina publice habitarum fasciculus* (Altdorf, 1727); *Biographiae professorum medicinae, qui in Academia Altorfina unquam vixerunt* (Nuremberg-Altdorf, 1728); "Sciagraphia Musei sui. Accendunt supplementa *Oryctographiae noricae*," in *Acta physico-medica Academiae Caesareae Leopoldina-Carolinae Naturae Curiosorum, 2* (1730), Appendix, also published separately (Nuremberg, 1730); *Oryctographia norica sive rerum fossilium et ad minerale regnum pertinentium in territorio Norimbergensi eiusque vicinia observatorum succincta descriptio. Cum supplementis*

a. 1730 editis (Nuremberg, 1758); *Epistolae ad viros eruditos eorumque responsiones historiam literariam et physicam specialem explanantes, curante filio Ferdinando Jacobo Baiero* (Frankfurt-Leipzig, 1760); and "Oryctographia Norica and Supplements," translated from the Latin by Hermann Hornung, with paleontological explanations by Florian Heller, edited and explicated by Bruno von Freyberg, in *Erlanger geologische Abhandlungen, 29* (1958).

II. SECONDARY LITERATURE. Works on Baier are Bruno von Freyberg, "250 Jahre geologische Forschung in Franken," in *Geologische Blätter für Nordost-Bayern und angrenzende Gebiete, 8* (1958), 34–43; "Einführung (in Baiers wissenschaftliches Lebenswerk)," in *Erlanger geologische Abhandlungen, 29* (1958), 7–12; and "Memoria viri perillustris, magnifici excellentissimique domini Joanni Jacobi Baieri," in *Acta physico-medica Academiae Caesareae Leopoldina-Carolinae Naturae Curiosorum, 4,* Appendix, Biographies (1737), 35–48; and Ernst Stromer von Reichenbach, "Johann Jakob Baier, einer der ersten deutschen Paläontologen, ein Beispiel der Willkür des Nachruhmes," in *Natur und Volk, 75/76* (1946), 25–31.

B. V. FREYBERG

BAILAK AL-QABAJAQĪ. See **Baylak al-Qibjāqī.**

BAILEY, EDWARD BATTERSBY (*b.* Marden, England, 1 July 1881; *d.* London, England, 19 March 1965), *geology.*

Bailey was a son of John Battersby Bailey, medical practitioner, and Louise Florence Carr, daughter of a farmer. He was educated at Kendal Grammar School and at Clare College, Cambridge, where he graduated with First-Class Honours in geology and physics in 1902. In 1914 Bailey married Alice Meason, by whom he had a son and a daughter. Alice Meason died in 1956, and six years later he married Mary Young.

While at Cambridge, the reading of a translation of Suess's great synthesis, *Das Antlitz der Erde,* inspired Bailey with a passionate enthusiasm for geological research—an enthusiasm favored by his robust health, remarkable physique, and unusually fertile mind. Temperamentally gay, exuberant, and self-confident, he wrote in a clear, distinctive style characterized by picturesque phrases. In religious matters he was an atheist.

Upon graduation from Cambridge, Bailey became geologist, and later district geologist, with the Geological Survey of Great Britain (in Scotland). He held the latter post until 1929. He then became professor of geology at Glasgow University, and in 1937 returned to government service as director of the Geological Survey and Museum. He retired in 1945. Bailey's many honors included fellowship of the Royal Society, six honorary doctorates, and seven scientific medals. He was knighted in 1945.

His work on the Geological Survey was interrupted from 1915 to 1919, when he served as an artillery subaltern on the Western Front and was twice wounded, losing an eye. By his gallantry he gained the Military Cross, the Croix de Guerre, and the Legion of Honor.

Bailey made notable contributions to tectonics and metamorphism, to igneous and general geology and to the history of the development of geological ideas. His revolutionary tectonic reinterpretation of Dalradian schists in the Scottish Highlands was inspired by the work of his colleagues C. T. Clough and H. B. Maufe, and by excursions in Switzerland and Scandinavia. In Scotland from 1910 onward he introduced new or modified stratigraphical groupings and reinterpreted structure in terms of great recumbent folds and contemporaneous slides (fold faults) that had locally cut out parts of the succession and had then been refolded (1916, 1922, 1925, 1937). Bailey's syntheses met with criticism, details of which may be found in "Discussions" following his *Quarterly Journal* papers and in Read and MacGregor (1948). From time to time he modified his ideas (1930, 1934, 1938), notably because of evidence provided by the current-bedding criterion for stratigraphical order introduced to Scotland in 1930 by T. Vogt and T. L. Tanton. Bailey's mature views (e.g. 1916, revision of 1960) are, in the main, now accepted.

In northern Scotland, Bailey dealt with tectonics and metamorphism in the Moine Thrust areas of Skye and the northwest mainland (1951, 1955). He supported the correlation of Moinian and Torridonian, and the Caledonian age of Moinian and Dalradian metamorphism (1955).

In 1929 Bailey published an account of the Paleozoic mountain systems of Europe and North America, in which he suggested that the crossing of Caledonian and Hercynian chains, begun in southern Wales and Ireland and completed in New England, may be evidence of continental drift. His *Tectonic Essays* (1935) explain Alpine terminology and structure. In later years he produced tectonic reassessments of parts of Iran, Turkey (1953), Provence, Gibraltar, and Liguria (1963).

Bailey's main contributions to Scottish igneous geology stemmed from work with C. T. Clough and H. B. Maufe. In the Glen Coe area they demonstrated a Devonian ring fracture accompanied by a ring intrusion and a central 1,000-foot caldron subsidence of an oval block of schists and Devonian lavas several miles in diameter. A northeasterly dyke swarm was also mapped. These remarkable discoveries were described by Bailey (1909, 1916). Both editions of *The Geology of Ben Nevis* (1916, 1960) include detailed petrographic accounts of Devonian lavas, dykes, and granitic plutons. In a wider study, Bailey inferred that the hornblendic parental Devonian magma was relatively richer in water than the pyroxenic parental British Tertiary magma (1958).

Bailey's compilation of the memoir on the Tertiary volcanic complex of Mull (1924), and its accompanying intricate map, was recognized as a major scientific achievement. He and his colleagues found evidence of a caldera with pillow lavas, innumerable cone sheets, a northwesterly dyke swarm, and massive ring dykes locally modified by gravitative differentiation. Bailey and H. H. Thomas studied the petrology of the complex and introduced the concept of "magma type." There has been controversy over the ring-dyke differentiation, involving Holmes (1936) and Koomans and Kuenen (1938), as well as over the parental magma, the magma-type concept, and the use of terms "tholeiite" and "tholeiitic," in which Kennedy (1933), Wells and Wells (1948), Holmes (1949), Tomkeieff (1949), Tilley (1950), Chayes (1966), Dunham (1966), and Tilley and Muir (1967) participated.

Bailey also reassessed the intrusion tectonics of the Arran granite (1926) and of the volcanic complex of Rhum (1945), both of the Tertiary period. With W. J. McCallien, he later studied pillow lavas and serpentines associated with radiolarian cherts in Scotland, Turkey, and the Apennines, and advocated their submarine origin (1953, 1957, 1960, 1963). In Ireland he and McCallien inferred that dolerite can crack before its crystallization has gone very far and can then be locally chilled by contact with invading colder acid magma (1956); such ideas, originally developed with L. R. Wager (1953), have been criticized by Reynolds (1953) and supported by Skelhorn and Elwell (1966). Bailey's general Scottish work included glaciation studies (1908, 1916, 1924) and an inference that Chalk seas had desert shores (1924).

With L. W. Collet and R. M. Field, Bailey published a reinterpretation of the Quebec and Lévis conglomerates; these were regarded as the products of submarine landslips, detached during successive subsidences along the hinge of the Logan Slope (1928). He was thus led to infer that Kimmeridgian boulder beds in Sutherland originated from movements along a submarine fault scarp (1932). He later suggested that submarine landslips produce graded bedding and may locally merge into submarine mud rivers (1930, 1936, 1940). Kuenen and Migliorini (1950) were led thereby to develop the idea of submarine turbidity currents of high density.

Bailey's historical writings include an invaluable chronological summary of the development of world tectonic research (1935); a history of the Geological Survey (1952); a biography of Sir Charles Lyell (1962); and an account of James Hutton's life and work which includes a commentary on each chapter of Hutton's *Theory of the Earth* (1967).

Obituary notices of Bailey have been written by Stubblefield (1965) and by MacGregor (1966); they contain bibliographies much more comprehensive than that given below.

BIBLIOGRAPHY

I. ORIGINAL WORKS. Bailey's writings include "The Glaciation of East Lothian South of the Garleton Hills," in *Transactions of the Royal Society of Edinburgh,* 46 (1908), 1–31, written with P. F. Kendall; "The Cauldron-subsidence of Glen Coe and the Associated Igneous Phenomena," in *Quarterly Journal of the Geological Society of London,* 65 (1909), 611–678, written with C. T. Clough and H. B. Maufe; *The Geology of Ben Nevis and Glen Coe and the Surrounding Country,* a memoir of the Geological Survey (Edinburgh, 1916, 1960), written with H. B. Maufe *et al.;* "The Structure of the South-west Highlands of Scotland," in *Quarterly Journal of the Geological Society of London,* 78 (1922), 82–131; "The Desert Shores of the Chalk Seas," in *Geological Magazine,* 61 (1924), 102–116; *The Tertiary and Post-Tertiary Geology of Mull, Loch Aline and Oban,* a memoir of the Geological Survey (Edinburgh, 1924), written with C. T. Clough *et al.;* "Perthshire Tectonics; Loch Tummel, Blair Atholl and Glen Shee," in *Transactions of the Royal Society of Edinburgh,* 53 (1925), 671–698; "Domes in Scotland and South Africa: Arran and Vredefort," in *Geological Magazine,* 63 (1926), 481–495; "Palaeozoic Submarine Landslips Near Quebec City," in *Journal of Geology,* 36 (1928), 577–614, written with L. W. Collet and R. M. Field; "The Palaeozoic Mountain Systems of Europe and America," in *Report of the British Association for 1928* (London, 1929), pp. 57–76; "New Light on Sedimentation and Tectonics," in *Geological Magazine,* 78 (1930), 77–92; "Submarine Faulting in Kimmeridgian Times: East Sutherland," in *Transactions of the Royal Society of Edinburgh,* 57 (1932), 429–467, written with J. Weir; "West Highland Tectonics: Loch Leven to Glen Roy," in *Quarterly Journal of the Geological Society of London,* 90 (1934), 462–525; *Tectonic Essays, Mainly Alpine* (Oxford, 1935); "Sedimentation in Relation to Tectonics," in *Bulletin of the Geological Society of America,* 47 (1936), 1713–1726; "Perthshire Tectonics: Schichallion to Glen Lyon," in *Transactions of the Royal Society of Edinburgh,* 59 (1937), 79–117, written with W. J. McCallien; "Northwestern Europe: Caledonides," in *Regionale Geologie der Erde,* II, pt. 2 (Leipzig, 1938), 1–76, written with O. Holtedahl; "American Gleanings: 1936," in *Transactions of the Geological Society of Glasgow,* 20 (1940), 1–16, issued as an offprint in 1938; "Tertiary Igneous Tectonics of Rhum (Inner Hebrides)," in *Quarterly*

Journal of the Geological Society of London, 100 (1945), 165–191; "Scourie Dykes and Laxfordian Metamorphism," in *Geological Magazine,* 88 (1951), 153–165; *Geological Survey of Great Britain* (London, 1952); "Basic Magma Chilled Against Acid Magma," in *Nature,* 172 (1953), 68–69, written with R. L. Wager; "Serpentine Lavas, the Ankara Mélange and the Anatolian Thrust," in *Transactions of the Royal Society of Edinburgh,* 62 (1953), 403–442, written with W. J. McCallien; "Moine Tectonics and Metamorphism in Skye," in *Transactions of the Edinburgh Geological Society,* 16 (1955), 93–166; "Composite Minor Intrusions and the Slieve Gullion Complex, Ireland," in *Liverpool and Manchester Geological Journal,* 1 (1956), 466–501, written with W. J. McCallien; "The Ballantrae Serpentine," in *Transactions of the Edinburgh Geological Society,* 17 (1957), 33–53, written with W. J. McCallien; "Some Chemical Aspects of Southwest Highland Devonian Igneous Rocks," in *Bulletin of the Geological Survey,* 15 (London, 1958), 1–20; "Some Aspects of the Steinmann Trinity, Mainly Chemical," in *Quarterly Journal of the Geological Society of London,* 116 (1960), 365–395, written with W. J. McCallien; *Charles Lyell* (London, 1962); "Liguria Nappe: Northern Apennines," in *Transactions of the Royal Society of Edinburgh,* 65 (1963), 315–333, written with W. J. McCallien; and *James Hutton —The Founder of Modern Geology* (Amsterdam-London-New York, 1967).

II. SECONDARY LITERATURE. Writings dealing with Bailey or his work are F. Chayes, in *American Journal of Science,* 264 (1966), 128–145; K. C. Dunham, in *The Geology of Northern Skye,* a memoir of the Geological Survey (Edinburgh, 1966), p. 157; A. Holmes, in *Geological Magazine,* 73 (1936), 228–238, and *ibid.,* 86 (1949), 71–72; W. Q. Kennedy, in *American Journal of Science,* 25 (1933), 239–256; C. Koomans and P. H. Kuenen, in *Geological Magazine,* 75 (1938), 145–160; P. H. Kuenen and C. I. Migliorini, in *Journal of Geology,* 58 (1950), 91–127; A. G. MacGregor, in *Bulletin of the Geological Society of America,* 77 (1966), "Proceedings," 31–39; H. H. Read and A. G. MacGregor, *British Regional Geology: The Grampian Highlands,* 2nd ed. (Edinburgh, 1948), pp. 16–38; D. L. Reynolds, in *Nature,* 172 (1953), 69; R. R. Skelhorn and R. W. D. Elwell, in *Transactions of the Royal Society of Edinburgh,* 66 (1966), 294; C. J. Stubblefield, in *Biographical Memoirs of the Royal Society of London,* 11 (1965), 1–21; T. L. Tanton, in *Geological Magazine,* 67 (1930), 73–76; C. E. Tilley, in *Quarterly Journal of the Geological Society of London,* 106 (1950), 37–61; C. E. Tilley and I. D. Muir, in *Geological Magazine,* 104 (1967), 337–343; S. I. Tomkeieff, *ibid.,* 86 (1949), 130; T. Vogt, *ibid.,* 67 (1930), 68–73; and M. K. Wells and A. K. Wells, *ibid.,* 85 (1948), 349–357.

A. G. MACGREGOR

BAILEY, LIBERTY HYDE, JR. (*b.* South Haven Township, Michigan, 15 March 1858; *d.* Ithaca, New York, 25 December 1954), *botany, horticulture, agriculture.*

Bailey was the youngest son of Liberty Hyde Bailey, who had migrated from Townshend, Vermont, and Sarah Harrison Bailey, who came of a distinguished Virginia family. At an early age he manifested his precocity in the study of plants, birds, insects, and unusual rocks of the region. Since he grew up in an area abounding in orchards, he was also interested in the grafting of apple tree varieties.

At nineteen, Bailey entered Michigan State (Agricultural) College, where his genius for plant study was soon recognized by William James Beal, a former student of Asa Gray and a pioneer in the laboratory method of teaching botany. Bailey also studied Darwinian evolution, and in 1880 the *Botanical Gazette* (**5** [1880], 76–77) published his article "Michigan Lake Shore Plants." When Bailey received the B.S. degree in 1882, he had been trained in the use of compound microscopes and had begun experiments with *Rubus* and other plants. A brief stint as a reporter on the Springfield, Illinois, *Monitor* followed; but a visit to the herbarium of Michael Schuck Bebb testifies to his continued interest in plants. Late in 1882 Asa Gray of Harvard employed Bailey "at Cambridge . . . for a year or two" as assistant curator of the university herbarium. He was also assistant in physiological experiments and had charge of nomenclature for gardens, greenhouses, and the students' and garden herbaria. In June 1883 he married Annette Smith, of a farm near Lansing, Michigan.

From 1884 through 1900 Bailey published many papers on *Carex,* his first being a catalog that was presented in fuller form in 1887. In 1885 Michigan State (Agricultural) College called him to serve as professor of horticulture and landscape gardening. In that same year the American Pomological Society awarded Bailey its Wilder medal for an exhibit of native nuts and fruits. No later than 1886 he began making crosses and varietal studies in *Cucurbita,* another group on which he became an authority. His instruction in horticulture, in both classroom and field, embraced every facet of the subject as it was then conceived, and introduced such innovations as classification and nomenclature of fruits and vegetables, hybridization, and cross-fertilization of plant varieties. Also in 1886 Bailey was elected president of the Ingham County Horticultural Society, received the M.S. degree from Michigan State, and, with Joseph Charles Arthur, participated in a botanical survey in Minnesota. The first three of his more than sixty books appeared during this period.

In 1888 Bailey was summoned to Cornell University to occupy its chair of practical and experimental horticulture, the first such chair in an American university. He held it with distinction as horticulturist, botanist, rural sociologist, nature-study proponent,

editor, poet, philosopher, and world traveler until 1903, when he became the second director of the College of Agriculture. In May 1904 he was made first dean of the New York State College of Agriculture and director of its experiment station.

Bailey wrote hundreds of papers, but the magnitude of his work may best be indicated by enumerating some of his many honors. He was a founder and first president of the American Society for Horticultural Science (1903), a founder and president of the Botanical Society of America (1926), and twice president of the American Nature-Study Society (1914–1915). He also served as president of the American Association of Agricultural Colleges and Experiment Stations (1906), the American Pomological Society (1917), the American Association for the Advancement of Science (1926), the Fourth International Botanical Congress (1926), the American Country Life Association (1931), and the American Society of Plant Taxonomists (1939). Honorary degrees were conferred on him by Alfred University and the universities of Wisconsin, Vermont, and Puerto Rico, and he was a member of, among many organizations, the National Academy of Sciences, the American Philosophical Society, the American Academy of Arts and Sciences, and the Academy of Natural Sciences of Philadelphia.

In 1908 President Theodore Roosevelt appointed Bailey chairman of his Country Life Commission, which investigated the possibilities of improving rural conditions and, until 1911, submitted recommendations that were nationwide in scope. Bailey was also the founder, developer, and donor of the Bailey Hortorium of the New York State College of Agriculture, which publishes the quarterly journal *Baileya,* devoted to the botany of cultivated plants, their identification, nomenclature, classification, and history. Another periodical, *Gentes herbarum,* founded by Bailey, has attained worldwide influence.

Bailey was a recognized authority on *Carex, Rubus, Cucurbita,* the palms, *Vitis,* and certain of the cultivated groups, notably *Brassica.* He will be most remembered, however, for his great encyclopedias and important manuals of horticulture and agriculture; his summaries of progress; his texts; his books on principles of cultivation, harvesting, plant breeding, and evolution; his (and his daughter Ethel's) *Hortus;* his beautiful and informative "garden" books; and his so-called background books.

BIBLIOGRAPHY

Additional works on Bailey are addresses published in *Baileya,* **6,** and delivered at Cornell University, mid-March

1958, on the celebration of the Liberty Hyde Bailey centennial; E. Eugene Barker, "Liberty Hyde Bailey, Philosopher and Poet," in *Cornell Countryman,* **14,** no. 1 (1958), 13 f.; Lewis Knudson, "Liberty Hyde Bailey," in *Science,* **121** (1955), 322–323; George H. M. Lawrence, "Liberty Hyde Bailey, 1858–1954," in *Baileya,* 3 (1955), 27–40, with a list of degrees, honors, and societies and a bibliography; "Liberty Hyde Bailey, the Botanist," in *Bulletin of the Torrey Botanical Club,* **82** (1955), 300–305; "Professor L. H. Bailey," in *Nature,* **175** (1955), 451–452; and "The Bailey Hortorium, Its Past and Present," in *Baileya,* **4,** no. 1 (1956), 1–9; Andrew Denny Rodgers III, *Liberty Hyde Bailey, A Story of American Plant Sciences* (Princeton, 1949), see "Acknowledgments" for source materials—also a facsimile of 1949 ed. (New York, 1965), and "*Portrait* Liberty Hyde Bailey," in *American Scholar* (Summer 1951), 336–340.

ANDREW DENNY RODGERS III

BAILEY, LORING WOART (*b.* West Point, New York, 28 September 1839; *d.* Fredericton, Canada, 10 January 1925), *geology.*

Loring Bailey was born at the United States Military Academy, where his father, Jacob Whitman Bailey, was professor of chemistry, mineralogy, and geology. His mother was Maria Slaughter Bailey. He received both his bachelor of arts degree (1859) and his master's degree (1861) from Harvard University. He thereupon moved to Canada, where from 1861 until his retirement in 1907 he held the chair of chemistry and natural science at the University of New Brunswick in Fredericton. In August 1863, Bailey married Laurestine Marie d'Avray.

The position at the university required that Bailey teach physics, chemistry, zoology, physiology, botany, and geology. After several years, however, the first two subjects were assigned to a colleague. At the beginning he had some knowledge of chemistry but little of the other fields—least of all geology. Yet geology captured his attention, primarily because of the complex stratigraphical relations of New Brunswick, which the previous studies by Abraham Gesner, J. William Dawson, and James Robb had done little to elucidate. Together with George F. Matthew and Charles F. Hartt, Bailey was the first to find fossils of Cambrian age in New Brunswick (near St. John), thus establishing the base for deciphering the chronostratigraphic interrelationships of a large area. Bailey's numerous studies of the region not only provided an extensive foundation for further work in New Brunswick but also contributed to the understanding of the geology of neighboring New England, especially Maine. His *Report on the Mines and Minerals of New Brunswick* and his *Observations on the Geology of Southern New Brunswick* are classics of regional geology. Most of Bailey's numerous publications were in the form of official reports, lectures, and newspaper and magazine articles.

After his retirement from professorial duties and from summer field work, Bailey continued his biological researches, in particular the microscopic investigation of diatoms. (His first publication, in 1861, had been the completed form of his father's "Microscopical Organisms from South America," which the elder Bailey had left unfinished at his death in 1857.) During the course of his research, which was carried out in conjunction with the St. Andrews Marine Biological Station, the number of known New Brunswick diatoms increased from fifty to about four hundred. His work resulted in a catalog of Canadian diatoms, which was issued late in 1924. In 1888 and 1918 Bailey served as president of the geology section of the Royal Society of Canada, of which he was a charter member.

BIBLIOGRAPHY

The only published list of Loring Bailey's works is contained in *Loring Woart Bailey: The Story of a Man of Science* (St. John, 1925), his reminiscences, collected and edited by his son, Joseph Whitman Bailey. His most important regional studies are *Report on the Mines and Minerals of New Brunswick* (Fredericton, 1864); "Notes on the Geology and Botany of New Brunswick," in *Canadian Naturalist,* **1** (1864), 81–97; *Observations on the Geology of Southern New Brunswick . . . with a Geological Map* (Fredericton, 1865); and *The Mineral Resources of the Province of New Brunswick,* Geological Survey of Canada, Annual Report, n.s. **10,** part M (Ottawa, 1898). His microscopic biology begins with "Notes on New Species of Microscopical Organisms from the Para River, South America," in *Boston Journal of Natural History,* **7** (July 1861), 329–351, and concludes with "An Annotated Catalogue of the Diatoms of Canada showing their Geographical Distribution," in *Contributions to Canadian Biology,* n.s. **2** (1924), 31–68.

The biography by his son provides little insight into or information on Bailey's scientific achievements; for such see W. F. Ganong's memoir in *Proceedings and Transactions of the Royal Society of Canada* (May 1925), pp. xiv–xvii.

BERT HANSEN

BAILEY, SOLON IRVING (*b.* Lisbon, New Hampshire, 29 December 1854; *d.* Norwell, Massachusetts, 5 June 1931), *astronomy, meteorology.*

Bailey pioneered in studies in the southern hemisphere for the Harvard Observatory, at a time when there were no large telescopes south of the equator. His two main contributions to astronomy were studies of variable stars in globular clusters and his long-exposure photographs, which not only helped to elucidate the structure of our galaxy but also showed the value of photography in detecting extragalactic objects too faint to be observed visually.

Graduating from Boston University with an A.M. degree in 1884, Bailey began a career with the Harvard Observatory that was to last forty-four years. He earned a second A.M. degree from Harvard in 1888 and was then sent to South America by E. C. Pickering (director of the Observatory), to find a suitable location for Harvard's proposed southern observing post.

Bailey traveled throughout Peru and Chile, trying out various sites. No information on weather patterns was available to make his task easier, so he established a chain of meteorological stations—from sea level up to 19,000 feet. He published the data that he accumulated over the following thirty-seven years in his "Peruvian Meteorology" (1889 to 1930). As a result of his survey, Harvard's Boyden station, with the 24-inch Bruce doublet as its main telescope, was established near the city of Arequipa in Peru and remained in operation from 1890 until 1927.

Bailey took with him to Peru the visual photometer used for the original "Harvard Photometry," a compilation of standard magnitudes for stars located north of declination −30° (1884, 1885), and with it completed Harvard's coverage of the sky (1895). He then began photographing ω Centauri and other globular clusters, to get light curves for over a hundred of the stars now called cluster variables (1902, 1916); this work proved fundamental to estimates of astronomical distances subsequently made by Harlow Shapley and others.

Bailey's photographs of regions in and away from the plane of the Milky Way were made with exposures ranging up to nineteen hours and twenty-seven minutes (1908, 1913, 1917). They were used for relative star counts and also revealed more than 3,000 new extragalactic objects.

Bailey served as acting director of the Harvard Observatory from 1919 to 1921, between the tenures of Pickering and Shapley. During his fifth and final stay in Arequipa, in 1923, the University of San Agustín awarded him an honorary Sc.D. degree. His other honors included election to the National Academy of Sciences in Washington. After retiring in 1925 he completed his *History and Work of the Harvard Observatory, 1839–1927* (1931).

BIBLIOGRAPHY

I. ORIGINAL WORKS. Except for the *History and Work of the Harvard College Observatory, 1839–1927,* which was published as Harvard Observatory Monograph No. 4 (Cambridge, Massachusetts, 1931), all works cited in the text appeared in *Annals of the Astronomical Observatory of Harvard College.* The original "Harvard Photometry" had appeared as "Observations with the Meridian Photometer during the years 1879–1882," by E. C. Pickering, Arthur Searle, and Oliver C. Wendell, in *Annals,* **14,** part I (1884), 1–324, and **14,** part II (1885), 325–512; Bailey's extension of it was "A Catalogue of 7922 Southern Stars Observed with the Meridian Photometer during the years 1889–1891" (reduced under the direction of E. C. Pickering), *ibid.,* **34** (1895), 1–259. The other papers by Bailey were "A Discussion of Variable Stars in the Cluster ω Centauri," *ibid.,* **38** (1902), 1–252; "Globular Clusters," *ibid.,* **76** (1916), 43–82; "A Catalogue of Bright Clusters and Nebulae," *ibid.,* **60** (1908), 199–229; "The Southern Milky Way," *ibid.,* **72** (1913), 71–78, with 9 half-tone plates; and "The Northern Milky Way," *ibid.,* **80** (1917), 83–89, with 9 half-tone plates.

Bailey's "Peruvian Meteorology," covering the period 1888–1925, appeared in the *Annals* in six parts: **39,** part I (1889), 1–153; **39,** part II (1906), 157–292; **49,** part I (1907), 1–103; **49,** part II (1908), 107–232; **86,** part III (1923), 123–194; and **87,** part 2A (1930), 179–217.

II. SECONDARY LITERATURE. Annie Jump Cannon wrote two obituaries of Bailey: one in *Monthly Notices of the Royal Astronomical Society,* **92** (1932), 263–266; the other, with a portrait, appeared in *Publications of the Astronomical Society of the Pacific,* **43** (October, 1931), 317–323 and was reprinted, with the addition of a list of 95 publications by Bailey, in *Biographical Memoirs of the National Academy of Sciences* (Washington), **15** (1934), 193–203.

SALLY H. DIEKE

BAILLIE, MATTHEW (*b.* Shots Manse, Lanarkshire, Scotland, 27 October 1761; *d.* Duntisbourne, Gloucestershire, England, 23 September 1823), *medicine.*

Baillie's father was a Presbyterian minister in Shots, and later professor of divinity at Glasgow University. His mother, Dorothy Hunter Baillie, was the sister of the famous surgeons John and William Hunter. His sister, Joanna Baillie, was a well-known playwright and poet, who was an intimate friend of Sir Walter Scott. Baillie attended Hamilton Grammar School, Glasgow University, and, for a year, Balliol College, Oxford. He had won a scholarship to Oxford shortly after his father died, and before moving to Oxford he stayed in London with his uncle William Hunter, who operated the famous Windmill Street School of Anatomy. He soon was affiliated with the school, and when his uncle died in 1783, Baillie, then twenty-two, became master of the school. His uncle also left him the use of his medical museum for twenty years (after which it was to revert to Glasgow University) and a considerable fortune. In 1787 Baillie was elected physician to St. George's Hospital, a position he held for thirteen years. He received the M.D. from Oxford in 1789 and soon after became a fellow of the Royal College of Physicians as well as of the Royal Society. In 1791 he married Sophia Denman, sister of the Lord Chief Justice. The couple had two children.

Baillie's great importance is in the field of pathology. His *Morbid Anatomy of Some of the Most Important Parts of the Human Body* (1795) was the first English text on pathology, and the first systematic study in any language. Although Joseph Lieutaud and Giovanni-Battista Morgagni had earlier published studies in the field, Baillie was the first to take the various organs of the body serially and set forth the diverse morbid conditions of each. He believed that by studying the altered structure of morbid anatomy, it might be possible for the physician to learn what had caused the changes. Baillie was, however, careful not to go beyond his observations, and his modest goal prevented him from analyzing, correlating, or theorizing about his data. Most of his descriptions are based upon his own firsthand observations, many of them from specimens preserved by his uncles in their medical museum. Although explanations of morbid appearances have changed radically since his time, Baillie's descriptions are still of value. His work is limited primarily to thoracic and abdominal organs and the brain; he ignored changes observed in the skeleton, muscles, nerves, and spinal cord. In general, Baillie was quite logical in his procedures, and he carefully distinguished between inflamed states, thickenings, hardenings, softenings, ulcers, tubercles, aneurysms, and the like. The second and subsequent editions of his work included sections on symptoms to be observed. Most subsequent pathology textbooks have been modeled on his.

Once his study of morbid anatomy had been published, and then revised and illustrated, Baillie concentrated on the practice of medicine. By 1800 he had the largest medical practice in London, and he has been called the most popular physician of his time. His bust was later placed in Westminster Abbey; and when the London Pathological Society was founded in 1846, its members put Baillie's portrait on their seal. He left a fortune of over £80,000.

BIBLIOGRAPHY

I. ORIGINAL WORKS. Baillie's major work is *The Morbid Anatomy of Some of the Most Important Parts of the Human Body* (London, 1795; rev. 1797, 1799), the 1799 ed. illustrated with engravings. Earlier he had edited a MS by his uncle William Hunter that is often credited to Baillie:

Anatomy of the Gravid Uterus (London, 1794). Many of his essays, accompanied by a brief sketch of his life, were published in *The Works of Matthew Baillie,* James Wardrop, ed., 2 vols. (London, 1825).

II. SECONDARY LITERATURE. Information about Baillie's career is usually included in various works that discuss William and John Hunter. There is, for example, a brief biographical sketch of him in Richard Hingston Fox, *William Hunter, Anatomist, Physician, Obstetrician* (London, 1901), pp. 26–29. See also William Macmichael, *The Gold Headed Cane,* 7th ed. (Springfield, Ill., 1953), pp. 165–185; and Benjamin Ward Richardson, *Disciples of Aesculapius,* 2 vols. (London, 1900), II, 554–572. For an assessment of his importance, see Lester S. King, *The Medical World of the Eighteenth Century* (Chicago, 1958), pp. 277–281.

VERN L. BULLOUGH

BAILLOU, GUILLAUME DE, also known as **Baillon** and **Ballonius** (*b.* Paris, France, *ca.* 1538; *d.* Paris, 1616), *medicine.*

Baillou was the son of a mathematician and noted architect. He became a physician in 1570 and dean of the Faculty of Medicine in 1580. He had a reputation for dialectics and was known as "the bane of the bachelors," but he also was the most erudite and well-read doctor of his time—famous for his eloquence, the clarity of his courses, and his writings, almost all of which were published posthumously. Baillou fought against the tradition of Arab medicine and revived the Hippocratic tradition of clinical observation, human understanding, and macrocosmic concepts of illnesses and their treatment. Consequently, he thought that solar eclipses and the position of the stars were important in medical practice, and restored a little of the astrology completely eliminated by Jean Fernel—whose pupil he never was, despite claims to the contrary.

During the many epidemics in Paris between 1570 and 1579, Baillou developed the idea of the ephemerides, which influenced the work of Thomas Sydenham. He was thus the first Occidental epidemiologist since Hippocrates. He left excellent descriptions of the plague (and possibly of typhoid fever); of measles, which he distinguished from variola; and of diphtheria, whose choking false membranes he identified. Baillou is also credited with the first mention of adhesive pericarditis complicated by edema, and of whooping cough (*tussis quinta*). The latter is uncertain, however, for whooping cough seems to have been diagnosed in the *Khulasat-ul Tajjarib* (1501) of Baha'-ul-Douleh, an Iranian doctor.

Baillou brought rheumatism into nosology, and in this connection he gave a learned presentation of Fernel's, Lepois's, and Felix Platter's rather vague conceptions of the overflow of phlegm and aqueous humors. Fernel thought the *distillatio* was a superfluous humor running down from the head into the declivitous parts of the human organism and was the sole cause of chronic arthritis and crural neuralgia. He had located these ailments, two hundred years before Domenico Cotugno, in the sciatic notch, which was the seat of the diffusion of pain. Baillou attributed to rheumatism all pain in the external *habitus corporis,* that is, all areas situated between the skin and the internal parts of the body. The *habitus corporis* therefore included cellular tissues, muscles, tendons, aponeuroses, bones, and joints. He went on to describe a rheumatic diathesis (not necessarily articular) with painful localizations in the limbs. This was in the form of gout, sciatica, and arthritis or *morbus articularis* (rheumatic fever or subacute or chronic rheumatism). To this infinitely variable disease Baillou related all pains of the external body, from scurvy, smallpox, and lead poisoning to those thought to be caused by wind, worms, and other obscure agents.

BIBLIOGRAPHY

I. ORIGINAL WORKS. Baillou's writings are *Comparatio medici cum chirurgo ad castigandum quorumdam chirurgicorum audaciam* (Paris, 1577); *Consiliorum medicinalium libri duo* (Paris, 1635–1639), also published separately (Vol. II only) by Jacques Thévart (Paris, 1640); *Definitionum medicinalium liber* (Paris, 1639); *De convulsionibus libellus* (Paris, 1640); *Epidemiorum et ephemeridum libri duo* (Paris, 1640), also in Ralph Mayor, *Classic Descriptions of Disease* (Lawrence, Kans., 1932), pp. 94–96, 159–160, and translated into French by Prosper Yvaren as *Épidémies et éphémérides* (Paris, 1858); *Liber de rhumatismo et pleuritide dorsali* (Paris, 1642), trans. by Barnard in *British Journal of Rheumatism,* **2** (1940), 141–162; *Commentarius ad libellum Theophrasti de Vertigine. De virginum et mulierum morbis liber* (Paris, 1643); *Opuscula medica de arthritide, de calculo et urinarum hypostasi* (Paris, 1643); *Adversaria medicinalia* (Paris, 1644); and *Opera omnia medica,* 4 vols. (Paris, 1685), also Tronchin, ed., 4 vols. (Geneva, 1762).

II. SECONDARY LITERATURE. Works on Baillou are A. Chéreau, "Baillou," in *Dictionnaire encyclopédique des sciences médicales,* VIII (Paris, 1878); A. Delpeuch, *Histoire des maladies—La goutte et le rhumatisme* (Paris, 1900); Charles Fiessinger, *La thérapeutique des vieux maîtres* (Paris, 1897), pp. 110–115; E. W. Goodhall, "A French Epidemiologist of the Sixteenth Century," in *Annals of Medical History,* **7** (1935), 409–427, and "De Baillou Clinician and Epidemiologist," in *Journal of the American Medical Association,* **195** (1966), 957; and Philippe Very, "Il y a 350 ans mourait Guillaume de Baillou," in *Scalpel,* **119** (1966), 677–678.

PIERRE HUARD

BAILLY, JEAN-SYLVAIN (*b.* Paris, France, 15 September 1736; *d.* Paris, 12 November 1793), *astronomy.*

Bailly was born in the Louvre, where his father, Jacques, as keeper of the king's paintings, had an apartment. His father also owned a house in Chaillot, a fashionable suburb of Paris. Bailly later took up residence there, where he met Madame Gaye, a widow whom he married in 1787. Little is known of his youth, but it appears that he received schooling that would prepare him to assume his father's office, a position held by a member of the family since Bailly's great-grandfather. He succeeded to the title in 1768. Bailly was relieved of his functions in 1783 but continued to receive the pension accorded to the position and to be known as honorary keeper. When he was about twenty, he received mathematics lessons from Montcarville of the Collège Royal. Shortly thereafter he met Nicolas de Lacaille, France's greatest observational astronomer, and Alexis Clairaut, France's greatest theoretical astronomer. The further studies that he pursued with them directed him into his lifework.

Bailly undertook his first astronomical research in 1759—concerned, appropriately, with Halley's comet. His paper on the comet's theory, read to and published by the Académie des Sciences, pointed out that one could not conclude the duration of its revolution from that of its visibility. This paper was based upon the observations of Lacaille.

In 1760 Bailly established his own observatory in the Louvre. Although not ideal, the site served him well, and he felt it important for an astronomer to base his theories on his own observations. He now began to do this with Jupiter's satellites, reading two papers on this subject in 1762 and adding a third near the end of 1763.

By the time he read the third report, Bailly had become a member of the Académie. In January 1763 Bailly was elected to the vacancy created by the death of Lacaille, probably because he had been Lacaille's protégé and was engaged in editing an unfinished work of his. He had also shown greater promise than his competitors, Jeaurat and Messier, of significant theoretical researches.

Bailly approached the problem of inequalities in the motions of the four known satellites of Jupiter with Clairaut's lunar theory in mind. Improvements had been made in tables of the motions since Cassini's 1668 ephemerides, but these improvements had been made empirically. Bailly was the first to attempt to achieve better tables theoretically, by treating each satellite in turn as the third body in a three-body problem. His success was not complete—there were considerable discrepancies between his theoretical formulation of orbitary elements and their observed values—but he did demonstrate that the problem was amenable to solution by Newtonian principles.

Bailly's memoirs sparked interest in this subject, and the Académie made it the topic of its essay contest for 1766. As an Academician, Bailly could not win the prize; nevertheless, he considered himself in competition with the astronomers who entered, and therefore synthesized and extended his earlier researches to produce his major *Essai*. Although excellent, this work was greatly overshadowed by the prize-winning entry of Lagrange. As Bailly himself later admitted, Lagrange's use of the new method of the variation of parameters allowed him to resolve almost completely the problem of five simultaneously perturbed bodies, as opposed to his own continuing series of three-body treatments.

In 1766 there arose the possibility of Bailly's succeeding the ailing Grandjean de Fouchy as perpetual secretary of the Académie. To prepare for this position, Bailly wrote several *éloges*. He did not achieve his goal, however; in 1770 Fouchy named Condorcet as his assistant.

Bailly followed this setback with one of his best scientific papers, his 1771 memoir on the inequalities of the light of Jupiter's satellites. Fouchy had earlier noted that a satellite disappeared before its total immersion and that, at its emersion, it was observed only when a small segment had already emerged from the planet's shadow. He concluded that the size of the segment involved depended upon the amount of the particular satellite's light. Utilizing a new observational technique, Bailly confirmed Fouchy's theory while coupling his study of light intensities with determinations of the diameters of the satellites. The resultant paper added greatly to contemporary knowledge of Jupiter's satellites and suggested a standard observing method to reduce instrument and observer errors. Because the fourth satellite had not been eclipsing during the period of his observations, the memoir dealt only with the first three satellites. Bailly never completed the study, for this paper was his last theoretical effort.

Having moved to his father's house in Chaillot, Bailly turned his attention to literary pursuits. These were given direction by his scientific activity, as shown in the four-volume history of astronomy that he published between 1775 and 1782. These tomes represent his most lasting achievement and were responsible for additional honors. In 1783 he was elected to the Académie Française, and two years later he was named to the Académie des Inscriptions et Belles-Lettres. This made him a triple academician, the only Frenchman besides Bernard de Fontenelle to achieve this distinction.

Meanwhile, Bailly continued to work within the Académie des Sciences, although not at astronomical pursuits. In 1784 he was named to the commission appointed to investigate the extravagant claims then being made for "animal magnetism" by Mesmer and others, and he drafted the commission's damning report on that alleged phenomenon. It was probably for this service that, near the end of 1784, Bailly was made a supernumerary pensioner within the Académie. A year later he was appointed to a commission to investigate the Hôtel Dieu, the hospital of the poor of Paris; again he prepared the findings. Three reports submitted between 1786 and 1788 deplored the miserable conditions existing at the hospital and suggested means for their correction.

It was chiefly acclaim through these reports that catapulted Bailly into public affairs at the beginning of the French Revolution; the movement culminated on 15 July 1789 in his unanimous proclamation as the first mayor of Paris. He was reelected for a second term in August 1790, but in this second year he lost popularity, particularly after the unfortunate massacre of the Champ-de-Mars. Although he retired from office in November 1791 and left Paris in July 1792, he was not forgotten. Arrested in September 1793, Bailly was soon tried, found guilty, and condemned to the guillotine. Like those of his victims, his head fell on the Champ-de-Mars.

BIBLIOGRAPHY

I. ORIGINAL WORKS. Bailly's first paper, the "Mémoire sur la théorie de la comète de 1759," was published in the *Mémoires de mathématiques et de physique présentés à l'Académie Royale des sciences par divers savans et lûs dans ses assemblées,* **5** (1768), 12–18. The Académie employed this journal, generally known as its collection of memoirs *par savants étrangers,* as an outlet for papers by scientists who, like Bailly at that time, were not members of the Académie and, thus, were "foreign" to it. This would have been the case with his first two papers "sur la théorie des satellites de Jupiter," except that he reread them to the Académie after attaining membership; thus, these and the third were published in the regular *Mémoires de l'Académie Royale des sciences* for 1763. He also placed many subsequent papers there, including, most importantly, his "Mémoire sur les inégalités de la lumière des satellites de Jupiter, sur la mesure de leur diamètres, et sur un moyen aussi simple que commode de rendre les observations comparables, en remédiant à la différence des vues et des lunettes" (1771), pp. 580–667. His *Essai sur la théorie des satellites de Jupiter,* on the other hand, was issued as a separate volume with *privilège* granted by the Académie (Paris, 1766).

Two of Bailly's *éloges,* those of Corneille and Leibniz, won prizes. They were published separately by the appropriate institutions: the Académie des Sciences, Belles-Lettres & Arts of Rouen (Rouen, 1768) and the Académie Royale des Sciences et des Belles-Lettres of Berlin (Berlin, 1769), respectively. These were incorporated with others, including that of Lacaille, in a collection (Berlin, 1770). But all of these and some later ones may be most conveniently consulted in Vol. I of the two-volume *Discours et mémoires* (Paris, 1790).

The first of Bailly's historical works was the *Histoire de l'astronomie ancienne, depuis son origine jusqu'à l'établissement de l'école d'Alexandre* (Paris, 1775). Its argument for an antediluvean astronomy that prepared the way for the astronomers of recorded history brought him into conflict with Voltaire and resulted in the publication of his *Lettres sur l'origine des sciences* (Paris-London, 1777) and the similar *Lettres sur l'Atlantide de Platon* (Paris-London, 1778). These were sidelights, however, and he continued to work on the larger theme. His *Histoire de l'astronomie moderne* appeared in two stages. Two volumes, devoted to the period up to 1730, were published in 1779, and were followed by a third that brought the story up to 1782, the year of its publication. To these he added a special *Traité de l'astronomie indienne et orientale* (Paris, 1787).

The *Rapport des commissaires chargés par le roi de l'examen du magnétisme animal* was published separately by order of the king (Paris, 1784), as were the three hospital reports (Paris, 1786, 1787, 1788). The latter were subsequently reprinted in the *Histoire de l'Académie Royale des sciences,* which prefaces each volume of the regular *Mémoires,* but in association with incorrect years, as follows: (1785), 1–110; (1786), 1–9, 13–40. As with his earlier *éloges,* all of these and other reports may be consulted in his *Discours et mémoires,* Vol. II.

Bailly's own treatment of his political career is contained in the three-volume *Mémoires de Bailly, avec une notice sur la vie, des notes et des éclaircissemens historiques* (Paris, 1821), which constitute Vols. VIII–X of Berville and Barrière's *Collection des mémoires relatifs à la révolution française. . . .*

II. SECONDARY LITERATURE. A definitive biography has not yet been written. The most important general account by a contemporary is that by Bailly's friend Mérard de Saint-Just: *Éloge historique de Jean-Sylvain Bailly au nom de la république de lettres, par une société de gens de lettres; suivi de notes et de quelques pièces en prose et en vers* (London, 1794). Providing more insight into his astronomical work are J. J. Lalande's "Éloge de Bailly," originally published in the *Décade philosophique* of 30 pluviôse an III, **4** (1795), 321–330, but more easily consulted in his *Bibliographie astronomique . . .* (Paris, 1803), pp. 730–736; J. B. J. Delambre's treatment in his *Histoire de l'astronomie au dix-huitième siècle* (Paris, 1827), pp. 735–748; and D. F. Arago's "Bailly, biographie lue en séance publique de l'Académie des Sciences, le 26 février 1844," in his *Oeuvres complètes,* II (Paris, 1854), 247–426. On Bailly's observa-

tory, see G. Bigourdan, *Histoire de l'astronomie d'observation et des observatoires en France,* part 2 (Paris, 1930), 125–132.

Ignoring works that concentrate on his political career, the best modern study is E. B. Smith, "Jean-Sylvain Bailly; Astronomer, Mystic, Revolutionary, 1736–1793," in *Transactions of the American Philosophical Society,* n.s., **44** (1954), 427–538. Based entirely upon printed sources—and, in fact, providing a comprehensive checklist of Bailly's printed works and an extensive bibliography—Smith's work should be supplemented by an article devoted to demonstrating the existence of various as yet unused manuscript sources on Bailly: R. Hahn, "Quelques nouveaux documents sur Jean-Sylvain Bailly," in *Revue d'histoire des sciences,* **8** (1955), 338–353.

SEYMOUR L. CHAPIN

BAILY, FRANCIS (*b.* Newbery, Berkshire, England, 28 April 1774; *d.* London, England, 30 August 1844), *astronomy, metrology.*

Baily was one of the founders of the Astronomical Society of London (later the Royal Astronomical Society). His enthusiasm and organizing ability served to arouse interest in astronomy and to put its practical aspects on a firm footing. Today he is remembered (although frequently with his name misspelled) for "Baily's beads," an effect seen during solar eclipses by many men before Baily but never so vividly described.

Baily, the third son of a banker, received only an elementary education. At the age of fourteen he was apprenticed to a London mercantile firm. As soon as his seven years of apprenticeship were up, Baily set sail for the United States and two years of rugged adventures at sea and in the backwoods, which he described in his *Journal.* He returned to England in 1798, hoping to spend his life as an explorer. When all efforts to obtain backing for such a career proved fruitless, he became a stockbroker instead. Before the end of the Napoleonic wars he had published several actuarial tables, *An Epitome of Universal History,* and an astronomical paper (1811).

Having prospered on the stock exchange, Baily retired at the age of fifty to devote his full time to astronomy. He had become a fellow of the Royal Society in 1821 and was to serve the Astronomical Society as president during four two-year terms, the first beginning in 1825 and the last interrupted by his death.

Baily's first substantial astronomical work dealt with methods of determining latitude and time by the stars. Since no up-to-date star catalog was available for this purpose, Baily calculated the mean positions of 2,881 stars for the epoch 1 January 1830; this work, published in 1826, earned him his first Gold Medal from the Astronomical Society. (The second came in 1843, for his redetermination of the density of the earth.)

Work on the standard pendulum, the standard yard, and the ellipticity of the earth followed, interspersed among revisions of many star catalogs. In the course of preparing a new edition of the *Historica coelestis* of 1712, Baily found and published (1835) evidence that Edmund Halley, the second astronomer royal, had unduly maligned his predecessor, John Flamsteed.

It was during the annular eclipse of 15 May 1836, which he observed from Inch Bonney in Scotland, that Baily first saw the "beads." They are a transient phenomenon often seen at the beginning and end of totality in a solar eclipse, when the edge of the moon is close to inner tangency and a thin crescent of sunlight shines between mountains on the moon's limb. In Baily's own words, they appear as "a row of lucid points, like a string of bright beads . . . running along the lunar disc with beautiful coruscations of light." His report (1838) included a list of all previous observers, beginning with Halley in 1715, and aroused keen interest. For the solar eclipse of 8 July 1842, many astronomers accordingly journeyed to Italy, where the eclipse was to be total. The British astronomer royal, George B. Airy, who was in Turin, looked for, but did not see, "Mr. Baily's beads"; Baily himself, in Pavia, did see them but only at the beginning of totality (1846).

Astronomical Society, **10** (1838), 1–42; "Some Remarks on the Total Eclipse of the Sun on July 8th, 1842," *ibid.,* **15** (1846), 1–8.

Ninety-one publications are listed in the preface to Baily's travel diary, *Journal of a Tour in Unsettled Parts of North America in 1796 and 1797,* Augustus de Morgan, ed. (London, 1856), pp. 61–69; fifty appear in the Royal Society of London's *Catalogue of Scientific Papers,* I (London, 1867), 158–160. Baily's long articles constitute the bulk of the first fifteen volumes of the *Memoirs of the* [*Royal*] *Astronomical Society of London* (1822–1846)—his edition of Tobias Mayer's star catalog in **4** (1831), 391–445; of the Abbé de La Caille's catalog in **5** (1833), 93–124; of the catalogs of Ptolemy, Ulugh Beigh, Tycho Brahe, Halley, and Hevelius in **13** (1843), prefaces 1–48, tables (1)–(248), with errata facing p. 1; his work on the earth's ellipticity in **7** (1834), 1–378; on the standard yard in **9** (1836), 35–184; and on the earth's density in **14** (1843), 1–120 with tables on i–ccxlvii. His paper on correcting a pendulum to vacuum is in *Philosophical Transactions of the Royal Society of London,* **122** (1832), 399–492. Three more star catalogs were completed and published posthumously: a revision of Jérôme Lalande's *Histoire céleste française* and of La Caille's southern hemisphere stars (both London, 1847) and finally the ultimate evidence of Baily's industry, the British Association for the Advancement of Sciences' catalog of almost 10,000 stars (London, 1845).

II. SECONDARY LITERATURE. Baily's entry in *Dictionary of National Biography,* II (London, 1885), 427–432, written by Agnes M. Clerke, includes an appraisal of his achievements. An obituary by Sir John Herschel appeared in *Philosophical Magazine* (London), ser. 3, **26** (1845), 38–75, and was reprinted, with additions, as part of the preface to Baily's *Journal.*

SALLY H. DIEKE

BIBLIOGRAPHY

I. ORIGINAL WORKS. Baily's works mentioned in the text are *Tables for the Purchasing and Renewing of Leases for Terms of Years Certain and for Lives* (London, 1802; 3rd ed., 1812); *The Doctrine of Life-Annuities and Assurances Analytically Investigated* (London, 1810; appendix 1813); "On the Solar Eclipse Said to Have Been Predicted by Thales," in *Philosophical Transactions of the Royal Society,* **101** (1811), 220–241; *An Epitome of Universal History,* 2 vols. (London, 1813); "On the Construction and Use of Some New Tables for Determining the Apparent Places of Nearly 3000 Principal Fixed Stars," in *Memoirs of the* [*Royal*] *Astronomical Society of London,* **2** (1826), whole appendix: Baily's Preface iii–xli, auxiliary tables xlii–liv, the general catalog lv–ccxxi, supplementary tables ccxx–ccxxiii, errata ccxxiv; *An Account of the Revd. John Flamsteed, the First Astronomer Royal* (London, 1835; facsimile reprint, omitting the star catalog, London, 1966); "On a Remarkable Phenomenon that Occurs in Total and Annular Eclipses of the Sun," in *Memoirs of the Royal*

BAIN, ALEXANDER (*b.* Aberdeen, Scotland, 11 June 1818; *d.* Aberdeen, 18 September 1903), *philosophy, psychology.*

Alexander Bain was the son of George Bain, a handloom weaver. Poverty forced the father to take young Alexander out of school at the age of eleven, and for the next seven years the boy had to work for a living. However, he spent his spare time studying Latin, Greek, mathematics (chiefly algebra), and some mechanics. He became very proficient in these subjects, and in 1836 he won a bursary to study at Marischal College, in Aberdeen. He excelled at his studies during his four years at Marischal, and when he received his degree of master of arts in 1840, he was adjudged the best candidate of the year. He had acquired a training both in the humanities and the natural sciences.

After receiving his degree, Bain taught mental and moral philosophy for five years at Marischal. During these years he did much of his thinking on psychology. For the next fifteen years he held various lectureships for short durations. It was also during this time that he became a close friend of John Stuart Mill. In 1860 he was elected to the chair of logic at the newly formed Aberdeen University (a union of Marischal and King's colleges). Bain remained in this post until he retired in 1880. In 1876 he founded, and for sixteen years edited, the philosophical journal *Mind,* which has remained an important journal in the field to the present day. He served as rector of the university from 1882 to 1886. Bain was married twice. His first wife, Frances, whom he married in 1855, died in 1892. In April 1893 he married Barbara Forbes.

After an early interest in the natural sciences, Bain turned his attention to philosophical psychology. Here his training in the philosophy of Reid and Beattie, the influence of his friends Mill and George Grote, and the writings of Comte and Whewell are apparent. He had a great respect for facts and a mistrust of speculative metaphysics. He was also impressed by the physiological theories of Johannes Müller and was convinced that they were essential to the study of psychology.

Two powerful and complementary ideas of Bain's philosophy concerned the unity of the mind and the active power of the mind: "The argument for the two substances have, we believe, now entirely lost their validity; they are no longer compatible with ascertained science and clear thinking. The one substance with two sets of qualities, the physical and mental—a double-faced unity—would comply with all the exigencies of the case" (*Mind and Body,* p. 196). Bain's study of the nervous system gave him a way of correlating every mental process with some physiological process. For example, the will is identified with surplus energy in the nervous system.

The active nature of the mind is emphasized not only with respect to the feelings and volitions of an individual but also to the sensations. The mind can discriminate between sensations and can retain some of them; and he found that greater retention of some sensations is connected closely with greater discriminations of these sensations. Bain also believed that instinct, which includes reflex actions and primitive combined movements, is another active principle of the mind. Thus Bain presented the mind as an active unity, which superseded the then reigning theory of the faculties of the mind.

In ethics Bain followed the utilitarian position set out by Mill. He also followed Mill in logic, even in criticizing the Aristotelian syllogism as fallacious; but later, in a note in *Mind* (reprinted in *Dissertations*), he renounced this position.

BIBLIOGRAPHY

For a complete bibliography of Bain's work, see his *Autobiography* (London, 1904). Articles of primary importance include "Electrotype and Daguerrotype," in *Westminster Review,* **34** (Sept. 1840), 434; "Constitution of Matter," *ibid.,* **36** (July 1841), 69; "An Attempt to Generalise and Trace to One Sole Cause—viz. the Liberation of Latent Heat—All Cases of Terrestrial Heat," read to the Aberdeen Philosophical Society (6 Jan. 1843), manuscript in the Aberdeen University Library; "On a New Classification of the Sciences," read to the Aberdeen Philosophical Society (1 Dec. 1843), manuscript in the Aberdeen University Library; and "On the Definition and Classification of the Human Senses," read to the Aberdeen Philosophical Society (9 Dec. 1844), manuscript in the Aberdeen University Library. See also "On the Impediments to the Progress of Truth from the Abuse of Language," an 1845 MS in the Aberdeen University Library. For major books by Bain see *The Senses and the Intellect* (London, 1855); *The Emotions and the Will* (London, 1859); *An English Grammar* (London, 1863); *Mental and Moral Science—a Compendium of Psychology and Ethics* (London, 1868); *Logic,* part I, "Deduction" (London, 1870), part II, "Induction" (London, 1870); *Mind and Body: The Theories of Their Relation,* International Scientific Series, Vol. IV (London, 1872); *Mental Science: Psychology and History of Philosophy* (London, 1872); *Moral Science: Ethical Philosophy and Ethical Systems* (London, 1872); *Education as a Science,* International Scientific Series, Vol. XXV (London, 1879); *James Mill: A Biography* (London, 1882); *John Stuart Mill: A Criticism With Personal Recollections* (London, 1882). Some of Alexander Bain's most important articles, chiefly from the journal *Mind,* can be found in *Dissertations on Leading Philosophical Topics* (London, 1903). Works edited by Bain include *Paley's Moral Philosophy,* with dissertations and notes, Chamber's Instructive and Entertaining Library (Edinburgh, 1852); *James Mill's Analysis of the Human Mind,* with notes, 2 vols. (London, 1869); *Grote's Aristotle,* with G. C. Robertson (London, 1872); and *Grote's Minor Works,* with critical remarks (London, 1873).

JAGDISH N. HATTIANGADI

BAIRD, SPENCER FULLERTON (*b.* Reading, Pennsylvania, 3 February 1823; *d.* Woods Hole, Massachusetts, 19 August 1887), *zoology, scientific administration.*

Baird's father was Samuel Baird, a lawyer of local prominence; his mother was the former Lydia MacFunn Biddle of Philadelphia. Upon Samuel's death in 1833, Lydia and her seven children moved to Carlisle, Pennsylvania, where Spencer Baird entered Dickinson College in 1836, receiving a B.A. in 1840 and an M.A. in 1843. In November 1841, Baird went to New York City to study medicine, but two months later he abandoned his studies and returned to Carlisle, determined to pursue a career in zoology despite the limited opportunities then available to American biologists. Since the United States lacked institutions offering professional training in science, Baird's education consisted of self-study and informal instruction from established naturalists, including James Dwight Dana, John James Audubon, and George N. Lawrence. In 1846 he married Mary Helen Churchill, daughter of a well-known army officer, and in the same year became professor of natural history at Dickinson College. Lucy Hunter Baird, the couple's only child, was born in 1848.

In 1850 Baird's writings in systematic zoology; his translation and revision of the four-volume *Iconographic Encyclopaedia of Science, Literature, and Arts,* compiled in cooperation with many leading American scientists; and recommendations from politicians and scientists secured his appointment as assistant to Joseph Henry at the Smithsonian Institution. For the next thirty-seven years Baird used numerous governmental expeditions, plus a network of private collectors, to bring distinguished zoological and anthropological collections to the Smithsonian's National Museum. He became a member of the National Academy of Sciences in 1864, over the opposition of Louis Agassiz, who had personal differences with Baird and also contended that, as a descriptive biologist, Baird contributed no new knowledge to science. In 1871 Congress established the U.S. Fish Commission under Baird's direction. This agency conducted basic research in marine biology, propagated food fishes, and aided the fishing industry. In 1878 he succeeded Joseph Henry as secretary of the Smithsonian, a position he held until his death. Baird was noted for his serenity and modesty, but in his private dealings he was forceful and persistent in pursuing his ambitions. He gradually drifted from his Protestant upbringing, and after 1875 did not attend religious services.

Baird's bibliography includes more than a thousand titles, of which about ninety were formal scientific contributions. The remaining writings were largely official reports or brief review articles in the *Annual Record of Science and Industry,* a semipopular series of eight volumes that he edited from 1871 to 1878. His most notable scientific papers were taxonomic studies of birds and mammals, but he also wrote on reptiles, amphibians, and fishes, usually in collaboration with Charles Girard.

His scientific writings earned Baird his reputation as the leading vertebrate zoologist of mid-nineteenth-century America. Four of his works were especially significant. The first two, *Mammals* (1857) and *Birds* (1858), were comprehensive monographs based on

American collections taken north of Mexico by fifteen governmental surveys and by numerous individual naturalists. From this extensive material, Baird was able to describe seventy species of mammals and 216 bird species not previously known. Moreover, he completely recast the nomenclature and classification of the two classes. Because of the accuracy and originality of his descriptions, and his use of several specimens to establish the characteristics of a particular species, Baird's methods were in themselves an advance. According to David Starr Jordan, Baird's "minute exactness" thereby "departed widely from the loose and general type of description" of his predecessors, especially by "using a particular individual and then indicating with precision any deviations due to age, sex, geographical separation or other influences which might appear in other specimens" ("Spencer Fullerton Baird and the United States Fish Commission," p. 101). The two works replaced studies prepared in the preceding two decades by Audubon and John Bachman, and remained standard sources at the time of Baird's death. Many of the species identified by Baird are now considered to be synonyms or subspecies.

A third major work, "The Distribution and Migrations of North American Birds," was Baird's only important attempt at scientific generalization. This 1865 paper was notable for the definition of biological zones and the discussion of "general laws" showing "certain influences exerted upon species by their distribution . . . and by their association with each other" ("Distribution," p. 189). Baird noted that an understanding of environmental influences allowed taxonomists to reduce the number of nominal species. The paper's larger import was to reveal Baird's support of organic evolution. It was recognized by his contemporaries as one of the major commentaries on Darwinian evolution produced by American naturalists during this era.

In 1874 Baird, assisted by Thomas M. Brewer and Robert Ridgway, published his final major work, a three-volume study of land birds entitled *A History of North American Birds.* Baird and Ridgway prepared the technical descriptions while Brewer, working primarily from field notes forwarded to the Smithsonian by Baird's collectors, contributed accounts of the habits of individual species. The *History* was notable for presenting the first comprehensive information on the behavior of birds in Arctic breeding grounds. It remained a standard treatise on ornithological life history throughout the nineteenth century.

Baird's significance as a teacher and as a molder of scientific institutions was probably greater than his personal scientific work. He was the patron of numerous naturalists who collected for him or studied informally at the Smithsonian. Among his most important protégés were George Brown Goode, C. Hart Merriam, Robert Ridgway, and William Healey Dall. Baird's simultaneous direction of the U.S. Fish Commission, the U.S. National Museum, and the Smithsonian during the last ten years of his life indicates his influence on American scientific institutions. From 1871 through 1887, the Fish Commission's research ships and volunteer scientists undertook the first sustained biological study of American waters. The U.S. National Museum, along with Harvard's Museum of Comparative Zoology, were the leaders in American zoology during this period. The Smithsonian, under Baird's administration, was no longer restrained by its modest private income. In contrast with Joseph Henry, who feared that government funds would lead to political interference, Baird did not hesitate to seek congressional appropriations to expand the work of the Smithsonian.

BIBLIOGRAPHY

I. ORIGINAL WORKS. For a comprehensive bibliography of Baird's writings, see George Brown Goode, *The Published Writings of Spencer Fullerton Baird, 1843–1882* (Washington, D.C., 1883). Baird's two monographs on mammals and birds were initially published as Vols. VIII and IX of *Reports of Explorations and Surveys to Ascertain the Most Practicable and Economical Route for a Railroad from the Mississippi River to the Pacific Ocean* (Washington, D.C., 1857, 1858). An abstract of "The Distribution and Migrations of North American Birds," read to the National Academy of Sciences in 1865, appears in *The American Journal of Science and Arts,* 2nd ser., **41** (Jan.–May 1866), 78–90, 184–192, 337–347.

Two valuable sources presenting portions of Baird's scientific correspondence are Ruthven Deane, "Unpublished Letters of John James Audubon and Spencer F. Baird," in *The Auk,* **23** (Apr. and July 1906), 194–209, 318–334, and **24** (Jan. 1907), 53–70; and Elmer Charles Herber, ed., *Correspondence Between Spencer Fullerton Baird and Louis Agassiz, Two Pioneer American Naturalists* (Washington, D.C., 1963).

Baird's personal papers and letters documenting his work as a Smithsonian official are held by the Smithsonian Institution, Washington, D.C. The comprehensive records of the U.S. Fish Commission are in the U.S. National Archives, Washington, D.C.

II. SECONDARY LITERATURE. The only biography is William Healey Dall, *Spencer Fullerton Baird: A Biography* (Philadelphia, 1915). Dall presents much useful data, but the work is now dated. He slights the last seventeen years of Baird's career.

Among the most useful brief sketches of Baird are John Shaw Billings, "Memoir of Spencer Fullerton Baird,

1823–1887," in *Biographical Memoirs of the National Academy of Sciences,* III (Washington, D.C., 1895), 141–160; George Brown Goode, "The Three Secretaries," in *The Smithsonian Institution, 1846–1896,* George Brown Goode, ed. (Washington, D.C., 1897), pp. 115–234; and David Starr Jordan, "Spencer Fullerton Baird and the United States Fish Commission," in *The Scientific Monthly,* **17** (Aug. 1923), 97–107. A detailed assessment of Baird's personal scientific work is presented in T. D. A. Cockerell, "Spencer Fullerton Baird," in *Popular Science Monthly,* **68** (Jan. 1906), 63–83.

A recent and extended discussion of Baird's career, concentrating on his work with the Fish Commission, is Dean C. Allard, "Spencer Fullerton Baird and the U.S. Fish Commission: A Study in the History of American Science," unpublished Ph.D. diss. (Washington, D.C., 1967). This work contains a lengthy bibliography of published literature relating to Baird.

DEAN C. ALLARD

BAIRE, RENÉ LOUIS (*b*. Paris, France, 21 January 1874; *d*. Chambéry, France, 5 July 1932), *mathematics.*

Baire was one of three children in a modest artisan's family. His parents had to sacrifice in order to send him through high school. Having won a scholarship competition for the city of Paris in 1886, he entered the Lycée Lakanal as a boarding student; there he completed his advanced classes in 1890 after having won two honorable mentions in the Concours Général de Mathématiques.

In 1891 Baire entered the section for special mathematics at the Lycée Henri IV, and in 1892 was accepted at both the École Polytechnique and the École Normale Supérieure. He chose the latter, and during his three years there attracted attention by his intellectual maturity. He was a quiet young man who kept to himself and was profoundly introspective. During this period he was found to be in delicate health.

Although he placed first in the written part of the 1895 *agrégation* in mathematics, Baire was ranked third because of a mistake in his oral presentation on exponential functions, which the board of examiners judged severely. In the course of his presentation Baire realized that his demonstration of continuity, which he had learned at the Lycée Henri IV, was purely an artifice, since it did not refer sufficiently to the definition of the function. This disappointment should be kept in mind, because it caused the young lecturer to revise completely the basis of his course in analysis and to direct his research to continuity and the general idea of functions. While studying on a scholarship in Italy, Baire was strengthened in his decisive reorientation by Vito Volterra, with whom he soon found himself in agreement and who recognized the originality and force of his mind.

On 24 March 1899 Baire defended his doctoral thesis, on the theory of the functions of real variables, before a board of examiners composed of Appell, Darboux, and Picard. The few objections, which Baire fully appreciated, proved that he had embarked on a new road and would not find it easy to convince his listeners.

Baire began his teaching career in the *lycées* of Troyes, Bar-le-Duc, and Nancy, but he could not long endure the rigors of teaching the young. In 1902, as lecturer at the Faculty of Sciences of Montpellier, he wrote a paper on irrational numbers and limits. In 1904 he was awarded a Peccot Foundation fellowship to teach for a semester at the Collège de France. At that time this award went to young teachers to enable them to spend several months, free of routine duties, in developing their own specialties. Baire chose to work on a course in discontinuous functions, later edited by his pupil A. Denjoy and published in the Collection Borel, a series of monographs on the theory of functions.

Upon his return to Montpellier, Baire experienced the first violent attack of a serious illness that became progressively worse, manifesting itself in constrictions of the esophagus. After the crisis passed, he began drafting his paper "Sur la représentation des fonctions discontinues." Appointed professor of analysis at the Faculty of Science in Dijon in 1905, to replace Méray, he devoted himself to writing an important treatise on analysis (1907–1908). This work revivified the teaching of mathematical analysis. His health continued to deteriorate, and Baire was scarcely able to continue his teaching from 1909 to 1914. In the spring of 1914 he decided to ask for a leave of absence. He went first to Alésia and then to Lausanne. War broke out while he was there, and he had to remain—in difficult financial circumstances—until the war ended.

Baire was never able to resume his work, for his illness had undermined his physical and mental health. He now devoted himself exclusively to calendar reform, on which he wrote an article that appeared in the *Revue rose* (1921). While still at his retreat on the shores of Lake Geneva, Baire received the ribbon of the Legion of Honor, and on 3 April 1922 was elected corresponding member of the Academy of Sciences. A pension granted him in 1925 enabled him to live in comparative ease, but the devaluation of the franc soon brought money worries. His last years were a struggle against pain and worry.

Thus Baire was able to devote only a few periods, distributed over a dozen years, to mathematical research. In addition to the already mentioned works, of particular importance are "Sur les séries à termes continus et tous de même signe" and "Sur la non-applicabilité de deux continus à n et $n + p$ dimensions." His writings, although few, are of great value.

Baire's doctoral thesis solved the general problem of the characteristic property of limit functions of continuous functions, i.e., the pointwise discontinuity on any perfect aggregate. In order to imagine this characteristic, one needed very rare gifts of observation and analysis concerning the way in which the question of limits and continuity had been treated until then. In developing the concept of semicontinuity—to the right or to the left—Baire took a decisive step toward eliminating the suggestion of intuitive results from the definition of a function over a compact aggregate. But in order to obtain the best possible results, one needed a clear understanding of the importance of the concepts of the theory stemming from aggregates.

> Generally speaking, in the framework of ideas that here concerns us, every problem in the theory of functions leads to certain questions in the theory of sets, and it is to the degree that these latter questions are resolved, or capable of being resolved, that it is possible to solve the given problem more or less completely [*Sur les fonctions*].

In this respect, Baire knew how to use the transfinite in profoundly changing a method of reasoning that had been applied only once before—and this in a different field.

> From the point of view of derivative sets that interests us here, it may be said that if α is a number of the first type, then P^α is the set derived from $P^{\alpha-1}$, and if α is of the second type, P^α is by definition the set of points that belongs to all $P^{\alpha'}$ where α' is any number smaller than α. Independently of any abstract considerations arising from Cantor's symbolism, P^α represents a fully determined object. Nothing more than a convenient language is contained in the use we shall be making of the term "transfinite number" [*Ibid.*, p. 36].

Until the arrival of Bourbaki, his success greatly influenced the orientation of the French school of mathematics.

In line with his first results, Baire was led to approach the problem of integrating equations with partial derivatives at a time when their solution was not subjected to any particular condition of continuity. But it is in another, less specialized field that Baire's name is associated with lasting results.

Assigning to limit functions of continuous functions the name of Class 1 functions, Baire first endeavored to integrate functions of several variables into this class. Thus he considered those functions that are separately continuous in relation to each of the variables of which they are a function. Then he defined as Class 2 functions the limits of Class 1 functions, and as Class 3 functions the limits of Class 2 functions. Having established basic solutions for these three classes, he obtained a characteristic common to the functions of all classes.

Since the beginning of the nineteenth century, mathematicians had been interested in the development of the theory of functions of real variables only incidentally and in relation to complex variables. Baire's work completely changed this situation by furnishing the framework for independent research and by defining the subject to be studied.

If Baire did not succeed, even in France and despite intensive efforts, in overcoming the mistrust of the transfinite, he nevertheless put an end to the privileged status of continuity and gave the field to aggregate-oriented considerations for the definition and study of functions. Baire's work, held in high esteem by Émile Borel and Henri Lebesgue, exerted considerable influence in France and abroad while its author found himself incapable of continuing or finishing the task he had set himself.

There can be no doubt that the progress of modern mathematics soon made obsolete Baire's work on the concept of limit and the consequences of its analysis. But this work, written in beautiful French, has an incomparable flavor and merits inclusion in an anthology of mathematical thought. It marks a turning point in the criticism of commonplace ideas. Moreover, the class of Baire's functions, according to the definition adopted by Charles de la Vallée Poussin, remains unattainable as far as the evolution of modes of expression is concerned. This model of a brief and compact work is part of the history of the most profound mathematics.

BIBLIOGRAPHY

I. Original Works. Baire's writings are *Sur la théorie analytique de la chaleur* (Paris, 1895), his ed. of Henri Poincaré's 1893–1894 lectures; *Sur les fonctions de variables réelles* (Milan, 1899), his doctoral thesis (Faculté des Sciences, Paris, no. 977); "Sur les séries à termes continus et tous de même signe," in *Bulletin de la Société mathématique de France,* no. 32 (1904), 125–128; *Leçons sur la théorie des fonctions discontinues,* A. Denjoy, ed. (Paris, 1905, 1930); *Théorie des nombres irrationnels, des limites et de la continuité* (Paris, 1905, 1912, 1920); "Sur la représentation des fonctions discontinues," in *Acta mathematica,* no. 30 (1906), 1–48, and no. 32 (1909), 97–176; "Sur la non-applicabilité de deux continus à n et $n + p$

dimensions," in *Bulletin des sciences mathématiques* (Darboux), no. 31 (1907), 94–99; *Leçons sur les théories générales de l'analyse,* 2 vols. (Paris, 1907–1908); and "Origine de la notion de semi-continuité," in *Bulletin de la Société mathématique de France,* no. 55 (1927), 141–142.

Baire's works are now being collected.

II. Secondary Literature. Works dealing with Baire are Émile Borel, *L'espace et le temps* (Paris, 1922), p. 123; A. Buhl and G. Bouligand, "En mémoire de René Baire," in *L'enseignement mathématique,* **31,** nos. 1–3 (1932); Constantin Caratheodory, *Vorlesungen über reellen Funktionen* (Vienna, 1918), pp. 178, 393–401; Hans Hahn, *Reellen Funktionen* (Vienna, 1932), pp. 276–324; H. Lebesgue, notice in *Monographies de l'enseignement mathématique,* no. 4 (1958); Marijon, notice in *Annuaire de l'Association amicale des anciens élèves de l'École normale supérieure* (1933), pp. 82–87; Paul Montel, "Quelques tendances dans les mathématiques contemporaines," in *Science (L'encyclopédie annuelle;* 1 Mar. 1937); P. Sergescu, *Les sciences mathématiques (tableau du XXe siècle)* (Paris, 1933), pp. 77–79, 170; and C. de la Vallée Poussin, *Intégrales de Lebesgue, fonctions d'ensemble, classes de Baire* (Paris, 1916, 1934), pp. 113–160.

Pierre Costabel

AL-BAIRŪNĪ. See **al-Bīrūnī.**

IBN AL-BAIṬĀR. See **Ibn al-Bayṭār.**

IBN BĀJJA, ABŪ BAKR MUḤAMMAD IBN YAḤYĀ IBN AL-ṢĀ'IGH, also known as **Avempace** or **Avenpace** (*b.* Saragossa, Spain, end of the 11th century; *d.* Fez, Morocco, 1138/1139), *philosophy.*

Ibn Bājja was a Muslim philosopher who wrote in Arabic. Besides Saragossa and Fez, he lived and worked in Seville and Granada. He is said to have been a vizier serving an Almoravid prince and to have been poisoned by physicians who were jealous of his medical skill. Ibn Bājja is often described as the earliest Arabic Aristotelian in Spain, which is correct but rather less significant than a characterization made by a friend and editor of his work, Abu'l-Hasan ʿAlī of Granada, who indicates that Ibn Bājja had a preeminent part in establishing in Spain a systematic method for the study of the philosophical sciences. Such a method was already in existence in the Muslim East, but not in the peripheral Muslim West.

It can be taken as certain that, in working out his curriculum, Ibn Bājja, like the philosophers of the East, attached the greatest importance to the study of the *corpus Aristotelicum.* In spite of far-reaching doctrinal divergences he appears to have modeled his philosophical method on that of al-Fārābī rather than on that of Ibn Sīnā (Avicenna), whose influence was at that time predominant in the eastern centers of learning. In this and in various other respects he seems to have been responsible for the distinctive character of Spanish Aristotelianism, which counts among its representatives Ibn Rushd (Averroës) and Moses Maimonides. Among his extant works are the following:

Tadbīr al-mutawaḥḥid ("The Regimen of the Solitary"). The work deals with the various categories of men—those interested only in the bodily functions, those swayed by such "spiritual" faculties as imagination, and those governed by reason—in relation to man's final end, which is intellectual perfection; with various regimens; and with the position that the philosopher should adopt in relation to the imperfect communities in which he has to live (the reference is to the Islamic states of the time). In the absence of any hope for the creation of a perfect philosophical body politic (the conception of which goes back to Plato), the philosopher should regard himself as a stranger in his own community and as a citizen of the ideal State constituted by the happy few, i.e., the men, in whatever country they live, who in the past or the present have attained intellectual perfection.

A treatise on the union of man with the Active Intellect.

Risālat al-widāʿ ("The Epistle of Farewell"). The work treats some of the themes discussed in the *Tadbīr.*

A book on the soul.

Commentaries and notes on some works or parts of works belonging to the *corpus Aristotelicum,* including treatises of the *Organon* (there is also a commentary on Porphyry's *Isagoge*), the *Physics, De generatione et corruptione,* the *Meteorologica,* and *The Book of Animals.* There is also a "Book of Plants."

In a letter to Abū Jaʿfar Yūsuf Ibn Ḥasday, Ibn Bājja gives some details concerning his intellectual biography. After having learned the art of music, he studied astronomy; he then went on to study Aristotle's *Physics.* In astronomy Ibn Bājja rejected the theory of epicycles as being incompatible with the (Aristotelian) physical doctrine (see Maimonides, *The Guide of the Perplexed,* II, 24). He thus seems to have been one of the initiators of the tendency—which, after him, came to the fore in Muslim Spain—to reject and attempt to replace the Ptolemaic system.

Ibn Bājja's dynamics, as set forth in his notes on the seventh book of Aristotle's *Physics,* may, *inter alia,* be regarded as an attempt to unify the Aristotelian theory of movement by replacing the multiform concept of cause with the notion of force. The Arabic term used by Ibn Bājja is a translation of the Greek *dynamis,* but in the context it seems to have an exclusively active sense (which the term also has in Book VII of Aristotle's *Physics,* in certain texts of pagan Neoplatonic philosophers, and in John Philoponus' writings); it is in no way a potentiality. The unifying function of Ibn Bājja's concept of force may to some extent be classified by a consideration of the notion of "fatigue" (a term used in somewhat similar but not identical contexts by Alexander of Aphrodisias and by John Philoponus), which in Ibn Bājja's doctrine is associated with it. According to Ibn Bājja, the force of a mover may become "fatigued" (1) by the mere fact that it is exerted in moving a body and (2) because of the reaction of the body that is moved, when this body is other than the mover.

In relation to the first factor Ibn Bājja's statements give rise to some perplexity. One of them seems to purport that the "natural" motions of simple bodies do not cause fatigue, the reason being that in these motions there is no opposition between the mover and the moved body. It would thus appear that factor (1) causes fatigue only when it is accompanied by factor (2). The latter factor produces fatigue because a body moved by another body (and also a living being moved by its soul) causes in its turn (apparently in proportion to its fatigue) motion in its mover and thus fatigues the latter. In other words, there are an action and a reaction, the two being essentially comparable. While this view can be regarded as a development of some conceptions implicitly contained in the seventh book of Aristotle's *Physics,* it does not agree with other Aristotelian texts, which tend to assimilate the relation between a mover and a moved body to the relation between an agent and the thing acted upon or between a cause and an effect; that is to say, to relations that from the Peripatetic point of view do not lend themselves easily, and perhaps do not lend themselves at all, to being quantified. As against this, there is no theoretical difficulty about the quantification of the relation of action and reaction postulated by Ibn Bājja.

This view could, as it seems, be expressed in the following formula (whose validity would, however, be restricted to the instant in which a given body is moved): $M = F_1 - F_2$, M being the motion, F_1 the force of the mover, and F_2 the force of the moved body. This formula does not take into consideration the progressive weakening, or in Ibn Bājja's terminology "fatigue," of the force of the mover, which in all probability (although this is not explicitly stated by Ibn Bājja) is directly proportional to the duration of the motion.

It is indicated in a rather vague way that in accordance with the formulas of Book VII of the *Phys-*

ics, the distance covered by a body in motion is directly proportional to the relation between the force of the mover and the force of the moved body. The formula breaks down, however, in the case of a moved body that weighs too little "to fatigue," i.e., to move, its mover.

In the case of descent on an inclined plane, the fatigue (perhaps the slowing down) of the falling body is proportional to the angle formed by the inclined plane and a perpendicular drawn to the surface of the earth from the point on the plane at which the falling body happens to be. Ibn Bājja is possibly the earliest author known to us who has outlined, admittedly in a very summary way, a dynamic theory of descent on an inclined plane.

In his explanation of the motion of projectiles, Ibn Bājja follows Aristotelian lines. According to him, the continued motion of an arrow shot from a bow and of a stone thrown by the hand is due to their being pushed by particles of air, the motion of which is, in the last analysis, due to air's being pushed by the action of the hand or the bow. He seems to ignore the theory of violent inclination, similar to the theory of impetus, which was propounded by such philosophers of the Muslim East as Ibn Sīnā. As an Aristotelian philosopher, Ibn Bājja believed that a projectile moves more quickly at the middle of its course than at its beginning.

In Ibn Bājja's view a magnet does not directly cause a piece of iron that is not immediately contiguous to it to move; the latter's motion is occasioned by the air, or some other body, such as a piece of copper or silver, that is placed between the magnet and the piece of iron. In another context Ibn Bājja refers to, but rejects, the belief that an attraction of the earth, similar to the attraction exerted upon a piece of iron by a magnet (rather than the tendency to reach their natural place), is the cause of the downward motion of heavy bodies.

In Latin Europe, the most influential of Ibn Bājja's physical theories was the one sometimes described as the doctrine concerning the original time of motion. This theory attacks the Peripatetic conceptions concerning the role of the resistance of the medium (air or water), regarded as one of the factors determining the velocity of a moving body. According to the Aristotelians, the function of this factor is such that, in the absence of any resistance on the part of a medium, i.e., in a vacuum, the velocity of a moving body must become infinite. The impossibility of this proves that there is no vacuum. Although Ibn Bājja did not hold a brief for the existence of a vacuum, he refuted the Aristotelian argumentation. His view on this question is similar to a doctrine set forth by

his contemporary Abu'l-Barakāt al-Baghdādī as well as by John Philoponus, by whom Ibn Bājja may have been influenced, but it also derives in a logical way from Ibn Bājja's theory concerning the relation between a mover and a moved body. As stated above, it is this relation that determines the velocity of a moved body. Ibn Bājja contends that, in the absence of a medium, the body would move with this original velocity, which is clearly finite. This velocity would decrease in proportion to the resistance of a medium. As has been shown by E. A. Moody, this theory, which was known in Latin Europe through the exposition of Ibn Rushd, who refuted it, influenced Thomas Aquinas, Duns Scotus, and other Schoolmen.

BIBLIOGRAPHY

I. ORIGINAL WORKS. Miguel Asín Palacios has provided the Arabic text and Spanish translation of the following works by Ibn Bājja: "Avempace Botánico" ("Book of Plants"), in *Al-Andalus,* **5** (1940), 259–299; "Tratado de Avempace sobre la unión del intelecto con el hombre" ("The Union of Man With the Active Intellect"), *ibid.,* **7** (1942), 1–47; "La carta de adiós de Avempace" ("The Epistle of Farewell"), *ibid.,* **8** (1943), 1–85; and *El régimen del solitario* ("The Regimen of the Solitary"; Madrid–Granada, 1946), English trans. by D. M. Dunlop in *Journal of the Royal Asiatic Society* (1945), 61–81.

II. SECONDARY LITERATURE. Further information on Ibn Bājja can be found in E. A. Moody, "Galileo and Avempace," in *Journal of the History of Ideas,* **12** (1951), 163–193, 375–422; and S. Pines, "La dynamique d'Ibn Bājja," in *Mélanges Alexandre Koyré,* I, *L'aventure de la science* (Paris, 1964), 442–468.

SHLOMO PINES

BAKER, HENRY (*b.* London, England, 8 May 1698; *d.* London, 25 November 1774), *microscopy.*

Henry Baker did valuable work on the teaching of the deaf and dumb, but he is especially noted for his popularization of the use of the microscope and for his contribution to the study of crystals. His father, William, was a Clerk in Chancery, and his mother, the former Mary Pengry, was "a midwife of great practice." At the age of fifteen Baker was apprenticed to a bookseller whose business later passed into the hands of Robert Dodsley, the printer of Baker's microscopical works. In 1720, at the close of his indentures, Baker went to stay with John Forster, a relative and an attorney, whose daughter had been born deaf. Baker felt inspired to teach the child to read and speak, and was so successful that he became in great demand as a teacher both of the deaf and dumb, and of those with speech defects. He amassed a considerable fortune, and possibly it was for financial reasons that he kept his teaching methods secret. Four manuscript volumes of exercises written by his pupils have, however, survived, and are in the library of the University of Manchester.

Baker's work with the deaf attracted the interest of Daniel Defoe, one of whose early novels, *The Life and Adventures of Duncan Campbell* (1720), was about a deaf conjurer. This book shows that Defoe was familiar with the methods for teaching the deaf used by John Wallis. Baker married Defoe's youngest daughter, Sophia, in 1729. The year before, Defoe and Baker had established the *Universal Spectator and Weekly Journal,* Baker using the pseudonym Henry Stonecastle. The magazine existed until 1746, and Baker was in charge of its production and a frequent contributor until 1733. His annotated volume containing copies of the journal, from the first copy until April 1735, is now in the Bodleian Library, Oxford. Baker's early literary efforts also included several volumes of verse, both original and translated. In 1727 he published *The Universe: a Philosophical Poem intended to restrain the Pride of Man,* which was much admired and reached a third edition, incorporating a short eulogy of the author, in 1805. This poem reveals Baker's keen interest in natural philosophy, as well as his pious approach to the wonders of nature, and includes a reference to the microscope.

In January 1740, Baker became a fellow of the Society of Antiquaries, and in March 1741 a fellow of the Royal Society. For the next seventeen years he was a frequent contributor to the *Philosophical Transactions,* on subjects as diverse as the phenomenon of a girl "able to speak without a tongue" and the electrification of a myrtle tree. Microscopical examinations of water creatures and fossils were, however, the subject of the majority of his papers and were included in his books on microscopy. In 1742 there was considerable interest among fellows of the Royal Society in the freshwater polyp (*Hydra viridis*) as a result of the recent discovery and description of this animal by Abraham Trembley, and with Martin Folkes Baker carried out experiments on this animalcule which he published in 1743 under the title *An Attempt towards a Natural History of the Polype.* The first edition of *The Microscope Made Easy* appeared in 1742; it ran to five editions in Baker's lifetime and was translated into several foreign languages. The Copley Medal of the Royal Society was awarded to Baker in 1744 "For his curious Experiments relating to the Crystallization or Configuration of the minute particles of Saline Bodies dissolved in a menstruum."

Baker was an indefatigable correspondent with scientists and members of philosophical societies all over Europe. He introduced the alpine strawberry into England with seeds sent to him from a correspondent in Turin, and the rhubarb plant (*Rheum palmatum*) sent from a correspondent in Russia. Eleven years after the appearance of *The Microscope Made Easy,* Baker published a second microscopical work, *Employment for the Microscope,* which was as successful as its predecessor. In 1754 the Society for the Encouragement of Arts Manufactures and Commerce was established, and Baker was the first honorary secretary. He died in his apartments in the Strand at the age of seventy-six, and left the bulk of his property to his grandson, William Baker, a clergyman. Neither of his two sons had a successful career, and both predeceased their father. He bequeathed the sum of £100 to the Royal Society for the establishment of an oration, which was called the Bakerian Lecture. Among notable Bakerian lecturers in the fifty years following Baker's death were Tiberius Cavallo, Humphry Davy, and Michael Faraday. Baker's considerable collection of antiquities and objects of natural history was sold at auction in the nine days beginning 13 March 1775.

Henry Baker was in many respects a typical natural philosopher of the eighteenth century. His interests ranged widely, and his skills were equally various; he was by no means dedicated to one branch of study, nor did he do research in the modern sense. Yet he deserved the title "a philosopher in little things"; and he had the rare gift of communicating his knowledge of, and above all his enthusiasm for, the microscope to others. This was what made his two books so widely popular. He regarded the microscope with reverence, as a means to the deeper appreciation of the wonders of God's world. "Microscopes," he wrote in the introduction to *The Microscope Made Easy,* "furnish us as it were with a new sense, unfold the amazing operations of Nature," and give mankind a deeper sense of "the infinite Power, Wisdom and Goodness of Nature's Almighty Parent." *The Microscope Made Easy* is divided into two parts, the first dealing with the various kinds of microscopes, how each may be best employed, the adjustment of the instrument, and the preparation of specimens. Part II has chapters devoted to the examination of various natural objects, in the manner of Robert Hooke's *Micrographia*—e.g., the flea, the poison of the viper, hairs, and pollen. Part I of *Employment for the Microscope* is devoted to the study of crystals, and Part II is a miscellany of Baker's microscopical discoveries. Both books were deliberately written for the layman.

Apart from his work as an instructor in the techniques of microscopy, Baker's most important scientific achievements were the observation under the microscope of crystal morphology, for which he received the Copley Medal, and his account of an examination of twenty-six bead microscopes bequeathed to the Royal Society by Antony van Leeuwenhoek. His measurements of these unique microscopes (lost during the nineteenth century) are most valuable historical material.

BIBLIOGRAPHY

I. Original Works. Baker's writings are *The Universe: a Philosophical Poem* (London, 1727); *Universal Spectator and Weekly Journal,* Henry Stonecastle [Henry Baker], ed. (London, 1728–1735), annotated volume Bodl. Hope F103; *The Microscope Made Easy* (London, 1742); *An Attempt towards a Natural History of the Polype in a Letter to Martin Folkes* (London, 1743); and *Employment for the Microscope* (London, 1753). Some twenty papers were published between 1740 and 1758 in *Philosophical Transactions of the Royal Society.* The following are manuscript materials relating to Baker: letters from Baker—Bodl.MS Montague D11, ff.70–75, 79; BM Add.MS4426, f.242; BM Add.MS4435, ff.255–259; indentures relating to Baker—BM MS Egerton 738, ff.2–5; four volumes of exercises written by Baker's pupils, formerly in Arnold Library—Special Collection, Manchester University, 371 924 B1, Vols. I–IV; legal agreements concerning teaching—Special Collection, Manchester University, 371 92092 f B4.

II. Secondary Literature. Works on Baker are A. Farrar, *Arnold on the Education of the Deaf: A Manual for Teachers,* Book 1, "Historical Sketch" (London, 1932), 33; William Lee, *Daniel Defoe: His Life and Recently Discovered Writings,* 3 vols. (London, 1869), I, 439, 441, 455–459; and John Nichols, *Biographical and Literary Anecdotes of William Bowyer* (London, 1782), pp. 413–416, 596, 645; and *Literary Anecdotes of the Eighteenth Century,* 9 vols. (London, 1812–1816), V, 272–278.

G. L'E. Turner

BAKER, JOHN GILBERT (*b.* Guisborough, England, 13 January 1834; *d.* Kew, England, 16 August 1920), *botany.*

Baker's parents, John Baker and Mary Gilbert, moved from Guisborough to Thirsk, Yorkshire, in 1834. A Quaker, he attended the Friends' School at Ackworth; when he was twelve, he was transferred to the Friends' School at Bootham, York, which then enjoyed a reputation for natural history study. His formal education ended in 1847, and he spent the next eighteen years in a drapery business in Thirsk. This uncongenial occupation did not impede Baker's enthusiasm for natural history; when only fifteen, he communicated a new record of a rare *Carex* to *The*

Phytologist. In 1854 he collaborated with J. Nowell in a supplement to Baines's *Flora of Yorkshire.* Baker's zeal helped to create the Botanical Exchange Club of the Thirsk Natural History Society; when the society was dissolved in 1865, the club moved to London, with Baker as one of the two curators. In May 1864 Baker's home and business premises were completely destroyed by fire and his entire herbarium and library were lost, including the stock of his book *North Yorkshire* (1863). This catastrophe caused him seriously to consider his future career, and when an opportunity was offered to engage in botanical research, he readily abandoned the drapery business.

The opportunity arose from an invitation by J. D. Hooker, director of the Royal Botanic Gardens, Kew, to join the staff of its herbarium. In 1866 Baker was appointed first assistant in the Kew Herbarium, with the initial task of finishing W. J. Hooker's *Synopsis Filicum,* left incomplete on his death in 1865. To supplement his slender salary, Baker lectured on botany at the London Hospital Medical School from 1869 to 1881; the following year he was appointed lecturer in botany at the Chelsea Physic Garden. In 1890 he became keeper of the herbarium and library at Kew, serving until his retirement in 1899.

His very able work on Hooker's *Synopsis Filicum* earned Baker wide recognition as an expert on vascular cryptogams, and he was invited by Martius to undertake the volume on ferns in his monumental *Flora Brasiliensis;* Baker later contributed the *Compositae* to the same work. An early interest in *Rosa,* manifested in a review of the genus in *The Naturalist* for 1864, was followed by a monograph on British roses in 1869; he also wrote the botanical descriptions for E. A. Willmott's *Genus Rosa* (1910–1914). He published monographic accounts of other plant families and genera, and made substantial contributions to *Flora of Tropical Africa, Flora Capensis,* and *Flora of British India.* Baker was one of the great English taxonomists and a pioneer investigator in plant ecology. Botany was his *raison d'être;* his enormous capacity for work and his output were impressive by any standard.

Baker was a notably effective lecturer, clear and concise, and had an instinctive sympathy for the problems of his students. His long, fruitful career was attended by numerous distinctions: fellowship of the Royal Society in 1878, the Victoria Medal of Honour of the Royal Horticultural Society in 1897, in acknowledgment of his valuable services to horticulture, and the Linnean Medal in 1899. His first child (he married Hannah Unthank in 1860), Edmund Gilbert Baker, emulated his father by choosing botany as his vocation.

BIBLIOGRAPHY

I. ORIGINAL WORKS. Baker's writings include *Supplement to Baines' Flora of Yorkshire* (London, 1854), written with J. Nowell; *North Yorkshire* (London, 1863); the completion of Sir W. J. Hooker's *Synopsis Filicum* (London, 1868, 1874); "A Monograph of the British Roses," in *Journal of the Linnean Society,* **11,** no. 52 (1869), 197–243; *Handbook of the Fern-allies* (London, 1887); *Handbook of the Amaryllideae* (London, 1888); *Handbook of the Bromeliaceae* (London, 1889); and *Handbook of the Irideae* (London, 1892). He wrote over 400 papers, most of which are listed in the *Royal Society Catalogue of Scientific Papers, 1867–1914*: I, 164–165; VII, 74–75; IX, 102–104; XIII, 253–254.

II. SECONDARY LITERATURE. Obituary notices are *Botanical Society and Exchange Club of the British Isles,* **6** (1920), 93–100; James Britten, in *Journal of Botany,* **58** (1920), 233–238; and Sir David Prain, in *Proceedings of the Royal Society of London,* **92B** (1921), xxiv–xxx.

R. G. C. DESMOND

BAKEWELL, ROBERT (*b.* England, 1768; *d.* Hampstead, England, 15 August 1843), *geology.*

Bakewell's parentage and birthplace are not known, although he may have come from Nottingham. He was not related to Robert Bakewell (1725–1795), the celebrated Leicestershire husbandman with whom he has often been confused. That he became interested in science, particularly geology, about the middle of his life perhaps explains the emphasis in his works on presenting science to his readers in clear, simple language, scorning merely technical distinctions and abstruse vocabulary. He wrote for the general reader but without undue popularization. During much of his life he lived in London, working as a mineralogical surveyor and teaching mineralogy and geology.

Bakewell's *Introduction to Geology* appeared in 1813. The work was widely read and appreciated, largely because it used examples and illustrations taken from the English countryside. A second, enlarged edition appeared in 1815, a third edition in 1828, a fourth edition in 1833, and a final edition in 1838. The second and third editions were translated into German. In 1829, Benjamin Silliman published an American edition, in which he included his own lecture notes.

Bakewell's brightly ironic style contributed greatly to the popularity of the *Introduction,* and perhaps accounts for the book's continued success despite its being outdated by advances in the subject. William Smith's ideas of using fossils for the correlation of strata, for example, were never included in the *Introduction.* Bakewell appreciated James Hutton's "plutonic" ideas while failing to grasp the principle of uniformity—Hutton's greatest contribution. He was highly critical of the geognosy of the Wernerian school, missing no opportunity to disparage it, and he rejected "neptunism," depending almost entirely on volcanic processes to account for rock formations. Like Baron Cuvier, a French contemporary, Bakewell found evidence in the rocks for geological revolutions of great magnitude with quiet intervals lasting tens of thousands of years.

In addition to the *Introduction,* Bakewell wrote many articles on geological and biological subjects. Most of these appeared in the *Philosophical Magazine,* although one was published by the Geological Society of London, to which Bakewell was never admitted as a member. One of his sons, also named Robert Bakewell, wrote on geology, and the three articles on the Falls of Niagara listed for the elder Bakewell in the *Royal Society Catalogue of Scientific Papers* were written by his son.

BIBLIOGRAPHY

In addition to *An Introduction to Geology, . . . and Outline of the Geology and Mineral Geography of England* (London, 1813; 5th ed. 1838), Bakewell wrote *An Introduction to Mineralogy* (London, 1819) and *Travels . . . in the Tarentaise,* 2 vols. (London, 1823). Further details of Bakewell's life may be found in the *Dictionary of National Biography.*

BERT HANSEN

BAKH, ALEKSEI NIKOLAEVICH. See **Bach, Aleksei Nikolaevich.**

AL-BAKRĪ, ABŪ ʿUBAYD ʿABDALLĀH IBN ʿABD AL-ʿAZĪZ IBN MUḤAMMAD (*b. ca.* 1010; *d.* 1094), *geography.*

Al-Bakrī was a Hispano-Arabic geographer who belonged to a family of landowners that took advantage of the fall of the caliphate of Córdoba to declare itself independent in Huelva and Saltes. When his father was deposed by al-Muʿtaḍid, al-Bakrī moved to Córdoba, where he studied with the historian Ibn Ḥayyān (*d.* 1075) and the geographer al-ʿUdhrī (*d.* 1085). For much of his life al-Bakrī was a member of al-Muʿtaṣim's court at Almería, and late in life he became acquainted with the writer Ibn Khāgān. He spent much time in Seville, and was there when El Cid arrived to collect the tributes due Alfonso VI.

A man of wide-ranging knowledge, al-Bakrī was a good poet and philologist who devoted much of his time to geography, even though it appears that he never traveled outside the Iberian Peninsula. His main scientific works are the following:

(1) *Mu'jam mā ista'jam,* a collection of place names that are mainly Arabian and that are frequently misspelled in common use. The analytical part is preceded by an introduction detailing the geographic framework of the region under study.

(2) *Kitāb al-masālik wa'l-mamālik* (completed in 1068), only part of which has been preserved. As the title ("Book of the Roads and Kingdoms") implies, it is a description of land and sea routes written to facilitate travel. Aside from the purely geographical facts, al-Bakrī also includes historical and social data. The description of the coasts is in some instances so precise that it makes one wonder if the author's source was a navigation or prenavigation text of the western Mediterranean. The book is independent of the works of the same title written by Oriental geographers. Still extant is a general introduction that contains a description of the Slavic and Nordic peoples; it has been published only in fragments. There is also a description of North Africa and Spain (*al-Mughrib fī dhikr Ifrīqiyya wa'l-Maghrib*). The first part presents interesting data about the Sahara routes and the origins of the Almoravid movement. We have only fragments of the second part, which was used by Alfonso X (el Sabio). The main source of the work (aside from al-Bakrī's teacher al-'Udhrī), of which many fragments about Spain have been preserved, is the book about Ifrīqiyya written by Muḥammad ibn Yūsuf al-Warrāq (*d.* 973). Al-Bakrī also had access to Latin sources, such as the *Etimologiae* of St. Isidore, the *History* of Orosius, and many others known in Córdoba either in Arabic versions or in oral tradition. In addition, he utilized the description of the trip of Ibrāhīm ibn Ya'qūb, a Jew from Tortosa, to the north of Europe in the tenth century. The *Kitāb al-masālik wa'l-mamālik* was influential in Arabic literature for centuries.

(3) Al-Ghafiqī and Ibn al-Bayṭār cite al-Bakrī as an authority several times in their pharmacological compilations. From this we can deduce that he wrote a treatise, since lost, entitled *A'yān al-nabāt* or *Kitāb al-nabāt,* about simple medicines, quoted by Ibn Khayr (*Fahrasa,* 377, Codera and Ribera, eds. [Zaragoza, 1894–1895]).

BIBLIOGRAPHY

I. ORIGINAL WORKS. There is a list of al-Bakrī's manuscripts in Brockelmann, *Geschichte der arabischen Literatur,* I (Weimar, 1898), 476, and Supp. I (Leiden, 1937), 875–876. The *Mu'jam mā ista'jam* was edited by F. Wüstenfeld and published as *Das geographische Wörterbuch* (Göttingen–Paris, 1876; Cairo, 1945–1949). The manuscript of the *Kitāb al-masālik wa'l-mamālik* is in Paris (BN 5905); the part dealing with North Africa was published in French trans. by de Slane as "Description de l'Afrique septentrionale," in *Journal asiatique* (1858–1859), and as a book (2 vols., Algiers, 1911–1913; 1 vol., Paris, 1965). It has often been reprinted with original and translation combined. The part dealing with the Slavs was translated into Russian by A. Kunik and V. Rosen (St. Petersburg, 1878); it also appears in A. Seippel's *Rerum normanicorum fontes arabici* (Oslo, 1896–1928). The best edition with Polish and Latin versions is that of T. Kowalski (Krakow, 1946).

II. SECONDARY LITERATURE. The Arabic sources for the life of al-Bakrī are listed in Khayr al-Dīn al-Ziriklī, *al-A'lām,* 2nd ed., IV, 233; secondary listings may be found in the above sources and in George Sarton, *Introduction to the History of Science,* I, 768; and E. Lévi-Provençal, in *Encyclopédie de l'Islam,* 2nd ed., I, 159–161. See also the important text by his teacher al-'Udhrī, published by al-Ahwānī, in *Fragmentos geográficos-históricos de al-Masālik ilā Gamī' al-Mamālik* (Madrid, 1965), and the note by J. Vernet in *Revista del Instituto de estudios islámicos,* **13** (1965–1966), 17–24.

J. VERNET

BALANDIN, ALEKSEY ALEKSANDROVICH (*b.* Yeniseysk, Siberia, Russia, 20 December 1898; *d.* Moscow, U.S.S.R., 22 May 1967), *chemistry.*

Balandin was the founder of an important school of catalytic chemistry. He graduated from Moscow University in 1923. Professor of chemistry from 1934, he was elected a corresponding member of the Soviet Academy of Sciences in 1943 and a full member in 1946.

As a result of his quantitative studies of the kinetics of catalytic reactions of hydrogenation and dehydrogenation of cyclic hydrocarbons, Balandin established that two factors play a decisive role in all catalytic processes: (1) a similarity between the structure of the reacting molecules and the surface of the catalyst and (2) comparable energy values for the chemical bonds of the molecular reagents and the energy of chemical interaction of these molecules with the surface of the catalysts. In 1929 Balandin made this discovery the basis of his universal catalysis theory, which became known as the universal "multiplet" theory of catalysis.

For the first time in the history of chemistry, Balandin proposed and demonstrated physically the principle of an active transitional state characterized by the formation of an unstable complex containing not fully valent chemical bonds (i.e., bonds with less than two electrons). With some modifications, this principle has been incorporated into one of the most universal theories of chemical processes, the theory of the absolute reaction rates.

Balandin showed that the active, or multiplet, complex (formed as a transition state in hydrogenation and dehydrogenation processes of cyclic hydrocarbons) can take on an orientation that conjoins either the plane or a facet of a molecule with the surface of the catalyst. The practical outcome of this work was that Balandin was able to predict catalytic activity for a number of metals in group VIII of the periodic table, as well as for chromium and vanadium oxides. Chromium sesquioxide later became a commercial-type catalyst.

Having worked out quantitative methods to determine a catalyst's maximum activity, Balandin showed that the peak activity is located in the vicinity of an adsorption potential, q, equal to one half of the total energy of the reacting bonds, s, i.e., at the $q = s/2$ point. This relationship gives a solution to the problem of selecting catalysts by experimental determination of their absorption potential. In addition, Balandin determined the conditions for enhancing the activity of mixed catalysts and found explanations for poisoning—promoting and utilizing these conditions in the control of the activity. He was thus able to forecast the sequence of reactions in stepwise processes.

On the basis of the multiplet theory, Balandin proposed a classification of the organic catalytic reactions that reflected the positions of the atoms in the reacting molecule on the catalyst surface in relation to the active center. The importance of this classification for catalytic organic synthesis is equivalent to that of the system of forms used in crystallography. New types of processes can be forecast by means of this system of classification. For example, in 1935 Balandin predicted the then unknown types of paraffin and olefin dehydrogenation processes that now form the basis for the production of monomers used in the synthesis of rubber.

Balandin introduced a number of basic concepts and equations into chemical kinetics. In 1929–1930 he was one of the first (together with F. Constable) to indicate the importance of activation energy determinations in the study of heterogenous processes; he established a logarithmic dependence between ε and k_0 in the Arrhenius equation $k = k_0 \cdot e^{-\varepsilon/rt}$ (ε being the empirical value of activation energy). In 1930–1935 he gave a precise equation of reaction kinetics in a flow system and derived a general equation for monomolecular reactions complicated by adsorption equilibrium. Having studied the kinetics of the dehydrogenation of butane and butylene to butadiene and of ethylbenzene to styrene, Balandin was the first to find conditions under which the yield of these most valuable monomers approached the thermodynamically feasible maximum.

Balandin's work in catalysis is closely connected with petrochemical synthesis. Together with N. D. Zelinski and his aides, Balandin participated in the discovery and study of the alkane and cyclane (cycloparaffin) reactions and, in particular, in the dehydrocyclization of paraffins, aromatization, and hydrogenolysis. In 1950 he applied the multiplet theory to fermentation processes, demonstrating the special role of the matrix effect by imposing substituents on the surface of ferment (entropy factor) and by lowering the potential barrier of the reaction and of the heat of adsorption (energy factor).

BIBLIOGRAPHY

I. ORIGINAL WORKS. Among Balandin's writings are "Khimiya i struktura" ("Chemistry and Structure"), a series of articles in *Izvestiia Akademii nauk SSSR* (1940), 295–310; (1940), 571–584; (1942), 168–178, 286–296; (1943), 35–42; "Teoria slozhnykh reaktsy" ("Theory of Complex Reactions"), in *Zhurnal fizicheskoi khimii*, **15** (1941), 615–628; "Tochny metod opredelenia adsorbtsionnykh koeffitsientov" ("A Precise Method of Determining Adsorption Coefficients"), in *Izvestiia Akademii nauk SSSR* (1957), 882–884; "Printsipy strukturnogo i energeticheskogo sootvetstvia v fermentativnom katalize" ("Principles of Structural Energetic Conformity in Fermentative Catalysis"), in *Biokhimiya*, **23** (1958), 475–485; and *Multipletnaya teoria kataliza* ("Multiple Catalysis Theory"), 2 vols. (Moscow, 1963–1965).

II. SECONDARY LITERATURE. Works on Balandin are *Materialy k biobibliografy uchenykh SSSR. Aleksey Aleksandrovich Balandin* ("Bibliographical Material Concerning the Lives of USSR Scientists. Aleksey Aleksandrovich Balandin"; Moscow, 1958); A. M. Rubinstein, "Akademik Aleksey Aleksandrovich Balandin" ("Academician Aleksey Aleksandrovich Balandin"), in *Uspekhi khimii*, **18** (1949), 38 (issued on the occasion of his fiftieth birthday); H. S. Taylor, "Geometry in Heterogeneous Catalysis," in *Chemical Architecture* (New York, 1948), pp. 8–18; and B. M. W. Trapnell, "Balandin's Contribution to Heterogeneous Catalysis," in *Advances in Catalysis and Related Subjects,* III (New York, 1951), 1–25.

V. I. KUZNETZOV

BALARD, ANTOINE JÉROME (*b.* Montpellier, France, 30 September 1802; *d.* Paris, France, 30 March 1876), *chemistry.*

Balard was born into a family of modest circumstances; his parents were wine-growers. His godmother noticed his intelligence, however, and enabled him to attend the *lycée* in Montpellier. In 1819, upon his graduation, he began to train for a career in pharmacy. While training in Montpellier, he served as *préparateur* in chemistry to Joseph Anglada of the Faculté des Sciences and *préparateur* at the École de Pharmacie. At the latter he studied chemistry and physics under Jacques Étienne Bérard, who permitted Balard to do research at the chemical factory of which Bérard was the director. Balard received his degree in pharmacy in 1826, having written a thesis on cyanogen and its compounds.

It was in this period, about 1825 (the date is uncertain but was before 28 November), that Balard made his discovery of the element bromine. The discovery of a new chemical element by a young and obscure provincial pharmacist caused a sensation in Parisian, and subsequently in foreign, scientific circles. Balard's achievement was recognized by the Académie des Sciences and he was awarded a medal by the Royal Society of London. Professionally he advanced steadily, first in Montpellier, where he succeeded Anglada in 1834, and later in Paris, where he assumed Louis Jacques Thénard's chair at the Sorbonne in 1842 and that of Théophile Jules Pelouze at the Collège de France in 1851. For this last position, Balard's chief competitor was Auguste Laurent. In 1844 Balard was elected to the Académie des Sciences.

Balard's mode of life was modest, even in his successful years in Paris. Moreover, his abstemiousness influenced the style of his scientific research; both Jean Baptiste Dumas and Charles Adolphe Wurtz testified to Balard's preference for simple apparatus and homemade reagents over elaborate techniques and materials. He was amiable and generous both to his colleagues and to his students.

Balard was principally an experimental chemist, although his experimentation was guided by a keen awareness of the analogies between the substances he was investigating and others of which the chemistry was better known. He did not publish a great deal, but what did appear was of high quality and great interest.

The discovery of bromine, Balard's first and greatest achievement, actually was a by-product of his more general chemical investigations of the sea and its life forms. In the course of his studies, Balard devised a reliable test for the presence of iodine, the content of which he was determining in plants taken from the Atlantic and the Mediterranean. Chlorine water was added to the test solution, to which starch and sulfuric acid had already been added. The iodine was manifested by its characteristic blue color at the interface of the test solution and the chlorine water. Then Balard noticed that, in some samples, above the blue layer there appeared a yellow-orange layer, which had its own characteristic odor. He isolated the substance causing the yellow color, which proved to be a red liquid. He first collected it by simple distillation, but soon he found a more effective method: shaking the chlorinated sample with ether and treating the resultant orange layer with caustic potash. The crystallized precipitate was then distilled with manganese dioxide and sulfuric acid to produce the red vapor of elemental bromine, which Balard dried with calcium chloride and condensed to a liquid.

At first he thought the substance might be a combination of chlorine and iodine, but he was unable to detect the presence of iodine and the liquid did not decompose under electrolysis. Balard concluded that he had discovered a new element, which, at the suggestion of Anglada, he named muride, subsequently changed to bromine. He proceeded to study its properties, which he found to be analogous to those of chlorine and iodine.

A number of German chemists, including Justus Liebig, had in fact isolated bromine before Balard without realizing its elemental nature. Carl Jacob Löwig, while still a student, isolated it almost simultaneously with Balard. The discovery of this element had a significance greater than that of the isolation of most other elements, for it made manifest the most striking "family" of elements—the halogens—in which bromine possessed an atomic weight that was approximately the arithmetic mean between those of chlorine and iodine.

In 1834 Balard published the results of his study of the bleaching agent Javelle water. In the course of working out the chemistry of this chlorine bleach, he succeeded in preparing hypochlorous acid and chlorine monoxide.

The project to which Balard devoted the most time was the inexpensive extraction of salts from the sea. Beginning in 1824, he spent many years developing techniques for precipitating sodium sulfate and potassium salts, publishing his method in 1844. Unfortunately for Balard, cheaper techniques for producing sodium sulfate were developed and huge deposits of potassium sulfate were discovered at Stassfurt.

Two other chemical studies by Balard deserve mention: the discovery of oxamic acid from the decomposition by heat of ammonium hydrogen oxalate (ammonium bioxalate) and the study and naming of amyl alcohol.

Of perhaps greater importance than his chemical researches was the interest Balard took in his students' careers, particularly those of Louis Pasteur and Marcelin Berthelot. Balard petitioned to have Pasteur assigned to him as an assistant in 1846, and in 1851 he secured a similar position for Berthelot at the Collège de France. He maintained close friendships with both these pupils, coming to Pasteur's defense in the spontaneous-generation controversy and securing the creation of the chair in organic chemistry at the Collège de France for Berthelot.

BIBLIOGRAPHY

I. ORIGINAL WORKS. For a listing of Balard's scientific papers, see the Royal Society of London's *Catalogue of Scientific Papers,* I, 166–167, and VII, 76. His most important papers are "Note pour servir à l'histoire naturelle de l'iode," in *Annales de chimie,* 2nd ser., **28** (1825), 178–181; "Mémoire sur une substance particulière contenue dans l'eau de la mer (le brôme)," *ibid.,* **32** (1826), 337–384; "Recherches sur la nature des combinaisons décolorantes de chlore," *ibid.,* **57** (1834), 225–304; "Note sur la décomposition du bioxalate d'ammoniaque par la chaleur et les produits qui en résultent," *ibid.,* 3rd ser., **4** (1842), 93–103; "Mémoire sur l'alcool amylique," *ibid.,* **12** (1844), 294–330; and "Sur l'extraction des sulfates de soude et de potasse des eaux de la mer," in *Comptes-rendus de l'Académie des Sciences,* **19** (1844), 699–715.

II. SECONDARY LITERATURE. Works on Balard are J. B. Dumas, "Éloge de M. Antoine-Jérome Balard," in *Mémoires de l'Académie des Sciences,* 2nd ser., **41** (1879), lv–lxxx; M. Massol, "Centenaire de la découverte du brôme par Balard," in *Bulletin de la Société Chimique de France,* 4th ser., **41** (1927), 1–9; J. R. Partington, *A History of Chemistry,* IV (London, 1964), 96–97; M. E. Weeks, *Discovery of the Elements,* 4th ed. (Easton, Pa., 1939), 360–362; and C. A. Wurtz, "Discours qui M. Wurtz, membre de l'Académie des Sciences, se proposait de prononcer aux funérailles de M. Balard, le 3 Avril, 1876," in *Journal de pharmacie et chimie,* 4th ser., **23** (1876), 375–379.

SEYMOUR H. MAUSKOPF

BALBIANI, EDOUARD-GÉRARD (*b.* Port-au-Prince, Haiti, 31 July 1823; *d.* Meudon, France, 25 July 1899), *biology.*

Balbiani's father, German by birth but of Italian descent, married a French Creole and went to Haiti to set up a banking firm. While still young, Balbiani was sent to Frankfurt am Main, and about 1840 he went to Paris to finish his studies, his mother having

settled there. For a time Balbiani attended law school, but he was soon attracted by the natural sciences as they were being taught at the Muséum National d'Histoire Naturelle by de Blainville.

Balbiani became *licencié ès sciences naturelles* in 1845 and *docteur en médecine* on 30 August 1854. His thesis, "Essai sur les fonctions de la peau considérée comme organe d'exhalation, suivi d'expériences physiologiques sur la suppression de cette fonction," was on a far higher level than the usual medical thesis.

His financial situation made it possible for Balbiani not to practice medicine, but to devote himself entirely to microscopic studies. As early as 1858 he communicated the first results of his research to the Academy. Balbiani founded the Société de Micrographie and was a faithful member of the Société de Biologie and the secretary of the *Journal de physiologie.* He was already well known in 1867, when Claude Bernard, who often praised him, asked him to direct the histological research at the laboratory of general physiology at the Muséum. On 13 February 1874 he became professor of embryogeny at the Collège de France, a post he held for the rest of his life.

Balbiani's work was extensive. His early research concerned protozoa, which at the time were subject to various interpretations. Some naturalists, following Ehrenberg, considered the infusoria as complete organisms with differentiated groups of organs. Others, such as Dujardin, saw in the protozoa only a mass of "sarcoda" without any organization whatever. These extreme views eventually were reconciled, but it is not possible to consider them here without outlining the history of protozoology. Balbiani discovered sexual reproduction in the ciliata, a finding that aroused much controversy until Bütschli confirmed Balbiani's research and gave it its true interpretation. While studying the binary fission of the infusoria, Balbiani set forth its laws in 1861. This work led him to perform genuine microsurgical experiments that enabled him to specify the role of the nucleus. He also introduced the technique and the term "merotomy."

Balbiani's research on the formation of the sexual organs of the *Chironomus* demonstrated that the sexual cells derive directly from the egg and are differentiated before the blastoderm appears—and that consequently they precede the individual itself. This essential fact was later observed in other species and eventually was responsible for the general theory of the autonomy of the germ cell. Notice should also be made of Balbiani's investigations on the reproduction of aphids and of his work on pebrine, the disease of the silkworm that later attracted Pasteur's attention.

Balbiani is known eponymously through his research on cytoplasmic inclusions. He described in the yolks of young ovules a special formation that Milne-Edwards called the Balbiani vesicle (1867). This had already been pointed out by Julius Carus (1850) under the name "vitelline nucleus," but Henneguy proposed calling it "corps vitellin de Balbiani" (1893). This body, interpreted by turns as a derivative of the centrosome or as an equivalent of the chondriome, has received new attention with the development of the electron microscope.

A solitary worker, Balbiani did not seek recognition through his lectures at the Collège de France. His publications were numerous, and with Ranvier he founded *Archives d'anatomie microscopique,* which is still published.

BIBLIOGRAPHY

L. F. Henneguy has written two works that provide additional information on Balbiani: *Leçons sur la cellule* (Paris, 1896), and "Balbiani, E. G.—Notice biographique," in *Archives d'anatomie microscopique,* **3** (1900), i–xxxi, with a complete bibliography of Balbiani's publications and a portrait.

MARC KLEIN

BALBUS (BALBUS MENSOR [?]) (*fl. ca.* A.D. 100), *surveying, mathematics.*

For information on the life of Balbus, we must depend upon the scanty data appearing in his works. He served as an officer in the campaign that opened Dacia to the Romans (see Lachmann, p. 93). Since Balbus does not name the reigning emperor, this may have been either the war of Domitian, which started in A.D. 85, or one of the campaigns of Trajan, which terminated in A.D. 106 with the conversion of Dacia into a Roman province. The second possibility seems more likely. Immediately following his return from war, Balbus completed a treatise dedicated to a prominent engineer named Celsus, about whom nothing has come down to us.

Authenticated Works. Balbus' work in its oldest manuscript, the so-called Arcerianus B, is entitled "Balbi ad Celsum expositio et ratio omnium formarum."[1] Other manuscripts name Frontinus—or even Fronto—as the author. The work is a geometric manual for surveyors. Starting with a summary of standard measurements, it contains definitions of geometric concepts (point, line, area, types of angles, figures). The work, which refers back to the works

of Hero of Alexandria (Hultsch, pp. 103 f.; Cantor, pp. 101 f.), is distorted by gaps and interpolations (see Lachmann's ed.; and Bubnov, pp. 419 f.) and undoubtedly is not preserved in full, for its contents do not match its title. Probably the end of the preserved text (Lachmann, p. 107)[2] was followed by examples of the calculation of triangles, rectangles, and polygons, such as can be found in Hero's works.

Works of Uncertain Origin. The oldest surveying codices have handed down a list of cities (*liber coloniarum I,* Lachmann, I, 209–251). Repeatedly mentioned as the source is a Balbus *mensor* (surveyor), who is said to have lived at the time of Augustus. Mommsen has demonstrated that this Balbus could not have been a contemporary of Augustus, so it is possible that this surveyor Balbus is identical with the author of *Expositio.* Nevertheless, the *liber coloniarum* does not form part of *Expositio,* since the latter almost certainly contained only geometry and not surveying material.

In 1525 Fabius Calvus of Ravenna published a short treatise on fractions (*De asse minutisque eius portiunculis*) as a fragment derived from a larger work by Balbus. However, this Balbus has no connection with the author of *Expositio:* Christ (*Sitzungsberichte der Bayerischen Akademie der Wissenschaften zu München* [1863], p. 105) and Hultsch (*Metrologicorum scriptorum reliquiae,* II [Leipzig, 1866], 14) found that the treatise on fractions originated between the time of Alexander Severus (222–235) and Constantine I (306–337).

Whether other works in the *Corpus agrimensorum* must be attributed to Balbus is uncertain.

Some chapters in the *Collection of the Surveyors* go back to Balbus (for example, Lachmann, I, 295.17–296.3). Particularly clear references to Balbus appear in the two works on geometry ascribed to Boethius: similar formulations in the five-book work on geometry have been grouped by Bubnov, p. 426. In the two-book work on geometry edited by G. Friedlein almost the entire section pp. 393.12–395.2; pp. 401.15–403.24 relates back to Balbus. At one place (p. 402.28–29 of Friedlein's edition) its anonymous author credits Frontinus with a definition actually derived from Balbus.

NOTES

1. The translation of *forma* as "geometric figure" is corroborated by Balbus' own definition (p. 104), despite the contrary views of Lachmann (*forma* as *mensura,* or "measure"; Lachmann, II, 134) and Mommsen (*forma* as *Grundriss* or "plan"; Lachmann, II, 148).
2. The text (I, 107.10–108.8 of Balbus' text, edited by Lachmann),

which Lachmann himself considered spurious, is believed to be the work of Frontinus; compare C. Thulin, "Die Handschriften des *Corpus agrimensorum Romanorum*," in *Abhandlungen der Preussischen Akademie der Wissenschaften,* Phil.-hist. Kl., no. 2 (1911), p. 23. In the London MS, BM Add. 47679, the only prehumanistic codex containing the ending of Balbus' work, this text is preceded by excerpts from Balbus and followed by abstracts from Frontinus. There are no headings. On this codex, so far neglected but a must for the reconstruction of the Balbus text, see M. Folkerts, *Zur Überlieferung der Agrimensoren: Schrijvers bisher verschollener "Codex Nansianus,"* which is to be printed in the *Rheinisches Museum für Philologie.*

BIBLIOGRAPHY

There is an edition of the *Expositio* by K. Lachmann in K. Lachmann et al., *Die Schriften der römischen Feldmesser,* I (Berlin, 1848), 91–107.

Works on Balbus are N. Bubnov, *Gerberti opera mathematica* (Berlin, 1899), pp. 400, 419–421; M. Cantor, *Die römischen Agrimensoren* (Leipzig, 1875), pp. 99–103; Gensel, in Pauly-Wissowa, II, 2820–2822; F. Hultsch, in *Ersch und Grubers allgemeine Encyclopaedie,* **92** (1872), 102–104; K. Lachmann, "Über Frontinus, Balbus, Hyginus und Aggenus Urbicus," in K. Lachmann, Blume, and Rudorff, *Die Schriften der römischen Feldmesser,* II (Berlin, 1852), 131–136; T. Mommsen, "Die *libri coloniarum,*" *ibid.,* 145–214; and Schanz and Hosius, *Geschichte der römischen Literatur,* 4th ed., II (1935), 802 f.

MENSO FOLKERTS

BALDI, BERNARDINO

BALDI, BERNARDINO (*b.* Urbino, Italy, 5 June 1553; *d.* Urbino, 10 October 1617), *mechanics.*

After a classical education by private tutors at Urbino, Baldi studied mathematics with Guido Ubaldo del Monte, under Federico Commandino, beginning about 1570. At Commandino's suggestion he translated the *Automata* of Hero of Alexandria into Italian, but left it unpublished until 1589. He also translated the *Phenomena* of Aratus of Soli and wrote didactic poems on the invention of artillery and the nautical compass, but did not publish them. In 1573 he enrolled at the University of Padua, and when it was closed shortly afterward because of plague, Baldi returned to Urbino. He was with Commandino during the latter's final illness in 1575, and obtained from him an account of his life. Baldi's studies at Padua centered on philology and literature, but he obtained no degree.

In 1580 Baldi went to Mantua in the service of Ferrante II Gonzaga, who in 1585 secured him the post of abbot of Guastalla. He then put in order his biographies of some 200 mathematicians, a work conceived during the writing of Commandino's biography and completed in 1588–1589. About that time he also wrote his principal contribution to physics, a commentary on the pseudo-Aristotelian *Questions of Mechanics,* posthumously published in 1621. In 1589 he published his translation of Hero's *Automata,* prefaced by a history of mechanics.

Baldi visited Urbino in 1601 to compile materials for a life of Federico di Montefeltro, and in 1609 he resigned his abbacy to enter the service of the duke of Urbino as historian and biographer, remaining there until his death. A vast work on geography on which he worked in his later years remains unpublished, although many of his poetic and literary compositions were printed in his lifetime. His final scientific contribution was a translation of Hero's *Belopoeica* into Latin, accompanied by the Greek text and by Baldi's Latin *Life of Hero* (1616). Brief extracts from his lives of the mathematicians were published in 1707, and about forty of those biographies have since been published in full. Most of the work, however, remains in manuscript.

Except for that of Henri de Monantheuil, with which Baldi was certainly unacquainted, Baldi's commentary on the *Questions of Mechanics* was the most important work of its kind to appear up to that time. He was probably influenced in his ideas on the continuance of motion by the earlier commentary of Alessandro Piccolomini. His account of dynamic equilibrium in spinning tops was superior to that of G. B. Benedetti, with whose principal work he appears to have been unfamiliar. The most significant aspect of Baldi's approach to mechanics lay in the development and application of the concept of centers of gravity, particularly with regard to stable and unstable equilibrium. It was the opinion of Pierre Duhem that Baldi drew his chief ideas from manuscripts of Leonardo da Vinci. Duhem accepted the year 1582 for the original composition of Baldi's commentary, as given by Baldi's first biographer. That date is, however, inconsistent with passages in Baldi's own preface and in the text of the work, which imply the year 1589. The latter year is also supported by textual indications that Baldi's principal inspiration was drawn from Commandino's translation of Pappus and from Guido Ubaldo's commentary on the *Plane Equilibrium* of Archimedes, both of which were published in 1588. The influence of Baldi's work was doubtless diminished by its delay in publication until after the Archimedean ideal had largely supplanted the Aristotelian among students of mechanics.

BIBLIOGRAPHY

I. ORIGINAL WORKS. An essentially complete bibliography of Baldi's published works is given in Pierre

Duhem, *Études sur Léonard de Vinci,* I (Paris, 1906; repr. 1955), 93–99; those of scientific interest are *Di Herone Alessandrino de gli automati . . .* (Venice, 1589; repr. 1601); *Scamilli impares Vitruviani . . .* (Augsburg, 1612); *De Vitruvianorum verborum significatione . . .* (Augsburg, 1612); *Heronis Ctesibii Belopoeeca . . . et . . . Heronis vita . . .* (Augsburg, 1616); *In mechanica Aristotelis problemata exercitationes . . .* (Mainz, 1621); *Cronica de' matematici . . .* (Urbino, 1707); "Vita di Federigo Commandino," in *Giornale de' letterati de'Italia,* **19** (1714), 140 ff.; "Vite inedite di matematici italiani," in *Bollettino di bibliografia e di storia delle scienze,* **19** (1886), 335–640; **20** (1887), 197–308; and *L'invenzione del bossolo da navigare,* G. Canerazzi, ed. (Leghorn, 1901).

II. SECONDARY LITERATURE. Principal biographical sources are Fabritio Scharloncini, *De vita et scriptis Bernardini Baldi Urbinatis,* prefaced to Baldi's *In mechanica Aristotelis . . .*; Ireneo Affò, *Vita di Bernardino Baldi* (Parma, 1783); and R. Amaturo, "Bernardino Baldi," in *Dizionario biografico degli Italiani,* V (Rome, 1963), 461–464. For Baldi's scientific work and its influence, see Duhem, *op. cit.,* pp. 89–156; for his relation to the central Italian mathematicians, see S. Drake and I. E. Drabkin, *Mechanics in Sixteenth-Century Italy* (Madison, Wis., 1968).

STILLMAN DRAKE

BALFOUR, FRANCIS MAITLAND (*b.* Edinburgh, Scotland, 10 November 1851; *d.* near Courmayeur, Switzerland, 19/20 July 1882), *embryology.*

The third son of James Maitland Balfour and Lady Blanche, daughter of the marquis of Salisbury, Francis Balfour came from an illustrious family, the outstanding member of which was his oldest brother, the prominent philosopher and statesman Arthur James Balfour. Francis spent his childhood at Whittingham. He attended the preparatory school at Hoddesdon, Hertfordshire, and in 1865 enrolled at Harrow. A keen naturalist as a boy, at Harrow Balfour wrote a prize-winning essay for the school's scientific society, "The Geology and Natural History of East Lothian," which was judged and highly praised by Thomas H. Huxley.

Balfour matriculated at Trinity College, Cambridge, in 1870; he took a first in the Natural Science Scholarships the following year, and by 1872 was working under the direction of the physiologist Michael Foster. During the winter of 1873/1874 he began his investigation of the embryology of elasmobranchs at the Stazione Zoologica in Naples, work he pursued intermittently, both in Italy and in Cambridge, until 1878, when he completed his outstanding monograph on elasmobranch development. He began lecturing on morphology and embryology at Trinity College in the fall term of 1873 and became director of the university's morphological laboratory, where

he attracted an extraordinarily enthusiastic group of students. Balfour was elected to the Royal Society in 1878, became vice-president of the biological section of the British Association for the Advancement of Science in 1880, and won the Royal Society's Royal Medal the following year upon completion of his two-volume text on comparative embryology.

Balfour's star had risen so quickly and his reputation as a remarkable teacher was so well known that it was not surprising that both Oxford and the University of Edinburgh tried to lure him away from Cambridge. In 1882, at the urging of Foster, Cambridge created a professorship of animal morphology that Balfour was to hold for his lifetime; but before the year was out, Balfour was dead. For several years he had spent his vacations mountain climbing in Switzerland and had become an experienced alpinist. On 18 July 1882 he set out with his Swiss guide to scale the unconquered peak Aiguille Blanche de Peteret in the Chamonix district. They failed to return; their bodies were recovered at the foot of an icefall several days later.

Balfour's embryological contributions exemplify the descriptive studies that characterized the two decades of embryology following the publication of Darwin's *Origin of Species.* He began his research in Naples at a time when Ernst Haeckel, Aleksandr Kovalevski, E. Ray Lankester, and Anton Dohrn, among others, were emphasizing comparative embryology and placing a premium on the search for homologies and phylogenetic links. Balfour's work was unquestionably directed by similar concerns, but his painstaking microscopic examinations and his crisp ordering of embryological details permitted him to draw certain sound generalizations about development that are far more impressive to the historian than the wilder speculations of his peers.

His monograph on elasmobranchs was a closely knit document of nearly 300 pages. At the outset, Balfour avoided the customary phylogenetic discussion; instead, he began by describing the development of the ovum and the segmentation of the fertilized egg. He carried the description forward by embryonic stages until, at the end of the treatise, he could give a detailed analysis of the major organ systems and interpret their development in relation to that in other animals. Balfour's analysis of germ-layer formation in elasmobranchs is a good example of his detailed microscopic examination and also demonstrates his ability to draw far-reaching generalizations. Carefully tracing the migration of lower-level cells during the formation of the segmentation cavity, he argued that both the segmentation cavity and the alimentary canal were formed by a delamination in the hypoblast. At first glance this conclusion had grave implications for Haeckel's *gastraea* theory, to which Balfour himself subscribed, because Haeckel had maintained that the alimentary canal of all vertebrates was formed by an involution of the epiblast—that is, in the same manner that the archenteron of his hypothetical *gastraea* had been formed in eons past.

At this juncture Balfour introduced quite a different question: If the segmentation cavity and alimentary canal in *amphioxus,* elasmobranchs, amphibians, and birds were to be considered homologous, how should one interpret their different germ-layer origins? He concluded that one must take into consideration the quantity of yolk in the egg and its degree of segmentation at the time of germ-layer formation. Thus, he argued that since there was little yolk in *amphioxus* and amphibian eggs, there existed perforce an anus of Rosconi and an involution of the epiblast at the dorsal lip of the blastopore; however, his argument continued, since there was a large quantity of yolk in elasmobranch eggs, there existed only a temporary anal opening and a delamination of the hypoblast. As for bird eggs, which held an extremely large quantity of yolk, Balfour claimed that no anus of Rosconi could possibly exist, nor could the epiblast invaginate. In this explanation Balfour indicated an appreciation for the mechanical influences of cellular movement that forced different embryos to develop along different lines, irrespective of their phylogenetic connections.

Balfour's recognition of the mechanical influence of the mass of yolk may have prompted his inquiry into the meaning of the primitive streak of the chick embryo. Comparing the positions of amphibian and selachian embryos, which are asymmetrically situated on the blastoderm, with the chick embryo, which lies on the center, Balfour argued that the primitive streak was the homologue of the blastopore in the lower vertebrates. In collaboration with one of his students, Balfour further explained that the mesoblast of the chick was derived through a simultaneous differentiation from both the hypoblast and the epiblast, which lay along the axial line of the primitive streak. Such evidence again implicitly challenged a too rigid belief in the specificity of the germ layers. Balfour, however, did not draw the ultimate conclusions but faithfully adhered to the germ-layer doctrine.

In his study of elasmobranchs, Balfour included a detailed and superb description of the development of the excretory system. Although this work was anticipated in many respects by Karl Semper's similar study, Balfour definitively pointed out the initial segmental character of the Wolffian duct ("segmental duct") and traced the manner in which the Müllerian duct arose from the Wolffian duct's ventral side. He then described in detail how the Müllerian duct in the female became converted to the oviduct and how the Wolffian duct in the male was utilized by the testes as the *vas deferens.* Considering the various modes of development in the abdominal opening of the Müllerian duct in elasmobranchs, amphibians, and birds, Balfour argued that there were sufficient differences to indicate three lines of urogenital evolution that diverged from a more general and primitive state. Although it is clear that the reconstruction of an evolutionary tree was a concern which constantly framed his detailed research, Balfour again minimized a discussion of the phylogenetic implications of his work.

When one surveys his many shorter articles, it is surprising to discover how strategically Balfour covered portions of the animal kingdom. A clear pattern emerges from his studies of elasmobranchs, *Lepidosteus* (a ganoid), *amphioxus, Peripatus* (an aberrant arthropod), and *Araneina* (a true spider), in which Balfour appears intent upon locating possible links between major taxa. Although he did not commit himself to any current theory concerning the link between invertebrates and vertebrates, he believed that any protochordate must have been segmental in character and must have had a suctorial mouth on the ventral surface. He believed, moreover, that any claimant of the title "missing link" must show undeniable signs of a primitive notochord.

Even taking these broader interests in phylogeny into consideration, it is still remarkable that within three years of the completion of his monograph on elasmobranchs, Balfour finished his two-volume *Treatise on Comparative Embryology* (1880–1881). According to Waldeyer, this was the first successful attempt at a complete comparative embryology text; it was translated into German the same year, and one finds important references to it for decades thereafter. Not only did Balfour survey developments peculiar to each phylum and give a comparative survey of the embryology of each organ system, but he also included introductory chapters on gamete formation, fertilization, and early cleavage, additions that demonstrated his keen interest in the most recent advances in cytology. By 1882 microscopy had made such rapid gains that many of Balfour's facts, particularly about the nucleus, were already dated. There are certain signs, however, that he would have become more involved in this direction of research; in fact, as indicated above, there are even signs that he would have appreciated the type of question which the experimental embryologists in Germany began asking of the embryo from about 1882. Reflecting upon these interests, one can only muse how the embryological sciences in England would have progressed had Balfour not died at the age of thirty.

BIBLIOGRAPHY

The Works of Francis Maitland Balfour, Michael Foster and Adam Sedgwick, eds., 4 vols. (London, 1885), contains all of Balfour's published works, including *A Monograph on the Development of the Elasmobranch Fishes* (London, 1878) and *A Treatise on Comparative Embryology,* 2 vols. (London, 1880–1881).

There are only a few scanty biographical notices on Balfour, and even fewer discussions of his work. Besides Michael Foster's introduction to the collected works, W. Waldeyer, "Francis Maitland Balfour, Ein Nachruf," in *Archiv für mikroskopische Anatomie,* **21** (1882), 828–835, and Henry Fairfield Osborn, "Francis Maitland Balfour," in *Science,* **2** (1883), 299–301, are useful. Balfour's work is placed in its historical context in E. S. Russell, *Form and Function, a Contribution to the History of Animal Morphology* (London, 1916), pp. 268–301.

F. B. CHURCHILL

BALFOUR, ISAAC BAYLEY (*b.* Edinburgh, Scotland, 31 March 1853; *d.* Haslemere, England, 30 November 1922), *botany.*

Balfour possessed a distinguished academic pedigree: his father, John Hutton Balfour, was professor of botany at Edinburgh University and his mother, Marion Spottiswood Bayley, was the daughter of Isaac Bayley, writer to the signet; his ancestry also included George H. Baird, principal of Edinburgh University, and geologist James Hutton.

At Edinburgh University he obtained his B.S. in 1873 and M.B. in 1877, then continued his botanical studies, particularly morphology and physiology, at the universities of Würzburg and Strasbourg. He accompanied the transit of Venus expedition to Rodriguez Island in 1874 as botanist and geologist. The botanical results of this expedition, published in the *Philosophical Transactions* in 1879, clearly indicated that Balfour was a taxonomist of considerable promise. In 1879–1880 he collected plants on the island of Socotra, and in 1888 published his description of the island's flora, which included many new species. He observed that the flora had affinities with that of the African mainland and argued that Socotra had once formed part of that continent.

After his appointment to the chair of botany at Glasgow University in 1879, Balfour revealed his capacity for organization. In his five years there he rebuilt the principal range of greenhouses, saved the herbarium from imminent destruction, and improved the laboratory facilities for students. In 1884 he was elected Sherardian professor of botany at Oxford, where his energy and administrative skill revitalized the ancient but neglected botanic garden. The herbaceous beds were remodeled, and the valuable herbarium and library thoroughly reorganized. Having established good relations with the Clarendon Press in Oxford, he persuaded them to undertake, under his editorship, the publication of translations of standard German botanical texts. The press also launched the *Annals of Botany* in 1887, with Balfour as joint editor with S. H. Vines and W. G. Farlow until 1912.

He moved to Edinburgh in 1888 as professor of botany, queen's botanist in Scotland, and Regius keeper of the Royal Botanic Garden, holding these offices, as did his father before him, for thirty-four years. During this time Balfour gradually accomplished many of his desired reforms: a massive wall that obstructed the redesigning of the botanic garden was removed; the plant collections were enriched, particularly with alpines, for which a splendid new rock garden was created; and the greenhouses were rebuilt. Under his direction Edinburgh became an exemplar of horticultural practice.

A capacity for unrelenting work brought Balfour distinction in several fields of activity: taxonomy, teaching, horticulture, and administration. The pressures of a full life never hindered his botanical research, in which he concentrated on *Rhododendron* and *Primula*. His taxonomic papers on these two genera appeared in *Notes From the Royal Botanic Garden, Edinburgh,* which he founded in 1900. He was an authority on the vegetation of the Himalayas and western China, and successfully grew at Edinburgh many of the new plants introduced by George Forrest from that region. A gifted lecturer, Balfour modernized the teaching methods of three universities, and for a generation Edinburgh was the main center for the teaching of taxonomy. In short, he was that *rara avis,* an all-round botanist with an aptitude for organization.

Balfour was elected a fellow of the Royal Society in 1884; awarded the Victoria Medal of Honour of the Royal Horticultural Society in 1897, and the Linnean Medal in 1919; and created K.B.E. in 1920 for services rendered during World War I. He married Agnes Boyd in 1884, and had one son and one daughter.

BIBLIOGRAPHY

I. ORIGINAL WORKS. Among Balfour's writings are "Botany [of Rodriguez]," in *Philosophical Transactions of the*

Royal Society of London, **168** (1879), 302–387; and "Botany of Socotra," which constitutes *Transactions of the Royal Society of Edinburgh,* **31** (1888).

II. SECONDARY LITERATURE. Obituaries include F. O. Bower, in *Proceedings of the Royal Society of Edinburgh,* **43**, no. 3 (1923), 230–236; J. B. Farmer, in *Annals of Botany,* **37**, no. 146 (1923), 335–339; *Kew Bulletin* (1923), 30–35; Sir David Prain, in *Proceedings of the Royal Society of London,* **96B**, no. 678 (1924), i–xvii; and W. Wright Smith, in *Transactions and Proceedings of the Botanical Society of Edinburgh,* **28**, no. 4 (1923), 192–196.

R. G. C. DESMOND

BALFOUR, JOHN HUTTON (*b.* Edinburgh, Scotland, 15 September 1808; *d.* Edinburgh, 11 February 1884), *botany.*

The eldest son of Andrew Balfour, an army surgeon who became a printer and publisher in Edinburgh, John Balfour received his basic education at the High School, Edinburgh, and the universities of Edinburgh and St. Andrews. He resisted his parents' wishes that he enter the church, and chose medicine for his future career. He graduated M.D. at Edinburgh in 1832, and after a period of further study in a medical school in Paris, returned to his native city to practice medicine in 1834.

Like so many other physicians before him, Balfour found himself irresistibly drawn to botany. He first became seriously interested in the subject when he was about eighteen, and he was allowed to attend Robert Graham's botanical lectures for four sessions. He was a founding member in 1836 of the Botanical Society of Edinburgh, and two years later he established the Edinburgh Botanical Club. In 1840 he enjoyed some success as a lecturer on botany in the extramural School of Medicine.

In 1841 Balfour abandoned medicine on succeeding Sir William J. Hooker as professor of botany at Glasgow University. His few years at Glasgow were not marked by any radical changes, although he arranged the removal of the botanic garden, which was becoming hemmed in by adjacent streets, to a new site at Kelvinside. Upon the death of Graham in 1845, he was elected to the chair of botany at Edinburgh and the associated posts of queen's botanist in Scotland and Regius keeper of the Royal Botanic Garden. At Edinburgh, Balfour was fortunate in having as successive curators William and James McNab, father and son, and through their horticultural skill marked improvements were effected in the botanic garden: the grounds were enlarged from fourteen to forty-two acres, an arboretum was established, and a fine palm house and botanical museum were erected.

It is, however, as a teacher that Balfour is remembered. He made extensive use of the microscope in his demonstrations—not a common practice at that time—and placed great emphasis on the value of botanical excursions. These excursions had always been a characteristic feature of the teaching of botany in Scottish universities, and Balfour, like his predecessor Graham, used them for the dual purposes of instruction and supplying the botanical garden with specimens suitable for cultivation. Through these excursions he explored the greater part of Scotland, inculcating in his students not only a knowledge of the flora but also an appreciation of ecological diversity. His manner of teaching, lucid and displaying an impressive wealth of detail, was distinguished by an enthusiasm that he communicated to his audience. A number of useful students' textbooks, which went through numerous editions, came from his pen, including *Manual of Botany* (1849) and *Class Book of Botany* (1852).

His father had been a strict Presbyterian, and Balfour himself was a deeply religious man who sought in nature confirmation of God's existence. Among his botanico-religious books were *Phyto-Theology* (1851), the title of which was changed to *Botany and Religion* in the third edition, *Plants of the Bible* (1857), and *Lessons From Bible Plants* (1870).

Balfour was an editor of the *Edinburgh New Philosophical Journal.* That his original work should have been slight was the inevitable consequence of the time he devoted to teaching and administration. Elected a fellow of the Royal Society of Edinburgh in 1835, he was its secretary for many years; he also acquired the secretaryship of the Royal Caledonian Horticultural Society and was dean of the Medical Faculty at Edinburgh for thirty years. He was elected a fellow of the Linnean Society in 1844, and of the Royal Society in 1856. On his retirement in 1879, the universities of Edinburgh, St. Andrews, and Glasgow each conferred on him the LL.D.

BIBLIOGRAPHY

Among Balfour's works are *Manual of Botany* (London, 1849); *Phyto-Theology* (Edinburgh, 1851); *Class Book of Botany* (Edinburgh, 1852); *Outlines of Botany* (Edinburgh, 1854); *Plants of the Bible* (London, 1857); *Flora of Edinburgh* (Edinburgh, 1863), written with J. Sadler; and *Lessons From Bible Plants* (Glasgow, 1870).

There is an article on Balfour by his son, Isaac, in F. W. Oliver, ed., *Makers of British Botany* (Cambridge, 1913), pp. 293–300.

R. G. C. DESMOND

BALIANI

BALIANI, GIOVANNI BATTISTA (*b.* Genoa, Italy, 1582; *d.* Genoa, 1666), *physics.*

Baliani, the son of a senator, was trained in the law and spent most of his life in public service. His scientific interests appear to have begun about 1611, when he was prefect of the fortress at Savona. There he noted the equal speed of fall of cannon balls differing greatly in weight. About the same time he devised an apparatus for cooking by frictional heat—an iron pot rotating on a concave iron base.

In 1613 Filippo Salviati met Baliani and wrote of him to Galileo, who began corresponding with Baliani concerning the experimental determination of the weight of air. In 1615 Baliani visited Galileo at Florence and met Benedetto Castelli. The intermittent correspondence that lasted for many years shows Baliani to have been a talented experimentalist and an ingenious speculator. In 1630 he wrote to Galileo of the failure of a siphon that had been expected to carry water over a rise of about sixty feet (eighty *piedi*). Baliani attributed the action of a lift pump to atmospheric pressure, but doubted that the total weight of a column of air many miles high could be less than that of a thirty-foot column of water, at which height Galileo had already noted the failure of lift pumps.

In astronomy, although Baliani preferred Tycho Brahe's system to that of Copernicus, he speculated on a terrestrial motion as the possible cause of tides.

In 1638 Baliani published a short treatise on the motions of heavy bodies, which he reprinted in 1646 with many additions. In the first edition he gave correct laws for free fall, motion on inclined planes, and pendulums. In the second edition he speculated on the possibility that in unmeasurably small successive finite times, the spaces traversed by a falling body might increase in proportion to the natural numbers, assuming that the body received very rapid successive impulses and retained them unimpaired. Baliani's argument embodied an important step toward the concept of mass and the analysis of acceleration, but it was widely misunderstood as intended to contradict the law that both he and Galileo had explicitly stated: that for successive equal measurable times, the spaces traversed by a falling body are as the odd numbers 1, 3, 5,···. The misunderstanding caused Baliani's name to become associated with the false hypothesis, specifically rejected by Galileo, that velocity in free fall increases in proportion to space traversed. Although Baliani did not uphold the false law of acceleration, he rejected the parabolic trajectory in such a way as to show that his idea of inertial motion was inexact.

In 1647 Baliani published a treatise on the plague, suggesting a chemical explanation of its nature and its contagious character. In this work he stated the principle that the rate of human population increase as related to arable land and food production would necessarily result in famine were it not for the occurrence of war and pestilence. The quantitative nature of his argument entitles him to be regarded as a predecessor of the Malthusian law.

Baliani returned to Savona in 1647 as governor of its fortress, a post he held until 1649. He was then elevated to membership in the principal governing body of Genoa, where he remained until his death.

Baliani's previously unpublished works were collected and printed in 1666. They include several philosophical dialogues and discussions of light, action at a distance, the existence of a vacuum and of motion therein, and some prismatic experiments. The works were republished in 1792 with an anonymous life of Baliani and a number of letters praising his achievements.

The direct influence of Baliani on other scientists probably was not great; he worked as an amateur with notable ability and success, but his principal fields of interest were those that were simultaneously receiving attention from Galileo and his disciples. He did not arrive at the laws of falling bodies independently of Galileo, and although their explanation in terms of incremental impulse was probably his own, a similar analysis had been published by G. B. Benedetti in 1585. His correct conception of atmospheric pressure remained unpublished, although it may have become known to Torricelli through conversations with Galileo, who rejected it. Baliani's most important contribution, a discussion of elastic shock, seems to have gone unnoticed until recently, and hence probably did not influence the development of the laws of impact. No final evaluation of Baliani's place in the history of physics is possible, however, without an exhaustive study of his extant correspondence, for many of his germinal ideas were not published and are known only through his letters.

BIBLIOGRAPHY

I. ORIGINAL WORKS. Known copies of Baliani's works in North America not listed in the Union Catalogue are designated as follows: California Institute of Technology, CIT; University of Toronto Library, ULT. His works are *De motu naturali gravium solidorum Ioannis Baptistae Baliani patritii genuensis* (Genoa, 1638); *De motu gravium solidorum et liquidorum Io. Baptistae Baliani patritii genuensis* (Genoa, 1646; ULT); *Trattato della pestilenza di Gio. Battista Baliano* (Savona, 1647; ULT); *Di. Gio. Batista Baliani. Opere diverse* (Genoa, 1666); and *Opere diverse di Gio. Battista Baliani, patrizio genovese; aggiuntovi nell'avviso a chi legge, una compendiosa notizia di lui vita* (Genoa, 1792; CIT).

The Baliani-Galileo correspondence is included in *Le opere di Galileo Galilei*, Ed. Naz. (Florence, 1934–1937), Vols. XII–XVIII, *passim*. Baliani's correspondence with Mersenne has been published to 1640 in *Correspondance du P. Marin Mersenne*, Cornelis De Waard *et al.*, eds. (Paris, 1945–1965). Unpublished Baliani letters at Milan are described in Moscovici's 1965 article.

II. SECONDARY LITERATURE. A general discussion of Baliani and his published works is given in Alpinolo Natucci, "Giovan Battista Baliani letterato e scienzato del secolo XVII," in *Archives internationales d'histoire des sciences*, **12** (1959), 267–283. A critical examination of the misinterpretation by earlier writers of Baliani's law of acceleration occupies Ottaviano Cametti's *Lettera critico-meccanica* (Rome, 1758); its subsequent fate and its implications for the concepts of mass and inertia are discussed in S. Moscovici, *L' expérience de mouvement. Jean-Baptiste Baliani—disciple et critique de Galilée* (Paris, 1967), which discusses extensively the barometric correspondence with Mersenne and others and which has an appendix with many previously unpublished letters of Baliani. Other aspects of Baliani's physics are discussed in S. Moscovici, "Les développements historiques de la théorie galiléenne des marées," in *Revue d'histoire des sciences et de leurs applications*, **18**, no. 2 (1965), 193–220; and Cornelis De Waard, *L'expérience barométrique. Ses antécédents et ses explications* (Thouars, 1936), p. 95.

STILLMAN DRAKE

AL-BALKHĪ. See **Abū Maʿshar.**

BALLONIUS. See **Baillou, Guillaume.**

BALLOT, CHRISTOPH BUYS. See **Buys Ballot, Christoph.**

BALMER, JOHANN JAKOB (*b.* Lausen, Basel-Land, Switzerland, 1 May 1825; *d.* Basel, Switzerland, 12 March 1898), *mathematics, physics.*

Balmer was the oldest son of Chief Justice Johann Jakob Balmer and Elisabeth Rolle Balmer. He attended the district school in Liestal and the secondary school in Basel, studied mathematics at Karlsruhe and Berlin, and was granted a doctorate at Basel in 1849 with a dissertation on the cycloid. In 1868 he married Christine Pauline Rinck, who bore him six children. He taught at the girls' secondary school in Basel from 1859 until his death, and from 1865 to 1890 he also held a part-time lectureship at the University of Basel. His major field of professional interest was geometry; spectral series, the topic of his most noted contribution, was an area in which he became involved only late in life.

The earliest attempts to establish relationships between the observed lines of an elementary spectrum were organized primarily within the theoretical context of a mechanical acoustical analogy. Many investigators attempted to establish simple harmonic ratios, but in 1881 Arthur Schuster demonstrated the inadequacy of this approach. The essentially successful mathematical organization of the data began in 1885 with Balmer's presentation of the formula $\lambda = hm^2/(m^2 - n^2)$ for the hydrogen series. This formula could be used to generate, with considerable accuracy, the wavelengths of the known characteristic spectral lines for hydrogen when $n = 2$, $h = 3645.6 \times 10^{-8}$ cm., and $m = 3, 4, 5, 6, \cdots$ successively.

Initially, Balmer knew only Ångström's measurements for the first four visible hydrogen lines, but he calculated the next, or fifth, result of the formula using $m = 7$, obtaining the wavelength of a line that, if it existed, would be barely on the edge of the visible spectrum. Jakob Edward Hagenbach-Bischoff, a friend and colleague at the University of Basel who had stimulated his interest in this topic, informed him that this fifth line had been observed, and that a number of other hydrogen lines had been measured. Comparisons between the calculated results obtained using Balmer's formula for these lines and the observed values showed close agreement, differences being at most approximately one part in one thousand. Later investigators demonstrated that the formula, with a slightly altered constant, represented the whole series, including additional lines, with unusual accuracy. Balmer speculated that values for other hydrogen series in the ultraviolet and infrared regions would be generated if n were assigned integer values other than two. Such predicted series were experimentally found later and are known as the Lyman, Paschen, Brackett, and Pfund series.

Balmer's relationship was so different from the simple harmonic ratios expected on the acoustical analogy, that investigators were bewildered as to what sort of mechanism could produce such lines. In spite of this disturbing feature, Balmer's work served as a model for other series formulas, especially the more generalized formulas of Johannes Robert Rydberg (1854–1919), Heinrich Kayser (1853–1940), and Carl Runge (1856–1927). Balmer published only one further paper on spectra, in which he extended his considerations to the spectra of several other elements (1897).

BIBLIOGRAPHY

I. ORIGINAL WORKS. Balmer's major article on the hydrogen spectrum is "Notiz über die Spektrallinien des

Wasserstoffs," in *Verhandlungen der Naturforschenden Gesellschaft in Basel*, **7** (1885), 548–560, 750–752; also in *Annalen der Physik*, 3rd ser., **25** (1885), 80–87. His second and only other spectral article is "Eine neue Formel für Spektralwellen," in *Verhandlungen der Naturforschenden Gesellschaft in Basel*, **11** (1897), 448–463; and in *Annalen der Physik*, 3rd ser., **60** (1897), 380–391. It is also available in *Astrophysical Journal*, **5** (1897), 199–209. A short note of historical interest is Jakob Edward Hagenbach-Bischoff's "Balmer'sche Formel für Wasserstofflinien," in *Verhandlungen der Naturforschenden Gesellschaft in Basel*, **8** (1890), 242.

II. Secondary Literature. For discussions on aspects of Balmer's life and works, see August Hagenbach, "J. J. Balmer und W. Ritz," in *Die Naturwissenschaften*, **9** (1921), 451–455, and "Johann Jakob Balmer," in Edward Fueter, ed., *Grosse Schweizer Forscher* (Zurich, 1939), pp. 248–249; L. Hartmann, "Johann Jakob Balmer," in *Physikalische Blätter*, **5** (1949), 11–14; and Eduard His, "Johann Jakob Balmer," in *Basler Gelehrte des 19. Jahrhunderts* (Basel, 1941), pp. 213–217.

C. L. Maier

BAMBERGER, EUGEN (*b.* Berlin, Prussia, 19 July 1857; *d.* Ponte Tresa, Switzerland, 10 December 1932), *chemistry*.

In 1875 Bamberger entered the University of Breslau as a medical student. The next summer he studied at Heidelberg with Robert Bunsen. He later returned to Berlin, worked with Carl Liebermann, and completed his degree under A. W. Hofmann. He then became an assistant to Karl Rammelsberg at the Technische Hochschule of Berlin-Charlottenburg. In 1883 Bamberger went to Munich as Baeyer's assistant, first in the analytic, then in the organic, laboratory. He gave his inaugural lecture in 1885 and in 1891 became extraordinary professor of organic chemistry. In 1893 he accepted a professorship at the Eidgenössische Technische Hochschule in Zurich. He relinquished this position in 1905, however, because of a nervous condition that left his right arm paralyzed. He nevertheless continued private research with the aid of an assistant.

In his dissertation Bamberger worked on derivatives of guanine, then turned to similar substances. He investigated aromatic hydrocarbons and elucidated the structures of retene, chrysene, pyrene, and the glycoside picein. As he pursued his work with naphthalene derivatives, he noticed that some compounds in which hydrogen had been added to the substituted ring no longer retained their aromatic properties. He called these alicyclic because they behaved like aliphatic compounds but had a closed-ring structure. In connection with this work he also extended the centric formula of benzene to naph-

thalene and supported this view with his work on benzimidazole and isoquinoline. Turning to by-products of reactions previously studied, Bamberger examined such mixed nitrogen compounds as the hydrazones and formaryl derivatives. He then directed his attention to organic nitrogen compounds, and discovered the isodiazo compounds. He found that, unlike normal diazo compounds, in the isodiazo compounds the NO could be oxidized to NO_2. This led Bamberger to believe that a formula similar to that of nitrosamines could be used to represent those isodiazo compounds which on hydrolysis yielded normal diazo compounds. In 1894 this view was sharply criticized by Arthur Hantzsch. He suggested that the differences between the two types of diazo compounds could be explained by isomerism. As a classical organic chemist, Bamberger countered most of Hantzsch's arguments by studying the chemical activity of the supposed isomer, but he admitted the cogency of the physicochemical arguments by replacing his proposed formula with one containing the phenylazo radical. The controversy continued for years, and only with the rejection of pentavalent nitrogen could a new formula for diazo compounds be proposed.

Bamberger then turned to the oxidation and reduction of nitrogen compounds. He reduced nitrobenzene to nitrosobenzene and phenylhydrozylamine with zinc dust in a neutral solution, but refused to patent the process. His preparation of dimethylaniline oxide supported the idea of the pentavalence of nitrogen. Following the diazo controversy Bamberger paid more attention to physical properties, investigating the optical properties of anthranil derivatives and the photochemical properties of benzaldehyde derivatives. In spite of this, however, he remained a classical organic chemist devoted to theory. He investigated natural compounds, using minimum material and the simplest equipment, and studied all by-products thoroughly.

BIBLIOGRAPHY

I. Original Works. An extensive list of Bamberger's works is in Poggendorff. Among his writings are "Ueber die Constitution des Acenaphtens und der Naphthalsäure," in *Bericht der Deutschen chemischen Gesellschaft*, **20** (1887), 237–244, written with Max Philip; "Ueber α-tetrahydronaphtylene," *ibid.*, **21** (1888), 1786–1795, 1892–1904, written with Max Althausse; "Ueber Aethyl-α-naphtylamin," *ibid.*, **27** (1894), 2469–2472, written with Carl Goldschmidt; "Zur Kenntnis des Diazotirungsprocess," *ibid.*, 1948–1953; "Ueber das Phenylhydrozylamin," *ibid.*, 1548–1557; "Ueber die Reduction der Nitroverbindungen," *ibid.*,

1347–1350; "Ueber die 'Stereoisomeren' Diazoamidverbindungen von A. Hantzsch," *ibid.,* 2596–2601; "Weiteres über Diazo- und Isodiazoverbindungen," *ibid.,* 914–917; and "Zur Geschichte der Diazoniumsalze," *ibid.,* **32** (1899), 2043–2046, 3633–3635.

II. SECONDARY LITERATURE. Works dealing with Bamberger are "E. Bamberger zum 75. Geburtstag," in *Zeitschrift für angewandte Chemie,* **45** (1932), 514; Louis Blangey, "Eugene Bamberger," in *Helvetica chimica acta,* **16** (1933), 644–676; and Eduard Hjelt, *Geschichte der organischen Chemie von altester Zeit bis zur Gegenwart* (Brunswick, 1916). J. R. Partington, *A History of Chemistry,* IV (London, 1964), discusses Bamberger's contributions to organic chemistry on pp. 840–842 and gives an account of the controversy with Hantzsch under "Hantzsch," pp. 842–847.

RUTH ANNE GIENAPP

BANACH, STEFAN (*b.* Krakow, Poland, 30 March 1892; *d.* Lvov, Ukrainian S.S.R., 31 August 1945), *mathematics.*

Banach's father, a railway official, and mother turned their son over to a laundress, who became his foster mother and gave him her surname. From the age of fifteen he supported himself by giving private lessons. After graduating from secondary school in Krakow in 1910, Banach studied at the Institute of Technology in Lvov but did not graduate. He returned to Krakow in 1914, and from 1916, when he met H. Steinhaus, he devoted himself to mathematics. His knowledge of the field was already fairly extensive, although it probably was not very systematic. Banach's first paper, on the convergence of Fourier series, was written with Steinhaus in 1917 and was published two years later. Also in 1919 he was appointed lecturer in mathematics at the Institute of Technology in Lvov, where, in addition, he lectured on mechanics. In the same year he received his doctorate with an unusual exemption from complete university education. Banach's thesis, "Sur les opérations dans les ensembles abstraits et leur application aux équations intégrales," appeared in *Fundamenta mathematicae* in 1922. The publication of this thesis is sometimes said to have marked the birth of functional analysis.

In 1922 Banach became a *Dozent* on the basis of a paper on measure theory (published in 1923). Soon afterward he was made associate professor, and in 1927 he became full professor at the University of Lvov. In 1924 he was elected corresponding member of the Polish Academy of Sciences and Arts. Banach's research activity was intense, and he had a number of students who later became outstanding mathematicians: S. Mazur, W. Orlicz, J. Schauder, and S. Ulam, among others. Banach and Steinhaus

founded the journal *Studia mathematica,* but often Banach had little time left for scientific work because the writing of both college texts (of which the book on mechanics is of special importance) and secondary-school texts took most of his time and effort.

From 1939 to 1941 Banach was dean of the faculty at Lvov and was elected a member of the Ukrainian Academy of Sciences. In the summer of 1941, Lvov was occupied by the German army, and for three years Banach was compelled to feed lice in a German institute that dealt with infectious diseases. After the liberation of Lvov in the autumn of 1944, he resumed his work at the university. His health was shattered, however, and he died less than a year later.

Banach's scientific work comprises about fifty papers and the monograph *Théorie des opérations linéaires* (1932). Although he laid the foundations of contemporary functional analysis, most of his papers are closely connected with the field but are not precisely in it.

Banach made a significant contribution to the theory of orthogonal series, and his theorem on locally meager sets is of lasting importance in general topology. In the descriptive theory of sets and mappings, he extended to mappings some theorems previously known only for numerical functions. A number of results, many of which can now be found in textbooks, concern derivation and absolute continuity, as well as related properties. Banach made a substantial contribution to the theory of measure and integration, results that stimulated a great number of papers and, apparently, the discovery of the Radon-Nikodým theorem. The questions of the existence of measures investigated by Banach have proved to be closely connected with the axiomatic theory of sets.

Despite the great importance of these results and the unusual lucidity and force of mathematical thinking manifested in them, functional analysis is Banach's most important contribution. His work started, of course, from what was achieved during the decades following Vito Volterra's papers of the 1890's on integral equations. Before Banach there were either rather specific individual results that only much later were obtained as applications of general theorems, or relatively vague general concepts. Papers on the so-called general analysis (mainly by E. H. Moore) formed a significant trend, but these were none too comprehensible and, for that period at least, much too general. Ivar Fredholm's and David Hilbert's papers on integral equations marked the most substantial progress. The concepts and theorems they had discovered later became an integral part of functional analysis, but most of them concern only a single linear space (later called Hilbert space).

Later, more or less simultaneously with Banach, several mathematicians—O. Hahn, L. Fréchet, E. Helly, and Norbert Wiener, among others—attained many of the concepts and theorems forming the basis of Banach's theory. None of them, however, succeeded in creating as comprehensive and integrated a system of concepts and theorems and their applications as that of Banach, his co-workers, and his students.

From 1922 on, Banach introduced through his papers the concept of normed linear spaces and investigated them (and metric linear spaces), particularly regarding the assumption of completeness (complete normed linear spaces are now generally known as Banach spaces). The concept was introduced at almost the same time by Norbert Wiener (who about a quarter of a century later founded cybernetics), but he did not develop the theory, perhaps because he did not see its possible application. Banach proved three fundamental theorems of the theory of normed linear spaces: the theorem on the extension of continuous linear functionals, now called the Hahn–Banach theorem (they proved it independently, and Hahn actually did so first); the theorem on bounded families of mappings, now called the Banach–Steinhaus theorem; and the theorem on continuous linear mappings of Banach spaces. He also introduced and examined the concept of weak convergence and weak closure, and gave a series of applications of the general theorems on normed linear spaces.

Further development of functional analysis proved that metric linear spaces are not sufficient for the needs of analysis and that it is essential to use more general, and also richer and more special, objects and structures. Nevertheless, the theory of Banach spaces has—often in combination with other methods—numerous applications in analysis. The theory of these spaces is both an indispensable tool and the basis of contemporary theory of more general linear spaces; it also provided the stimulus and the starting point for other branches of functional analysis.

The fact that functional analysis originated as late as Banach and his school, although favorable conditions seemingly existed at the beginning of the century, is due largely to the way mathematics had developed until then. In fact, sufficiently detailed knowledge about the different concrete instances of linear spaces was not achieved until the 1920's. Also, by that time the applications of some methods of the theory of sets, such as transfinite construction, were clarified, and some theorems on general topology (e.g., Baire's theorem on complete metric spaces and some propositions from the descriptive theory of sets) became widely known and applied.

BIBLIOGRAPHY

I. ORIGINAL WORKS. Banach's major work is *Théorie des opérations linéaires* (Warsaw, 1932). Numerous papers are in *Fundamenta mathematicae* and *Studia mathematica*. See also "Sur le problème de la mesure," in *Fundamenta mathematicae*, 4 (1923), 7–33; and *Mechanika w zakresie szkol akademickich,* Vols. 8 and 9 in the series Monografie Matematyczne (Warsaw–Lvov–Vilna, 1938), translated into English as *Mechanics* (Warsaw–Breslau, 1951). The first volume of his collected works, *Oeuvres* (Warsaw, 1967), contains, besides papers by Banach, up-to-date comments on almost every article.

II. SECONDARY LITERATURE. A short biography, a practically complete list of scientific papers, and an analysis of Banach's work are in *Colloquium mathematicum,* 1, no. 2 (1948), 65–102. Also see H. Steinhaus, "Stefan Banach," in *Studia mathematica,* special series, 1 (1963), 7–15; and S. Ulam, "Stefan Banach 1892–1945," in *Bulletin of the American Mathematical Society,* 52 (1946), 600–603.

MIROSLAV KATĚTOV

BANACHIEWICZ, THADDEUS (*b.* Warsaw, Poland, 13 February 1882; *d.* Krakow, Poland, 17 November 1954), *astronomy*.

The younger son of Arthur Banachiewicz, a landowner in the Warsaw district, and Sophia Rzeszotarska, Banachiewicz received his bachelor's degree in astronomy in 1904 from Warsaw University, where one of his astronomical papers had earlier won a gold medal. He continued his studies in Göttingen under Schwarzchild and in Pulkovo. After his return to Warsaw he was junior assistant at the Warsaw Observatory in 1908–1909. In 1910 he received the master's degree in astronomy from Moscow University and soon afterward was appointed assistant at the Engelhardt Observatory, near Kazan, where he stayed until 1915. For the next three years he taught at Dorpat. He returned to Warsaw in 1918 and for a short time was *Dozent* of geodesy at the Warsaw Polytechnic High School. Toward the end of that year he accepted the professorship of astronomy at the University of Krakow and directorship of the Krakow Observatory. He spent the rest of his life in Krakow, the only interruption occurring in the winter of 1939/1940, when the Krakow faculty was taken to the Gestapo concentration camp at Sachsenhausen, near Berlin.

Banachiewicz's work concerned many important problems of astronomy, geodesy, geophysics, mathematics, mechanics, and numerical calculus. His principle of repeated verification made his 240 published papers safe from errors. His most important astronomical and geodetical work was theoretical. As early as 1906 a paper of his that dealt with Lagrange's three-body problem was presented to the Paris Academy by Poincaré. The paper, "Über die Anwendbarkeit der Gyldén-Brendelschen Störungstheorie auf die Jupiternahen Planetoiden," gave a brilliant analysis of Gyldén-Brendel's theory, pointing out its illusiveness when applied to small planets in the vicinity of Jupiter.

He also published several papers on Gauss's equation and gave useful tables to facilitate its numerical solution. These tables have been reprinted in J. Bauschinger and G. Stracke's *Tafeln zur theoretischen Astronomie.*

Banachiewicz paid considerable attention to multiple solutions in the determination of parabolic orbits. Legendre, Charlier, Vogel, and others claimed to have solved the question in the sense that the two equations obtained in the process of determining a parabolic orbit from three observations lead to a single solution. Banachiewicz showed that they were basing their reasoning on Lambert's equation, which fails in certain circumstances. In these exceptional cases three solutions are possible, as he demonstrated with a fictitious numerical example.

One of Banachiewicz's great achievements in theoretical astronomy was the simplification of Olbers' method of determining parabolic orbits. These new methods used a much improved technique of computing, for which Banachiewicz had invented the cracovian calculus. The cracovians are related to Cayley's matrices but differ in the definition of the product, the cracovians being multiplied column by column. This change in the product rule leads to considerable differences between the theories of Cayley and Banachiewicz and makes cracovians more suitable for machine computation. The invention of rotary cracovians enabled Banachiewicz to obtain the solution of the general problem of spherical polygonometry, which had been sought for over a century. Having these new formulas at his disposal, he simplified Bessel's classic method of reducing heliometric observations of the moon's libration. He successfully applied the cracovians to the correction of orbits and gave a simple, practical, and elegant solution of the problem. Convenient cracovian formulas were introduced by Banachiewicz for computing the precessional effect of star coordinates, and his orthogonal transformation formulas facilitated the reduction of the vectorial elements of planets and comets from one epoch to another.

Banachiewicz's investigations into the theory of linear equations produced interesting applications of the cracovian method to such problems as the reduction of astrographic plates; here cracovian formulas led to a general solution that comprised the formulas of Turner and those of the dependency method. He also simplified the classical method of least squares. The cracovian method is well suited to numerical computation. Its importance lies in the fact that the unknowns and their weights are found simultaneously during the process of computation, which is not the case in Gauss's method.

Banachiewicz was not only a prominent theorist but also a gifted and assiduous observer. While a student he promoted observations of occultations of stars by the moon, insisting on their importance for the study of the moon's motion, and developed a purely mathematical method for predicting occultations of stars that had great advantages over the graphical methods. He was also interested in occultations of stars by planets. His ephemerides drew attention to the occultation of 6G Librae by Ganymede, Jupiter's III satellite, on 13 August 1911, which was unique in the history of astronomy because it was the only occultation of a bright star by a planet's satellite to be predicted and observed. From probability considerations one may conclude that an occultation of a star of magnitude $\leq 7^n$ by Ganymede occurs once in a thousand years. While in Kazan he carried out very precise observations of the moon's libration with a four-inch heliometer. Banachiewicz attached much importance to observations of eclipsing variables and introduced them into the working program of the Krakow Observatory. He considered eclipsing binaries the clue to many important questions of the sidereal universe and insisted on gathering observational material for "the future Kepler of eclipsing binaries."

Since he was interested in higher geodesy, Banachiewicz took part in gravimetric observations when he was at Kazan. He later organized gravimetric observations and first-order leveling in Poland. He was Poland's representative to the Baltic Geodetic Commission. At its 1928 meeting Banachiewicz reported the results obtained by the Polish expedition to Lapland (12 June 1927) in timing a solar eclipse by his "chrono-cinematographic" method. This method makes use of Baily's beads and thus greatly increases the number of observed contacts of the two heavenly bodies. Thus the difference in right ascension of moon–sun could be established for the Lapland eclipse with a mean error of $\pm 0.''04$. Banachiewicz proposed to use total eclipses for "lunar triangulations" capable of connecting distant points of the earth's surface.

In astrophysics Banachiewicz was especially interested in photometric problems. Besides the photometry of variable stars he was interested in the illumination of planetary disks and of our sky. He was the first in Poland to appreciate the value of radio signals for the time service and of phototubes in photometry. At his urging the first Polish radio telescope was installed at Fort Skala, a branch station of the Krakow Observatory. Polish astronomy is also indebted to him for his organizational activity. Because of the poor observing conditions at the old Krakow Observatory, he set up a branch station on Mount Lubomir, about nineteen miles south of Krakow. Many observations of variable stars were made there, and several new comets were discovered. The station was burned down by a Gestapo detachment in 1944, but shortly before his death Banachiewicz began the building of a new branch station at Fort Skala.

Banachiewicz was founder and editor of *Acta astronomica, Ephemerides of Eclipsing Binaries,* and *Circulaire de l'Observatoire de Cracovie.*

BIBLIOGRAPHY

I. ORIGINAL WORKS. Among Banachiewicz's numerous publications are "Sur un cas particulier du problème des *n* corps," in *Comptes rendus de l'Académie des sciences* (26 Feb. 1906); "Sur les occultations de l'étoile BD—12° 4042 le 13 août 1911," in *A. N.* 4508; "Sur le mouvement d'un corps céleste à masse variable," in *Comptes-rendus de la Société des sciences de Varsovie,* **6,** fasc. 8 (1913), 657–666; "Sur la méthode d'Olbers et ses solutions multiples," in *Comptes rendus de l'Académie des sciences* (9 Aug. 1915); "Sur la théorie de l'erreur de fermeture dans le cas de la détermination de la latitude géographique" (in Russian), in Kazan, Université Impériale (1915), pp. 1–11; "Tri eskiza po teorii refrakcii," *ibid.;* "Sur la résolution de l'équation de Gauss dans la détermination d'une orbite planétaire," in *Bulletin de l'Académie impériale des sciences,* Petrograd (1916), 739–750; "Tables auxiliaires pour la résolution de l'équation de Gauss sin $(z - q) = m \sin^4 z$" (Paris, 1916), pp. 3–19; "Bemerkungen zu Teil V der Photometrie von Lambert," in *A. N.* **207** (1918), 113–118; "Sur les points d'inflexion des courbes généralisées de Cassini," in *Bulletin de l'Académie polonaise,* ser. A (1921); "Calcul de la précession en coordonnées orthogonales," *ibid.* (1923); "Sur un théorème de Legendre relatif à la détermination des orbites cométaires," *ibid.* (1924), 1–7; "Ueber die Anwendbarkeit der Gyldén-Brendelschen Störungstheorie auf die jupiternahen Planetoiden," in *Circulaire de l'Observatoire de Cracovie,* **22** (1926); "Les rélations fondamentales de la polygonométrie sphérique," *ibid.,* **25** (1927), and *Comptes rendus de l'Académie des sciences* (21 Nov. 1927); "Sur un théorème de Poincaré relatif aux marées océaniques" (in Polish), in *Comptes-rendus de l'Académie polonaise,* Krakow (7 Mar. 1927); "Voies nouvelles dans l'astronomie mathématique," in *Bulletin de l'Académie polonaise* (1927); "Determination of the Constants of the Position of an Orbit From Its Ecliptic Elements," in *Monthly Notices of the Royal Astronomical Society* (Dec. 1928), 215–217;

"Méthodes arithmométriques de la correction des orbites," *Acta astronomica,* **1** (1929), 71–86; "Coordonnées sélénographiques relatives aux occultations," *ibid.* (1930), 127–130; "Sur la détermination de l'orbite de Pluton," in *Comptes rendus de l'Académie des sciences,* **191** (1930), 1–3; "Sur l'amélioration d'une orbite elliptique," in *Bulletin astronomique,* **7,** fasc. 1 (1932), 1–11; "Ueber die Anwendung der Krakoviane in der Methode der kleinsten Quadrate," in *Verhandlungen der 6 Tagung d. Balt. Geod. Kommission* (1933); "Quelques points fondamentaux de la théorie des orbites," in *Acta astronomica,* **3** (1933), 53–56; "On the Prediction of Occultations by the Moon," *ibid.* (1934), 67–76; "Divers points de la théorie des étoiles à éclipses," in *CRM Cracovie* (1936); "Calcul des déterminants à l'aide de cracoviens," in *CRM de l'Académie polonaise des sciences,* **3,** no. 1 (1937); "Contrôle des opérations avec les cracoviens," in *Acta astronomica,* **3** (1938), 133–143; "Einfluss der Gewichte auf die Resultate einer Ausgleichung nach der Methode der kleinsten Quadrate," *ibid.,* 109–118; "Méthode de la résolution numérique des équations linéaires," in *Bulletin de l'Académie polonaise,* ser. A (1938), 393–404; "Principes d'une nouvelle technique de la méthode des moindres carrés," *ibid.,* 134–135; "Sur les rotations dans l'espace à 4 dimensions," *ibid.,* 127–133; "On the Computation of Inverse Arrays," in *Acta astronomica,* **4** (1948), 26–30; "An Outline of the Cracovian Algorithm of the Method of Least Squares," in *Astronomical Journal,* **50** (1942), 38–41; "Improvement of a 9 Cosine Table by Least Squares and Cracovians," in *Acta astronomica,* **4** (1948), 78–80; "La précision d'une orbite provisoire," *ibid.,* **5** (1950), 37–50; "On the General Least Squares Interpolation Formula," *ibid.,* **4** (1950), 123–128; "Sur la détermination du profil de la lune," *ibid.,* **5** (1952), 19–32; and *The Cracovian Calculus* (in Polish) (Warsaw, 1959).

The International Supplement to *Rocrnik astronomiczny Obserwatorium Krakowskiego* ("Astronomical Annual of the Krakow Observatory"), founded by Banachiewicz, is published yearly. Supp. no. 39 for 1968 (1967) contains ephemerides of 754 eclipsing binaries, a list of eclipsing binaries and bases of the ephemeris 1968, RR-Lyrae-type variables, and auxiliary tables, including geocentric ephemeris of the oppositions of the libration points L_4 and L_5 in the earth–moon system. It is published in English.

II. SECONDARY LITERATURE. Banachiewicz's tables are reprinted in Julius Bauschinger, *Tafeln zur theoretischen Astronomie,* 2nd ed. by G. Stracke (Leipzig, 1934); table 22, "Auflösung der Gauss'schen Gleichung," pp. 126–130, is identical with Banachiewicz's. See also Stracke's *Bahnbestimmung der Planeten und Kometen,* ch. 13, which concerns Banachiewicz's method of determining parabolic orbits; fourteen of Banachiewicz's papers are also cited.

J. WITKOWSKI

BANCROFT, WILDER DWIGHT (*b.* Middletown, Rhode Island, 1 October 1867; *d.* Ithaca, New York, 7 February 1953), *chemistry.*

Bancroft was descended from an early New England family, his grandfather being George Bancroft the historian, secretary of the navy under James K. Polk, and founder of the United States Naval Academy. He became interested in chemistry at Harvard, where he received the B.A. in 1888 and assisted in the chemistry department in 1888–1889. He then journeyed to Europe and studied at Strasbourg; Berlin; Leipzig, where he received the Ph.D. under Wilhelm Ostwald in 1892; and Amsterdam, where he studied under van't Hoff. On returning to the United States, Bancroft taught at Harvard from 1893 to 1895 and at Cornell from 1895 to 1937. During World War I he joined the Chemical Warfare Service with the rank of lieutenant colonel. His ability in science, coupled with his good judgment in administrative matters, led his professional colleagues to elect him president of the American Chemical Society in 1910, and of the American Electrochemical Society in 1905 and 1919. In 1937 on the Cornell campus an automobile struck him, injuring him so severely that he was a semi-invalid for the remainder of his life.

Bancroft was one of the early physical chemists in the United States. He taught physical chemistry at Cornell, trained graduate students, wrote a text entitled *The Phase Rule* (1897), and founded the *Journal of Physical Chemistry* in 1896. He supported the *Journal* financially, coedited it until 1909, and edited it until 1932, when he gave it to the American Chemical Society. The value of the *Journal* in its early years lay not only in the information it transmitted, but also in the stimulus it gave to the study of physical and colloid chemistry in the United States.

In research Bancroft did not follow one line exhaustively, but preferred to roam into many fields, letting his curiosity lead him. Generally he had a number of investigations going on at one time. His early investigations were in electrochemistry, a subject he pursued into the practical field of electrodeposition of metals. At the same time he and his students took up the study of heterogeneous equilibria, which was then in an early stage of development, and applied the phase rule to a great variety of systems. They investigated freezing-point equilibria in three-component systems; showed that the minimum in boiling-point curves of binary liquid mixtures was caused by association of one or both components; and made intelligible the heterogeneous solid–liquid equilibria encountered in dynamic isomerides.

Bancroft's second specialty was colloid chemistry. His early work on emulsions and the chemistry of photography led him into theories of dyeing, of the color of colloids, and, toward the end of his career,

of the colloidal phenomena associated with anesthesia, asthma, insanity, and drug addiction.

Through his writings on contact catalysis, Bancroft clarified what was, around 1920, largely an empirical art and stimulated chemists to carry out investigations that placed the art on a firm theoretical foundation.

BIBLIOGRAPHY

I. ORIGINAL WORKS. Bancroft's writings include *The Phase Rule* (Ithaca, N.Y., 1897); *Applied Colloid Chemistry: General Theory* (New York, 1921; 3rd ed., 1932); and *Research Problems in Colloid Chemistry* (Washington, D.C., 1921). Bancroft's articles, of which there are scores, may be found by reference to *Chemical Abstracts*.

II. SECONDARY LITERATURE. Articles on Bancroft are A. Findlay, "Wilder Dwight Bancroft, 1867–1953," in *Journal of the Chemical Society* (London) (1953), 2506–2514, with portrait, also in Eduard Farber, ed., *Famous Chemists* (New York, 1961), pp. 1245–1261; H. W. Gillett, "Wilder D. Bancroft," in *Industrial and Engineering Chemistry*, **24** (1932), 1200–1201; and C. W. Mason, "Wilder Dwight Bancroft, 1867–1953," in *Journal of the American Chemical Society*, **76** (1954), 2601–2602, with portrait.

WYNDHAM DAVIES MILES

BANISTER, JOHN (*b.* Twigworth, Gloucestershire, England, 1650; *d.* on Roanoke River, Virginia, May 1692), *botany, entomology, malacology, anthropology.*

The first resident, university-educated naturalist of what is now the eastern United States, Banister contributed to English horticulture, to Linnaeus' understanding of the American flora, to Martin Lister's iconography of mollusks, and to James Petiver's catalog of insects. He would have influenced the course of colonial natural history even more but for his early death. Approximately 340 plant descriptions, specimens, and at least eighty plant drawings by Banister are behind the citations in John Ray's *Historia,* Robert Morison's *Historia,* and Leonard Plukenet's *Phytographia* and texts cited in Linnaeus' *Species plantarum* (1753). Jan Gronovius, working with Linnaeus on *Flora Virginica* (1739–1743), compared John Clayton's specimens with Plukenet's—and thus Banister's—illustrations and the descriptions in Ray and Morison.

Lister reproduced, without acknowledgment, at least fourteen of Banister's drawings of Virginia shells in his *Historia conchyliorum,* and published material from four of Banister's letters in *Philosophical Transactions.* Banister's "Collectio insectorum [et arachnidorum]," dealing with about a hundred specimens, and sent probably to Lister in 1680, was published by Petiver in *Philosophical Transactions* in 1701. Banister was one of the first to describe the internal anatomy of a snail, and the first to explain the function of balancers of *Diptera*. He spent the last several years of his life composing his significant "Natural History of Virginia." His "Of the Natives," and undoubtedly some geographical and economic materials, were used by Robert Beverley in *History and Present State of Virginia* (1708): indeed Beverley lifted paragraphs and sentences intact from Banister. Banister's citations are a comprehensive bibliography of the natural history of the New World.

With James Blair as the other minister, Banister was appointed to the committee to establish the College of William and Mary and was named a trustee. He had assembled at least twenty-eight natural history and travel books, which were later acquired by William Byrd I, thus adding immeasurably to the luster of the library at Westover in the time of William Byrd II and III.

Banister's matriculation record at Magdalen College, Oxford, dated 21 June 1667, states that he was the son of John Bannister, "pleb." He was a chorister, receiving the B.A. in 1671 and the M.A. in 1674; was "clerk" (and/or librarian, *fide* his grandson) for two years; and chaplain from 1676 to 1678. That he was well acquainted with American plants growing at Oxford is attested by his carefully labeled *hortus siccus* with author citations. He probably took this with him to Virginia, leaving its catalog at Oxford.

Although Banister arrived as an Anglican minister in Virginia in 1678, after a pause probably in Barbados and Grenada, his ambition from the beginning was his "Natural History," modeled on Robert Plot's *Natural History of Oxfordshire* (1677). Banister's name is absent from the Bristol Parish register of ministers for 1680. Virginians were reluctant to assume the financial burden imposed by induction: thus Banister was financially insecure. He received at least encouragement and hospitality from William Byrd I, trader at the falls of the James River, and from Theodorick Bland, then of Westover. He probably received some assistance from the Temple Coffee House Botany Club in London: Bishop Compton, Lister, Plukenet, and Samuel Doody, to all of whom, and to John Ray, who called him "eruditissimus," he sent specimens.

Banister finally realized that in order to maintain his status in the colony, to have sufficient income, and to have time to complete his "Natural History," he must become a planter. In 1690 he was able to patent 1,735 acres near the Appomattox River in return for importing thirty-five persons, including two Negroes.

He married a young widow named Martha sometime before 16 April 1688, and had one son, John.

A fall from a horse and at least one "fit of sickness" impeded Banister's field excursions. One longer trip of several days, probably up the James River, took his party well toward the Appalachians before Indians discouraged their further progress. In May 1692 he joined a party going to the Roanoke River, where he was accidently shot while botanizing among the river rocks.

The originals of his catalogs (after being copied?), some drawings, dried plants, seeds, and shells were sent to Bishop Compton, who passed them on: the botanical material was given to Plukenet, who loaned much of it to Petiver. Upon Petiver's death his vast accumulation of natural history materials, still containing some of Banister's and Plukenet's specimens and letters, was purchased by Sir Hans Sloane.

Banister's devotion to natural history is well expressed in his letter of 1688: "Had I an Estate would bear out my Expense, There is no part of this, or any other Country that would afford new matter, though under ye Scorching Line, or frozen Poles my genius would not incline me to visit."

BIBLIOGRAPHY

Banister's known letters and manuscripts are in the British Museum, Sloane MSS 3321 and 4002; the Bodleian Library, Oxford, Sherard MSS B26 and B37; and Lambeth Palace, letter from "the Falls" (Apr. 1679). These are reproduced in Joseph and Nesta Ewan, *John Banister and His Natural History of Virginia* (Urbana, Ill., in press).

Printed excerpts and information come mainly from Martin Lister, "Extracts of Four Letters From Mr. John Banister to Dr. Lister . . .," in *Philosophical Transactions of the Royal Society,* **17** (1693), 667–672; Robert Morison, *Plantarum historiae universalis Oxoniensis,* Jacob Bobart the younger, ed., III (Oxford, 1699)—although not acknowledged in the Preface, Banister is mentioned in the discussion of many species; James Petiver, "Herbarium Virginianum Banisteri," in *Monthly Miscellany or Memoirs for the Curious,* Decad no. 7 (Dec. 1707), and "Some Observations Concerning Insects Made by Mr. John Banister in Virginia, A.D. 1680 . . .," in *Philosophical Transactions of the Royal Society,* **22** (1701), 807–814; Leonard Plukenet, *Opera,* especially the *Phytographia* (London, 1691–1705); John Ray, *Historia plantarum,* 3 vols. (London, 1686–1704), esp. II, Preface and 1926–1928, and III, Preface and *passim;* and Arthur Foley Winnington-Ingram, *The Early English Colonies* (London–Milwaukee, 1908), pp. 192–201.

JOSEPH EWAN

BANKS, JOSEPH

BANKS, JOSEPH (*b.* London, England, 13 February 1743; *d.* Isleworth, England, 19 June 1820), *botany.*

Joseph Banks was the only son of William Banks of Revesby Abbey, Lincolnshire, and his wife Sarah, the eldest daughter of William Bate of Derbyshire. The Banks family first became well known in the seventeenth century, and by the eighteenth century was firmly established among the landed gentry. Joseph's great-grandfather, a prosperous attorney of the same name, was a man who acquired property and rendered public service as a member of Parliament, first for Grimsby and later for Totnes. In the next generation another Joseph was sheriff of the county and a member of the Royal Society of London. His second son, Joseph's father, continued the tradition of public service and took particular interest in the drainage of the Fenland. Thus the inheritance of the family was a happy if not unusual one. In the early eighteenth century the Banks family elevated its social position by marrying into the Grenville family and the family of the earl of Exeter.

The early years of Banks's life were spent at Revesby Abbey. In 1752 he entered Harrow, transferring in 1756 to Eton. Henry Brougham, in a biographical sketch published after Banks's death, commented that the young Joseph was not particularly "bookish," and his school record bears this out. At the age of fifteen, while still at Eton, Banks became aware of his interests and found a goal for his life, the study of botany. One summer evening, after swimming with schoolmates, he remained behind his companions and returned to school alone. While he was wandering along a country lane, the beauty of the flowers and the solitude overwhelmed him. He told a friend, Sir Everard Home, of the experience, and Home repeated the story in his Hunterian Oration of 1822:

> He stopped and looking round, involuntarily exclaimed, How beautiful! After some reflection, he said to himself, it is surely more natural that I should be taught to know all these productions of Nature, in preference to Greek and Latin; but the latter is my father's command and it is my duty to obey him; I will however make myself acquainted with all these different plants for my own pleasure and gratification. He began immediately to teach himself Botany; and, for want of more able tutors, submitted to be instructed by the women, employed in culling simples, as it is termed, to supply The Druggists and Apothecaries shops, paying sixpence for every material piece of information.

When he next went home on holiday, Banks found a battered copy of John Gerarde's *The Herball or Historie of Plants* (1598); the woodcuts illustrating the text were of the very same plants he had been collecting at school. He proceeded to broaden his interest in natural history, turning to the study of insects, shells, and fossils as well as plants.

In 1760 Banks entered as a gentleman commoner at Christ Church, Oxford. The classical curriculum was far from his taste, but he was able to begin his formal training in botany. This was due to his own initiative, however, rather than to the challenge of the curriculum. The professor of botany at Oxford, Humphrey Sibthorp, never gave lectures. At Sibthorp's suggestion, Banks turned to the professor of botany at Cambridge, who found him an instructor, Israel Lyons. Lyons came to Oxford and gave instruction to Banks and other interested students. Lyons was supported by Banks with income from his estate, the estate that was to be the source of support for many scientific projects during Banks's long life. As Linnaeus somewhat chauvinistically remarked later: "I cannot sufficiently admire Mr. Banks who has exposed himself to so many dangers and has bestowed more money in the service of Natural Science than any other man. Surely none but an Englishman would have the spirit to do what he has done."

Banks's father had died in 1761, and in 1764, at his majority, Joseph came into his well-managed inheritance. During his lifetime he was spoken of as a man of large fortune, and estimates of his yearly income varied from £6,000 to £30,000. It was not his wealth that made him a prominent man; rather, it was his vision and interests that could be furthered by his income. A modest man when it came to his scientific prowess, he spoke of himself as a botanizer rather than as a botanist. His chief reputation was not based on his scientific ability as much as it was on his ability to organize and administer scientific affairs. He became a patron of science. Owing to his background, connections, interests, and pleasant personality, he became a person of importance and influence early in life.

Finding the atmosphere of Oxford not conducive to his interests, Banks left the university without a degree and settled in London. In 1766 he made the first of several voyages. These trips appealed to him because of the opportunity they presented to collect new botanical specimens. His first voyage, lasting from April to November 1766, took him to Labrador and Newfoundland. He indulged his interests to the full, bringing back specimens that marked the beginning of the famous Banks Herbarium. In the same year he was elected a fellow of the Royal Society of London.

In 1768 the governments of Europe, in cooperation with scientific academies, were planning a series of observations of the transit of Venus in 1769. The English government was to send an expedition to the South Seas; the Admiralty and the Royal Society planned the expedition. Banks asked for and gained permission to join the voyage as a naturalist. He became a participant in the famous first voyage of Captain James Cook on the *Endeavour*. Besides observing the transit of Venus, the expedition was to conduct explorations in the South Seas for the southern continent that was thought to exist. Although the two aims of the voyage, geography and astronomy, were far from Banks's interests, he easily accommodated himself to the ship and its company. His preparations were extensive. He was accompanied by his own party of eight men with their equipment, all paid for from his own pocket. One of his companions was a Swede, Daniel Carl Solander.

One of Linnaeus' outstanding pupils, Solander had come to England in 1760 at the request of Peter Collinson and John Ellis, English naturalists who corresponded with Linnaeus. He became well known in England and spread his master's teachings in the British Isles. As early as 1762 he was invited to attend meetings of the Royal Society. In the same year the St. Petersburg Academy of Sciences offered him a professorship in botany. Solander did not wish to leave England, for he found it much to his liking, both professionally and personally. By 1764 he was made an assistant at the British Museum and in the same year was elected a member of the Royal Society. Banks's other companions, aside from personal servants, were Armon Sporing, a naturalist; Sydney Parkinson, a skilled artist; and A. Buchan, another artist, who died early in the voyage.

The preparations for the expedition by Banks and Solander were extensive. With these preparations there developed a close personal and professional relationship between the two men that ended only with the death of Solander in 1782. A letter from James Ellis to Linnaeus, written on the eve of the voyage, reveals the careful planning:

No people ever went to sea better fitted out for the purpose of Natural History. They have got a fine library of Natural History; they have all sorts of machines for catching and preserving insects; all kinds of nets, trawls, drags and hooks for coral fishing, they have even a curious contrivance of a telescope, by which, put into the water, you can see the bottom at a great depth, where it is clear. They have many cases of bottles with ground stoppers of several sizes, to preserve animals in spirits. They have the several sorts of salts to surround the seeds; and wax, both beeswax and that of Myrica; besides there are many people whose sole business it is to attend them for this very purpose. They have two

painters and draughtsmen, several volunteers who have a tolerable notion of Natural History; in short Solander assured me this expedition would cost Mr. Banks £10,000. All this is owing to you and your writings.

Banks was also well informed about the problem of scurvy on long voyages. Cook provided quantities of sauerkraut for the crew. Banks preferred to use lemon juice, which he brought along on the voyage. Both of these remedies worked well in keeping the crew free of the disease.

Fortunately, Banks was a man of easy disposition, and from the beginning he and Cook were friendly. Cook was the navigator, Banks the botanizer. After the astronomical aspects of the voyage were accomplished, the expedition turned to exploring for the southern continent. Although the hope of discovery was not realized, Cook did conduct explorations in New Zealand and Australia. The gathering of specimens was of marked importance for descriptive botany and zoology. During the voyage over 800 previously unknown specimens were collected. Banks took great interest in the native languages and customs, and was the only person on the trip who gained any mastery of Tahitian, although he had little facility in foreign languages. The voyage acted as an intellectual stimulus to Banks, then in the full vigor of youth. Most of all, this expedition, one of the first to carry a professional naturalist, made a reputation for Banks that would greatly aid him in his later career. On their return in 1771, both Banks and Cook were acclaimed as heroes.

Banks kept an extensive journal of this three-year period. The publication of the journal was delayed for over a century, however, and not until 1962 was an accurate and well-edited version published. Banks was not himself a man of letters, and seems to have felt hesitation in putting his journal into a publishable form. He had hoped to publish the journals with handsome illustrations, but the death of his associate and librarian Solander in 1782 delayed publication for the moment. This delay continued until his death. His herbarium and library were willed to his last librarian and custodian, Robert Brown, a noted botanist in his own right. In his will Banks provided that the bequest would go to the British Museum at Brown's death, unless Brown chose to deposit the collection at the museum during his lifetime. Brown elected the latter course and became keeper of the botanical department of the British Museum in 1827, his chief job being the supervision of the collections left by Banks. Because his journal and private papers were ignored by his heirs for some time after his death, Banks was not very well known in the fields of his greatest competence and interest until several generations after his death. Instead, his name and reputation were associated with the Royal Society of London. Banks dominated the scientific community of England and presided over its affairs for many years in the same way that Samuel Johnson presided over the literary community. In 1772 Banks made a brief visit to Iceland, the last of his voyages.

Banks has been best remembered for his long tenure of office as president of the Royal Society. Elected at the age of thirty-five in 1778, he continued in that office until his death in 1820. At the time of his election nonscientists made up the majority of the society membership, a situation that had existed since its founding. Although boasting of the sovereign as its patron, the society lacked any regular income from royal or parliamentary grants. Often membership was given to men of influence who might bring benefaction, if not scientific knowledge, to the society. During Banks's long tenure the proportion of scientific to nonscientific members did not increase significantly. Early in his presidency he was criticized for packing the council of the society with his favorites, for being dictatorial in selection of new members, and for not possessing an appropriate mathematical bent. Only the last was true. Although somewhat high-handed in introducing nominations for membership and appointments to the council, this was not necessarily favoritism on his part, but may have represented an attempt to strengthen the membership rolls of the society. Yet Banks was not an innovator and made no attempt to redress the lack of balance between professional scientists and amateurs in the society. In this respect he maintained the status quo.

Banks considered the presidency of the Royal Society the greatest honor bestowed upon him in his lifetime and was faithful in attending to the duties of his office. During his forty-one years of service there were 450 meetings of the council, and he presided over 417 of them, although later in life he was crippled with gout and could move only with difficulty. He made the society much better known both at home and abroad. After 1777 his house in Soho Square became an unofficial headquarters for scientists in London. His weekly receptions, his famous breakfast parties for noted guests, and his large library, available to students, all contributed to the enhancement of the reputation of the society. And Banks did not hesitate to use the prestige of his office to further causes connected with science. He was one of the founders of the Linnean Society, assisted in the founding of the Royal Institution, and took an active interest in the affairs of the Board of Longitude.

Banks was made a baronet in 1781, a knight of the Order of the Bath in 1795, and a member of the Privy Council in 1797. Oxford University had already awarded him an honorary degree on his return from his voyage to the South Seas. One of the great pleasures of his life came in 1771, when he was introduced to King George III. The two men immediately struck up a friendship that grew with their common interest in horticulture and agriculture. It was Banks who persuaded the king to turn Kew Gardens, already noted for their beauty, into a botanical research center. Banks became the king's chief adviser in connection with Kew, and plants from all over the world were brought there for study and cultivation. Sir Joseph had the foresight to recognize that various plants could be adapted for cultivation in the broad reaches of the British Empire. He suggested the growing of Chinese tea in India, and his desire to cultivate the breadfruit tree in the West Indies led to the ill-fated voyage of the *Bounty*. A later expedition succeeded in bringing plants to the West Indies, but unfortunately the tree did not adapt itself very successfully to its new environment.

Kew Gardens became a bond between Banks and George III. The king was interested, as were others, in the possibility of bringing merino sheep from Spain in order to improve the quality of English wool. However, the sheep, long valued for the fine quality of their wool, were carefully protected and Spanish law forbade their sale to foreigners. Earlier in the century a few of the sheep had been obtained in France and Silesia. Banks managed the delicate transaction of obtaining sheep for England; in later years, during the Peninsular War, merino sheep became more available.

The friendship of the king for Banks undoubtedly assisted his election to the presidency of the Royal Society. The king had been severely displeased with Sir John Pringle, Banks's predecessor. In 1775 a committee of the society, among whom was Benjamin Franklin, had conducted, at the request of the government, a series of experiments to determine the most effective type of lightning rod. In its report the committee had advocated the use of lightning rods with pointed conductors, as opposed to blunt or knobbed conductors. The knobbed conductors had their advocates, however, and as a result, a spirited argument arose. With the outbreak of the American Revolution in 1776, Franklin's name became associated with rebellion as well as with pointed conductors, and a scientific question thus became a political question as well. Pringle backed Franklin, and on being urged by the king to change his opinion, is supposed to have said: "Sire, I cannot reverse the laws and operations of nature." Pringle's decision to retire in 1778 made it possible for the society to elect as president a person who, in addition to other qualifications, was a friend of the king.

Banks's interest in the South Seas did not lag after his return from the *Endeavour* voyage. Throughout the remainder of his life he continued to be concerned about the prospects of obtaining botanical specimens from these areas. And both Banks and Cook had been impressed with the east coast of Australia, which in both climate and soil was appealing as a prospective site for European colonization. As early as 1779 Banks appeared before a committee of the House of Commons to urge the use of Botany Bay as a place to send English convicts who had long terms to serve. The defection of the American colonies, which in the past had received some of these convicts, made a new destination urgent. Not until 1783 did the government begin to make plans for a convict settlement in New South Wales. In 1786, when the formal plans were made, Banks was consulted, and most probably was the author of a document entitled "Heads of the Plan," which described the proposed voyage and the aims of the settlement. The plan pointed out that New Zealand flax would undoubtedly thrive in Australia and would give an additional and superior supply of material for making canvas for both the navy and the merchant marine.

From the beginning of the colony in 1788 there was a constant problem for the military governors in dealing with the convicts, problems of supply, and the general lack of interest of the government at London—due in large part to the French Revolution. Throughout the extended period of war following the Revolution, the various governors sent not only official dispatches and pleas to London but also private letters to Banks outlining their problems and asking for help and advice. He did much to aid the struggling colony. At first Banks did not encourage the raising of sheep in the new land because the coastal area that Banks had explored had not seemed good for pasturage. An early governor had also reported that a flock of seventy sheep had died shortly after their arrival from the Cape Colony. As sheep raising became successful, Banks slowly changed his mind.

One of the most outstanding contributions that Banks made to the scientific world was his interest in maintaining close contacts in the international scientific community. He had been impressed with Franklin's protection of Captain Cook during the American Revolution; Franklin had made it possible for Cook to sail unmolested by ships of the new republic. The outbreak of war with France in 1793 provided a great challenge to the free exchange of ideas between French and English scientists. Throughout the long war Banks was a constant advocate of maintaining contact with French scientists. He also spent much time in attempting to maintain a free exchange of scientific publications at a time when communications with the enemy were strictly forbidden.

Scientists frequently became prisoners of war, and when appeals were made to Banks, his efforts to gain their release were often successful. Enemy ships, captured on their return from scientific expeditions, often carried valuable botanical specimens, and Banks would arrange for the release and return of this valuable scientific cargo to French ports. The French geologist Dolomieu, returning from the Egyptian expedition of Napoleon, was imprisoned by the king of Naples. When Banks found that it was impossible to obtain his release, he used all of the influence at his command to make Dolomieu's confinement easier. His correspondence with Frenchmen in this period is impressive. Such names as Lalande, Du Pont de Nemours, Delambre, and Cuvier appear; they wrote to Banks concerning such diverse matters as the release of a hostage, a copy of the *Nautical Almanac,* and letters of safe passage for scientific workers. In 1802 Banks was elected to membership in the Institut, an honor he accepted with pride.

Until his death Banks maintained his interest in science and his encouragement of scientific pursuits. His own scientific writings are few and of no importance; and he would have been the first to admit that such was the case. His great collection of specimens and his library are now in the British Museum. Long remembered by many as an autocrat in his rule of the Royal Society and often associated with the patronizing characterization of him by Sir Humphry Davy, Banks is assessed much more fairly in Cuvier's *éloge* of 1821:

> The works which this man leaves behind him occupy a few pages only; their importance is not greatly superior to their extent; and yet his name will shine out with lustre in the history of the sciences. In his youth, resigning the pleasures which an independent fortune had placed at his command, he devoted himself to Science and in her cause braved the dangers of the sea and the rigors of the most opposite climates. During a long series of years, he has done good service to the cause of Science by exciting in its favour all the influences arising from his fortunate position and friendship with men in power; but his special claim to our homage rests on the fact that he always considered the labourers in the field of science as having a rightful claim on his interest and protection.

BIBLIOGRAPHY

Little recognition was given to Banks by writers until many years after his death. A convenient listing of early memorials and reminiscences of Banks, along with the titles of Banks's scientific treatises, can be found in B. D. Jackson, "Sir Joseph Banks," in *Dictionary of National Biography.* The first biography, a typical life-and-letters biography of the Edwardian period, is Edward Smith, *The Life of Sir Joseph Banks* (London, 1911). George Mackaness, *Sir Joseph Banks, His Relations With Australia* (Sydney, 1936), is of some help, although the title is somewhat misleading. The best biography is Hector Charles Cameron, *Sir Joseph Banks, K.B., P.R.S., The Autocrat of the Philosophers* (London, 1952). Halldor Hermannsson, "Sir Joseph Banks and Iceland," in *Islandica,* **18** (1928), gives a good account of the voyage to Iceland and Banks's continued interest in the island.

Warren R. Dawson, *The Banks Letters; A Calendar of the Manuscript Correspondence of Sir Joseph Banks* (London, 1958), is an invaluable guide to Banks's extensive correspondence. Sir Gavin de Beer, *The Sciences Were Never at War* (London, 1960), supplies interesting correspondence of Banks in connection with his attempts to maintain communication with France during the French Revolution and the Napoleonic Wars. A good, brief account of Banks's presidency of the Royal Society can be found in Henry Lyons, *The Royal Society, 1660–1940* (Cambridge, 1944). The work of J. C. Beaglehole in the study of Banks's career is most important. His editing of *The Endeavour Journal of Joseph Banks, 1768–1771,* 2 vols. (Sydney, 1962), is not only a model of editing but also supplies, in the authoritative introduction to the journals, by far the best account of Banks's life in this formative period.

GEORGE A. FOOTE

IBN AL-BANNĀʾ AL MARRĀKUSHĪ, also known as **ABŪ'L-ʿABBĀS AHMAD IBN MUHAMMAD IBN ʿUTHMĀN AL-AZDĪ** (*b.* Marrakesh, Morocco, 29 December 1256; *d.* Marrakesh [?], 1321), *mathematics.*

Some authors, following Casiri, say Ibn al-Bannāʾ was a native of Granada. In any case, he studied all the literary and scientific subjects that had cultural value in Fez and Marrakesh. Muhammad ibn Yahyā al-Sharīf taught him general geometry and Euclid's *Elements;* Abū Bakr al-Qallūsī, nicknamed al-Fār ("the Mouse"), introduced him to fractional numbers; and Ibn Hajala and Abū ʿAbd Allāh ibn Makhlūf al-Sijilmāsī rounded out his training in mathematics. He also studied medicine with al-Mirrīkh, but he did not delve deeply into the subject. The mystic al-Hazmirī was responsible for directing a great part of Ibn al-Bannāʾ's work to the study of the magic properties of numbers and letters.

He taught arithmetic, algebra, geometry, and astronomy in the *madrasa* al-ʿAttārīn in Fez. Among his disciples were Abū Zayd ʿAbd al-Rahmān . . . al-Lajāʾī (*d. ca.* 771/1369), teacher of Ibn Qunfudh, who left us an excellent biographical sketch of Ibn al-Bannāʾ; Muhammad ibn Ibrāhīm al-Abūlī (*d.* 770/1368); Abu'l-Barakāt al-Balāfiqī (*d.* 771/1370), who had Ibn al-Khatīb and Ibn Khaldūn as disciples; and Ibn al-Najjār al-Tilimsānī.

H. P. J. Renaud lists eighty-two works by Ibn al-Bannāʾ. The most important scientific ones are an introduction to Euclid; a treatise on areas; an algebra text dedicated to Abū ʿAlī al-Hasan al-Milyānī; a book about acronical risings and settings (*Kitāb al-anwāʾ*), which is not as good as his other works on astronomy, such as the *Minhāj;* and an almanac that is possibly the earliest known, in which the word *manākh* appears for the first time in its Arabic form. The works of greatest merit, however, are the *Talkhīs* and the *Minhāj.*

The *Talkhīs,* as its title indicates, is a summary of the lost works of the twelfth- or thirteenth-century mathematician al-Hassār. It was later summarized in verse by Ibn al-Qādi (*d.* 1025/1616) and was often commented on and glossed. Outstanding commentaries are the *Rafʿ al-hijāb* by Ibn al-Bannāʾ himself, with notes by Ibn Haydūr, and that of al-Qalasādī of Granada. These works contain a type of fraction that corresponds to what are today called continuing ascending fractions and an approximate method for extracting square roots that corresponds, more or less, to the third or fourth reduction in the development of the continuous fraction, and is similar to al-Qalasādī's

$$a + \frac{r}{2a} - \frac{\left(\frac{r}{2a}\right)^2}{2a + \frac{r}{2a}}.$$

The possible connection between this formula and that of Juan de Ortega seems evident, but the transmission has not been sufficiently proved. The works also contain sums of cubes and squares according to the formulas

$$1^3 + 3^3 + 5^3 + \cdots + (2n - 1)^3 = n^2(2n^2 - 1)$$

$$1^2 + 3^2 + \cdots + (2n - 1)^2 = \left(\frac{2n + 1}{6}\right)2n(2n - 1).$$

One cannot be sure that Ibn al-Bannāʾ was responsible for introducing a system of mathematical notation.

The *Kitāb minhāj al-tālib li taʿdīl al-kawākib* is a very practical book for calculating astronomical ephemerals, thanks to the attached tables that are based upon those that Ibn Isḥāq al-Tūnisī calculated for the year 1222. The theoretical part does not contribute anything new and sometimes gives incorrect relationships between contradictory theories.

Ibn al-Bannāʾ is credited with a *Risāla* ("epistle") on the astrolabe called *ṣafīḥa shakāziyya,* a variation of the *ṣafīḥa zarqāliyya,* or "al-Zarqālī's plate," which is the topic of many manuscripts in the libraries of north Africa. An examination of some of these manuscripts does not show the differences that should, in theory, exist between the two instruments.

BIBLIOGRAPHY

I. ORIGINAL WORKS. Manuscripts of works by Ibn al-Bannāʾ are listed in Brockelmann, *Geschichte der arabischen Litteratur,* II (Berlin, 1902), 255, 710; Supp. II (Leiden, 1938), 363–364; J. Vernet, "Los manuscritos astronómicos de Ibn al-Bannāʾ," in *Actes du VIIIe Congrès International d'Histoire des Sciences* (1956), 297–298; and Griffini in *RSO,* 7 (1916), 88–106. A. Marre published a French translation of the *Talkhīṣ* in *Atti dell'Accademia pontificia de Nuovi Lincei,* 17 (5 July 1864); the commentary of al-Qalaṣādī was translated by M. F. Woepcke, *ibid.,* 12 (3 April 1859). The *Minhāj* has been edited, translated into Spanish, and studied by J. Vernet (Tetuán, 1951). The *Kitāb al-anwāʾ* was edited, translated into French, and commented on by H. J. P. Renaud (Paris, 1948).

II. SECONDARY LITERATURE. The Arabic sources for Ibn al-Bannāʾ's life are listed in al-Ziriklī, *al-Aʿlām,* 2nd ed., I, 213–214; especially in H. P. J. Renaud, "Ibn al-Bannāʾ de Marrakech, ṣūfī et mathématicien," in *Hesperis,* 25 (1938), 13–42. The *Muqaddima* of Ibn Khaldūn is fundamental; see the English translation by F. Rosenthal, 3 vols. (New York, 1958), indexes and esp. III, 121, 123, 126, 137. Also consult H. P. J. Renaud, "Sur les dates de la vie du mathématicien arabe marocain Ibn al-Bannāʾ," in *Isis,* 27 (1937), 216–218; and "Sur un passage d'Ibn Khaldoun relatif à l'histoire des mathématiques," in *Hesperis,* 31 (1944), 35–47.

Additional information can be found in George Sarton, "Tacuinum, taqwīm. With a digression on the word 'Almanac,'" in *Isis,* 10 (1928), 490–493, and *Introduction to the History of Science,* II, 998–1000; H. Suter, *Die Mathematiker und Astronomen der Araber und ihre Werke* (Leipzig, 1900), 162–164, 220, 227; J. A. Sánchez Pérez, *Biografías de matemáticos árabes que florecieron en España,* no. 44, pp. 51–54; M. Cantor, *Vorlesungen ueber Geschichte der Mathematik,* I (Leipzig, 1907), 805–810; *Encyclopaedia of Islam,* II, 367; M. Steinschneider, "Rectification de quelques erreurs relatives au mathématicien Arabe Ibn al-Banna," in *Bulletino di bibliografia e di storia delle scienze matematiche e fisiche,* 10 (1877), 313; and F. Woepcke, "Passages relatifs à des sommations de séries de cubes," in *Journal des mathématiques pures et appliquées,*

2nd ser., 10 (1865), reviewed by M. Chasles in *Comptes rendus des séances de l'Académie des Sciences* (27 March 1865).

J. VERNET

BANTI, GUIDO (*b.* Montebicchieri, Italy, 8 June 1852; *d.* Florence, Italy, 8 January 1925), *pathology.*

Banti, the most eminent Italian pathologist of the early twentieth century, was born in a typical village of Tuscany, in the lower valley of the Arno River. He was the son of Dr. Scipione Banti, a physician, and Virginia Bruni. He studied medicine at the University of Pisa, but was graduated in 1877 from the Medical School of Florence. He was then appointed assistant at the Archihospital of Santa Maria Nuova in Florence and, at the same time, assistant at the Laboratory of Pathological Anatomy. Banti was a tireless worker. Chief of the hospital medical service from 1882, in 1890 he became temporary professor and, in 1895, ordinary professor of pathological anatomy at the Medical School of Florence. His medical service at the hospital ended in 1924, after forty-seven years; he died the following year, his thirty-fifth year of teaching.

As a result of then existing arrangements, Banti could observe patients in bed and later study their corpses through autopsy as well as through laboratory tests: he wrote that clinical observation, anatomical report, and laboratory examination are three links in the same chain. Banti's numerous writings are original, and few men of science have spoken or written with such conciseness and clarity.

Banti was a perspicacious clinician, as evidenced by his study on heart enlargement (1886) and his notes for the surgical treatment of hyperplastic gastritis (1898) and acute appendicitis (1905). He was also a precise histologist who studied cancer cells (1890–1893) and a capable bacteriologist who published the first Italian textbook of bacteriological technique, *Manuale di Tecnica Batteriologica* (Florence, 1885). Thus, he contributed decisively to the advancement of the study of human pathology.

As a bacteriologist, Banti integrated bacteriology with the pathogenesis of infectious diseases. His works on typhoid fever (1887, 1891) and his paper *Le setticemie tifiche* (1894) contained the first observations of typhoid without intestinal localizations. Of fundamental importance were his studies (1886–1890) on *Diplococcus pneumoniae Fraenkelii.* In particular, Banti analyzed the characteristics of the types *hemolytic* and *viridans.* In 1890 he affirmed the hematogenic pathogenesis of acute pneumonia. In his remarkable experimental work on the destruction of bacteria in organisms (1888), Banti contributed to the development of Metchnikoff's views on the phagocytic defense of the organism against bacterial invasion.

As a histologist, Banti wrote his *Endocarditi e nefriti* (Florence, 1895), in which he illustrated several forms of endocarditis and described arteriosclerosis of the kidney. He also anticipated the modern view of nephrosis. Opposing Ludwig Pfeiffer, who in *Die Protozoen als Krankheitserreger* (1890) interpreted as parasites some cytoplasmatic corpuscles in the cancerous cells, Banti denied the parasitic nature of these corpuscles and showed that it is only a question of a pathology of the mytosis (see his *Su i parassiti del carcinoma*, 1893). At that time, when every pathological process anatomically characterized by fibrinous exudation was attributed to an infectious agent, Banti illustrated the existence of a fibrinous pericarditis as caused by a dismetabolic etiopathogenesis (1894).

As an anatomist, Banti contributed to the understanding of aphasia (1886); and in his paper of 1907, *A proposito dei recenti studi sulle afasie,* he confuted Pierre Marie's views on the motor type of aphasia.

Banti is especially remembered, however, for his contributions to knowledge of pathology of the spleen and of leukemia. In 1913, he gave his nosographic definition of the leukemias and demonstrated the relationship of the spleen to hemolysis *in vivo*.

From 1882 to 1914 Banti studied the so-called primitive splenomegalies—enlargements of the spleen that are neither degenerative nor infectious. In his first work on the spleen ("Dell'anemia splenica," in the second volume of *Archivio di anatomia patologica* [1882]), Banti had already directed attention to the relation between some splenomegalies and a peculiar form of hypochromic progressive anemia in adults. From further observations he was able by 1894 to describe a new morbid entity, later known as Banti's disease, characterized by anemia with splenomegaly, and, in the terminal stage, by cirrhosis of the liver with ascites. This disease, of unknown cause and of several years' duration, is histologically defined by a peculiar picture of the spleen (*fibroadenia*). A timely splenectomy, performed when the spleen is enlarged, leads to permanent recovery, because this procedure prevents or halts the development of cirrhosis of the liver. Discussion of Banti's disease has resulted in an improved knowledge of the spleen's physiopathology and anatomy.

Banti also developed knowledge of the spleen in relation to hemolysis. He demonstrated (1895–1912) that the spleen is the principal site for the destruction of red blood cells, and that this normal function is exaggerated when the spleen becomes enlarged pathologically. Banti stated that only splenectomy can stop the hemolytic process, and the first splenectomy for hemolytic jaundice was performed in Florence, on his advice, on 20 February 1903.

But Banti's name is primarily connected with leukemia: "All leukemias belong to the sarcomatosis," he wrote in 1903, in opposition to the views of Arthur Pappenheim and Carl Sternberg. With further observations Banti completed his definition in 1913. He concluded that the leukemias are systematic diseases arising from hemopoietic structures, lymph glands, and bone marrow, and that they are the consequence of the limitless proliferative power of staminal blood cells (the lymphoblast and the myeloblast: Banti was always a confirmed dualist), which have lost their maturative capacity. This is still the basic definition of leukemia. Banti also was the first to demonstrate that leukemia produces erosion of the walls of the smallest blood vessels, as a result of the activity of the leukemic cells. If this erosion does not occur, then true leukemia is not present.

From 1907 to 1909 Banti was municipal adviser and also assessor of sanitation in Florence. A devout Roman Catholic, he also had a deep belief in science, which he often expounded in his lectures.

BIBLIOGRAPHY

I. ORIGINAL WORKS. Only the first of two volumes of *Trattato di anatomia patologica* was published (Milan, 1907); it covers infections, the pathology of the heart and lungs, and the leukemias. For the text of the second volume, which consisted of revisions of earlier works—the chapter on the pathology of the spleen, for example—it is necessary to consult Banti's original writings: *Afasia e sue forme* (Florence, 1886); "Sulle localizzazioni atipiche della infezione tifosa," in *La riforma medica,* **3** (1887), 1448–1449, 1454–1455; "Sulla distruzione dei batteri nell'organismo," in *Archivio per le scienze mediche,* **12** (1888), 191–221; "Carcinoma primitivo della tiroide," in *Archivio di anatomia normale e patologica,* **5** (1890), 131–142; "Sopra alcune localizzazione extrapolmonari del Diplococcus pneumoniae Fraenkelii," *ibid.,* 71–130; "Sulla etiologia delle pneumoniti acute," in *Lo sperimentale,* **44** (1890), 349–384, 461–474, 573–588; "L'epidemia di tifo in Firenze nei suoi rapporti con l'acqua potabile," *ibid.,* **45** (1891), 85–94 (see also "Adunanze Accademia Medico-Fisica Fiorentina"); "Su i parassiti del carcinoma," in *La riforma medica,* **9** (1893), 361–364; "Le setticemie tifiche," *ibid.,* **10** (1894), 674–680; "La splenomegalia con cirrosi epatica," in *Lo sperimentale,* **48** (1894), 407–420; "Ueber urämische Pericarditis," in *Centralblatt für allgemeine Pathologie und pathologische Anatomie,* **5** (1894), 461–468; *Endocarditi e nefriti* (Florence, 1895); "La milza nelle itterizie pleiocromiche," in *Lo sperimentale,* **49,** Sezione Clinica (1895), 41–42, 62–64; see also *Gazzetta degli ospedali e delle cliniche,* **16** (1895), 190–195, and *Deutsche medizinische Wochenschrift,* **31**

(1895), 493–495; "Pilorostenosi e intervento chirurgico nella malattia del Reichmann," in *Lo sperimentale,* **52** (1898), 138–152; "Splenomegalie primitive," in *La riforma medica,* **17** (1901), 590–592, 605–608, 614–617, 627–631; "Le leucemie," in *Atti della Società italiana di patologia* (Florence, 1903), and also in *Lo sperimentale,* **57** (1903), 786–789; "Sull'ufficio degli organi linfopoietici ed emopoietici nella genesi dei globuli bianchi del sangue," in *Archivio di fisiologia,* **1** (1904), 241–247; "Sulla cura delle appendiciti acute," in *Lo sperimentale,* **59** (1905), 891–896 (see also "Adunanze Accademia Medico-Fisica Fiorentina"); "A proposito dei recenti studi sulle afasie," in *Clinica moderna,* **13** (1907), 49–65; "Ueber Morbus Banti," in *Folia haematologica,* **10** (1910), 33–53; "La splenomegalia emolitica," in *Lo sperimentale,* **66** (1912), 91–122, and **67** (1913), 323–378; *The Clinical Aspects of Haemolysis,* report to the Seventeenth International Congress of Medicine (Oxford, 1913); "Le leucemie," report to the eighth meeting of the Italian Society of Pathology, in *Lo sperimentale,* **67** (1913), suppl., 10–19; "Malattie diplococciche," in A. Lustig, *Malattie infettive dell'uomo e degli animali,* I (Milan, 1913), 576–610; "La splenectomia nelle anemie," in *Ricerche di biologia dedicate al Professore Alessandro Lustig nel 25° anno del suo insegnamento universitario* (Florence, 1915), 677–680; "L'evoluzione nella materia e nella vita," in *Annuario 1902–1903 del Regio Istituto di studi pratici e di perfezionamento in Firenze.*

II. SECONDARY LITERATURE. Works on Banti and Banti's disease include in particular P. Franceschini, "La malattia di Banti," in *Il Sistema Istiocitario* (Florence, 1954), pp. 532–561, and "In ricordo di Guido Banti," in *Rivista di storia delle scienze mediche e naturali,* **43** (1952), 157–167, which has the complete inventory of his works; A. Lustig, "In memoria di Guido Banti," in *Lo sperimentale,* **79** (1925), I–XXXI (with Banti's portrait); F. Micheli, "Sul Morbo di Banti," in *Archivio per le scienze mediche,* **33** (1909), 351–377, 460–494, 495–514; G. Patrassi, *La questione del Morbo di Banti* (Bologna, 1942).

PIETRO FRANCESCHINI

BANTING, FREDERICK GRANT (*b.* Alliston, Ontario, 14 November 1891; *d.* near Musgrave Harbour, Newfoundland, 21 February 1941), *endocrinology.*

Youngest of the five children of William Thompson Banting and Margaret Grant, Banting grew up on a small Ontario farm and was educated in local schools. He entered the University of Toronto, to study for the ministry, but registered as a student of medicine the next year. He was attracted by the study of anatomy. When he reached the clinical years of the medical school program, he formed the resolve that his career was to be in surgery—more specifically, orthopedic surgery, an ambition inspired by C. L. Starr, surgeon-in-chief of the Hospital for Sick Children. Banting became a lieutenant in the Canadian Army Medical Corps in December 1916. Arriving in England early in the new year, he was assigned to

a special hospital at Ramsgate, planned as an orthopedic hospital; one of the members of the staff was W. E. Gallie, who succeeded Starr in the chair of surgery at Toronto. Banting was soon sent to France; near Haynecourt, in September 1918, he suffered a shrapnel wound in the right forearm. For his conduct in action on this occasion he was awarded the Military Cross.

After the war Banting resumed his work in orthopedic surgery under Starr, but after one year he began his first and only attempt at surgical practice, at London, Ontario. His hoped-for practice was slow in growing, and since London was the seat of Western University (now the University of Western Ontario), Banting became a demonstrator at its medical school. Here, for nearly a year, he taught anatomy and physiology. Under the direction of F. R. Miller, a distinguished neurophysiologist, he made his first foray into medical research, carrying out with Miller experiments on the excitability of the cerebellar cortex. On 30 October 1920, Banting conceived an idea in another area of physiology. The following day he was to talk to his students on the function of the pancreas. Stopping in the medical school library, he looked at the November copy, just received, of *Surgery, Gynecology and Obstetrics,* in which the first article was "The Relation of the Islets of Langerhans to Diabetes, With Special Reference to Cases of Pancreatic Lithiasis," by Moses Barron. Reviewing the literature, Barron had written, in part:

> Arnozan and Vaillard ligated the pancreatic ducts in rabbits and found that within twenty-four hours the ducts became dilated, the epithelial cells were desquamated, and there were protoplasmic changes in the acinic cell. . . . At the fourteenth day a great deal of the parenchyma had been replaced by connective tissue. . . . Ssobolew ligated the ducts in rabbits, cats, and dogs. He found a gradual atrophy and sclerosis of the organ with relatively intact islets and no glycosuria.

More evidence to the same effect was cited, and Barron pointed out the similarity between the degeneration that occurs in the pancreas following experimental ligation of the ducts, and the blocking of the ducts by gallstones. This meant that tying off the pancreatic ducts caused atrophy of all but a small portion of the gland, the islets of Langerhans (named by Laguesse in honor of Paul Langerhans, who first described them in a thesis presented in 1869). These islets were already thought to be the source of a hypothetical diabetes-preventing hormone, a hormone necessary for the utilization of sugar in normal metabolism. This was inferred from the absence of glycosuria after the tying off of the ducts and the atrophy of most of the gland, coupled with the important discovery by Mehring and Minkowski, in 1889, that removal of the entire pancreas from a dog was followed by all the symptoms of severe diabetes, terminating in death from inanition in the course of two or three weeks. Apparently the part of the gland that prevented the disease was the part that remained almost intact many weeks after ligation of the ducts.

Attempts to treat diabetes by oral administration of fresh pancreas or pancreatic extracts (as thyroid preparations were used when the thyroid was deficient) had all been unavailing. Neither were pancreatic extracts useful when injected subcutaneously or intravenously. Taken by mouth, such preparations might be presumed to be destroyed by digestive processes. Extracts made from the whole gland might be thought to be destroyed during extraction by the powerful ferment originating in the acinar tissue. This was Banting's hypothesis. In the small hours of the morning he wrote in a notebook, "Tie off pancreas ducts of dogs. Wait six or eight weeks. Remove and extract."

Banting's conception was not altogether correct, as later studies revealed. The digestive ferments of the pancreas must be activated in the bowel before they attain their destructive power; also, the islet tissue of the gland is affected, although much more slowly than the acinar tissue, by ligation of the duct. Neither was the concept altogether new. As early as 1906 Lydia de Witt, basing her experiments on the observations of Schulze, Ssobolew, and others, made extracts of the islet tissue of cat pancreas and found that they had no digestive powers but possessed distinct glycolytic properties. This work was by no means the first attempt to make use of pancreatic extracts, for Minkowski had conceived the idea and many attempts had been made to prepare such extracts. In 1908 Zuelzer, using an alcoholic extract of pancreas, obtained favorable results in five cases of diabetes mellitus, but unfortunately toxic results caused the work to be discontinued.

Meantime, Kleiner, Murlin, E. L. Scott, and Paulesco carried out physiological investigations on laboratory animals. In 1912 Scott prepared alcoholic extracts of the pancreas that were partially successful in treating experimental diabetes. He even attempted the de Witt–Banting procedure of preliminary duct-tying; probably because of excessive tightness of ligatures and consequent recanalization of ducts, complete atrophy did not take place. At this point Scott turned his energies to attempting to obtain more precise methods of estimating blood sugar. In 1913 Murlin prepared alkaline extracts of the pancreas and of the small intestine, and demonstrated that they reduce the elevated blood sugar of diabetic dogs. He found, however, that this result could be obtained by the administration of alkalies alone, and the investigation was abandoned. After the war Murlin resumed his investigations and found that the administration of perfusates of the pancreas was followed by an elevation of the respiratory quotient. Thus he could restore to the diabetic animal some of its lost power of burning carbohydrates.

F. R. Miller, deeply involved in neurophysiological research, advised Banting to put his idea before J. J. R. Macleod of the University of Toronto, a leading authority on carbohydrate metabolism. It is interesting that whereas Artur Biedl (*The Internal Secretory Organs,* 1913) had stated that the existence of an internal secretion of the pancreas was absolutely proved by Forschbach's parabiotic experiments, Macleod, in the latest edition of his textbook of physiology, asserted that there was as yet no proof of the existence of a pancreatic internal secretion, nor any way as yet of disproving the theory that the islet cells were detoxification centers. Despite a great deal of activity following the work of Mehring and Minkowski more than thirty years earlier, the situation was still altogether unclear. It is easy to see why Macleod did not welcome Banting's work as a revelation. Banting himself later remarked that if he had been thoroughly acquainted with the literature before beginning his research, he might never have begun. Macleod nevertheless agreed to give him a place to work for eight weeks, an undergraduate assistant, and an allotment of ten dogs. With this measure of support, Banting resigned his position at Western University and returned to Toronto.

A recent graduate, C. H. Best, who had just obtained his bachelor's degree in physiology and chemistry, joined Banting in mid-May 1921. With another senior student, E. C. Noble, he had been engaged in experimental studies of *piqûre* (puncture), or Claude Bernard, diabetes. Bernard had discovered that a lesion of the floor of the fourth ventricle was followed by excessive secretion of urine that contained an abundance of sugar. In their work on this phenomenon, Best and Noble had acquired certain special knowledge of carbohydrate metabolism and a number of useful skills in the performance of the necessary tests. Best was the first to assist Banting in the new project dealing with the pancreas, and Noble subsequently joined them.

Ligation of the pancreatic ducts of a number of dogs seemed relatively simple. Next came a more difficult task—to depancreatize. They tried, but later abandoned, the Hédon procedure of removing the pancreas in two stages, and adopted a technique, which Banting developed, for complete pancreatectomy in one operation. While this was going forward, the necessary weeks elapsed for the evaluation of the dogs in which the ducts had been tied, but unhappily the pancreas had not degenerated in most of them. This, too, proved to be a technical surgical problem. It was necessary to operate on all the dogs a second time, and although some were found to have fairly degenerated glands, it was decided to leave these another two weeks. Some ligatures had been too loose to block the ducts, others so tight that they caused recanalization. Therefore, in some cases Banting applied two or three ligatures at different tensions. It was 27 July before both a depancreatized dog and a duct-tied dog were ready. The signs, symptoms, and biochemistry of experimental diabetes had become familiar. Now a degenerated gland was chopped into small pieces in a chilled mortar and frozen in brine. The mass was ground up and about 100 cc. (a little more than three ounces) of saline solution were added. Of this extract 5 cc. were administered intravenously to the depancreatized dog. Samples of blood were taken at half-hour intervals and analyzed for sugar content. The blood sugar fell from 0.200 to 0.11 percent in two hours, and at the same time the clinical condition of the dog was much improved.

Thus encouraged, the experimenters not only repeated and extended this work, gradually eliminating possible sources of error by means of control experiments, but also tried other techniques, such as that of the "exhausted gland," for preparing the extract. Instead of the duct-tied gland they used a pancreas stimulated to the point of exhaustion by continued injection of secretin. A classroom experiment performed by Banting only a few years previously was thus repeated in a modified form. This, like the first method, was clearly a very limited means of production. Believing that the fetal pancreas contains relatively more islet tissue than the adult pancreas, Banting and Best obtained fetal glands from a Toronto abattoir and extracted the active principle from them, providing it at no expense to the laboratory and in quantities that permitted repeated trials and various extractions. This was the third method of preparing what they then called "isletin." It was based on the same fundamental idea as the others—the avoidance of trypsin—and while it made use of a more plentiful source of the new hormone than the other two methods, it, like them, did not appear capable of producing adequate amounts.

The work did not proceed in a perfectly orderly sequence, beginning with the first method and ending with the whole-gland extractions. As early as 17 August 1921, studies were made of the effect of whole, fresh gland extracts, and a page from the first notebook shows that on this date a very definite fall in blood sugar was obtained with an extract made up in Ringer's solution and with one that had been acidified. An effective product was secured by extraction with alcohol and acid, but the result was hard to reproduce until the right pH was used in extraction. Subsequent purification also presented problems, and relative success at an early stage was the consequence of the more or less accidental precipitation that followed attempts to eliminate trypsin, which in fact was not activated. The work on the whole gland was in any case suspended for a time, while other courses were followed. When Macleod returned from a summer in Scotland, the attempt had not only been resumed but a highly potent extract had also been prepared.

Nevertheless, much remained to be done, and Macleod enlisted the aid of the biochemist J. B. Collip, who took up afresh the task of purification. Fractionation had previously been discontinued at 65 percent alcohol because at this point the trypsin, for which tests were performed, had been eliminated. Collip stepped up the percentage of alcohol and removed the greater part of it, producing a practical extract. He himself said that what he added to the team effort, beginning at this point, was "only that which any well-trained biochemist could be expected to contribute." There is, nonetheless, a practical sense in which it is true that Collip's work marked the first major advance beyond the stage attained by Zuelzer some fourteen years earlier. A relatively pure extract (not so good as later preparations) resulted from Collip's fractional precipitation method, making possible the first clinical trials. Further contributions were made by Fitzgerald, Defries, E. L. Scott, Noble, Hepburn, and Latchford, as well as by Collip and by Best. Much of this work was done in the Connaught Laboratories at the University of Toronto. The next phase, however, leading toward the production of insulin in commercial quantity, utilized the talents of a number of American scientists. For instance, the idea of using strong acid (Banting and Best had originally used weak acid) did not originate in Toronto, but in the United States, with Walden and Shaffer.

In January 1922 the first clinical trials of insulin (a name introduced by Macleod but suggested as early as 1910 by Sharpey-Schafer) were carried out in the Toronto General Hospital on a fourteen-year-old boy who had diabetes. From the beginning there was a marked fall in blood sugar and slightly lowered sugar excretion, but the extract then used was so unsatisfactory, by later standards, that no clinical benefit was evidenced. Daily injections soon began, resulting in immediate improvement. Much less sugar was excreted, the acetone bodies disappeared from the urine, and the boy became brighter and more active. Then, for ten days, no insulin was given. During this time sugar again appeared in the urine in large amounts, along with traces of acetone. Administration of insulin in smaller doses again resulted in lowered sugar excretion and disappearance of acetone from the urine.

The use of insulin soon became the chief resource in the treatment of diabetes, but it was early realized that diet and insulin would be complementary methods of reaching the same end. Had insulin been discovered before the great work of Frederick M. Allen was accomplished, it would not have been possible to use it so promptly and with such intelligent discretion. W. R. Campbell and A. A. Fletcher were the clinicians assigned by Duncan Graham to work out the many problems presented to their colleagues in the era of therapy that was just beginning. The earliest reports bore the names of Banting, Campbell, and Fletcher, but Banting did not participate in writing them. On one side of the street he was "no physiologist," "no chemist"; on the other side he was "no clinician." This situation he often found difficult.

Meantime, production and purification problems continued to demand attention, and the task of commercial production had to be solved. The Eli Lilly Company was able, by November 1922, to effect a very substantial purification and concentration of the product by developing the isoelectric method of precipitation. Work carried out there and in the Connaught Laboratories provided insulin for 250 clinicians by January 1923. J. J. Abel of Baltimore succeeded in 1926 in preparing insulin in crystalline form, and D. A. Scott of Toronto introduced the fundamental method of doing so through the employment of zinc. H. C. Hagedorn, the Danish investigator, was able to prolong the effect of insulin by adding protamine, Scott once again demonstrating that in the absence of zinc the change would not take place and there would be little or no prolongation of action.

Before the decade was out, Banting had turned to other areas of research. His almost instantaneous worldwide fame was first attested by the "insulin rush," the descent on Toronto of diabetic patients from many countries. Once insulin had become more generally available, this impetus waned, but the celebrity was perhaps even greater. The Nobel Prize in physiology and medicine was awarded to Banting and Macleod in 1923; Banting immediately divided his share equally with Best, and Macleod divided with

Collip. In the same year Banting was awarded an annuity by the Canadian parliament. He became an honorary member of most of the major scientific and medical societies of the world, and awards followed each other in rapid succession. In 1930 the Banting Institute of the University of Toronto was opened, and Banting, who had been appointed professor of medical research in 1923, spent the rest of his life as director of the Banting–Best Department of Medical Research. His later research, before World War II, was devoted largely to cancer, coronary thrombosis, and silicosis.

Before, and more especially during, World War II, Banting was the leading figure in Canada's governmental support of medical science. He was chairman of the Medical Research Committee of the National Research Council and chairman also of the Associate Committee on Aviation Medical Research. Much of the wartime activity of the institute was devoted to research in this sector. An important part of Banting's own work consisted in establishing and maintaining research liaison with British colleagues through visits to England. In February 1941 he set off on such a journey and met his death in an air crash in Newfoundland.

BIBLIOGRAPHY

Among Banting's papers are "Effect of Pancreatic Extract (Insulin) on Normal Rabbits," in *American Journal of Physiology,* **62** (Sept. 1922), 162–176; "Internal Secretion of Pancreas," in *Journal of Laboratory and Clinical Medicine,* **7** (Feb. 1922), 251–326, written with C. H. Best; "Insulin in Treatment of Diabetes Mellitus," in *Journal of Metabolic Research,* **2** (Nov.–Dec. 1922), 547–604, written with W. R. Campbell and A. A. Fletcher; and "Pancreatic Extracts in Diabetes," in *Journal of the Canadian Medical Association,* **12** (Mar. 1922), 141–146, written with C. H. Best, J. B. Collip, W. R. Campbell, and A. A. Fletcher. A group of important early papers by Banting, Macleod, Collip, J. Hepburn, and E. C. Noble is in *Transactions of the Royal Society of Canada,* 3rd ser., **14,** sec. 5 (1922).

Biographies of Banting are Lloyd Stevenson, *Sir Frederick Banting* (Toronto, 1946; 2nd ed., rev., 1947), with a fuller bibliography in the later edition; and Seale Harris, *Banting's Miracle: The Story of the Discoverer of Insulin* (Philadelphia, 1946).

LLOYD G. STEVENSON

BANŪ MŪSĀ. Three brothers—**Muḥammad, Aḥmad,** and **al-Ḥasan**—always known under the one name, which means "sons of Mūsā" (*b.* Baghdad, Iraq, beginning of ninth century; *d.* Baghdad.

Muḥammad, the eldest, *d.* January or February A.D. 873), *mathematics, astronomy.*

Their father, Mūsā ibn Shākir, was a robber in his youth but later became a proficient astrologer. He died during the reign of Calif al-Ma'mūn (813–833), while his children were still young. Al-Ma'mūn recognized the mental ability of the brothers and enrolled them in the House of Wisdom—the first scientific institution in the Abbasid Empire and quite similar to the modern academy—which he himself had founded. Soon the Banū Mūsā excelled in mathematics, astronomy, and mechanics and became the most active members of the House of Wisdom. With Muḥammad ibn Mūsā al-Khwārizmī they led its scientific research. Al-Khwārizmī was the founder of the Arabic school of algebra, while the Banū Mūsā were especially interested in geometry. They also led the astronomical observations in Baghdad and organized a school of translators who rendered many Greek scientific manuscripts into Arabic. These translations were very useful in the development of science. Some important Greek works are now known only in their Arabic translations.

The most famous translators of that time worked under the guidance of the Banū Mūsā. Among them were Ḥunayn ibn Isḥāq, who became the foremost translator of medical works, and Thābit ibn Qurra, the famous scientist and translator of the ninth century, to whom are ascribed many works besides the translations of such Greek works as Euclid's *Elements* and three books of Apollonius' *Conics.* The Banū Mūsā were among the first Arabic scientists to study the Greek mathematical works and to lay the foundation of the Arabic school of mathematics. They may be called disciples of Greek mathematicians, yet they deviated from classical Greek mathematics in ways that were very important to the development of some mathematical concepts.

It is difficult to distinguish the role played by each of the brothers in their common works, but it seems that Ja'far Muḥammad was the most important. Muḥammad and al-Ḥasan were especially interested in geometry; Aḥmad was interested in mechanics. Muḥammad also did work in astronomy.

Of the many works ascribed to the Banū Mūsā, the most important was the geometrical treatise called *Book on the Measurement of Plane and Spherical Figures.* Manuscripts of this treatise are in Oxford, Paris, Berlin, Istanbul, and Rampur, India. One of these manuscripts, with a recension by the thirteenth-century mathematician Naṣīr al-Dīn al-Ṭūsī, has been published in Arabic. It was well-known in the Middle Ages in both Islam and Europe. The best evidence for this is the twelfth-century Latin translation by

Gerard of Cremona, entitled *Liber trium fratrum de geometria.* Manuscripts of this translation are in Paris, Madrid, Basel, Toruń, and Oxford. The main purpose of the treatise—as stated in the introduction—was to demonstrate the most important part of the Greek method of determining area and volume. In the treatise the method was applied to the measurement of the circle and the sphere.

In *Measurement of the Circle* and *On the Sphere and Cylinder,* Archimedes found the area of the circle and the surface and volume of the sphere by means of the method of Eudoxus, which was later called the "method of exhaustion." This method was based on the same ideas that underlie the limit theory of modern mathematics. After Archimedes, this method was followed without further development. In fact, there is no evidence of work on the measurement of areas and volumes until the ninth century.

The Banū Mūsā found the area of the circle by a method different from that of Archimedes but based on his ideas of infinitesimals. They used the "method of exhaustion" but omitted the main part of it, inscribing in the circle a sequence of right polygons with 2^k sides ($k = 2, 3, \cdots, n$) and finding their areas. Then they used the method of the "rule of contraries" to find the desired result. They omitted the transition to the limit condition, however; that is, they did not find the area of such a polygon when $k \to \infty$. Instead, they depended upon a proposition whose proof included the transition. This is the sixteenth proposition of the twelfth book of the *Elements.*

Using this theorem, the Banū Mūsā proved the following: If we have a circle of circumference C and a line of length L, and if $L < C$, then we can inscribe in this circle a right polygon of perimeter P_n (n is the number of sides) such that $P_n > L$. This means that we can find an integer, N, such that $C - P_n < C - L$ for every $n > N$. In the second part of this proposition the Banū Mūsā proved that if $L > C$, then we can circumscribe a right polygon of perimeter Q_n, such that $Q_n < L$. After this the proof of $A = r \cdot 1/2\ C$ (where A is the area of the circle and r its radius) becomes easy.

It should be noted that the Banū Mūsā defined the areas and volumes as equal to the products of certain values, while in Greek geometry they were expressed as comparisons with other areas and volumes. For example, Archimedes defined the volume of the sphere as four times the volume of the cone with the radius of the sphere as its height and the great circle of the sphere as its base. The Banū Mūsā found that the volume is equal to the radius of the sphere multiplied by one third of its surface. In other words, they used arithmetical operations for determining geometrical values. It was an important step to extend the number system and make it include irrationals as well as integers and rationals. In the sixth proposition the Banū Mūsā demonstrated the method of Archimedes for the approximate determination of the value of π. By means of inscription and circumscription of right polygons of ninety-six sides, Archimedes proved that π must lie between the values 3 1/7 and 3 10/71. The Banū Mūsā wrote that this method can be continued to get nearer to the boundaries of the value of π. This means that $\pi = \lim P_n$ (where P_n is the perimeter of the inscribed or circumscribed right polygon).

Like Archimedes, the Banū Mūsā determined that the surface of the sphere is four times its great circle, but their proof is different. Archimedes' proof is equivalent to the calculation of the definite integral

$$\int_0^\pi 2\pi r^2 \sin \phi \, d\phi = 4\pi r^2,$$

where r is the radius of the sphere. This cannot be said for the Banū Mūsā's proof, for they calculated only a finite sum of the sine series proving that

$$\cos \frac{\pi}{4n} \cdot \cot \frac{\pi}{4n} < 2 \sum_{K=1}^{n} \sin \frac{K\pi}{2n} < \csc \frac{\pi}{4n};$$

they did not extend this formula to the limit condition. Instead, they used the following fact without proving it: For any two concentric spheres we can inscribe in the larger a solid generated by rotating a right polygon about the diameter of the sphere that passes through two vertexes of the polygon, such that the surface of this solid does not touch or intersect the smaller sphere. This was proved by Euclid in the seventeenth theorem of the twelfth book of the *Elements*. The Banū Mūsā calculated the volume of the solid; then, using Euclid's theorem and the rule of contraries, they proved that $A = 4C$ (where A is the surface of the sphere and C is its great circle).

In addition to the measurement of the circle and the sphere, three classical Greek problems were solved in the treatise:

(1) In the seventh proposition of the treatise the Banū Mūsā proved the following theorem: If a, b, and c are sides of any triangle and A its area, then

$$A = \sqrt{p(p-a)(p-b)(p-c)},$$

where $p = (a + b + c)/2$. This theorem is often called Hero's theorem because Europeans met it for the first time in Hero's *Metrics*, but it existed in a lost book of Archimedes, which was known to the Arabs. The Banū Mūsā's proof, however, is different from that of Hero.

(2) The determination of two mean proportionals.

This problem concerns the determination of two unknowns, x and y, from the formula $a/x = x/y = y/b$, where a and b are given. This problem was solved for the first time by Archytas. The Banū Mūsā included this solution but stated that they had borrowed it from a geometrical treatise by Menelaos. Archytas found x and y through three intersecting curved surfaces: right cylinder $x^2 + y^2 = ax$, right cone $b^2(x^2 + y^2 + z^2) = a^2x^2$, and torus $x^2 + y^2 + z^2 = a\sqrt{x^2 + y^2}$. If x_0, y_0, and z_0 are the coordinates of the point of intersection of these surfaces, then it is clear that

$$\frac{a}{\sqrt{x_0^2 + y_0^2 + z_0^2}} = \frac{\sqrt{x_0^2 + y_0^2 + z_0^2}}{\sqrt{x_0^2 + y_0^2}} = \frac{\sqrt{x_0^2 + y_0^2}}{b}.$$

Therefore, $\sqrt{x_0^2 + y_0^2 + z_0^2}$ and $\sqrt{x_0^2 + y_0^2}$ are the required two mean proportionals between a and b. The Banū Mūsā gave a practical method for solving this problem by means of an instrument constructed from hinged rules. This instrument is very much like that devised by Plato for the same purpose.

(3) The trisection of the angle. Their solution to this problem, like all those given previously, is kinematic.

Thus, the contents of the Banū Mūsā's treatise are really within the boundaries of the ancient knowledge of geometry. This treatise, however, is not merely an exposition of Greek geometrical works, for it contains new proofs for the main theorems of the measurement of the circle and the sphere. Having studied the works of Greek mathematicians, the Banū Mūsā assimilated many of their methods. But in using the Greek infinitesimal method—the "method of exhaustion"—they omitted the transition to the limit conditions.

In the tenth and eleventh centuries a number of Arabic mathematical works on the measurement of figures were influenced by the Banū Mūsā's treatise, *On the Measurement of Plane and Spherical Figures.* The most important of these works were Thābit ibn Qurra's *On the Measurement of the Conic Section Named Parabola* and *On the Measurement of the Parabolic Solids,* and Ibn al-Haytham's *On the Measurement of Parabolic Solids* and *On the Measurement of the Sphere.* In the Middle Ages the treatise played a great role in spreading the tradition of Euclid and Archimedes in the Arabic countries and in Europe. Its influence upon European scientists in the Middle Ages can easily be seen in the *Practica geometrica* of Leonardo Fibonacci. In this book we can see some theorems of the Banū Mūsā that did not exist in the Greek books—for example, the theorem that says that the plane section of a right cone parallel to the base of the cone is a circle.

In addition to the treatise *On the Measurement of Plane and Spherical Figures,* the Banū Mūsā are credited with a number of other works that have been studied either insufficiently or not at all. Following is a list of the most important of these works.

(1) *Premises of the Book of Conics.* This is a recension of Apollonius' *Conics,* which was translated into Arabic by Hilāl al-Ḥimsī (Bks. I–IV) and Thābit ibn Qurra (Bks. V–VII). This recension was probably prepared by Muḥammad. Manuscripts of it are in Oxford, Istanbul, and Leiden.

(2) *Book of the Lengthened Circle.* This treatise, written by al-Ḥasan, seems to be on the "gardener's construction of the ellipse," that is, the construction of an ellipse by means of a string attached to the foci.

(3) *Qarasṭūn.* This is a treatise on the balance theory and its instruments.

(4) *On Mechanical Devices* (or *On Mechanics*). This treatise on pneumatic devices was written by Aḥmad. Manuscripts of it are in Berlin and the Vatican.

(5) *Book on the Description of the Instrument Which Sounds by Itself.* This work is on musical theory. A manuscript is in Beirut.

Some of these works deserve to be carefully studied, especially *Qarasṭūn* and *On Mechanical Devices.*

BIBLIOGRAPHY

I. ORIGINAL WORKS. There are two editions of the Banū Mūsā's main work, *On the Measurement of Plane and Spherical Figures: Kitāb maʿrifat misāḥat al-ashkāl al-basīṭa waʾl-kuriyya,* in *Rasāʾil al-Ṭūsī,* II (Hyderabad, 1940); and *Liber trium fratrum de geometria,* M. Curtze, ed., in *Nova acta Academiae Caesareae Leopoldino Carolinae germanicae naturae curiosorum,* **49** (1885).

II. SECONDARY LITERATURE. The Banū Mūsā's contributions are discussed in Marshall Clagett, *Archimedes in the Middle Ages,* I (Madison, Wis., 1964); M. Steinschneider, "Die Söhne des Musa ben Schakir," in *Bibliotheca mathematica* (Leipzig, 1887), pp. 44–48, 71–75; H. Suter, "Mathematiker und Astronomen der Araber und ihre Werke," in *Abhandlungen zur Geschichte der Mathematik* (Leipzig, 1900), and "Die Geometria der Söhne des Musa b. Shakir," in *Bibliotheca mathematica,* 3 (1902), 259–272. Information on the life and works of the Banū Mūsā can be found in C. Brockelmann, *Geschichte der arabischen Litteratur,* I (Leiden, 1936), p. 382 of Supp. I; G. Sarton, *Introduction to the History of Science,* I, 545–546, 560; Ibn al-Nadīm, *al-Fihrist,* G. Flügel, ed. (new ed., Beirut, 1964), I, 271; II, 126–127; Ibn al-Qiftī, *Taʾrīkh al-ḥukamāʾ,* Julius Lippert, ed. (Leipzig, 1903), pp. 315–316, 441–443. See also E. Wiedemann, "Zur Mechanik und Technik bei der Ara-

bern," in *Sitzungsberichte der Physikalisch-medizinischen Sozietät in Erlangen,* **38** (1906), esp. 6–8, which briefly discusses the Banū Mūsā's work on mechanics.

J. AL-DABBAGH

BÁRÁNY, ROBERT (*b*. Vienna, Austria, 22 April 1876; *d.* Uppsala, Sweden, 8 April 1936), *oto-rhino-laryngology.*

Bárány was the son of Ignaz Bárány, a bank official, and Marie Hock. He graduated from the University of Vienna on 2 April 1900, then trained in internal medicine with Noorden in Frankfurt am Main. He later studied with Kraepelin at the psychiatric-neurological clinic at Heidelberg and at the neurological clinic in Freiburg im Breisgau until April 1902. He received surgical training in the Vienna General Hospital until 30 September 1903. The next day Bárány entered service at the University of Vienna ear clinic under Adam Politzer, the founder of otology in Austria.

It is the task of the human ear not only to hear but also to be involved in the maintenance of equilibrium, the apparatus for which is found in the inner ear and consists of a space filled with fluid. The organ of equilibrium had hitherto only been the subject of investigations by various theoretical workers (Pierre Flourens, Ernst Mach, Josef Breuer, Julius Ewald), who had used pigeons and rabbits. On the basis of his observations concerning vertigo and equilibrium disturbances in patients, the French scientist Menière related these symptoms to the equilibrium system, thus terminating the period of theoretical speculative investigations of the organ.

Bárány's main contribution was the clinical application of these experimental data to humans, which led to the development of methods of investigating the human equilibrium system. It had been known for some time that this apparatus reacted to rotatory sensations. Bárány discovered the laws governing these rotatory reactions and thus was able to define the subjective sensations of dizziness by means of such objective indications as definite eye movements and reactions of the body's muscular system. His most important discovery was the caloric nystagmus. The organ of equilibrium can be stimulated by differences in temperature by irrigation of the ears with hot or cold liquid, a method that makes it possible to excite each organ separately. The technique is especially valuable because it can be used clinically at the bed of the patient. Bárány also proved the connection between the organ of equilibrium and centers in the brain. His work made possible the systematic interpretation of the colorful and many-sided aspects of vertigo and equilibrium disturbances, that is, to recognize them as ear-connected or originating in the nervous system. Incidentally, Bárány was able, in the course of his further studies, to investigate the relationship between the equilibrium apparatus and the nervous system, thus creating the basis for an entirely new field, otoneurology. For all these investigations he was given the title of *Dozent* in 1909, and in 1912 received half of the Politzer Prize. The following year he was awarded the ERB Medal of the German Neurological Society, and in 1914 the Guyot Prize for his contributions to otology.

In spite of ankylosis of the knee, Bárány volunteered for military service in 1914 in order to be able to test his ideas on the treatment of brain wounds. In 1915, while a Russian prisoner of war, he was awarded the Nobel Prize for medicine and physiology in recognition of his work on the vestibular apparatus, and was released. Two years later Bárány was appointed director of the University of Uppsala otorhino-laryngology clinic, a post he held until his death.

Bárány was a member or honorary member of numerous scientific societies. In 1924 he was awarded an honorary doctorate by the University of Stockholm.

A quiet, withdrawn researcher who worked with fanatical devotion, he lived happily with his wife, Ida Berger, who bore him two sons and a daughter, all of whom became physicians.

BIBLIOGRAPHY

I. ORIGINAL WORKS. Bárány published a total of 184 scientific papers. Some of his more important works are *Untersuchungen über den vom Vestibularapparat des Ohres reflektorisch ausgelösten rhythmischen Nystagmus und seine Begleiterscheinungen* (Berlin, 1906); *Physiologie und Pathologie des Bogengang-Apparates beim Menschen* (Leipzig–Vienna, 1907); *Funktionelle Prüfung des Vestibularapparates* (Jena, 1911), written with K. Wittmaack; *Klinik des Bogengangapparates* (Leipzig, 1913); "Primäre Wundnaht bei Schussverletzungen, speziell des Gehirns," in *Wiener klinische Wochenschrift*, no. 28 (1915), 525; and his Nobel address (11 Sept. 1916), in *Nordisk tidskrift för oto-rhino-laryngologi*, **1** (1916), 157.

II. SECONDARY LITERATURE. Works on Bárány include H. Hartmann, "Robert Bárány," in *Notring Jahrbuch* (Vienna, 1957), p. 21, and "Robert Bárány," in *Lexikon der Nobelpreisträger* (Frankfurt–Berlin, 1967), p. 9; C. O. Nylen, "Robert Bárány," in *Archives of Otolaryngology*, **82** (1965), 316; E. Wodak, *Kurze Geschichte der Vestibularisforschung* (Stuttgart, 1956), pp. 18 ff., 47 ff.; and K. Burian, "Robert Bárány," in *Österreichische Nobelpreisträger* (Vienna, 1961), p. 9.

E. H. MAJER

BARANZANO, GIOVANNI ANTONIO (*b.* Serravalle in Sesia, Vercelli, Italy, 1590; *d.* Montargis, France, 23 December 1622), *philosophy of astronomy.*

Baranzano began his studies at Crevalcuore and Vercelli, and continued them at Novara and Milan. On 11 March 1609 he took his vows as a Barnabite and assumed the name Redento. After finishing his religious and philosophical education, Baranzano studied Latin, Greek, Hebrew, and Chaldaic. In 1615 he was sent to teach philosophy in Annecy, at the college founded by Eustachio Chappuys. During this period he preached against the Calvinists in Thonon, Geneva, and Béarn.

In 1617 Baranzano published his most important work, *Uranoscopia seu De coelo,* in which he defended the Copernican system. This book was not well received by the Church, however, and Baranzano was called to Milan by the archbishop to make corrections. It is of some interest that he took with him on this occasion a letter written by his good friend Francis de Sales, testifying to his merits. Indeed, Baranzano clearly had a capacity for progressive thought; only his membership in a religious order and the ambient scholastic mentality made him turn back. Being obliged to withdraw his assertions, he wrote a small tract in which he presented his excuses for having departed *ex abundantia cordis* of the Scriptures. This was entitled *Nova de motu terrae Copernicolo iuxta Summi Pontificis mentem disputatio* (1618) and was appended, where possible, to the original *Uranoscopia.*

It is known that Baranzano had read Patrizi and Telesio, and he seems to have been in contact with Tobia Adami (a pupil of Tommaso Campanella), Tycho Brahe, Johannes Kepler, and Giovanni Magini. Francis Bacon, aware that Baranzano was the first to oppose Aristotle with the experimental method, wrote him a laudatory letter in 1622.

After the visit to Milan to correct his book, Baranzano was sent again to Annecy. In 1620 he was in Paris to obtain permission for the establishment of a Barnabite college in France. A college had just been founded at Montargis, and Baranzano held a teaching position there until his death, two years later.

BIBLIOGRAPHY

I. ORIGINAL WORKS. Baranzano's writings are *Uranoscopia, seu De coelo, in qua universa coelorum doctrina, clare, dilucide et breviter traditur* (Coloniae Allobrogum, 1617; 2nd ed., Paris, 1618); *Nova de motu terrae Copernicolo iuxta Summi Pontificis mentem disputatio* (Coloniae Allobrogum, 1618); *Prima summae philosophicae pars, seu*

Logica clare, breviter et subtiliter explicata (Lyons, 1618), also published in *Campus philosophicus* (see below); *Summa philosophica Anneciacensis, in qua omnes philosophicae quaestiones docte et breviter suo quaeque loco disponuntur* (Lyons, 1618), also published in *Campus philosophicus; Auscultatoriae disputationes quibus methodice lata corporis naturalis in genere cognitio comprehenditur* (Lyons, 1619); *Novae opiniones physicae, seu Tomus primus secundae partis Summae philosophicae Anneciacensis et physica auscultatoria octo physicorum libris explanandis accomodata* (Lyons, 1619); *Campus philosophicus in quo omnes dialecticae questiones breviter, clare et subtiliter suo quaeque loco agitantur* (Lyons, 1620); *De cometa ad Serenissimum Ducem Sabaudiae; Sur une fontaine de la Roche en Savoye; Sur la manière de se confesser* (Brussels, 1621); *Sur la manière de méditer la Passion de J. C.* (Brussels, 1621); and *Nuova teoria dei pianeti e dei moti celesti* and *Speculatio de arte militari,* both unpublished.

II. SECONDARY LITERATURE. Works pertaining to Baranzano are *Letters and Life of Bacon,* J. Spedding, ed., VII (London, 1874), 374–377; G. Boffito, *Scrittori barnabiti,* I (Florence, 1933), 75–80; G. Colombo, *Profili biografici d'insigni barnabiti,* I (Crema, 1870), 62, and *Intorno alla vita e alle opere del P. R. B.* (Turin, 1878); G. De Gregory, *Istoria della vercellese letteratura ed arti,* II (Turin, 1820), 66; C. Dionisotti, *Notizie biografiche dei vercellesi illustri* (Biella, 1862), p. 88; C. A. Ducis d'Annecy, *Notice sur d. Baranzano, père barnabite, professeur au Collège Chappuysien d'Annecy* (Annecy, 1881); Francis de Sales, *Oeuvres,* VIII (Annecy, 1912), 94, 97, 116; G. M. Mazzucchelli, *Gli scrittori d'Italia,* II, pt. 1ª (Brescia, 1758), 230 f.; J. P. Niçeron, *Mémoires pour servir à l'histoire des hommes illustrés dans la république des lettres, avec un catalogue raisonné de leurs ouvrages,* III (Paris, 1727), 43–48; C. R. Pasté, "Il p. Giov. Antonio B. vercellese e la questione galileiana," in *Archivio della Società vercellese di storia e d'arte,* **13,** nos. 1–2 (1921), 210–216; O. Premoli, *Storia dei Barnabiti nel cinquecento,* II (Rome, 1913), 72–75; G. Spini, *Ricerca dei libertini* (Rome–Florence, 1950), p. 310; and L. Thorndike, *A History of Magic and Experimental Science,* VII (New York, 1958), 112–114, 286–288.

MARIA LUISA RIGHINI-BONELLI

BARBA, ALVARO ALONSO (*b.* Lepe, Huelva, Spain, 15 November 1569; *d.* Potosí [?], Peru [now Bolivia], *ca.* 1640), *metallurgy.*

In 1588 Barba was sent by the Church to Peru, where he combined priestly duties with studies of mineral deposits, mining, and especially the treatment of silver ores by amalgamation. He traveled widely in the Peruvian provinces, living in Tarabuco (1590) and Tiahuanaco (1615). In 1617 he moved to Yotala in Los Lipez province, where he perfected his new procedures for treating silver ore. After 1624 Barba served the San Bernardo parish in the famous silver town of Potosí, where he presumably died sometime after 1639. His one book, *El arte de los metales*

(Madrid, 1640), brought him posthumous fame and is the main source of biographical information.

El arte was the first significant treatise on metals to be written in Spanish and is the only seventeenth-century treatise that was largely original. Barba dedicated it on 15 February 1637 to Juan de Lizarazu, president of the Real Audiencia de la Plata of Peru, who transmitted it to Spain with the approval of the mayor and of the Amalgamators Guild of Potosí. It went through approximately thirty editions in Spanish, English, German, and French. The work reflects Barba's rich enjoyment of the "qualities and Virtues [of the many] marvellous substances of this New World [which] will afford ample room for philosophic discourses when the bright Minds, now occupied in the tasks of taking out and enjoying the incomparable Riches of this Land, occupy themselves in the study of true Sciences" (Douglass and Mathewson, p. 10). He bowed to theory by citing alchemical literature on the origins of earths, minerals, and salts, but he added clear descriptions of them and wrote mainly as an observant, practical man.

Barba excelled in his account of the treatment of silver ores by amalgamation, using processes that he himself had discovered and that were in large measure responsible for the wealth of the province. (Only Biringuccio's outline of a simple process existed before this.) Barba's amalgamation was done over heat in copper vessels with mechanical stirring devices, and he strongly emphasized the importance of tests to find the correct kind and amount of additive for each kind of ore to improve collection of the silver by the mercury and to prevent flouring. Barba was one of the first writers to advocate what amounts to a laboratory control of an entire plant process as well as the computation of all costs (including fuel, mercury, additives, depreciation of equipment, and labor) before undertaking an operation. He describes the local pre-Columbian smelting practice, and the use of the reverberatory furnace for smelting considerably before its widespread adoption.

BIBLIOGRAPHY

Barba's only work was *El arte de los metales* (Madrid, 1640, 1680, 1729, 1768, 1770, 1811, 1852, 1932 [photo repro. of 1770 ed.]; Córdoba, 1675). There were also Spanish-American editions (Lima, 1817, 1842–1843; Santiago, 1877–1878; Norwood, Mass., 1925 [repro. of 1770 ed.]; La Paz, 1939). A partial English translation (Books I and II) was made by Edward Montagu, earl of Sandwich (London, 1670, 1674, 1738, 1739, 1740). The complete English translation is by R. E. Douglass and E. P. Mathewson (New York, 1923). French translations are by C. Hautin de Villars

(Paris, 1729, 1730) and by Lenglet-Dufresnoy, under the pseudonym Gosford (Paris, 1751; The Hague, 1752). It also appeared in German translation (Hamburg, 1676, 1739; Frankfurt, 1739; Vienna, 1749, 1767; Ephrata, 1763).

The sparse biographical information on Barba has been summarized in Eugenio Maffei and Ramón Rua-Figueroa, *Apuntes para una biblioteca española de libros . . . relativos al conocimiento y explotación de las riquezas minerales,* I (Madrid, 1872), 61–65.

C. S. SMITH

BARBIER, JOSEPH-ÉMILE (*b*. St.-Hilaire-Cotter, Pas-de-Calais, France, 18 March 1839; *d*. St.-Genest, Loire, France, 28 January 1889), *mathematics, astronomy.*

The son of a former soldier, Barbier was singled out in primary school for his mathematical and scientific aptitude. After secondary schooling at the Collège de St.-Omer, and then at the Lycée Henri IV in Paris, he was admitted in 1857 to the École Normale Supérieure, where he astonished his fellow students by his acute intelligence and his ability to grasp the deeper meanings of complex problems. He also had a taste for subtlety that led him to detect the errors in the most classic demonstrations.

In 1860 Barbier passed his *agrégation* and taught mathematics at the *lycée* of Nice, where he does not seem to have been appreciated by his students. Le Verrier, director of the Paris Observatory, was impressed by Barbier's keen insight and offered him a position as assistant astronomer. A good observer, Barbier showed himself also to be an able calculator. He was fully aware of the usefulness to astronomy of mathematics, physics, chemistry, and instrumental techniques, and he was thus a valuable collaborator. During this period he published numerous reports concerned with various problems in astronomy and the most diverse types of mathematics. His ingenuity led him to perfect a new type of thermometer.

But after a few years Barbier seemed to become more and more unstable and strange. In 1865 he left the observatory, and after attempting to enter a religious order broke off all contacts with his associates. Only in 1880 was he discovered in the asylum at Charenton-St.-Maurice, where he had been sequestered for several years. Joseph Bertrand, permanent secretary of the Académie des Sciences, encouraged him to return to scientific writing and was able to secure for him regular financial help from a foundation connected with the Academy. The numerous reports published thereafter were irreproachably sound and often most original. Although Barbier never recovered his sanity, the gentleness of his be-

havior caused him to be released, and he spent his last years in a more serene environment.

Barbier's work is scattered in thirty or more memoirs and reports, of which about two-thirds were published during his brief career as a professor and assistant astronomer (1860–1866); most of the others were published between 1882 and 1887.

Several of the studies in the first series bear on the mathematical aspects of astronomy (spherical geometry and spherical trigonometry), on the construction of new thermometers, and on other aspects of instrumental techniques. The others deal with infinitesimal calculus and elementary and infinitesimal geometry, as well as with the calculus of probabilities. The last works of Barbier dealt almost entirely with mathematics and made several interesting contributions to geometry (the theory of polyhedra, the indicatrix of Dupin), integral calculus, and the theory of numbers.

Despite the illness that ruined his career, Barbier deserves to be numbered among the good unspecialized mathematicians of the late nineteenth century.

BIBLIOGRAPHY

I. ORIGINAL WORKS. Barbier's scientific work consists of thirty or more memoirs and reports published in various French journals, particularly in *Nouvelles annales de mathématiques; Les mondes;* and *Comptes-rendus hebdomadaires de l'Académie des sciences.* Nearly complete lists of his publications are given in the *Catalogue of Scientific Papers* of the Royal Society: I (1867), 178; VII (1877), 85; IX (1891), 118–119; XIII (1914), 289; and Poggendorff, III (1898), 68, and IV (1904), 64.

II. SECONDARY LITERATURE. Articles on Barbier are J. Bertrand, in *Association des anciens élèves de l'École normale* (Paris, 1890), pp. 35–36; P. Gauja, *Les fondations de l'Académie des sciences (1881–1915)* (Hendaye, 1917), pp. 348–349; and A. M. Lautour, in *Dictionnaire de biographie française,* III (1951), col. 326.

RENÉ TATON

BARBOUR, HENRY GRAY (*b*. Hartford, Connecticut, 28 March 1885; *d*. New Haven, Connecticut, 23 September 1943), *physiology, pharmacology.*

Although a pharmacologist by profession, Henry G. Barbour made his single most important contribution to science in physiology, with his delineation of the reactions of the body temperature-regulating center in the brain. Barbour was graduated A.B. from Trinity College in Hartford in 1906, and M.D. from Johns Hopkins University in 1910. After a year at Johns Hopkins as a fellow in pathology, he traveled abroad (1911–1912), visiting research laboratories in Freiburg, Vienna, and London. Following his return to the United States he taught pharmacology at Yale University (1912–1921), McGill University (1921–1923), and the University of Louisville (1923–1931). In 1931 he returned to Yale, first as associate professor and in 1940 as research associate in pharmacology.

In 1885, twenty years after the appearance of Claude Bernard's concept of the physiologically constant *milieu intérieur*, E. Aronsohn and J. Sachs had disclosed the existence of a region in the corpus striatum of the brain concerned with the regulation of one of the most important factors in internal constancy, body temperature. A puncture of the nervous tissue in this region was shown to produce a characteristic fever. R. Kahn's experiments in 1904 on the heating of the blood in the carotid artery showed that the brain reacted to the increased heat of this blood with such cooling responses as peripheral vasodilation and increased perspiration.

In 1912 Barbour set out to test the effect of heat and cold applied directly to this temperature-responsive region of the brain. He punctured the brains of rabbits and inserted in each a tube through which water at different temperatures could be passed. The puncture itself induced a fever, but when water heated 46°C.–49°C. was passed through the tube, body temperature dropped sharply, almost 1.5 degrees C. in one hour. When cold water was passed through the tube, body temperature rose sharply.

Through observations of the veins in the ear of the rabbit, Barbour was able to correlate vasomotor reactions with the temperature of the water in the experiment. He reported a striking alteration in the ear's appearance: within two minutes after the start of hot water flow, the veins had dilated and filled with blood, and the entire ear felt warm. Cold stimulation of the temperature center produced opposite effects. The heat center of the brain therefore reacted to extreme temperatures by activating countervailing physiological mechanisms that brought the blood temperature back to normal.

From 1912 until well into the 1940's Barbour contributed to the amassing of more precise information on the phenomena of temperature regulation, and he became a leading authority on the mechanism of body temperature regulation and the effect of pyretic and antipyretic drugs. His primary contribution to this field was contained in his 1912 paper. After 1931, Barbour's work benefited from the added stimulus of Walter B. Cannon's ideas on the physiological elements contributing to homeostasis.

In a 1940 paper expanding on the work of Keller and Hare and others, Barbour showed, through the use of localized lesions to remove functions selectively, that there are two temperature control centers: a heat loss center in the anterior hypothalamus and a heating center in the posterior hypothalamus. In both cat and monkey brains, lesions of the anterior hypothalamus produced abnormally high body temperatures, while lesions of the posterior hypothalamus or the nervous paths related to that region resulted in greatly lowered temperatures. In the same series of experiments, control of water-shifting mechanisms, and therefore of the concentration of the bodily fluids, was found to be associated with the anterior hypothalamic region.

BIBLIOGRAPHY

I. ORIGINAL WORKS. Works by Barbour include "Die Wirkung unmittelbarer Erwärmung und Abkülung der Wärmezentra auf die Körpertemperatur," in *Archiv für experimentelle Pathologie und Pharmakologie*, **70** (1912), 1–26; and "Hypothalamic Control of Water Movement in Response to Environmental Temperature," in *Research Publications. Association for Research in Nervous and Mental Diseases*, **20** (1940), 449–485.

II. SECONDARY LITERATURE. No satisfactory biographical or bibliographical materials concerning Barbour exist. For work closely related to Barbour's, see E. Aronsohn and J. Sachs, "Die Beziehungen des Gehirns zur Körperwärme und zum Fieber," in *Pflügers Archiv für die gesamte Physiologie des Menschen und des Tiere*, **37** (1885), 233–301; R. H. Kahn, "Ueber die Erwärmung des Carotidblutes," in *Archiv für Anatomie und Physiologie* (1904), supp., 81–134; and A. Keller and W. Hare, "The Hypothalamus and Heat Regulation," in *Proceedings of the Society for Experimental Biology and Medicine*, **29** (1932), 1069–1070.

ALAN S. KAY

BARCHUSEN, JOHANN CONRAD (*b.* Horn, Germany, 16 March 1666; *d.* Utrecht, Netherlands, 2 October 1723), *chemistry, medicine.*

Little is known of Barchusen's life before he settled in Utrecht, but it appears that he studied pharmacy in several cities, including Berlin, Mainz, and Vienna. He also traveled in Hungary and Italy and, for a short period in the latter half of 1693, acted as physician to Francesco Morosini during the abortive Venetian expedition to the Peloponnesus. Sometime in 1694 Barchusen settled in Utrecht, where in September of that year he was granted permission by the city council to conduct chemistry courses for students attending the university. In April 1695, at the behest of the city fathers and with their financial support, he was provided with a laboratory. In these circumstances Barchusen taught chemistry as a *Privatdozent* until

1698, when, again on the initiative of the city council, he was awarded an honorary M.D., granted an annual salary, and given the title of "lector" in chemistry, which allowed him to teach publicly in the university. He was promoted to extraordinary professor of chemistry in 1703. In 1699 Barchusen married a native of Utrecht, Maria Johanna Pylsweert, who died without issue in 1717.

Barchusen's published work reflects his personal development from practicing pharmacist to professor of a new academic discipline, chemistry. His first book was a pharmaceutical text, *Pharmacopoeus synopticus* (1690). His chemical writings are contained in three works, published after his arrival in Utrecht: the *Pyrosophia* (1698), which was later revised and republished with the title *Elementa chemiae* (1718); the *Acroamata* (1703), a collection of his public lectures on chemistry; and the *Compendium ratiocinii chemici* (1712), a brief work that attempts to set out the principles of chemistry in the form of a geometry textbook, with definitions, postulates, theorems, and so on.

The *Pyrosophia* is a formal, systematic textbook that deals with the principles of chemistry, both theoretical and practical, and then attempts to demonstrate their applications to natural philosophy, medicine, metallurgy, and alchemy. The bulk of the work is descriptive, preparative iatrochemistry of a conventional type; but the syllabi of his laboratory courses for 1695 to 1697, included as an appendix to the volume, show an increasing tendency to emphasize chemistry as the analysis and synthesis of bodies by fire, relegating the preparative iatrochemistry to a secondary part of the course. All the syllabi contain sections devoted to metallurgical assay and to alchemy. In this last part, the students were shown how most alleged transmutations could be explained in terms of displacement reactions of metals. The *Elementa chemiae* contains a remarkable set of symbolic alchemical plates. The most interesting lectures in the *Acroamata* are his inaugural of 1703, on the antiquity and utility of chemistry; a lecture defending the technique of analysis by fire and the concept of chemical principles or elements, directed against Robert Boyle; and two lectures attacking John Mayow's ideas on nitro-aerial spirits. Throughout his chemical writings Barchusen seeks to combine an interpretation of chemical reactions in terms of principles or elements with a corpuscular view of matter. The most thoroughly mechanistic of his works is the short *Compendium*. Here (p. 12) he postulates that corpuscles of chemical substances differ not only in shape but also in weight. Although he cites Becher and Stahl several times, Barchusen makes no mention of phlogiston.

As a chemist, Barchusen contributed little to the practical or conceptual development of his subject; he has been credited with some originality in his ideas on chemical affinity, but these appear to be derived from Mayow, Homberg, and others. His activities at Utrecht, however, illuminate the Dutch academic chemistry from which his illustrious contemporary at Leiden, Hermann Boerhaave, emerged as the most influential teacher of chemistry in the first decades of the eighteenth century.

Barchusen's *Historia medicinae* (1710) is arranged in dialogue form, with several contemporary Dutch physicians discussing certain historical themes and systems in medicine. It was revised and republished with the title *De medicinae origine et progressu dissertationes* (1723) because of criticism of the dialogue form and the poor Latin style (a characteristic of all his writings). The *Collecta medicinae practicae generalis* (1715) arose out of Barchusen's dissatisfaction with the confusion of medical systems that he encountered in writing his history of medicine: here he collected some of the more important clinical observations in the work of ancient and modern physicians to support his view that true progress in medicine would be achieved through extensive clinical observation and empirical therapy.

BIBLIOGRAPHY

I. ORIGINAL WORKS. Since considerable confusion exists in the standard bibliographies, a full list of Barchusen's works follows. His chemical works are *Pharmacopoeus synopticus, seu synopsis pharmaceutica, plerasque medicaminum, compositiones, ac formulas, eorumque . . . conficiendi methodum exhibens* (Frankfurt, 1690; 2nd ed., Utrecht, 1696), 3rd ed. entitled *Synopsis pharmaciae* (Leiden, 1712); *Pyrosophia, succincte atque breviter iatrochemiam, rem metallicam et chrysopoeiam pervestigans. Opus medicis, physicis, chemicis, pharmacopoeis, metallicis ec. noninutile* (Leiden, 1698), 2nd ed., rev., entitled *Elementa chemiae, quibus subjuncta est confectura lapidis philosophici imaginibus repraesentata* (Leiden, 1718); *Acroamata, in quibus complura ad iatro-chemiam atque physicam spectantia, jocunda rerum varietate, explicantur* (Utrecht, 1703); and *Compendium ratiocinii chemici more geometrarum concinnatum* (Leiden, 1712). The medical works are *Historia medicinae* (Amsterdam, 1710), 2nd ed., rev., entitled *De medicinae origine et progressu dissertationes* (Utrecht, 1723); and *Collecta medicinae practicae generalis* (Amsterdam, 1715).

II. SECONDARY LITERATURE. The fullest account of Barchusen's early life is in Caspar Burmann, *Traiectum eruditum* (Utrecht, 1750), p. 14. His career at Utrecht is discussed in O. Hannaway, "Johann Conrad Barchusen (1666–1723)—Contemporary and Rival of Boerhaave," in

Ambix, **14** (1967), 96–111, where an extensive list of secondary literature is cited.

OWEN HANNAWAY

BARCLAY, JOHN (*b.* Perthshire, Scotland, 10 December 1758; *d.* Edinburgh, Scotland, 21 August 1826), *anatomy.*

John Barclay was the leading teacher of anatomy in Edinburgh at the beginning of the nineteenth century. The son of a Perthshire minister, Barclay was originally destined for the Church, and having taken his license after a good education at St. Andrews University, he acted as a preacher in the Church of Scotland before turning his attention to medicine and graduating M.D. at Edinburgh in 1796. He was thirty-eight years of age before he began to teach anatomy on his own account, after assisting John Bell in his class.

The house in High School Yards, in which he lectured, soon became too small to accommodate the students, and Barclay was obliged not only to remove to a larger classroom in Surgeons' Square but also to lecture on the same subject twice a day. In 1810 the number of students attending his class had risen to 300. Barclay had no monopoly on anatomical teaching; there were other extramural classes of anatomy that prospered, especially after the retirement of the second Monro from the university chair. Barclay was, however, the first teacher of anatomy in Edinburgh to confine his attention to anatomy and not to engage in practice. He made a number of valuable contributions to human and comparative anatomy, and indeed it was proposed that a chair of comparative anatomy should be created for him in the university.

This proposal aroused violent discussion, and was eventually abandoned. It is commemorated by a clever cartoon in Kay's *Edinburgh Portraits,* entitled "The Craft in Danger." Barclay is shown mounted on the skeleton of an elephant, being pushed into the university gate by some of his friends. His progress is resisted by his enemies.

The Barclay Collection of Comparative Anatomy was bequeathed by him to the Royal College of Surgeons. The result of twenty-seven years of collecting, it remains a monument to his industry.

Barclay was succeeded as conservator and teacher of anatomy by Robert Knox.

BIBLIOGRAPHY

I. ORIGINAL WORKS. Barclay's writings include *A New Anatomical Nomenclature* (1803); *Muscular Motions of the Human Body* (1808); and *The Arteries of the Human Body* (1812).

II. SECONDARY LITERATURE. There is no full-length biography of Barclay, but see Ballingall's short notice (1827) and Struthers' memoir in his *The Edinburgh Anatomical School* (1867).

DOUGLAS GUTHRIE

BARCROFT, JOSEPH (*b.* Newry, Ireland, 23 July 1872; *d.* Cambridge, England, 21 March 1947), *physiology.*

Barcroft was descended from a branch of a landed English family who had become Quakers and had moved to Ireland during the seventeenth century. His father, Henry Barcroft, was active in the management of a spinning company and a tramway company, and contributed mechanical inventions important to the operations of each. He was also an artist and was interested in natural history.

Joseph Barcroft grew up a Quaker and remained active within the Society of Friends until he came to disagree with its views during World War I. Sent to the Leys School at Cambridge in 1888 because of his interest in science, Barcroft took a B.Sc. at the University of London by passing the examinations while still a student at Leys. After a year off in 1892–1893 because of overstrain, he entered King's College, Cambridge, to study natural science. After his graduation in 1896 he began original research in the Cambridge Physiological Laboratory, founded and directed by Michael Foster. In 1899 he was elected to a fellowship at King's College, and in 1905 also became a lecturer of the college. He held these positions for nearly fifty years. In 1925, upon the death of John Newport Langley, Barcroft became professor of physiology. He married Mary Agnetta Ball in 1902.

Barcroft's first investigation was suggested to him in 1897 by Langley, who was then Foster's assistant. For many years Langley had been investigating the process of glandular secretion. Rudolf Heidenhahn had theorized that there are two types of nerves supplying the salivary glands, but Langley became convinced that there was no evidence for more than one kind of secretory nerve fiber, and that the differences in the character of salivary secretions obtained when the chorda tympani and the cervical sympathetic nerves leading to the gland are stimulated could be explained by vasomotor effects. Langley encouraged Barcroft to try to measure the effects of stimulating the submaxillary gland upon its metabolism, in order to throw light on the issue of its innervation.

When Barcroft took up the topic, however, the accurate measurement of the changes in the amounts of gases exchanged in the organ became in itself an absorbing problem, one on which he worked for several years. He had first to refine the methods for extracting blood gases so that he could analyze samples of blood much smaller than were customarily used. In 1901 he and John Scott Haldane developed a method by which he could measure quickly and accurately the gases contained in 1 cubic centimeter of blood. The physiological problem of estimating the gaseous exchange of the gland was, he saw, more complex than previously realized. It was not enough merely to measure the quantities of gases in equal volumes of arterial and venous blood and the amount of blood flowing out of the gland in a given time in order to calculate the rate of exchange, for he found that the hemoglobin in the venous blood was more concentrated because some of the water of the blood had been lost as salivary fluid. After he had taken such changes into account in his calculations, he was able to show that stimulation of the chorda tympani substantially increased the oxygen uptake and carbonic acid output.

In the following years Barcroft turned the methods he had developed for this research to the study of other organs. In 1904, in collaboration with Ernest Starling, he showed that the pancreas also consumes more oxygen and releases more carbonic acid when it is secreting than when it is not. Next he turned to the kidney and to the heart, finding in each case a correlation between increased or decreased activity and the rate of metabolism of the organ.

In his early blood gas analyses Barcroft dealt only with the amounts of these substances in the arterial and venous blood samples. Other physiologists, however, including especially Christian Bohr, had been investigating the relation between the percentage saturation of the blood with oxygen and the tension of the oxygen in the blood, the latter being proportional to the pressure of oxygen in the atmosphere with which the blood sample was in equilibrium. They were attempting to construct characteristic curves with which they could calculate either quantity when the other was known. Bohr emphasized that it was the oxygen tension in the plasma of the venous blood, rather than the percentage saturation of the hemoglobin with oxygen, which most directly determined the amount of oxygen that reaches the cells. Accordingly, he calculated from Barcroft's figures for the quantities of oxygen in the venous blood of the submaxillary gland the corresponding oxygen tension, and showed that it increased by 48 percent after the gland was stimulated.

Undoubtedly impressed by the application Bohr had made of his "own figures," Barcroft returned in 1905 to the submaxillary gland, to take up the problem inherent in Bohr's approach: how oxygen is transferred from the blood to the secretory cells. Barcroft noticed, however, a striking anomaly: the available analysis of saliva showed that it contained a larger percentage of oxygen than the blood plasma did, according to Bohr's calculations. It was hard to imagine how this concentration could occur. Barcroft thought that there was no recourse but to assume that there was active cellular secretion of oxygen in the capillary walls, unless the oxygen dissociation curves were incorrect, so that they gave a calculated oxygen tension that was too low. The problems thus raised in response to Bohr's discussion became prominent themes in Barcroft's work during the following years.

Examining more closely the previous literature on oxygen dissociation curves, Barcroft realized that the results were widely discordant. He decided, therefore, to check the curves for himself. At first he and his research associate, Mario Camis, seemed to obtain a uniformity of results that had eluded their predecessors. Blood of different kinds of animals, which before had given divergent results, came out the same for them. But when they used human blood, they could not obtain a similar agreement. Only after "six months of research which became weekly more depressing," as Barcroft recalled, did they finally discover that a variation in the salts present in a solution of hemoglobin alters the hemoglobin's dissociation curve for oxygen. Systematically examining the effects of other changes in the salts, they found that they could reproduce curves consistently whenever they kept the composition of the solution constant.

Following this success, Barcroft's main focus of research shifted to further elucidation of the oxygen dissociation curve. He pursued two distinct but interlocking lines of investigation. First, principally in collaboration with A. V. Hill, he tried to characterize the curves mathematically and derive from the characteristics of the reaction between hemoglobin and oxygen a theory of the mechanism of their interaction. Second, he continued to study the conditions that modify the curve. A rise in temperature from 36° to 41°C., he discovered, shifted the curve so that at a given tension the blood was less saturated with oxygen. The addition of lactic acid to the blood modified the curve in the same direction. He saw both these effects as having adaptive significance to the animal, for they would aid in the discharge of oxygen in the tissues when the latter were in conditions of stress, which require more rapid delivery of oxygen.

In his first paper on the dissociation curve, Barcroft considered some implications of the curve's properties for conditions at high altitudes. Shortly after, Nathan

Zuntz of Berlin invited him to join an expedition to the island of Tenerife. The group, whose purpose was to examine the biochemical effects of high climates and solar radiation, operated from three stations on the island: at sea level, 7,000 feet, and 11,000 feet. Because Bohr had shown that a change in the carbonic acid concentration in the blood displaces the oxygen dissociation curve, Barcroft expected that at high altitude, where the alveolar CO_2 pressure is reduced, the curve would be so modified. Contrary to his prediction, he found the results for blood samples taken at 11,000 feet to be the same as for those taken at sea level. If, on the other hand, he analyzed the blood sample taken at high altitude after putting it in equilibrium with carbonic acid at a pressure equivalent to the alveolar pressure at sea level, the curve was displaced. Consequently, the blood itself must have changed in such a way that its dissociation curve at the lower pressure duplicated that of normal blood at a higher pressure. He thought that probably some substance such as lactic acid was taken up in the blood in place of the decreased carbonic acid. "This change," he concluded, "compensated the change in alveolar CO_2 tension to such an extent that the actual dissociation curve under the conditions locally established did not alter." He considered it probable that this was one of the mechanisms produced in the process of evolution that enabled "the respiratory process to adapt itself to various unusual conditions."

After returning from Tenerife, Barcroft continued the two basic lines of research that he had established. He investigated the metabolism of the submaxillary gland, the kidneys, and the liver, becoming more deeply involved in the special problems each organ presented for measuring the gaseous exchange, the oxygen consumption, the work performed, and the relation between circulatory changes and activity. At the same time he delved further into the physical chemistry of hemoglobin. In 1910 A. V. Hill developed a mathematical equation from which he could derive the oxygen dissociation curve, and from which he could make deductions concerning such properties as the state of aggregation of the hemoglobin molecules. The equation also enabled Barcroft to treat more precisely and quantitatively the alterations of the dissociation curve with altitude and with other changes in conditions. In 1913 Barcroft summarized the results of his researches over the preceding sixteen years in *The Respiratory Function of the Blood,* generally regarded as a landmark in the development of respiratory physiology.

During World War I, Barcroft contributed to the national effort by investigating the effects of gas poisoning and methods for treating patients suffering from it. In 1915 he went to Boulogne to study gassed soldiers at the base hospital; in 1917 he was made a member of the Chemical Advisory Committee of the British government, and took charge of its physiological work in a laboratory established at Porton. His work was related to his prewar research, for he saw that the symptoms of gassed patients were often the result of inadequate respiration caused by damage to the lungs. "The fundamental idea on which our treatment is based," he reported, "is that the whole train of symptoms shown by these patients is the same as that exhibited at high altitudes." His wartime experiences also helped to broaden his view of the factors involved in respiration, by emphasizing to him the importance of the chemical buffers of the blood for controlling its alkalinity.

After the war Barcroft extended his study of high-altitude physiology. In 1922 he led an expedition to the Peruvian Andes to study the ways in which the human body adapts to an environment of low oxygen pressure by changes in the oxygen dissociation curve of its blood, increases in pulmonary ventilation and the concentration of hemoglobin in the blood, and other factors. He also continued to examine a question often debated among contemporary physiologists: whether the pulmonary epithelium secretes oxygen into the blood under such conditions. He concluded that his own evidence did not support the assertion that it does.

While making, incidental to this expedition, measurements of the total volume of human blood, Barcroft observed an anomaly that helped start him on a new line of research. To determine the volume, he had the subject inhale a known quantity of carbon monoxide and then measured its concentration in a few drops of the subject's blood. The object was to compare the volume at higher altitude with that at sea level, but the volume at sea level turned out to be greater when the temperature was high than when it was low. This result raised the question of whether there was in the body a reservoir of blood and hemoglobin not detectable by the carbon monoxide method. Suspecting the spleen to be such a site, Barcroft established that in animals exposed to carbon monoxide, that gas penetrated the hemoglobin of the spleen significantly more slowly than it did the hemoglobin of the general circulation, suggesting that the spleen does retain a store of hemoglobin. Between 1925 and 1928 he developed several methods for observing changes in the size of the spleen, so that he could tell whether it adds a significant amount of blood to the circulation when it contracts. He found not only that it does, but that its contractions are correlated with increased demands for circulating blood, so that the organ serves as a regulator of blood volume.

In 1928 Barcroft found "in a somewhat accidental way" that the spleen of a pregnant dog was contracted, an observation which made him wonder what quantity of blood was needed in the uterus during pregnancy. In 1932 he measured the amount and found it unusually large, even while the embryos were still very small. He then asked whether this quantity served for storing blood or whether an unusually large volume passed through the uterus. While measuring the blood flow and gaseous exchanges of the organ, he discovered that the percentage saturation with oxygen of the venous blood in the uterus gradually declined during pregnancy, until it reached such a low level that it was hard for him to imagine how any further oxygen could be transferred to the embryonic circulation. The gravity of the problem launched him on a full investigation of fetal respiration, which broadened into a study of embryonic circulatory and nervous development. He continued his research on fetal physiology until his death.

Although known chiefly as a resourceful experimentalist with a sure grasp of significant problems, Barcroft also took time to write more broadly on the nature of physiological processes. The most notable of these efforts was *Features in the Architecture of Physiological Function* (1934), in which he discussed general functional principles that he considered to be manifested repeatedly in specific mechanisms within animals. Among such principles were the fixity of the internal environment, the provision of stores of materials, "all-or-nothing responses," and the view that "every adaptation is an integration." Barcroft was regarded as an inspiring teacher and a warm, sensitive person, combining gaiety with seriousness, and disciplined, forceful leadership with generosity and informality.

BIBLIOGRAPHY

I. ORIGINAL WORKS. Barcroft's books include *The Respiratory Function of the Blood* (Cambridge, 1914); *The Respiratory Function of the Blood*, pt. I, *Lessons From High Altitudes* (Cambridge, 1925); *The Respiratory Function of the Blood*, pt. II, *Haemoglobin* (Cambridge, 1928); *Features in the Architecture of Physiological Function* (Cambridge, 1934); *The Brain and Its Environment* (New Haven, 1937); and *Researches on Pre-natal Life* (Oxford, 1946). The majority of his research papers appeared in the *Journal of Physiology*. Full bibliographies are given in the two works below.

II. SECONDARY LITERATURE. Works on Barcroft are Kenneth J. Franklin, *Joseph Barcroft 1872–1947* (Oxford, 1953); and F. J. W. Roughton, "Joseph Barcroft 1872–1947," in *Obituary Notices of Fellows of the Royal Society,* **6** (1949), 315–345.

FREDERIC L. HOLMES

BARKHAUSEN, HEINRICH GEORG (*b.* Bremen, Germany, 2 December 1881; *d.* Dresden, Germany, 20 February 1956), *electronic engineering.*

The son of a district judge, Barkhausen attended the Gymnasium in Bremen and then spent half a year as an engineering trainee in a railway maintenance depot before entering engineering college at Bremen. He soon turned to physics and attended the universities of Munich, Berlin, and Göttingen; at Göttingen he became an assistant in the Institute of Applied Electricity and received the doctorate in 1907 with the dissertation "The Problem of the Generation of Oscillations." His work attracted a good deal of attention in technical circles and led to his employment as a research worker in the Siemens & Halske laboratories in Berlin.

In 1911 the Technische Hochschule in Dresden created the first professorship anywhere in the communications branch of electrical engineering, and Barkhausen was appointed to it. From this important position, Barkhausen greatly influenced the development of the new field both scientifically and pedagogically. He made early, basic contributions to the theories of nonlinear switching elements and of spontaneous oscillation, and he formulated the still-used electron-tube coefficients and the equations relating them. Barkhausen wrote a four-volume text on electron tubes and their technological applications that remained the standard work for many years. He also contributed to acoustics and to magnetism. In acoustics, the method of subjective measurement of loudness and the use of the *phon* as a unit of loudness were first proposed by Barkhausen. In magnetism, he discovered by acoustical methods the discontinuities that occur as a ferromagnetic material is magnetized; this observation, known as the Barkhausen effect, played a part in the further elucidation of the discrete nature of magnetism by the domain theory.

Among engineers he is best known for the Barkhausen-Kurz oscillator (developed in 1920 with his collaborator Karl Kurz), an electron tube capable of continuous-wave oscillation at ultrahigh frequencies, which was the forerunner of a whole series of microwave tubes and contributed to the understanding of their underlying principle, velocity modulation.

Barkhausen's Institute of High-Frequency and Electron-Tube Technology in Dresden, which had survived most of World War II unscathed, was destroyed by bombing on 13 February 1945. After the war, Barkhausen returned from West Germany to his beloved Dresden and participated in the reconstruction of the institute, where he remained until his death. The buildings housing the institute are named the Barkhausenbau in his honor.

Barkhausen was renowned throughout the world. He received many honors in Germany and abroad, especially from Japan and the United States; he was awarded the Morris Liebmann Memorial Prize for 1933 by the Institute of Radio Engineers, of which he was vice-president in 1935. His scholarly, teaching, and research careers were all exceedingly fruitful. Dresden's excellence as a center of electronics research was in large measure due to Barkhausen; the influence he exercised through his works and his students came to be felt all over the world.

BIBLIOGRAPHY

A list of Barkhausen's major publications appears in Poggendorff, *Biographisch-literarisches Handwörterbuch,* vols. V, VI, and VII.

An obituary by his successor in the Dresden institute, Hans Frühauf, appears in *Jahrbuch der Deutschen Akademie der Wissenschaften zu Berlin* (1956), pp. 513–515; a more elaborate eulogy by Frühauf is in *Hochfrequenztechnik und Elektroakustik,* **65** (1957), 109–112.

CHARLES SÜSSKIND

BARKHAUSEN, JOHANN CONRAD. See **Barchusen, Johann Conrad.**

BARKLA, CHARLES GLOVER (*b.* Widnes, Lancashire, England, 27 June 1877; *d.* Edinburgh, Scotland, 23 October 1944), *physics.*

Barkla's father, John Martin Barkla, was secretary of the Atlas Chemical Company in Widnes; his mother, Sarah Glover, was of a local family of watch manufacturers. Barkla received his secondary education at the Liverpool Institute, and in October 1895, with scholarships, entered University College, Liverpool. He concentrated on mathematics and physics. After taking Honours in mathematics he specialized in experimental physics under Oliver Lodge and in 1898 was awarded First-Class Honours in the B.Sc. examination. He received the M.Sc. in 1899. While at Liverpool, Barkla served as first president of the

University Physical Society and as occasional substitute for Lodge.

In the autumn of 1899, with an 1851 Exhibition scholarship, Barkla entered Trinity College, Cambridge, as an advanced student. He attended lectures, including those of George Stokes on optics and hydrodynamics (where he was on occasion the sole auditor), and began researches at the Cavendish Laboratory, for which he eventually received the Cambridge B.A. After eighteen months at Trinity, Barkla moved to King's College in order to sing in its famous chapel choir—the chapel was jammed for his baritone solos. In 1901 Barkla's two-year scholarship was exceptionally renewed for a third year. The following year, refusing the opportunity to remain at Cambridge on a choral scholarship, Barkla returned to the University of Liverpool as Oliver Lodge Fellow for three years. He received Liverpool's D.Sc. in 1904; between 1905 and 1909 he was, successively, demonstrator, assistant lecturer, and special lecturer. In 1909 Barkla succeeded H. A. Wilson as Wheatstone professor of physics at King's College, London, and in 1913, only ten years after the publication of his first paper on X rays, Barkla was appointed professor of natural philosophy in the University of Edinburgh, where he remained until his death. He was elected a fellow of the Royal Society in 1912, appointed Bakerian lecturer for 1916, and in November 1918 was awarded the Nobel Prize for physics for 1917 for his discovery that each element emits a characteristic spectrum of X rays.

In 1907, after a special lectureship in advanced electricity had been created for him, Barkla married Mary Esther Cowell, elder daughter of the receiver-general of the Isle of Man. They had three sons and a daughter. Their residence was always in a rural setting. Barkla was a tall, solid, healthy man with delicate hands; he had a friendly, charming manner and a great fondness for children. His recreations were golf and singing. "Barkla," H. S. Allen records, "was a deeply religious man, and like his ancestors was a faithful adherent of the Methodist Church."

Barkla's first researches at the Cavendish were measurements, employing standing waves and Rutherford's magnetic detector, of the velocity of transmission of electromagnetic waves along wires of different materials and diameters, a question that J. J. Thomson and A. Sommerfeld, among others, had tackled theoretically. In his third year at Cambridge, he began investigations of the secondary X rays emitted by substances in the path of a beam of X radiation, a topic toward which virtually all his researches were to be directed in the following forty years. The first studies, completed at Liverpool and published in June 1903,[1] showed that the secondary radiation emitted by "all gases"—in fact, sulfur was the heaviest atom involved—was of the same absorbability (average wavelength) as that of the primary beam—not, as Georges Sagnac (1898) reported of secondary X rays from solids, of distinctly greater absorbability.

Demonstration of the existence of such an unmodified scattered radiation was strong support for the "ether pulse" theory. According to this theory, X rays are the narrow pulses of radiation that classical electromagnetic theory requires be emitted when the rapid motion of the electrons in the X-ray tube is arrested by impact upon the anode. The classical theory—in contrast with the subsequent quantum theory (Compton effect, 1923)—further requires that as this pulse passes through matter, the loosely bound electrons contained therein must undergo accelerations whose time dependence (frequency, wavelength) is that of the electric field of the pulse. Thus these electrons must, in turn, emit electromagnetic radiation with the same time dependence; the energy of this "scattered" radiation is drawn from the energy of the primary pulse. Barkla's discovery of this unmodified secondary radiation was most welcome, making it unnecessary to introduce extra hypotheses and analogical arguments (e.g., by J. J. Thomson[2]) to account for the theretofore accepted fact that the secondary radiation was softer (more absorbable, of greater average wavelength) than the primary.

Barkla also emphasized the not unexpected, but highly satisfactory, result that "this scattering is proportional to the mass of the atom." "This gives further support to the theory [the electron theory of matter] that the atoms of different substances are different systems of similar corpuscles, the number of which in the atom is proportional to its atomic weight."[3] The further possibility of using X-ray scattering for an experimental determination of this number was easily conceived when, in the autumn of 1903, J. J. Thomson published a calculation of the fractional energy loss of the X-ray beam per unit path length of the scattering substance due to this classical scattering process, obtaining $8\pi/3 \cdot Ne^4/m^2$, where e and m are the charge and mass of the electron, and N is the number of electrons per unit volume in the scattering substance.[4]

Barkla now measured the fractional energy loss due to scattering,[5] showing that, contrary to the general assumption,[6] this was not a negligible factor. From Thomson's formula there then came a value for N that Barkla described as in "close agreement" with "that calculated on the electronic theory of matter."[7] Actually, the results were rather embarrassing to this

theory which supposed atoms to be composed solely of electrons, for the number of electrons per atom (although Barkla did not express his results in these revealing terms) came out only about five times the atomic weight. Through these same measurements Barkla believed that he had confirmed a striking feature of Thomson's formula, namely, that the energy loss is independent of the wavelength (hardness) of the X rays.[8] As others soon emphasized, this result holds only in the long wavelength limit.

Meanwhile, Barkla had found another property of the secondary radiation which argued strongly that X rays were indeed transverse electromagnetic radiations. On the ether pulse hypothesis, the radiation scattered at 90° with respect to the primary beam should be plane polarized; the intensity of the radiation scattered from a plane polarized beam would be zero in the direction of the electric field of these polarized pulses and would reach a maximum in the plane perpendicular to this direction. R. L. Wilberforce suggested to Barkla that he look for this polarization by scattering the scattered radiation and observing the distribution of intensity of this—necessarily very weak—tertiary radiation in the plane perpendicular to the secondary radiation.

It was two years before Barkla was able to perform this difficult experiment,[9] but by March 1904 he had demonstrated the polarization in a much simpler way.[10] It occurred to him that the electrons impinging upon the anode of the X-ray tube should be more accelerated in the direction of their motion than perpendicular to it, and thus the radiation they would emit in the plane perpendicular to their motion would have a stronger electric field perpendicular to that plane than in it, i.e., the primary X-ray beam should be partially polarized. Rather than rotating his detector—an ionization chamber in which the density of ions was measured by the rate of leak of the charge on a gold-leaf electroscope—about the primary beam, Barkla rotated the plane of polarization of the beam by rotating the X-ray tube (and stream of cathode rays) about the beam as axis. A 15 percent variation of intensity was found.

Barkla became ever more firmly convinced of the ether pulse theory, for it had guided him to the discovery of new phenomena and had given his discoveries meaning and general significance. Understandably, he was aroused when in September 1907 W. H. Bragg published an attempt to construe the known facts about X rays, including Barkla's phenomenon of polarization, on the hypothesis that the rays are corpuscular, namely, a pair of oppositely charged particles with a net angular momentum.[11] Searching for a crucial experiment, Barkla hit upon the angular distribution of the scattered radiation with respect to the direction of the primary beam. Supposing the beam to be unpolarized, Barkla averaged the scattered radiation from electrons accelerated in all directions in the plane perpendicular to the beam—which, curiously, had not previously been done—and found $I_\theta = I_{\pi/2}(1 + \cos^2 \theta)$, the "Thomson" scattering distribution. He then verified the rather surprising conclusion that the intensity of the scattered radiation was a minimum at 90° with respect to the beam.[12] This "waist" in the distribution of the scattered radiation came to be generally regarded as one of the strongest pieces of evidence that X rays were electromagnetic radiations interacting with matter according to the Maxwell-Lorentz theory. The controversy with Bragg in the letter columns of *Nature* following Barkla's presentation of his "quite conclusive evidence in favor of the ether pulse theory"[13] attracted considerable attention and resulted in considerable personal stress for Barkla. Although Bragg had less right on his side, he outclassed Barkla as a strategist of controversy as well as of physical research.

It was by confining himself to the scattering by light elements that Barkla was able, at first, to deny that the secondary X radiation was softer than the primary, and thus to construe the emission of these secondary radiations as a classical scattering of the primary beam. In his polarization measurements of 1904 Barkla had found that the effect (i.e., variation of the intensity of the secondary radiation with the angle of rotation of the X-ray tube) tended to disappear as the atomic weight of the scatterer increased. This led him to recognize that a softened secondary radiation from heavier elements did indeed exist and moreover was emitted isotropically, thus with no relation to the direction or polarization of the primary beam. Barkla tried to fit these two leading characteristics (softer, isotropic) into the ether pulse theory by supposing that in heavier atoms the electrons were no longer free to follow the electric field of the pulse; rather, their motion was constrained by intra-atomic forces and neither the direction nor the time dependence of their accelerations was that of the electric field of the pulse.[14]

This physical picture did not, however, lead Barkla immediately to speculate that such secondary radiations may not be pulses but highly homogeneous wave trains, X-ray spectral lines. His first efforts were directed toward the intensity of this secondary radiation: ignorance of the peculiar constitution and conditions of excitation of these characteristic X rays almost inevitably led Barkla astray.[15] He then went off on a sidetrack, an attempt to determine the relative atomic weight of nickel through the dependence of the properties of secondary radiation upon atomic weight.[16] This was not a complete waste, for it raised the problem of precise discriminations of hardness—Barkla was beginning to fasten upon the hardness of the secondary radiation as characteristic of the element. At this point (early 1907) Barkla was joined by Charles A. Sadler, demonstrator in physics at Liverpool. Their first results, published that September, showed the homogeneity of this secondary radiation (the criterion being exponential decrease of intensity in traversing a homogeneous absorber).[17] During the next four years they followed up this fundamental discovery. Two groups, A and B (afterward labeled L and K, respectively), of homogeneous X rays from each heavy element were distinguished; and the condition (analogous to Stokes's law of fluorescence) was established that they could be excited only by exposing the element to X rays harder than its own characteristic X rays.[18] The natural and widespread—although not universal—assumption that these characteristic emissions were monochromatic X-ray "spectral lines" caused this work to be recognized immediately as "of the utmost importance."[19]

By 1911, after barely ten years of research on secondary X rays, Barkla had achieved an international reputation as the leading physicist in this field. Five years later he had lost this position and was rapidly isolating himself from the professional community he had led. To say this is not to dismiss him from further consideration. On the contrary, Barkla's later years are of great interest to the historian of science precisely because they offer a striking example of a man "passing out of physics"—departing so far from the accepted conceptual foundations and methodological canons of his field as to preclude acquiescence in its consensus. That Barkla had tended from the start to cite only his own work and to base theoretical conclusions solely on the phenomena he investigated himself may have helped prepare the way for the professional seclusion of his later years.

While it was evident to his contemporaries that Barkla was weak as a theorist, it was not at all evident to Barkla. By 1916 his sense of proportion had eroded so far that he devoted the larger part of his Bakerian lecture, "On X-rays and the Theory of Radiation,"[20] to his own theoretical considerations—an involved and confused attempt to express his results in terms of the quantum, energy levels, and energy balance in the excitation and emission of radiation by atoms. His conclusion that "absorption is *not* in quanta of primary radiation" was already scarcely defensible in 1916; it is an index of Barkla's increasing rigidity that he repeated himself, *verbatim,* in his Nobel lecture in 1920.[21]

After 1916 Barkla committed himself to the pursuit of a will-o'-the-wisp he called the "J-Phenomenon." Originally a radiation more penetrating (and thus, presumably, of shorter wavelength) than that of the K series, about 1920 the phenomenon was transferred to absorption, about 1925 to the conditions of excitation of the X-ray tube, and finally, about 1930, to a state of the absorbing-scattering substance. Barkla's reaction to the Compton effect—which seemed to threaten much of his own work, and all that he stood for—suggests that his J-Phenomenon served also to protect his personal conceptual world from external challenge. The J-Phenomenon shows that "a change in the activity (photoelectric action, ionization, absorption) of a radiation can take place without a change in the wave-length. . . . we are very sceptical as to whether a change in the diffraction angle in [Compton's] spectroscopic measurements really does correspond to a change of wave-length."[22]

NOTES

1. "Secondary Radiation from Gases Subject to X-Rays," in *Philosophical Magazine*, 6th ser., **5**, 685–698.
2. *The Conduction of Electricity Through Gases* (Cambridge, 1903), p. 270.
3. *Philosophical Magazine*, 6th ser., **5** (June 1903), 697.
4. Thomson, *op. cit.*, pp. 268–270. Due to an error in integration, which Barkla caught, Thomson found $4\pi/3$.
5. "Energy of Secondary Röntgen Radiation," in *Philosophical Magazine*, 6th ser., **7** (May 1904), 543–560.
6. E.g., E. Rutherford and R. K. McClung, *Philosophical Transactions of the Royal Society*, **A196** (1901), 38–39.
7. *Philosophical Magazine*, 6th ser., **7** (May 1904), 556–557.
8. This result, apparently at variance with the very notion of hardness, caused Thomson no difficulty because he did not think this process contributed appreciably to the absorption.
9. "Polarization in Secondary Röntgen Radiation," in *Proceedings of the Royal Society*, **A77** (Jan. 1906), 247–255.
10. "Polarization in Röntgen Rays," in *Nature*, **69** (17 Mar. 1904), 463.
11. W. H. Bragg, "On the Properties and Natures of Various Electric Radiations," in *Philosophical Magazine*, 6th ser., **14** (Sept. 1907), 429–449.
12. "The Nature of X-Rays," in *Nature*, **76** (31 Oct. 1907), 661–662.
13. *Ibid.*
14. "Secondary Röntgen Radiation," in *Nature*, **71** (9 Mar. 1905), 440; "Secondary Röntgen Radiation," in *Philosophical Magazine*, 6th ser., **11** (June 1906), 812–828.
15. "Secondary Röntgen Rays and Atomic Weight," in *Nature*, **73** (15 Feb. 1906), 365.
16. "The Atomic Weight of Nickel," in *Nature*, **75** (14 Feb. 1907), 368.
17. Barkla and Sadler, "Secondary X-Rays and the Atomic Weight of Nickel," in *Philosophical Magazine*, 6th ser., **14** (Sept. 1907), 408–422.
18. Barkla and Sadler, "The Absorption of Röntgen Rays," *ibid.*, **17** (May 1909), 739–760; Sadler, "Transformations of Röntgen Rays," *ibid.*, **18** (July 1909), 107–132; Barkla, "The Spectra of the Fluorescent Röntgen Radiations," *ibid.*, **22** (Sept. 1911), 396–412.
19. J. J. Thomson, "Röntgen Rays," in *Encyclopaedia Britannica* (11th ed., 1911).

20. *Philosophical Transactions of the Royal Society*, **A217** (1917), 315–360. Foreshadowed in "Problems of Radiation," in *Nature*, **94** (18 Feb. 1914), 671–672; "X-Ray Fluorescence and the Quantum Theory," *ibid.*, **95** (4 Mar. 1915), 7: "Indeed, the theory was forced upon the writer directly by the experimental results, and it was only afterwards that he was reminded of some similarity with the theory of Bohr. . . ."
21. "Characteristic Röntgen Radiation," in *Les Prix Nobel en 1914–1918* (Stockholm, 1920), Barkla's only publication in the five years 1918–1922.
22. Barkla and R. S. Khastgir, "The 'Modified Scattered' X-Radiation," in *Nature*, **117** (13 Feb. 1926), 228–229.

BIBLIOGRAPHY

An excellent chronological bibliography is appended to H. S. Allen, "Charles Glover Barkla, 1877–1944," in *Obituary Notices of Fellows of the Royal Society of London*, **5** (1947), 341–366. The only publications whose absence I have noted are Barkla's Nobel lecture (1920) and "'J'-Phenomenon and X-Ray Scattering," in *Nature*, **112** (12 Nov. 1923), 723–724. See also F. Horton, "Prof. C. G. Barkla, F.R.S.," *ibid.*, **154** (23 Dec. 1944), 790–791; Niels H. deV. Heathcote, *Nobel Prize Winners in Physics 1901–1950* (New York, 1953), pp. 141–150; but above all R. J. Stephenson, "The Scientific Career of Charles Glover Barkla," in *American Journal of Physics*, **35** (Feb. 1967), 140–152.

PAUL FORMAN

BARLOW, PETER (*b.* Norwich, England, October 1776; *d.* 1 March 1862), *mathematics, physics.*

Although he was self-educated, Barlow successfully competed for the position of assistant mathematics master at the Royal Military Academy, Woolwich, in 1801. While there he wrote mathematical articles for *The Ladies' Diary* and later for encyclopedias. He also published *An Elementary Investigation of the Theory of Numbers* (1811), *A New Mathematical and Philosophical Dictionary* (1814), and *New Mathematical Tables* (1814), later known as *Barlow's Tables*. The *Tables*, which gave the factors, squares, cubes, square roots, cube roots, reciprocals, and hyperbolic logarithms of all numbers from 1 to 10,000, was so accurate and was deemed so useful that a large part of it was reprinted and distributed by the Society for the Diffusion of Useful Knowledge (the last reprint was in 1947).

Barlow's reputation was established with the publication of his *Essay on the Strength and Stress of Timber* (1817), the result of experiments he conducted at the Woolwich dockyard and arsenal. He worked with Thomas Telford on the design of the Menai Strait suspension bridge and on the calculation of tides in the Thames as they would be affected by the removal of the old London Bridge. Barlow was made an honorary member of the Institution of Civil Engineers in 1820.

In 1819 Barlow became interested in the compass deviation caused by the iron in ships. He therefore investigated the action of terrestrial magnetism and conducted a series of experiments on the interaction of iron objects and compass needles. His results, published as *Essay on Magnetic Attractions* (1820), described a method of correcting ships' compasses by use of a small iron plate. For his discoveries in magnetism he was made a fellow of the Royal Society in 1823 and received the Copley Medal in 1825. He also received international recognition and several awards for his contribution to navigation. Barlow was also concerned with electromagnetism and unsuccessfully attempted to make an electric telegraph. Using a magnetic needle, he tried to produce a deflection by means of battery current sent through a length of wire, but the insulation failed.

Around 1827 Barlow became interested in the calculation for the curvature of achromatic object glasses, and in the course of his research he developed a telescope lens consisting of a colorless liquid between two pieces of glass. The "Barlow lens," a modification of this telescope lens, is a negative achromatic combination of flint glass and crown glass.

On several occasions in the 1830's and 1840's Barlow served as a royal commissioner of railroads. He was one of the first to conduct experiments and make calculations on the best shape for rails and the effect of gradients and curves.

BIBLIOGRAPHY

I. ORIGINAL WORKS. Forty-nine of Barlow's scientific papers are listed in the Royal Society's *Catalogue of Scientific Papers 1800–1863,* I, 182–184. He edited an edition of D. H. Mahan's *An Elementary Course of Civil Engineering* (Edinburgh–Dublin–London, 1845) and Thomas Tredgold's *Elementary Principles of Carpentry,* 5th ed. (London, 1870).

II. SECONDARY WORKS. Articles on Barlow are in *Dictionary of National Biography* and *Encyclopaedia Britannica* (1911). There is no full-length biography available.

HAROLD I. SHARLIN

BARLOW, WILLIAM (*b.* Islington, London, England, 8 August 1845; *d.* Great Stanmore, Middlesex, England, 28 February 1934), *crystallography.*

Barlow, a privately educated genius, was perhaps one of the last great amateurs in science. It was only when he was in his early thirties, however, after he attained the leisure afforded by an inheritance from his father, that he began to study and work in crystallography. His original view of the nature of crystalline matter united the mathematical system of symmetry, for which he wrote his own final chapter in the 1890's, with an anticipation of the new determinations of atomic structure that were to follow after 1910, and also with certain speculations on the relation of symmetry to structure that have not yet been fully elucidated.

The nineteenth century saw a succession of researches into the reason for the order exhibited by crystals. It was a search joined not only by mineralogists from C. S. Weiss to E. S. Fedorov, but also by mathematicians, notably Auguste Bravais, Louis Jordan, and Artur Schönflies.

Barlow's theories of the properties of crystals were based on the close packing of atoms. His first paper (1883) in some respects marked no great departure from earlier theories—some dating from the time of Kepler—in which a crystal was regarded as resembling an orderly stack of cannonballs. Barlow was probably unaware of these earlier theories, for by his time a considerable body of chemical theory emphasized the association of atoms into the molecular groupings of compounds. Nearly all of the two-element crystals that Barlow knew, principally the alkali halides, formed cubic crystals, whatever their chemical composition. As he stated in his introductory sentence of "Probable Nature of the Internal Symmetry of Crystals" (p. 186), this ". . . led him to believe that in the atom-groupings which modern chemistry reveals to us the several atoms occupy distinct portions of space and do not lose their individuality." Thus, by treating the atoms as individual spheres, Barlow was able to stack them in five arrangements[1] that he considered to be the only "very symmetrical" ones; these correspond to structures known today as body-centered cubic, simple cubic, face-centered cubic (cubic closest-packed), body-centered hexagonal (hexagonal closest-packed), and one kind of double hexagonal (but not closest-packed). Leonhard Sohncke criticized Barlow for including the last structure, claiming that it did not fulfill a strict definition of homogeneous symmetry around each sphere (the spheres in alternate layers are surrounded by different configurations). In this Sohncke was correct, but Barlow here showed for the first time that not all the atoms in a symmetrical structure need correspond to a single set of symmetrically equivalent points.

In his first paper, Barlow also recognized that body-centered cubic and simple cubic structures admit packing of spheres of two kinds (but of equal size), and are therefore suited to be structures of the alkali halides. Not until his definitive paper on structure, read before the Royal Society of Dublin in 1897, did Barlow explicitly display the variations possible in making the two kinds of spheres of two corresponding sizes. This was a correct guess for the structure of alkali halides, and through Barlow's collaboration with W. J. Pope, later professor of chemistry at Manchester, this structure was suggested by Pope to W. L. Bragg, who in 1913 confirmed it with the first structure determination by X-ray diffraction.

Barlow also suggested that face-centered cubic and body-centered hexagonal structures admitted of two kinds of spheres in the ratio 2:1, and ascribed the latter structure first to ice (wrong!) and then to calcite and aragonite only by writing the composition $CaC_2O_3 = Ca_2CO_3$ (worse!).[2] In this paper he also tentatively introduced the idea that while a structure might be nearly close-packed, slight changes of the groupings might be important for symmetry. His proposed structure for quartz was not borne out by X-ray diffraction, because quartz is not in the class of crystals that approximate close-packing. But he was on the right track when he used his hypothesis to explain the circular polarization in quartz, recognizing that a spiral of atoms could be left-handed or right-handed in similar structures. This was characteristic of Barlow's approach; he attempted to explain the widest range of crystal phenomena with his structures: cleavage, such polar properties as pyroelectricity, varieties of crystal growth, solid solution, and chemical reactivity. Most of those explanations were in principle correct, if not entirely original, and contributed to the unraveling of crystal physics in the ensuing thirty years.

Today it is clear that only a small fraction of crystalline species can be regarded as close-packed; most, but not all, are elements or simple compounds of dominantly ionic bonding. But many more crystals are nearly close-packed with interatomic distances and angles slightly deformed by covalent bonding. Barlow saw clearly that deformation of his "root forms" was necessary, and ascribed it to an unequal contraction of interatomic distances during crystallization from a more symmetrical but more loosely packed liquid. This led to the important concept of what is today known as pseudosymmetry, which Barlow used as a structural explanation of twinning, polymorphism, oriented overgrowth, and anomalous birefringence in crystals. Similar ideas were developed by E. S. Fedorov and T. V. Barker, between 1900 and 1930, into an elaborate system of "syngony" relating the morphology of crystals to similar but not equivalent angles. Although this system has had little direct use, the general basis set out by Barlow is still

fundamental to the understanding of these crystal properties.

In his first paper, it seems that Barlow was not aware of symmetry theory beyond the most elementary description of crystal systems. He was brought up short, apparently, by Sohncke's comments (1884), and a couple of years later took a course in crystallography from H. E. Armstrong and also began associations with H. A. Miers and W. J. Pope. In 1879 Sohncke published his "Entwickelung einer Theorie der Krystallstruktur," in which he expanded the work of Bravais to sixty-five infinite groups of equivalent points that might be possible in crystals. Since Sohncke confined himself to congruent equivalence, however, he could not explain the many known crystals with polar symmetry. Barlow realized the importance of this general mathematical approach, and in his usual independent and original fashion he set about fitting it into his models of structure. At the British Association for the Advancement of Science, on 26 August 1891, he ". . . concludes his paper by referring to some geometrical properties of the symmetrical systems of the crystallographer which he has discovered by an extension of the methods adopted by Bravais and by Sohncke, and which have greatly facilitated his work in finding symmetrical groupings to fit the forms and composition of a variety of different substances" (p. 582). For ten years, apparently unknown to Barlow, Fedorov had also been working (and publishing) on the problem of explaining crystal symmetry by systems of points, taking his departure from A. V. Gadolin and including both congruent and mirror-image (enantiomorphous) equivalence. In January 1891, Fedorov had published in Russian his complete derivation of the 230 space groups. Artur Schönflies, professor of applied mathematics at Göttingen, was also pursuing this problem independently, and following an exchange of letters with Fedorov, he published his version of the 230 space groups later in 1891 in the *Zeitschrift für Krystallographie*. Barlow did not get into print with his own derivation of the 230 space groups until 1894. In answering a criticism of his work that was published in the same journal in 1895, he complained that he did not have access to the original works of Schönflies and Fedorov.[3]

The differences in method by which the three authors derived the 230 space groups are no longer of much interest—both more elegant and simpler systems have since been published. Barlow was the last of the three to publish, and consequently has had little credit. In contrast with Fedorov and Schönflies, however, Barlow had as his goal nothing less than a total explanation of crystals in terms of structure.

His long paper on crystal structure appeared next, in 1897, and incorporated his work with space groups. He could not go further in solving the puzzle without one very important piece of information, however: the size, or at least the relative size, of the atoms. He had at one point assumed, on the model of Rudjer Bošković, that atoms were points with surrounding fields of attraction and repulsion; but the forms of these fields, or the corresponding sizes of the corresponding atoms, were illusory. For the next fifteen years, then, he worked with W. H. Pope in assembling data on solid-solution substitutions and the variation of the morphological axial ratios that should reflect variations in atomic size. While this approach was a valid one, it still contained a minimum ambiguity, which led Pope and Barlow to postulate that ionic volumes were proportional to valency. These papers were published in the *Journal of the Chemical Society* between 1906 and 1910; after only a few years, results from X-ray diffraction were sufficient to show that volumes of ions were, if anything, related to negative charge. But even in late (7 December) 1916 Barlow was still inclined to say, in a letter to G. F. Herbert Smith of the British Museum (Natural History), ". . . I regard the Paper in the Philosophical Magazine, so far as it relates to the Law of Valency Volumes, as a 'mare's nest' indeed feel confident that the x-ray results instead of weakening will greatly strengthen the case for the Law of Valency Volumes" (letter in files of the Mineralogical Laboratory).

Barlow was elected to the Royal Society in 1908 and was president of the Mineralogical Society in 1915–1918. His career spanned a critical stage in the development of crystallography. His self-educated guesses were sometimes off the mark, but often clear and to the point, and always provocative. In his obituary of Barlow, Pope says:

> Although X-ray analysis has increased our knowledge of crystal structure in an astounding way and has proved a most useful tool, it has not led to a mechanical theory of crystal structure; it reveals the atomic arrangement but offers no reason why the component atoms seem to be closely packed in some crystalline structures and often loosely in others. The required mechanical theory of crystal structure may be found in some kind of generalisation of Barlow's conception of equilibrium conditions [*Journal of the Chemical Society,* p. 1330].

NOTES

1. A sixth close-packed structure was added in his second paper (1886).

2. Corrected in his second paper, where packing of three kinds of atoms (still all the same size) was discussed.
3. "Meine einzige Quelle zur Zeit der Abfassung meiner Abhandlung war der Auszug von Fedorow's Arbeit in dieser *Zeitschr.* **20,** 25, und dieser bot mit durch seine Kürze gewisse Schwierigkeiten dar. Was Schoenflies' Darstellung betrifft, so konnte ich sie damals nur aus zweiter Hand erhalten, und hierdurch ist es veranlasst, dass ich Demselben einen Ausdruck zuschreib, welchen er nicht gebraucht hat. . . ." Yet Barlow's 1894 paper quotes Schönflies' book, citing page numbers, as well as Fedorov's discussion of Schönflies, which appeared in *Zeitschrift für Krystallographie,* **20** (1892), 25–75.

BIBLIOGRAPHY

I. ORIGINAL WORKS. Barlow's most important publications appeared in journals. Inasmuch as a proper bibliography has never been published, the main papers are listed here, in three groups.

(1) Papers on crystal structure and physical properties: The most important is "A Mechanical Cause of Homogeneity of Structure and Symmetry Geometrically Investigated; With Special Application to Crystals and to Chemical Combination," in *Scientific Proceedings of the Royal Society of Dublin,* **8** (1897), 527–690, still in print in 1958. The earlier papers are "Probable Nature of the Internal Symmetry of Crystals," in *Nature,* **29** (1883–1884), 186–188, 205–207, 404; "A Theory of the Connection Between the Crystal Form and the Atom Composition of Chemical Compounds," in *Chemical News,* **53** (1886), 3–6, 16–19, abstracted in *Report of the British Association for the Advancement of Science* (1885), 983–984; "On Atomgrouping in Crystals," *ibid.* (1890), 754–755; and "On the Connection Between the Crystal Form and the Chemical Composition of Bodies. The Symmetry of Crystals Accounted for by the Application of Boscovich's Theory of Atoms to the Atoms of the Chemist," *ibid.,* sec. A (1891), 581–582.

(2) Papers on space groups and other aspects of symmetry: The principal work is "Ueber die geometrischen Eigenschaften homogener starrer Structuren und ihre Anwendung auf Krystalle," in *Zeitschrift für Krystallographie,* **23** (1894), 1–63. Other discussions are "The Relation Between the Morphological Symmetry and the Optical Symmetry of Crystals," in *Report of the British Association for the Advancement of Science* (1895), 617–619; "The Relations of Circular Polarization, as Occurring Both in the Amorphous and Crystalline States, to the Symmetry and Partitioning of Homogeneous Structures, i.e., of Crystals," in *Philosophical Magazine,* **43** (1897), 110–117; "Nachtrag zu den Tabellen homogener Structuren und Bemerkungen zu E. von Fedorow's Abhandlung über regelmassige Punktsysteme," in *Zeitschrift für Krystallographie,* **25** (1896), 86–91; "On Homogeneous Structures and the Symmetrical Partitioning of Them, With Application to Crystals," in *Mineralogical Magazine,* **11** (1896), 119–136; and "Partitioning of Space Into Enantiomorphous Polyhedra," in *Philosophical Magazine,* **46** (1923), 930–956.

In collaboration with H. A. Miers and G. F. H. Smith, Barlow published a critical-historical review of the symmetry and structure of crystals, "The Structure of Crystals: Part I. Report on the Development of the Geometrical Theories of Crystal Structure, 1666–1901," in *British Association for the Advancement of Science, Glasgow Meeting, Sec. C* (1902). Part II was to deal with what Barlow calls the mechanical theory of structure, but it was never prepared. The modern reader will need a guide to the diverse nomenclature used by the various authors dealing with space groups at this time. A concordance is H. Hilton, "A Comparison of Various Notations Employed in 'Theories of Crystal Structure,'" in *Philosophical Magazine*, 6th ser., **3** (1902), 203–212; this includes the Schönflies notation, which in turn may be compared with the Hermann-Mauguin notation in the modern *International Tables for X-ray Crystallography*, I (Birmingham, 1952), 545.

(3) Papers on the valency-volume theory: With W. J. Pope, Barlow wrote "A Development of the Atomic Theory Which Correlates Chemical and Crystalline Structure and Leads to a Demonstration of the Nature of Valency," in *Journal of the Chemical Society*, **89** (1906), 1675–1774, and, with other titles, **91** (1907), 1150–1214; **93** (1908), 1528; **97** (1910), 2308–2388. By himself he wrote "Crystallographic Relations of Allied Substances Traced by Means of the Law of Valency Volumes," in *Mineralogical Magazine*, **13** (1916), 314–323.

Barlow also published a book, *New Theories of Matter and of Force* (London, 1885), but it apparently did not have much circulation or impact, for it was never cited, even by Barlow. It detailed his speculations on the nature of the ether, chemical elements, electricity, and other subjects; these preceded his work in crystallography but were not particularly pertinent to it.

The British Museum (Natural History) has several models of crystal structure made by Barlow, and a few of his letters, but otherwise his papers and MSS do not appear to have been preserved.

II. SECONDARY LITERATURE. Commentaries on specific papers of Barlow's were published by Sohncke, Lord Kelvin, Sollas, and Federov, among others. He is mentioned briefly in most histories of crystallography. Obituary notices are W. J. Pope, in *Journal of the Chemical Society* (1935), 1328–1330; in *Nature,* **133** (1934), 637–638; and in *Obituary Notices of Fellows of the Royal Society,* **1** (1935), 367–370, with portrait; G. F. H. Smith, in *Quarterly Journal of the Geological Society of London,* **91** (1935), lxxxv–lxxxvi; and L. J. Spencer, in *Mineralogical Magazine,* **24** (1936), 277–279. See also G. T. Moody and W. Mills's obituary of W. J. Pope, in *Journal of the Chemical Society* (1940), 697–715.

WILLIAM T. HOLSER

BARNARD, EDWARD EMERSON (*b.* Nashville, Tennessee, 16 December 1857; *d.* Williams Bay, Wisconsin, 6 February 1923), *astronomy.*

The second son of Reuben and Elizabeth Jane Haywood Barnard, Edward was born after the death of his father. He had only two months of formal schooling. In 1866, when not quite nine years old, he was sent to work in a portrait studio to help support his impoverished family. During the seventeen years he worked in this studio, Barnard became familiar with photography, which was gradually replacing painting as a portrait medium and which he was to exploit fully in later astronomical activity. Quite independently he developed a strong interest in astronomy during these years and made a name for himself as a comet seeker of extraordinary zeal and skill. In 1881 he married Rhoda Calvert, a sister of two English artists employed in the same portrait studio.

From 1883 to 1887 Barnard was associated with Vanderbilt University as both student and instructor. There he benefited from formal training, in a somewhat irregular curriculum dictated by the peculiar combination of his lack of previous schooling and the special requirements necessary for him to develop his astronomical potential. Since this training did not constitute a regular course of studies, he received no degree, although six years after leaving the university, he was given the D.Sc. in recognition of his many scientific contributions—particularly his brilliant discovery of Jupiter's fifth satellite—and his earlier studies. Barnard's personal life was marked by great modesty, unselfishness, and tolerance, no doubt engendered by his own struggle with distress and adversity. He was universally respected and loved, for he formed warm and enduring friendships. In his scientific writings he demonstrated the same tolerance and understanding, giving due credit to the work of others, even when he did not agree with them.

It can safely be said in retrospect that Barnard was the foremost observational astronomer of his time, ranking with Sir William Herschel in the range of his contributions and in the peculiar intuitive genius and native instinct that formal training may discipline and supplement, but never supplant. Hardly a branch of astronomy was not enriched by his attention, and his accomplishments in any one field would have sufficed for wide recognition. Barnard was primarily an observer, making use of his insatiable curiosity, keen perception, and sound judgment; his vision and his intimate familiarity with the sky are legendary. Ever impatient to catch any moment of clear sky and irate when clouds interfered, he was infinitely patient at the most demanding, tedious, or uncomfortable observational tasks. He was not a theorist, but his discoveries and subsequent studies of them were marked by original and imaginative interpretation.

Throughout his scientific career, Barnard was honored by learned societies and was the recipient of numerous awards and medals, including the Lalande gold medal of the French Academy of Sciences (1892), the Arago gold medal of the French Academy of Sciences (1893), the Gold Medal of the Royal Astronomical Society (1897), the Janssen gold medal of the French Academy of Sciences (1900), the Janssen Prize of the French Astronomical Society (1906), and the Bruce gold medal of the Astronomical Society of the Pacific (1917). He was vice-president of the American Association for the Advancement of Science (1898), a foreign associate of the Royal Astronomical Society, a member of the American Academy of Arts and Sciences, director of the B. A. Gould Fund of the National Academy of Sciences, and a member of the American Philosophical Society. In addition, Barnard was thrice awarded the Donohoe comet medal of the Astronomical Society of the Pacific in 1901 and 1902. Previously he had been awarded this medal for a comet discovery in 1889, but he declined it, pointing out that the comet was a rediscovery of a known comet, d'Arrest's comet. On five occasions he received a $200 prize given by H. H. Warner, of Rochester, New York (a manufacturer of patent medicine who endowed the Warner Observatory in Rochester) for each discovery of a new comet by an American observer. These cash prizes, coming at a crucial stage in his very early career, did much to encourage Barnard.

Barnard's scientific career may be conveniently broken into four periods: before 1883, an enthusiastic amateur working with his own five-inch telescope; 1883 to 1887, at Vanderbilt University, using the six-inch telescope; 1888 to 1895, at the Lick Observatory; and 1895 to 1923, at the Yerkes Observatory.

It is impossible to fix any date for Barnard's first astronomical experience, but it is clear that even as a child he was aware of and fascinated by the sky. His earliest recollections were recorded in an article he wrote for the *Christian Advocate* (Nashville, Tennessee, 5 July 1907, pp. 23–28), in which he described his childhood familiarity with the stars, their patterns in the sky, and their seasonal disappearance and reappearance. It is of interest, although of no scientific importance, that as a child Barnard unknowingly discovered the equation of time (the difference between the position of the actual sun and of a fictitious sun moving uniformly across the sky). His account of this discovery is to be found in the same *Christian Advocate* article referred to above.

In 1876, as Barnard's attention was increasingly focused on astronomy, he purchased a five-inch telescope for $380, which was about two-thirds of his annual income. He spent much of his time between 1876 and 1880 acquainting and amusing himself with the heavens, observing Jupiter's satellites and other planetary phenomena, keeping meticulous notes, and developing his ability to draw telescopic images. His first published notes concern the transit of Mercury of 6 May 1878, for which he set up his five-inch telescope at the state capitol, not far from the portrait studio where he worked.

Of considerable significance were his drawings of Jupiter, for Barnard carried out a systematic study of its surface features and their ever-changing forms in late 1879 and 1880. An excellent summary of this early work, together with forty-five of his drawings, appeared later in an article in *Publications of the Astronomical Society of the Pacific* (1889). In these studies he observed the Great Red Spot, hitherto unknown to him, the equatorial white spot, and the belt features, and noted a wealth of detail and change.

It is reported that he planned a small book on Mars around 1880, but it is doubtful that the book ever materialized. By 1883 he was a regular contributor to the local biweekly, *Artisan,* conducting a column devoted to astronomical events.

In 1877, upon being advised rather brusquely by Simon Newcomb that he could not expect to contribute much to astronomy without a knowledge of mathematics, unless it were the discovery of comets, Barnard directed himself toward both goals. He hired tutors and he sought comets. His search was rewarded by two comet discoveries: 1881 VI on 17 September 1881, and 1882 III on 13 September 1882. Actually, he discovered one on 12 May 1881 (verified again the following night), but since he was not then acquainted with the formal means of announcing comet discoveries, this comet was never officially named or recognized. Although it was not observed by any others, no comet authority has ever doubted the validity of the discovery. Another officially unrecognized discovery occurred on 14 October 1882, when Barnard found a group of about a dozen comets, probably fragments of the great comet of 1882 (1882 II). He secured positions of about seven or eight of these before dawn interfered with his work, and he communicated them, as before, to the Warner Observatory. But they were not officially announced by that office, probably on the assumption that the recipient of two recent Warner prizes had suddenly gone demented and wished to acquire a fortune, to paraphrase Barnard's own words.

After entering Vanderbilt University, Barnard continued his intensive observing with both the university's six-inch and his own five-inch telescopes, for his studies evidently constituted no greater handicap to this activity than had his previous full-time employment. Seven new comet discoveries during this period are credited to him:

Discovery Date	Comet
16 July 1884	1884 II
7 July 1885	1885 II
3 December 1885	1886 II
4 October 1886	1886 IX
23 January 1887	1886 VIII
15 February 1887	1887 III
12 May 1887	1887 IV

For the first three discoveries he received Warner prizes, after which the award was discontinued. He also discovered, one day too late but quite independently, comet 1885 V, on 27 December 1885; W. R. Brooks, another famous comet observer, had discovered it the previous night.

Comet seekers frequently discover nebulae and, indeed, pay attention to them because they look very like comets in the telescope. Barnard discovered his share of new nebulae at this time. In later years his work with nebulae was made more effective by photography.

Barnard was an independent discoverer of the *Gegenschein* in late 1883, and from observations of this difficult phenomenon, carried on over ensuing years, he was able to identify its true character and position (1918).

On the night of 5 November 1883 Barnard discovered the duplicity of the star β' Capricorni in a remarkable and unprecedented fashion. In an occultation of this star by the moon, the disappearance of the starlight, which as a rule is virtually instantaneous, occurred in an interrupted fashion: "First about nine-tenths of the light instantly disappeared, and for a space of one second there remained in its place a minute point of light, estimated of the tenth magnitude. This also instantly disappeared" (*Astronomische Nachtrichten*, **108** [1884], 369–372). The noninstantaneous occultation was witnessed by at least one other astronomer, but Barnard alone gave the correct interpretation: the star was a close and very unequal double. This interpretation was ultimately confirmed by S. W. Burnham, who was able to measure the pair, nearly a year later, with the 18 1/2-inch Dearborn refractor.

By 1887, Barnard's work with the Vanderbilt six-inch telescope and his own five-inch telescope became so widely known through his numerous contributions to the principal astronomical journals that he was invited to join a group of gifted and distinguished astronomers in staffing the new Lick Observatory being erected on Mount Hamilton, near San Jose, California.

In September 1887 Barnard went to California to take up the position offered him at the Lick Observatory. Since the observatory was not completed until the following summer, Barnard found himself stranded without work or income. He served as a clerk in a San Francisco lawyer's office and spent many frustrating months unable to observe. In June 1888 the operations of the Lick Observatory were begun, and after only a year's work Barnard had several significant accomplishments: four new comets—1888 V, 1889 I, 1889 II, and 1889 III—setting a record for rapidity of discovery; several new nebulae; the first photographs of the Milky Way; and further planetary observations. Among the latter was the observation of an eclipse of one of Saturn's moons, Iapetus, by Saturn's ring, during which he noticed that the illumination of Iapetus continued, thus demonstrating the discontinuous and particulate nature of the ring. Curiously he was the sole astronomer to observe or pay attention to this event.

Of great importance was the beginning Barnard made in photographing the Milky Way. It can fairly be said that, although photography had been used in astronomy to a limited and somewhat experimental extent, it was not until Barnard's wholesale use of it that the technique became a vital and spectacular part of regular astronomical observing.

His initial labors in this area were not easy, because funds for equipment were scarce, and he was the junior member under a somewhat crusty and autocratic director, E. S. Holden. Barnard was obliged to use a small telescopic camera, contrived from a 2 1/2-inch portrait lens with a focal length of thirty-one inches, initially strapped to the side of a 6 1/2-inch telescope for want of a suitable mounting and guiding arrangement. With so small a telescope, exposures were necessarily very long; moreover, photographic materials were still rather primitive and insensitive. Nevertheless, Barnard's Milky Way photographs revealed a wealth of both bright and dark nebulae, and star-clouds hitherto unknown. The long exposures (up to six hours) were made with extreme difficulty and required great patience, for the guiding telescopes were without illuminated reticles. He was obliged to use fine iron wires for cross hairs, and to throw the image of a bright star out of focus, maintaining equal intensity in all four quadrants separated by the wires' silhouette. Many of these remarkable photographs of the Milky Way and clusters, as well as of comets, were later assembled into Volume **11** of the *Publications of the Lick Observatory*.

Before leaving the Lick Observatory, Barnard discovered three more comets—1891 I, 1891 IV, and 1892 V—the latter being the first to be discovered photographically. Barnard also observed innumerable other comets, both recent discoveries by other observers and returns of previously known objects. He turned his attention more and more to detailed photographic studies of comets, and after 1892 he spent little time in actual comet seeking. His collection of thousands of expertly guided photographs constitutes a vast store of information on comet behavior and tail structure, a collection still used and referred to by cometary scholars.

By far his most sensational discovery at the Lick Observatory was that of Jupiter's fifth satellite, which is closer to the parent planet than the Galilean satellites and is very much fainter. Barnard, the junior astronomer, had never been given regular use of the thirty-six-inch great refractor until the summer of 1892, when he prevailed upon the director to permit him to use it one night per week. Before many weeks had passed, he noticed, while examining the vicinity of Jupiter, an object exceedingly difficult to see, and recognized from its motion with the planet that it could not be a star. This occurred on 9 September 1892. While he was trying to measure its position relative to the third satellite and the planet, it became lost in the glare of the planet. Barnard suspected that it was an unrecognized satellite but felt he should verify his discovery before making any announcement. He was given the use of the great refractor on the following night, through the kindness of his colleague Schaeberle, when he secured further measures of the new satellite's position. A telegram announcing the fifth satellite was sent out by the director the following morning, electrifying the scientific world. (The wording of the original telegram is not completely clear. A. A. Common, president of the Royal Astronomical Society, reports that Barnard's name was not mentioned in the first telegram received there; E. S. Holden has published what he claims to be the correct wording, in which Barnard's name figures twice.)

Barnard's extraordinary vision was responsible for other important, if less spectacular, discoveries. Once he was shown an extremely faint star within the trapezium in Orion by his colleague S. W. Burnham, another observer of remarkable vision, who asserted that no telescope smaller than the thirty-six-inch great refractor could show it. Thereupon Barnard pointed out an even fainter star near it, as well as a still fainter double star. Likewise, he was able to discover, visually, faint nebulae close to bright stars, such as the very close planetary nebula near Merope and the new expanding nebula that surrounded Nova Aurigae a few months after its outburst. His micrometric meas-

ures of the diameters and dimensions of planets, satellites, and asteroids were highly reliable, and later verification of them has often taxed the most refined techniques.

Although Barnard found his first fully professional experience at the Lick Observatory stimulating and rewarding, it is no secret that he felt unduly constrained by Holden's autocratic policies, and he was easily attracted away from the Lick Observatory to join Hale's promising group at the University of Chicago, then erecting the Yerkes Observatory in nearby Wisconsin. He joined the University of Chicago in October 1895 as professor of practical astronomy, with complete freedom from teaching, administrative, and editorial duties. For almost two years, during which there were various delays in completing the new observatory, his observing activity was distinctly curtailed, although he had the use of the modest Kenwood Observatory in Chicago.

His subsequent work at the Yerkes Observatory, although extensive, was less spectacular than that of earlier years. It was marked in part by personal disappointment, brought about, oddly enough, by his failure to take full advantage of photography in the study of stellar motions. He invested immense labor in micrometric measures of parallax and of stellar positions in clusters, anticipating that stellar motions would soon reveal themselves through systematic repetition of measures of this type. His colleagues were unable to persuade him that comparison of photographic plates, made at long intervals, could achieve more accurate results with far greater economy of effort. He did, however, draw the correct inference from the failure of his measures, made at ten-year and even twenty-year intervals, to reveal internal motions: evidently the clusters were much farther away and were much larger than had been hitherto assumed.

Much of Barnard's other work at Yerkes was more fruitful: studies and discovery (often visually) of variable stars, novae, double stars, and faint satellites; observations of Eros to determine the basic astronomical distance, the astronomical unit; continuation of his monumental studies of the forms of comet tails; extension of his Milky Way photography with the Bruce telescope, which was far superior to the equipment he employed earlier; ultimate recognition of dark nebulae as obscuring matter rather than voids in stellar distribution; planetary photography and drawing; aurorae; cometary positions; and solar and lunar eclipses.

Barnard was particularly mindful of his duty to carry out studies on the fainter objects, beyond the grasp of smaller telescopes, and to secure comet positions at very great distances. It is worth noting that he never agreed with Lowell's views about Mars. Barnard, with his extraordinary vision and skill, and with superior equipment at his command, never did see the surface markings commonly referred to as canals.

Among the unusual things Barnard did was to note gross spectral changes in novae, which were too faint to observe with a spectroscope, but which he detected through the change in focus of their light. He discovered a star having (until 1968) the largest known proper motion, 10 seconds of arc per year; it is now known as Barnard's star.

Barnard never had any students or protégés to whom he could pass on his enormous store of experience. Having missed the teacher-pupil and father-son relationships in his own youth, he could not see why everyone should not be self-made. He was, in fact, quite impatient with students and young assistants. His colleague E. B. Frost, director of Yerkes Observatory for many years, stated: "Mr. Barnard could not bring himself to lose time at the telescope in having a pupil take part in measurements, which he could himself make so much better, and he begrudged the possible loss, in quality, of a photograph if someone less skilled than himself took some part in the guiding" (*Astrophysical Journal,* 58 [1923], 33). Nevertheless, Barnard took much time in advising students and writing to schoolboys who expressed interest in becoming astronomers. His sympathetic encouragement brought several into professional astronomy.

In 1914 Barnard was stricken with diabetes and for a year was obliged to curtail his heavy schedule of observing. Upon regaining his strength, he resumed observing as vigorously as ever. It is recorded that he observed during virtually every clear hour, and when one telescope was in use by another observer, he would be busy at another.

Barnard had no children, and after his wife died in 1921, he became depressed and lonely, and lost some of his former drive. He was taken ill in late December 1922 and, although his colleagues and doctors expected recovery, he died on 6 February 1923. His last telescopic observations were made on 16 and 22 December 1922, but even from his death-bed he observed visually the 13 January 1923 occultation of Venus by the moon.

Barnard left a substantial amount of unpublished material. The more significant works were completed by his assistant and niece, Mary Calvert, and his associates E. B. Frost and G. Van Biesebroeck. A manuscript, almost complete, for a treatise on Mars was not published, and remains in the Barnard collection at Vanderbilt University.

BIBLIOGRAPHY

I. Original Works. The most complete bibliography of Barnard's publications, compiled by Mary Calvert, is appended to E. B. Frost's biographical sketch of him (see below). Among his publications referred to in this article are "Observations of Jupiter With a Five-inch Refractor, During the Years 1879–1886," in *Publications of the Astronomical Society of the Pacific,* 1 (1889), 89–111; "The Gegenschein and Its Possible Origin," in *Popular Astronomy,* 27 (1918), 109–112; "Recollections of an Astronomer," in *Christian Advocate* (5 July 1907), pp. 23–28; "Duplicity of β' Capricorni," in *Astronomische Nachtrichten,* 108 (1884), 369–372; "Photographs of the Milky Way and of Comets," in *Publications of the Lick Observatory,* 11 (1913), 1–560.

II. Secondary Literature. While Barnard was still at the Lick Observatory, his close friend and colleague S. W. Burnham wrote three articles describing his life and career; they appeared in *Popular Astronomy,* 1 (1894), 193–195, 341–345, 441–447. Toward the close of Barnard's career, J. T. McGill published an account of Barnard's work in three issues of the *Vanderbilt Alumnus,* 7 (1922), 70–73, 101–103, 183–186; these articles were approved and corrected by Barnard himself. Later they were assembled and reprinted, with a supplementary note, in *Journal of the Tennessee Academy of Science,* 3, no. 1 (1928), 32–56, which is the "Edward Emerson Barnard Memorial Number" and is devoted entirely to reminiscences of and tributes to Barnard by many of his friends and colleagues. After Barnard's death a number of his colleagues wrote biographical sketches and reviews of his remarkable career; the most comprehensive is that by E. B. Frost, "Biographical Memoir on Edward Emerson Barnard," in *Memoirs of the National Academy,* 21, no. 14 (1926), 1–23. Frost's article is also published, without bibliography, in *Astrophysical Journal,* 58 (1923), 1–35. Others are by Philip Fox, in *Popular Astronomy,* 31 (1923), 195–200; R. G. Aitken, in *Publications of the Astronomical Society of the Pacific,* 35 (1923), 87–94; J. A. Parkhurst, in *Journal of the Royal Astronomical Society of Canada,* 17 (1923), 97–103; and W. F. Denning, in *Monthly Notices of the Royal Astronomical Society,* 84 (1924), 221–225. A brief account of Barnard's early life in Nashville is in an article by Robert Hardie, in *Leaflets of the Astronomical Society of the Pacific,* nos. 415 and 416 (1964). A well-known astronomical hoax was perpetrated on Barnard and is described by H. D. Curtis in *Popular Astronomy,* 46 (1938), 71–75; and by A. H. Joy, in *Leaflets of the Astronomical Society of the Pacific,* no. 311 (1955). A. A. Commons' account of the announcement of the discovery of Jupiter's fifth satellite is in *Popular Astronomy,* 5 (1887), 2; E. S. Holden's is in *Publications of the Astronomical Society of the Pacific,* 4 (1892), 199.

Robert H. Hardie

BAROCIUS, FRANCISCUS, also known as **Francesco Barozzi** (*b.* Candia, Crete, 9 August 1537; *d.* Venice, Italy, 23 November 1604), *mathematics, astronomy.*

A Venetian patrician, Barocius received a humanistic education and achieved an admirable command of Greek and Latin. He studied at the University of Padua and, according to his own account, lectured there about 1559 on the *Sphere* of Sacrobosco. Barocius' edition of Proclus' commentary on the first book of Euclid's *Elements* was the first important translation of this work, for it was based on better manuscripts than previous efforts had been. The translation, published at Venice in 1560, was completed by Barocius at the age of twenty-two.

In 1572 he brought out a Latin translation of Hero's book on war machines, and in 1588 he completed his corrections, unpublished to this day, of a manuscript copy of Federicus Commandinus' translation of Pappus' *Collectio.* His translation of the Archimedean *De dimensionibus* also is still in manuscript. Barocius wrote in Italian on *rythmomachia* (1572), a number game that he attributed to Pythagoras but that appears to go back only to the eleventh century. The book is based on Boissière's work on the same subject (Paris, 1556). Barocius composed a Latin treatise on thirteen ways to draw two parallel lines in a plane (1572) and an elementary *Cosmographia* (1585), based on the *Sphere* of Sacrobosco and containing chapters on meteorology and physical geography. Barocius noted eighty-four errors in Sacrobosco's work, largely, according to Thorndike, matters of definition and order of treatment. The "errors" did not include the geocentric theory, and a marginal comment condemned as false the opinion of Aristarchus and Copernicus.

Barocius had a stormy career. In 1587 he was brought before the Inquisition on charges of sorcery, and more particularly of having caused a torrential rainstorm in Crete. He was sentenced to provide silver crosses at a cost of 100 ducats and condemned to remain in prison at the pleasure of the Holy Office (apparently a suspended sentence). After the trial the only work that he published was another edition of the *Cosmographia* (1598).

BIBLIOGRAPHY

I. ORIGINAL WORKS. Works by Barocius include *Opusculum, in quo una oratio, & duas questiones: Altera de certitudine & altera de medietate mathematicarum continentur* (Padua, 1560); *Procli Diadochi in primum Euclidis elementorum librum commentariorum libri IIII a Francisco Barocio . . .* (Padua, 1560); *Commentarius in locum Platonis obscurissimum, & hactenus a nemine recte expositum in principio dialogi octaui de Rep. ubi sermo habetur de numero geometrico, de quo prouerbium est, quod numero Platonis nihil obscurius* (Bologna, 1566); *Heronis mechanici liber de machinis bellicus, necnon liber de geodesia a Francisco Barocio . . . Latinitate donati* (Venice, 1572); *Il nobilissimo et antiquissimo givoco Pythagoreo nominato rythmomachia, cioe battaglia di consonanze di numeri, in lingua volgare a modo di parafresi composto* (Venice, 1572); *Cosmographia in quattuor libros distributa* (Venice, 1585, 1598; Italian trans., 1607); *Admirandum illud geometricum problema tredecim modis demonstratum, quod docet duas lineas in eodem plano designare, quae numquam invicem coincidant, etiam si in infinitum protahantur* (Venice, 1586). His *Descrittione dell'isola di Creta* was edited by Giuseppe Nicoletti (Venice, 1898).

Manuscripts include his corrections of Federicus Commandinus' translation of Pappus' *Collectio* (BN MS Lat. 7222$^{1-2}$) in the Bibliothèque Nationale and two manuscripts at Trinity College in Dublin: *Savasordae Judaei liber de arcis, infinitis erroribus expurgatis atque scholis et annotationibus illustratus* and *Archimedis liber de dimensionibus a Franc. Barocio restauratus.*

II. SECONDARY LITERATURE. Works concerning Barocius are B. Boncompagni, "Intorno alla vita ed ai labori de Francesco Barozzi," in *Bullettino di bibliographia e di storia delle scienze matematiche e fisiche,* **17** (1884), 795–848; Lynn Thorndike, *A History of Magic and Experimental Science,* VI (New York, 1941), 25, 47, 154–155, 199; Athanasius Pryor Treweek, "Pappus of Alexandria. The Manuscript Tradition of the *Collectio mathematica,*" in *Scriptorium,* **11,** no. 2 (1957), 195–233; Paul Ver Eecke, ed. and trans., *Proclus de Lycie, les commentaires sur le premier livre des Éléments d'Euclide* (Bruges, 1948), pp. xxi ff.; and the entry in *Dizionario biografico degli italiani,* VI (1964), 495–499.

MARJORIE NICE BOYER

BARRANDE, JOACHIM (*b.* Sangues, Haute-Loire, France, 11 August 1799; *d.* Frohsdorf, Austria, 5 October 1883), *paleontology, stratigraphy.*

Barrande was educated in Paris at the École Polytechnique and the École des Ponts et Chaussées. He became tutor to the grandson of Charles X and left France with the king's family after the July Revolution of 1830. The exiled royal family traveled to England and Scotland, then temporarily settled in Prague in 1832. When the family later moved to Görz (now Gorizia, Italy), Barrande remained in Prague, where he took a position as engineer for the construction of a horse-drawn railway. While surveying the proposed route, he became interested in the local fossils, and the acquisition of fossils and the examination of the strata near Prague became his chief occupation. When Murchison's *Silurian System* appeared

(1839), Barrande recognized the similarity between the rocks of central Bohemia and those Murchison described in Britain.

From 1840 to his death Barrande collected, described, and drew the fossils of the central Bohemian basin—this area has been called the Barrandian ever since. The strata of this basin are Proterozoic–early Paleozoic in age. At that time "Silurian" might be applied to strata that today are in the Cambrian, Ordovician, Silurian, or Devonian system. The results formed the outstanding monograph *Système silurien du centre de la Bohême* (Prague, 1852–1902), which appeared in eight parts forming thirty quarto volumes. Because this work is so comprehensive, its drawings so accurate, and its descriptions so fine, it is still used as a reference book by paleontologists. Barrande's enormous collection, with all his scientific manuscripts and his library, was given to the Prague Museum at his death. His will also provided 10,000 florins to defray the costs of the remaining volumes of the *Système silurien,* which the museum was to publish from the extensive notes he left.

The *Système silurien* would have been a significant contribution to the geology of the mid-nineteenth century if it had offered no more than the naming and analysis of over 4,000 new fossil species. Yet these investigations had even greater impact on geological thought. In 1851 Charles Lyell pointed out in the *Quarterly Journal of the Geological Society of London* (**7**, xxiii), on the basis of some of Barrande's preliminary studies:

> . . . it is not the least interesting circumstance attending these discoveries, to learn that all these fossils were obtained from a superficial area, not more extensive than one-sixtieth part of the Adriatic; and they certainly show that the Silurian Fauna was not only as rich, but as much influenced by geographical conditions, or as far from being uniform throughout the globe, as that of any subsequent era.

Barrande's meticulous efforts distinguished metamorphosis in several species of trilobites, and he even identified embryonic states. He described *Sao hirsuta,* of which twenty naturally occurring forms had previously been identified as eighteen species in ten genera.

Barrande never abandoned the Cuvierian conception of the constancy of species, which he acquired during his early training in Paris. Similarly, he persevered in his conception of "colonies," assemblages of more recent fauna found intercalated among older strata. They supposedly resulted from migrations, although his opponents argued that these anomalies were due to tectonic disturbances of the strata.

In an international controversy over the status of the Taconic system, proposed by the American geologist Ebenezer Emmons, Barrande actively joined Jules Marcou in supporting Emmons' claim to be the true discoverer of the primordial fauna.

BIBLIOGRAPHY

I. ORIGINAL WORKS. The *Système silurien du centre de la Bohême,* VII, pt. 1 (Prague, 1887), ix–xvi, contains a bibliography of Barrande's many articles. His *Défense des colonies* (Prague, 1861–1881) is a series of his articles, letters, and essays relevant to that controversy.

II. SECONDARY LITERATURE. A bibliography of secondary materials on Barrande is in K. Lambrecht, W. Quenstedt, and A. Quenstedt, eds., *Fossilium catalogus I: Animalia, pars 72: Palaeontologi catalogus bio-bibliographicus* (The Hague, 1938), p. 22. An interesting modern biography is Josef Svoboda and Ferdinand Prantl, *Barrandium: Geologie des mittelböhmisches Silur und Devon* (Prague, 1958), pp. 47–67.

BERT HANSEN

BARRÉ DE SAINT VENANT. See **Saint Venant, A. J. C. Barré de.**

BARRELL, JOSEPH (*b.* New Providence, New Jersey, 15 December 1869; *d.* New Haven, Connecticut, 4 May 1919), *geology.*

Barrell was well prepared for a fruitful and scholarly career in the earth sciences: he studied engineering at Lehigh University, graduating with high honors in 1892, and continued there for E.M. and M.S. degrees in 1893 and 1897. He received the Ph.D. in geology from Yale in 1900 and the D.Sc. from Lehigh in 1916. To defray the expense of such extended education, Barrell took part-time positions teaching mathematics, mining and metallurgy, geology, zoology, and astronomy; he considered this experience invaluable when he became professor of structural geology at Yale (1908–1919).

Although he was concerned with a variety of problems, from mining technology to the evolution of protoman, Barrell's chief contributions were in isostasy, sedimentology, and metamorphism. He preferred building theories to collecting data, and his most impressive papers were deductive interpretations of the work of others. When writing on a particular topic, Barrell followed what he called the method of multiple working hypotheses: beginning with a set of carefully considered assumptions, he attempted to derive a number of hypothetical explanations that could later be checked against existing facts and theories. His own conclusions were typically prefaced with lengthy and critical presentations.

Barrell's ideas on metamorphism grew out of fieldwork during the summers of 1897–1901. In 1901 he joined the U.S. Geological Survey in Montana, to study the Marysville mining district and large Marysville and Boulder granite batholiths. Dissatisfied with contemporary theories of their origin, he directed his efforts to an accurate description of the characteristics of igneous intrusions occurring in nature, and developed a theory of magmatic stoping. The method of invasion was by subsidence of roof blocks and the rise of magma. Superheated magma confined at great depths shows a maximum of marginal assimilation. In the zone of flowage, magmatic intrusions crowd aside their containing wall rock, with the development of peripheral schistosity, and in the zone of fracture they force strata apart, forming sheets, laccoliths, and dikes. Greatly confined magmas expand and give rise to volcanism. Charles Schuchert called the *Geology of the Marysville Mining District, Montana* (1907) a geological classic.

Many of Barrell's 150 published papers deal with topics in paleoclimatology and sedimentology. He was a pioneer dry-land geologist, greatly influencing the manner in which stratigraphic problems were subsequently approached and conceptualized. Before his work, it was generally held that most sedimentary strata were of marine origin. Barrell was convinced by examination of the floodplains of western deserts and Triassic deposits of New Jersey that at least a fifth of all land surfaces are mantled by continental, fluvial, or eolian sediments.

He early recognized causal relationships between climatic variation and sedimentation, emphasizing that the ratio of terrestrial to littoral and marine deposits fluctuates markedly through time. Barrell proposed that sedimentation is a complex repetition of many compound rhythms and that such cyclic events as diastrophism, erosion, temperature change, and rainfall variation influence and are influenced by topography and physical geography, by the depth and streaming force of water bodies. He outlined numerous covarying factors of deposition in "Criteria for the Recognition of Ancient Delta Deposits" (1912) and pointed out that the heterogeneity of stratified deposits is the result.

Barrell read the history of the earth in its strata and interpreted their irregularities as meaning that geological processes are halting and discontinuous. Antiuniformitarian arguments are forcefully presented in "Rhythms and the Measurements of Geologic Time" (1917), one of Barrell's more philosophical works. Here he tried to estimate the age of the earth by calculating the rates of denudation, sedimentation, uplifts and subsidences, deposition of salt in the sea, and emission of radioactivity. The figure he obtained, 1,400 million years to the Precambrian, was more than ten times the usual uniformitarian estimates.

Geodesic theory occupied Barrell's interest for a portion of his career. He published eight papers in the *Journal of Geology* (1914–1915), under the series title "Strength of the Earth's Crust," that present his views on isostasy and terrestrial dynamics. Positing two crustal layers, an outermost and stronger *lithosphere* (50–70 miles thick and of varying density) and a zone of flowage that he named the *aesthenosphere* (70–300 miles thick), he sought to explain geological phenomena by their dynamic interaction. Barrell said that isostatic equilibrium obtains in general, despite the effects of erosion and sedimentation. He wrote that the lithosphere is capable of supporting limited loads, uncompensated, however, if the vertical anomaly is inversely proportional to the area. Anomalies in excess of this proportion are compensated for by vertical displacement of the lithosphere against the foundation aesthenosphere (isostatic adjustment).

Although Barrell's concerns were seemingly diverse, they were actually variations on a common theme: the effects of physical agents on the evolution of the earth and its inhabitants. "The Origin of the Earth" (1916), a lecture delivered to Yale's Sigma Xi Society, discussed the conditions required for the genesis of the solar system and the development of the earth. His papers on sedimentology always relate sedimentological processes to the larger problems of historical geology, as do his treatments of structural geology. Barrell even maintained that biological evolution was the result of physical and chemical agents, in that these are the factors determining the environment of organisms.

BIBLIOGRAPHY

I. ORIGINAL WORKS. Barrell's writings include *Geology of the Marysville Mining District, Montana . . .,* U.S. Geological Survey, Professional Paper no. 57 (Washington, D.C., 1907); "Criteria for the Recognition of Ancient Delta Deposits," in *Bulletin of the Geological Society of America,* **23** (1912), 377–446; the series on the strength of the earth's crust: "Geologic Tests of the Limits of Strength," in *Journal of Geology,* **22** (1914), 28–48; "Regional Distribution of Isostatic Compensation," *ibid.,* 145–165; "Influence of Variable Rate of Isostatic Compensation," *ibid.,* 209–236; "Heterogeneity and Rigidity of the Crust as Measured by Departures From Isostasy," *ibid.,* 289–314; "The Depth of Masses Producing Gravity Anomalies and Deflection Residuals," *ibid.,* 441–468, 537–555; "Relation of Isostatic Movements to Sphere of Weakness," *ibid.*, 655–683; "Variation of Strength With Depth," *ibid.*, 729–741, and **23** (1915), 27–44; and "Physical Conditions Controlling the Nature of the Lithosphere and Aesthenosphere," *ibid.*, **23** (1915), 425–443, 449–515; "Rhythms and the Measurements of Geologic Time," in *Bulletin of the Geological Society of America*, **28** (1917), 745–904; and "The Origin of the Earth," in Sigma Xi Society, ed., *The Evolution of the Earth and Its Inhabitants* (New Haven, 1918), pp. 1–44.

II. SECONDARY LITERATURE. Works on Barrell are Herbert E. Gregory, "Memorial to Joseph Barrell," in *Bulletin of the Geological Society of America,* **34** (1923), 18–28; G. P. Merrill, "Joseph Barrell," in *Dictionary of American Biography,* I, 642–644; and Charles Schuchert, "Biographical Memoir of Joseph Barrell," in *Biographical Memoirs of the National Academy of Science,* **12** (1927), 1–40.

MARTHA B. KENDALL

BARRESWIL, CHARLES-LOUIS (*b.* Versailles, France, 13 December 1817; *d.* Boulogne-sur-Mer, France, 22 November 1870), *chemistry.*

Barreswil studied chemistry in Paris under the guidance of Robiquet and Bussy, and later under Jules Pelouze, whose laboratory on the Rue Dauphine he directed. It was there, from 1844 to 1849, that Barreswil worked side by side with Claude Bernard and gave the young physiologist, then far from his future eminence, extremely valuable assistance. They conducted experiments on themselves, such as subsisting only on gelatin and attempting to discover the influence of food on the chemical reaction in the urine.

At first Barreswil was especially interested in the improvement of chemical analysis; starting in 1843 he published several articles in this field, notably on a new process for separating cobalt from manganese (1846) and on the cupropotassic solution as a reagent facilitating the detection of sugar (1844). Rayer introduced the "blue liquid of Barreswil" into the systematic clinical detection of diabetes; only slightly altered, it is the Fehling solution used today.

Barreswil participated in Bernard's researches on digestion (1844); on the chemical composition of gastric juices, bile, and pancreatic juice (1844–1846); on the means of eliminating urea after the removal of the kidneys (1847); and especially on the role of sugar in the animal organism. Both Bernard and Barreswil signed the two basic communications on the presence of sugar in the liver (1848) and in egg whites (1849).

While carrying on his own research, Barreswil discovered a new chrome compound, blue chromic acid (1847), and prepared quinine tannate.

Having become professor of chemistry at the École Municipale Turgot, and later at the École Supérieure de Commerce in Paris, Barreswil abandoned physiological chemistry and became more interested in the problems of industrial chemistry, particularly those of coloring, of photographic chemistry, and of the manufacture of sulfuric acid. He also carried out useful and humanitarian work as inspector of child labor in the factories of the Department of the Seine and as secretary of a philanthropic organization for the protection of young workers.

BIBLIOGRAPHY

I. ORIGINAL WORKS. Barreswil's books include *Appendice à tous les traités d'analyse chimique* (Paris, 1848), written with A. Sobrero; *Chimie photographique* (Paris, 1854; 4th ed., 1864), written with Davanne; *Répertoire de chimie pure et appliquée,* 6 vols. (Paris, 1858–1866); and *Dictionnaire de chimie industrielle,* 3 vols. (Paris, 1861–1864), written with A. Girard *et al.* For the bibliography of his articles see *Royal Society of London, Catalogue of Scientific Papers,* I, 191–192.

II. SECONDARY LITERATURE. There is no proper biographical study of Barreswil. Short notices are in G. Vapereau, *Dictionnaire universel des contemporains,* 4th ed. (Paris, 1870), and *Dictionnaire de biographie française,* V (Paris, 1951).

M. D. GRMEK

BARROIS, CHARLES (*b.* Lille, France, 21 April 1851; *d.* Ste.-Geneviève-en-Caux, Seine Maritime, France, 5 November 1939), *geology, paleontology.*

Barrois belonged to a family of rich industrialists who had been liberals under the Restoration but became conservatives and ardent Catholics under the Second Empire. After studying with the Jesuits in Lille, Charles and his brother Jules wanted to be zoologists, an ambition encouraged by their parents. Jules became a specialist in invertebrate embryology, and Charles wrote his second doctoral thesis on the development of living *Spongiae* (1876). As early as 1871, however, he was caught up in Jules Gosselet's contagious enthusiasm for geology. He remained Gosselet's devoted disciple for half a century.

In 1871 Barrois was named assistant at the Faculté des Sciences of Lille, where he spent the rest of his career. He thereupon began a doctoral thesis on the Cretaceous formations of England, which he explored during four successive summers. His keen powers of observation were focused particularly on fossil fauna, which his training as a zoologist helped him to analyze. His thesis, presented in Paris in 1876 under Hébert's supervision, became the first volume of the *Mémoires de la Société géologique du Nord,* which was founded by Gosselet and Barrois himself. In this work Barrois extended to England the same paleontologic and stratigraphic zones found by Hébert in the French Cretaceous formation. Following Godwin-Austen, he observed that the axes of the deformations that affected the English Cretaceous were those active during the Primary era. This discovery was expanded by Marcel Bertrand in 1892 and by Eduard Suess as the theory of posthumous flections.

The English geologists were enthusiastic over Barrois's thesis. In 1908 Arthur Rowe declared his work to be that of a genius. According to E. Bailey (1940), Barrois was the most illustrious stratigrapher since Murchison. The compliment was slightly excessive, since Barrois owed a great deal to Gosselet and to Hébert. But his reputation benefited from the friendships that he made abroad, facilitated by his thorough command of languages and his personal fortune. His rather cold and haughty manner, the result of his education as a member of the high bourgeois, was mitigated by a gentle spirit and perfect manners. It was impossible to do other than like such a man, who was always as good as his word.

Once his thesis was finished, Barrois began a study of the Cretaceous formation of northern and eastern France. The most ancient formations of the globe had attracted him for many years, however, and after a period of study in the laboratory of Fouqué and Michel-Lévy at the Collège de France (where he became acquainted with the new methods of optical petrography), he undertook research on the Primary formations of northern Spain in 1877. He went on to make other field studies in Asturias and in Galicia that were the subject of an imposing memoir (1882). He also undertook a study of the Sierra Nevada with A. Offret in 1889; their stratigraphic results will long remain authoritative.

In 1878 Barrois had met the American geologist James Hall, who developed a paternal affection for him and took him back to the United States. Hall conducted him on a tour of the most important stratigraphic sequences in New York State, and Barrois wrote to Hébert, "One learns more in one hour in Albany than in a week anywhere else."

Back in France, Barrois was named lecturer at the Faculté des Sciences at Lille (1878) and embarked on his great work: mapping the geological formations of Brittany. This was a difficult task, for the Precambrian and Primary formations, overthrown by Hercynian flections and made unrecognizable by meta-

morphism, are practically always without fossils; moreover, they are often concealed by the present vegetation. Barrois hunted for outcrops in road cuts, small quarries, or barren land where the bedrock was visible. From 1880 to 1909 he published twenty geological maps on the scale of 1:80,000, representing more than 25,000 square kilometers. After his retirement from teaching in 1926, he returned to his beloved Brittany, where until his death he tried to improve his previous observations.

Although Brittany did not suggest any original hypotheses to Barrois (who rather dreaded them), it gave him the opportunity to verify new theories put forward by others. He showed the great diversity in the age of granites, and in the field he followed the transformation, through metamorphism, of bands of sandstone into veins of quartzite or quartz, and that of carbonaceous sediments into graphitic layers. He dated the numerous volcanic eruptions that affected Brittany during the Primary epoch and established the existence of a marine transgression during the Lower Carboniferous. He also collected specimens of Lamballe's *phtanites,* which L. Cayeux found to be one of the oldest microfauna of Europe, possibly going back to the Precambrian era.

As early as 1888 Barrois was made *professeur-adjoint* at the University of Lille, and in 1902 he became director of the Institute of Geology of Lille, following Gosselet. He also was an ingenious museologist, as is shown by the Musée Houiller, which he founded in 1907 to help train students, engineers, and technicians for the coal-mining industry. Barrois chose valuable collaborators, such as Pierre Pruvost, his successor; Paul Bertrand, a specialist in fossil flora; and André Duparc, who pioneered the microscopic study of coal. In 1905 Léon Bertrand's views on the structure of the Franco-Belgian coal basin were prevalent. It was conceived as a mildly folded depression where enormous reserves of coal had been deposited, the thick beds at the bottom and the thinner coals on top. Using a detailed stratigraphic and paleontological study, Barrois and his disciples designed a completely different tectonics for the basin, seeing it as crosshatched by faults. This led them to anticipate far smaller coal reserves. It was the triumph of minute observation over simplistic theory.

Barrois, who had a remarkable ability to discover and describe paleontological species, became interested in the fossil corals, the Spongiae, the Bryozoa, the brachiopods, and especially the graptolites. He also wrote an extensive monograph on the Devonian fauna of Erbray (1888). Pierre Pruvost said, however, that Barrois "defined his species in terms of their value as characteristic [guide and index] fossils, and he avoids . . . philosophical meditation on the origin and relationships of living beings. Paleontology is for him a chronology of organic life, as exact as possible . . . for the use of the geologist." When Barrois undertook the unrewarding but useful task of translating into French the five large volumes of Zittel's *Handbuch der Palaeontologie* (1883–1894), he made it difficult for others to publish treatises on paleontology that openly praised theories of evolution. Although he wrote "All scientific effort broadens our freedom of action," he was inhibited from speaking freely by his religious convictions: he and his friend Albert de Lapparent had been among the militants of what he called the Catholic party. He did not scorn honors and became a corresponding member of numerous academies; although not a resident of Paris, he was successful in being elected a titular member of the Académie des Sciences, after several defeats. During the last year of his life the pope made him a member of the Pontifical Scientific Academy.

Barrois was one of the last geologists to be *complet,* as Pruvost put it—that is, to be capable of carrying his research almost to perfection in both the field and the laboratory, whether the research was paleontological or petrographic. Barrois would have been outstanding among geologists had he been a bit more daring and had he had more of a feeling for synthesis.

BIBLIOGRAPHY

I. ORIGINAL WORKS. A list of Barrois's scientific works includes 268 titles, of which twenty-five are geological maps; it may be found on pp. 251–262 of Pruvost's article in *Bulletin de la Société géologique de France* (see below). His principal works are *Recherches sur le terrain crétacé supérieur de l'Angleterre et de l'Irlande,* his thesis (Paris, 1876), *Mémoires de la Société géologique du Nord de la France,* 1; "Mémoire sur le terrain crétacé des Ardennes . . .," in *Annales de la Société géologique du Nord de la France,* 5 (1878), 227–287; *Recherches sur les terrains anciens des Asturies et de la Galice, Mémoire de la Société géologique du Nord de la France,* 2 (1882); *Mémoire sur la faune du Calcaire d'Erbray (Loire-inférieure), Mémoire de la Société géologique du Nord de la France,* 3 (1889); "Mémoire sur la constitution géologique du Sud de l'Andalousie . . .," in *Académie des sciences, Mémoires des savants étrangers,* 2nd ser., 30 (1889), 79–169, written with Albert Offret; "Étude des strates marines du terrain houiller du Nord," in *Gîtes minéraux de la France* (1912), pt. 1; "Description de la faune siluro-dévonienne de Liévin," in *Mémoires de la Société géologique du Nord de la France,* 6, fasc. 2 (1922), 67–223, written with P. Pruvost and Georges Dubois; and "Les grandes lignes de la Bretagne," in *Livre jubilaire de la Société géologique de France* (1930), pp. 83 ff.

II. SECONDARY LITERATURE. Barrois's pupil and friend Pierre Pruvost analyzed the man and his work in *Bulletin de la Société géologique de France,* 5th ser., 10 (1950), 231–262, with a portrait. Charles Jacob attempted a sketch of the social milieu in which Barrois lived in *Obituary Notices of Fellows of the Royal Society,* 5 (1947), 287–293, with a portrait.

FRANCK BOURDIER

BARROW, ISAAC (*b.* London, England, October 1630; *d.* London, 4 May 1677), *geometry, optics.*

Barrow's father, Thomas, was a prosperous linendraper with court connections; his mother, Anne, died when Isaac was an infant. A rebel as a dayboy at Charterhouse, Barrow came later, at Felsted, to accept the scholastic disciplining in Greek, Latin, logic, and rhetoric imposed by his headmaster, Martin Holbeach. In 1643, already as firm a supporter of the king as his father was, he entered Trinity College, Cambridge, as pensioner. There he survived increasingly antiroyalist pressure for twelve years, graduating B.A. in 1648, being elected a college fellow (1649), and receiving his M.A. (1652), the academic passport to his final position as college lecturer and university examiner. In 1655, ousted by Cromwellian mandate from certain selection as Regius professor of Greek (in succession to his former tutor, James Duport), he sold his books and set out on an adventurous four-year tour of the Continent. On his return, coincident with the restoration of Charles II to the throne in 1660, he took holy orders and was promptly rewarded with the chair previously denied him. In 1662 he trebled his slender income by concurrently accepting the Gresham professorship of geometry in London and acting as locum for a fellow astronomy professor; he was relieved of this excessive teaching load when, in 1663, he was made first Lucasian professor of mathematics at Cambridge.

During the next six years, forbidden by professorial statute to hold any other university position, Barrow devoted himself to preparing the three series of *Lectiones* on which his scientific fame rests. In 1669, however, increasingly dissatisfied with this bar to advancing himself within his college, he resigned his chair (to Newton) to become royal chaplain in London. Four years later he returned as king's choice for the vacant mastership of Trinity, becoming university vice-chancellor in 1675. Barrow never married and, indeed, erased from his master's patent the clause permitting him to do so. Small and wiry in build, by conventional account he enjoyed excellent health, his early death apparently being the result of an overdose of drugs. He was remembered by his contemporaries for the bluntness and clarity of his theological sermons (published posthumously by Tillotson in 1683–1689), although these were too literary and long-winded to make him a popular preacher. His deep classical knowledge resulted in no specialized philological or textual studies. Although he was one of the first fellows of the Royal Society after its incorporation in 1662, he never took an active part in its meetings.

As an undergraduate, Barrow, like Newton a decade later, endured a traditional scholastic course, centered on Aristotle and his Renaissance commentators, which was inculcated by lecture and examined by disputation; but from the first he showed great interest in the current Gassendist revival of atomism and Descartes's systematization of natural philosophy. (His 1652 M.A. thesis, *Cartesiana hypothesis de materia et motu haud satisfacit praecipuis naturae phaenomenis,* is based on a careful study of Descartes and Regius.) That, also like Newton, he mastered Descartes's *Géométrie* unaided is unlikely. The elementary portion of Euclid's *Elements* was part of Barrow's college syllabus, but some time before 1652 he went on to read not only Euclidean commentaries by Tacquet, Hérigone, and Oughtred, but also more advanced Greek works by Archimedes and possibly Apollonius and Ptolemy. His first published work, his epitomized *Euclidis Elementorum libri XV* (probably written by early 1654), is designed as a quadrivium undergraduate text, with emphasis on its deductive structure rather than on its geometrical content, its sole concessions to contemporary mathematical idiom being its systematic use of Oughtred's symbolism and a list "ex P. Herigono" of numerical constants relating to inscribed polyhedra. To its reedition in 1657, Barrow added a similar epitome of Euclid's *Data,* and in his 1666 Lucasian lectures expounded a likewise recast version of Archimedes' method in the *Sphere and Cylinder;* a full edition, in the same style, of the known corpus of Archimedes' works, the first four books of Apollonius' *Conics,* and the three books of Theodosius' *Spherics* appeared in 1675. Overloaded with marginal references, virtually bare of editorial amplification, and fussy in their symbolism, these texts can hardly have been easier to read than their Latin originals, and only the conveniently pocket-sized *Euclid* reached a wide public. Barrow himself commented that his Apollonius had in it "nothing considerable but its brevity." His early attempt at a modern approach to Greek mathematics was a short, posthumously edited *Lectio* in which he analyzed the Archimedean quadrature method in terms of indivisibles on the style of Wallis' *Arithmetica infinitorum.*

Barrow's Gresham inaugural, still preserved, tells little of the content of his lost London lectures: perhaps they were similar to works of his on "Perspective, Projections, Elem^ts of Plaine Geometry" mentioned by Collins. The first of his Lucasian series, the *Lectiones mathematicae* (given in sequence from 1664 to 1666), discourse on the foundations of mathematics from an essentially Greek standpoint, with interpolations from such contemporaries as Tacquet, Wallis, and Hobbes (usually cited only to be refuted). Such topics as the ontological status of mathematical entities, the nature of axiomatic deduction, the continuous and the discrete, spatial magnitude and numerical quantity, infinity and the infinitesimal, and proportionality and incommensurability are examined at length. Barrow's conservatism reveals itself in his artificial preservation of the dichotomy between arithmetic and geometry by classifying algebra as merely a useful logical (analytical) tool which is not a field of mathematical study in itself. The *Lectiones geometricae* were, no doubt, initially intended as the technical study of higher geometry for which the preceding course had paved the way, and the earlier lectures may indeed have been delivered as such.

About 1664, having heard (as he told Collins) that "Mersennus & Torricellius doe mencōn a generall method of finding ye tangents of curve lines by composition of motions; but doe not tell it us," he found out "such a one" for himself, elaborating an approach to plane geometry in which the elements were suitably compounded rotating and translating lines. In his first five geometrical lectures he took some trouble to define the uniformly "fluent" variable of time which is the measure of all motion, and then went on to consider the properties of curves generated by combinations of moving points and lines, evolving a simple Robervallian construction for tangents. Later lectures (6–12), evidently thrown together in some haste, are in large part a systematic generalization of tangent, quadrature, and rectification procedures gathered by Barrow from his reading of Torricelli, Descartes, Schooten, Hudde, Wallis, Wren, Fermat, Huygens, Pascal, and, above all, James Gregory; while the final *Lectio,* 13, is an unconnected account of the geometrical construction of equations. We should (despite Child) be careful not to overemphasize the originality of these lectures: the "fundamental theorem of the calculus," for example, and the *compendium pro tangentibus determinandis* in *Lectio 10* are, respectively, restylings, by way of propositions 6 and 7 of Gregory's *Geometriae pars universalis* (1668), of William Neil's rectification method (in Wallis' *De cycloide,* 1659) and of the tangent algorithm thrashed out by Descartes and Fermat in their 1638 correspondence (published by Clerselier in 1667). In theory, as Jakob Bernoulli argued in 1691, Barrow's geometrical formulations could well have been the basis on which systematized algorithmic calculus structures were subsequently erected; but in historical fact the *Lectiones geometricae* were little read even by the few (Sluse, Gregory, Newton, Leibniz) qualified to appreciate them, and their impact was small. Perhaps only John Craige (1685) based a calculus method on a Barrovian precedent, and then only in a single instance (*Lectio 11*,1).

Barrow's optical lectures, highly praised on their first publication by Sluse and James Gregory, had an equally short-lived heyday, being at once rendered obsolete by the Newtonian *Lectiones opticae,* which, both in methodology and in subject matter, they inspired. In his introduction he lays down the scarcely novel mechanical hypothesis of a lucid body (a "congeries corpusculorum ultra pene quam cogitari potest minutorum" or "collection of particles minute almost beyond conceivability") as the propagating source of rectilinear light rays. His hypothesis of color (in *Lectio 12*) as a dilution in "thickness" and swiftness, of white light through red, green, and blue to black, is no less shadowy than the Cartesian explanation to which it is preferred. Structurally, the technical portion of the *Lectiones* is developed purely mathematically from six axiomatic "Hypotheses opticae primariae et fundamentales [seu] leges . . . ab experientiâ confirmatae," notably the Euclidean law of reflection and the sine law of refraction, and presents a reasonably complete discussion of the elementary catoptrics and dioptrics of white light. Not unexpectedly, the organization and mathematical detail are Barrow's, but his topics are mostly taken from Alhazen, Kepler, Scheiner, Descartes, and others: thus, his improvement of the Cartesian theory of the rainbow (*Lectio 12,* 14) derives from Huygens by way of Sluse. The most original contributions of the work are his method for finding the point of refraction at a plane interface (*Lectio 5,* 12) and his point construction of the diacaustic of a spherical interface (*Lectio 13,* 24): both were at once subsumed by Newton into his own geometrical optics, and the latter (in ignorance) was triumphantly rediscovered by Jakob Bernoulli in 1693.

Barrow's relationship with Newton, although of considerable historical importance, has never been clarified. That Newton was Barrow's pupil at Trinity is a myth, and Barrow's name does not appear in the mass of Newton's extant early papers; nor is there good evidence for supposing that any of Newton's early mathematical or optical discoveries were in any way due to Barrow's personal tutelage. In his old age, the furthest that Newton would go in admitting a

mathematical debt to Barrow was that attendance at his lectures "might put me upon considering the generation of figures by motion, tho I not now remember it." It may well be that Barrow came to know Newton intimately only after his election to senior college status in 1667. Certainly by late 1669 there was a brief working rapport between the two which, if it did not last long, at least resulted in Newton's consciously choosing to continue the theme of his predecessor's lectures in his own first Lucasian series.

BIBLIOGRAPHY

I. ORIGINAL WORKS. The contents of Barrow's library at the time of his death are recorded in "A Catalogue of the Bookes of Dr Isaac Barrow Sent to S.S. by Mr Isaac Newton . . . July 14. 1677" (Bodleian, Oxford, Rawlinson D878, 33^r–59^r). His *Euclidis Elementorum libri XV breviter demonstrati* appeared at Cambridge in 1655; to its 1657 reedition (reissued in 1659) was appended his edition of Euclid's *Data.* Both reappeared in 1678, together with Barrow's *Lectio . . . in qua theoremata Archimedis De sphaera & cylindro per methodum indivisibilium investigata exhibentur* (Royal Society, London, MS XIX). An English edition of the *Elements; the Whole Fifteen Books* (London, 1660) was reissued half a dozen times in the early eighteenth century, and an independent English version by Thomas Haselden of the *Elements, Data,* and *Lectio* together appeared there in 1732. The manuscript of Barrow's *Archimedis opera: Apollonii Pergaei Conicorum libri IIII: Theodosii Sphaerica: Methodo novo illustrata, & succincte demonstrata* (London, 1675) is now in the Royal Society, London (MSS XVIII–XX): a proposed appendix epitomizing Apollonius' *Conics,* 5–7 (from Borelli's 1661 edition) never appeared. His *Lectiones mathematicae XXIII; In quibus Principia Matheseôs generalia exponuntur: Habitae Cantabrigiae A.D. 1664, 1665, 1666* was published posthumously at London in 1683 (reissued 1684 and 1685); an English version by John Kirkby came out there in 1734. The rare 1669 edition of Barrow's *Lectiones XVIII Cantabrigiae in scholis publicis habitae; In quibus opticorum phaenomenωn genuinae rationes investigantur, ac exponuntur* was speedily followed (1670) by his *Lectiones geometricae: In quibus (praesertim) generalia curvarum linearum symptomata declarantur*: these were issued (both together and separately) at London in 1670, 1672, and 1674. Unpublished variant drafts of geometrical lectures 10, 11, and 13 are extant in private possession.

The optical lectures were reprinted, none too accurately, in C. Babbage and F. Maseres' *Scriptores optici* (London, 1823), and all three Lucasian series were collected, together with Barrow's inaugural, in W. Whewell's *The Mathematical Works of Isaac Barrow D.D.* (Cambridge, 1860). A mediocre English translation of the geometrical lectures by Edmund Stone (London, 1735) is more accurate than J. M. Child's distorted abridgment, *The Geometrical Lectures of Isaac Barrow* (Chicago-London, 1916). Alexander

Napier's standard edition of Barrow's *Theological Works* (9 vols., Cambridge, 1859), based on original manuscripts in Trinity College, Cambridge, and otherwise restoring the text from Tillotson's "improvements," is scientifically valuable for the *Opuscula* contained in its final volume: here will be found the texts of Barrow's early academic exercises and college orations, as well as of his professorial inaugurals. The extant portion of Barrow's correspondence with Collins has been published several times from the originals in possession of the Royal Society, London, and the Earl of Macclesfield, notably in Newton's *Commercium epistolicum D. Johannis Collins, et aliorum de analysi promota* (London, 1712) and in S. P. Rigaud's *Correspondence of Scientific Men of the Seventeenth Century,* II (Oxford, 1841), 32–76.

II. SECONDARY LITERATURE. Existing sketches of Barrow's life (by Abraham Hill, John Aubrey, John Ward, and, more recently, J. H. Overton) are mostly collections of unsupported anecdote, both dreary and derivative. Percy H. Osmond's *Isaac Barrow, His Life and Times* (London, 1944) has few scientific insights but is otherwise a lively, semipopular account of Barrow's intellectual achievement. In "Newton, Barrow and the Hypothetical Physics," in *Centaurus,* **11** (1965), 46–56, and *Atomism in England From Hariot to Newton* (Oxford, 1966), p. 120, Robert H. Kargon argues that Barrow's scientific methodology, as expounded in the *Lectiones mathematicae,* should be interpreted as a rejection of hypothetical physics rather than as Archimedean classicism, but he is uncritical in his acceptance of Barrow's early influence on Newton.

D. T. WHITESIDE

BARRY, MARTIN (*b.* Fratton, Hampshire, England, 28 March 1802; *d.* Beccles, Suffolk, England, 27 April 1855), *embryology, histology.*

Barry was trained for a career in his father's Nova Scotia-based mercantile concern, which sent ships to various parts of North America and the West Indies. After a short time in business, Barry began medical studies to prepare himself for work in science. Before receiving the M.D. at Edinburgh in 1833 he studied medicine at London, Paris, Erlangen, and Berlin. After graduation he specialized in anatomy and physiology for about a year under Friedrich Tiedemann at Heidelberg. On his return to Edinburgh, Barry attended the Royal Infirmary to further his medical knowledge.

Since he had a private income, Barry never had to practice medicine and did not hold any permanent appointment. As a result, he was able to divide his residency between Scotland, England, and Germany. In 1843 he presented a course of physiological lectures at St. Thomas' Hospital, London. The following year Barry became house surgeon at the new Royal Maternity Hospital, Edinburgh, and made observations on the position of the fetus both before and during delivery. These observations were noted by Sir James Young Simpson in various papers. Barry had a partiality for his obstetric work, of which Simpson spoke highly, but he soon had to resign this position because of recurring ill health.

Barry received the Royal Society's Royal Medal in 1839 for his 1838 and 1839 papers on embryology, and the following year was elected a fellow of the Royal Society. Other societies in which he was active were the Royal Society of Edinburgh and the Wernerian Society.

In 1835 Barry began to study the embryological literature, having been led into microscopical researches by an embryological work given to him by Robert Jameson. This was soon after K. E. von Baer and his fellow workers in Germany had stimulated the study of embryology. His interest in embryology led him into general histological studies at about the time that the cell theory was being formulated. The bulk of microscopic research was then being published in German, and Barry was one of few British scientists interested in and conversant with the German microscopic literature of the 1830's and 1840's.

Barry's first embryological paper was "On the Unity of Structure in the Animal Kingdom," in which he started from the assumption that all of nature is part of the same grand design. Barry recognized that the germ cells of several species of animals were essentially the same and that there is a general law directing the development of animal structure from a homogeneous or general state to a heterogeneous or special one. He adapted his description of the general development of animals from Baer, on whom he relied quite heavily.

In 1837 Barry was in Germany again, this time using the facilities of Johannes Müller, C. G. Ehrenberg, Rudolph Wagner, and Theodor Schwann. After his return to England he presented his results to the Royal Society as "Researches in Embryology" (1838–1840). In this three-part series Barry tried to follow the history of the mammalian ovum from its first appearance within the ovary through its early stages of development. His numerous observations (mostly on rabbits) resulted in a series of descriptions and illustrations (drawn by himself) that give a good account of that development.

Barry made two notable embryological observations: the segmentation of the yolk in the fertilized mammalian ovum and the penetration of the spermatozoon into the mammalian ovum. In 1839 he pictured the two-, four-, eight-, and sixteen-cell stages in mammals and described as similar to a mulberry that stage which Ernst Haeckel later named the morula. Barry concluded that the process he described in the mammal was similar to that already recognized in fishes and batrachians, thus strengthening his belief in the unity of the animal world.

In 1839 Barry avoided discussing the problem of whether contact of the seminal fluid with the ovum was necessary for impregnation. He did mention, however, that in some instances he had found spermatozoa on the surface of the ovary. The following year Barry reported that he had seen a spermatozoon within the *zona pellucida* with its head directed toward the interior of the ovum. Barry read a note to the Royal Society on 8 December 1842 in which he announced that he had recently seen spermatozoa within the ova of a rabbit. As far as he knew, this was an original observation. He showed one or more of these ova to Richard Owen, William Sharpey, and Richard Grainger, all of whom, he said, agreed that the spermatozoa were within the ova. Theodor Bischoff refused to believe that Barry had seen spermatozoa within ova, and Barry answered him in 1844, pointing out Bischoff's errors in obtaining and preserving ova. Only in 1851 did Alfred Nelson confirm Barry's observations; further proof came from George Newport and Georg Meissner, and finally from Bischoff himself.

Barry presented a second series of papers, "On the Corpuscles of the Blood," to the Royal Society in 1840–1841, and concluded it in a fourth part, "On Fibre," in 1842. A later, expanded version of the 1842 paper was translated into German by J. E. Purkinje, with whom Barry had been living, and was published in Müller's *Archiv* (1850). The histological work in these papers was an outgrowth of Barry's embryological studies, being prompted particularly by the appearance of the rabbit's generative organs when they were in a highly vascular condition. Barry was interested in the origin of the red blood corpuscles and the changes they undergo. The basic idea in his hypothesis of red corpuscle formation was that the nucleus of a parent cell somehow broke into several "discs," all but two of which eventually disappeared. A cell then formed around each of these two "discs," and when the new cells were complete with their own membranes, the membrane of the parent cell disappeared, leaving two new cells. Barry based these ideas on the observations he had made on the fertilized ovum and its development to the morula stage, during which time there is no appreciable increase in the total organic mass.

Barry thought that all of the animal structures which he had studied arose from red blood corpuscles, or corpuscles very similar to them. The bulk of his four-part series of papers was devoted to his observations on many types of tissues and his arguments that

they had all arisen in the same manner from the same basic elements, thus developing further his ideas about the unity of all animal life. He also thought that a knowledge of the formation of various tissues might lead to an understanding of the role of the blood corpuscles in nutrition. In a later paper he tried to show that John Goodsir's work in nutrition supported his ideas.

The greatest portion of Barry's later work was aimed at promoting his conclusions on the origin of blood corpuscles and the formation of animal tissues from them. Often he was overly concerned with his own priority and tried to show that other workers had merely confirmed his theories, even when there were scant grounds for such a claim.

Barry's contemporaries generally thought highly of, and accepted, his observations and the illustrations accompanying his papers. His conclusions, however, were often considered highly speculative and were sometimes assailed. In addition to a number of valuable observations, Barry should also be credited with stimulating microscopic studies in Great Britain and increasing his countrymen's acquaintance with the German literature in his field.

BIBLIOGRAPHY

I. ORIGINAL WORKS. Barry's first embryological paper was "On the Unity of Structure in the Animal Kingdom," in *Edinburgh New Philosophical Journal*, **22** (1837), 116–141, 345–364. His main embryological results are in "Researches in Embryology. First [Second and Third] Series," in *Philosophical Transactions of the Royal Society*, **128** (1838), 301–341; **129** (1839), 307–380; **130** (1840), 529–593; and in a short note, "Spermatozoa Observed Within the Mammiferous Ovum," *ibid.,* **133** (1843), 33. The important histological papers are the series "On the Corpuscles of the Blood," *ibid.,* **130** (1840), 595–612; **131** (1841), 201–216, 217–268; and the continuation "On Fibre," *ibid.,* **132** (1842), 89–135. Many of these observations and conclusions, with some new material, were summarized in a paper read before the Wernerian Society, "On the Nucleus of the Animal and Vegetable 'Cell,'" in *Edinburgh New Philosophical Journal*, **43** (Apr.–Oct. 1847), 201–229. The 1842 paper, "On Fibre," was expanded, translated into German by J. E. Purkinje, and published as "Neue Untersuchungen über die schraubenförmige Beschaffenheit der Elementarfasern der Muskeln, nebst Beobachtungen über die muskulöse Natur der Flimmerhärchen," in Müller's *Archiv* (1850), 529–596. See the Royal Society's *Catalogue of Scientific Papers*, 1st ser., I, 194–195, for Barry's other papers, most of which treat the same material.

II. SECONDARY LITERATURE. The most complete account of Barry's life and work is in the *Edinburgh Medical*

Journal, **1** (1856), 81–91. This consists of a memoir of Barry by J. B., pp. 81–87, and a letter to the editor by Allen Thomson, pp. 87–91. Thomson knew Barry and his scientific endeavors, having at times worked with him, and he gives a short comment on Barry's achievements.

WESLEY C. WILLIAMS

BARTELS, JULIUS (*b*. Magdeburg, Germany, 17 August 1899; *d*. Göttingen, Germany, 6 March 1964), *geophysics.*

Bartels was educated at the University of Göttingen, graduating Ph.D. in 1923 and then working in close association with the distinguished geomagnetician Adolph Schmidt for four years. He was head of the Meteorological Institute at the Fortliche Hochschule in Eberswalde from 1927 to 1941, professor of geophysics at the University of Berlin from 1941 to 1945, and professor of geophysics and director of the Geophysical Institute of the University of Göttingen from 1945 on. From 1956 he was also director of the Max Planck Institute of Aeronomy at Lindau and, from 1954 to 1957, president of the International Association of Geomagnetism and Aeronomy.

At the time Bartels began his research, the mathematical theory of statistics was emerging as a major scientific tool. Bartels saw how it could be used to improve the quality of inferences in important sections of geomagnetism. Accordingly, he developed rigorous statistical procedures that both served as a pattern in subsequent geomagnetic analyses and led to new results of much importance. He himself applied the procedures skillfully and fruitfully.

Bartels' statistical analyses led him to make the first clear discrimination between the geomagnetic variations caused by wave and particle radiation from the sun, and from this to develop reliable measures, based on geomagnetic observations, of the two types of radiation. Some of the indexes he introduced in his treatment of geomagnetic variations came to be used internationally, e.g., a sensitive geomagnetic index of the influx of solar particles into the auroral region and his planetary indexes K_p. His procedures further enabled Bartels to elucidate features of tides in the earth's atmosphere that are caused by the moon's gravitational attraction. In investigating twenty-seven-day variations in geomagnetic activity, which are connected with the sun's rotation, he was led to postulate the existence in the sun of certain magnetically active regions (*M* regions), which astronomers later connected with the development of sunspots. He also showed that the sun's surface is never wholly active or wholly quiet.

BIBLIOGRAPHY

Among Bartels' works are "Statistical Methods for Research on Diurnal Variations," in *Terrestrial Magnetism and Atmospheric Electricity,* **37** (1932), 291–302; "Twenty-Seven-Day Recurrence in Terrestrial Magnetic and Solar Activity, 1932–33," *ibid.*, **39** (1934), 201–202; "Random Fluctuations, Persistence and Quasi-persistence in Geophysical and Cosmical Periodicities," *ibid.*, **40** (1935), 1–60; "The Eccentric Dipole Approximating the Earth's Magnetic Field," *ibid.*, **41** (1936), 225–250; "Geophysical Lunar Almanac," *ibid.*, **43** (1938), 155–158, written with G. Fanselau; "Harmonic Analysis of Diurnal Variations for Single Days," *ibid.*, **44** (1939), 137–156; "Some Problems of Terrestrial Magnetism and Electricity," in J. A. Fleming, ed., *Physics of the Earth VIII: Terrestrial Magnetism and Electricity* (New York–London, 1939), pp. 385–430; "The Three-Hour-Range Index Measuring Geomagnetic Activity," in *Terrestrial Magnetism and Atmospheric Electricity,* **44** (1939), 411–454; *Geomagnetism,* 2 vols. (Oxford, 1940, 1951, 1962), written with Sydney Chapman; "Geomagnetic Data on Variations of Solar Radiation. Part 1—Wave-radiation," in *Terrestrial Magnetism and Atmospheric Electricity,* **51** (1946), 181–242; "Geomagnetic and Solar Data," in *Journal of Geophysical Research,* **54** (1949), 295–299; "Geomagnetically Detectable Local Inhomogeneities in Electrical Conductivity Below the Surface," in *Nachrichten. Akademie der Wissenschaften in Göttingen,* **5** (1954), 95–100; "Solar Influences on Geomagnetism," in *Proceedings of the National Academy of Sciences,* **43** (1957), 75–81; and "Discussion of Time-variations of Geomagnetic Activity Indices K_p and A_p, 1932–1961," in *Annales de géophysique,* **19** (1963), 1–20.

Bartels was also editor of Vols. XLVII and XLVIII of *Handbuch der Physik* (Berlin, 1957).

K. E. BULLEN

BARTHEZ, PAUL-JOSEPH (*b*. Montpellier, France, 11 December 1734; *d*. Paris, France, 15 October 1806), *physiology.*

Barthez was an extraordinarily influential French physician who helped to popularize vitalistic doctrines at a time when the most unsophisticated forms of mechanism still held sway in biology and medicine. Succeeding generations have regarded Barthez's theories as hopelessly naïve, but the general point of view that he advocated was adopted by many important biologists of the early nineteenth century.

The son of Guillaume Barthez de Marmorières, chief engineer of Languedoc, Barthez received his early schooling in Narbonne and Toulouse and entered the medical school at Montepellier at the age of sixteen. Completing his degree in three years, he went to Paris, where he became a protégé of Falconnet, physician to Louis XV. He frequented the intellectual circles of the capital and became particularly intimate with d'Alembert. From 1755 to 1757 he served as a physician with the French army. Upon returning to Paris, he was employed first as a royal censor and then as an editor of the *Journal des savants.* During this time he also contributed to the *Encyclopédie* edited by his friend d'Alembert.

Barthez returned to Montpellier about 1760 as professor of medicine and remained there for twenty years, becoming chancellor of the medical school in 1773. During this period he developed his vitalistic doctrines, expounding them in three books: *De principio vitali hominis* (1773), *Nova doctrina de fonctionibus naturae humanae* (1774), and his most important work, *Nouveaux éléments de la science de l'homme* (1778).

Barthez's vitalism is based on the distinction between three different types of phenomena—matter (*la matière*), life (*la vie*), and soul (*l'âme*). He argued that even if like effects follow from like causes, we cannot assume that the laws which govern one type of phenomenon will be meaningful when applied to another; life cannot be subsumed under the laws that govern matter, and it cannot be described in the same manner as the behavior of the soul. Barthez denied both the mechanistic doctrines of Borelli and Boerhaave and the vitalism of Stahl and van Helmont. He thought that their approaches to physiology were illogical and—even worse—totally useless, since they yielded results that were either obviously wrong or incapable of being tested. In his view, life was a valid subject for investigation, but it needed its own distinctive science with unique principles and techniques.

One important aspect of this new science was the development of clinical teaching and research. Barthez thought that physicians should return to the inductive method of Hippocrates, learning the principles of physiology as they manifest themselves in the whole, living body. Although such clinical research later became the basis for the superiority of French medical science in the nineteenth century, the idea was opposed by Barthez's colleagues, and the controversy that it aroused caused him to resign his position at Montpellier in 1781.

Once again Barthez returned to the literary and intellectual life of Paris. He was awarded many honors, among them membership in the Académie des Sciences and the Société Royale de Médecine. The Revolution stripped him of these honors and sent him into retirement in southern France, where he spent the last two decades of his life studying and writing. In 1798 he published *Nouvelle méchanique des mouvements de l'homme et des animaux,* in which he demonstrated, through very intricate anatomical analysis,

that the simple hydraulic explanations offered by the iatromechanists (particularly Borelli) would never explain the delicate balance and control of muscles that are needed for such motions as walking and swimming. During these years Barthez also published several practical medical handbooks and revised his *Nouveaux éléments,* which had been very popular in its earlier version.

With the coming of the Directorate, Barthez regained some of his former prominence. At the time of his death in 1806 he was personal physician to Napoleon and honorary professor of medicine at Montpellier. He had been appointed to the Légion d'Honneur and the Institut National, and had served with Corvisart as a medical member of Napoleon's consular government.

Unfortunately, Barthez did not really practice what he had preached on the subject of clinical research. His works are almost wholly theoretical, and he was particularly adept at producing the teleological explanations which were anathema to later generations of physiologists. Despite these failings his influence was widely felt; and his attitude toward physiology is mirrored in the work of Xavier Bichat and Johannes Müller, and even in that of the antivitalists François Magendie and Claude Bernard.

BIBLIOGRAPHY

I. ORIGINAL WORKS. The two most important works for an understanding of Barthez's physiological doctrines are *Nouveau éléments de la science de l'homme* (Montpellier, 1778; 2nd ed., Paris, 1806) and *Nouvelle méchanique des mouvements de l'homme et des animaux* (Carcassonne, 1798). Other works include *De principio vitali hominis* (Montpellier, 1773); *Nova doctrina de fonctionibus naturae humanae* (Montpellier, 1774).

II. SECONDARY LITERATURE. For reliable discussions of Barthez's life and theories see Jacques Lordat, *Exposition de la doctrine medical de Barthez et mémoire sur la vie de Barthez* (Paris, 1818); A. C. E. Barthez, *Sur la vitalisme de Barthez* (Paris, 1864).

RUTH SCHWARTZ COWAN

BARTHOLIN, CASPAR (*b.* Malmö, Denmark [now Sweden], 12 February 1585; *d.* Sorø, Denmark, 13 July 1629), *theology, anatomy.*

Bartholin's father, Bertel Jespersen, was court chaplain; his mother, Ane Rasmusdotter Tinckel, the daughter of a clergyman from Skåne. Because of his aptitude for languages Caspar was sent to grammar school when he was only three; at eleven he delivered lectures in Greek and Latin. In 1603 he matriculated at the University of Copenhagen, but transferred the following year to Wittenberg, where he studied philosophy and theology for the next three years. He was *respondens* at theses, lectured, and was elected master of philosophy and humane arts in 1608 with the thesis *Exercitatio physica de natura.* In 1606 Bartholin traveled through Germany to Holland, France, and England, visiting the universities and meeting learned physicians and philosophers. During a stay at Leiden he began to study medicine, but without giving up theology. After a short visit home he returned to Wittenberg, where in 1606 he published *Exercitatio de stellis,* which was reissued seven times, with queries and corrections, as *Astrologia sive de stellarum naturae, emendiator et auctior.*

In 1607 Bartholin went to Basel, where he lectured and worked with Felix Platter, Gaspard Bauhin, and Jacob Zwinger. While there he was offered the M.D. degree, but declined it. From 1608 to 1610 Bartholin was in Italy, where he studied anatomy and performed dissections at Padua with Fabricius ab Aquapendente and Casserio, and at Naples, where he was offered a professorship in anatomy. He helped to prepare the engravings for Casserio's work on the sense organs, *Pentaesthesicon* (1609), and his anatomical studies here formed the basis for the manual *Anatomicae institutiones corporis humani* (1611), which made him famous. During this time he also published several manuals of logic, physics, and ethics: *Enchiridion logicum ex Aristotele* (1608), *Janitores logici bini* (1609), *Disp. physica Basileensis* (1610), and *Enchiridion metaphysicum ex philosophorum coryphaei* (1610).

During a visit to Basel in 1610 Bartholin was made doctor of medicine after defending his *Paradoxa CCXL pathologica, simiotica, diaetetica.* When he returned to Denmark in 1611 he was appointed *professor eloquentia* at the University of Copenhagen. His marriage in 1612 to Anna Fincke, daughter of the professor of medicine Thomas Fincke, strengthened his ties to the university. He became professor of medicine in 1613, inaugurating his lectures with a speech on the use of philosophy in medicine. During the next ten years he wrote prolifically and lectured on medicine, physics, and religion, but he performed no dissections at Copenhagen. By 1622 his health had failed and, tortured by renal stones and rheumatism, he sought recovery at Carlsbad.

Vowing to continue his theological studies, upon his cure in 1624 Bartholin accepted a professorship of theology at the University of Copenhagen. Two years later he was made a doctor of divinity, and in the following years he published such works as *De natura theologiae* (1627), *De auctoritate Sacrae Scripturae* (1627), *Benedictio Aharonis* (1628), and

Systema physicum (1628). A mild religious tone is found in his writings, especially in *De studio theologico ratione inchoando et continuando* (1628), where he urges the young to study Holy Writ in both the vernacular and the original language. In 1629, when he was dean of the University of Copenhagen for the second time, Bartholin went to visit his children, who had been removed to Sorø for fear of the plague at Copenhagen. He died there, of renal failure, in the home of his friend J. Burser (1583–1639), a botanist.

Bartholin's fame is due not to his originality, but to his learning and reputation as a teacher; as a strict Aristotelian he clarified the essential points in the doctrines of his time, eliminating obsolete and superfluous theories. As a theologian his personal life was marked by piety and Lutheran orthodoxy. His anatomical manual *Institutiones,* well arranged and handy but without illustrations, was reprinted five times. It became still more famous when his son Thomas brought out an enlarged and illustrated edition, *Novis recentiorum opinionibus* (1641). In addition to four main sections on the abdomen, thorax, head, and extremities there were four *libelli* on the blood vessels, nerves, and skeleton. It was the first manual to describe the olfactory nerves, found by Casserio, as the first pair of cerebral nerves. Bartholin called the suprarenal glands, recently discovered by Bartolomeus Eustachius, the *capsulae atrabiliares,* in the belief that they were hollow and the source of black bile. In 1628 Bartholin published an excellent textbook, *De studio medico,* for his sons.

BIBLIOGRAPHY

I. ORIGINAL WORKS. A full catalog of Bartholin's works is in H. Ehrencron-Müller, *Forfatterlexikon,* I (Copenhagen, 1924), 258–264. Individual works are *Exercitatio de stellis* (Wittenberg, 1606), reissued as *Astrologia sive de stellarum naturae, emendiator et auctior* (Wittenberg, 1606; 6th ed., 1627); *Enchiridion logicum ex Aristotele* (Augsberg, 1608); *Exercitatio physica de natura* (Wittenberg, 1608); *Janitores logici bini* (Wittenberg, 1609); *Disp. physica Basileensis* (Basel, 1610); *Enchiridion metaphysicum ex philosophorum coryphaei* (Augsburg, 1610); *Paradoxa CCXL pathologica, simiotica, diaetetica* (Basel, 1610); *Anatomicae institutiones corporis humani* (Wittenberg, 1611); *De auctoritate Sacrae Scripturae* (Copenhagen, 1627); *De natura theologiae* (Copenhagen, 1627); *Benedictio Aharonis* (Copenhagen, 1628); *De studio medico* (Copenhagen, 1628); *De studio theologico ratione inchoando et continuando* (Copenhagen, 1628); and *Systema physicum* (Copenhagen, 1628). The *Institutiones* was translated by Simon Paulli as *Künstliche Zerlegung menschlichen Leibes* (Copenhagen, 1648) and also into Italian (Florence, 1651).

II. SECONDARY LITERATURE. V. Ingerslev, *Danmarks*

Laeger og Laegevaesen, I (Copenhagen, 1873), 270–274, and G. A. Sommelius, *Lexicon eruditor. Scanensium,* I (Lund, 1776), 133–146, give biographical information, while E. Gotfredsen, *Medicinens historie* (Copenhagen, 1964), p. 230, treats Bartholin's time.

E. SNORRASON

BARTHOLIN, ERASMUS (*b.* Roskilde, Denmark, 13 August 1625; *d.* Copenhagen, Denmark, 4 November 1698), *mathematics, physics.*

Erasmus Bartholin was the son of Caspar Bartholin (1585–1629) and the brother of Thomas (1616–1680). He matriculated at the University of Leiden in 1646 and remained in Holland for several years, studying mathematics. Later he traveled in France, Italy (he received his M.D. at Padua in 1654), and England. Upon his return to Copenhagen, Bartholin was appointed professor of mathematics in 1656 but transferred to an extraordinary chair of medicine in 1657 and to an ordinary one in 1671. He served the University of Copenhagen as dean of the faculty of medicine, librarian, and rector, and was appointed royal physician and privy councilor.

Bartholin wrote little on medicine, although he and his brother Thomas played some part in introducing cinchona bark to Denmark; he also contributed to the journal founded and edited by Thomas, *Acta medica et philosophica Hafniensia.*

His publications in pure mathematics were fairly numerous, but not of great importance. As an exponent of the Cartesian tradition, Bartholin's main interest was in the theory of equations; in this he was directly influenced by Frans Van Schooten. Besides his own works, he issued in almost every year from 1664 to at least 1674 a *Dissertatio de problematibus geometricis* consisting of theses propounded by himself and defended by his students.

Bartholin also worked in astronomy. Like many others, he observed the comets of 23 December 1664–9 April 1665. In this effort he was assisted by Ole Rømer. He did not reach a conclusion about the true orbits, for he was skeptical of all statements about either the place of comets in the heavens (including Tycho Brahe's) or their physical nature (including Descartes's).

Also in 1664 Bartholin began, at the direction of Frederick III of Denmark, to prepare for publication the collected manuscript observations of Tycho Brahe, which the king had bought from Ludwig Kepler. In this task he was again assisted by Rømer. The king's death prevented the project's completion, and its only result was Bartholin's critique of the imperfect *Historia coelestis* of Albert Curtz.

Bartholin's major contribution to science was un-

doubtedly his study of Icelandic spar (specially collected by an expedition sent to Helgusta ir in Reyðarfyorðr, Iceland, in 1668). In physics, as in mathematics, Bartholin was a fervent admirer of Descartes (of whom he wrote: "Miraculum reliquum solus in orbe fuit"), as is evident in his attempt to deal with the newly discovered phenomenon of double refraction. Having shown that both rays (*solita* and *insolita*) are produced by refraction, and given a construction for determining the position of the extraordinary image, he argued that double refraction could be explained in the Cartesian theory of light by assuming that there was a double set of "pores" in the spar. This puzzling phenomenon proved to be of great theoretical interest to both Huygens and Newton. Bartholin was in fairly close touch with both French and German scientists and, through the latter (initially), with the Royal Society. The copy of his *Experimenta crystalli Islandici* that he sent to Henry Oldenburg is now in the British Museum; from it Oldenburg prepared an excellent English précis.

BIBLIOGRAPHY

I. ORIGINAL WORKS. Bartholin's works are in *Francisci à Schooten Principia matheseos universalis* (Leiden, 1651); *Dissertatio mathematica qua proponitur analytica ratio inveniendi omnia problemata proportionalium* (Copenhagen, 1657), a monograph on harmonic proportionals ($2ac = ab + bc$) leading into a short discussion of the resolution of equations; a translation of a minor Greek optical text by Damianos, or Heliodorus of Larissa (Copenhagen, 1657); a completion of two papers of Florimond de Beaune as *De aequationum natura, constitutione & limitibus,* in Descartes's *Geometria* (Amsterdam, 1659); *Auctarium trigonometriae ad triangulorum sphaericorum et rectilineorum solutiones* (Copenhagen, ca. 1663/1664); and *Dioristice, seu Aequationum determinationes duabus methodis propositae* (Copenhagen, 1663). The *Dissertatio, Dioristice,* and *Auctarium* (and perhaps others) were issued under the title *Selecta geometrica* (Copenhagen, 1664). Also see *De cometis anni 1664 et 1665 opusculum* (Copenhagen, 1665); his critique of Albert Curtz's *Historia coelestis* (Augsberg, 1668) in *Specimen recognitionis nuper editarum observationum astronomicarum N. V. Tychonis Brahe* (Copenhagen, 1668); and *Experimenta crystalli Islandici disdiaclastici quibus mira & insolita refractio detegitur* (Copenhagen, 1669). *De naturae mirabilibus quaestiones academicae* (Copenhagen, 1674) is a collection of reprinted essays and addresses (original dates in brackets): "The Study of the Danish Language" [1657], "The Shape of Snow" [1660], "The Pores of Bodies" [1663], "On Cartesian Physics" [1664], "On Attraction" [1665], "On Custom" [1666], "On Nature" [1666], "On Judgment and Memory" [1667], "On Experiment" [1668], "On Physical Hypotheses" [1669], "On the Shapes of Bodies" [1671], and "Secrets of the Sciences" [1673]; the article on the Danish language has attracted some interest from modern Danish scholars. *De aere Hafniensi dissertatio* (Frankfurt, 1679) is a pamphlet on climatology that alludes to medieval Iceland. There may well be other tracts by Bartholin.

II. SECONDARY LITERATURE. Works dealing with Bartholin include Axel Garboe, "Nicolaus Steno and Erasmus Bartholinus," in *Danmarks geologiske undersøgelse*, 4th ser., **3**, no. 9 (1954), 38–48; V. Maar, *Den første anvendelse af kinabark i Danmark* (Leiden, 1925); Kirstine Meyer, *Erasmus Bartholin. Et Tidsbillede* (Copenhagen, 1933); and Henry Oldenburg's précis of the *Experimenta crystalli Islandici*, in *Philosophical Transactions of the Royal Society*, **6**, no. 67 (16 Jan. 1671), 2039–2048.

A. RUPERT HALL

BARTHOLIN, THOMAS (*b.* Copenhagen, Denmark, 20 October 1616; *d.* Copenhagen, 4 December 1680), *physiology, anatomy.*

Thomas Bartholin was the second of the six sons in the famous family produced by Caspar and Anna (Fincke) Bartholin. He entered the University of Copenhagen in 1634 and in 1637 went to Leiden, where he decided on medicine as his vocation. Like his renowned father, who successively was professor of anatomy and religion at the University of Copenhagen, he retained a strong interest in the humanities. In Leiden, with the help of Sylvius (Franciscus de le Boë) and Johannes de Wale, he produced in 1641 the first of the many revised editions of his father's *Institutiones anatomicae* (1611). Notably, the new edition recognized the work of Aselli and Harvey. In 1640, threatened by pulmonary tuberculosis, Bartholin went to Paris, then to Orléans and Montpellier, and finally to Padua, where he regained his health, only to develop chronic renal stones. In Padua, he studied with a fellow countryman, Johan Rhode, and the anatomist Johann Vesling. The latter assisted him with a second revision of the *Institutiones,* published in 1645.

In the winter of 1643–1644, Bartholin visited Rome and Naples, where he gained the enduring friendship of Marco Aurelio Severino; in the following spring he visited Sicily and Malta. At Messina he was offered, but declined, a professorship in philosophy. During this time he wrote a thesis (never published) on fossil sharks' teeth (*glossopetrae*), which were thought to have value as medicine. When he returned to Padua, he produced a related treatise, *De unicornu* (1645). The peripatetic Bartholin then moved to Basel, where he obtained a medical degree, and in October 1646 he returned to Copenhagen and joined the faculty of the university. Three years later he married Else Christoffersdatter. Of their children, the most notable was Caspar Bartholin, known eponymously

for Bartholin's gland (*Glandula vestibularis major*) and Bartholin's duct (*Ductus sublingualis major*).

After teaching mathematics for a time, in 1649 Bartholin was chosen to succeed Simon Paulli in the chair of anatomy. Thus Paduan anatomy was introduced to Copenhagen. Hitherto, human dissection had been performed infrequently, was somewhat restricted, and was performed only at the discretion of the king, who sometimes observed from a concealed position. Bartholin's most famous student was Niels Stensen. In his new post, Bartholin was able to study anatomy extensively and regularly, and this is reflected in the third revised edition of the *Institutiones* (1651), an edition much superior in text to the second, which had been severely criticized, both justly and unjustly, by Caspar Hoffmann and Jean Riolan. The third edition was also noteworthy for the illustrations from Casserius and Vesling that replaced the earlier Vesalian figures.

After being informed by his brother Erasmus Bartholin of Pecquet's discovery in dogs of the thoracic duct (*ductus thoracicus*) and the cisterna chyli (*receptaculum chyli*), Bartholin undertook a search for them in the cadavers of two criminals, donated for the purpose by the king. He found the duct, which he reported in *De lacteis thoracis in homine brutisque nuperrime observatis* (1652), but apparently he overlooked the cisterna chyli and declared that it is not always present in man. Bartholin's greatest contribution to physiology was his discovery that the lymphatic system is an entirely separate system. At first he sought to explain the lymphatics, already recognized as anatomical structures, as providing the liver with chyle for the manufacture of blood. On 28 February 1652, working with his assistant, Michael Lyser, Bartholin concluded that the lymphatics formed a hitherto unrecognized physiological system. This was reported in *Vasa lymphatica nuper hafniae in animalibus inventa et hepatis exsequiae* (1653). Failure, in this edition, to indicate the date of discovery by more than the term "28 February" and the inclusion of the further date "1652" in the second edition led to the belief by many that the true year of discovery was 1653. Such was the opinion of Olof Rudbeck, who claimed priority of discovery by reason of his demonstration of the lymphatics in April 1652. Although there was extended controversy, there is now little doubt of Bartholin's priority. In *Vasa lymphatica in homine nuper inventa* (1654), he confirmed the existence of the human lymphatic system.

Continuing attacks of renal stones forced Bartholin to give up his anatomical duties in 1656, after which he turned his attention to a wider range of medical problems. His *Dispensatorium hafniense*

(1658) was the first Danish pharmacopeia. The *Historarium anatomicarum rariorum centuria I-VI* (1654–1661) dealt with numerous limited problems of human and comparative anatomy, and *Cista medica hafniensis* (1662) was a medical miscellany. Bartholin immediately recognized the significance of Malpighi's work on the lungs, *De pulmonibus* (Bologna, 1661)—not least because it provided the first account and illustration of the capillaries, the link between arteries and veins hypothesized by Harvey as a requirement for a systemic circulation of the blood and now proved to exist. Consequently, he included these two celebrated letters in *De pulmonum substantia et motu* (1663), their second publication in Europe. In 1661, Bartholin was elected *professor honorarius,* which freed him from all academic duties, and in 1663 he bought the estate of Hagestedgaard, forty-five miles from Copenhagen. There he devoted himself largely to literary, historical, antiquarian, and medicophilosophical studies, such as *De insolitis partus humani viis* (1664), *De medicina danorum domestica* (1666), *De flammula cordis epistola* (1667), *Orationes et dissertationes omnino varii argumenti* (1668), and *Carmina varii argumenti* (1669). Many unpublished works were lost in 1670 in a disastrous fire at Hagestedgaard, described in *De bibliothecae incendio* (1670).

As the most distinguished physician in Denmark and held in high esteem by the king, Bartholin was responsible for the royal decree of 1672 that decided the organization of Danish medicine for the next hundred years. In 1673 he established the first examination in midwifery at Copenhagen, and in the same year he began publication of the first Danish scientific journal, *Acta medica et philosophica hafniensa.* His health continued to decline, and in 1680 Bartholin sold Hagestedgaard and returned to Copenhagen, where he died. He is buried in the cathedral, the Vor Frue Kurke (Church of Our Lady), but unfortunately the location of his grave is not known.

BIBLIOGRAPHY

I. ORIGINAL WORKS. Bartholin's works, which are discussed in the text, are *Institutiones anatomicae* (Leiden, 1641, 1645, 1651), revised editions of his father's work; *De unicornu* (Padua, 1645); *De lacteis thoracis in homine brutisque nuperrime observatis* (Copenhagen, 1652); *Vasa lymphatica nuper hafniae in animalibus inventa et hepatis exsequiae* (Copenhagen, 1653); *Vasa lymphatica in homine nuper inventa* (Copenhagen, 1654); *Historarium anatomicarum rariorum centuria I-VI* (Copenhagen, 1654–1661); *Dispensatorium hafniense* (Copenhagen, 1658); *Cista medica hafniensis* (Copenhagen, 1662); *De pulmonum substantia*

et motu (Copenhagen, 1663); *De insolitis partus humani viis* (Copenhagen, 1664); *De medicina danorum domestica* (Copenhagen, 1666); *De flammula cordis epistola* (Copenhagen, 1667); *Orationes et dissertationes omnino varii argumenti* (Copenhagen, 1668); *Carmina varii argumenti* (Copenhagen, 1669); *De bibliothecae incendio* (Copenhagen, 1670).

II. SECONDARY LITERATURE. Despite the destruction of a number of his manuscripts in the fire of 1670, Bartholin's bibliography remains extensive. The fullest list is H. Ehrencron-Müller, *Forfatterlexikon omfattende Danmark, Norge og Island indtil 1814,* I (Copenhagen, 1924), 276–290. Bartholin's work on the lymphatics has been translated from Latin into Danish by F. Lützhøft and G. Tryde as *Lymfekarrene af Thomas Bartholin* (Copenhagen, 1936); and by G. Tryde as *Thomas Bartholins skrifter om opdagelsen af lymfekarsystemet hos dyrene og mennesket* (Copenhagen, 1940). There is an English version of Bartholin's youthful travels and of the burning of Hagestedgaard, translated by C. D. O'Malley: *Thomas Bartholin on the Burning of His Library and on Medical Travel* (Lawrence, Kans., 1961).

The fullest biographical account is that of Axel Garboe, *Thomas Bartholin et bidrag til dansk natur-og laegevidenskabs historie i det 17. aarhundrede,* 2 vols. (Copenhagen, 1949–1950).

C. D. O'MALLEY

BARTOLI, DANIELLO (*b.* Ferrara, Italy, 12 February 1608; *d.* Rome, Italy, 12 January 1685), *physics.*

Bartoli entered the Society of Jesus at the age of fifteen and studied with the Jesuits at Piacenza and Parma. After teaching rhetoric at Parma for a time, he proceeded to Milan and Bologna for theological studies. At Bologna he studied under G. B. Riccioli. He took his vows in 1643. In 1650, after extensive travel, he was made historian of the Jesuits, and thereafter resided principally in Rome. From 1671 to 1673 he was rector of the Collegio Romano (now the Gregoriana), the principal Jesuit university.

Bartoli's major published works comprise histories of the first century of Jesuit activity in England, Italy, China, and Japan. He also wrote extensively on Italian literary matters and on morals. In the scientific field he did much to expound and popularize the work of contemporary physicists, particularly barometric experiments and the concept of atmospheric pressure (1677). He also wrote works on the physical analysis of sound, sound waves, and the sense of hearing (1679), and on the phenomena of freezing (1681). The last-mentioned work was severely criticized by Giuseppe Del Papa, professor of philosophy at the University of Pisa, in a published letter to Francesco Redi.

Although not distinguished by valuable original contributions, Bartoli's scientific expositions were generally objective, clear, and attractively written; they evidence wide reading and a spirit of true inquiry. Bartoli sought to link the speculative and experimental approaches in science. He did not hesitate to mention Galileo with praise and to quote from his works (which were still on the *Index*) and from those of such foreign writers as William Harvey, Marin Mersenne, and Pierre Gassendi. Occasionally he disputed Galileo's opinions, especially on harmonic theory. To judge by their numerous editions and translations, his books were widely read and did much to render the scientific debates of his day interesting and accessible to the general reader, as well as to inculcate a taste for impartial consideration of scientific evidence.

Thomas Salusbury, the English translator of Galileo's works, published in 1660 a translation of Bartoli's *Dell'huomo di lettere difeso, et emendato*. The book was designed to encourage the pursuit of scholarship under such difficulties as poverty, hostile criticism, and neglect of one's published work; to stimulate public appreciation of original ideas; and to discourage plagiarism or the worship of authority by students. Bartoli's work was undoubtedly effective, both in Italy and abroad, in increasing interest among lay readers in the burgeoning physics of the seventeenth century.

BIBLIOGRAPHY

Bartoli's collected works (*Opere*) were published in fifty volumes (Florence, 1829–1837). His letters were published with a biography by G. Boero in *Lettere edite ed inedite del p. Daniello Bartoli* (Bologna, 1865). The works of scientific interest include *Dell'huomo di lettere difeso, et emendato* (Rome, 1645), translated by Thomas Salusbury as *The Learned Man Defended and Reformed* (London, 1660); *La ricreazione del savio* (Rome, 1659); *La tensione, e la pressione* (Rome, 1677); *Del suono, de' tremori armonici, e dell'udito* (Rome, 1679); and *Del ghiaccio e della coagulazione* (Rome, 1681). An exhaustive bibliography appears in C. Sommervogel, S. J., *Bibliothèque de la compagnie de Jésus* (Louvain, 1960).

The biographical article by A. Asor-Rosa in *Dizionario biografico degli italiani*, VI (Rome, 1964), includes a modern critical appraisal of Bartoli's literary and historical activities.

STILLMAN DRAKE

BARTOLOTTI, GIAN GIACOMO (*b.* Parma, Italy, *ca.* 1470; *d.* after 1530), *medicine, history of medicine.*

Bartolotti came from a family of doctors; his father, Pellegrino, was competent in both pharmacy and surgery. Gian Giacomo studied philosophy and medi-

cine at the universities of Bologna and Ferrara; at the latter he was a pupil of Antonio Cittadini and of Sebastiano Dell'Aquila, both of secondary importance in the medical ranks of Ferrara. He was there in 1494, among those who witnessed the conferring of degrees, and in 1497 he attended an anatomical dissection. A year later, although not included on the list of professors holding regular appointments at Ferrara, he was assigned to teach a course on the fourth "fen" of the first book of the *Canon* of Ibn Sīnā (Avicenna). He prefaced the course with a series of historical lessons that he also used as an introduction to his *Opusculum de antiquitate medicinae*. Toward the close of the century he was practicing medicine, and in the early sixteenth century he was doing so at Venice.

In 1758 Mazzuchelli revealed an Italian translation that Bartolotti had made of the *Table* (*Pinax*), a dialogue attributed to Cebes, the Theban philosopher who was a disciple of Socrates and Philolaus.

In his *Opusculum de antiquitate medicinae,* a brief treatise on the history of ancient medicine, Bartolotti exhibits praiseworthy zeal, even though the work is based on obvious critical naïveté regarding historical-scientific orientation of the ancient period. Nevertheless, he reveals a good knowledge of classical medical literature, and in the early chapters he analyzes the origins of medical thought.

BIBLIOGRAPHY

I. ORIGINAL WORKS. MS of Cebe's *Table,* translated into the vernacular at the request of Niccolò Maria d'Este, bishop of Adria, is preserved in the Library of the Somaschi Fathers of the Salute in Venice, Codex Vaticanus 288, and bears the notation "Ferrariae 1498, die 28. Aprilis." *Opusculum de antiquitate medicinae,* Codex Vaticanus 5376, was translated, along with introduction, into English by Dorothy M. Schullian and, in the same volume, into Italian by Luigi Belloni (Milan, 1954). Mention must also be made of *Tractatus de natura daemonum* (1498) and *Tractatus complessionum* (1520), which are in the MS Vaticanus latinus 5376.

II. SECONDARY LITERATURE. Mention of Bartolotti may be found in I. Affo, *Memorie degli scrittori e letterati parmigiani* (Parma, 1791), pp. 178–179; and G. M. Mazzuchelli, *Gli scrittori d'Italia,* II, pt. 1 (Brescia, 1758), 479.

LORIS PREMUDA

BARTON, BENJAMIN SMITH (*b.* Lancaster, Pennsylvania, 10 February 1766; *d.* Philadelphia, Pennsylvania, 19 December 1815), *botany, zoology, ethnography, medicine.*

Barton was the author of the first botanical textbook published in the United States, *Elements of*

Botany (1803), which ran to six editions (three during his lifetime); an influential teacher at the University of Pennsylvania (his students included William Darlington, William Baldwin, Charles Wilkins Short, Thomas Horsfield, and Meriwether Lewis); the patron of Frederick Pursh and Thomas Nuttall, with whose specimens he hoped to produce a flora of North America; and the owner of the largest private natural history library of his time. Between 1797 and 1807 he assembled what was then the largest herbarium of native plants (1,674 specimens).

His father, Thomas Barton, attended Trinity College, Dublin; came to Pennsylvania in 1750; and married David Rittenhouse's older sister, Esther, in 1753. Ordained in the Anglican Church, he worked with the Indians around Carlisle, and settled on Conestoga Creek. Benjamin's mother died in 1774, and his father in 1780, leaving Benjamin an orphan at fourteen. Educated by his older brother, William, and at an academy in York, Pennsylvania, he early showed a liking for history, natural history, and drawing, but recurrent gout soon plagued his health. He commenced medical training at eighteen under Dr. William Shippen of Philadelphia. During 1785 he joined his uncle David Rittenhouse, commissioned to survey the western boundary of Pennsylvania. During the first of his two years (1786–1787) of medical studies at the University of Edinburgh, although twice ill, he won for his dissertation on black henbane the Harveian Prize, which he did not receive until about 1813. He had been made one of four annual presidents of the Royal Medical Society of Edinburgh and had been entrusted with a sum of the Society's money, which he was unable to return before his departure.

Barton did not receive a medical degree from Edinburgh, nor is there confirmation that he did from Göttingen, but he received a diploma from Lisbon Academy, Portugal. He took no pride in the Lisbon diploma, however, and in 1796 he wrote (but may not have sent) a letter to D. Christopher Ebeling of Hamburg University, seeking a degree from that or another German university. In 1801 *A Memoir concerning the disease of Goitre, as it prevails in different parts of North America* (Philadelphia, 1800) was published in Portuguese in Lisbon (his doctoral thesis?) and in 1802 in German in Göttingen.

Barton's "irritable and even cholerick" disposition with his colleagues, influenced by his gout, was no doubt worsened by the consciousness of the sum unreturned to the Medical Society. As his nephew, W. P. C. Barton, wrote (p. 283): " . . . the struggles he made in early life through the most discouraging, nay appalling influence of want, added to the direful ravages of disease—his subsequent elevation appears astonishing. . . . He whose mental exertions survive such a fate, and who perseveres through it, is not, believe me, a common man!"

In 1789, at the age of twenty-three, Barton returned to Philadelphia to become professor of natural history and botany; in 1795 he succeeded to the professorship of materia medica, and in 1813 he added the professorship of the practice of physic to his already too busy life. For ten years (1790–1800) he served as one of the American Philosophical Society's curators, and from 1802 to 1815 as one of its vice-presidents. In 1797 he married Mary Pennington, by whom he had two children, Thomas Pennant and Hetty. He visited Thomas Jefferson at Monticello in 1802, and revisited Virginia in 1805.

Barton was continually publishing short papers on his observations, or those related to him by his associates, not always with permission or acknowledgment. His prose was diffuse and sometimes redundant; he seldom revised but expostulated in an intimate style. His interpretations of complex phenomena generally followed the views of the antiquarians. His bibliography is a farrago, for he continually announced projected works, varying their titles. He began a revision of Gronovius' *Flora Virginica,* and a "Flora of Pennsylvania." In 1808 he began editing successful European works, relating the content to American readers. Meanwhile, to the dismay of Jefferson and others, his natural history of the Lewis and Clark expedition lay unfinished.

In 1815 Barton revisited France and England, then died within two weeks of his return to Philadelphia. Barton had, said Elliott Coues, "every qualification of a great naturalist except success, his actual achievements being far from commensurate with his eminent ability and erudition."

BIBLIOGRAPHY

I. Original Works. Barton's papers are preserved in the Academy of Natural Sciences of Philadelphia, the American Philosophical Society, the Pennsylvania Historical Society, the Boston Public Library, the Library of Congress, and the possession of John R. Delafield. Barton launched the *Philadelphia Medical and Physical Journal* (1804–1809), to which he contributed numerous articles on medicine, natural history, physical geography, and lives of naturalists. Lists of his writings are found in Max Meisel, *Bibliography of American Natural History,* 3 vols. (New York, 1924–1929); *Elements of Botany,* 6th ed., William P. C. Barton, ed. (Philadelphia, 1836), pp. 27–30, illustrated, as were all editions, with drawings by William Bartram; Whitfield J. Bell, Jr., *Early American Science, Needs and*

Opportunities for Study (Williamsburg, Va., 1955), p. 45; and Francis W. Pennell, "Benjamin Smith Barton as Naturalist," in *Proceedings of the American Philosophical Society,* **86** (1942), 108–122. W. L. McAtee edited "Journal of Benjamin Smith Barton on a Visit to Virginia, 1802," in *Castanea,* **3** (1938), 85–117.

II. SECONDARY LITERATURE. Additional sources, any of which must be read with caution as to the known facts and/or the bias of the writer in mind, are Jeannette E. Graustein, "The Eminent Benjamin Smith Barton," in *Pennsylvania Magazine of History and Biography,* **85** (1961), 423–438; John C. Greene, "Early Scientific Interest in the American Indian: Comparative Linguistics," in *Proceedings of the American Philosophical Society,* **104** (1960), 511–517; [John E. Hall] "Life of Benjamin S. Barton M.D.," extracted from the paper read by W. P. C. Barton before the Philadelphia Medical Society shortly after his uncle's death, in *The Port Folio,* 4th ser., **1** (1816), 273–287; Francis Harper, "Proposals for Publishing Bartram's *Travels,*" in *Library Bulletin of the American Philosophical Society* (1945), 27–38; Francis W. Pennell, "The Elder Barton—His Plant-Collection and the Mystery of His Floras," in *Bartonia,* no. 9 (1926), 17–34; and Edgar Fahs Smith, "Benjamin Smith Barton," in *Papers of the Lancaster County Historical Society,* **28** (1924), 59–66. Barton presents his future biographer a challenge matched by few men of his period. The acidulous estimates of his students Charles Caldwell and James Rush may be balanced by the regard of DeWitt Clinton.

JOSEPH EWAN

BARTRAM, JOHN (*b.* Marple, Pennsylvania, 23 May 1699; *d.* Kingsessing, Pennsylvania, 22 September 1777), *botany.*

The eldest child of William Bartram and his first wife, Elizabeth Hunt, both members of the Society of Friends, John Bartram was born on his father's farm near Darby, Pennsylvania. He had only a common country schooling; but, from the age of twelve, as he later said, he had "a great inclination to Botany and Natural History," although for a time medicine and surgery were his "chief study." On reaching manhood, Bartram inherited from an uncle a farm on which he established himself and his young family; he sold it in 1728 and bought another, of 102 acres, on the banks of the Schuylkill River at Kingsessing, four miles from Philadelphia. Here he converted the marshy lands into productive meadows by draining them; and, through intelligent use of fertilizer and crop rotation, he was soon reaping more abundant crops than most of his neighbors. By 1730 he had laid out a small garden where he cultivated plants, shrubs, and trees from different parts of America. As Bartram's interest in scientific botany grew, James Logan, chief justice of the province and a learned amateur of science, encouraged him with loans and gifts of books. About 1734 Bartram was introduced to the London mercer and enthusiast of science Peter Collinson as "a very proper person" to provide specimens of the products of American fields and forests; and thus his career was launched.

Collinson ordered seeds, plants, and shrubs; got Bartram other customers; advised him on what would sell in England; and instructed him how to pack and ship the specimens and even how to behave toward his patrons. The dukes of Richmond, Norfolk, Argyll, and Bedford; Lord Petre; Philip Miller, author of *The Gardener's Dictionary*; Sir Hans Sloane; and Thomas Penn all enriched their gardens and greenhouses with plants obtained from Bartram. In this way Bartram introduced more than a hundred American species into Europe. Collinson and his friends annually raised a fund to pay for their purchases and thus to underwrite Bartram's collecting. Sometimes they sent him botanical works as gifts so that he could identify the plants he found, and Collinson persuaded the Library Company of Philadelphia to give Bartram a membership so that he might use its collections. In addition, Collinson introduced Bartram by letter to Linnaeus, Gronovius, G. L. Buffon, and other European naturalists, and also to Americans who shared his interests.

With a market for his plants thus assured, Bartram began to make a series of botanical journeys to distant parts of the country. The first, in 1736, was to the sources of the Schuylkill River. In 1738 he traveled to Virginia and the Blue Ridge, covering 1,100 miles in five weeks and spending but a single night in any town. He made shorter expeditions to the New Jersey coast and pine barrens and to the cedar swamps of southern Delaware. The yield to science from these explorations was so great that in 1742 Benjamin Franklin and other Philadelphians opened a subscription to enable Bartram "wholly to spend his Time and exert himself" in discovering and collecting plants, trees, flowers, and other natural products. The subscription was abandoned when Logan opposed it, and Bartram never had the kind of financial independence he repeatedly sought. Nonetheless, in the summer of 1742 he tramped over the Catskill Mountains, and in 1743, with Conrad Weiser, the province interpreter, and the cartographer Lewis Evans, he traveled through Pennsylvania into the Indian country of New York as far as Oswego and Lake George. "Our way . . . lay over rich level ground," Bartram wrote of one day's journey, in a good example of both his life in the woods and his prose style,

> . . . but when we left it, we enter'd a miserable thicket of spruce, opulus, and dwarf yew, then over a branch

of Susquehannah, big enough to turn a mill, came to ground as good as that on the other side of the thicket; well cloathed with tall timber of sugar birch, sugar maple, and elm. In the afternoon it thunder'd hard pretty near us, but rained little: We observed the tops of the trees to be so close to one another for many miles together, that there is no seeing which way the clouds drive, nor which way the wind sets: and it seems almost as if the sun had never shone on the ground since the creation.

By 1750 Bartram was famous. Copies of his journals circulated in manuscript in London, and that of the trip to Onondago was published there in 1751. Such American naturalists as Dr. John Mitchell of Virginia and such philosophers as Cadwallader Colden of New York sought him out. Peter Kalm spent so much time at Kingsessing that Logan complained that during an eight-month visit to Philadelphia the Swedish botanist had seen no one but Franklin and Bartram. Dr. Alexander Garden of Charleston wrote of a visit to Bartram in 1754:

His garden is a perfect portraiture of himself, here you meet with a row of rare plants almost covered over with weeds, here with a Beautifull Shrub, even Luxuriant Amongst Briars, and in another corner an Elegant & Lofty tree lost in common thicket. On our way from town to his house he carried me to severall rocks & Dens where he shewed me some of his rare plants, which he had brought from the Mountains &c. In a word he disclaims to have a garden less than Pensylvania & Every den is an Arbour, Every run of water, a Canal, & every small level Spot a Parterre, where he nurses up some of his Idol Flowers & cultivates his darling productions. He had many plants whose names he did not know, most or all of which I had seen & knew them. On the other hand he had several I had not seen & some I never heard of [Earnest, p. 21].

Bartram's observations were not limited to things botanical. He collected shells, insects, hummingbirds, terrapin, and wild pigeons. He described the mussels of the Delaware River, rattlesnakes, wasps, and the seventeen-year locust; and from his letters about them Collinson fashioned communications that were printed in the Royal Society's *Philosophical Transactions*. Except for the introduction and notes for a Philadelphia edition of Thomas Short's *Medicina Britannica* and two short pieces on snakeroot and red cedar for *Poor Richard's Almanack*, Bartram wrote almost nothing for publication; even the Onondago journal, in Kalm's estimate, contained not "a thousandth part of the great knowledge which he has acquired in natural philosophy and history."

Bartram was also interested in every scheme to promote scientific inquiry in America, and he offered several of his own. In 1739 he suggested that "ingenious & curious men" be organized into a society or college for "the study of natural secrets arts & syances." The suggestion was premature, but in 1743 Franklin succeeded in establishing for a few years a less ambitious group, the American Philosophical Society, to which Bartram was especially devoted. In a letter to Garden in 1756 he proposed a kind of geological survey of the mineral resources of the North American continent. Bartram was always ready to become a traveling naturalist, supported by the government or private patrons and reporting his discoveries to his sponsors. As increasing numbers of explorers and collectors uncovered and carried away mammoth fossils from Big Bone Lick, Kentucky, in the 1750's and 1760's, Bartram expressed the hope that wealthy "curiosos" would "send some person that will take pains to measure every bone exactly, before they are broken and carried away, which they soon will be, by ignorant, careless people, for gain."

Single-minded and untiring in pursuit of natural history, Bartram grumbled and complained when anything impeded his work. On the other hand, he was friendly and open to those who shared his devotion. Kalm gratefully acknowledged that he owed Bartram much, "for he possessed that great quality of communicating everything he knew." Everyone who knew him was impressed with Bartram's industry, his capacity for accurate observation and recall, and his independence. When Kalm repeated Mark Catesby's theory that trees and plants decrease in size and strength when they are taken north, Bartram answered that if the question were "more limited," Catesby's answer "would prove more worthwhile"—some trees grow better in the south, others in the north.

This independent turn of mind also showed itself in Bartram's religious views, which were deeply influenced by his studies of nature. He was contemptuous of ecclesiastical formalities and theological points; he was scornful of Quaker pacifism, which he believed made men hypocrites, "for they can't banish freedom of thought"; and, unlike his coreligionists, he judged that the only way to establish lasting peace with the Indians was to "bang them stoutly." He was in fact a deist, and when he persisted in expressions of disbelief in the divinity of Jesus, the Friends disowned him in 1757. He continued to attend Quaker meetings, however—and to express his unorthodox views. "My head runs all upon the works of God, in nature," he wrote in 1762. "It is through that telescope I see God in the sky." Over the window of his house in 1770 he carved the words, "'Tis God alone, Almighty Lord,/The Holy One, by me ador'd."

The sentiment, his son William remembered, gave offense to pious neighbors.

The close of the French and Indian War brought Great Britain a vast increase of territory in North America, and Bartram set out to explore it. He traveled in 1761 to the forks of the Ohio River and to the springs of western Virginia, crawling "over many deep wrinkles in the face of our antient mother earth"; and in 1764 he appealed to Collinson to raise funds to send him on an exploration of Florida. In consequence of his friend's representations, in 1765 Bartram was named king's botanist with an annual stipend of fifty pounds. Although he complained that it was not enough, Bartram set out all the same, accompanied by his son William. Entertained by governors and other officials, he traveled from Charleston through Georgia into Florida, visiting plantations, noting the quality of the soils, and recording trees, plants, and fossils. During these journeys he discovered the lovely *Franklinia altamaha,* which has never since been found in its native soils and survives today only in descent from a specimen Bartram brought back to his garden. In Florida, Bartram went up the St. John's River to Fort Picolata, where he and William witnessed an impressive Indian treaty ceremonial.

This was Bartram's last trip. He was aging, and his sight was failing. He spent his remaining years at Kingsessing, surrounded by family and friends, tending his garden, visited by the great and the curious. One visitor, J. Hector St. John de Crèvecoeur, later published a pleasing, although romanticized, account of Bartram's life and manner of living. Inevitably honors came to Bartram. The Royal Academy of Sciences of Sweden made him a member in 1769, and in 1772 "A Society of Gentlemen in Edinburgh" who were interested in propagating arts and sciences, awarded him a gold medal for his services. Before he died, his fellow citizens and European friends of America had ranked Bartram with Franklin and David Rittenhouse as one of the country's authentic natural geniuses.

Bartram was married twice: in 1723 to Mary Maris of Chester Monthly Meeting, by whom he had two sons; and in 1729 to Ann Mendenhall, of Concord Monthly Meeting, who bore him five sons and four daughters. His sons Isaac and Moses became apothecaries, John inherited the farm and famous garden, and William achieved lasting fame as a botanical traveler, artist, and author. John Bartram, in William's words, was "rather above the middle size, and upright," with a long face and an expression that was at once dignified, animated, and sensitive. A painting by John Wollaston in the National Portrait Gallery in Washington is thought to be a portrait of Bartram.

BIBLIOGRAPHY

I. ORIGINAL WORKS. Bartram's published writings are *Observations on the Inhabitants, Climate, Soil, Rivers, Productions, Animals, and Other Matters . . . From Pensilvania to Onondago, Oswego and the Lake Ontario, in Canada* (London, 1751); and "Diary of a Journey Through the Carolinas, Georgia, and Florida . . . ," Francis Harper, ed., in American Philosophical Society, *Transactions,* **33,** part 1 (1942–1944), 1–120.

II. SECONDARY LITERATURE. Works on Bartram are William Bartram, "Some Account of the Late Mr. John Bartram, of Pennsylvania," in *Philadelphia Medical and Physical Journal,* **1,** part 1 (1804), 115–124; William Darlington, *Memorials of John Bartram and Humphry Marshall* (Philadelphia, 1849); Ernest Earnest, *John and William Bartram: Botanists and Explorers* (Philadelphia, 1940); Peter Kalm, *Travels in North America,* A. B. Benson, ed., 2 vols. (New York, 1937); Leonard W. Larabee et al., eds., *The Papers of Benjamin Franklin* (New Haven, Conn., 1959–   ), II, 298–299, 355–357, 378–380, *et passim;* Francis D. West, "John Bartram's Journey to Pittsburgh in the Fall of 1761," in *Western Pennsylvania Historical Magazine,* **38** (1955), 111–115; "John Bartram and the American Philosophical Society," in *Pennsylvania History,* **23** (1956), 463–466; and "The Mystery of the Death of William Bartram, Father of John Bartram the Botanist," in *Pennsylvania Genealogical Magazine,* **20** (1956–1957), 253–255.

WHITFIELD J. BELL, JR.

BARTRAM, WILLIAM (*b.* Kingsessing, Pennsylvania, 9 April 1739; *d.* Kingsessing, 22 July 1823), *botany, ornithology.*

William Bartram, third son of the botanist John Bartram and his second wife, Ann Mendenhall, was born on his father's farm at Kingsessing, four miles from Philadelphia. In 1752 he was sent to the Academy of Philadelphia; his studies there included Latin and French, but botany and drawing, his father wrote, were "his darling delight." The father encouraged his son in these directions, taking him on botanizing trips to the Catskill Mountains in 1753 and to Connecticut in 1755, and letting him sketch on Saturday afternoons and Sundays, instead of working and going to meeting. Samples of William's work were sent to Peter Collinson, his father's London friend and patron, who was much pleased with them. Before he left the Academy in 1756, William was making natural history drawings for Collinson and for George Edwards, who used them and William's descriptions of Pennsylvania birds in his *Gleanings of Natural History.* Two of William's drawings of turtles were printed in the *Gentleman's Magazine.*

William had no idea what profession or trade he should enter. His father, sure only that he did not "want him to be what is called a gentleman," consulted Collinson and Benjamin Franklin. He considered medicine, surveying, printing, and engraving for the lad; but finally, in 1757, apprenticed him to a merchant. In 1761 William moved to Cape Fear, North Carolina, where he opened a trading store that soon failed. Nothing, in fact, went well for him, and by 1764 he seemed to Collinson, who liked him, to be "lost in indolence and obscurity."

In 1765 John Bartram, setting out on his trip to Florida, asked William to accompany him. When the journey was over, William chose to remain in the south. Turning down an invitation from Major John G. W. DeBrahm to join him as a draftsman on his survey of Florida, he settled as a planter of rice and indigo, living in a mean hovel on the St. John's River. His father did not approve and could not understand—Billy, he lamented, was "so whimsical and so unhappy." The young man succeeded no better as a planter than as a merchant. He returned to Pennsylvania, eked out a poor living by various means, and made a few drawings for Dr. John Fothergill, the London Quaker physician who had succeeded Collinson as the Bartrams' patron. But the lure of the Carolinas and Florida was strong, and in 1771 William was in the south again. Fothergill encouraged him to visit Florida, offered him fifty pounds a year, and agreed to purchase any drawings he made. With this assurance William set out in March 1773 on the travels that were to make his reputation.

For four years he traveled through South Carolina, Georgia, and Florida. Much of the way he went alone; and so patent were his innocence and devotion to nature that colonial governors—even in wartime—let him come and go freely, and the Indians everywhere welcomed him, naming him *Puc-puggy,* the "Flower Hunter." Bartram made notes on birds, animals, fishes, and plants, which were everywhere in profusion, and he recorded the life of the Indians. He wandered along meandering streams, refreshed himself from crystal springs, took refuge in dark caves from crashing thunderstorms, marveled at the terrifying roar and thrash of angry alligators, and stood in awe before forests of azalea so bright that the very mountains seemed on fire. In this world, which was as much of his own making as nature's, Bartram found peace. He returned to Kingsessing in January 1778, however, and never left again. His brother John, who had inherited their father's farm and garden, made him welcome; and so, after John's death, did their sister and her husband. William never-married.

He worked in the garden, planting, grafting, and performing the many other chores the nursery required. In 1782 the University of Pennsylvania offered him the professorship of botany, but he declined it.

He wrote up his notes and sometimes shyly showed them to visitors; but he was in no hurry to publish, and the *Travels* did not appear until 1791. The book was reprinted in London in 1792 and 1794; and before the decade closed, other editions appeared in Paris, Dublin, Vienna, Berlin, and Holland. Most reviewers praised Bartram's descriptions of natural products and of the Indians; but almost all criticized his style as florid, luxuriant, imaginative, imprecise, and personal. Yet it is for its style that the *Travels* is best known, and for its influence on romantic literature that it has its most lasting fame. Coleridge, Wordsworth, and Chateaubriand filled pages of their notebooks with excerpts from the *Travels;* and from these notebooks Bartram's figures and sense of nature passed through the poets' richly imaginative minds and reappeared, still recognizable, in *Ruth,* "Kubla Khan," "The Rime of the Ancient Mariner," *Atala,* and other works. Bartram, in short, was one of the earliest voices, and one of the authentic sources, of the nineteenth-century romantic movement.

The fame of the *Travels,* in addition to John Bartram's reputation, brought a procession of visitors to Kingsessing; otherwise, William's life was unchanged. He wrote down his observations of the Creek and Cherokee Indians for Benjamin Smith Barton, made most of the drawings for Barton's *Elements of Botany* (1803), and wrote a few papers for Barton's *Philadelphia Medical and Physical Journal,* among them a biographical sketch of his father. To the Philadelphia Society for Promoting Agriculture, which elected him a member in 1785, he sent "Observations on the Pea-Fly or Beetle." At its founding in 1812, the Academy of Natural Sciences made him a member. He was also a member of the American Philosophical Society, but took no interest in its work and never attended a meeting.

Gentle, loving, and well loved, "the happiest union of moral integrity with original genius and unaspiring science," William Bartram lived out his life in harmony with the numberless lives in nature all about him. Without formal education in science, he was nonetheless recognized, as his father had been, for his unequaled knowledge of the natural world. Many sought his help, and he cheerfully shared all he knew. Thomas Nuttall, F. A. Michaux, Thomas Say, and Palisot de Beauvois felt they could hardly begin their work without his advice and blessing. In particular, the ornithologist Alexander Wilson owed much of his training to Bartram, lived for a time at the garden, and urged his benefactor to accompany him on his ornithological journeys. On 22 July 1823, having completed in his study a note on the natural history of a plant, Bartram took a few steps, collapsed, and died in the house where he was born. A portrait by Charles Willson Peale, done in 1808, is in the Independence National Historical Park collection, Philadelphia.

BIBLIOGRAPHY

I. ORIGINAL WORKS. William Bartram's works are "Observations on the Creek and Cherokee Indians, 1789," in American Ethnological Society, *Transactions,* **3,** part 1 (1853), 1–81; "Travels in Georgia and Florida, 1773–74: A Report to Dr. John Fothergill," Francis Harper, ed., in American Philosophical Society, *Transactions, 33,* part 2 (1943), 121–242; and *Travels Through North & South Carolina, Georgia, East & West Florida, . . .* (Philadelphia, 1791). Of many subsequent printings and editions of the *Travels,* that edited by Francis Harper (New Haven, Conn., 1958) is most useful for scholars.

II. SECONDARY LITERATURE. Works concerning Bartram are William Darlington, *Memorials of John Bartram and Humphry Marshall* (Philadelphia, 1849); Ernest Earnest, *John and William Bartram: Botanists and Explorers* (Philadelphia, 1940); N. Bryllion Fagin, *William Bartram, Interpreter of the American Landscape* (Baltimore, 1933); John Livingston Lowes, *The Road to Xanadu* (Boston, 1927).

The drawings Bartram made for Fothergill, now in the British Museum (Natural History), have been published, in color and with an introduction and notes by Joseph Ewan, by the American Philosophical Society (Philadelphia, 1968).

WHITFIELD J. BELL, JR.

BARUS, CARL (*b.* Cincinnati, Ohio, 19 February 1856; *d.* Providence, Rhode Island, 20 September 1935), *physics.*

Barus was the son of German immigrants. His father, Carl Barus, Sr., was a musician and choirmaster; his mother, Sophia Moellmann, was a clergyman's daughter. Despite persistent financial difficulties, he attended Columbia University's School of Mines from 1874 to 1876 and from 1876 to 1879 studied at Würzburg, where he took his Ph.D. under Friedrich Kohlrausch. Barus worked for the United States Geological Survey (1880–1892), the United States Weather Bureau (1892–1893), and the Smithsonian Institution (1893–1894), where he assisted Samuel P. Langley with the development of the flying machine. Appointed to the Hazard professorship of physics at Brown University in 1895, he became dean of the graduate school in 1903 and taught until his retirement in 1926. Barus was married in 1887 to Annie G. Howes of Massachusetts, a graduate of Vassar College who was active in civic and social reform.

While at the Geological Survey, Barus worked in collaboration with the geologist Clarence King, an advocate of aiding the study of geological evolution with the laboratory analysis of rocks and minerals under high temperatures and pressures. Perhaps Barus' most significant achievement was the development, independently of Châtelier, of methods of measuring, with thermocouples, temperatures over a range of some 1,000° C. Internationally known as an authority on pyrometry, he was elected to the National Academy of Sciences in 1892 and awarded the Rumford Medal of the American Academy of Arts and Sciences in 1900. A founder of the American Physical Society in 1899, he served as its president from 1905 to 1906.

At the Weather Bureau, Barus' research shifted to the condensation of water vapor on nuclei, but his departure interrupted his experiments. Resuming this work about 1900, he studied the effects of X rays and radioactivity on condensation in a fog chamber. The chamber, a cylinder made of wood impregnated with resin, was filled with moist air at atmospheric pressure and connected through a stopcock to another chamber at lower pressure. When the stopcock was opened, the air became supersaturated.

Barus concluded that ionization was relatively unimportant in condensation, but C. T. R. Wilson pointed out that his apparatus was unreliable. Wilson had published two authoritative papers in 1899 showing that ions produced by X rays and radioactivity were significant in condensation. He had used a chamber made almost wholly of glass; supersaturation was achieved by expansion at the sudden drop of a piston. Wilson sharply criticized Barus for ignoring the contaminating effect of the resin in his chamber and for failing to recognize that the stopcock method of expansion allowed condensation to occur before maximum supersaturation. In addition, Barus had failed to shield the chamber from the strong electric field of his X-ray apparatus.

Rutherford, who disliked the fragility of Wilson's glass equipment, encouraged Barus to improve the fog chamber so as to explore the nature of X rays. But Barus soon dropped this work entirely, and by the 1920's, despite continued publication, he had fallen into professional obscurity.

BIBLIOGRAPHY

Barus' papers are in the Brown University Archives, the John Hay Library, Brown University, Providence, R.I. The collection consists of his 269-page unpublished autobiography, a frank account of his personal and professional life; a file of about 750 letters, mostly to Barus from personal and scientific correspondents, covering 1879–1935; ten letterpress books for the years 1882–1897, particularly useful for his work at the Geological Survey; and a small group of miscellaneous scientific papers and notes.

R. Bruce Lindsay, "Carl Barus," in *National Academy of Sciences Biographical Memoirs,* **22** (1943), 171–213, is far better than the usual official memoir by a former student. Based on the Barus papers, it is a sympathetic and perceptive account and contains an apparently complete bibliography of Barus' many publications.

DANIEL J. KEVLES

BARY, HEINRICH ANTON DE. See **DeBary, Heinrich Anton.**

BASIL VALENTINE. See **Valentine, Basil.**

BASSANI, FRANCESCO (*b.* Thiene, Vicenza, Italy, 29 October 1853; *d.* Capri, Italy, 26 April 1916), *paleontology.*

The son of Antonio Bassani and Anna Brolis, Bassani studied geology at Padua with Giuseppe Meneghini and, especially, Giovanni Omboni, who introduced him to fossil fishes. After assisting Omboni for two years, he continued his studies at Paris in 1877 under Hébert, Gaudry, and Sauvage, and in Vienna in 1878 with E. Suess and M. Neumayr. He also studied in Munich with Zittel. From 1879 to 1887 Bassani taught natural history, geology, and mineralogy in secondary schools in Padua, Modena, and Milan, and actively investigated and published on fossil fishes of northern Italy and adjacent regions. In 1887 he was called to the chair of geology at Naples, which he occupied until his death.

Bassani was an outstanding teacher, combining the zest and talent for research with the gift of communicating his discoveries and aspirations clearly and understandably to others. As director of the Geological Institute in Naples he brought about extensive improvements in laboratory facilities and collections. He married Everdina Dowkes Dekker, a native of the Netherlands, whose drawings of fossils illustrate his monographs; they had two sons. In his last years he was afflicted with diabetes, in spite of which he continued his research with the aid of assistants.

Bassani was primarily a student of fossil fishes. He also investigated other geological problems, particularly those of the stratigraphic relations and geologic age of various formations in southern Italy, volcanic phenomena at Vesuvius and Solfatara, the contemporaneity of man and extinct animals on Capri, and marine mammals. Many of his short papers pointed out solutions to problems that led to rapid advances

in regional geology. While still a student, he collaborated in translating Charles Darwin's *Expression of Emotions in Man and Animals* into Italian. In 1885 he published a textbook of zoology for secondary schools.

Bassani's earliest studies were of the Eocene fishes of Bolca (Verona), and he wrote a total of eight papers describing and interpreting these famous fossils; a monographic review commenced shortly before his death was completed by his student D'Erasmo in 1922. The slightly later deposit at Chiavòn (Vicenza) was written up in 1889. His studies of the Cretaceous fishes of Comen (Istria) in 1880 and the island of Lesina (Hvar) in 1882 are more important for the extensive comparisons between numerous Cretaceous faunas of the Mediterranean basin than for their systematic or descriptive portions. In 1886 he described a collection of fishes and reptiles from the Triassic bituminous shales of Besano, near the southern tip of Lake Lugano.

Soon after his appointment at Naples, Bassani investigated the fishes from limestones of the Sorrento Peninsula; these proved to belong to the alpine Triassic fauna, and he was able to show that the main dolomitic limestones of southern Italy, which up to that time had been regarded as Jurassic or Cretaceous, were actually Triassic. About the same time he wrote a monograph on the Miocene fishes of Sardinia; in 1899, on the Eocene fishes of Gassino, in Piedmont; in 1905, those of the Pleistocene marls of Taranto and Nardo; and in 1915, on the fishes of the Miocene of Lecce. At least nine of Bassani's papers are devoted exclusively to fossil sharks, and studies of this group of fishes form prominent parts of other reports. He became expert at discriminating shark teeth and eventually concluded that all Pliocene sharks belonged to existing species.

Bassani's most significant work consisted of faunal revisions; he reviewed nearly all important fossil fishes of the Mesozoic and Cenozoic in Italy. Characteristically, he studied entire fossil assemblages rather than reviewing genera or other systematic groups. His reports include full surveys of earlier studies, carefully organized and detailed descriptions of the fossils, and logically developed conclusions about the environmental implications of the fauna and its geological age. He made extensive use of comparative range charts and based his correlations upon the indications of the bulk of the fauna rather than a few "index" species. As his familiarity with faunas of many ages grew, he developed a concept of fish species evolving slowly through geologic time; in accordance with this, he believed that many of the differently named fossils from faunas of different ages actually belonged to the same species, but in the absence of adequate proof of identity he refrained from relegating them to synonymy. He was widely regarded as one of the leading paleoichthyologists of his day.

BIBLIOGRAPHY

I. ORIGINAL WORKS. Lists of Bassani's publications are in the memorial by D'Erasmo, pp. lxviii–lxxvi, and those by Lorenzo and Parona. See also A. S. Romer, N. E. Wright, T. Edinger, and R. van Frank, "Bibliography of Fossil Vertebrates Exclusive of North America, 1509–1927," in *Memoirs of the Geological Society of North America,* no. 87, I (1962), 100–103.

Individual works by Bassani are *L'espressione dei sentimenti nell'uomo e negli animali* (Turin, 1878), a translation of Darwin's *Expression of Emotions in Man and Animals,* with G. Canestrini; *Elementi di zoologia descrittiva al uso delle scuole secondarie* (Milan, 1885, 1889); "Sui fossili e sull'età degli scisti bituminosi triasici di Besano in Lombardia," in *Atti della Società italiana di scienze naturale,* **29** (1886), 15–72; "Ricerche sui pesci fossili di Chiavòn (strati di Sotzka, Miocene inferiore)," in *Atti della Reale Accademia delle scienze, scienze fisiche e matematiche di Napoli,* 2nd ser., **3,** no. 6 (1889), 1–103; "Sui fossili e sull'età degli scisti bituminosi di Monte Pettine presso Giffoni Valle Piana in provincia di Salerno," in *Memorie della Società italiana delle scienze detta dei XL,* 3rd ser., **9,** no. 3 (1892), 1–27; "Contributo alla paleontologia della Sardegna. Ittioliti miocenici," in *Atti della Reale Accademia delle scienze, scienze fisiche e matematiche di Napoli,* 2nd ser., **4,** no. 3 (1892); "La ittiofauna del calcare eocenico di Gassino in Piemonte," *ibid.,* **9,** no. 13 (1899), 1–41; "La ittiofauna delle argille marnose pleistoceniche di Taranto e di Nardò," *ibid.,* **12,** no. 3 (1905), 1–59; "La ittiofauna del calcare cretacico di Capo d'Orlando presso Castellammare," in *Memorie della Società italiana delle scienze,* 3rd ser., **17** (1912), 185–243, written with G. D'Erasmo; and "La ittiofauna della pietra leccese (Terra d'Otranto)," in *Atti della Reale Accademia delle scienze, scienze fisiche e matematiche di Napoli,* 2nd ser., **16,** no. 4 (1915), 1–52.

II. SECONDARY LITERATURE. Articles on Bassani are G. D'Erasmo, "Commemorazione di F. Bassani," in *Bollettino della Società geologica italiana,* **35** (1916), xlix–lxxvi, including a bibliography of 105 titles; G. de Lorenzo, "Commemorazione di F. Bassani," in *Rendiconti della Reale Accademia delle scienze, scienze fisiche e matematiche di Napoli,* 3rd ser., **22** (1916), 69–88; C. F. Parona, "Cenno necrologico," in *Atti dell'Accademia delle scienze di Torino* (Classe di scienze fisiche, matematiche e naturali), **51** (1915–1916), 945–950, and "A ricordo di F. Bassani," in *Bollettino. Comitato geologico d'Italia,* 5th ser., **6** (1919), 89–102; and C. Stefani, "Commemorazione del Prof. F. Bassani," in *Atti dell'Accademia nazionale dei Lincei. Rendiconti,* 5th ser., **26** (1917), 335–336.

JOSEPH T. GREGORY

BASSI, AGOSTINO MARIA (*b.* Mairago, Italy, 25 September 1773; *d.* Lodi, Italy, 6 February 1856), *law, agriculture, natural science.*

Bassi experimented over many years to determine the cause of the *mal del segno,* or muscardine, the silkworm disease then prevalent. His discovery of the microscopic fungus parasite that caused this malady, commonly believed to be of spontaneous origin, was published in 1835 and contributed importantly to the understanding of contagious disease.

He was one of twins born to Rosa Sommariva and Onorato Bassi. After his early schooling in Lodi, he entered the University of Pavia. He studied law, but at his parents' desire, he later wrote. His study of physics, chemistry, mathematics, natural science, and some medicine is evidence of his interest in science. Among his teachers were Antonio Scarpa, the anatomist, Alessandro Volta, the physicist, and Giovanni Rasori, professor of pathology and a strong proponent of the *contagium vivum* theory at a time when this was in dispute. Bassi was able to attend the lectures of Lazzaro Spallanzani, who had opposed the doctrine of spontaneous generation and carried out experiments to disprove it. He received his doctorate in jurisprudence in 1798 and was named provincial administrator and police assessor in Lodi, newly under French administration. Subsequently he held various positions in the civil service. Failing eyesight forced his return to Mairago, to his father's farm, where, except for a brief period in public service in 1815, he remained for the rest of his life.

As early as 1807 Bassi's attention was drawn to the silkworm disease, but while he conducted his experiments over the years, he maintained a number of agricultural interests, ranging from the importation and breeding of merino sheep and the publication of *Il pastore bene istruito* (1812) to potato cultivation and winemaking, on which he also published.

The silkworm disease, known in Italy as *mal del segno,* or as *calcino* or *calcinaccio,* because of the white efflorescence and calcined appearance that developed after the worms had died of its ravages, had caused heavy losses to the silkworm industry in Italy and in France, where it was called *la muscardine.* Bassi at first accepted the opinion of the silkworm breeders that the disease arose spontaneously. He experimented, therefore, upon various premises: considering the possibility that environmental factors of food, atmospheric conditions, or methods of breeding were responsible, he maltreated the worms in many ways; they died, but not of the muscardine. Then, suspecting excessive acidity to be the cause, he used phosphoric acid, but was unsuccessful in producing the disease. When Bassi obtained worms that seemed to be calcified after death, he found that they lacked the contagious property that characterized *mal del segno.*

After some years, Bassi concluded that the disease was due to external agents and was transmitted by food, by contact with the dead worms that showed white efflorescence, and by the hands and clothing of the silkworm breeders. The germs were also carried by animals and flies. The contagion contaminated the air in rooms where the worms had become infected with the disease. Bassi reproduced the muscardine by inoculating healthy worms with the white dust, or with matter from diseased worms. He infected caterpillars of other species and then, in turn, produced the same disease in silkworms again. Bassi's microscopic investigations showed that the disease was caused by a cryptogam, a fungus parasitic upon the silkworm. The fine efflorescence, which usually appeared following the death of the animal, was composed of a multitude of minute plants bearing the "seeds," and only when they developed did the disease become infectious. The seeds, transmissible in numerous ways, penetrated the bodies of healthy worms and there nourished themselves. The worms eventually died, and, upon maturation, the small plants produced new seeds. The latent life of the seeds was somewhat under two years, but under certain circumstances it was three.

Bassi presented his results at the University of Pavia in 1833, and in the following year repeated his experiments to the satisfaction of a nine-member committee of the faculties of philosophy and medicine. He reported his experiments and conclusions in *Del mal del segno, calcinaccio o moscardino, malattia che afflige i bachi da seta e sul modo di liberarne le bigattaje anche le più infestate* (1835–1836). He was reviving the *contagium vivum* theory of Rasori, he remarked; it had already been suggested that the disease was caused by a fungus, but only on the basis of odor. It was Bassi who first demonstrated through experiments that a living fungus parasite was the cause of a disease in animals. We know the white efflorescence actually is a mass of spores. During the life of the silkworm the mycelium grows at the expense of the animal and the worm, in time, dies. The hyphae, which penetrate the skin, bear the fine, white, dustlike spores which only then appear.

The first part of the *Del mal del segno* contained a theory proposing that some contagions of plants and animals had their source in the "germs" of plant or animal parasites, and that possibly certain diseases of man were caused by vegetable organisms. The second part was devoted to practical methods of preventing and eliminating the silkworm disease through the avoidance of contamination, the disinfection of rooms where the disease had occurred, and the boiling of implements. He included fresh air and sunlight among his disease preventives and disinfectants.

The minute fungus parasite discovered by Bassi was examined by the botanist Giuseppe Balsamo-Crivelli, professor at the University of Milan. He described it as the vegetable parasite *Botrytis paradoxa,* of the family *Mucedinaceae,* and later named it for Bassi, *Botrytis bassiana* (today *Beauvaria bassiana*).

Confirmation of Bassi's discovery by Jean-Victor Audouin and others came soon after the publication of *Del mal del segno.* The significance of this work was recognized as far greater than its immediate value to practical agriculturists. Johann Lukas Schönlein of Zurich remarked upon the implications for pathogenesis in Bassi's discovery of the fungus origin of muscardine. He recounted his own repetition of Bassi's experiments, for with these in mind he had microscopically examined material from the pustules of favus, and had found the disease to be caused by a vegetable parasite, a fungus. Bassi's influence has been traced in the subsequent investigations of David Gruby, Miles J. Berkeley, and others who considered fungus parasites as a cause of disease in both animals and plants. Bassi's conviction that parasites were actively involved in most contagions was also reflected in Jakob Henle's classic paper of 1840, "Von den Miasmen und Contagien und von den miasmatisch-contagiösen Krankheiten." Over the ensuing years, the clearer understanding of the nature of parasitism affected concepts of infectious disease and contributed to the undermining of the doctrine of spontaneous generation. Bassi's use of experimental inoculation showed his understanding of the importance of this means of tracing the life history of the invading organism. It was to be utilized by the mycologist Anton de Bary in later years.

With time Bassi's increasing loss of eyesight precluded further microscopic observations. His later writings showed his continuing interest in contagion, for he suggested that parasites, animal or vegetable, were the cause of various diseases, including plague, smallpox, syphilis (1844), and cholera (1849). Since the minute germs spread, he advocated quarantine and various modes of prevention and disinfection, employing both asepsis and antisepsis.

Bassi's outstanding and enduring contribution to the understanding of the origin of infectious disease was his demonstration of the fungus cause of the silkworm disease.

BIBLIOGRAPHY

I. ORIGINAL WORKS. Bassi's outstanding publication was *Del mal del segno, calcinaccio o moscardino, malattia che afflige i bachi da seta e sul modo di liberarne le bigattaje anche le più infestate,* 2 pts. (Lodi, 1835–1836; 2nd ed., Milan, 1837; facsimile of 1st ed., Pavia, 1956). The American Phytopathological Society has published a translation of pt. 1 by P. J. Yarrow in Phytopathological Classics, no. 10, C. G. Ainsworth and P. J. Yarrow, eds. (Baltimore, 1958). Three medical works are *Sui contagi in generale e specialmente su quelli che affliggono l'umana specie* (Lodi, 1844); *Discorsi sulla natura e cura della pellagra* (Milan, 1846); and *Istruzioni per prevenire e curare il colera asiatico* (Lodi, 1849). *Opere di Agostino Bassi* (Pavia, 1925) contains a collection of his works. *Documenti Bassiani,* Luigi Belloni, ed. (Milan, 1956), including an autobiographical writing (1842), portraits, facsimiles, and manuscripts, was issued to commemorate the centenary of Bassi's death, and is a valuable source of material on his life and contributions. In the same year there appeared *Studi su A. Bassi,* Luigi Cremascoli, Luigi Belloni, Letizia Vergnano, and Attilio Zambianchi, eds. (Lodi, 1956), with the autobiographical fragment and lists of works, manuscripts, documents, portraits, and illustrations. It also contains a catalog of the 1956 commemorative exhibition relating Bassi's work to other writings, both earlier and later, on *contagium vivum* and the etiology of infectious disease.

II. SECONDARY LITERATURE. Works on Bassi are C. G. Ainsworth, "Agostino Bassi, 1773–1856," in *Nature,* **177** (1956), 255–257; Giovanni P. Arcieri, *Agostino Bassi in the History of Medical Thought, A. Bassi and L. Pasteur* (New York, 1938; Florence, 1956), which stresses his role as a founder of microbiology; Bajla, "Agostino Bassi da Lodi, 1773–1856," in *La clinica veterinaria,* **47** (1924), 186–189; William Bulloch, in *The History of Bacteriology* (London, 1938, 1960), which presents Bassi's doctrine of pathogenic microorganisms in its historical relation to concepts of disease and to the investigations of parasitic cryptogams that followed his work on the silkworm disease; Ralph H. Major, "Agostino Bassi and the Parasitic Theory of Disease," in *Bulletin of the History of Medicine,* **16,** no. 2 (1944), 97–107; Adalberto Pazzini, "The Influence of Agostino Bassi on the Evolution of Microbiology," in *Scientia medica italica,* 2nd ser., English ed., **3** (1954), 187–195; and G. C. Riquier, "Agostino Bassi, 1773–1856," in *Rivista di storia delle scienze mediche e naturali,* **6** (1924), 48–51. Gian Battista Grassi's "Commentario all'opera parasitologica (sui contagi) di Agostino Bassi" is included in the *Opere di Agostino Bassi,* pp. 11–48, and in the booklet accompanying the facsimile edition of *Del mal del segno,* pp. 5–33. Luigi Belloni, "La scoperta di Agostino Bassi nella storia del contagio vivo," is in *Studi su A. Bassi,* pp. 55–86, and in *Actes du VIIIᵉ Congrès international d'histoire des sciences* (Florence-Milan, 1956), II, 897–909.

GLORIA ROBINSON

BASSLER, RAYMOND SMITH (*b.* Philadelphia, Pennsylvania, 22 July 1878; *d.* Washington, D.C., 31 October 1961), *paleontology.*

In his presidential address to the Paleontological Society in 1933, Bassler lamented the passing of an era when training was acquired more in the field than in the classroom: The modern student, attaining maturity before deciding on paleontology as his lifework, loses precious years of interest and experience. As a youth, Bassler had himself spent many hours collecting marine fossils in the dusty Ordovician outcrops near his Cincinnati home, and had worked after high school every day as technical assistant to E. O. Ulrich.

Bassler's close association with Ulrich lasted well beyond his high-school days. When the elder scientist moved to Washington, the younger withdrew from the University of Cincinnati and followed him. Ulrich's influence colored his entire career. He adopted Ulrich's methods and approaches to problems, his interest in paleontology, and his passion for collections and catalogs.

Bassler did graduate work at George Washington University, taking the M.S. and Ph.D., and during this time was employed by the United States National Museum. He was affiliated with these two institutions for nearly four decades.

A world authority on Silurian and Ordovician Bryozoa, Bassler assembled an outstanding collection of these fossils, now at the Smithsonian Institution. He also published valuable bibliographic indexes relating to them: "Bibliographical Index of American Ordovician and Silurian Fossils" (1915), "Early Bryozoa of the Baltic Provinces" (1911), and "Synopsis of American Fossil Bryozoa" (1900). His study of other phyla resulted in the compilation of the *Bibliographic Index of Paleozoic Ostracoda* (1934) and *Bibliographic and Faunal Index of Paleozoic Echinoderms* (1943), as well as shorter papers on tetra corals, Cystoidea, and conodonts.

In the 1933 presidential address, Bassler advocated the classical geological practice of retouching photographs of specimens, a position that has led modern paleontologists to characterize his work as "enthusiastic."

BIBLIOGRAPHY

I. ORIGINAL WORKS. Bassler's writings include "A Synopsis of American Fossil Bryozoa," in *Bulletin of the U.S. Geological Survey,* no. 173 (1900), 9–663, written with J. M. Nickles; "A Revision of Paleozoic Bryozoa," in *Smithsonian Miscellaneous Collections,* **45** (1904), 256–296; **47** (1904), 15–45, written with Ulrich; "The Early Bryozoa of the Baltic Provinces," in *Bulletin of the U.S. National Museum,* **77** (1911), 1–382; "Bibliographic Index of American Ordovician and Silurian Fossils," *ibid.,* **92** (1915), 1–1521 (in 2 vols.); "Development of Invertebrate Paleontology in America," in *Bulletin of the Geological Society of America,* **44** (1933), 265–286; *Bibliographic Index of Paleozoic Ostracoda,* Geological Society of America, special paper no. 1 (Washington, D.C., 1934); and *Bibliographic and Faunal Index of Paleozoic Echinoderms,* Geological Society of America, special paper no. 45 (Washington, D.C., 1943).

II. SECONDARY LITERATURE. Articles on Bassler are Kenneth Caster, "Memorial to Raymond S. Bassler," in *Bulletin of the Geological Society of America, 76,* no. 11 (1965), 167–173; and *National Cyclopedia of American Biography,* XLIX (1966), 482.

MARTHA B. KENDALL

BASSO, SEBASTIAN (*fl.* second half of the sixteenth century), *natural philosophy.*

Although Basso was famous as a reviver of the atomic philosophy, and was mentioned by Descartes, Gassendi, and Jungius, there is little biographical information about him. He is known only as the author of *Philosophiae naturalis adversus Aristotelem,* which tells us that he was a physician and had studied at the new Academia Mussipontana (Pont à Mousson).

In the choice and arrangement of topics, Basso follows the Aristotelian tradition of the sixteenth century. The authors most discussed are Scaliger, Toletus, Piccolomini, Zabarella, and the Conimbricenses. But Basso's aim is to oppose Peripatetic opinions, and to prove that many puzzling problems in natural philosophy can be solved satisfactorily only by reviving the doctrines of such pre-Aristotelian thinkers as Empedocles, Democritus, Anaxagoras, and Plato. Basso's central doctrines are that all matter consists of very small atoms of different natures and that a very fine, corporeal ether extends throughout the universe and fills the pores between the atoms. The atomic doctrine is invoked, in a sustained polemic with Scaliger, to prove that the forms of the constituents really persist in the compound. Particles of the four elements combine into groupings of the second order, third order, and so on, and produce the characteristic properties of a specific body. The predominant element determines whether an inorganic, compound body is *solida, liquida, fusilia,* or *meteoria.* Transmutation of the elements is held to be impossible, since the ultimate particles are immutable. When water evaporates, it turns into steam, not air: the fiery particles penetrate the water, and drive the watery particles farther apart and into the air.

The ether, or *spiritus,* which Basso likens to the universal ether of the Stoics, governs the motion and arrangement of the atoms, and is responsible for all material change. The immediate instrument of God

in moving and directing all things, it is different from fire, which consists of *spiritus* plus very fine and sharp corpuscles. Basso is convinced that the vacuum of Democritus signifies nothing but the ether of the Stoics. He attempts to explain a wide range of phenomena by assigning to the ether the function of bringing together likes and driving apart unlikes. He opposes Zabarella's opinions when discussing the acceleration of falling bodies and the motion of projectiles: Acceleration of falling bodies is due to increasing pressure from the air above and diminishing resistance of the air beneath.

Basso considers such traditional questions as the influence of the planets on men, especially of the moon on critical days and tides, and tries to explain them (like Pomponazzi and Fracastoro, among the Aristotelians) in terms of contact-action: very fine and fiery spirits emanate from the planets. Their action begins at birth; before that the body of the mother shields the fetus from their influence.

In attacking Aristotelian philosophy, reviving the pre-Socratics and atomists, and offering corpuscular explanations of physical change, Basso was seen as a precursor by some of the founders of the mechanical philosophy in the seventeenth century.

BIBLIOGRAPHY

Basso's only printed work is *Philosophiae naturalis adversus Aristotelem libri XII. In quibus abstrusa veterum physiologia restauratur, & Aristotelis errores solidis rationes refelluntur* (Geneva, 1621; Elzevir ed., Amsterdam, 1649). It has not been possible to trace a 1574 edition that Jöcher claims was published at Rome.

Works on Basso are I. Guareschi, "La teoria atomistica e Sebastiano Basso con notizie e considerazioni su William Higgins," in *Memoria della Regale Accademia dei Lincei, Classe di Scienze Fisiche, Matematiche e Naturali,* **11** (1916), 289–388; Kurt Lasswitz, *Geschichte der Atomistik vom Mittelalter bis Newton,* I (Hamburg–Leipzig, 1890), 467–481, and *Vierteljahrschrift für wissenschaftlichen Philosophie,* **8** (1884), 18–55; Lynn Thorndike, *A History of Magic and Experimental Science,* VI (New York, 1941), 386–388; and J. R. Partington, *A History of Chemistry,* II (London, 1961), 387–388.

P. M. RATTANSI

BASTIAN, HENRY CHARLTON (*b.* Truro, England, 26 April 1837; *d.* Chesham Bois, England, 17 November 1915), *neurology, bacteriology.*

Little is known of Bastian's early life except that his father was named James and that the boy showed great interest in natural history. In 1856 he entered University College London, and seven years later was graduated M.B. At first he worked at St. Mary's Hospital, London, as assistant physician and lecturer on pathology, but returned to his *alma mater* in 1867 as professor of pathological anatomy, having received the M.D. a year before. He continued to practice clinical medicine, and in 1878 was promoted to physician to University College Hospital. From 1887 to 1898 Bastian held the chair of the principles and practice of medicine and also had an appointment at the National Hospital in Queen Square, London, from 1868 to 1902. Early in his career he worked on the problem of abiogenesis, or spontaneous generation, and the return of this interest determined his premature retirement from clinical neurology.

Bastian married Julia Orme in 1866, and had three sons and a daughter. He was elected a fellow of the Royal Society of London in 1868, at the age of thirty-one; served as a censor of the Royal College of Physicians of London from 1897 to 1898; and received honorary fellowship of the Royal College of Physicians of Ireland and an honorary M.D. from the Royal University of Ireland. From 1884 to 1898 Bastian was crown referee in cases of supposed insanity, and a few months before he died, he was awarded a Civil List pension of £150 a year in recognition of his services to science. He is said to have been a close friend of Herbert Spencer, but the philosopher makes only very slight reference to Bastian in his lengthy autobiography. As one of Spencer's executors, Bastian helped to publish the latter work.

Bastian's earliest scientific work was with guinea worms and other nematodes, but his investigations ended suddenly when he developed a strange allergy to these creatures. His clear analytical mind, sound reasoning, and acute powers of observation drew him to clinical neurology, and he spent the rest of his hospital and academic life in this discipline. Beginning in 1869, he published a series of papers on speech disorders. At a time when it was thought that speech was controlled by independent brain centers, Bastian was the most important of those who represented this view by means of diagrams almost akin to electrical circuits. He described a visual and an auditory word center, and in 1869 he gave the first account of word blindness (alexia) and of word deafness, which is known today as "Wernicke's aphasia." His views on aphasia, which were founded on an assumption that there is a direct relationship between psychological functions and localized areas of brain, were an oversimplification and are no longer accepted. They are presented, with supporting clinical data, in *A Treatise on Aphasia and Other Speech Defects* (1898).

The many publications on clinical and clinico-pathological neurology prepared by Bastian reveal his outstanding practical, philosophical, and literary skills, which he exercised to the full in a specialty of medicine that was then emerging as a more precise science. Nevertheless, his work was overshadowed by that of some of his contemporaries who excelled him. His book *The Brain as an Organ of Mind* (1880) and those on paralyses (1875, 1886, 1893), although important, were less popular than those of other writers; and the claim that he and his contemporaries John Hughlings Jackson and William Gowers founded neurological science in Britain is difficult to justify. Nevertheless, he was an important pioneer of neurology as a science; in addition, his anatomical skill is revealed by the discovery in 1867[1] of the anterior spinocerebellar tract of the spinal cord—now known, however, as "Gowers' tract" because of the more detailed investigation of it made by Gowers in 1880. In 1887 Bastian published his important paper on "muscular sense," which he thought was represented in the cerebral cortex, whereas, in contrast with Ferrier and Beevor, in particular, he considered the cortical motor centers to be unnecessary. In 1890 he showed for the first time that complete section of the upper spinal cord abolishes reflexes and muscular tone below the level of the lesion; this has been known occasionally as Bastian's law.

Bastian himself claimed that his studies on abiogenesis were more significant; and there were two periods of activity in this field, approximately 1868–1878 and 1900–1915. Contrary to accepted biological and bacteriological opinion, he believed that there was no strict boundary between organic and inorganic life. He denied the doctrine of *omne vivum ex ovo* and argued that since living matter must have arisen from nonliving matter at an early stage in evolution, such a process could still be taking place. His battle was fought mostly alone; and eventually he was the last scientific opponent of Pasteur, Tyndall, Koch, and the other pioneers of bacteriology. This was an important role, for he pointed out many of their mistakes; and thus, in a negative way and quite against his purpose, he helped to advance the germ theory of fermentation and of disease. As Pasteur's main opponent, he was responsible for the development of some of the techniques that advanced bacteriology.

Thus, Bastian denied that boiling destroyed all bacteria, as Pasteur claimed, and thereby opened the way for the discovery of heat-resistant spores. On the whole, his criticisms of Pasteur's logic were more effective than the multitude of experiments he cunningly conceived and carried out, for the techniques he used are now known to have been frequently defective. His views and supporting experimental data were set forth in a large book of over 1,100 pages, *The Beginnings of Life* (1872). Concerning the role of bacteria in fermentation, he concluded that "These lowest organisms are, in fact, to be regarded as occasional concomitant products rather than invariable or necessary causes of all fermentative changes."[2] A controversy with Tyndall concerning the existence of airborne germs closed his first period of interest in bacteriology. His opponent's comments summarize the situation in 1878: "Neither honour to the individual nor usefulness to the public is likely to accrue from its [the controversy's] continuance, and life is too serious to be spent in hunting down in detail the Protean errors of Dr. Bastian."[3] He began again to devote all his time to his neurological practice and writings.

Bastian returned to his biological studies in 1900 and devoted the last fifteen years of his life to the fundamental problem of the origin of life. He was the last scientific believer in spontaneous generation, for he succeeded in converting no one to his cause. He had been self-instructed in the field of biological research, and although he learned such recording procedures as photomicrography, he was eventually left behind as the technology of the new science of microbiology developed apace, mainly in the hands of the French and German pioneers. Bastian thought that abiogenesis included "archebiosis," living things arising from inorganic matter, or from dead animal or plant tissues, through new molecular combinations, and "heterogenesis," the interchangeability of the lowest forms of animal and vegetable life, both among themselves and with each other; thus ciliates and flagellae could arise from amoebae.

In this regard Bastian was criticized by biologists who accused him of insufficient knowledge of lower forms of life. He attempted to substantiate these phenomena in *Studies in Heterogenesis* (1904), illustrated by 815 photomicrographs, and in *The Nature and Origin of Living Matter* (1905). Each contains similar arguments, in which he compares the unit of living matter with crystals and suggests that the persistence of lower organisms can be adequately ascribed to their successive evolution. Bastian made solutions containing colloidal silica and iron, and put them in sealed glass tubes that were heat-sterilized and stored under regulated conditions of light and temperature. His claim was that after a time, such organisms as bacteria, torulae, and molds grew, but no one could or would repeat these observations. *The Evolution of Life* (1907) dealt exclusively with archebiosis. Many of his papers were rejected by the Royal Society of London and by other learned bodies; this

was the case with the material of his last book, *The Origin of Life* (1911). Two years later *The Lancet* summarized the scientists' judgment of this losing battle: "To our mind the position is quite unchanged, and we ourselves still remain unconvinced, save, of course, of the courage and good faith of Dr. Bastian."[4]

After Bastian's death his son challenged bacteriologists and others to disprove his father's work on abiogenesis. The correspondence thus stimulated[5] reveals that several investigators thought they had done so, but certain findings are still unexplained. Careful repetition of crucial experiments and a dialectical analysis of his results are still needed. Of Bastian's industry, tenacity, logic, and experimental versatility—although perhaps misplaced—there can be no question.

NOTES

1. "On a Case of Concussion-Lesion . . .," in *Medical-Chirurgical Transactions,* 2nd ser., **32** (1867), 499–537.
2. *Modes of Origin,* p. 108.
3. "Spontaneous Generation. A Last Word," in *Nineteenth Century,* **3** (1878), 497–508, see 508.
4. *The Lancet* (1913), **i,** 970.
5. *Ibid.* (1919), **i,** 951–952, 1000–1001, 1044–1045, 1133–1134; **ii,** 216–217, 458.

BIBLIOGRAPHY

I. ORIGINAL WORKS. Bastian's writings include *The Modes of Origin of Lowest Organisms* (London, 1871); *The Beginnings of Life,* 2 vols. (London, 1872); *On Paralysis From Brain Disease in Its Common Forms* (London, 1875); *The Brain as an Organ of Mind* (London, 1880), also trans. into French and German; *Paralyses, Cerebral, Bulbar and Spinal* (London, 1886); "The 'Muscular Sense'; Its Nature and Cortical Localisation," in *Brain,* **10** (1888), 1–137; *Various Forms of Hysterical or Functional Paralysis* (London, 1893); *A Treatise on Aphasia and Other Speech Defects* (London, 1898), also trans. into German and Italian; *Studies in Heterogenesis* (pub. in 4 pts., London, 1901–1903; pub. together, 1904); *The Nature and Origin of Living Matter* (London, 1905; rev. and abbr. ed., 1909); *The Evolution of Life* (London, 1907), also trans. into French; and *The Origin of Life* (London, 1911, 1913). There is a complete list of Bastian's writings in an unpublished biography by Mercer Rang, "The Life and Work of Henry Charlton Bastian 1837–1915" (1954), MS in Library of University College Hospital Medical School, London.

II. SECONDARY LITERATURE. There is no published work comparable with the Rang MS. Obituaries are *British Medical Journal* (1915), **2,** 795–796; *The Lancet* (1915), **2,** 1220–1224 (including portrait and brief bibliography); and F. W. M[ott], in *Proceedings of the Royal Society of London,*

89 (1917), xxi–xxiv. See also J. K. Crellin, "The Problem of Heat Resistance of Micro-organisms in the British Spontaneous Generation Controversies of 1860–1880," in *Medical History*, **10** (1966), 50–59; Lothar B. Kalinowsky, "Henry Charlton Bastian," in Webb Haymaker, ed., *The Founders of Neurology* (Springfield, Ill., 1953), pp. 241–244; and Mercer Rang, "Henry Charlton Bastian (1837–1915)," in *University College Hospital Magazine*, **39** (1954), 68–73.

EDWIN CLARKE

BATAILLON, JEAN EUGÈNE (*b.* Annoire, Jura, France, 22 October 1864; *d.* Montpellier, France, 1 November 1953), *biology, zoology.*

Bataillon was the son of a stone mason. Although he had a scholarship to the *petit séminaire* of Vaux-sur-Poligny, he refused to prepare for an ecclesiastic career. After he had passed the first part of his *baccalauréat ès lettres* in 1882, he became a *surveillant* at the Collège d'Arbois; after passing the second, he was made assistant master at the Belfort *lycée* and started work on his *licence* in philosophy. Bataillon next went to Lyons as master at the *lycée* and, when he had passed his *baccalauréat ès sciences*, he became a student under the physiologist Fernand Arloing. As a *licencié ès sciences naturelles,* he became an assistant in zoology at the University of Lyons in 1887 and learned the elementary techniques of experimental embryology under Laurent Chabry.

On 17 April 1891, Bataillon presented a thesis for the doctorate in science, *La métamorphose des amphibiens anoures.* Seconded by Pasteur, he was made acting lecturer at the Faculté des Sciences at Lyons and deputy lecturer in zoology and physiology at Dijon in 1892. There he became professor of general biology (the first chair so named in France) in 1903, and dean in 1907. It was in Dijon that he discovered the traumatic parthenogenesis of the batrachians. Appointed professor at the University of Strasbourg, which was being reorganized in 1919, he first set up a new laboratory and then temporarily served as rector. He became rector of the University of Clermont-Ferrand in 1921 but left this administrative position in 1924 to accept a professorship of zoology and comparative anatomy at Montpellier. There he met his principal collaborator, Chou Su, who thereafter helped him in his research. In 1932 Chou Su had to return to China to teach, and Bataillon decided to retire ahead of time. He went to live with one of his sons at Castelnau-le-Lez and later on the outskirts of Montpellier, where he died. He had become a corresponding member of the Académie des Sciences in 1916 and a full member in 1946. He was awarded the Osiris Prize of the Academy in 1951.

The experimental attempts to produce parthenogenesis with sodium chloride and sugar hypertonic solutions or butyric acid had failed, resulting only in an abortive segmentation of the egg (simple activation). During an experimental attempt to fertilize *Bufo calamita* with sperm of *Triturus alpestris,* Bataillon, struck by the resemblance of the spermatozoa to fine needles, thought of substituting glass or platinum stylets for them. On a Sunday in March 1910 the experiment performed on *Rana temporaria* was successful and resulted in 90 percent of the eggs being segmented, of which about 10 percent evolved into normal larvae able to survive.

The analysis of these results demonstrated that besides the simple pricking (first activating factor) there is a second regulating factor, which can be identified as a cell or an inoculated cellular fragment. Operating upon eggs freed of their gelatin coating by potassium cyanide, Bataillon demonstrated, in an elegant experiment, using horse blood that had been defibrinated and sedimented, that the element inoculated was a leukocyte. Later, J. Shaver revealed that the active element is a cytoplasmic fragment rich in ribonucleoproteins.

By this interpretation Bataillon corrected Guyer's error. Guyer had attributed to the nucleus of the leukocyte, released inside the egg by the pricking, the power to divide itself and to direct the embryogenesis. The activator thus provoked the "proper reaction" of the egg membrane, making any further fertilization impossible; there followed a special monocentric rhythm, a succession of monopolar mitoses that were, of course, abortive. The second regulating factor was necessary to determine the sequence of the bipolar mitoses (dicentric or amphiastral rhythm), the only ones capable of bringing about segmentation and, consequently, normal development. An intermediate type of mitosis, bipolar but anastral, appeared when the regulation was insufficient.

Electric shocks, pricking by galvanocautery, and the action of fat solvents could all be the activating factor, but only a biological factor could be the regulator. The latter, however, was not a specific: blood of other anurans, urodeles, fish, or mammals could replace the blood of *Rana.* The action of potassium cyanide as a chemical unsheathing agent was a fortuitous discovery which confirmed that unfertilized eggs pricked, but not smeared with blood, never undergo morphogenesis; it also made possible the experiment with defibrinated and sedimented horse's blood, which could be performed only on naked eggs. Eggs sheathed in serum before pricking showed no regular cleavage; those sheathed in red corpuscles showed only 1 percent; and those sheathed in leukocytes showed 75 percent. The extract of hepatopancreas from the *Astacus* was useful in distinguishing the nonactivated eggs, which were cytolyzed, from the activated ones; the latter, through strengthening of the activating membrane, were able to resist cytolysis. This membrane had to be "modified in thickness," a concept confirmed by modern electronic microscopic research (the bursting of the cortical granules liberated their contents, which then reinforced the vitelline membrane).

Bataillon emphasized this paradox: the spermatozoa of *Rana*, when penetrating the eggs of *Bufo*, caused fewer normal developments than did the *Rana* blood inoculated in *Bufo* eggs. He gave the explanation that the inoculated leukocyte acts only as regulator and does not cause any intervention due to chromosome incompatibilities. G. Hertwig, causing irradiated spermatozoa of *Rana* to act upon eggs of *Bufo*, obtained the same results and came to absolutely the same conclusion. Traumatic parthenogenesis generally leads to haploid larvae, but occasionally diploids may result either from an ovule whose polar mitosis aborted or from a secondary regulation through the fusion of divided nuclei. In such cases a few diploid larvae undergo metamorphosis. The regulation factor therefore can substitute dicentric mitosis for monocentric mitosis but cannot double the number of chromosomes that remain haploid. The role of this factor was confirmed by research done with Chou Su on immature and overmature eggs, and subsequently on "false hybrids," where incompatible nuclei act only as regulation factors.

Bataillon's work, although extremely original, is little known, and his role as a precursor is underestimated. His own modesty and deliberate reticence have lessened his reputation. His unchallenged discovery of traumatic parthenogenesis is important, but even more important is his remarkable analysis of the process, which clarified the complex phenomena of fertilization.

BIBLIOGRAPHY

I. ORIGINAL WORKS. Among Bataillon's writings are "L'embryogenèse complète provoquée chez les amphibiens par piqûre de l'oeuf vierge, larves parthénogénésiques de *Rana fusca*," in *Comptes rendus de l'Académie des sciences*, **150** (1910), 996–998; "Les deux facteurs de la parthénogenèse traumatique chez les amphibiens," *ibid.*, **152** (1911), 920–922; and *Une enquête de trente cinq ans sur la génération*, J. Rostand, S.E.D.E.S., ed. (Paris, 1955), which sums up his work.

II. SECONDARY LITERATURE. Writings on Bataillon include R. Courrier, "Notice sur la vie et les travaux d'Eugène Bataillon," in *Notices et discours de l'Académie des sciences*, 3 (1954), 1–26, which sums up his work; M. F. Guyer, "The Development of Unfertilized Frog Eggs Injected With Blood," in *Science*, **25** (1907), 910–911; G. Hertwig, "Parthenogenesis bei Wirbeltieren hervorgerufen durch artfremden radiumbestrahlten Samen," in *Archiv für mikroskopische Anatomie*, **81** (1913), 87; and J. Shaver, "The Role of Cytoplasmic Granules in Artificial Parthenogenesis," in *Journal de cyto-embryologie belgonéerlandaise* (1949), 61–66.

PAUL SENTEIN

BATE, HENRY. See **Henry Bate of Malines.**

BATEMAN, HARRY (*b.* Manchester, England, 29 May 1882; *d.* Pasadena, California, 21 January 1946), *mathematics, mathematical physics.*

The son of Marnie Elizabeth Bond and Samuel Bateman, a druggist and commercial traveler, Bateman became interested in mathematics while at Manchester Grammar School. He attended Trinity College, Cambridge, where he received a B.A. in 1903 and an M.A. in 1906. After a tour of Europe in 1905–1906 he taught for several years, first at Liverpool University and then at Manchester. In 1910 he emigrated to the United States, where he taught for two years at Bryn Mawr College, then held a three-year research fellowship and lectured at Johns Hopkins from 1912 to 1917, taking his Ph.D. there in 1913. Although by this time he had an international reputation as a mathematician, he worked part time on meteorology at the Bureau of Standards. In 1917 Bateman was appointed professor of mathematics, theoretical physics, and aeronautics at Throop College (which later became California Institute of Technology) in Pasadena, California, where he taught until his death. He was made a fellow of the Royal Society in 1928 and a member of the U.S. National Academy of Sciences in 1930, was elected vice-president of the American Mathematical Society in 1935, and delivered the Society's Gibbs lecture in 1943.

General theories had little attraction for Bateman; he was a master of the special instance. Much of his work consisted of finding special functions to solve partial differential equations. After some geometrical studies, he used definite integrals to extend E. H. Whittaker's solutions of the potential and wave equations to more general partial differential equations (1904). These and later results he applied to the theory of electricity and, with Ehrenfest, to electromagnetic fields (1924).

While in Göttingen in 1906, Bateman became

familiar with the work of D. Hilbert and his students on integral equations. He applied integral equations to the problem of the propagation of earthquake waves, determining, from the time of contact at various surface points, the velocity of the motion at interior points. In 1910 he published a comprehensive report on research concerning integral equations.

Bateman's most significant single contribution to mathematical physics was a paper (1909) in which, following the work of Lorentz and Einstein on the invariance of the equations of electromagnetism under change of coordinates of constant velocity and constant acceleration, he showed that the most general group of transformations which preserve the electromagnetic equations and total charge of the system and are independent of the electromagnetic field is the group of conformal maps of four-dimensional space.

Bateman was one of the first to apply Laplace transform methods to integral equations (1906), but he felt that he never received recognition for this. In 1910 he solved the system of ordinary differential equations arising from Rutherford's description of radioactive decay. From 1915 to 1926 Bateman worked on problems of electromagnetism and classical atomic models that were solved by the quantum theory (1926). His interests shifted to hydrodynamics and aerodynamics; in 1934 he completed a monumental 634-page report on hydrodynamics for the National Academy of Sciences.

In 1930 Bateman set out to find complete systems of fundamental solutions to the most important equations of mathematical physics, and he wrote a text describing many of the methods of solving these equations (1932). Much of the remainder of his life was dedicated to completing the task of collecting special functions and integrals that solve partial differential equations. He developed many of these, such as Bateman's expansion and Bateman's function. Bateman kept references to the various functions and integrals on index cards stored in shoe boxes—later in his life these began to crowd him out of his office. His memory for special facts was phenomenal. Mathematicians both telephoned and wrote to him, asking about particular integrals; and after consulting his files, Bateman supplied the questioner with formulas and extensive references. After his death the Office of Naval Research assembled a team of mathematicians headed by Arthur Erdelyi to organize and publish Bateman's manuscripts. Only parts of the resulting volumes on transcendental functions and integral transforms made extensive use of Bateman's files.

BIBLIOGRAPHY

For bibliographies of Bateman's books and papers and biographical material, see Arthur Erdelyi, "Harry Bateman 1882-1946," in *Obituary Notices of Fellows of the Royal Society,* **5** (London, 1948), 591-618; and F. D. Murnaghan, "Harry Bateman," in *Bulletin of the American Mathematical Society,* **54** (1948), 88-103. The volumes resulting from the Bateman Manuscript Project are Arthur Erdelyi, ed., *Higher Transcendental Functions,* 3 vols. (New York, 1953-1955), and *Tables of Integral Transforms,* 2 vols. (New York, 1954).

C. S. FISHER

BATES, HENRY WALTER (*b.* Leicester, England, 8 February 1825; *d.* London, England, 16 February 1892), *natural history.*

The eldest son of Henry Bates, a hosiery manufacturer at Leicester, Henry received his elementary education in the schools there before attending Mr. H. Screaton's boarding school at Billesden, a village about nine miles from Leicester. Although Bates was an excellent student, his formal education was terminated in midsummer 1838, and he was apprenticed to a local hosiery manufacturer, for whom he labored thirteen hours a day. His capacity for work was prodigious, however, and he also took night classes at the local Mechanic's Institute, where he excelled in Greek, Latin, French, drawing, and composition. (Later, while in South America, he taught himself German and Portuguese.) Throughout his life Bates read very widely and was particularly fond of reading Homer in the original and Gibbon's monumental *Decline and Fall of the Roman Empire.* Music also engaged some of his time: he sang in the local glee club, played the guitar, and maintained a strong interest in classical music throughout his life.

In addition to these numerous activities, Bates was an avid entomologist and, with his brother Frederick, scoured the woods of nearby Charnwood Forest for specimens during his holidays. His earliest scientific work, a short paper on beetles (1843), was published in the first issue of *The Zoologist* when he was eighteen years old.

His supervisor died several years before Bates's apprenticeship was completed, and Bates assumed management of the firm for the son before becoming a clerk in nearby Burton-on-Trent. He strongly disliked his work, however; entomology was a much more congenial occupation, and he habitually spent much of his time writing detailed accounts of his expeditions and captured treasures. In 1844 (or 1845) Bates befriended Alfred Russel Wallace, a mutually beneficial act that profoundly influenced both their lives. Wallace was then a master at the Collegiate School at Leicester and in his spare time enthusiastically pursued his own amateurish interests in botany. Bates introduced him to entomology, and the two friends continued to correspond and exchange specimens after Wallace moved from Leicester early in 1845.

While exchanging specimens in 1847, Wallace audaciously suggested to Bates that they should travel to the tropical jungles to collect specimens, ship them home for sale, and gather facts "towards solving the problem of the origin of species"—a frequent topic of their conversations and correspondence. Wallace's attention had been directed to South America by the vivid prose of William H. Edwards' *Voyage up the River Amazon, Including a Residence at Pará* (1847); conversations with the author increased their interest, as did Edward Doubleday of the British Museum, who showed them some exquisite new species of butterflies collected near Pará (Belém), Brazil, and offered other encouragement. Arrangements were soon made, and after a swift voyage of thirty-one days, the two amateur naturalists disembarked on 28 May 1848 at Pará, near the mouth of the Amazon River. Although Wallace returned to England in July 1852, Bates remained for a total of eleven years, exploring and collecting within four degrees of the equator. Frequently discouraged by his chronically destitute condition and his isolation, he was nevertheless held there by an intense passion for collecting: the "exquisite pleasure of finding another new species of these creatures supports one against everything." Bates conservatively estimated that he had collected 14,712 animal species (primarily insects) while in South America; more than 8,000 of these were new to science. Despite the richness of his collections, he received a profit of only about £800 for his efforts—or about £73 a year.

From Pará Bates traveled almost 2,000 miles deep into the wilderness. He resided in Pará for a total of nearly eighteen months, returning there periodically for a few months after each of his shorter excursions to the interior. On 26 August 1848 Bates and Wallace embarked on a journey up the Tocantins River; they arrived in October 1849 at what was to be Bates's headquarters for three years—Santarém, a small town of 2,500 inhabitants some 475 miles from the sea at the mouth of the Tapajós River. By mutual agreement Bates and Wallace parted company on 26 March 1850 at Manaus, the latter departing for the Rio Negro and the Uaupés. Manaus, at the confluence of the Rio Negro and the upper Amazon (Solimões), was a classic hunting ground for naturalists, having

been a favorite spot for the celebrated travelers J. B. von Spix and K. F. P. von Martius, who had stayed there in 1820. On 6 November 1851 Bates set out to explore the Tapajós and Solimões river basins, spending a total of seven and one-half years there. His headquarters during his four and one-half years in the Solimões area was at Ega (Tefé), at the foot of the Andes. In September 1857 he plunged deep into the wilderness to São Paulo, some 1,800 miles from Pará. Finally, on 11 February 1859, Bates left Ega for Pará and England, his chronically poor health at its nadir.

After arriving in England in the summer of 1859, Bates began work on his enormous collections under the influence of a specific biological concept. In the previous year the now famous papers of Charles Darwin had been presented to the Linnean Society of London, and in November 1859 Darwin published *On the Origin of Species by Means of Natural Selection.* Bates was an immediate convert, and had some substantial and impressive evidence of his own to contribute to Darwin's arguments. (Bates's Unitarian religious views did not hinder his acceptance of natural selection.) On 21 November 1861 Bates first expounded his ideas on mimicry in his famous paper "Contributions to an Insect Fauna of the Amazon Valley. *Lepidoptera: Heliconidae,*" which he read before the Linnean Society. With typical enthusiasm for works by his followers, Charles Darwin commented that Bates's article was "one of the most remarkable and admirable papers I have ever read in my life."

Responding to Darwin's exhortations, Bates published early in 1863 a two-volume narrative of his travels in South America, *The Naturalist on the River Amazon.* This splendid work was one of the finest scientific travel books of the nineteenth century. The *Naturalist* went through many editions and was translated into several languages; nevertheless, popular and remunerative as it was, Bates remarked that he would rather spend another eleven years on the Amazon than write another book.

In 1862 Bates failed to secure a position in the zoology department at the British Museum—a post that went instead to A. W. E. O'Shaughnessy, a poet who, Bates said, was probably sponsored by Richard Owen. In 1864, however, Bates was appointed assistant secretary of the Royal Geographical Society of London, serving with distinction for twenty-eight years. Besides editing the *Journal* and *Proceedings* of the Society, as well as carrying on an immense correspondence with travelers and others throughout the world, Bates actually managed the Society and made arrangements for various meetings, including those held by the Geographical Section of the British Association.

During his tenure as assistant secretary, Bates's published works were devoted almost exclusively to entomology, primarily systematics, and numerous editions of travel works, such as Peter E. Warburton's *Journey Across the Western Interior of Australia* (1875), Thomas Belt's *The Naturalist in Nicaragua* (1873), and six volumes of Cassell's *Illustrated Travels: A Record of Discovery, Geography and Adventure* (1869–1875). His greatest contribution to systematic entomology appeared in various volumes of the *Biologia Centrali-Americana,* edited by F. D. Godman and O. Salvin (see his works on Coleoptera: Adephaga, Pectinicornia [Passalidae and Lucanidae], Lamellicornia [Scarabaeidae], and Longicornia [Cerambycidae]), and his fame as a preeminent authority on Coleoptera was worldwide. He contributed more than one hundred scientific papers to scholarly journals, corresponded with many entomologists, and served as consultant or assistant to various scientific journals, including the *The Entomologist.* (He also published anonymously purely literary works, and was at one time on the staff of the *Atheneum.*)

Many honors were bestowed on Bates, although he was strongly disinclined to discuss them. In 1861 he was elected to the Entomological Society of London and served as president in 1868, 1869, and 1878. He was elected fellow of the Linnean Society in 1871, fellow of the Zoological Society in 1863, and fellow of the Royal Society in 1881. Although he was secretary of the Geographical Section of the British Association, he declined the office of president. For his work in Brazil, the emperor of that country bestowed on Bates the Order of the Rose, a distinction rarely conferred upon foreigners. In 1863 he married Sara Ann Mason of Leicester, who bore him one daughter and three sons, two of whom emigrated to New Zealand.

That Bates was an immediate, early convert to Darwinian natural selection is understandable, for he had long been an evolutionist, as had his friend and traveling companion Alfred Russel Wallace. However, Bates appears not to have been converted as quickly as Wallace was by the evolutionary explanations adduced by Robert Chambers in his heretical, but quite popular, *Vestiges of the Natural History of Creation* (1844 *et seq.*). In a letter to Wallace in 1845, Bates apparently had described Chambers' ideas as hasty generalizations, a charge that Wallace felt compelled to answer at some length. By March 1850,

when the two parted company to explore by themselves, they had often discussed the species question and had reached some tentative conclusions. Nevertheless, Bates expressed surprise at Wallace's paper "On the Law Which Has Regulated the Introduction of New Species."[1] In this important work Wallace argued that every species has arisen "coincident in both space and time with a pre-existing closely allied species," thus supporting species creation through natural laws—as opposed, by implication, to numerous special creations by God.

Bates wrote Wallace from the Amazon that he was at first startled to see that he was "already ripe for the enunciation of the theory," commenting, however, "the theory I quite assent to, and, you know, was conceived by me also, but I profess that I could not have propounded it with so much force and completeness." Wallace replied from the Malay Archipelago that his paper naturally would appear more clear to Bates than "to persons who have not thought much on the subject," adding that the "paper is, of course, only the announcement of the theory, not its development. . . ."[2] Precisely what Bates meant by "the theory . . . was conceived by me also" is a matter for conjecture, for Wallace apparently was the earlier convert to the evolutionary hypothesis and, in fact, pleaded the evolutionist's case quite forcefully to Bates. Furthermore, Wallace certainly had a far more pregnant imagination than Bates, and it was he who perceived in 1858 the solution to the problem. Bates's original contribution to evolutionary biology appeared shortly after the *Origin* was published and fully corroborated Darwin's theory of natural selection.

Before 1861, naturalists had observed that certain butterflies belonging to distinct groups inhabiting the same geographical area bear remarkable superficial resemblances in appearance, shape, and color. In 1836 J. A. Boisduval had described the African swallow-tailed butterfly, which was copied by quite distinct butterflies. The distinguished English entomologists William Kirby and William Spence had observed in 1817 that the flies of the genus *Volucella* enter bees' nests to deposit their eggs so that their larvae may feed on the bee larvae and that the flies curiously resemble the bees on which they are parasitic. They concluded that the resemblance exists to protect the flies from possible attacks by the bees. In an article published in 1861, the German entomologist A. Rössler enumerated many examples of mimicry, which he explained as a device to protect insects from their enemies. In general, however, belief in the handiwork of God sufficed to explain the phenomenon, although some thought that there might be an innate tendency in insects to vary in a particular direction.

Bates was the first naturalist to venture a comprehensive scientific explanation for the phenomenon that he labeled "mimicry" (Batesian mimicry). Batesian mimicry should here be differentiated from Müllerian mimicry. According to Cott:

> In Batesian mimicry a relatively scarce, palatable, and unprotected species resembles an abundant, relatively unpalatable or well-protected species and so becomes disguised. In Müllerian mimicry, on the other hand, a number of different species all possessing aposematic attributes and appearance, resemble one another, and so become easily recognized [*Adaptive Coloration in Animals,* p. 398].

One therefore leads to deception of enemies and the other to the education of enemies by warning colors. Bates, and others, at first confused the two kinds of mimicry.

Bates's discussion of mimicry was unobtrusively buried in his classic article on the heliconid butterflies of the Amazon, which were frequently mimicked by counterfeits so perfect that even Bates was unable to distinguish them in flight. The Leptalides (*Dismorphia*) butterflies, although quite different structurally from the Heliconidae, are especially proficient mimics. Other examples abound. In various parts of the world beetles, spiders, flies, and grasshoppers mimic ants. While spiders may have a body configuration resembling that of ants, other mimics may use optical illusions to produce the appearance of a narrow antlike waist. Certain bees on the banks of the Amazon, as Bates observed, are also mimicked; indeed, many moths and longicorn beetles in the tropics mimic bees, wasps, and other hymenopterous insects. (Bates also adduced numerous examples of insects imitating inanimate objects.) In every case the mimic benefited to some extent from protection afforded by the original. The Heliconidae, which fly slowly and in plain sight of many potential enemies, are rendered foul-smelling and unpalatable by a glandular secretion. Birds and reptiles, to a lesser extent than insects, also mimic protected species. Bates observed an extraordinary example of a very large caterpillar that imitated a small, venomous snake. The first three segments behind the head could be dilated at will by the insect, and on each side of its head was a large pupillated spot resembling the eye of the poisonous snake. The general consternation produced among the natives when Bates displayed his specimen attests to the excellence of the imitation.

Granted that mimics are adaptations to their environment, the important question was why such remarkably close analogies exist. Bates ruled out direct action of physical conditions because in limited districts where these conditions were the same, the most widely contrasting varieties may be found coexisting. Likewise, sports (mutations) did not explain mimicry. To Bates it was quite clear that natural selection had produced these phenomena, "the selecting agents being insectivorous animals which gradually destroy those sports or varieties which are not sufficiently like [the protected species] to deceive them." The closer the resemblance of the mimic to the original, the greater will be its protection. Imperfect copies will be eliminated slowly, unless they have some supplementary protection of their own. (In fact, as V. Grant observed, "most animals in general have several alternative means of defense against their enemies" [*The Origin of Adaptations,* p. 112].) By observing the different forms of the mimic as it approximated (or diverged from) the original, species change itself could be carefully observed: "Thus, although we are unable to watch the process of formation of a new race as it occurs in time, we can see it, as it were, at one glance, by tracing the changes a species is simultaneously undergoing in different parts of the areas of distribution."[3] As Bates so aptly observed, it was "a most beautiful proof of natural selection."

Darwin was thoroughly delighted with Bates's paper, for it fully corroborated his theory and presented him with an excellent opportunity to rebut his critics in a short, unsigned review in the *Natural History Review* for 1863. He confronted the creationists with the embarrassing case of the mimicking forms of Leptalides (*Dismorphia*) butterflies, which could be shown through a graduated series to be varieties of one species; other mimickers clearly were distinct varieties, species, or genera. To be logically consistent—and they were not always—the creationists had to admit that some mimickers had been formed by commonly observed variations, while others were specially created. They would further be required to admit that some of these forms were created in imitation of forms known to arise through the ordinary processes of variation. The difficulties of such a position were insurmountable, and the arguments for Batesian mimicry were widely accepted. Moreover, A. R. Wallace soon extended these arguments in two excellent articles: "On the Phenomena of Variation and Geographical Distribution as Illustrated by the *Papilionidae* of the Malayan Region" (1865) and "Mimicry and Other Protective

Resemblances Among Animals" (1867). Thereafter, the literature was rich with references to mimicry, reaching a high point toward the end of the century with extensive discussions by Wallace, Poulton, and Beddard.

On the other hand, Bates, the author of the theory of mimicry, never published an extensive review of the subject, nor did he ever again write a philosophical or interpretative paper comparable to his article on mimicry. Unable to spin hypotheses as easily as did Darwin and Wallace, he devoted himself instead to numerous works on systematic entomology, such as his catalog of the Erycinidae (Riodinidae) butterflies, the foundation upon which subsequent authors worked. After selling his collections of Lepidoptera, Bates concentrated on Coleoptera, especially Adephaga, Lamellicornia and Longicornia.

That Bates failed to produce further works comparable to those on mimicry and his *Travels* has generally been attributed to the press of his many duties at the Royal Geographical Society. However, the character of his later work on entomological systematics may have been strongly influenced by other factors as well. In his presidential address to the Entomological Society in 1878, Bates discussed the "prevailing exclusively descriptive character of the entomological literature of the day," which he thought resulted primarily from the difficulty of describing the prodigious influx of newly discovered species. Nature was proving to be far more prolific, and her products more varied, than had previously been thought. "Thus our best working Entomologists are led to abandon general views from lack of time to work them out, and the consciousness that general views on the relations of forms and faunas are liable to become soon obsolete by rapid growth of knowledge." This, he felt, did not totally excuse the systematists' excessive narrowness, for it led them to neglect natural affinities that greatly illuminated evolution, which in his opinion was the greatest problem in biology. While Bates himself searched for natural affinities and focused attention on the important problems of the geographical distribution of animals, his general observation about systematists may also have applied to him, as his friend D. Sharp observed. Nevertheless, his erudite papers formed the substance for those who were able to develop theories, while his paper on mimicry and his *Travels* stand as classics in their own right.

NOTES

1. *Annals and Magazine of Natural History,* 2nd ser., **16** (1855), 184–196.

2. Bates to Wallace, 19 November 1856, and Wallace to Bates, 4 January 1858, in Marchant, *Alfred Russel Wallace: Letters and Reminiscences,* pp. 52–55.
3. "Contributions to an Insect Fauna . . .," in *Transactions of the Linnean Society of London,* **23** (1862), 512–513.

BIBLIOGRAPHY

I. ORIGINAL WORKS. Bates's best-known works are "Contributions to an Insect Fauna of the Amazon Valley. *Lepidoptera: Heliconidae,*" in *Transactions of the Linnean Society of London,* **23** (1862), 495–566, in which he announced his theory of mimicry, and *The Naturalist on the River Amazon,* 2 vols. (London, 1863; repr. London, 1892). Many other contributions to the insect fauna of the Amazon appeared in entomological journals. His presidential addresses to the Entomological Society of London, in its *Proceedings* for 1868, 1869, and 1878, are valuable for understanding his general opinions on entomology and biology.

II. SECONDARY LITERATURE. There are a number of informative obituaries on Bates; his neighbor and friend Edward Clodd had direct access to his papers (which have disappeared), which makes his account particularly valuable. See his memoir of Bates prefaced to the 1892 reprint of the first edition of Bates's *Travels.* Other obituaries are R. McLachlan, "Obituary of Henry Walter Bates, F. R. S.," in *The Entomologist's Monthly Magazine,* 2nd ser., **3** (1892), 83–85; *Proceedings of the Royal Geographical Society,* **14** (1892), 245–257; D. Sharp, "Henry Walter Bates," in *The Entomologist,* **25** (1892), 77–80; and Alfred Russel Wallace, "H. W. Bates, the Naturalist of the Amazons," in *Nature,* **45** (1892), 398–399.

Except for letters to Darwin at Cambridge, scarcely any of Bates's correspondence remains. Fortunately, however, some of his important letters have been published in the following works: Francis Darwin, ed., *The Life and Letters of Charles Darwin,* II (London, 1887), 378–381, 391–393; Francis Darwin and A. C. Seward, eds., *More Letters of Charles Darwin,* Vol. I (New York, 1903), *passim;* James Marchant, ed., *Alfred Russel Wallace: Letters and Reminiscences* (New York, 1916), pp. 52–59; and A. R. Wallace, *My Life: A Record of Events and Opinions,* I (London, 1905), 350–379.

On mimicry see Frank E. Beddard, *Animal Coloration* (London, 1892); Hugh B. Cott, *Adaptive Coloration in Animals* (London, 1940, 1957); Verne Grant, *The Origin of Adaptations* (New York-London, 1963); E. B. Poulton, *The Colours of Animals, Their Meaning and Use* (London, 1890); Charles L. Remington, "Mimicry, a Test of Evolutionary Theory," in *Yale Scientific Magazine,* **22,** no. 1 (October 1957), 10–11, 13–14, 16–17, 19, 21, written with Jeanne E. Remington; and "Historical Backgrounds of Mimicry," in *Proceedings of the XVI International Congress of Zoology,* IV (Washington, D. C., 1963), 145–149; and A. R. Wallace, *Darwinism* (London, 1889), pp. 232–267.

H. LEWIS MCKINNEY

BATESON, WILLIAM (*b.* Whitby, England, 8 August 1861; *d.* Merton, London, England, 8 February 1926), *morphology, genetics.*

Bateson was the son of William Henry and Anna Aiken Bateson. His father, a classical scholar, had become master of St. John's College, Cambridge (1857), and Bateson lived in that university town until 1910. In that year he moved to London and remained there until his death.

Marked as "a vague and aimless boy" while at Rugby, Bateson confounded the doubters by taking first-class honors in the natural science tripos at Cambridge, from which he received the B.A. in 1883. A student and later (1885–1910) a fellow of St. John's College, his interest early came to focus on zoology and morphology. Contributing largely to his scientific development were A. Sedgwick and W. F. R. Weldon at Cambridge and, while he was in Maryland and Virginia during 1883 and 1884, W. K. Brooks at Johns Hopkins. Bateson was ill-trained in physics and chemistry and knew virtually no mathematics. His abilities as a classicist were outstanding.

Bateson's career may be divided into three periods. During the first period (1883–1900) he turned from orthodox embryological Darwinizing to the rigorous study of heredity and variation. Dissatisfied with old truths, he was seeking a new approach to evolutionary studies. His views were distinctly out of favor with conventional zoologists, and he won no regular university teaching appointments. Bateson's Mendelian period opened in 1900 and continued until about 1915. His contributions toward the establishment of the Mendelian conception of heredity and variation were enormous, and he finally began to harvest popular and professional esteem. The third period (*ca.* 1915–1926) reintroduced the discordant element. Bateson continually attacked the new glory, chromosome theory, and concentrated upon problems of somatic segregation. Once a radical, furiously disturbing his zoological elders, he now seemed conservative. His science, genetics (so named by Bateson in 1905–1906), turned largely toward chromosomes and genes. As a result, Bateson, who had been a central figure, became isolated from current developments.

Bateson received the Balfour Studentship at Cambridge in 1887. His other Cambridge positions included deputy in zoology to Alfred Newton in 1899, reader in zoology in 1907, and finally professor of genetics in 1908. His was the first such chair in Britain. In 1910 he became the first director of the John Innes Horticultural Institution, then at Merton. He was elected a fellow of the Royal Society in 1894 and belonged to numerous other societies. Among his many honors were the Darwin Medal (1904), presi-

dency of the British Association for the Advancement of Science (1914), the Royal Medal (1920), and election as a trustee of the British Museum (1922).

Bateson's Cambridge training had emphasized genealogical reconstruction. Such work promised the recovery of a generalized view of the history of life, but it could tell very little about how such great changes had actually come to pass. True progress in evolutionary studies must, Bateson believed, reject customary phylogenetic ambitions and turn to the process wherein evolutionary novelty emerges, that is, the phenomena of heredity and, particularly, variation. From about 1887 such detailed investigation dominated Bateson's activity. He searched the literature and began experimental hybridization, demanding exact knowledge of the transmission of heritable features from parent to immediate offspring. Then, in May 1900, he read Mendel's report of 1866 on breeding experiments with peas.

The rediscovery of Mendel's work transformed Bateson's career. He reinterpreted experimental data already available in Mendelian terms. Simultaneously with L. Cuénot he proved that Mendelian behavior holds for animals as well as plants. His research group, which included R. C. Punnett, E. R. Saunders, and L. Doncaster, demonstrated the existence of epistatic modifications of simple Mendelian ratios and the phenomena of reversion and (as it was subsequently designated) linkage. As spokesman for the new discipline Bateson knew no peer, yet his work was financed with great difficulty and only by personal funds, private gifts, and the Evolution Committee of the Royal Society. Reports to the latter body were the main vehicle of Mendelian publication in Britain until Bateson and Punnett began the *Journal of Genetics* in 1910.

Behind all technical achievements persisted Bateson's concern for the "salt of biology," evolution theory, and its indispensable adjunct, the determinative mechanism(s) of inheritance. The chromosome theory of inheritance, rising from bare enunciation in 1902 to evident triumph around 1920, offered a formed, material element in the cell nucleus as the agent of heredity. But Bateson demanded a direct— indeed, a visible—correlation between any chromosome and consequent bodily feature, and he found none. Moreover, chromosome theory was patently materialistic, and this, for numerous and complex reasons, he could not tolerate. In place of the chromosome theory Bateson devised an ostensibly nonmaterialistic vibratory theory of inheritance, founded on force and motion. This theory and the phenomena that appeared consistent with it (especially plant variegation) were utterly unacceptable to most geneticists, and in its defense Bateson became increasingly an advocate without adversaries. Significant discussion of his views largely disappeared from leading genetics journals.

An ardent evolutionist, Bateson vigorously opposed the doctrine of natural selection. Like Fleeming Jenkin and St. G. Mivart, he failed to see how few and slight variations, the raw material for Darwinian selection, could be truly useful. He rejected the entire "utility" aspect of orthodox Darwinism. What, then, could be the source of undeniable evolutionary change? The answer was found in the organismic quality of any significant biological variation. Genuine evolutionary novelty was, therefore, not the product of gradual accumulation of seemingly trivial variations but the consequence of saltatory or major modifications. Variation was the driving force of evolutionary change, and Bateson always hoped to find its explanation in his vibratory theory of heredity. Perhaps the disputatious Bateson's most famous public battle was against the biometrical school led by W. F. R. Weldon and Karl Pearson. At issue was the nature of evolutionary change and how it might best be studied. Bateson emphasized the imprecision in individual instances of statistical analyses and decried the biometricians' ardent defense of natural selection. In straightforward Mendelism he found both support for evolutionary discontinuities and a dependable experimental approach to matters of descent.

Bateson's broad interests and remarkable personality greatly influenced his scientific thought. A man of deep and well-cultivated aesthetic sensibilities (he was a major collector of Oriental works of art and the creations of William Blake), he despaired before the harsh spiritual and economic realities of late Victorian England. He was at once a radical empiricist, wanting his facts absolutely secure, and a rather unconscious intuitionist. From his intuition, fed by insights taken from transcendental morphology, he developed his conception of the functionally integral organism. The same view informs his conception of human society, in which an intellectual elite is struggling desperately against a rising and insensitive middle-class horde bent on leveling all men to their own mediocrity. To Bateson this was not life, but mere existence. This complex of ideas and intuitions set Bateson firmly against utilitarian rationalism and its near neighbor, materialism. In natural selection and the chromosome theory he saw both at work, and would have none of them.

BIBLIOGRAPHY

I. ORIGINAL WORKS. With few and unimportant exceptions Bateson's scientific contributions were collected and reissued by R. C. Punnett as *Scientific Papers of William Bateson,* 2 vols. (Cambridge, 1928). His often remarkable general biological and social essays are available in B. Bateson, ed., *William Bateson, F.R.S. Naturalist. His Essays and Addresses* (Cambridge, 1928). Bateson's major publications are *Materials for the Study of Variation Treated with Especial Regard to Discontinuity in the Origin of Species* (London, 1894); *Reports to the Evolution Committee of the Royal Society, I–V* (London, 1902–1909); *Mendel's Principles of Heredity. A Defence* (Cambridge, 1902); *Mendel's Principles of Heredity* (Cambridge, 1909, 1913); and *Problems of Genetics* (New Haven, 1913). Punnett has provided a bibliography of Bateson's writings in *Scientific Papers,* II, 487–494.

The Bateson papers, in the possession of his family, constitute an extensive and exceptionally valuable archive. A comprehensive selection of scientific items from this collection has been microfilmed (a copy is deposited in the Library of the American Philosophical Society, Philadelphia) and roughly catalogued. All aspects of Bateson's career are represented, including his large and interesting correspondence, unpublished speculative essays, and abundant documentation to published works. These papers are described in *The Mendel Newsletter,* no. 2 (Philadelphia, 1968). Lesser collections of Bateson MSS are held by the John Innes Institute (to join the University of East Anglia, Norwich, *ca.* 1970), the Royal Society of London, and the American Philosophical Society.

II. SECONDARY LITERATURE. The principal biographical source is B. Bateson, "Memoir," in *William Bateson, F.R.S. Naturalist,* pp. 1–160. Other notices, particularly concerned with his scientific endeavor, are R. C. Punnett, "William Bateson," in *Edinburgh Review,* **244** (1926), 71–86; and T. H. Morgan, "William Bateson," in *Science,* **63** (1926), 531–535. See also O. Renner, "William Bateson and Carl Correns," in *Sitzungsberichte der Heidelberger Akademie der Wissenschaften,* Mathematische-naturwissenschaftliche Klasse, **6** (1960–1961), 159–184; L. C. Dunn, *A Short History of Genetics* (New York, 1965), pp. 55–87; and C. D. Darlington, *The Facts of Life* (London, 1953), pp. 95–116. An excellent discussion of Bateson's peculiar later conception of the heredity mechanism is R. C. Swinburne, "The Presence-and-Absence Theory," in *Annals of Science,* **18** (1962), 131–145. Bateson's refusal to pursue phylogenetic reconstruction is recorded in W. Coleman, "On Bateson's Motives for Studying Variation," in *Actes du XIᵉ Congrès International d'Histoire des Sciences,* V (Warsaw-Cracow, 1968), 335–339.

WILLIAM COLEMAN

BATHER, FRANCIS ARTHUR (*b.* Richmond, Surrey, England, 17 February 1863; *d.* Wimbledon, England, 20 March 1934), *paleontology.*

Francis Arthur Bather, the son of Arthur H. and Lucy Bloomfield Bather, attended Winchester School and New College, Oxford, where he earned the bachelor of arts degree in 1886. Bather received the master of arts degree in 1890 and the doctor of science in 1900, both from Oxford. In 1887 he took a position as assistant geologist in the British Museum, and in 1924 he was promoted to keeper of the geology department. Bather enjoyed his curatorial duties and took great interest in museum administration, finding ways to improve exhibits, corresponding with other curators around the world, and visiting natural history museums on the Continent.

In addition to his curatorial work, Bather carried out research in paleontology and contributed many fundamental studies on echinoderm morphology. Among the echinoderms the Pelmatozoa were his specialty. In 1893 his *Crinoidea of Gotland* (part 1) was published by the Royal Swedish Academy. His *The Echinoderma,* one volume in E. R. Lankester's *Treatise of Zoology* (1900), remained the leading exposition of echinoderm morphology for decades, with new discoveries fitting easily into the scheme that Bather established. Intensive study of fossil morphology did not hinder Bather's appreciation of the environment and an animal's place in it. The study of paleoecology interested him, and he particularly recommended this study to others. In such ways he brought biological concepts to bear on fossil studies. Although Bather began his museum work nearly thirty years after the publication of Darwin's *Origin of Species,* the classification of echinoderms had been untouched by evolutionary ideas.

Bather retired from the British Museum in 1928. Among the many honors he received for his scientific contributions were the Rolleston Prize of Oxford and Cambridge (1892) and the Wollaston Fund (1897) and the Lyell Medal (1911) of the Geological Society of London. He also served as president of the Geological Society, the Museums Association, and the British Association for the Advancement of Science.

BIBLIOGRAPHY

In addition to the works cited above, see Bather's presidential address to the Geological Society, "Biological Classification: Past and Future," in *Quarterly Journal of the Geological Society of London,* **83** (1927), lxii–civ. Besides his general views, the address contains a lucid historical review of classificatory schemes. Further biographical material is to be found in memoirs by W. D. Lang, in *Nature,* **133** (1934), 485–486; and Percy E. Raymond, in *Proceedings of the Geological Society of America* (June 1935), pp. 173–186. The latter contains a complete bibliography of Bather's writings, compiled by Thomas H. Withers.

BERT HANSEN

AL-BATTĀNĪ,[1] **ABŪ ʿABD ALLĀH MUḤAMMAD IBN JĀBIR IBN SINĀN AL-RAQQĪ AL-ḤARRĀNĪ AL-ṢĀBIʾ,** also **Albatenius, Albategni** or **Albategnius** in the Latin Middle Ages; *astronomy, mathematics.*

One of the greatest Islamic astronomers, al-Battānī was born before 244/858,[2] in all probability at or near the city of Ḥarrān (ancient Carrhae) in northwestern Mesopotamia, whence the epithet al-Ḥarrānī. Of the other two epithets, al-Raqqī, found only in Ibn al-Nadīm's *Fihrist,*[3] refers to the city of al-Raqqa, situated on the left bank of the Euphrates, where al-Battānī spent the greater part of his life and carried out his famous observations; al-Ṣābiʾ indicates that his ancestors (al-Battānī himself was a Muslim; witness his personal name Muḥammad and his *kunya* Abū ʿAbd Allāh) had professed the religion of the Ḥarranian Sabians,[4] in which a considerable amount of the ancient Mesopotamian astral theology and star lore appears to have been preserved and which, tolerated by the Muslim rulers, survived until the middle of the eleventh century. The fact that al-Battānī's elder contemporary, the great mathematician and astronomer Thābit ibn Qurra (221/835–288/901) hailed from the same region and still adhered to the Ṣabian religion, seems indicative of the keen interest in astronomy that characterized even this last phase of Mesopotamian star idolatry. As for the cognomen (*nisba*) al-Battānī, no reasonable explanation of its origin can be given. Chwolsohn's conjecture[5] that it derives from the name of the city of Bathnae (or Batnae; Gr., Βάτναι; Syr., Baṭnān) near the ancient Edessa, was refuted by Nallino[6] with the perfectly convincing argument that the possibility of a transition of Syriac *t* into Arabic *t* (Baṭnān to Battān) has to be strictly excluded; since there is no evidence of the existence of a city or town named Battān, Nallino suggests that this name, rather, refers to a street or a district of the city of Ḥarrān.

Nothing is known about al-Battānī's exact date of birth and his childhood. Since he made his first astronomical observations in 264/877, Nallino is on safe ground assuming the year 244/858 as a *terminus ante quem* for his birth. His father, in all probability, was the famous instrument maker Jābir ibn Sinān al-Ḥarrānī mentioned by Ibn al-Nadīm,[7] which would explain not only the son's keen astronomical interest but also his proficiency at devising new astronomical instruments, such as a new type of armillary sphere.

On al-Battānī's later life too the information is scanty. According to the *Fihrist*[8] and to Ibn al-Qifṭī's *Taʾrīkh al-Ḥukamāʾ,*[9] al-Battānī was

. . . one of the illustrious observers and foremost in geometry, theoretical and practical [lit., computing]

astronomy, and astrology. He composed an important *zīj* [i.e., work on astronomy with tables] containing his own observations of the two luminaries [sun and moon] and an emendation of their motions as given in Ptolemy's *Almagest*. In it, moreover, he gives the motions of the five planets in accordance with the emendations which he succeeded in making, as well as other necessary astronomical computations. Some of the observations mentioned in his *Zīj* were made in the year 267 H.[10] [A.D. 880] and later on in the year 287 H. [A.D. 900]. Nobody is known in Islam who reached similar perfection in observing the stars and in scrutinizing their motions. Apart from this, he took great interest in astrology, which led him to write on this subject too; of his compositions in this field [I mention] his commentary on Ptolemy's *Tetrabiblos*.

He was of Ṣabian origin and hailed from Ḥarrān. According to his own answer to Jaʿfar ibn al-Muktafī's question, he set out on his observational activity in the year 264 H. [A.D. 877] and continued until the year 306 H. [A.D. 918]. As an epoch for his [catalog of] fixed stars in his *Zīj* he chose the year 299 H. [A.D. 911].[11]

He went to Baghdad with the Banu'l-Zayyāt, of the people of al-Raqqa, on account of some injustice done them.[12] On his way home, he died at Qaṣr al-Jiṣṣ in the year 317 H. [A.D. 929].[13]

He wrote the following books: *Kitāb al-Zīj* [*Opus astronomicum*], in two recensions;[14] *Kitāb Maṭāliʿ al-Burūj* ["On the Ascensions of the Signs of the Zodiac"];[15] *Kitāb Aqdār al-Ittiṣālāt* ["On the Quantities of the Astrological Applications"], composed for Abu'l-Ḥasan ibn al-Furāt; *Sharḥ Kitāb al-Arbaʿa li-Baṭlamiyūs* ["Commentary on Ptolemy's *Tetrabiblos*"].[16]

It seems to have been a widespread belief among Western historians that al-Battānī was a noble, a prince, or even a king of Syria. Not the slightest allusion to it can be found in Arabic writers, so the source of this misunderstanding must be sought in Europe. The earliest reference quoted by Nallino[17] is Riccioli's *Almagestum novum*,[18] where al-Battānī is called "dynasta Syriae." J. F. Montucla[19] makes him a "commandant pour les califes en Syrie" and J. LaLande[20] a "prince arabe," as does J.-B. Delambre,[21] probably on LaLande's authority, since he expressly says that he used a copy, formerly in LaLande's possession, of the 1645 Bologna edition of al-Battānī's *Zīj*, although its title contains no reference to the author's alleged nobility.[22]

From al-Battānī's work, only one additional fact on his life can be derived: he mentions in his *Zīj*[23] that he observed two eclipses, one solar and one lunar, while in Antioch, on 23 January and 2 August A.D. 901, respectively.

The book on which al-Battānī's fame in the East and in the West rests is the *Zīj*, his great work on astronomy. Its original title, in all probability, was that indicated by Ibn al-Nadīm and Ibn al-Qiftī: *Kitāb al-Zīj*, or just *al-Zīj*. Later authors also often call it *al-Zīj al-Ṣabiʾ* ("*The Ṣabian Zīj*").[24] The word *zīj*, derived from the Middle Persian (Pahlavi) *zīk* (modern Persian, *zīg*), originally meant the warp of a rug or of an embroidery. As Nallino points out,[25] by the seventh century this had become a technical term for astronomical tables. In Arabic, it soon assumed the more general meaning "astronomical treatise," while for the tables themselves the word *jadwal* ("little river") came into use.[26]

Of the two recensions mentioned by Ibn al-Qiftī, the first must have been finished before 288/900 because Thābit ibn Qurra, who died in February 901, mentions one of its last chapters.[27] Since the manuscript preserved in the Escorial[28] and the Latin version by Plato of Tivoli (Plato Tiburtinus) contain the two observations of eclipses mentioned above, the first of which occurred immediately before, and the second six months after, Thābit's death, Nallino concludes[29] that they must both have been copied (or translated) from the second recension.

In the preface to the *Zīj*,[30] al-Battānī tells us that errors and discrepancies found in the works of his predecessors had forced him to compose this work in accordance with Ptolemy's admonition to later generations to improve his theories and inferences on the basis of new observations, as he himself had done to those made by Hipparchus and others.[31] The Arabic version of the *Almagest*, on which he relied, seems to have been a translation from the Syriac, which Nallino shows on several occasions was not free from errors. All quotations from the *Almagest* are carefully made and can be verified.

A comparison of the *Zīj* with the *Almagest* at once reveals that it was far from al-Battānī's mind to write a new *Almagest*. To demonstrate this, it suffices to point out a few striking differences:

The arrangement of the fifty-seven chapters is dictated by practical rather than by theoretical considerations. Thus, contrary to al-Farghānī, who, writing half a century before al-Battānī, devotes his nine first chapters[32] to the same questions that are treated in *Almagest* I, 2–8 (spherical shape of the heavens and of the earth; reasons for the earth's immobility; the earth's dimensions and habitability; the two primary motions; etc.), al-Battānī starts his *Zīj* with purely practical definitions and problems: the division of the celestial sphere into signs and degrees, and prescriptions for multiplication and division of sexagesimal fractions. In chapter 3, corresponding to *Almagest* I, 11, he develops his theory of trigonometrical functions (see below); in chapter 4 he presents his own observations that resulted in a value for the obliquity of the ecliptic (23°35′) that is more than 16′ lower than Ptolemy's (23°51′20″; *Almagest* I, 12);[33] the next chapters (5–26), corresponding roughly to *Almagest* I, 13–16 and the whole of Book II, contain a very elaborate discussion of a great number of problems of spherical astronomy, many of them devised expressly for the purpose of finding solutions for astrological problems.

The Ptolemaic theory of solar, lunar, and planetary motion in longitude is contained in chapters 27–31. Then follows a discussion of the different eras in use and their conversion into one another (chapter 32),[34] serving as an introduction to the next sixteen chapters (33–48), in which detailed prescriptions for the use of the tables are given (chapters 39 and 40 deal with the theory of lunar parallax and the moon's distance from the earth, necessary for the computation of eclipses). Chapters 49–55 treat of the chief problems in astrology: chapter 55 has the Arabic title "Fī maʿrifat maṭāliʿ al-burūj fī-mā bayna 'l-awtād fī arbaʿ al-falak" ("On the Knowledge of the Ascensions of the Signs of the Zodiac in the Spaces Between the Four Cardinal Points of the Sphere"),[35] which is identical with Ibn al-Nadīm's title of one of al-Battānī's minor works. It is possible that this chapter actually existed as a separate treatise, but it is also possible that it was only due to an error that we find it listed separately in the *Fihrist* and in later biographies.

Of the two last chapters, 56 deals with the construction of a sundial indicating unequal hours (*rukhāma,* "marble disk"), and 57 with that of a novel type of armillary sphere, called *al-bayḍa* ("the egg"), and of two more instruments, a mural quadrant and a *triquetrum* (Ptolemy's τεταρτημόριον, *Almagest* I, 12, and ὄργανον παραλλακτικόν, *Almagest* V, 12).

Contrary to Ptolemy's procedure in the *Almagest,* the practical aspect of the *Zīj* is so predominant that it sometimes impairs the clarity of exposition and even evokes a totally wrong impression. This is felt more than anywhere else in chapter 31, which deals with the theory of planetary motion. The Arabic text consists of little more than five pages, only three of which deal with the theoretical (i.e., kinematic) aspect of the problem. Here the reader trained in Ptolemy's careful and sometimes slightly circumstantial way of exposing his arguments, and familiar with al-Farghānī's excellent *epitome,* will needs be struck by the brevity and—this is worse—by the insufficiency and inaccuracy of al-Battānī's outline. To point out some particularly bewildering features:[36] No distinction is made between, on the one hand, the theory of the three superior planets and Venus, and, on the other, the ingenious and intricate mechanism devised by

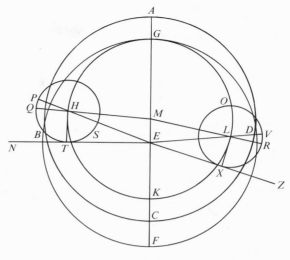

FIGURE 1

Ptolemy to represent Mercury's perplexing motion. With the aid of only one figure, which is wholly defective and misleading, al-Battānī tries—and of course fails—to demonstrate the motion of all of the five planets alike. In this figure, reproduced here (Fig. 1), the equant (*punctum aequans*), the essential characteristic of the Ptolemaic theory, is not indicated, nor is it referred to in the accompanying text, according to which the center, *M*, of the deferent itself is to be regarded as the center of mean motion (!). Moreover, the nodes of the planetary orbit are placed at right angles to the line of apsides (which of course is not true of any of the five planets), and for the planet's position in the epicycle, in the two cases indicated in the figure, the very special points are chosen in which the line earth-planet is tangent to the epicycle.

It is easy to point out all these errors and, as G. Schiaparelli has done at Nallino's request,[37] to show how the figure ought to look, were it drawn in accordance with Ptolemy's theory (Fig. 2). But Schiaparelli's surmise that al-Battānī's correct figure was distorted by some unintelligent reader or copyist does not exhaust the question. For, if so, who would dare at the same time to mutilate the text in such a way that the equant disappears from it altogether? And which uninitiated reader might have had the courage to suppress in this context the theory of Mercury, without which Ptolemy's system of planetary motions remains a torso? Since the Escorial manuscript and Plato of Tivoli's translation[38] have both the same erroneous figure and text, the alleged mutilation must have occurred, at the latest, in the eleventh century, during the lifetime of the great Spanish-Muslim astronomer al-Zarqālī (Azarquiel) or of one of his renowned

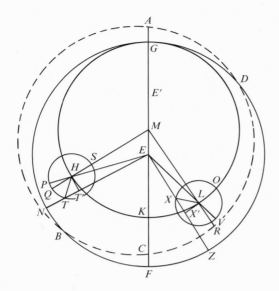

FIGURE 2

predecessors. To me it seems utterly improbable that an arbitrary disfiguring of one of the crucial chapters of al-Battānī's great *Zīj* could have escaped their attention and that no measures should have been taken to delete such faulty copies and to restore the original text. I am inclined, thus, to ascribe the matter to al-Battānī's carelessness rather than to anything else, in view of the circumstance that no other reasonable conjecture seems to square with the facts. Similar examples can be adduced from the writings even of the greatest astronomers; in this context I refer to a grave slip (although of lesser consequence) committed by al-Bīrūnī, which I have pointed out in an earlier paper.[39] It need not be emphasized that al-Battānī actually knew better; to prove this, it suffices to mention that his tables of planetary motion, far more elaborate than Ptolemy's, could not have been drawn up without a thorough familiarity with the Ptolemaic system, including all its finesses and intricacies.

While al-Battānī takes no critical attitude toward the Ptolemaic kinematics in general, he evidences, as said before, a very sound skepticism in regard to Ptolemy's practical results. Thus, relying on his own observations, he corrects—be it tacitly, be it in open words—Ptolemy's errors. This concerns the main parameters of planetary motion no less than erroneous conclusions drawn from insufficient or faulty observations, such as the invariability of the obliquity of the ecliptic or of the solar apogee.

The Islamic astronomers' interest in the question of the variability of the obliquity of the ecliptic started astonishingly early. This is the more remarkable because the effect, being on the order of magnitude of 0.5" a year, is definitely of no practical use. According

to Ibn Yūnus (*d.* 399/1009),[40] the first measurement since Ptolemy was made shortly after 160/776, yielding 23°31', which was 4'–5' too low;[41] after this he reports quite a number of different values, all in the vicinity of 23°33', made during and after the time of al-Ma'mūn (*d.* 215/830). Hence, al-Battānī's determination is nothing exceptional, but it is important for us because he gives a careful description of the procedure by which his value (23°35'), which squares perfectly with the modern formula, was obtained.

In chapter 28 of the *Zīj*, al-Battānī discusses his observations of the lengths of the four seasons, from which, employing Hipparchus' method as described in *Almagest* III, 4, he infers that the sun's apogee and its eccentricity have both changed since antiquity: the apogee, found at 65°30' by Hipparchus and erroneously claimed to be invariable by Ptolemy, had moved to 82°17', and the eccentricity had diminished from $2^p29'30''$ to $2^p4'45''$ ($1^p = 1/60$ of the radius).

Despite contrary assertions, however, al-Battānī was not the first since Ptolemy to check on these values. According to al-Bīrūnī,[42] who relies on Abū Ja'far al-Khāzin's (*d. ca.* 350/961) commentary on the *Almagest,* the first observations serving the purpose of a new determination of the apogee were carried out, on the basis of the specially devised new "method of the four *fuṣūl*,"[43] in the Shammāsiyya quarter of Baghdad in A.D. 830. In spite of this methodological improvement, the result was extremely poor: it yielded a value no less than 20° too small. One year after, Thābit ibn Qurra or the Banū Mūsā, using the old Ptolemaic method, obtained the excellent value 82°45'.[44] Comparing this with Hipparchus' value (65°30') and rejecting Ptolemy's obviously wrong confirmation of the latter, he (or they) found that the motion of the apogee amounts to 1° in sixty-six years. Then, from the fact that he had also found the same value for the motion of precession, Thābit concluded that they must of necessity be identical—in other words, that the apogee of the sun remains fixed once and for all in regard to the fixed stars (for this type of reasoning and concluding, European scholasticism has invented the term "Ockham's razor").

Al-Battānī's value for the sun's apogee (82°17') is not quite as good as Thābit's (or the Banū Mūsā's), although the perfect accordance of the latter with the one resulting from the modern formula must be considered to some degree accidental: for A.D. 831, Leverrier's formula yields 82°50'22" (Thābit, 82°45'); for A.D. 884, 83°45'10"[45] (al-Battānī, 82°17'). It is of interest in this context that Hipparchus' value, 65°30' (*ca.* 140 B.C.), also squares exceedingly well with the modern, 65°21'.

Thus, it is evident that al-Battānī has no special

claim to the discovery of the motion of the solar apogee. Apart from this, he was no more able than Thābit to decide whether this motion was identical with that of precession. It was only 150 years later that al-Bīrūnī furnished the theoretical foundation for such a distinction,[46] but even he had to admit that the data at his disposal did not allow him to make a conclusive statement. The first who actually made a clear (and very correct) numerical statement concerning the proper motion—1° in 299 Julian years, or 12.04″ in one year (modern: 1.46″), was al-Zarqālī (second half of the eleventh century) of Toledo. But his result is impaired by his belief in the reality of trepidation, which he shared with Thābit.

Al-Battānī's value for the eccentricity of the solar orbit ($2^p4'45''$), corresponding to an eccentricity in the modern sense of 0.017326 (instead of 0.016771, according to our modern formula, for A.D. 880) must be called excellent, while Ptolemy's value (0.0208 instead of 0.0175) is much too high.[47]

Among al-Battānī's many other important achievements is his improvement of the moon's mean motion in longitude;[48] his measurements of the apparent diameters of the sun and of the moon and their variation in the course of a year, or of an anomalistic month, respectively, from which he concludes that annular solar eclipses (impossible, according to Ptolemy) must be possible;[49] and his new and elegant method of computing the magnitude of lunar eclipses.[50]

For the precession of equinoxes, he accepts and confirms Thābit's value (1° in sixty-six years), far better than Ptolemy's (1° in 100 years), but about 10 percent too fast (correct, 1° in seventy-two years). Accordingly, his tropical year ($365^d5^h46^m24^s$) is too short by 2^m22^s (correct, $365^d5^h48^m46^s$), while Ptolemy's ($365^d5^h55^m12^s$) is too long by 6^m26^s.

Al-Battānī's catalog of fixed stars[51] is far less comprehensive than Ptolemy's (489 as against 1,022 stars). The latitudes and magnitudes are taken over (perhaps with a few corrections) from the *Almagest,* while the longitudes are increased by the constant amount of 11°10′, which corresponds, for the interval of 743 years between the epochs of the two catalogs (A.D. 137 and 880), to the motion of precession indicated, viz., 1° in sixty-six years.

While Ptolemy's *Almagest* is often cited, his *Tetrabiblos* is mentioned on only one occasion (end of chapter 55). It is uncertain whether al-Battānī knew and used Ptolemy's *Geography.*[52] Ptolemy's *Hypotheses* (called by later authors *Kitāb al-Iqtiṣāṣ* or *Kitāb al-Manshūrāt*)[53] are made use of in chapter 50, which deals with the distances of the planets, but al-Battānī ascribes the underlying theory of contiguous spheres,

according to which the distances are computed, to "more recent scientists [who lived] after Ptolemy." Since al-Farghānī mentions no name at all in this connection,[54] it seems probable that al-Battānī's reference to "scientists after Ptolemy" reflects a passage from Proclus' *Hypotyposis,*[55] in which Ptolemy's name also does not occur, and that Ptolemy's authorship became known only when, some time before al-Bīrūnī, the *Hypotheses* were translated into Arabic.

Of other astronomical works from antiquity, only Theon of Alexandria's *Manual Tables* are mentioned. In the section of chapter 6 dealing with geographical questions,[56] al-Battānī refers to "the ancients" without further specification. Nallino[57] has shown that this expression, there, means Greco-Syriac sources.

In spite of the circumstance that al-Battānī, as demonstrated before, has a good deal in common with the Banū Mūsā, Thābit, and al-Farghānī, no reference whatever appears in his *Zīj* to his Islamic predecessors. In his terminology he abstains from using foreign (Persian or Indian) words, as found in earlier writings of his countrymen, such as *awj* for the apogee of the eccentric (circumstantially called by al-Battānī *al-buʿd al-abʿad min al-falak al-khārij al-markaz,* "the [point having] maximum distance in the eccentric"), *jayb* for the sine (al-Battānī: *watar munaṣṣaf,* "half-chord," or just *watar,* "chord"), *buht* for the (unequal) motion of a planet in the course of one day (a concept not used by al-Battānī), *jawzahar* for the ascending node (al-Battānī: *al-ra's,* "the head [of the dragon]"), *haylāj* for the astrological "significator" or "aphet" (Gr.: ἀφέτης; al-Battānī: *dalīl*), and so on.[58] His aversion to foreign terms, however, certainly springs not from any "purism of language" but, rather, from the circumstance that the words in question did not occur in the *Almagest* translations at his disposal; this explains why in some cases he does not hesitate to employ clumsy transliterations of Greek terms, such as *afījiyūn* for ἀπόγειον ("apogee") and *farījiyūn* for περίγειον ("perigee").

Al-Battānī uses the sine instead of the chord (of twice the angle), following the example of his Arab predecessors who had fused into one whole the new Indian notion (*Siddhānta*) and the old Greek notion. Besides the sine he also employs the cosine (*watar mā yabqā li-tamām . . . ilā tisʿīn,* "the sine of the complement of . . . to 90°") and the versine (R − cosine, called *watar rājiʿ,* "returning sine"), for which later authors also employed the term *jayb maʿkūs* ("inverted sine"), as opposed to *jayb mustawī* ("plain sine") or *sahm* ("arrow"), whence the medieval Latin *sagitta.* Tangents and cotangents do not occur in al-Battānī's formulas, which therefore often become as clumsy as Ptolemy's. He uses them only in his gnomonics, where they refer, as in the *Siddhāntas,* to a twelve-partite gnomon. For the cotangent, he employs the term *ẓill mabsūṭ* ("umbra extensa"; called by others also *ẓill mustawī,* "umbra recta"); for the tangent, *ẓill muntaṣib* ("umbra erecta"; called by others *ẓill maʿkūs,* "umbra versa").[59] By applying considerations based on the principle of orthographic projection, al-Battānī introduced new and elegant solutions into spherical trigonometry. In Europe, this principle was adopted and developed by Regiomontanus (1436–1476).

The epoch of al-Battānī's chief era (*Taʾrīkh Dhiʾl-Qarnayn,* "Epoch of the Two-Horned [Alexander]") is Saturday (mean noon, Raqqa), 1 September 312 B.C., which precedes by thirty days the epoch *Dhuʾl-Qarnayn* used by all other Arabic authors: Monday, 1 October 312 B.C. It is combined with the Julian year; for the months he uses the "Syrian" names: *aylūl* (September), *tishrīn* I and II, *kanūn* I and II, *subāṭ, ādhār, nīsān, ayyār, ḥazīrān, tammūz,* and *āb.* The epoch of the Coptic era (*Taʾrīkh al-Qibṭ*) is Friday, 29 August 25 B.C., while all other Arabs used this term to denote one of the following three: the era of Nabunassar (1 Thoth = 26 February 747 B.C.), the era of Philippus Arrhidaeus (12 November 324 B.C., mentioned in the *Almagest* as the "era of Alexander's death"), or the era of Diocletian (29 August 284, also called *Taʾrīkh al-Shuhadāʾ,* "era of the martyrs").[60]

A Latin translation of the *Zīj* made by the English Robertus Retinensis (also cited as R. Ketenensis, Castrensis, or Cestrensis; Nallino believes the correct form to be Cataneus),[61] who flourished about the middle of the twelfth century, has not survived. The only Latin version extant is the one by Plato of Tivoli, who flourished in Barcelona in the first half of the twelfth century. This translation was printed twice. The *editio princeps* (Nuremberg, 1537) carries the title *Rudimenta astronomica Alfragrani* [sic].[62] *Item Albategnius peritissimus de motu stellarum ex observationibus tum propriis tum Ptolemaei, omnia cum demonstrationibus geometricis et additionibus Ioannis de Regiomonte;* the title of the second edition (Bologna, 1645), printed without al-Farghānī's *Elements,* is *Mahometis Albatenii de scientia stellarum liber cum aliquot additionibus Ioannis Regiomontani. Ex Bibliotheca Vaticana transcriptus.*

A Spanish translation, made at the order of King Alfonso el Sabio (1252–1284), is preserved in the Bibliothèque de l'Arsenal in Paris.[64]

Although no Hebrew translation of the *Zīj* seems to have existed, its impact on Jewish scholarship was great. It was mentioned and praised by Abrāhām bar Ḥiyyāʾ (d. *ca.* 1136) and Abrāhām ibn ʿEzrā (*ca.* 1090–1167). Maimonides (1135–1204) follows al-Battānī closely, but without mentioning his name, in the eighth treatise of Book III of his *Mishne Tōrā,* which bears the title "Hilkōt qiddūsh ha-ḥōdesh."[65] In chapters 12–14 the parameters used (mean motion in longitude of the sun and of the moon, mean anomalistic motion of the moon, equation of the sun) are exactly the same as in al-Battānī's tables, except that the values for the solar equation are rounded off to minutes.[66] In his prescriptions for determining the limits of visibility of the new moon, too, Maimonides closely follows the elegant method devised by al-Battānī.

Among Islamic astronomers and historians, al-Battānī holds a place of honor. The great al-Bīrūnī composed a book entitled *Jalaʾ al-Adhhān fī Zīj al-Battānī* ("Elucidation of Genius in al-Battānī's *Zīj*"),[67] and Ibn Khaldūn (1332–1406)[68] counts his works among the most excellent in Islamic astronomy.

In Byzantine writings, al-Battānī's name is mentioned as δΠατανής, but Greek translations apparently have not existed. A great many medieval Latin authors who knew the *Zīj* or at least mention the name of its author can be enumerated. Among them are Henry Bate (1246–*ca.* 1310), who, in composing his *Magistralis compositio Astrolabii anno 1274 scripta,* makes ample use of the contents of the *Zīj*—not without giving its author due credit for it; Gerard of Sabbionetta; Albertus Magnus; Lēvi ben Gersōn (in the Latin translation of his *Astronomy*);[69] and, not least, Regiomontanus, whose keen interest in the work is evident from the great number of annotations in his handwriting found in his copy of Plato of Tivoli's version and printed as an appendix to the Nuremberg and the Bologna editions. His teacher Georg Peurbach's (1423–1461) *Theoricae planetarum,* printed and edited by Regiomontanus,[70] mentions al-Battānī's name on only one occasion (fol. 18r),[71] where he relates that "Albategni," contrary to those who defended the theory of trepidation, claimed that the stars move 1° in sixty years and four months,[72] and always toward the east. Since all Arab astronomers, in accordance with the text and the translations extant, state that al-Battānī accepted a motion of 1° in sixty-six years,[73] it is a mystery how this erroneous value, which cannot be due to a copyist's slip, could have found its way into Peurbach's book. As for his masterful presentation of planetary kinematics according to Ptolemy, it is a matter of course—in view of what I have said about al-Battānī's chapter 31[74]—that it could not be modeled after al-Battānī's fallacious chapter, while the influence of al-Farghānī seems perceptible in many places.

The indebtedness of Copernicus to al-Battānī is well known. He quotes him fairly often, especially—as does Peurbach—in the chapters dealing with the problems of solar motion and of precession.[75] Much more frequent references to him are found in Tycho Brahe's writings and in G. B. Riccioli's *New Almagest;*[76] in addition, Kepler and—only in his earliest writings—Galileo evidence their interest in al-Battānī's observations.

From the point of view of the history of astronomy, the names of two men are to be mentioned, although with a totally different weight. In 1819 Delambre published his *Histoire de l'astronomie du moyen âge.*[77] In chapter 2 he devotes fifty-three pages to a very thorough analysis of the *Zīj,* on the basis of the Bologna edition of Plato of Tivoli's translation. Even to the modern reader the chapter is of interest, in spite of the fact that a certain superciliousness, characteristic of all Delambre's historical works, is sometimes embarrassing. For it is, of course, not as interesting to learn how one problem or the other could have been solved in a less circumstantial way as it would be to get an insight into the historical situation in which al-Battānī's work came into being. This, however, was beyond Delambre, for even if he had possessed a sufficient knowledge of Arabic (he had none at all), the only extant manuscript would not have been within his reach. Thus he had to rely on Plato of Tivoli's version, whose errors and misunderstandings naturally led him astray in more than one case.

Eighty years after Delambre, in 1899, the young Italian orientalist C. A. Nallino published his model edition of the complete Arabic text of al-Battānī's *Zīj.*[78] The two other volumes, containing a Latin translation and exceedingly detailed and learned commentaries, followed during the next eight years. In a time like ours, characterized by the abuse of superlatives, it is hard to describe Nallino's work in appropriate terms. Al-Battānī's Arabic style, which at first sight looks simple and straightforward, but which reveals itself difficult and even obscure on many occasions, is rendered here in a Latin whose purity and clarity deserve the highest praise. In reading this book, which is Nallino's *magnum opus,* one understands that it was not due purely to a whim that he decided to compose it in Latin. As for the technical aspect, Nallino's work bears witness to a great familiarity with the mathematical and astronomical problems occurring in al-Battānī's *Zīj,* and no less with the historical facts that form its background. This third Latin translation, written eight centuries after the first two, will always stand as one of the masterpieces of the history of science.

Until recently it was believed that none of the three minor works (all of astrological content) listed in the *Fihrist* and in Ibn al-Qifṭī's *Ta'rīkh al-ḥukamā'*[79] had survived, since, on the one hand, the authenticity of

a manuscript preserved in Berlin seemed dubious[80] and, on the other, the only extant manuscript expressly titled "Commentary on Ptolemy's *Tetrabiblos,*" which figures still in Casiri's catalog,[81] could no longer be found in the Escorial library, as stated by H. Derenbourg[82] in 1884 and confirmed by Nallino in 1894 and by Father Pedro Blanco Soto in 1901.[83] Fortunately, however, the lost manuscript seems to have been recovered: in H.-P.-J. Renaud's new catalog,[84] it is listed as no. 969, 2 (not 966, as in Casiri), under the title *Kitāb al-arbaʿ maqālāt fī aḥkām ʿilm al-nujūm,* the copy dating from 939/1533 and comprising sixty folios. The word *sharḥ* ("commentary") does not appear in the title, but Renaud's and Casiri's descriptions read "Commentary on Ptolemy's *Quadripartitum*" (i.e., *Tetrabiblos*). It will require a special study to establish whether the Berlin and the Escorial manuscripts are identical in text. The fact that the latter also contains tables (which the Greek original does not have) suggests the existence in the text of rules and prescriptions for their use that might justify calling it a "commentary."

In this context,[85] Nallino mentions that the Egyptian ʿAlī ibn Riḍwān (latinized as Haly Heben Rodan, *d.* 453/1061) states that he has never come across any paraphrase (*glossa*) of the *Tetrabiblos* at all, whereas Abu'l-Ḥasan ʿAlī ibn Abi'l-Rijāl (Albohazen Haly filius Abenragel, *fl. ca.* 1050) counts al-Battānī among those who, like Ptolemy, attributed special importance to astrological prognostications made on the basis of eclipses that occur during the years of planetary conjunctions. Nallino evidently believes this refers to *Tetrabiblos* II, 6,[86] which deals with the same subject matter. The case, however, is different. In the Saib (Ismāʿīl Sāʾib) Library at Ankara there is preserved a volume (no. 1/199) containing three different works, the second of which (fols. 27r–42v) bears the title *Kitāb [Muḥammad ibn] Jābir b. Sinān al-Ḥarrānī al-Battānī fī dalāʾil al-qirānāt wa'l-kusūfāt* ("Jābir . . . al-Battānī's Book on the Significations of Conjunctions and Eclipses").[87] It is undoubtedly this book, not listed in any of the great oriental bibliographies, on which bears Albohazen's remark. Judging from a cursory inspection of a photostatic copy in the possession of the Institute for the History of Science of the University of Frankfurt, I see no reason to doubt its authenticity.

Another manuscript, entitled *Tajrīd uṣūl tarkīb al-juyūb*[88] ("Construction of the Principles of Establishing [Tables of] Sines"), also carries al-Battānī's name. From the fact that al-Battānī, at least in his *Zīj,* avoids using the term *jayb* (plural, *juyūb*) for "sine,"[89] it might be inferred that this manuscript is spurious.

For a number of other definitely spurious works existing only in Latin translations, see the list (with comprehensive discussions) found in Nallino.[90]

NOTES

1. The transliteration system used in this article is that of the *Encyclopaedia of Islam*, 2nd ed., with the following simplifications: *j* instead of *dj*; *q* instead of *k* (NB: *qu* is pronounced *ku*, not as English *qu*); no underlinings to indicate compound consonants: *kh* instead of *kh* for the Scottish *ch*-sound, *th* and *dh* for the English voiceless and voiced *th*, respectively.

2. Of two numbers separated by a slash, the first indicates the year according to the Muslim calendar and the second its beginning according to the Christian calendar. In quotations from Arabic texts, Muslim years are denoted by H. (Hegira), and the corresponding Christian years are added in brackets. Note that the Muslim year is 3 percent shorter than the Julian.

3. *Kitāb al-Fihrist* (composed *ca.* A.D. 987 by Ibn al-Nadīm), G. Flügel, ed. (Leipzig, 1871–1872), I, 279. See also C. A. Nallino, *Al-Battānī sive Albatenii Opus astronomicum, ad fidem codicis escurialensis arabice editum, latine versum, adnotationibus instructum*, I (Milan, 1903), viii ff. This *magnum opus* (Vol. II, 1907; Vol. III, 1899), cited hereafter as *O.A.*, will always remain the chief source of information in Arabic astronomy and on al-Battānī in particular.

4. See B. Carra de Vaux, "al-Ṣābi'a," in *Encyclopaedia of Islam*, 1st ed., IV; and, for comprehensive information (although obsolete in certain parts), D. Chwolsohn, *Die Ssabier und der Ssabismus*, Vols. I/II (St. Petersburg, 1856).

5. *Die Ssabier*, I, 611.

6. *O.A.*, I, xiii.

7. *Fihrist*, p. 285.

8. p. 280.

9. J. Lippert, ed. (Leipzig, 1903), p. 280. Ibn al-Qifṭī, the author of this "History of Learned Men," died in 646/1248. His chapter on al-Battānī (which I follow in my translation), according to his own words, relies on Ṣā'id al-Andalusī. It contains information not found in the *Fihrist*.

10. Owing to a scribal error, the *Fihrist* and Qifṭī have 269.

11. Instead of 299/911, read 267/880 (scribal error). The epoch of the catalog is actually 267/880.

12. The meaning, evidently, is "because unjust taxes had been requested of them." The text leaves open whether "them" includes al-Battānī. Cf. Nallino, *O.A.*, I, viii. As for the Banu'l-Zayyāt, Nallino (*ibid.*, pp. xvii f.) considers it almost certain that they are the descendants of the famous poet and vizier 'Abd al-Malik ibn Abān al-Zayyād (executed by Caliph Mutawakkil in 233/847). It was to his great-grandson's son, Abū Ṭālib Aḥmad al-Zayyād, that Ibn Waḥshiyya dictated, in 318/930, his alleged "translation from the Syriac" of his book on the Nabataean agriculture.

13. In Ibn Khallikān's (*d.* 681/1282) biographical dictionary (Eng. trans. by Mac Guckin de Slane, Paris–London, 1843–1871, IV, 317–320; Arabic original: *Ibn Challikan, Vitae illustrium virorum*, F. Wüstenfeld, Göttingen, 1835–1842, no. 719 [cited after *O.A.*, I, ix, n. 6]), the place of al-Battānī's death is Qaṣr al-Ḥaḍr. Nallino has shown (*O.A.*, p. xviii) that Jiṣṣ (of which Ḥaḍr is nothing but a graphical corruption) is the correct form.

14. Ibn al-Nadīm and Ibn Khallikān add the words "a first and a second; the second is better."

15. Ibn al-Nadīm adds the words *fī mā bayna arbāʿ al-falak* ("in the spaces between the four cardinal points of the sphere"). The book gives mathematical solutions of the astrological problem of finding the direction of the *aphet* (*tasyīr al-dalīl*).

16. Not listed by Ibn al-Nadīm.

17. *O.A.*, I, xvii, n. 1.

18. Bologna, 1651, II, xxix.

19. *Histoire des mathématiques,* new ed. (Paris, 1797–1800), I, 363.

20. *Astronomie,* 3rd ed. (Paris, 1792), I, 123.

21. *Histoire de l'astronomie du moyen âge* (Paris, 1819; repr. New York–London, 1965), pp. 4, 10.

22. In this title, the author is called "Mahometus, filius Geber, filius Crueni, qui vocatur Albategni." The strange name Cruenus is obviously due to a misreading of Sinanus, which may have been found spelled Cinenus.

23. Ch. 30, *O.A.*, I, 56.

24. Thus Ibn Khallikān and Ḥājjī Khalīfa (1017/1609–1067/1657); see *Haji Khalfae Lexicon bibliographicum et encyclopaedicum,* ed. and trans., with commentary, by G. Flügel (Leipzig–London, 1835–1858), III, 564, no. 6946.

25. *O.A.*, I, xxxi, n. 3.

26. In Byzantine Greek, the word is found as ζῆσι and identified with σύγταξις; see *O.A.*, I, xxxi, n. 5.

27. Ch. 57, which treats the theory of trepidation, refuted by al-Battānī but accepted by Thābit. The reference to al-Battānī is found in Thābit's letter to Isḥāq ibn Ḥunayn, preserved by Ibn Yūnus. See *O.A.*, I, 298.

28. Originally no. 903 (M. Casiri, *Bibliotheca arabico-hispanica Escurialensis,* Madrid, 1760, I, 342–343), now no. 908. Unbelievable as it sounds, only this copy of one of the most important books written in the Middle Ages has survived in the Arabic original.

29. *O.A.*, I, xxxii.

30. Ch. 1, *O.A.*, I, 5.

31. *Almagest*, III, 1 (German trans. by Karl Manitius, *Des Claudius Ptolemäus Handbuch der Astronomie,* Leipzig, 1912, p. 141). The wording there is a little different and contains no such express "admonition" or "order" (*amr*).

32. Except for ch. 1, which deals with the various eras and their mutual conversions, practically identical with al-Battānī's ch. 32. Cf. J. Golius' ed. and Latin trans.: *Muhammedis fil. Ketiri Ferganensis, qui vulgo Alfraganus dicitur, Elementa astronomica* (Amsterdam, 1669).

33. See W. Hartner, "The Obliquity of the Ecliptic According to the Hou-Han Shu and Ptolemy," in *Silver Jubilee Volume of the Zinbun-Kagaku-Kenkyusyo* (Kyoto, 1954), pp. 177–183; repr. in Hartner's *Oriens-Occidens* (Hildesheim, 1968), pp. 208–214.

34. See n. 32.

35. See p. 508 and n. 15.

36. See the figure and the accompanying text, *O.A.*, III, 96 f. (Arabic) and *O.A.*, I, 64 f. (Latin), from which Figure 1 in the text is reproduced.

37. *O.A.*, I, 237 f. Figure 2 in the text is reproduced from Schiaparelli's.

38. Nallino, *O.A.*, I, lxii, states that the Arabic original, from which Plato of Tivoli translated, and the Escorial MS (written, according to Nallino, about 1100) must both have belonged to the same archetype.

39. "Mediaeval Views on Cosmic Dimensions and Ptolemy's *Kitāb al-Manshūrāt*," in *Mélanges Alexandre Koyré,* I (Paris, 1964), 254–282; repr. in W. Hartner, *Oriens-Occidens* (Hildesheim, 1968), pp. 319–348.

40. Bibliothèque Nationale, MS Ar. 2495, p. 222 (cited after *O.A.*, I, 157).

41. For an exact verification and comparison with modern formulas (Newcomb, de Sitter), the effect of refraction and of solar parallax has to be taken into account; by this the values derived from observation are reduced by about 40″, which of course is of no interest here (see n. 33).

42. Masʿūdic Canon, VI, chs. 7 and 8 (*al-Qānūnal-Masʿūdī,* pub. by The Dāʾirat al-Maʿārif Oṣmānia, II (Hyderabad-Dn., 1374/1955), pp. 650–685. Cf. W. Hartner and M. Schramm, "Al-Bīrūnī and the Theory of the Solar Apogee: An Example of Originality in Arabic Science," in A. C. Crombie, ed., *Scientific Change* (London, 1963), pp. 206–218.

43. Observation of the sun's passage through the points 15° Taurus, 15° Leo, 15° Scorpio, and 15° Aquarius.

44. According to the *Kitāb fī sanat al-shams bi'l-arṣād,* MS London India Office no. 734, fol. 6r, ll. 13 ff.

45. Schiaparelli (*O.A.,* I, 215) gives the erroneous value 83°50′51″ for A.D. 884.

46. Cf. Hartner and Schramm (n. 42), pp. 216–218.

47. Cf. *O.A.,* I, 213 f. For comparing the ancient with the modern values (elliptic eccentricity), the former must of course be halved: $2^p4'45''/60 = 0.034653 = 2 \cdot 0.017326$.

48. Cf. *O.A.,* I, 225 f.

49. Cf. *ibid.,* 58, 236. He either is unaware or avoids mentioning that his own observations of the moon's apparent diameter at apogee ($d_1 = 29.5'$) and at perigee ($d_2 = 35.3'$) are in the ratio 5:6. According to Ptolemy's and his own theory, they ought to be in the ratio 17:33, or nearly 1:2.

50. Cf. *ibid.,* 99 f.

51. Arabic text, *O.A.,* III, 245–274; Latin, *O.A.,* II, 144–177.

52. Cf. *O.A.,* I, xli and 20 (end of ch. 4).

53. See W. Hartner, "Mediaeval Views on Cosmic Dimensions" (n. 39), and B. R. Goldstein, "The Arabic Version of Ptolemy's *Planetary Hypotheses,*" in *Transactions of the American Philosophical Society,* n.s. **57,** pt. 4 (1967).

54. Ch. 21, pp. 80–82; see n. 32.

55. *Procli Diadochi Hypotyposis astronomicarum positionum,* ed. and trans. into German by K. Manitius (Leipzig, 1909), ch. 7, 19 (p. 220). As I have shown in "Mediaeval Views . . ." (see n. 39), it can no longer be doubted that the idea of contiguous spheres was conceived by Ptolemy. The final proof for the correctness of my assertion has been furnished by Goldstein (see n. 53), who found that the extant Arabic and Hebrew versions of the *Hypotheses* contain the part missing from J. L. Heiberg's edition (*Claudii Ptolemaei opera,* II, *Opera astronomica minora,* Leipzig, 1907, 69–145) at the end of Book I. It has exactly the same parameters and ratios as indicated in my paper.

56. *O.A.,* I, 17–19.

57. *Ibid.,* 165–177.

58. Cf. *ibid.,* xlii f.

59. On the back of astrolabes, preference is given to the terms *ẓill mabsūṭ* for the shadow cast by a vertical gnomon on a horizontal plane, and *ẓill maʿkūs* (sometimes *mankūs*) for the shadow of a horizontal gnomon on a vertical plane.

60. For further information, see *O.A.,* I, 242–246.

61. See *O.A.,* I, xlix f. There can be no doubt that the name means Robert of Chester, a friend of Hermannus Dalmata. He was the first to translate the Koran into Latin (1143) and also one of the first translators of Muḥammad ibn Mūsā al-Khwārizmī's *Algebra.* See L. C. Karpinski, "Robert of Chester's translation of al-Khowarizmi," in *Bibliotheca mathematica,* **11** (1911), 125–131. Robertus Retinensis is not identical with Robertus Anglicus, who lived in the thirteenth century.

62. Cf. the other edition of al-Farghānī's *Elements,* quoted in n. 32. The division into chapters is different in the two editions.

63. For C. A. Nallino's Latin translation and edition, see p. 513.

64. Described by Rico y Sinobas in *Libros del saber de astronomía del Rey D. Alfonso X de Castilla,* V, pt. 1 (Madrid, 1867), 19 f.

65. Cf. *O.A.,* I, xxxiv; and S. Gandz, trans., "The Code of Maimonides, Book III, Treatise 8, Sanctification of the New Moon: With Supplementation and an Introduction by J. Obermann and an Astronomical Commentary by Otto Neugebauer," in J. Obermann, ed., *Yale Judaica Series,* XI (New Haven, 1956), 47–56.

66. *O.A.,* II, 20, 22, 75, and 78 ff. Note that for the sun's mean motion, the values given in the tables on pp. 22 and 75 differ by 1″ and 2″ for the arguments 9^d and 10^d. The figures on p. 75 are the correct ones: 9^d, $8°52'15''$; 10^d, $9°51'23''$.

67. *Jalāʾ al-adhhān fī Zīj al-Battānī,* according to al-Bīrūnī's own bibliography, published in E. Sachau, ed., *Chronologie orientalischer Völker von Albêrûnî* (Leipzig, 1878), p. xxxxvi.

68. Cf. de Slane, trans., *Les prolégomènes d'Ibn Khaldûn* (Paris, 1863–1868), III, 148; cf. F. Rosenthal, trans., *Ibn Khaldûn, The Muqaddimah,* III (New York, 1958), 136.

69. Cod. Vat. Lat. 3098 (cited after *O.A.,* I, xxxvi).

70. Nuremberg, *ca.* 1473 (the exact year of this incunabulum cannot be established).

71. In the chapter "De motu octavae sphaerae." The folios carry no numbers.

72. "Albategni vero dicebat eas moveri uno gradu in sexaginta annis et quatuor mensibus semper versus orientem."

73. Cf. p. 510.

74. See p. 509.

75. See e.g., Copernicus, *De revolutionibus,* III, 13.

76. See n. 18.

77. See n. 21.

78. See n. 3.

79. See p. 508.

80. Staatsbibliothek, MS no. 5875; see W. Ahlwardt, *Verzeichniss der arabischen Handschriften der Kgl. Bibliothek zu Berlin,* V, 273 f. The MS, written *ca.* 800/1397 by Aḥmad ibn Tamīm and comprising 62 folios, lacks the title page and the first pages of the text. At the end is the grammatically incorrect phrase *tamma kitāb al-arbaʿa* [*sic!*] *sharḥ al-Battānī* ("Here ends the Book of the Four [Maqālas] of al-Battānī's commentary"), which obviously alludes to Ptolemy's *Tetrabiblos.* According to Ahlwardt, no division into four *maqālas* and no sections marked as commentaries (*sharḥ*) are recognizable. As Nallino (I, xxi ff.) has shown, the subjects treated and their sequence are, with few exceptions, those of the *Tetrabiblos.*

81. See n. 28. I, 399: "Cod. CMLXVI, nr. 2°: Commentarius in Quadripartitum Ptolemaei de astrorum iudiciis: subiectis tabulis. Auctor est vir clarissimus Mohammad Ben Geber Albategnius."

82. *Les manuscrits arabes de l'Escurial* (Paris, 1884), I, xxiv.

83. *O.A.,* I, xx.

84. "Les manuscrits arabes de l'Escurial décrits d'après les notes de Hartwig Derenbourg," in *Publications de l'École Nationale des Langues Orientales Vivantes,* 6th ser., **5,** 2, fasc. 3 (1941), 116.

85. *O.A.,* I, xxiii.

86. Cited after the anonymous Latin translation *C. Ptolemaei de praedictionibus astronomicis, cui titulum fecerunt Quadripartitum, libri IV. Ed. posterior* (Frankfurt, 1622).

87. This important MS was discovered by Fuat Sezgin, Institut für Geschichte der Naturwissenschaften, University of Frankfurt. It dates from the sixth/thirteenth century.

88. Istanbul, Carullah 1499, fol. 81v, written in 677/1278, consisting of only one page. This MS was discovered by Fuat Sezgin.

89. See p. 511.

90. *O.A.,* I, xxiii–xxxi.

BIBLIOGRAPHY

Consult the following works by C. A. Nallino: *Al-Battānī . . . Opus astronomicum* (see note 3); "Al-Battānī," in *Encyclopaedia of Islam,* Vol. I, repr. with augmented bibliography, *ibid.,* 2nd ed., Vol. I; "Astronomy," *ibid.;* "Astrologia e astronomia presso i Musulmani," in his *Raccolta di scritti editi e inediti,* Maria Nallino, ed., V (Rome, 1944), 1–87, esp. 52; "Storia dell'astronomia presso gli Arabi nel Medio Evo," *ibid.,* pp. 88–329, trans. by Maria Nallino from the Arabic original, *ʿIlm al-Falak . . .* (Rome, 1911–1912); and "Albatenio," in *Enciclopedia italiana,* repr. in his *Raccolta,* V, 334–336.

See also H. Suter, "Die astronomischen Tafeln des Muḥammad ibn Mūsā al-Khwārizmī," in *Det Kgl. Danske Videnskabernes Selskabs Skrifter,* 7. Række, Historisk og Filologisk Afdeling, **3,** no. 1 (1914); J. M. Millás-Vallicrosa,

Estudios sobre Azarquiel (Madrid–Granada, 1943–1950); E. Honigmann, "Bemerkungen zu den geographischen Tabellen al-Battānī's," in *Rivista degli studi orientali*, **11** (1927), 169–175; and E. S. Kennedy and Muhammad Agha, "Planetary Visibility Tables in Islamic Astronomy," in *Centaurus*, **7** (1960), 134–140.

WILLY HARTNER

IBN BAṬṬŪṬA (*b.* Tangier, Morocco, 24 February 1304; *d.* Morocco, *ca.* 1368–1369), *Muslim traveler.*

Muḥammad, the son of ʿAbdallāh, whose family name was Ibn Baṭṭūṭa and who was descended from members of the Berber tribe of the Lawāta, left his native Tangier on 14 June 1325 in order to make the pilgrimage to Mecca. He returned to Morocco, to Fez, almost a quarter of a century later, in November 1349, after having visited much of Asia, going as far east as China. He went through northern Africa to Egypt, which he reached in the spring of 1326. He traveled through Egypt, Palestine and Syria, the Ḥijāz, South Arabia, and down the east coast of Africa from Mogadishu to Kilwa. Ibn Baṭṭūṭa visited southwestern Persia and Iraq, Anatolia, and southern Russia in the region of the Crimea. From there, he paid an imaginary visit to the city of Bulghār on the Volga and undertook an overland trip to Constantinople that has occasionally been doubted but seems to have taken place. He then went through central Asia to India, where he took up residence in Delhi. He spent about eight years in India, traveling along the coasts and through various sections of the subcontinent. He stayed in the Maldives for more than a year and a half, then visited Ceylon, Sumatra, and China.

Soon after his return to Morocco, Ibn Baṭṭūṭa left on a trip to Spain and then turned south to visit the mighty Mālī-Mandinka state, in particular, the cities of Timbuktu and Gawgaw (Gao). He returned to Morocco early in 1354. He dictated the story of his travels to Ibn Juzayy—a Spanish scholar and official at the court of Sultan ʿInān of Fez—who edited it in a very short time. No more is heard of Ibn Baṭṭūṭa after this.

All the details of Ibn Baṭṭūṭa's life and accomplishments come from his *Travels* (in Arabic, *Riḥla*). His family in Tangier belonged to the legal establishment, and he received the usual legal-religious education. Going on the pilgrimage meant visiting and, on occasion, studying with the famous scholars to be met en route. These customary study trips often extended over many years; but in the case of Ibn Baṭṭūṭa, although he always kept in contact with scholars and mystics, the original purpose was soon forgotten and travel became an end in itself. He thoroughly enjoyed what for most other medieval Muslims was a necessary evil, and seized every opportunity to see new cities and regions. Only a very small part of his time abroad was spent outside the realm of Islam; and when he stayed in places not under Muslim political control, he preferred to move in the circles of his fellow expatriate coreligionists, where his upbringing and his linguistic background stood him in good stead. The judicial functions he exercised for the first time on his way from Morocco to Egypt and then as a Mālikite judge in India suggest a career not unlike the one he would have pursued had he never left Morocco. He made his living from gifts and stipends—some, he says, very generous—from rulers or high officials wherever he went. He apparently undertook occasional commercial ventures on the side. Some of his marriages may have procured helpful family connections for him. He speaks often of the women he married in the various places he visited and the many slave girls who always accompanied him. He also refers to children born to his women, children whom he did not see again or who did not live to maturity.

If the summary of his travels has been left rather vague, it is not for a lack of precise dates, which are amply present in his work. It is because these dates have been recognized as frequently incorrect. Attempts to harmonize them and to establish a coherent chronology of his travels necessarily involve repeated choices between indications furnished by the author for reasons that are never absolutely cogent. Even the date he gives for his arrival in India, 12 September 1333, has been questioned. This date cannot be correct if one chooses to credit his statement that he was in Mecca during the pilgrimage a year earlier. His itinerary often cannot be followed in exact detail. He lists places, in seemingly chronological succession, that he can be assumed to have visited on different trips. He reports abruptly on side excursions that do not fit into the main itinerary. On occasion he uses literary sources, reports on events of contemporary history that he did not witness, and can be shown to present as having seen himself what he can only have been told by others. All this does not detract from the credibility of his information. It is explained not so much by slips of memory (the question of whether he had been able to keep written notes to help him in his recollections is much debated) as by the spirit and purpose of medieval Muslim literature.

Although exceptionally rich in personal data, the *Travels* was not meant to constitute a personal record in terms of the circumstances of the author's life or the proper sequence of his itinerary. Its purpose was to enlighten the reader about remarkable and often marvelous things and events that could be observed in other countries and to deepen his understanding of human society and his respect for the divine handiwork in all its richness and variety. This purpose was uniquely achieved and has given the *Travels* its lasting greatness.

Ibn Baṭṭūṭa was not a scientist. He was not even a productive scholar in the traditional Muslim sense. While his general qualifications in the legal field must have been acceptable, the fact that he did not give the final form to his work clearly shows that he did not belong to the scholarly sector of Muslim society. His travels did not involve any scholarly or scientific research pursuits. In the traditional manner he reported the things that struck him as unusual and remarkable. He deeply believed in and reported on supernatural events, the miracles of saintly men, and their dreams and predictions. He was interested in political conditions and the glories of foreign rulers; in economic factors; in all sorts of strange customs, such as those of marriage and burial; in the construction of Indian beds and the kind of fuel used in China; in strange inventions, such as wagons in the Crimea or a supposed way of getting rid of vermin; in remarkable animals, minerals, and, to a greater degree, trees and plants, especially those useful to man (for example, the coconut, on which he lived in the Maldive Islands). The only systematic treatment of observed facts concerns the trees, fruits, and grains of South Arabia, India, and the Maldives. His curiosity about buildings and ancient ruins was not particularly great. He believed in alchemy; but while he was credulous of religious stories, he showed himself quite skeptical of marvelous natural phenomena, such as fables about the origin of the coconut, the strange shape of the vagina of certain Turkish women, or the purported age of some old man.

Ibn Baṭṭūṭa's work is a source of unmatched importance for fourteenth-century India (to which about one-fifth of it is devoted), and even more so for the Maldives, southern Russia, and especially Negro Africa. Ibn Baṭṭūṭa often is the only medieval author to give us information on these areas; and where there is additional material, the value of his observations remains undisputed. He also contributes considerably to our knowledge of comparatively well-known areas, such as contemporary Anatolia. Whether observed fact, hearsay, or legend, whether indubitably true or suspect, his data are often the only ones we have to fill voids in our knowledge. His personal contribution lies in the single-mindedness with which he traveled in order to learn more and more about man and nature, in the skill he showed for ferreting out meaningful facts, and in his realization of the importance of these facts for the growth of human knowledge. In

contrast with Christian explorers, whose journeys took them out of their own limited world and who thus brought back to it an entirely new experience, he remained spiritually and for the most part physically within the boundaries of the world of Islam. Yet he clearly belongs in the select circle of the men who, often misunderstood or not understood by their contemporaries, paved the way for the modern age of discovery.

BIBLIOGRAPHY

I. ORIGINAL WORKS. The original edition of the *Travels* was published in four volumes, with a French translation, by C. Defrémery and B. R. Sanguinetti (Paris, 1853–1858). There is an English translation of the first two volumes by H. A. R. Gibb (Cambridge, 1958–1962), Hakluyt Society, 2nd ser., nos. 110 and 117. For a translation of the section on India, the Maldives, and Ceylon, see Mahdi Husain, *The Reḥla of Ibn Baṭṭūṭa* (Baroda, 1953). For the section dealing with Negro Africa, see G. S. P. Freeman-Grenville, *The East African Coast* (Oxford, 1962), pp. 27–32; and R. Mauny et al., *Textes et documents relatifs à l'histoire de l'Afrique* (Dakar, 1966), University of Dakar, Section d'Histoire, Publication 9.

II. SECONDARY LITERATURE. Works on Ibn Baṭṭūṭa include G.-H. Bousquet, "Ibn Baṭṭūṭa et les institutions musulmanes," in *Studia Islamica*, **24** (1966), 81–106; H. A. R. Gibb, "A Provisional Chronology of Ibn Baṭṭūṭa's Travels in Asia Minor and Russia," II, 528–537, of his translation; I. Hrbek, "The Chronology of Ibn Baṭṭūṭa's Travels," in *Archiv Orientální*, **30** (1962), 409–486; H. F. Janssens, *Ibn Batouta, le voyageur de l'Islam* (Brussels, 1948); É. Lévi-Provençal, "Le voyage d'Ibn Baṭṭūṭa dans le royaume de Grenade," in *Mélanges offerts à William Marçais* (Paris, 1950), pp. 205-224; and George Sarton, *Introduction to the History of Science*, III, pt. 2 (Baltimore, 1948), 1614–1623.

FRANZ ROSENTHAL

BAUDRIMONT, ALEXANDRE ÉDOUARD (*b.* Compiègne, France, 25 February 1806 [Partington; 7 May in Micé and Poggendorff]; *d.* Bordeaux, France, 24 January 1880), *chemistry, physiology*.

Baudrimont had an impressive range of scientific interests, but he accomplished nothing of major importance in any one of them. He was the son of Marie Victor Baudrimont, an inspector of bridges and roads, and Adélaïde Sauvage. At the age of twelve, Baudrimont was apprenticed to a pharmacist, to be trained in that profession, although he himself hoped to become a doctor. In 1823 he went to Paris to continue his training in pharmacy, taking up the study of medicine as well in 1825. He received his medical degree in 1831 and his first-class degree in pharmacy in 1834.

In the meantime, Baudrimont had developed his abilities as a chemist, first as a research assistant to E. R. A. Serres, with whom he published his first paper, in 1828, and then as an industrial chemist in Valenciennes, where he went in 1830 to earn money for his education.

After returning to Paris to receive his medical degree in 1831, Baudrimont went back to Valenciennes to practice medicine. But Paris was where he wished to live and work. During the 1830's and 1840's, he attempted to obtain a post in one of the scientific or medical centers in the capital, but he never advanced beyond minor positions at the Collège de France and the Faculté de Médecine. It was nevertheless a creative period for Baudrimont: he published the *Introduction à l'étude de la chimie par la théorie atomique* (1833), a mineralogy and geology textbook (1840), and the two-volume *Traité de chimie générale et expérimentale* (1844–1846). In addition, he wrote various theses either to obtain scientific degrees or to compete for academic posts in Paris; the most important of these was that on organic chemistry which he submitted in 1838 in competition for the chair of organic chemistry at the École de Médecine.

His "Recherches anatomiques et physiologiques sur le développement du foetus et en particulier l'évolution embryonnaire des oiseaux et des batraciens," written with Gaspard Martin Saint-Ange, won the Académie des Sciences's grand prize in physical sciences for 1846. His interest in applied chemistry was shown in contributions he made to the *Dictionnaire de l'industrie commerciale et agricole* in agricultural and industrial chemistry. In addition, Baudrimont obtained his degrees in pure science—his licentiate in 1839 and his doctorate in 1847. He was probably impelled to secure them by his failure to obtain a post teaching medical chemistry.

In 1847 he accepted a post as assistant to Auguste Laurent at the University of Bordeaux. Two years later he was awarded the chair of chemistry, and he remained in Bordeaux for the rest of his life. He had married in 1842, and had one son, Édouard. His nephew, Marie Victor Ernest Baudrimont, became a distinguished professor of pharmacy.

Baudrimont worked primarily in chemistry and physiology. In chemistry, he was active both as a theorist and as an experimentalist. In chemical theory, Baudrimont devoted his attention to molecular structure. He was greatly influenced by Ampère's ideas on this subject. Like Ampère, he thought that molecules, at least in the solid state, were polyhedral, and like both Ampère and Gaudin, he thought that these molecular shapes could be determined from chemical and crystallographical data. Moreover, he came to believe that in many cases atoms were grouped together in submolecular units within the molecule. He worked out a hierarchy of such units: merons, which roughly corresponded to chemical radicals; merules, which made up merons; and mericules, which composed merules. In his late publications, Baudrimont attempted to explain all physical phenomena in terms of the oscillations or rotations of one or another of these units.

Baudrimont's interest in molecular structure led. him to adumbrate a theory of chemical types. He himself claimed to have used chemical types for classificatory purposes as early as 1835, but he did not develop his ideas on them until his 1838 thesis on organic chemistry. He engaged in a priority dispute with both Dumas and Laurent over the type theory, although Laurent did give him credit for first employing the term *type chimique* (*Méthode de chimie*, p. 358). Baudrimont claimed that his ideas on chemical types were developed independently of the theory of substitution propounded by Dumas and Laurent.

As a theorist, Baudrimont was also one of the few proponents of Avogadro's gas hypothesis in the 1830's and 1840's.

In experimental chemistry, Baudrimont made an important study of aqua regia in 1843, which he published in 1846. Distilling this substance, he produced and condensed a red gas (most likely nitrosyl chloride mixed with some free chlorine) that he thought was the active ingredient in aqua regia. Gay-Lussac disproved Baudrimont's hypothesis but used his method of collecting the gaseous constituent. Baudrimont and F. J. M. Malaguti discovered the presence of sulfur in cystine in 1837.

Throughout his career Baudrimont was interested in physiological research and wrote extensively on physiology. The work that won him the greatest recognition was that done with Martin Saint-Ange. They studied the chemical changes that took place in embryonic development in chickens and amphibia and the toxological effects of various gaseous substances on the embryo.

Baudrimont's other interests can only be indicated here, since they were so varied. His concern with material structure extended into physics; in the 1830's he performed experiments testing the tenacity, ductibility, and malleability of metals. His interest in agricultural chemistry was lifelong and figured importantly in his work at Bordeaux. He also published works on geometry, philosophy of science, music theory, and linguistics.

BIBLIOGRAPHY

I. ORIGINAL WORKS. Baudrimont was a prolific writer. Numerous articles in many fields were published in the *Annales de chimie et de physique,* the *Comptes-rendus hebdomadaires de l'Académie des sciences,* and, especially after 1847, in the *Mémoires de la Société des sciences physiques et naturelles de Bordeaux* and the *Actes de l'Académie des sciences, belles-lettres et arts de Bordeaux.* The works listed here are the ones most relevant to the discussion of his scientific career: *Introduction à l'étude de la chimie par la théorie atomique* (Paris, 1833); "Quel est l'état actuel de la chimie organique, et quel secours a-t-elle reçu des recherches microscopes?," thesis submitted in competition for the chair of organic chemistry and pharmacy of the École de Médecine (Paris, 1838); "Théorie de substitution, discussion de M. Dumas et de M. Pelouze; nouvelle classification des corps moléculaires définis; réclamations de M. Baudrimont," in *Revue scientifique et industrielle,* **1** (1840), 5–60; *Traité de chimie générale et expérimentale,* 2 vols. (Paris, 1844–1846); "Recherches sur l'eau régale et sur un produit particulier auquel elle doit ses principales propriétés," in *Annales de chimie,* 3rd ser., **17** (1846), 24–42; and "Recherches anatomiques et physiologiques sur le développement du foetus et en particulier sur l'évolution embryonnaire des oiseaux et des batraciens," in *Mémoires présentés par divers savants à l'Académie des sciences,* 2nd ser., **11** (1851), 469–692, written with Martin Saint-Ange.

II. SECONDARY LITERATURE. Works on Baudrimont are L. Micé, "Discours d'ouverture de la séance publique du 19 mai 1881 (éloge de M. Baudrimont)," in *Actes de l'Académie de Bordeaux,* 3rd ser., **42** (1880), 729–766; and "Éloge de M. Baudrimont, notes complémentaires," *ibid.,* **44** (1882), 557–624, a typically laudatory *éloge,* very detailed in its account of Baudrimont's life and publications, that is his only extensive biography; and J. R. Partington, *A History of Chemistry,* IV (London, 1964), 391–393.

SEYMOUR H. MAUSKOPF

BAUER, EDMOND (*b.* Paris, France, 26 October 1880; *d.* Paris, 18 October 1963), *physics, physical chemistry.*

The son of a businessman, Bauer was educated at the *lycées* Condorcet and Janson de Sailly, and graduated from the University of Paris. At Paris he was first assistant to Jean Perrin; he worked for some time under Rubens and Nernst; and he engaged in theoretical and experimental research on luminescence and blackbody radiation under Langevin, writing his thesis on the latter work (1912). Bauer was married in 1911 and had four children. Severely wounded at Charleroi in 1914, he was a prisoner of war in Germany for three years. Once Alsace had been returned to France in 1919, he was appointed to the University of Strasbourg under Pierre Weiss; in 1928 Langevin asked him to be *sous-directeur* of his laboratory at

the Collège de France. During World War II, Bauer did not accept an invitation to go to the United States, and stayed in Vichy France; after the Gestapo arrested his daughter, who was fighting in the Resistance with her brothers, he had to seek refuge in Switzerland. His daughter was sent to Ravensbrück, but survived the war. His eldest son also was captured, and died in Neuengamme. Bauer's last position was as professor of physical chemistry at the University of Paris.

Bauer's main experimental and theoretical research dealt with radiation emitted by flames and metallic vapors, which he showed to be thermal; precise determination of the Stefan constant; diffusion of light by high-altitude atmosphere at the Mont Blanc observatory, involving Avogadro's number, the coming of night, and second twilight; the ferromagnetic equation of state; group theory and quantum mechanics; hydrogen bonding and the structure of water and ice, determined from vibration spectra; differential infrared detection of impurities in gas; dielectric dispersion and phase transformation, involving relaxation time and lifetime of hydrogen bonds; and chemical kinetics.

Throughout his life Bauer was keenly interested in the origin and development of the fundamental notions of physics. He contributed to treatises on the history of science and conducted much original research in that field.

Bauer's activity as a professor and an initiator of research stimulated a generation of French physicists. A man of great culture and inexhaustible generosity, he made himself always available to any scientist asking for help or direction in research. Thus, the sum of his work was more than what has been published under his name.

BIBLIOGRAPHY

I. ORIGINAL WORKS. Bauer's books on physics include *La théorie de Bohr* (Paris, 1922); *Les bases expérimentales immédiates de la théorie de quanta* (Paris, 1933), written with Pierre V. Auger, Louis de Broglie, and M. Courtines; *Introduction à la théorie des groupes et à ses applications à la physique quantique* (Paris, 1933), trans. by Paul E. H. Meijer as *Group Theory, the Application to Quantum Mechanics* (Amsterdam, 1962, 1965), and by N. D. Ershovoï as *Vvedenie v teoriu grup i ee prilozhenie k kvantovoï fizike* (Kiev, 1937); *La théorie de l'observation en mécanique quantique* (Paris, 1939), written with Fritz London (analysis, more concise than von Neumann's, of the modification of information on a system by the act of observation; the difference in statistical meaning between representation of information by a wave function and by a density matrix is clearly outlined); and *Champs de vecteurs et de tenseurs* (Paris, 1955).

He also wrote more than fifty original papers on his experimental and theoretical research in physics and physical chemistry. They include "Les coefficients d'aimantation des gaz paramagnétiques et la théorie du magnétisme," in *Journal de physique*, 6th ser., **1** (1920), 97–128, written with Auguste Piccard; "Les propriétés thermoélastiques des métaux ferromagnétiques et le champ moléculaire," *ibid.,* **10** (1929), 345–359; "Sur la déformation des molécules en phase condensée et la liaison hydrogène," *ibid.,* 7th ser., **9** (1938), 319–330, written with M. Magat; "Sur la théorie des diélectriques polaires," in *Cahiers de physique,* no. 20 (1944), 1–20; no. 21 (1944), 21–37; no. 27 (1945), 33–38; and "A Theory of Ultrasonic Adsorption in Unassociated Liquids," in *Proceedings of the Physical Society,* **52** (1949), 141–154.

Bauer's contributions to the history of science include *L'électromagnétisme, hier et aujourd'hui* (Paris, 1929); "L'oeuvre scientifique de Coulomb," in *Bulletin de la Société française des radioélectriciens,* 5th ser., **7** (1937), 1–18; and the chapters on electricity and magnetism in R. Taton, ed., *Histoire générale des sciences:* II, *La science moderne* (1958), 520–539; III, pt. 1, *Le XIXe siècle* (1961), 201–260; and III, pt. 2, *Le XXe siècle* (1964), 239–253. He also wrote all the chapters on the history of science in the seven vols. of Malet and Isaac's *Cours d'histoire,* the official textbook in all French secondary schools since 1928.

II. Secondary Literature. Information on Bauer's life and work is in the obituary by K. K. Darrow in *Physics To-day,* **17** (June 1964), 86–87; and in M. Letort, G. Champetier, J. Wyart et al., "Hommage à Edmond Bauer," in *Journal de chimie physique,* **61** (1964), 955–984.

Daniel Massignon

BAUER, FERDINAND LUCAS (*b.* Feldsberg, Lower Austria, 20 January 1760; *d.* Hietzing, near Vienna, Austria, 17 March 1826), *scientific illustration.*

Bauer's fame rests chiefly on his illustrations for John Sibthorp's *Flora Graeca,* the most beautiful flora of all time. With his brothers Joseph and Franz, he was educated by Father Boccius, prior of the monastery of the Merciful Brothers in Feldsberg, then worked under Nikolaus von Jacquin, professor of botany in Vienna. When Sibthorp, Oxford's professor of botany, came to Vienna in search of the *Codex vindobonensis* of Dioscorides, he learned of Bauer's work and traveled to Feldsberg to see Boccius' fourteen-volume manuscript, *Hortus botanicus,* the 2,750 plates of which were chiefly the work of Ferdinand and his brothers. So impressed was Sibthorp that he immediately engaged Bauer to serve as artist on his expedition to Greece and the Levant. In the ensuing twenty-two months (March 1786 to December 1787) Bauer painted nearly 1,000 watercolors of plants, 363 of animals, and 131 sepia landscapes. Only the plant

watercolors were eventually published in the *Flora Graeca,* a herculean work that took from 1806 to 1840 and cost over £30,000.

Bauer worked on the *Flora* in Oxford until 1801, when he joined Matthew Flinders on his voyage to Australia. There Bauer and the botanist Robert Brown made a rich collection of material that included over 2,000 sketches by Bauer, 1,541 being of plants. Few of these were ever published, although Endlicher used some for his *Prodromus florae Norfolkicae.* Bauer attempted to use them in his *Illustrationes florae Novae Hollandiae,* a project that failed commercially, and in 1814 he left England for Hietzing, which was close to the gardens of Schönbrunn.

Bauer sketched rapidly and colored little on the spot, but noted gradations with a number code so that he could finish his illustrations later. Untroubled by the rigors of travel, he worked hard and achieved an incredible output. Goethe admired the three-dimensional quality of his work, and all botanists respected his accuracy. The overthrow of Linnaean taxonomy was partly due to the Australian work of Bauer and Brown.

BIBLIOGRAPHY

I. Original Works. Bauer's only writing was *Illustrationes florae Novae Hollandiae* (London, 1813). Plates are in Boccius, *Hortus botanicus,* Vols. I–IX, MS at Vaduz, Liechtenstein; Stephan Endlicher, *Prodromus florae Norfolkicae* (Vienna, 1833); Matthew Flinders, *A Voyage to Terra Australis* (London, 1814); A. B. Lambert, *A Description of the Genus Pinus* (London, 1803–1824); John Lindley, *Digitalium monographia* (London, 1821); and John Sibthorp, *Flora Graeca* (London, 1806–1840).

II. Secondary Literature. There is no detailed biography of Bauer, few of his letters have survived, and no portrait is extant. The best accounts are Wilfred Blunt, *The Art of Botanical Illustration* (London, 1950), and William Stearn, "Franz and Ferdinand Bauer, Masters of Botanical Illustration," in *Endeavour,* **19**, no. 73 (Jan. 1960), 27–35. For details of Bauer manuscripts see C. Nissen, *Die botanische Buchillustration,* 2nd ed. (Stuttgart, 1966).

R. Olby

BAUER, FRANZ ANDREAS (*b.* Feldsberg, Lower Austria, 4 October 1758; *d.* Kew, England, 11 December 1840), *botanical illustration, microscopy.*

Bauer was educated by Father Boccius in Feldsberg and worked under Jacquin in Vienna. In 1788 he accompanied Jacquin's son, Joseph, on his travels through Europe. In London they met Sir Joseph Banks and worked in his magnificent library and herbarium. Banks then engaged Bauer as artist at the

Royal Garden, Kew, and at the attractive salary of £300 a year Bauer remained there for the rest of his life. His output was not so great as that of his brother Ferdinand, for his services were not adequately utilized and much of the time he followed his own fancy. This led him into the intricacies of flower structure in strelitzias and orchids, the nature of red snow, and the structure of pollen grains. He also illustrated the works of friends with microscopical and anatomical drawings: Banks's works on cereal diseases and apple blight, Robert Brown's description of *Rafflesia* and *Woodsia,* Home's *Lectures on Comparative Anatomy,* and John Smith's account of his discovery of the apomictic plant dovewood.

Bauer achieved recognition as a microscopist but made no lasting contribution to the field. For instance, while others correctly attributed the color of red snow to an alga, he believed the causal organism was a fungus. In his study of the rye ergot he inclined to the view that nutritional factors were responsible until John Smith showed him hyphae of the fungal agent in the infected ears. On the difficult subject of the fertilization mechanism in orchids Bauer, like Robert Brown, came to the wrong conclusions because he did not know that they are cross-pollinated by insects.

Bauer's plant paintings are of outstanding beauty and scientific accuracy. From the beginning he tended to use a pure wash, whereas his brother Ferdinand relied more on body color; yet much of Ferdinand's later work is indistinguishable from that of Franz. Since the cell theory and staining and fixing techniques had not yet been developed, it is understandable that Bauer's microscopical paintings have little scientific worth.

BIBLIOGRAPHY

I. ORIGINAL WORKS. Bauer's writings include *Delineations of Exotic Plants Cultivated in the Royal Garden at Kew* (London, 1796); *Strelitzia depicta* (London, 1818); "Microscopical Observations on the Red Snow," in *Quarterly Journal of Literature, Science and the Arts,* **7** (1819), 222–229; "Some Experiments on the Fungi Which Constitute the Colouring Matter of the Red Snow Discovered in Baffin's Bay," in *Philosophical Transactions of the Royal Society,* **110** (1820), 165–172; "Croonian Lecture," *ibid.,* **113** (1823), 1–16; *Illustrations of Orchidaceous Plants* (London, 1830–1838); and "The Ergot of Rye," in *Transactions of the Linnean Society of London,* **18** (1841), 509–512. Plates by Bauer are in E. Home, *Lectures on Comparative Anatomy,* 4 vols. and 2 supps. (London, 1814–1828); and W. J. Hooker, *Genera Filicum* (London, 1842).

II. SECONDARY LITERATURE. Obituaries are in *Proceedings of the Linnean Society of London,* **1** (1849), 101–104; and *Proceedings of the Royal Society,* **4** (1843), 342–344. On Bauer's art see W. Blunt, *The Art of Botanical Illustration* (London, 1950), pp. 195–202.

R. OLBY

BAUER, GEORG. See **Agricola.**

BAUER, LOUIS AGRICOLA (*b.* Cincinnati, Ohio, 26 January 1865; *d.* Washington, D.C., 12 April 1932), *geophysics.*

Bauer, the founder of the department of terrestrial magnetism of the Carnegie Institution of Washington, was of that line of students of magnetism starting with Halley, and including Gauss and Sabine, who have considered this topic one of the great scientific problems. Originally trained as a civil engineer, he worked from 1887 to 1892 as a computer, primarily on geomagnetism, for the U.S. Coast and Geodetic Survey. From 1892 to 1895 he studied at the University of Berlin and earned the Ph.D. for a thesis on the secular variation of the earth's magnetism.

On his return from Europe, Bauer taught at the University of Chicago (1895–1896) and the University of Cincinnati (1897–1899). While at the latter he also directed the magnetic work of the Maryland Geological Survey, and from 1899 to 1906 he supervised the expanded geomagnetic work of the Coast and Geodetic Survey. During this period he became convinced that determination of the physical nature of terrestrial magnetism and the explanation of its secular variation required a great increase in observational data. When the Carnegie Institution of Washington was founded in 1902, Bauer proposed a worldwide program of research on the magnetic and electrical condition of the earth and its atmosphere and was appointed head of the new department in 1904.

Undoubtedly the most heroic aspect of Bauer's work at the Carnegie Institution was the extensive mapping of the earth's magnetic field on a vast area of the seas, quite like the efforts of Halley and Sabine. Like Gauss and Sabine, he also promoted the establishment of magnetic stations and was active in the mathematical analysis of observations and in the development of a mathematical theory. Bauer paid considerable attention to instrumentation. Although much of his work was devoted to the main magnetic field, he was also interested in atmospheric electricity and extraterrestrial influences on the earth's magnetism. An example of the latter is his work on the effects of solar eclipses.

Bauer was very active in various international geophysical organizations, such as the International Union of Geodesy and Geophysics. In 1896 he founded the periodical *Terrestrial Magnetism* (later

Terrestrial Magnetism and Atmospheric Electricity), which he edited until 1927. Now known as the *Journal of Geophysical Research,* the periodical was influential, highly regarded, and played an important role in stimulating geophysical investigations at a time when interest in classical physics was being overshadowed by newer intellectual pursuits.

Bauer commited suicide at the age of sixty-seven.

BIBLIOGRAPHY

I. ORIGINAL WORKS. Bauer has over 300 titles to his credit. While no comprehensive bibliography exists, H. D. Harradon, "Principal Published Papers of Louis A. Bauer," in *Terrestrial Magnetism and Atmospheric Electricity,* **37** (Sept. 1932), 220–224, is a good introduction to Bauer's writings.

Bauer documents are in the Archives of the Carnegie Institution of Washington and the records of the U.S. Coast and Geodetic Survey in the U.S. National Archives, Washington, D.C. The W. F. G. Swann Papers at the American Philosophical Society Library, Philadelphia, and the George Ellery Hale Papers at the Millikan Library, California Institute of Technology, Pasadena, California, contain interesting Bauer correspondence.

II. SECONDARY LITERATURE. *Terrestrial Magnetism and Atmospheric Electricity,* **37** (Sept. 1932), 203–420, was the Bauer Memorial Number; it contains a scattering of comments on Bauer, as well as many articles showing the state of development of fields he worked in. Both the *Annual Report* of the U.S. Coast and Geodetic Survey and the *Yearbook* of the Carnegie Institution of Washington for the years when Bauer was with them are replete with information on his career. The best general secondary source on Bauer's principal intellectual interest is Sydney Chapman and Julius Bartels, *Geomagnetism,* 2 vols. (Oxford, 1940), which has many specific references to Bauer. An additional virtue of the work is that the authors have, implicitly and explicitly, attempted to place recent works in a historical perspective.

NATHAN REINGOLD

BAUHIN, GASPARD (*b.* Basel, Switzerland, 17 January 1560; *d.* Basel, 5 December 1624), *anatomy, botany.*

Bauhin was the younger son of Jean Bauhin, a French Protestant physician and surgeon from Amiens, who sought refuge from religious persecution by settling in Basel in 1541 and became attached to the university. From childhood, Bauhin was taught anatomy by his father and botany by his brother Jean (almost twenty years his senior), who became a botanist of some repute. In 1572 Gaspard entered the University of Basel, where Felix Plater and Theodore

Zwinger were among his teachers. He received the degree of Bachelor of Philosophy in 1575, and conducted his first medical disputation in 1577. In October of that year he went to Padua, where for eighteen months he studied anatomy with Girolamo Fabrizio (Fabricius ab Aquapendente), saw seven bodies dissected, "and even assisted myself in the private dissections." He also attended the teaching of Marco de Oddi and Emilio Campolongo at the Hospital of St. Francis, and probably that of Melchior Wieland (Guillandinus) in the botanical garden. At some time during this period he visited Bologna and received instruction in anatomy from Giulio Cesare Aranzio. In the spring of 1579 he signed the register of the University of Montpellier, but by his own account he spent more time in Paris attending the anatomies conducted by Séverin Pineau, professor of anatomy and surgery, "whom I assisted in dissecting at his request." In May 1580 he was in Tübingen. Early the following year he returned to Basel, where "at the urgent request of the College of Physicians, I began to dissect bodies." He held his first public anatomy on 27 February. The disputation for his doctor's degree took place on 19 April and had as its subject *De dolore colico.* He received the doctorate on 2 May, and on 13 May he was made a member of the Faculty of Medicine.

In April 1582 Bauhin was made professor of Greek; two years later he became *consiliarius* in the Faculty of Medicine, an office he held until his death. He was dean of the faculty nine times (beginning in 1586), and four times rector of the university (1592, 1598, 1611, 1619). Despite his professorship of Greek, he continued to teach both anatomy and botany, holding public anatomies in the winter and taking the students on botanical expeditions in the summer. As a result of his efforts, work was begun on a permanent theater for anatomical demonstrations, and a botanical garden was laid out. In September 1589 he was rewarded by the creation of a special chair in anatomy and botany. During these years Bauhin's private medical practice grew, and in 1597 he was associated with his brother Jean as physician to Duke Frederick of Württemberg. From 1588 on, he was occupied with the writing and publishing of a series of books on anatomy. His first major botanical work was *Phytopinax* (1596). When his *Pinax* appeared in 1623, it was said to be the result of forty years' work. On the death of Felix Plater in 1614, Bauhin succeeded him as archiater to the city of Basel. The following year he was appointed professor of the practice of medicine. He was married three times: in 1581 to Barbara Vogelmann of Montbéliard, by whom he had one daughter; in 1596 to Maria Bruggler of Bern;

and sometime after 1597 to Magdalena Burckhardt, by whom he had two daughters and one son, Jean Gaspard, who succeeded his father as professor of anatomy and botany in 1629 and became professor of the practice of medicine in 1660. In 1658 Jean Gaspard published the first volume, all that was ever published of the intended twelve, of his father's *Theatrum botanicum.*

No great anatomical discoveries can be ascribed to Bauhin. He himself believed that he was the first to describe the ileocecal valve, which was long known as the *valvula Bauhini;* and in a number of his anatomical writings he gives an account of how he first found it during a private dissection that he performed as a student in Paris in 1579. His greatest contribution to anatomy was the reform he introduced into the nomenclature, particularly into that of muscles. Because it is very easy to make mistakes in the enumeration of muscles if they are merely called first, second, third, etc., and because different anatomists had named different muscles in this way, not agreeing on the order of the enumeration, Bauhin decided that it was better to use another kind of terminology. He therefore named some muscles according to their substance (semimembranosus, etc.), others according to their shape (deltoid, scalene, etc.), some according to their origin (arytenoideus, etc.), and others according to their origin and insertion (styloglossus, crycothyroideus, etc.). Some he named according to the number of their heads (biceps, triceps), some according to their amount (vastus, gracilis), some according to their position (pectoralis, etc.), and others according to their use (supinator, pronator, etc.). He also decided that veins and arteries should be named according to their use or course, and nerves according to their function. The system had so many obvious advantages over the old method that it was adopted by all subsequent anatomists.

There is no doubt that Bauhin's contribution as a teacher of anatomy was considerable, particularly through his many books on the subject. His first textbook was *De corporis humani partibus externis* (1588), written at the request of his students after the public anatomy he had given two years before. It was intended to be a succinct, methodical account of the external parts of the body suitable for beginners and to be used in conjunction with the *Tabulae* of Vesalius. The second volume, dealing with "similar and spermatic" parts, was published in 1592. Meanwhile, in 1590, Bauhin published his first complete textbook, *De corporis humani fabrica: Libri IIII.* It was a systematic account written from the point of view of dissection, and intended for students rather than professors of anatomy. It respected ancient findings

and theories, but did not hesitate to correct them when the results of actual dissections made it necessary. Its appearance provoked a storm of abuse from the Galenists. Corrected and enlarged by a description of female anatomy, it was republished in 1597 as *Anatomica corporis virilis et muliebris historia.* In 1605 all these anatomical writings were brought together, revised and enlarged, and published in Bauhin's most celebrated anatomical textbook, *Theatrum anatomicum,* which was accompanied by copper engravings based on the drawings of Vesalius and entitled *Vivae imagines partium corporis.* The *Theatrum anatomicum* soon acquired the reputation of being the best anatomical textbook available. It was systematic, gave adequate consideration to the ancient authorities, did not go into too much detail over the controversies, had a series of eminently useful footnotes, and mentioned anatomical anomalies and pathological findings. Its illustrations, although poor in comparison with those of Vesalius, were adequate for anyone using the book to accompany an actual dissection. It was this work that William Harvey chose as the basis for his Lumleian Lectures to the College of Physicians in London in 1616. It was translated into English in 1615 by Helkiah Crooke and, conflated with the textbook of Laurentius, was published under the title of *Microcosmographia, A Study of the Body of Man.*

Although Bauhin said that his anatomical works contained few novelties, he did include new anatomical findings that were obviously true, for he believed firmly that truth demonstrable to the beholder outweighs the opinions of the authorities. In this way, in his *Libri IIII* of 1590 he included a description of the valves in the veins, as demonstrated sixteen years previously by Girolamo Fabrizio in Padua. (Fabrizio's own account was not published until 1603.) In the same work he pointed out that there was no need to suppose the existence of pores in the interventricular septum of the heart, for the venous blood could more easily go to the lungs from the right ventricle through the pulmonary artery, there be refined and mixed with air, and return to the left ventricle through the pulmonary vein. He gives no authorities for this view, and it is open to conjecture whether he formulated it independently. In the end, it is a view he seems to have rejected, for in his later works he repeats Galen's traditional teaching, supported by his own findings of conspicuous pores in the septum of an ox's heart, which had been prepared by boiling.

Bauhin's medical works include treatises on the bezoar stone, on Caesarean section, on hermaphrodites and other monstrous births, and on the pulse.

His two pharmacological writings are designed as handbooks for young physicians.

As in anatomy, Bauhin's great contribution to botany was to nomenclature. He was primarily a taxonomist, concerned with the collecting and classifying of a great variety of plants. He is also remembered for separating botany from materia medica. His botanical fame rests chiefly on two works, *Prodromos* (1620) and *Pinax* (1623). In the latter he discarded the old alphabetical manner of enumeration and stated that any sound method of classification must be based on affinities. Consequently, he distinguished between genus and species and introduced a system of binomial nomenclature. He made little or no progress in classifying the genera into orders and classes. Although the system was not his invention, he vastly improved it, and thereafter it was generally adopted. His botanical work was commemorated by L. P. C. Plumier, who gave the name *Bauhinia* to a family of tropical trees; and Linnaeus, in memory of both Gaspard and his brother Jean, called one species of this family *Bauhinia bijuga*.

Although in a final assessment of his work in botany and anatomy it can be said that little was truly original, Bauhin's influence in both fields lasted for well over a century. His great merit was his ability to treat his subjects in an orderly and methodical manner, for he had a capacity to think clearly and an ability to work without tiring. Quiet and reserved, he can be remembered in William Harvey's words concerning him: "a rare industrious man."

BIBLIOGRAPHY

I. ORIGINAL WORKS. Bauhin's anatomical and medical writings, presented in the order that best indicates their relationships, are ΑΠΟΘΕΡΑΠΕΙΑ ΙΑΤΡΙΚΗ *Quam medicae laureae causa Casparus Bauhinus . . . subibit* (Basel, 1581); ΥΣΤΕΡΟΤΟΜΟΤΟΚΙΑ *Francisci Rousseti, Gallicè primum edita, nunc vero Caspari Bauhini . . . Latine reddita* (Basel, 1588), which contains Bauhin's account of Caesarean section in the "Appendix varias et novas historias continens . . . a Casparo Bauhino addita," repr. many times in various eds. of Rousset's work; *De corporis humani partibus externis Tractatus* (Basel, 1588), repr. as *Anatomes . . . liber primus* (Basel, 1591); *Anatomes liber secundus partium similarium spermaticarum tractationem . . . continens* (Basel, 1592), repr. with *Anatomes . . . liber primus* (Basel, 1597); *De corporis humani fabrica: Libri IIII. Methodo anatomico in praelectionibus publicis proposita . . .* (Basel, 1590), enl. and repr. as *Anatomica corporis virilis et muliebris historia* (Lyons, 1597) and repr. as *Institutiones anatomicae corporis virilis et muliebris historiam exhibentes* (Lyons, 1604; Basel, 1609; Frankfurt, 1616);

Praeludia anatomica (Basel, 1601), also known as *Disputatio prima; Disputatio secunda de partibus humani corporis* (Basel, 1602); *Disputatio tertia. De ossium natura* (Basel, 1604); "Introductio in doctrinam pulsuum ad tyrones," in *Ars sphygmica . . . à Josepho Struthio . . . conscripta . . .* (Basel, 1602), pp. 1–23; *Theatrum anatomicum novis figuris aenis illustratum . . .* (Frankfurt, 1605; new and enl. ed., 1621); *Appendix ad Theatrum anatomicum . . . sive Explicatio characterum omnium . . .* (Frankfurt, 1600), frequently bound with the *Theatrum anatomicum* of 1605; *Vivae imagines partium corporis humani aeneis formis expressae & ex Theatro anatomico . . . desumptae* (Frankfurt, 1620, 1640), frequently bound with the 1621 ed. of *Theatrum anatomicum; De compositione medicamentorum sive medicamentorum componendorum ratio et methodus* (Offenbach, 1610); *De lapidis Bezaar . . . ortu, natura, differentiis, veròque usu* (Basel, 1613, 1624, 1625); *De homine oratio* (Basel, n.d.), an oration delivered to the Faculty of Medicine 16 Nov. 1614; *De hermaphroditorum monstrosorumque partuum natura* (Oppenheim, 1614); and *De remediorum formulis Graecis, Arabibus & Latinis usitatis . . . libri duo, Iuniorum medicorum usum editi* (Frankfurt, 1619).

Bauhin's botanical works are *De plantis a divis sanctisve nomen habentibus . . . Ioanni Bauhini* (Basel, 1591, 1595), which contains letters from Gaspard Bauhin to Conrad Gesner; ΦΥΤΟΠΙΝΑΞ *seu enumeratio plantarum ab herbariis nostro seculo descriptarum. . . . Additis aliquot hactenus non sculptarum plantarum vivis iconibus* (Basel, 1596); *Animadversiones in historiam generalem plantarum Lugduni editam. Item catalogus plantarum* (Frankfurt, 1601); ΠΡΟΔΡΟΜΟΣ *Theatri botanici in quo plantae supra secentae ab ipso primum descriptae cum plurimis figuris proponuntur* (Frankfurt, 1620; Basel, 1671); *Catalogus plantarum circa Basileam spontè nascentium . . . in usum scholae medicae* (Basel, 1622; 3rd ed., 1671; 2nd ed. unknown); ΠΙΝΑΞ *Theatri botanici sive Index in Theophrasti, Dioscoridis, Plinii et botanicorum qui à seculo scripserunt opera* (Basel, 1623, 1671, 1740); and *Theatri botanici sive Historiae plantarum . . . liber primus*, Jean Gaspard Bauhin, ed. (Basel, 1658).

In addition, Bauhin edited a number of anatomical and botanical works by other writers, of which the most notable is his ed. of P. A. Mathioli's *Opera quae extant omnia* (Frankfurt, 1598). Letters written by Bauhin on medical and anatomical subjects are in J. Hornung, *Cista medica* (Nuremberg, 1625); and Wolfgang Wedel, *Ephemeriden Academiae Naturae Curiosorum* (1673). Unpublished letters in holograph, both Latin and vernacular, are in the library of the University of Basel.

II. SECONDARY LITERATURE. Albrecht Burckhardt, *Geschichte der Medizinischen Fakultät zu Basel, 1460–1900* (Basel, 1917), pp. 95–123, provides a good account of Bauhin's life and a bibliography of his writings. Older studies are J. von Hess, *Bauhins Leben* (Basel, 1860); and Ludovic Legré, *Les deux Bauhins* (Marseilles, 1904). References to Bauhin's botanical works are in R. J. Harvey-Gibson, *Outlines of the History of Botany* (London, 1919); G. A. Pritzel, *Thesaurus literaturae botanicae* (Leipzig, 1851; new ed.,

Milan, 1871); and *Sachs' History of Botany 1530–1860*, trans. Garnsey and Balfour (Oxford, 1890).

GWENETH WHITTERIDGE

BAUHIN, JEAN (*b.* Basel, Switzerland, 12 February 1541; *d.* Montbéliard, principality of Württemberg–Montbéliard, 26 October 1613), *botany*.

Bauhin's father, Jean, a Protestant from Amiens, was physician to Margaret of Navarre; while in Paris he married Jean Fontaine. The revival of religious persecution under Francis I resulted in the exile of the Bauhin family to Basel in 1541; there the younger Jean, eldest of seven children, was born shortly afterward. His younger brother was Gaspard Bauhin.

Bauhin's basic education was in Basel; his early teachers were the religious reformer Coelius Secundus Curione, an Italian exile who was professor of belles lettres at Basel University, and Conrad Gesner of Zurich. Bauhin completed his studies by paying short visits to foreign universities between 1560 and 1563. His most prolonged stay was in Montpellier, from 1561 to 1562. It has generally been assumed that he obtained an M.D. at Montpellier, but this is not supported by the university records. Nevertheless, he established a medical practice at Lyons in 1563 and married Denyse Bornand (Bernhard) in 1565. Of the six children born to them, three daughters lived to maturity, all of whom married doctors.

Renewed religious persecution forced Bauhin into exile in Geneva, where he again practiced medicine, in 1568; two years later he was appointed professor of rhetoric at Basel. Finally, in 1571 he became physician to Duke Frederick of Württemberg, the ruler of the dual principality of Württemberg–Montbéliard and an enlightened and sympathetic patron. Bauhin established botanical gardens, in which he grew both native and exotic plants, at Montbéliard and Stuttgart. He excavated the ruins of Mandurium (Mandeure) and displayed his archaeological collections in a museum at Duke Frederick's chateau. Bauhin was also appointed archiater by Frederick. In 1675 he was instrumental in establishing the College of Medical Practitioners in Montbéliard, which regulated the duties of all practitioners and provided free medical services to the poor. His second marriage, in 1598, was to Anne Grégoire, a Protestant refugee from Besançon.

Botany was Bauhin's primary interest from his youth. His teacher and friend, Conrad Gesner, spent his last years compiling a *Historia plantarum,* a work on descriptive botany paralleling his published *Historia animalium;* the first documentary evidence relating to Bauhin's concern with botany is his correspondence with Gesner from 1560 to 1565. He collected plants and sent the herbarium specimens to Gesner, whose artist and engraver prepared appropriate illustrations. Gesner's death left this great collaborative enterprise incomplete, and the unfinished *Historia plantarum* was not published until the eighteenth century. Bauhin's *Historia plantarum* may be regarded as a reconstruction of Gesner's work, carrying on the latter's humanistic learning and enthusiasm for exploration and description. Yet Bauhin realized that a comprehensive description of flora could not be undertaken single-handed, and he relied on informants from many countries.

Bauhin's longest journeys were made during his medical studies. In 1561 he accompanied Gesner on a tour of the Rhaetian Alps, during which they pioneered the study of the alpine flora, particularly in the Mount Albula region. Upon Gesner's advice, in the same year he traveled to Tübingen to meet Leonhard Fuchs. He next spent more than a year at Montpellier under Rondelet, one of the most gifted Renaissance naturalists and medical teachers. He conducted further systematic explorations in the Montpellier region, and in 1562 he reported to Gesner that he was compiling a *Catalogum stirpium Monspeliensium.* This was never published separately, but information from it was incorporated into the *Historia plantarum.* References in this work show that Bauhin and his colleagues Jacques Raynaudet and Leonard Rauwolff explored Provence and Languedoc. Most of 1563 was spent studying the flora of north Italy and the Apennines. He also visited botanical gardens in Padua and Bologna, which later provided him with materials for his own gardens. His first garden was established about 1564 at Lyons, where he collaborated with Jacques Daleschamps in studying the local flora. It is not certain whether Bauhin played any significant role in the compilation of the anonymous *Historia plantarum generalis* (1586), which is generally attributed to Daleschamps. Bauhin's duties at Montbéliard did not interrupt his explorations, which were often undertaken in connection with the missions of Duke Frederick. In his later years Bauhin's closest collaborator was his son-in-law Jean-Henri Cherler, who had married his youngest daughter, Geneviève. Cherler contributed a knowledge of the floras of Belgium and England, and was named as joint author of the *Historia plantarum*—an honor he scarcely deserved.

The two botanical works published by Bauhin in 1591 and 1593 give no intimation of the *Historia plantarum,* for each is a very specific exercise. The first, *De plantis a divis sanctisve nomen* (1591), is an alphabetical list of plants named after saints, with full citations to the botanical literature. Bauhin showed that commonly more than one species—and often quite unrelated ones—were named after a particular saint. The other work, *De plantis Absynthii nomen* (1593), underlines the great confusion that existed over a single type. He quoted a list, covering twelve pages, of authors who had used the name *Absynthium* and then attempted to identify each type, indicating the synonyms used by botanists. Although these works may seem obscure, they illustrate Bauhin's critical talents, his great knowledge of the botanical literature, and his ability to solve problems of nomenclature.

Bauhin's reputation as a botanist rests upon the encyclopedic *Historia plantarum universalis* (1650–1651), which was not published until thirty-seven years after his death. It completely overshadows the works published during his lifetime, which give only a limited indication of his originality. He was reluctant to publish, and most of his works were concentrated in the years 1593–1598. Most of them dealt with subjects peripheral to his main botanical interests, although they displayed the erudition and caution of his later botanical works. A specifically medical work described the remedies for diseases contracted as a result of animal bites (*Histoire notable de la rage*, 1591). More significant is the description of swarms of locusts and grasshoppers that Felix Platter and François Valleriol had recorded at Arles in 1553, and the swarms of insects at Porrentruy, Montbéliard, in 1590 (*Traicté des animauls, aians aisles*, 1593). He suggested that these phenomena were a manifestation of the power of Providence and asserted that insects were a cause of disease. His longest and most popular medical work was a description of European mineral waters and baths, based on a study of the springs at Bad Boll, near Groppingen, Württemberg (*Historia novi et admirabilis fontis*, 1598). This was the most detailed work on the subject written in the sixteenth century, and contains a lengthy appendix that gives an intimation of Bauhin's abilities as a naturalist. It consists of a series of illustrations, most of his fossil collections, that was probably inspired by Gesner's *De rerum fossilium* (1565). The most original were the illustrations of sixty varieties of apples and thirty-nine of pears, all collected in the alpine region. These large and distinctive woodcuts show the value of illustration for depicting fine morphological distinctions.

From 1600 until his death, Bauhin was engaged in compiling the *Historia plantarum*. The virtually complete manuscript passed to Dominic Chabrey, an Yverdon physician, who published a summary of the work in 1619. Eventually, François Louis de Graffen-ried of Yverdon financed the publication of the work, which appeared in three volumes. Despite the delay in publication, the work was not obsolete. It contained the description and synonyms of 5,226 plants, primarily from Europe, but with some Eastern and American floras. This represented the fruits of the explorations of Bauhin and his informants, and compilation from ancient and contemporary literature. It also indicates the great progress of botany in the sixteenth century: Brunfels had described 240 plants in 1532; the less accurate *Historia plantarum generalis* of 1587 reached 3,000; the only works to describe more than this number in the succeeding century were by Jean Bauhin and his brother Gaspard. Jean's work was paralleled by his brother's *Pinax theatri botanici* (1623). This contained 6,000 plants but gave only names and synonyms. Hence the particular value of Jean's work was its concise and accurate description of each type.

BIBLIOGRAPHY

I. ORIGINAL WORKS. Bauhin's works are *Histoire notable de la rage des loups advenue l'an MDXC, avec les remèdes pour empescher la rage* . . . (Montbéliard, 1591), trans. into Latin and German the same year; *De plantis a divis sanctisve nomen habentibus . . . Additae sunt Conradi Gesneri epistolae hactenus editae a Casparo Bauhino* (Basel, 1591); *De plantis Absynthii nomen habentibus, caput desumptum ex clarissimi ornatissimique viri D. Doct. Ioannis Bauhin . . . Tractatus item de absynthiis Claudii Rocardi* (Montbéliard, 1593; repr. 1599); *Traicté des animauls, aians aisles, qui nuisent par leurs piqueures ou morsures, auec les remèdes* . . . (Montbéliard, 1593); *Historia novi et admirabilis fontis balneique Bollensis in Ducatu Wirtembergico* . . . (Montbéliard, 1598), trans. into German (Stuttgart, 1602) and also reissued under two other titles: *De thermis aquisque medicatis Europae praecipuis opus succinctum* (Montbéliard, 1600) and *De aquis medicatis nova methodus libri quatuor* (Montbéliard, 1607/1608, 1612); *Histoire ou plustot un simple et véritable récit des merveilleux effects qu'une salubre fontaine située au comté de Montbéliard* . . . (Montbéliard, 1601), also trans. into German (Montbéliard, 1602); *De auxiliis adversus pestem* (Montbéliard, 1607), reported to have been trans. into German by Thiebaud Noblot in the same year; *Joh. Bauhini et Joh. Henr. Cherleri, Historiae plantarum generalis novae et absolutissimae, quinquaginta annis elaboratae jam prelo commissae, Prodromus* (Yverdon, 1619); and *Historia plantarum universalis, nova et absolutissima, cum consensu et dissensu circa eas. Auctoribus Joh. Bauhino et Joh. Henr. Cherlero philos. et med. doctoribus Basiliensibus; Quam recensuit et auxit Dominicus Chabraeus, med. doct. Genevensis; Juris vero publici fecit Franciscus Lud. a Graffenried*, 3 vols. (Yverdon, 1650–1651).

II. SECONDARY LITERATURE. Works dealing with Bauhin and his accomplishments are A. Arber, *Herbals*, 2nd ed. (Cambridge, 1953), pp. 70, 85, 93, 113–119; P. Delaunay, *La zoologie au seizième siècle* (Paris, 1962), pp. 71, 225, 229, 230, 238, 302; L.-M. Dupetit-Thouars, in *Biographie universelle*, III, 556–559; C. Duvernay, *Notices sur quelques médecins, naturalistes et agronomes nés ou établis à Montbéliard dès le seizième siècle* (Besançon, 1835), pp. 1–24; É. and É. Haag, *La France protestante*, 2nd ed., I (Paris, 1887), 1016–1023; C. Jenssen, in *Allgemeine deutsche Biographie*, II, 149–151; L. Legré, *La botanique en Provence au XVIe siècle. Les deux Bauhin, Jean Henri Cherler et Valerand Dourez* (Marseille, 1904); J. E. Planchet, *Rondelet et ses disciples ou la botanique à Montpellier au XVIme siècle* (Montpellier, 1866); C. Roth, "Stammtafeln einiger ausgestorbener Gelehrtenfamilien," in *Basler Zeitschrift für Geschichte und Altertumkunde*, **15** (1916), 47–55; and C. P. J. Sprengel, *Geschichte der Botanik* (Leipzig, 1817–1818), pp. 364–369.

CHARLES WEBSTER

BAUMÉ, ANTOINE (*b.* Senlis, France, 26 February 1728; *d.* Paris, France, 15 October 1804), *chemistry, pharmacy.*

The son of Guillaume Baumé, who ran two inns in Senlis, Antoine Baumé seems to have had the advantages of a fairly well-to-do home. About 1743 he was apprenticed to a pharmacist in Compiègne, but by 1745 he was working in C. J. Geoffroy's dispensary in Paris, where he was able to indulge and develop his interest in theoretical chemistry as well as in pharmacy. In 1752 he became *maître apothicaire,* and opened his own dispensary in the Rue St.-Denis, Paris, the following year; it was moved to the Rue Coquillère in 1762.

In addition to its role as a local pharmacy, Baumé's dispensary supplied drugs in bulk to pharmacies and hospitals over a very wide area and manufactured drugs and other chemicals in large quantities. In 1767 he began the first large-scale production of sal ammoniac in France; he doubtless owed something in this connection to Geoffroy, who had been the first in France to make sal ammoniac. Baumé also supplied industrial and laboratory apparatus, some of which he designed himself. In particular, his areometer (1768) was an important step forward, in that it possessed a scale having two fixed points (the density of distilled water and that of a salt solution of known concentration), thus enabling properly calibrated instruments to be produced. In 1777, Baumé won first prize for an essay on the best furnaces, alembics, and other apparatus to be used in the distillation of wine.

In 1757, Baumé and Macquer began a series of courses in chemistry and pharmacy that continued

for sixteen years. Baumé equipped the laboratory, supplied the funds, and prepared all the experiments to be carried out. An outline of this course, *Plan d'un cours de chymie expérimentale et raisonnée . . .,* was published in 1757. Apart from this, Baumé published a number of works on chemistry and pharmacy that ran into several editions. He also contributed to the *Dictionnaire des arts et métiers* (1766).

From 1755 until the end of his life, Baumé produced many memoirs, the first of these being a dissertation on ether. (One of the many bitter wrangles he entered into with his fellow scientists was a dispute with L. C. Cadet de Gassicourt concerning the best and cheapest method of preparing ether [1775].) Baumé's many disputes nearly cost him membership in the Académie des Sciences, but he was finally elected as *adjoint-chimiste* on 25 December 1772; he became *associé* in 1778 and *pensionnaire* in 1785.

Despite his perceptiveness in some matters—he pointed out that two affinity tables were necessary (*Chymie expérimentale et raisonnée,* **1** [1773], 22), one for reactions done in the wet way and one for reactions done in the dry way—Baumé resisted the new theories in chemistry until the end of his life. He remained a determined phlogistonist—as late as 1797 he stated quite categorically that water could not be decomposed. With the coming of the Revolution, Baumé lost his fortune, including his pension as a member of the Academy, but in 1795, as a result of an appeal to the Committee of Public Instruction, he received a sum of money that enabled him to open another dispensary in 1796. At the newly formed Institut de France, he obtained only a place as *associé non résidant,* which carried a minimum of privileges.

BIBLIOGRAPHY

An excellent and detailed bibliography of Baumé's works is given in René Davy, *L'apothicaire Antoine Baumé (1728–1804)* (Cahors, 1955), pp. 141–147.

Other works on Baumé are L. C. Cadet de Gassicourt, *Éloge de Baumé, apothicaire* (Brussels, an XIII [1805]); Delunel, "Éloge de Baumé," in *Société de pharmacie de Paris, séance publique* (an XIV [1806]), p. 27; and N. Deyeux, "Éloge de Baumé," in *Annales de chimie et de physique,* **4** (30 messidor an XIII [1805]), 105.

E. McDONALD

BAUMHAUER, EDOUARD HENRI VON (*b.* Brussels, Belgium, 18 September 1820; *d.* Haarlem, Netherlands, 18 January 1885), *chemistry.*

The son of a solicitor-general at the High Court of Justice, Brussels, Baumhauer attended the Latin

School of Brussels, then studied classical literature and natural sciences at Utrecht, graduating with a degree in classical literature in 1843 and one in natural sciences in 1844. From 1845 to 1847 he was professor of physics and chemistry at the Royal Athenaeum in Maastricht, and from 1848 to 1865, professor of chemistry at the Athenaeum Illustre in Amsterdam. From 1865 until his death Baumhauer was perpetual secretary of the Dutch Society, Haarlem, and edited the *Archives néerlandaises des sciences exactes et naturelles.*

Baumhauer was primarily a teacher. During his stay in Amsterdam, however, he did a great deal of work in practical chemistry. In 1853 and the years following, he developed a method for the quantitative determination of oxygen in organic substances. His investigations on drinking water led in 1854 to the establishment of a waterworks in Amsterdam which drew its water from the coastal dunes. Baumhauer analyzed milk in 1857, and the following year he effected the passage of a municipal regulation calling for the inspection of food. In 1859 he began work on the accurate determination of the strength of alcohol, which was important for the levying of taxes.

Baumhauer published papers on a great variety of subjects, including diamonds, marine pileworms, and meteorology. After oil had been discovered in great quantities, he analyzed a number of samples from the Dutch East Indies and gave advice to those drilling for oil in that territory.

As a theoretical chemist Baumhauer was of minor significance. His analysis of meteoric stone, the subject of his thesis (1844), led him to theoretical speculations. He supposed, as Nördenskjöld did later, that meteorites were condensed nebulae, which, as small planets surrounded by noncondensed matter, described their own paths before they were attracted by the earth. He also held that when noncondensed matter, consisting of loose atoms, came within the earth's atmosphere, it gave rise to shooting stars, fireballs, and other forms of light phenomena associated with thermochemical effects. He believed that the aurora borealis originated from the oxidation of elementary iron and nickel particles attracted into the atmosphere by the earth's magnetic field. This theory was not accepted.

BIBLIOGRAPHY

I. ORIGINAL WORKS. Almost all of Baumhauer's work was published in Dutch journals, and some has been translated in German and French periodicals. A complete bibliography is in Gunning, pp. 49–57, and is supplemented in

Van der Beek, p. xv. Individual works are *Specimen inaugurale continens sententias veterum philosophorum Graecorum de visu, lumine et coloribus* (Utrecht, 1843); *Specimen meteorologico-chemicum de ortu lapidum meteoricorum, annexis duorum lapidum analysibus chemicis* (Utrecht, 1844); "Ueber den muthmasslichen Ursprung der Meteorsteine," in *Annalen der Physik und Chemie,* **66** (1845), 465–503; and *Beknopt leerboek der onbewerktuigde scheikunde,* 3rd ed. (Amsterdam, 1864).

II. SECONDARY LITERATURE. Works on Baumhauer are J. W. Gunning, "Levensbericht van E. H. von Baumhauer," in *Jaarboek van de Koninklijke Akademie van Wetenschappen, 1887* (Amsterdam, 1887), pp. 1–57; and J. H. Van der Beek, *E. H. von Baumhauer. Zijn betekenis voor de wetenschap en de Nederlandse economie* (Leiden, 1963).

H. A. M. SNELDERS

BAUMHAUER, HEINRICH ADOLF (*b.* Bonn, Germany, 26 October 1848; *d.* Fribourg, Switzerland, 1 August 1926), *chemistry, mineralogy.*

Baumhauer, the son of a lithographer and merchant, studied chemistry under Kekulé at Bonn and in 1869 earned his degree with the dissertation "Die Reduction des Nitrobenzols durch Chlor- und Bromwasserstoff." After a further year of study at Göttingen he briefly held three teaching posts before serving as teacher of chemistry at the agricultural school of Lüdinghausen, Westphalia, from 1873 to 1896. In that year he was called to the young University of Fribourg as its first professor of mineralogy; during his first ten years there he also taught inorganic chemistry.

Although Baumhauer was trained as a chemist, crystallography and mineralogy were his principal interests and he is generally regarded as a mineralogist. In spite of a heavy work load—he was a conscientious teacher—Baumhauer always had time for research, which at first was chemical. In 1870 he wrote a tract on the relation between atomic weights and the properties of elements. In it he commented on the work of Mendeleev and Lothar Meyer, and proposed a spiral arrangement for the periodic table. He also wrote a textbook of inorganic chemistry (1884) and one of organic chemistry (1885).

At Lüdinghausen, Baumhauer's interest turned to crystallography and mineralogy. He wrote a short text on mineralogy (1884) and, soon thereafter, a popular work on crystallography. Baumhauer is best known for his study of the etch figures produced on crystal faces by various solvents, a method of study that for a long time provided one of the principal means for establishing the symmetry of crystals. His *Die Resultate der Aetzmethode* (1894) was the standard and only work on the subject until it was supplemented in 1927 by A. P. Honess' book.

Soon after the appearance of *Resultate,* Baumhauer added other fields to the scope of his research. He became the foremost authority on the sulfosalts of the Binnental occurrence, and made extensive morphological studies of minerals. During his last decades his chief interest was comparative crystal morphology. He gathered material for a book on this subject, which was edited by his successor, Leonhard Weber, and published as an extended article.

BIBLIOGRAPHY

Complete bibliographies of Baumhauer's works are in Poggendorff, III, 84; IV, 78–79; and V, 75; in *Schweizerische mineralogische und petrographische Mitteilungen,* **6** (1926), 391–397, following a short autobiography dated July 1896; and in *Verhandlungen der Schweizerischen Naturforschenden Gesellschaft,* **107** (1926), Anhang, 3–15, following a fine biographical sketch by Leonhard Weber.

Among his books are *Die Beziehungen zwischen dem Atomgewichte und der Natur der chemischen Elemente* (Brunswick, 1870); *Kurzes Lehrbuch der Mineralogie (einschliesslich Petrographie)* (Freiburg im Breisgau, 1884); *Leitfaden der Chemie. I. Anorganische Chemie* (Freiburg im Breisgau, 1884); *Leitfaden der Chemie. II. Organische Chemie* (Freiburg im Breisgau, 1885); *Das Reich der Kristalle* (Leipzig, 1889); and *Die Resultate der Aetzmethode in der krystallographischen Forschung* (Leipzig, 1894). His articles include "Über die Einwirkung von Brom- und Chlorwasserstoff auf Nitrobenzol," in *Zeitschrift für Chemie,* n.s. **5** (1869), 198; "Über die Einwirkung von Bromwasserstoff auf Nitrobenzol," in *Berichte der Deutschen chemische Gesellschaft,* **2** (1869), 122; and "Beitrag zur vergleichenden Kristallographie," Leonhard Weber, ed., in *Schweizerische mineralogische und petrographische Mitteilungen,* **5** (1925), 348–426.

Arthur P. Honess, *The Nature, Origin and Interpretation of Etch Figures on Crystals* (New York, 1927), is the principal work continuing the studies summarized in the *Resultate* and contains many references to Baumhauer.

A. PABST

BAYEN, PIERRE (*b.* Châlons-sur-Marne, France, 7 February 1725; *d.* Paris, France, 15 February 1798), *chemistry, pharmacy.*

Bayen received his early education at the Collège de Troyes. After deciding on a career in pharmacy, he was placed with the pharmacist Faciot in Rheims. In 1749 he went to Paris and studied under P. de Chamousset and G. F. Rouelle.

With G. F. Venel, Bayen was commissioned by the government in 1753 to analyze all the mineral waters of France, but this work had to be suspended when he was sent as chief pharmacist on an army expedition in 1755. Later, after continuing the analyses alone for many years, he finally had to abandon the work for lack of funds. From 1763 to 1793 Bayen was *apothicaire-major des camps et armées du roi,* and he became *pharmacien inspecteur* to the Conseil de Santé in the latter year. He was never elected to the Academy but became a member of the Institut de France when it was founded in 1795.

Bayen's first publication was an analysis of the mineral waters of Bagnères-de-Luchon (1765), a long and detailed work published only incompletely in his *Opuscules.* However, his most important contribution to chemistry was a series of four memoirs on the precipitates of mercury (1774–1775). His observations led him to doubt the phlogiston theory, for he noticed that when red precipitate (mercuric oxide) was heated alone (in which case, there was no reducing agent to supply phlogiston to it), it was reduced to mercury and a large quantity of an elastic fluid was produced. He made careful quantitative observations of all that took place and concluded that when mercury was calcined, it did not lose phlogiston but combined intimately with the elastic fluid, and that this addition of elastic fluid to the mercury was responsible for its increase in weight. He failed to identify the elastic fluid (oxygen), however, and did not even apply the simple test of plunging a lighted taper into it.

Bayen helped to make known the work of Jean Rey, the seventeenth-century Périgord doctor whose theory of calcination was very similar to his own.

In 1781, Bayen produced a report, commissioned by the Paris College of Pharmacy, on the alleged presence of arsenic in tin. Henckel and Marggraf had reported that commercial tin contained arsenic, which would have made its use in kitchen equipment dangerous. Bayen concluded that, at the most, the tin contained only a trace of arsenic.

In addition to these researches, Bayen published analyses of minerals (1776, 1778, 1785, 1798). Some of his work, however, cannot be traced, because he burned all his manuscripts during the Terror.

Bayen was a thorough and careful worker, and often spent years examining a material, seeking the least destructive method of analysis in an attempt to imitate nature and preserve the constituents intact. That he was forty when he published his first memoir was doubtless a consequence of this reluctance to commit himself to paper before he had conducted the most exhaustive research.

BIBLIOGRAPHY

I. ORIGINAL WORKS. A detailed bibliography of Bayen's writings is in A. Balland, ed., *Travaux scientifiques des pharmaciens militaires français* (Paris, 1882), pp. 6–8. His works were collected in *Opuscules chimiques de Pierre Bayen,* P. Malatret, ed., 2 vols. (Paris, 1798), in which the memoir "Analyse des eaux de Bagnères-de-Luchon, par ordre du ministre de la guerre" is incomplete. A complete version of this memoir is in Richard, *Recueil d'observations de médecine des hôpitaux militaires,* II (Paris, 1772), 633–778; it was originally published, complete, in an octavo volume (Paris, 1765).

II. SECONDARY LITERATURE. Works on Bayen are A. Balland, "En mémoire de Bayen," in *Journal de pharmacie et chimie,* 8th ser., **1** (1925), 83–94; P. A. Cap, "Étude biographique sur Pierre Bayen," *ibid.,* 4th ser., **1** (Jan. 1865); P. Lassus, "Notice historique sur Bayen," in *Annales de chimie,* **26** (an VI [1798]), 278–288, also published as "Notice sur la vie et les ouvrages du C^{en} Bayen," in *Mémoires de l'Institut national des sciences mathématiques et physiques,* **2** (fructidor, an VII [1799]), hist., 144–152; A. A. Parmentier, "Eloge de Pierre Bayen," in Bayen's *Opuscules,* I, xxxiii–lxxiv; see also "Discours préliminaire," *ibid.,* pp. iii–xxxii, which contains sections of another *éloge,* not published elsewhere, in which some of Bayen's ideas are discussed; M. B. Reber, "Une lettre inédite de Pierre Bayen, suivie de quelques observations," in *Bulletin de la Société française d'histoire de la médecine,* **9** (1910), 50–63; and A. F. Silvestre, "Notice sur le Citoyen Bayen," in *Rapports généraux des travaux de la Société philomathique de Paris,* I (1793), 233–240.

E. McDONALD

BAYER, JOHANN (*b.* Rain, Germany, 1572; *d.* Augsburg, Germany, 7 March 1625), *astronomy.*

Bayer, a lawyer who was an amateur astronomer, established the modern nomenclature of stars visible to the naked eye. He enrolled at Ingolstadt University on 19 October 1592 as a student of philosophy, but later moved to Augsburg. There, on 1 September 1603, he dedicated his *Uranometria,* a popular guide to the starry heavens, to two leading citizens and the city council, which promptly rewarded him with an honorarium of 150 gulden. On 13 December 1612, Bayer was appointed legal adviser to the city council of Augsburg, at an annual salary of 500 gulden. He died a bachelor.

The oldest surviving star catalogue, contained in Ptolemy's *Syntaxis,* lists forty-eight constellations, with each star located in reference to a constellation by means of a verbal description. This was often cumbersome, and did not always direct every observer to the same star, particularly after the original Greek expression had been translated into one or more languages. This lack of compactness and of precision had long prevailed when Bayer undertook his reform by unambiguously and succinctly identifying every star visible to the naked eye.

In essence, the novelty of Bayer's method consisted of assigning to each star in a constellation one of the twenty-four letters of the Greek alphabet. For constellations with more than two dozen stars, he resorted to the Latin alphabet after exhausting the Greek letters. He placed these Greek and Latin letters on his star charts, beautiful copper-plate engravings by Alexander Mair. In addition, Bayer reproduced the traditional numeration of the stars in the constellations, as well as the many and very different names used by Ptolemy and his successors, whose works Bayer studied with painstaking care. In this way he sought to facilitate the identification of any star in his *Uranometria* with the same star as it had been recorded by his various predecessors. Thus, just a few years before the invention of the telescope enormously increased the number of stars visible with the aid of an optical instrument, Bayer produced a stellar nomenclature that astronomers still use for most stars visible to the naked eye.

In Bayer's own time the popularity of his work was further enhanced by his forty-ninth plate, which displayed twelve new southern constellations. These had recently been defined by the Dutch navigator Pieter Dirckszoon Keyzer (Petrus Theodori) of Emden, who corrected the older observations of Amerigo Vespucci and Andrea Corsali, as well as the report of Pedro de Medina.

On the other side of the ledger, two aspects of Bayer's *Uranometria* created difficulties. In the first place, what his predecessors had called the right side of a constellation's figure, he labeled the left side (Table 4, verso). Second, in bracketing stars of the same magnitude in each constellation (Table 1, recto), Bayer failed to indicate on what basis he assigned the letters within each bracket. The widespread assumption that he used the order of decreasing magnitude led to considerable confusion in the study of variable stars. The alternative assumption that he used some spatial arrangement is likewise open to serious objection.

BIBLIOGRAPHY

I. ORIGINAL WORKS. Bayer's main work is *Uranometria, omnium asterismorum continens schemata, nova methodo delineata, aereis laminis expressa* (Augsburg, 1603). *Explicatio characterum aenei Uranometrias imaginum tabulis insculptorum* reprints the text of Bayer's *Uranometria* but omits its plates. Bayer also collaborated on Julius Schiller's *Coelum stellatum Christianum* (Augsburg, 1627).

II. SECONDARY LITERATURE. There is no biography of Bayer. Some information about his life is provided in Franz Babinger, "Johannes Bayer, der Begründer der neuzeitlichen Sternbenennung," in *Archiv für die Geschichte der*

Naturwissenschaften und der Technik. **5** (1915). 108–113. Bayer's reliability is analyzed in F. W. A. Argelander, *De fide Uranometriae Bayeri* (Bonn, 1842). Bayer's collaboration with Schiller is discussed by Ernst Zinner in *Vierteljahrsschrift der astronomischen Gesellschaft,* **72** (1937), 64–68.

EDWARD ROSEN

BAYES, THOMAS (*b.* London, England, 1702; *d.* Tunbridge Wells, England, 17 April 1761), *probability.*

Bayes was a member of the first secure generation of English religious Nonconformists. His father, Joshua Bayes, F.R.S., was a respected theologian of dissent; he was also one of the group of six ministers who were the first to be publicly ordained as Nonconformists. Privately educated, Bayes became his father's assistant at the presbytery in Holborn, London; his mature life was spent as minister at the chapel in Tunbridge Wells. Despite his provincial circumstances, he was a wealthy bachelor with many friends. The Royal Society of London elected him a fellow in 1742. He wrote little: *Divine Benevolence* (1731) and *Introduction to the Doctrine of Fluxions* (1736) are the only works known to have been published during his lifetime. The latter is a response to Bishop Berkeley's *Analyst,* a stinging attack on the logical foundations of Newton's calculus; Bayes's reply was perhaps the soundest retort to Berkeley then available.

Bayes is remembered for his brief "Essay Towards Solving a Problem in the Doctrine of Chances" (1763), the first attempt to establish foundations for statistical inference. Jacques Bernoulli's *Ars conjectandi* (1713) and Abraham de Moivre's *The Doctrine of Chances* (1718) already provided great textbooks of what we now call probability theory. Given the probability of one event, the logical principles for inferring the probabilities of related events were quite well understood. In his "Essay," Bayes set himself the "converse problem": "*Given* the number of times in which an unknown event has happened and failed: *Required* the chance that the probability of its happening in a single trial lies somewhere between any two degrees of probability that can be named." "By chance," he said, "I mean the same as probability."

In the light of Bernoulli's *Ars conjectandi,* and of a paper by John Arbuthnot (1710), there was some understanding of how to reject statistical hypotheses in the light of data; but no one had shown how to measure the probability of statistical hypotheses in the light of data. Bayes began his solution of the problem by noting that sometimes the probability of a statistical hypothesis is given before any particular events are observed; he then showed how to compute the probability of the hypothesis after some observations are made. In his own example:

Postulate: 1. I suppose the square table or plane ABCD to be so made and levelled that if either of the balls O or W be thrown upon it, there shall be the same probability that it rests upon any one equal part of the plane as another, and that it must necessarily rest somewhere upon it.

2. I suppose that the ball W shall be first thrown, and through the point where it rests a line *os* shall be drawn parallel to AD, and meeting CD and AB in *s* and *o,* and that afterwards the ball O shall be thrown $p + q$ or n times, and that its resting between AD and *os* after a single throw be called the happening of the event M in a single trial.

For any fractions f and b (between zero and one), Bayes was concerned with the probability of assertions of the form

$$f \leq \text{probability of M} \leq b.$$

From his physical assumptions about the table ABCD, he inferred that the prior probability (i.e., the probability before any trials have been made) is $b - f$. He proved, as a theorem in direct probabilities, that the posterior probability (i.e., the probability, on the evidence, that M occurred p times and failed q times) is

$$\int_f^b x^p(1 - x)^q \, dx \Big/ \int_0^1 x^p(1 - x)^q \, dx.$$

A generalization on this deduction is often, anachronistically, called Bayes's theorem or Bayes's formula. In the case of only finitely many statistical hypotheses, $H_1, \cdots, H_n$, let there be prior data D and some new observed evidence E. Then the prior probability of H_i is Prob (H_i/D); the posterior probability is Prob $(H_i/D \text{ and } E)$; the theorem asserts:

$$\text{Prob } (H_i/D \text{ and } E)$$
$$= \frac{\text{Prob } (H_i/D) \text{ Prob } (E/H_i \text{ and } D)}{\sum\limits_{j=1}^{j=n} \text{Prob } (H_j/D) \text{ Prob } (E/H_j \text{ and } D)}.$$

A corresponding theorem holds in the continuum; Bayes's deduction essentially involves a special case of it.

The work so far described falls entirely within probability theory, and would now be regarded as a straightforward deduction from standard probability axioms. The striking feature of Bayes's work is an argument found in a *scholium* to the paper, which does not follow from any standard axioms. Suppose we have no information about the prior probability of a statistical hypothesis. Bayes argues by analogy that, in this case, our ignorance is neither more nor less than in his example where prior probabilities are known to be entirely uniform. He concludes, "I shall take for granted that the rule given concerning the event M . . . is also the rule to be used in relation to any event concerning the probability of which nothing at all is known antecedently to any trials made or observed concerning it."

If Bayes's conclusion is correct, we have a basis for the whole of statistical inference. Richard Price, who sent Bayes's paper to the Royal Society, seems to imply in a covering letter that Bayes was not satisfied with his argument by analogy and, hence, had declined to publish it. Whatever the case with Bayes, Laplace had no qualms about Bayes's argument; and from 1774 he regularly assumed uniform prior probability distributions. His enormous influence made Bayes's ideas almost unchallengeable until George Boole protested in his *Laws of Thought* (1854). Since then, Bayes's technique has been a constant subject of controversy.

Today there are two kinds of Bayesians. Sir Harold Jeffreys, in his *Theory of Probability,* maintains that, relative to any body of information, even virtual ignorance, there is an objective distribution of degrees of confidence appropriate to various hypotheses; he often rejects Bayes's actual postulate, but accepts the need for similar postulates. Leonard J. Savage, in his *Foundations of Statistics,* rejects objective probabilities, but interprets probability in a personal way, as reflecting a person's personal degree of belief; hence, a prior probability is a person's belief before he has made some observations, and his posterior probability is his belief after the observations are made. Many working statisticians who are Bayesians, in the sense of trying to argue from prior probabilities, try to be neutral between Jeffreys and Savage. In this respect they are perhaps close to Bayes himself. He defined the probability of an event as "the ratio between the value at which an expectation depending upon the happening of the event ought to be computed, and the value of the thing expected upon its happening." This definition can be interpreted in either a subjective or an objective way, but there is no evidence that Bayes had even reflected on which interpretation he might prefer.

BIBLIOGRAPHY

I. ORIGINAL WORKS. Bayes's works published during his lifetime are *Divine Benevolence, or an Attempt to Prove That the Principal End of the Divine Providence and Government Is the Happiness of His Creatures* (London, 1731); and *An Introduction to the Doctrine of Fluxions, and a Defence of the Mathematicians Against the Objections of the Author of* The Analyst (London, 1736). "An Essay Towards Solving a Problem in the Doctrine of Chances" was published in *Philosophical Transactions of the Royal Society of London,* **53** (1763), 370–418, with a covering letter written by Richard Price; repr. in *Biometrika,* **45** (1958), 296–315, with a biographical note by G. A. Barnard. Also of interest is "A Letter on Asymptotic Series from Bayes to John Canton," in *Biometrika,* **45** (1958), 269–271; repr. with the paper from the *Philosophical Transactions* in *Facsimiles of Two Papers by Bayes* (Washington, D.C., n.d.), with a commentary on the first by Edward C. Molina and on the second by W. Edwards Deming.

II. SECONDARY LITERATURE. Supplementary information may be found in John Arbuthnot, "An Argument for Divine Providence Taken From the Constant Regularity of the Births of Both Sexes," in *Philosophical Transactions of the Royal Society of London,* **23** (1710), 186–190; George Berkeley, *The Analyst* (London–Dublin, 1734); Jacques Bernoulli, *Ars conjectandi* (Basel, 1713); George Boole, *An Investigation of the Laws of Thought* (London, 1854); Harold Jeffreys, *Theory of Probability* (Oxford, 1939; 3rd ed., 1961); Pierre Simon Laplace, "Mémoire sur la probabilité des causes par les événements," in *Mémoires par divers savants,* **6** (1774), 621–656, and *Théorie analytique des probabilités* (Paris, 1812); Abraham de Moivre, *The Doctrine of Chances* (London, 1718; 3rd ed., 1756); and Leonard J. Savage, *The Foundations of Statistics* (New York–London, 1954).

IAN HACKING

BAYLAK AL-QIBJĀQĪ (fl. Cairo, Egypt, *ca.* 1250), *mineralogy,* probably also *mathematics, technology.*

Baylak's period of activity is determined from his signature, dated 1282, in the *Kanz al-tujjār.* An autobiographical note there states that in 1242/1243 he undertook a trip by sea from Tripoli, Syria, to Alexandria. He must have had connections at the court of Ḥamā, Syria, for the *Kanz* is dedicated to either the Ayyūbid ruler al-Malik al-Muẓaffar II (1229–1244) or his son al-Malik al-Manṣūr II (1244–1284). If Baylak is identical with the mathematician—and this can be assumed—who in 1260 prepared a copy of a work on the knowledge and use of the clocks of Riḍwān al-Khurāsānī, and if he is also the one who made a handwritten mark of ownership on another mathematical manuscript (1269/1270), both preserved in Istanbul, then he was concerned with at least three areas of mathematics and natural science. However, in the *Kanz* his father apparently is named Muḥammad, and in the manuscript on clocks he is definitely ʿAbdallāh. The authenticity of these details is open to investigation, but in any case, all dates mentioned fall within the lifetime of one particular mature man.

Baylak's only known book is his mineralogical work *Kanz al-tujjār* [or *al-tijār*] *fī maʿrifat al-aḥjār* ("Treasure of the Merchants on the Knowledge of Minerals"). If this was dedicated to al-Malik al-Muzaffar II, then the autograph of 1282 must be a copy of the original prepared by the author himself, for by 1282 al-Malik al-Manṣūr II was the ruler of Hamā. Apparently, however, 1282 was the year in which the original was written, for the note on the sea voyage is composed in such a manner that the *Kanz* can hardly have been written before 1244, the year of al-Malik al-Muzaffar's death. If one is to judge by excerpts of the book published by Clément-Mullet in 1868, the book contains little that is original; and this little is further reduced if one compares it with other texts additional to those preserved in the Paris manuscripts used by Clément-Mullet, and especially if it is compared with the older mineralogical books that have been discovered and published within the past hundred years.

Baylak was the first author writing in Arabic to treat the use of the magnetic needle as a ship's compass. On the trip to Alexandria, he watched one starless night as the captain stuck a needle through a straw so that the two objects formed a cross. This apparatus was then floated in a vessel of water. The needle responded to the circular movement of a nearby magnet. At the sudden removal of the magnet, the needle came to rest with a north-south orientation. Baylak had also heard that seamen in the Indian Ocean used hollow iron fish as compasses. His report on the magnetic needle was translated into French by Klaproth, then by Clément-Mullet (with the original Arabic text), and finally by De Saussure; Ferrand emended the latter translation at the time of its reprinting. Wiedemann translated the report into German in 1904.

BIBLIOGRAPHY

C. Brockelmann, *Geschichte der arabischen Literatur,* I (1898), 495; Supp. I (1937), 904; 2nd ed., I (1943), marginal 495—with contradictory details in each place; J. Clément-Mullet, "Essai sur la minéralogie arabe," in *Journal asiatique,* 6th ser., **11** (1868), 5–81, 105–253, 502–522, esp. 13 f., 146 ff., also published separately (1869); L. De Saussure, "L'origine de la rose des vents et l'invention de la boussole," repr. in Gabriel Ferrand, *Introduction à l'astronomie nautique arabe* (1928), pp. 80 ff.; F. Kern, in *Mitteilungen des Seminars für orientalische Sprachen in Berlin, Westasiatische Studien,* **11** (1908), 268 f.; Jules Klaproth, *Lettre à A. de Humboldt sur l'invention de la boussole* (1834), p. 59; M. Krause, "Stambuler Handschriften islamischer Mathematiker," in *Quellen und Studien zur Geschichte der Mathematik, Astronomie und Physik,* Abt. B, **3** (1936), 490 f.; G. Sarton, *Introduction to the History of Science,* II (1931), 1072, with several mistakes; MG. de Slane, *Bibliothèque Nationale, Catalogue des manuscrits arabes* (Paris, 1883–1895), MS No. 2779; G. Vajda, *Index général des manuscrits arabes musulmans de la Bibliothèque Nationale de Paris* (1953), p. 420, which differs from de Slane; and E. Wiedemann, "Beiträge zur Geschichte der Naturwissenschaften (II)," in *Sitzungsberichte der physikalisch-medizinischen Sozietät in Erlangen,* **39** (1904), 330 f. (the quotation from an Arabic author of 854 does not refer to the naval compass), and "Maghnaṭīs," in *Encyclopaedia of Islam,* III (1936).

MARTIN PLESSNER

BAYLISS, LEONARD ERNEST (*b.* London, England, 15 November 1900; *d.* London, 20 August 1964), *physiology.*

The youngest son of Sir William Maddock Bayliss and Gertrude Starling Bayliss, sister of the physiologist Ernest H. Starling, Bayliss grew up near Hampstead Heath, on the northern fringe of London. His parents entertained generously and attracted many overseas physiologists to meet their British colleagues in an atmosphere of tennis, good fellowship, and unending, searching arguments about the fundamentals of physical, biological, and medical sciences. Here his father had his private laboratory and workshop although, like Starling, he was also a professor in the physiological laboratory of University College, London. In such a home Bayliss developed his "do-it-yourself" attitude toward apparatus and his capacity for exacting and informed analysis of scientific problems.

After graduating from University College School, a day school for boys fairly near his home, Bayliss entered Trinity College, Cambridge, and graduated in physiology in 1922. He stayed on in the physiology department as Michael Foster Student and in 1925 received the Ph.D. with the thesis "Tone in Plain Muscle." From 1926 to 1929 he was Sharpey Scholar at University College, and in 1928–1929 he worked under A. N. Richards at the University of Pennsylvania on a Rockefeller Fellowship; he returned in 1929 to University College, where he was awarded the Schäfer Prize (given for original work by a young physiologist associated with University College). In 1933 Bayliss was appointed physiologist at the Marine Biological Station, Plymouth, and the following year he became lecturer in physiology at the University of Edinburgh, from which he "retired" in 1939, hoping to be free to prepare a revised version of his father's famous book *Principles of General Physiology,* the last edition of which had appeared in 1924, soon after his father's death. Bayliss returned to University College as honorary part-time research assistant in the same year.

Bombing and fire interrupted Bayliss' work in physiology in 1940, and he joined a group of pioneering scientists in the Army Operational Research Group, where he was later put in charge of research on antiaircraft gunnery and accuracy of fire against aircraft at various heights and against guided missiles.

Bayliss returned to physiology and to battered University College as full-time reader from 1945 to 1950. He resigned in 1950 in order to concentrate on rewriting *Principles of General Physiology* but retained his room near the Medical Sciences Library at the college. His accessibility to students and colleagues continued, and he pursued his research and writing with the title of honorary research associate. He also made an important contribution to advanced teaching of physiology. By 1960 he had completed his project, entirely rewriting the *Principles* and expanding it to two volumes.

His bibliography reveals Bayliss' wide interests in physical approaches to physiology and in relevant instrumentation, but he was a reluctant and unambitious publisher; much work never reached the journals at all or did so only in the papers of friends. A great deal of his time was always given to helping others, and he was sought after as perhaps the most learned, ingenious, and cooperative of English physiologists. His early papers on the pH of blood (1923, 1926) were written when the newly developed glass electrode, still of very high resistance, was connected to a delicate electrometer—quite a challenge even to skilled experimenters in the sulfurous atmospheres of towns. While at University College he also worked with Starling on the metabolism of dog heart-lung preparations; devised pump-oxygenator perfusion techniques for kidneys; and studied serotonins in defibrinated blood, water diuresis, and glomerular permeability in both cold-blooded and warm-blooded animals. His interest in invertebrates, as shown in a 1930 paper, was strengthened at the Plymouth Marine Biological Station.

The rheology of blood was a major but intermittent interest during Bayliss' later years. It began about 1930 with Fahraeus' papers showing that the viscosity of blood, relative to water in the same tube, diminished as the diameter diminished, down to 0.03 millimeters, at which point cells blocked the tube. Bayliss had been making and using micropipettes, and had encountered the problem of cell clumping in his blood perfusion experiments with pumps and tubes. He extended the range of tube diameters down as far as that of arterioles and found the apparent viscosity

nearly halved. This finding was published as a "personal communication" by colleagues (1933) and again in the second edition of *Human Physiology* (1936). Bayliss' first definitive paper on blood viscosity did not appear until 1952, and many experimental findings have remained unpublished.

In 1939 Bayliss married M. Grace Palmer Eggleton, a physiologist at University College, whom he had known since about 1930. They took an apartment at the top of a tall old building near the college and, except for the early war years, lived there happily and frugally until his death. Also in the year of their marriage they bought a weekend cottage, isolated in the East Sussex countryside, and Bayliss spent much energy and ingenuity in improving and enlarging both house and garden, in anticipation of their retirement in 1966. He was physically active and enjoyed good health. Among his avocations were mountain climbing and playing the piano. He was quietly courteous to students and friends but unyielding in essentials.

Bayliss was a fellow of the Royal Society of Edinburgh and a member of the Physiological Society, the Society for Experimental Biology, and the Marine Biological Association.

BIBLIOGRAPHY

Bayliss' earliest book was *Human Physiology* (London, 1930; 3rd ed., 1948; 5th ed., 1962), written with F. R. Winton. His major work was the complete revision and rewriting of his father's *Principles of General Physiology,* 2 vols. (London, 1959–1960). His *Living Control Systems* appeared in the New Science Series (London, 1966).

His papers are "A Comparison Between the Colorimetric and the Electrometric Methods of Determining the Hydrogen Ion Concentration of Blood," in *Journal of Physiology,* **58** (1923), 101–107, written with Ruth Conway-Verney; "Reversible Haemolysis," *ibid.,* **59** (1924), 48–60; "The Determination of the Hydrogen-ion Concentration of the Blood," *ibid.,* **61** (1926), 448–454, written with Phyllis Tookey Kerridge and Ruth Conway-Verney; "A Conductivity Method for the Determination of Carbon Dioxide," in *Biochemical Journal,* **21** (1927), 662–664; "The Action of Insulin and Sugar on the Respiratory Quotient and Metabolism of the Heart-lung Preparation," in *Journal of Physiology,* **65** (1928), 33–47, written with E. A. Müller and E. H. Starling; "The Energetics of Plain Muscle," *ibid.,* i–ii; "A Method of Oxygenating Blood," *ibid.,* **66** (1928), 443–448, written with A. R. Fee and E. Ogden; "A Simple High-speed Rotary Pump," in *Journal of Scientific Instruments,* **5** (1928), 278–279, written with E. A. Müller; "The Adductor Mechanism of *Pecten,*" in *Proceedings of the Royal Society,* **106B** (1930), 363–376, written with E. Boyland and A. D. Ritchie; "A Combined Flow Recorder and Pump Control," in *Journal of Physiology,* **69** (1930), v, written with A. R. Fee; "The Electrical Conductivity of Glomerular Urine From the Frog and From Necturus," in *Journal of Biological Chemistry,* **87** (1930), 523–540; "Studies in Water Diuresis. Part III. A Comparison of the Excretion of Urine by Innervated and Denervated Kidneys Perfused With the Heart-lung Preparation," in *Journal of Physiology,* **69** (1930), 135–143, written with A. R. Fee; "Studies in Water Diuresis. Part IV. The Changes in the Concentration of Electrolytes and Colloids in the Plasma of Decerebrate Dogs Produced by the Ingestion of Water," *ibid.,* **70** (1930), 60–66, written with A. R. Fee; "The Action of Cyanide on the Isolated Mammalian Kidney," *ibid.,* **74** (1932), 279–293, written with E. Lundsgaard; "Fourteenth International Physiological Congress," in *Nature,* **130** (1932), 705–707, written with P. Eggleton; "The Excretion of Protein by the Mammalian Kidney," in *Journal of Physiology,* **77** (1933), 386–398, written with Phyllis Tookey Kerridge and Dorothy S. Russell; "'Vaso-tonins' and the Pump-oxygenator-kidney Preparation," *ibid.,* 34P–35P, written with E. Ogden; "The Action Potentials in *Maia* Nerve Before and After Poisoning With Veratrine and Yohimbine Hydrochlorides," *ibid.,* **83** (1935), 439–454, written with S. L. Cowan and D. Scott, Jr.; "Digestion in the Plaice (*Pleuronectes platessa*)," in *Journal of the Marine Biological Association of the United Kingdom,* **20** (1935), 73–91; "A Drop Recorder for A.C. Mains," in *Journal of Physiology,* **84** (1935), 57P; "A Stimulation Unit for A.C. Mains," *ibid.,* 58P–59P, written with P. Eggleton; "Recent Developments in Physical Instruments for Biological Purposes," in *Journal of Scientific Instruments,* **12** (1935), 1–5, written with Phyllis Tookey Kerridge; "Some New Forms of Visual Purple Found in Sea Fishes With a Note on the Visual Cells of Origin," in *Proceedings of the Royal Society,* **120B** (1936), 95–113, written with R. J. Lythgoe and Katharine Tansley; "The Photographic Method for Recording Average Illuminations," in *Journal of the Marine Biological Association of the United Kingdom,* **23** (1938), 99–118; "The Visco-elastic Properties of the Lungs," in *Quarterly Journal of Experimental Physiology,* **29** (1939), 27–47, written with G. W. Robertson; "A Circulation Model," in *Journal of Physiology,* **97** (1940), 429–432; "The Part Played by the Renal Nerves in the Production of Water Diuresis in the Hypophysectomized and Decerebrate Dog," *ibid.,* **98** (1940), 190–206, written with A. Brown; "Schack, August Steenberg Krogh," in *Yearbook of the Royal Society of Edinburgh* (1948–1949); "Rheology of Blood and Lymph," in A. Frey-Wyssling, ed., *Deformation and Flow in Biological Systems* (Amsterdam, 1952), pp. 355–418; "A Mechanical Model of the Heart," in *Journal of Physiology,* **127** (1955), 358–379; "The Use of a Roller Pump for Long-continued Infusion," *ibid.,* **128** (1955), 29P–30P; "The Process of Secretion," in F. R. Winton, ed., *Modern Views on the Secretion of Urine: The Cushny Memorial Lectures* (London, 1956), pp. 96–127; "The 'Brown Dog' Affair," in *Potential: Journal of the Physiological Society of University College London,* no. 2 (1957), 11–22; "The Axial Drift of the Red Cells When Blood Flows in a Narrow Tube," in *Journal of Physiology,* **149** (1959), 593–613; "The Anomalous Viscosity of Blood," in A. L. Copley and G. Stainsby, eds., *Flow Properties of Blood and Other Bio-* *logical Systems* (Oxford, 1960), pp. 29–62; "William Maddock Bayliss, 1860–1924: Life and Scientific Work," in *Perspectives in Biology and Medicine,* **4** (1961), 460–479; "The Rheology of Blood," in *Handbook of Physiology,* sec. 2, W. F. Hamilton, ed., I (Washington, D.C., 1962), 137–150; "Some Factors Concerned in Temperature Regulation in Man," in *Journal of Physiology,* **172** (1964), 8P–9P, written with S. E. Dicker and M. Grace Eggleton; and "The Flow of Suspensions of Red Blood Cells in Capillary Tubes. Changes in the 'Cell-free' Marginal Sheath With Changes in the Shearing Stress," *ibid.,* **179** (1965), 1–25.

F. R. WINTON

BAYLISS, WILLIAM MADDOCK (*b.* Wednesbury, Staffordshire, England, 2 May 1860; *d.* London, England, 27 August 1924), *general physiology.*

W. M. Bayliss was the only son of Moses Bayliss and Jan Maddock to survive infancy. His father was a manufacturer of galvanized goods and founder of the Wolverhampton firm of Bayliss, Jones and Bayliss.

William received his early education at a private school in Wolverhampton, Staffordshire, and was then apprenticed to a local general practitioner.

When, in 1880, the elder Bayliss moved to London, William continued his studies at University College, London, where in 1881 he gained a medical entrance exhibition and a science exhibition at the preliminary scientific examination. In 1882 he took the B.Sc. degree with a scholarship in zoology and physics, and began to study physiology and anatomy, but at the second M.B. examination he failed in anatomy. He then relinquished medical studies to concentrate on physiology.

Two men who influenced him at this stage were John Burdon-Sanderson, Jodrell professor of physiology at University College, and Ray Lankester, professor of zoology. Physiology was at that time emerging as a subject separate from anatomy, and the Jodrell chair, founded in 1874, was the first separate chair of physiology in Great Britain. When the Waynflete chair of physiology was established at Oxford in 1882, Burdon-Sanderson was elected to it, and in 1885 Bayliss followed him to Oxford as an undergraduate of Wadham College. He took a first-class degree in physiology in 1888 and then returned to University College, where, in the meantime, E. A. Schäfer (afterward Sir Edward Sharpey-Schafer) had succeeded to the Jodrell chair. Bayliss worked for the remainder of his life at University College, first as assistant, then in 1903 as assistant professor, and from 1912 onward as professor of general physiology.

He attended an Anglo-Catholic church, but was largely tolerant in religious matters. Politically, he was somewhat to the left of liberal, with a sympathy for reasonable minority movements, but had little interest in politics as such.

In 1893 he married Gertrude Starling, the sister of E. H. Starling; and, after his father's death in 1895, he returned to live in the family home in Hampstead, London. He had three sons and one daughter; the youngest son, Leonard (1900–1964), was also a physiologist. Bayliss was well-off financially, his married life was happy, and until shortly before his death from a blood dyscrasia his health was excellent. In their large house, set in a four-acre garden with two tennis courts and a private laboratory, the Baylisses entertained often and liberally, mainly colleagues and visiting physiologists.

Bayliss was elected to membership in the Physiological Society in 1890 and served as secretary from 1900 to 1922, and treasurer from 1922 to 1924. He was editor of *Physiological Abstracts* from 1923 to 1924, and joint editor of the *Biochemical Journal* from 1913 to 1924.

In 1903 he was elected a fellow of the Royal Society, serving on its council from 1913 to 1915. He was Croonian lecturer (jointly with Starling) in 1904 and was awarded a Royal Medal in 1911 and the Copley Medal in 1919. He also received honorary degrees from the universities of Oxford, St. Andrews, and Aberdeen and was elected to the Royal Danish Academy of Science, the Royal Academy of Belgium, and the Société de Biologie of Paris. In 1917 he was awarded the Baly Medal of the Royal College of Physicians and in 1918 gave the Oliver-Sharpey lectures, and the Sylvanus Thompson lectures in 1919. He was created a knight bachelor in 1922.

During World War I he served on the Food (War) Committee of the Royal Society, and on the Wound Shock Committee of the Medical Research Committee; he visited the front in France in 1917. From 1917 to 1924 he served on the Medical Research Council's committee to study the biological action of light.

In 1922 he visited the United States to deliver the Herter lectures at Baltimore, a Harvey lecture at New York, and to talk to the Research Club at Harvard.

The placid tenor of his life was interrupted in 1903 by the urgent necessity to take out an action for libel against Stephen Coleridge, secretary of the National Antivivisection Society. The trial, before the lord chief justice, occupied four days and Bayliss won the day, with £2,000 damages. He presented the money to University College for furtherance of research in physiology. The interest on the capital sum is still used for that purpose.

Bayliss devoted his life almost solely to his work in physiology. He was fond of music and played the violin. He was of a merry and gentle disposition, good with his hands, and would accept little help from others, although he gladly gave his own. Photography was more than a hobby to him; the illustrations for his books and papers were his own work.

Bayliss' generation entered the scene at the beginning of a period of exponential growth of science, and his outlook can be seen as a projection into the twentieth century of that of Claude Bernard (1814–1878), Ludwig (1816–1895), and Helmholtz (1821–1894). To him all science was one, although fundamentally he was a biologist who was deeply interested in the emergence of physical chemistry and biochemistry and in their relations to the problems of general physiology. The foundations of Hoppe-Seyler's *Zeitschrift für physiologische Chemie* (1877) and Ostwald's *Zeitschrift für physikalische Chemie* (1887) were harbingers of what was to follow, and Bayliss availed himself of the tools offered by these new subjects.

The frequent coupling together of the names of Bayliss and Starling in important publications might lead to the inference that their partnership was an essential condition for either or both of them, but nothing could be further from the truth. They were both great physiologists and in their collaboration were largely complementary. Bayliss was the more fundamental and erudite, but of a retiring disposition; Starling was a pragmatic and forceful extrovert, with an essentially medical outlook. Bayliss preferred to work alone, without even technical help, but collaboration was imposed upon them for a time; until a new Institute of Physiology was built there was inadequate space and equipment in the department. After 1909 they never collaborated, although they frequently conferred at the daily tea meetings.

Bayliss' researches can be divided into roughly the following six phases:

Electrophysiology. When Bayliss started at University College, electrophysiology was the central feature of the research work in the department. Bayliss worked with Dr. (afterward Sir John) Rose Bradford in studying, with the aid of a Thomson galvanometer, the changes in electric potential involved in the act of secretion, first in the salivary glands of a frog and then in the skin. In his second paper, "The Electromotive Phenomena of the Mammalian Heart," he collaborated with Starling, partly at Oxford; they were able to use the relatively rapidly responding capillary electrometer, which Lippmann had introduced in 1873. The hearts of mammals, frog, tortoise, and man (the two authors) were studied, the electrical changes shown to be triphasic, and the time relations of the cardiac cycle observed.

Vascular System. This work, which was begun in 1892 with Starling, resulted in two papers, one on a new form of optically registered blood pressure apparatus and one "On Some Points in the Innervation of the Mammalian Heart." He also worked with Bradford on the innervation of the vessels of the limbs. At about this same time, he began his own investigations, starting with the physiology of the depressor nerve, which led on to an examination of vasomotor reactions in general and of their central coordination. The nature of the antidromic reaction, which he showed to be an axon reflex, was another important outcome of this work. By 1894 Bayliss and Starling were working on circulatory problems, including venous and capillary pressures and intraventricular and aortic pressure curves.

Intestinal Movements. The partners now turned their attention to the study of the movements of the small and large intestines, and of their innervation. The most important result of this work was the elucidation of the peristaltic wave.

Pancreatic Secretion. Bayliss' interest in secretion led him, with Starling, to study the anomalous secretion of pancreatic juice which occurred when acid was introduced into the duodenum. At that time the only known means by which glands were excited to secrete was by the mediation of secretory nerves, as exemplified by the pioneer work of Ludwig (1851) on the submaxillary gland. Pavlov had shown that secretion of pancreatic juice was evoked on stimulation of the vagus nerves, but it could also be produced by the introduction of acid into the upper intestine, even after section of both vagi; this acid-provoked secretion, he concluded, could only be brought about by a local reflex from the intestinal mucosa. Bayliss and Starling showed, however, that introduction of acid into the duodenum still induced secretion of pancreatic juice after division of both vagi and of all the nerves to the upper intestine, so that the only means of communication of the pancreas with the intestine was via the bloodstream. The excitant must, therefore, be not a nervous but a chemical stimulus, a substance derived from the intestine and carried in the bloodstream to the pancreas, which it excited to secrete. This they proved by showing that the intravenous injection of an acid extract of intestinal mucosa resulted in the secretion of pancreatic juice. They called the excitant substance *secretin,* and thus recognized the existence of a new class of chemical messengers, the hormones (from the Greek *horman,* "to set in motion"), a name first promulgated by Starling in his Croonian lecture of 1905, in which he foreshadowed other hormone actions.

Enzyme Action. Bayliss and Starling next studied the activation of trypsin in the pancreatic juice. As secreted, the juice has no proteolytic action, but it becomes activated by contact with enterokinase in the intestinal juice. Pavlov regarded this activation to be the result of an enzyme action by which the precursor, trypsinogen, was converted into the active form, trypsin, by the separation from it of part of its molecule. Opponents had thought of the action as a *combination* between inactive enzyme and activator. Bayliss and Starling gave support to Pavlov's view by showing that the reaction was catalytic and not stoichiometric.

Bayliss now turned to study enzyme action, in the light of physical chemistry. He used trypsin as the enzyme, caseinogen or gelatin as substrate, and followed the course of the digestion by measurement of the electrical conductivity, correlated with other measurements such as viscosity, refractive index, optical rotation, osmotic pressure, etc. These studies led on to further work on the velocity of enzyme action, final equilibria, reversibility, and the effect of temperature, in the course of which he showed that enzyme action is largely influenced by adsorption effects in which there is combination between enzyme and substrate, a viewpoint developed by Michaelis and Menten in 1913.

Colloids. Bayliss' study of the osmotic pressure of Congo red, showing that this colloid exerted the same osmotic pressure that it would if it were in true solution, led on to the study of the electrical equilibrium set up when Congo red and sodium chloride solutions are separated by a semipermeable membrane. This work gave support to the studies of Donnan on the theory of membrane equilibria, and its relation to Nernst's equation for a concentration cell.

War Problems (1914–1918). Bayliss' most valuable contribution to the war effort was his work on wound shock, which led to the practice of replacing lost blood with a gum saline solution. He had shown the importance of maintaining an adequate colloidal osmotic pressure in the circulating blood.

Books. Bayliss' great book, on which he spent many years, was his *Principles of General Physiology,* which first appeared in 1914. It can be regarded as an extension into the twentieth century of Claude Bernard's *Phénomènes de la vie commune aux animaux et aux végétaux* (1878–1879). The *Principles* stands as a landmark in the history of biological literature. When Bayliss visited the United States in 1922, he was pleased, but embarrassed, to find that at some universities there were Bayliss clubs, formed to discuss the contents of the book.

BIBLIOGRAPHY

I. ORIGINAL WORKS. *Articles.* "On the Physiology of the Depressor Nerve," in *Journal of Physiology,* **14** (1893),

303–325; "On the Origin From the Spinal Cord of the Vaso-Dilator Fibres of the Hind Limb and on the Nature of These Fibres," *ibid.,* **26** (1901), 173–209; "Further Researches on Antidromic Nerve Impulses," *ibid.,* **28** (1902), 276–299; "The Kinetics of Tryptic Action," in *Archives des sciences biologiques,* **11** (1904), 261–296, supp., *Pavlov Jubilee Volume;* "On Some Aspects of Adsorption Phenomena, with Especial Reference to the Action of Electrolytes, and to the Ash Constituents of Proteins," in *Biochemical Journal,* **1** (1906), 175–232; "On Reciprocal Innervation in Vaso-Motor Reflexes, and on the Action of Strychnine and of Chloroform Thereon," in *Proceedings of the Royal Society,* **80B** (1908), 339–375; "The Excitation of Vaso-Dilator Fibres in Depressor Reflexes," in *Journal of Physiology,* **37** (1908), 264–277; "The Osmotic Pressure of Congo Red, and of Some Other Dyes," in *Proceedings of the Royal Society,* **81B** (1909), 269–286; "On Adsorption as Preliminary to Chemical Reaction," *ibid.,* **84B** (1911), 81–98; "The Osmotic Pressure of Electrolytically Dissociated Colloids," *ibid.,* pp. 229–254; "Researches on the Nature of Enzyme Action. II. The Synthetic Properties of Anti-Emulsin," in *Journal of Physiology,* **43** (1912), 455–466; "Researches on the Nature of Enzyme Action. III. The Synthetic Action of Enzymes," *ibid.,* **46** (1913), 236–266; "The Action of Insoluble Enzymes," *ibid.,* **50** (1915), 85–94; "Methods of Raising a Low Arterial Pressure," in *Proceedings of the Royal Society,* **89B** (1916), 380–393, and in *British Medical Journal* (1917); "The Action of Gum Acacia on the Circulation," in *Journal of Pharmacology and Experimental Therapeutics,* **15** (1920), 29–74; "Reversible Gelation in Living Protoplasm," in *Proceedings of the Royal Society,* **91B** (1920), 196–201.

Collaborations. J. R. Bradford: "The Electrical Phenomena Accompanying the Process of Secretion in the Salivary Glands of the Dog and Cat," in *Internationale Monatsschrift für Anatomie und Physiologie,* **4** (1885), 109–136; "Proc. Physiol. Soc.," in *Journal of Physiology,* **6** (1889), xiii–xvi; and "The Innervation of the Vessels of the Limbs," *ibid.,* **16** (1894), 10–22.

W. B. Cannon: "Note on Muscle Injury in Relation to Shock," in *Special Report of the Medical Research Committee,* no. 26 (1919), 19–23.

Leonard Hill: "On the Intra-Cranial Pressure and the Cerebral Circulations," in *Journal of Physiology,* **18** (1895), 334–362.

E. H. Starling: "On the Electromotive Phenomena of the Mammalian Heart," in *Internationale Monatsschrift für Anatomie und Physiologie,* **9** (1892), 256–281; "On Some Points in the Innervation of the Mammalian Heart," in *Journal of Physiology,* **13** (1892), 407–418; "On the Form of the Intraventricular and Aortic Pressure Curves Obtained by a New Method," in *Internationale Monatsschrift für Anatomie und Physiologie,* **11** (1894), Heft 9; "The Movements and Innervation of the Small Intestine," in *Journal of Physiology,* **24** (1899), 99–143; "The Mechanism of Pancreatic Secretion," *ibid.,* **28** (1902), 325–353; "The Proteolytic Activities of the Pancreatic Juice," *ibid.,* **30** (1903), 61–83; and "The Chemical Regulation of the Secretory Process," Croonian Lecture pub. in *Proceedings of the Royal Society,* **73B** (1904), 310–322.

Books. The Nature of Enzyme Action, 5 eds. (London, 1908–1925); *An Introduction to General Physiology* (London, 1919); *Principles of General Physiology,* 4 eds. (London, 1919–1924); *The Physiology of Food and Economy in Diet* (London, 1917); *Intravenous Injections in Wound Shock,* Oliver-Sharpey Lectures (London, 1918); *The Vasomotor System* (London, 1923); *The Colloidal State in Its Medical and Physiological Aspects* (Oxford, 1923); *Interfacial Forces and Phenomena in Physiology,* Herter Lectures (London, 1923).

II. SECONDARY LITERATURE. L. E. Bayliss, "William Maddock Bayliss (1860–1924)," in *Perspectives in Biology and Medicine,* **4** (1961), 460–479; C. Lovatt Evans, First Bayliss-Starling Memorial Lecture, *Reminiscences of Bayliss and Starling* (Cambridge, 1964), p. 17; E. H. Starling, obit. of W. M. Bayliss in *The Times* (28 Aug. 1924).

CHARLES L. EVANS

IBN AL-BAYṬĀR AL-MĀLAQĪ, ḌIYĀ' AL-DĪN ABŪ MUḤAMMAD 'ABDALLĀH IBN AḤMAD

(*b.* Málaga, Spain, *ca.* 1190; *d.* Damascus, Syria, 1248), *pharmacology, botany.*

Ibn al-Bayṭār may have belonged to the Bayṭār family of Málaga, on which considerable information is available in the biographical dictionaries of the period. His Hispano-Roman ancestry, suggested by Francisco Javier Simonet, has not been proved. He studied in Seville, and while there he gathered herbs with his teachers Abu'l-'Abbās al-Nabātī, 'Abdallāh ibn Ṣāliḥ, and Abu'l-Hajjāj. We know he preferred to study the works of al-Ghāfiqī, al-Zahrāwī, al-Idrīsī, Dioscorides, and Galen.

Around 1220 Ibn al-Bayṭār migrated to the Orient, crossing North Africa and possibly sailing from there to Asia Minor and Syria in 1224. He finally settled in Cairo, where the Ayyūbid Sultan al-Kāmil named him chief herbalist, a post he continued to occupy under the sultan's successor, al-Ṣāliḥ. He traveled sporadically through Arabia, Palestine, Syria, and part of Iraq, accompanied most of the time by his disciples. The most outstanding of his followers was Ibn Abī Uṣaybi'a, who in his *'Uyūn* has left us a eulogistic passage about his teacher.

Ibn al-Bayṭār's *Al-Mughnī fi'l-adwiya al-mufrada* is dedicated to Sultan al-Ṣāliḥ and deals with the simple medicines appropriate for various illnesses. *Al-Jāmi' li-mufradāt al-adwiya wa'l-aghdhiya* enumerates alphabetically some 1,400 animal, vegetable, and mineral medicines, relying on his own observations as well as some 150 authorities, including, besides those already mentioned, al-Rāzī and Ibn Sīnā (Avicenna). The main contribution of Ibn al-Bayṭār was the systematization of the discoveries made by Arabs during the Middle Ages, which added between 300 and 400 medicines to the thousand known since antiquity. One must also point out his preoccupation

538

with synonymy (technical equivalents between Arabic and Persian, Berber, Greek, Latin, Arab dialects, and Romance, taken in part from the *Sharḥ asmā' al-'uqqār* by Maimonides, which he knew well because he had translated it).

Meyerhof and Sobhy have cast doubt on the originality of this work, suspecting that it is a plagiarism of the pharmacopoeia of al-Ghāfiqī, which Ibn al-Bayṭār quotes more than 200 times. This hypothesis is difficult to prove, because the concept of intellectual property was very different among the medieval Arabs from what it is now and because al-Ghāfiqī's work has been preserved only in a résumé by Barhebraeus. The *Jāmi'* had great influence upon later pharmacopoeias in the Near East, both in and out of the Islamic world—as, for example, on the Armenian Amir Dowlat. On the other hand, his influence in the West was less, for the era of great translations from Arabic to Latin ended in the middle of the thirteenth century. Nevertheless, Andrea Alpago used the *Jāmi'* in his works on Ibn Sīnā, and later it was the object of attention by such Arabists as William Portel and Antoine Galland, who published both a résumé and a manuscript in French.

The other works of Ibn al-Bayṭār have received much less attention than the aforementioned two. They are *Mīzān al-ṭabīb; Risāla fi'l-aghdhiya wa'l-adwiya; Maqāla fi'l-laymūn,* also attributed to Ibn Jumaʿ, which exists in a Latin version by Alpago; and *Tafsīr kitāb Diyusqūrīdis,* a commentary on Dioscorides, a manuscript of which has recently been found. In it he inventories 550 medicines that are to be found in the first four books of Dioscorides and frequently gives synonyms for them.

BIBLIOGRAPHY

I. ORIGINAL WORKS. An inventory of the MSS is in C. Brockelmann, *Geschichte der arabischen Literatur,* I, 492, and Supp. I, 896; and Albert Dietrich, *Medicinalia Arabica* (Göttingen, 1966), p. 147. Ibn al-Bayṭār's second work, the *al-Jāmi',* is not available in a good edition, although there is a defective German translation by J. Sontheimer, 2 vols. (Stuttgart, 1840–1842), and a very useful French edition by Lucien Leclerc in the series Notices et Extraits, XXIII, XXV, and XXVI (Paris, 1877–1883).

II. SECONDARY LITERATURE. Arabic sources for the biography of Ibn al-Bayṭār may be found in César E. Dubler, "Ibn al-Bayṭār en armenio," in *Al-Andalus,* **21** (1956), 125–130; Max Meyerhof, "Esquisse d'histoire de la pharmacologie et botanique chez les musulmans d'Espagne," *ibid.,* **3** (1935), 31–33; George Sarton, *Introduction to the History of Science,* II, pt. 2 (Baltimore, 1931), 663–664; and Ziriklī, *Aʿlām,* IV (Cairo, n.d.), 192.

A résumé of the work by al-Ghāfiqī may be found in *The Abridged Version of the "Book of Simple Drugs"* of . . . *al-Ghāfiqī by Gregorius Abu-l-Farag (Barhebraeus),* Max Meyerhof and G. P. Sobhy, eds., fasc. 1 (Cairo, 1932), 32–33. An article on the *Tafsīr kitāb Diyusqūrīdis* is M. al-Shihābī, in *Majallat Maʿhad al-Makhṭūṭāt al-ʿArabiyya,* **3,** no. 1 (1957), 105–112.

J. VERNET

BEALE, LIONEL SMITH (*b.* London, England, 5 February 1828; *d.* London, 28 March 1906), *microscopy.*

Beale's father, Lionel John Beale (1796–1871), was a prominent London surgeon and medical author; his mother was Frances Smith. After attending Highgate, a private school, Beale entered King's College School, London, in 1840. From then on, his life and career were intimately connected with institutions under the direction of the council of King's College. He studied at King's College School until 1844, and during the last three years was also apprenticed to an apothecary-surgeon, Joseph Ross, of Islington. In 1845 Beale entered the medical department of King's College, University of London, and two years later matriculated with honors in chemistry and zoology. He then spent two years at Oxford as assistant to Henry Acland (1815–1900) in the Anatomical Museum.

Beale was licensed by the Society of Apothecaries in 1849, and in 1851 he graduated M.B. from the University of London, having already served (1850–1851) as resident physician at King's College Hospital. In 1852 he established a private laboratory in Carey Street, near the hospital, where he pioneered in teaching the use of the microscope in pathological anatomy. In 1853, at the age of twenty-five, he succeeded Robert Bentley Todd as professor of physiology and general and morbid anatomy at King's College, sharing the duties for two years with William Bowman, who had been Todd's assistant. Beale later served King's College as professor of pathological anatomy (1869–1876) and as professor of the principles and practice of medicine (1876–1896). Upon his retirement in 1896, he was nominated professor emeritus and honorary consulting physician to King's College Hospital.

Conspicuous among the many honors conferred upon Beale were those of the Royal College of Physicians: membership (1856), fellowship (1859), the Baly Medal (1871), and the post of Lumleian lecturer (1875). Elected fellow of the Royal Society in 1857, he delivered the Croonian lecture for 1865. He also was president of the Microscopical Society from 1879 to 1880.

In 1859 Beale married Frances Blakiston; their son, Peyton Todd Bowman Beale, served as assistant surgeon to King's College Hospital. Beale's death, in his seventy-eighth year, was attributed to pontine hemorrhage.

Beale's contemporary reputation derived primarily from his practical books on the microscope and from his vocal opposition to the mechanistic interpretation of life. The books are basic laboratory manuals, a natural and useful outgrowth of the Carey Street course on the use of the microscope. Beale's opposition to T. H. Huxley and the other "physicalists" commanded attention because his scientific credentials were impressive. He had, in fact, been elected to his first teaching position at King's College despite Huxley's candidacy.

The high quality of Beale's histological studies is demonstrated by his series of lectures, "On the Structure of the Simple Tissue of the Human Body," delivered before the Royal College of Physicians in April and May 1861, and published in book form later that year under the same title. These lectures reveal a careful microscopist at work and demonstrate Beale's mastery of the recently introduced techniques of vital staining. Like most of his works, they are illustrated by excellent plates executed by Beale himself. To a great extent, his plates and conclusions confirmed the work of Ferdinand Cohn, Max Schultze, and others who were working toward a redefinition of the cell and a deemphasis of the cell wall. But Beale, a strong-willed and independent figure, proposed a unique terminology, insisting upon an absolute distinction between what he called "germinal matter" (essentially equivalent to protoplasm) and "formed matter" (all other tissue constituents). Germinal matter was the living substance; formed matter had ceased to live.

Beale was also committed to a special interpretation of the living substance, and after Huxley had in 1868 delivered a mechanistic manifesto on the nature of protoplasm,[1] Beale countered with *Protoplasm,* a polemical work in which he asserted that a vital force was necessary for life. Generally regarded as the defender of religion and morality against the inroads of the mechanistic heresy, he wrote often, especially near the end of his life, on religious and moral considerations.

Beale seems to have been polemical by nature. Besides his spectacular attack against Huxley, he was also suspicious of Darwinian evolution, and was involved in an extended controversy with the German histologists Wilhelm Kühne and Rudolf von Kölliker over the termination of the nerve endings in voluntary muscles. Beale denied their belief that the nerves terminate in ends, insisting instead that the cells and fibers of each nervous apparatus form a continuous loop, "an uninterrupted circuit." In his book *On Disease Germs* (1870), Beale attacked both those who believed that the agents of contagion were bacteria (i.e., plants) and those who believed that disease germs did not exist; he proposed instead the unique theory that disease germs are minute particles of degraded protoplasm derived by direct descent from the normal protoplasm of the diseased organism. It is typical of Beale that he attacked Darwin's now discredited hypothesis of pangenesis "with much acerbity and some justice."[2]

Beale was an amazingly prolific writer, but many of his works cover essentially the same ground. Between 1857 and 1870 he edited a periodical called *Archives of Medicine.* Two eponyms were awarded to Beale: "Beale's solution," carmine in ammonia, is an effective histological stain, and "Beale's cells" are the pyriform nerve ganglion cells.

NOTES

1. T. H. Huxley, "On the Physical Basis of Life," in *Fortnightly Review,* 5 (1869), 129–145. Later published in his *Lay Sermons, Addresses, and Reviews* (London, 1870), pp. 132–161.
2. Charles Darwin, *The Variation of Animals and Plants Under Domestication,* auth. ed. (New York, 1899), p. 339, n. 1.

BIBLIOGRAPHY

I. ORIGINAL WORKS. Among Beale's writings are *The Microscope, and Its Application to Clinical Medicine* (London, 1854; 4th ed., 1878), later editions varying slightly in title; *How to Work With the Microscope. A Course of Lectures on Microscopical Manipulation, and the Practical Application of the Microscope to Different Branches of Investigation* (London, 1857; 5th ed., 1880); "Some Points in Support of Our Belief in the Permanence of Species," in *Edinburgh New Philosophical Journal,* 11 (1860), 233–242; "Remarks on the Recent Observations of Kühne and Kölliker Upon the Terminations of the Nerves in Voluntary Muscle," in *Archives of Medicine,* 3 (1862), 257–265; *Kidney Diseases, Urinary Deposits, and Calculous Disorders; Their Nature and Treatment,* 3rd ed., enl. (London, 1869), earlier eds. (1861, 1864) under somewhat different titles; *Protoplasm; or Life, Matter, and Mind,* 2nd ed., rev. (London, 1870; 4th ed., 1892); and *On Slight Ailments: Their Nature and Treatment* (London, 1880; 4th ed., 1896). Nearly all of Beale's scientific papers are listed in the *Royal Society Catalogue of Scientific Papers,* I, 221–222; VII, 111–112; IX, 152; and XIII, 370.

II. SECONDARY LITERATURE. Sketches of Beale's life and work can be found in *Bulletin de l'Académie royale de médecine de Belgique,* 4th ser., 20 (1906), 348–351; *Dictionary of National Biography,* Supp. 2, I, 118–120; *Journal of the American Medical Association,* 46 (1906), 1392; *Lancet* (7 Apr. 1906), 1004–1007; *Medical History,* 2 (1958),

269–273; *Nature,* **73** (1905–1906), 540; and *Proceedings of the Royal Society,* **79B** (1907), lvii–lxiii.

GERALD L. GEISON

BEAUGRAND, JEAN (*b.* Paris [?], France, *ca.* 1595 [?]; *d.* Paris [?], *ca.* 22 December 1640), *mathematics.*

In spite of the important role he played in the mathematics of the 1630's, what little is known or surmised about Beaugrand has had to be pieced together from sources dealing with his friends and enemies, and only rarely with him directly. There are few manuscripts or letters, and no records. He may have been the son of Jean Beaugrand, author of *La paecilographie* (1602) and *Escritures* (1604), who was chosen to teach calligraphy to Louis XIII. He studied under Viète and became mathematician to Gaston of Orléans in 1630; in that year J. L. Vaulezard dedicated his *Cinq livres des zététiques de Fr. Viette* to Beaugrand, who had already achieved a certain notoriety from having published Viète's *In artem analyticam isagoge,* with scholia and a mathematical compendium, in 1631. Some of the scholia were incorporated in Schooten's edition of 1646.

Beaugrand was an early friend of Fermat[1] and Étienne Despagnet (the son of Jean Despagnet); later of Mersenne and his circle; and for a time, before their bitter break, of Desargues. He seems to have been an official Paris correspondent to Fermat and was replaced in that function by Carcavi.[2] In 1634 he was one of the scientists who officially examined Morin's method for determining longitudes.[3] The following year he assumed the functions of *secrétaire du roi,* possibly under Pierre Séguier, who was appointed chancellor in the same year.

Sometime before 1630 Beaugrand visited England;[4] he met Hobbes in Paris, at the home of Mersenne, in 1634 and 1637.[5] He spent a year in Italy, from February 1635, as part of Bellièvre's entourage.[6] While there, he visited Castelli in Rome,[7] Cavalieri in Bologna,[8] and Galileo in Arcetri,[9] and communicated to them some of Fermat's results in a conversation alluded to in his *Géostatique.* All of them, especially Cavalieri, appear to have been impressed with Beaugrand as a mathematician, and he continued to correspond with them after his return to Paris in February 1636.[10] He conveyed results of the French mathematicians without always bothering about provenance, a habit that resulted in misunderstandings.

Although Beaugrand's *Géostatique* (1636) was well received by Castelli and Cavalieri, it was a disappointment in France; and his violent polemical exchanges with Desargues, his anonymous pamphlets against Descartes, and the disdain that characterizes

Descartes's references to him, as well as the cooling of his relations with Fermat, seem to stem from the period of its publication. Its main thesis is that the weight of a body varies as its distance from the center of gravity. Fermat[11] had adopted this law, and sought to demonstrate it in a satisfactory manner by arguing from a thought-experiment in which Archimedean arguments were applied to a lever with its fulcrum at the earth's center. Thus he defended a law of gravity later taken up independently by Saccheri in his *Neo-Statica* (1703).

Fermat's proposition gave rise to a long debate involving Étienne Pascal, Roberval, and Descartes.[12] Desargues appended a text inspired by this controversy to his *Brouillon projet.* Beaugrand in turn claimed that the proposition which occupies most of the *Brouillon projet* is nothing but a corollary to Apollonius, *Conics* III, prop. 17.[13] This attack was preserved by Desargues's enemies and occasioned Poncelet's rediscovery of Desargues's work 150 years later. Beaugrand's attacks on Descartes[14] took a similar form, including a charge of plagiarism from Harriot,[15] and are to be found in three anonymous pamphlets and a letter to Mersenne claiming that Viète's methods were superior and that Descartes had derived his *Géométrie* from them.[16]

NOTES

D, F, and *M* below refer to the respective standard editions (see bibliography) of the correspondence of Descartes, Fermat, and Mersenne.

1. *M,* V, 466 f.
2. Cf. C. de Waard, in *Bulletin des sciences mathématiques,* 2nd ser., **17** (June 1918).
3. Bigourdin, "La conférence des longitudes de 1634," in *Comptes rendus de l'Académie des sciences,* **163** (1916), 229–233.
4. *M,* II, 514.
5. *D,* III, 342.
6. *M,* V, 271.
7. Paris, B.N., f. fr. 15913, 15914.
8. *M,* V, 429. Cf. C. de Waard, in *Bollettino di bibliografia di storia delle scienze matematiche* (1919), 1–12.
9. *M,* V, 454; Galileo, Edizione nazionale, XVI (1905), 335–337, 340–344.
10. *Lettres de Chapelain,* Tamizey de Larroque, ed., I (1880), 109.
11. *F,* V, 100–103.
12. Cf. Descartes to Mersenne, 13 July 1638.
13. R. Taton, *L'oeuvre mathématique de Desargues* (Paris, 1937), *passim.*
14. P. Tannéry, *Oeuvres scientifiques,* V, 503–512; VI, 206 ff.
15. *M,* VII, 201 f.
16. *Ibid.,* 87–104.

BIBLIOGRAPHY

References to Beaugrand are scattered throughout the standard eds. of the correspondence of Fermat (P. Tannéry and C. Henry, eds. [Paris, 1891–1912], supp. vol., N. de Waard, ed. [Paris, 1922]), Descartes (Adam and P. Tannéry, eds. [Paris, 1897–1913]), and Mersenne (Paris, 1933–   ).

The extant writings by Beaugrand, besides his ed. of Viète's *In artem analyticam isagoge* (Paris, 1631) and *Géostatique* (Paris, 1636), pub. in Latin as *Geostatica* (Paris, 1637), are a letter on tangents in Fermat's *Oeuvres,* supp. vol. (1922), pp. 102–113; a letter to Desargues, in R. Taton, *L'oeuvre mathématique de Desargues* (Paris, 1951), pp. 186–190; four writings against Descartes, "Lettre de M. de Beaugrand (10 Aug. 1640)," in Descartes, *Oeuvres,* V, 503–512; letter to Mersenne (Apr. [?] 1638), in Descartes, *Correspondance* (1903); three anonymous pamphlets, in P. Tannéry, *Mémoires scientifiques,* VI (Paris, 1896), 202–229 ("La correspondance de Descartes dans les inédits du fonds Libri"); and Mersenne, *Harmonie universelle,* II, *Livre I des instrumens,* props. 14, 15, 31, and his *Correspondance,* IV, 429–431.

See also Guy de Brosse, *Éclaircissement d'une partie des paralogismes . . .* (1637); P. Costabel, "Centre de gravité et équivalence dynamique," in *Les conférences du Palais de la Découverte,* ser. D, no. 34 (Paris, 1954); and P. Duhem, *Les origines de la statique* (Paris, 1906), pp. 178 ff. For the confused priority controversy over the cycloid, see Pascal, *Oeuvres,* L. Brunschvicq and E. Boutroux, eds., VIII (Paris, 1914), 181–223.

HENRY NATHAN

BEAUMONT, ÉLIE DE. See **Élie de Beaumont, Jean B.**

BEAUMONT, WILLIAM (*b.* Lebanon, Connecticut, 21 November 1785; *d.* St. Louis, Missouri, 25 April 1853), *physiology.*

William Beaumont was the son of a farmer. Deciding not to follow his father's occupation, he left home in the winter of 1806. He set out with a horse and cutter, a barrel of cider, and $100 and drove northward, arriving at Champlain, New York, in the spring of 1807. There he became the village schoolmaster and taught for three years. During this period, Beaumont employed his spare time to read medical books borrowed from Dr. Seth Pomeroy, a Burlington, Vermont, physician. Having decided to study medicine, he became an apprentice to Dr. Benjamin Chandler, a general practitioner in St. Albans, Vermont. In June 1812, after two years of study, he received a license to practice from the Medical Society of Vermont. That month war broke out between Great Britain and the United States, and in September, Beaumont joined the army as acting surgeon's mate. After resigning from the army in 1815, he practiced at Plattsburg for five years, but then took a commission as a post surgeon and was ordered to Fort Mackinac, now in Michigan.

Here, on 6 June 1822, an accident occurred. A shotgun had been carelessly loaded and had gone off. A nineteen-year-old French Canadian, Alexis St. Martin, a trapper employed by the American Fur Company, had been standing about two or three feet from the muzzle of the gun and received the entire charge in his left side. Beaumont was called to care for the trapper. Despite a very poor prognosis, St. Martin recovered. After ten months his wound was to a large extent healed. However, extensive parts of the injured lung and of the stomach sloughed off, and as a result of the union between the lacerated edges of the stomach and the intercostal muscles, a gastric fistula developed. Touched by the young trapper's misfortune, Beaumont took him into his own home, where he remained almost two years, until he was completely recovered. But the large fistula into his stomach remained.

The idea of carrying out experiments on digestion in a human subject occurred to Beaumont in the spring of 1825, and in May he began his investigations. From 1825 to 1833 Beaumont carried out four groups of experiments while stationed at several army posts (Mackinac, Niagara, Crawford, St. Louis). These studies were interrupted for varying periods, ranging from several months to four years, because of St. Martin's trips to Canada. It was not by accident that Beaumont recognized the opportunity presented by St. Martin's gastric fistula. Although he was self-educated, he had a curious mind and was eager to learn. From his writings it is clear that he was abreast of the scientific literature concerned with gastric physiology and pathology, and he employed the knowledge available to him to organize his experiments and observations. Aware of his limited knowledge of chemistry, he requested the assistance of Robley Dunglison, professor of physiology at the University of Virginia, and of Benjamin Silliman, professor of chemistry at Yale University. Both of them analyzed specimens of St. Martin's gastric juice, and established the presence in it of free hydrochloric acid. A portion of the gastric juice was sent by Silliman to the Swedish chemist Berzelius, but his investigation was incomplete and arrived too late to be included in Beaumont's book. In 1834, Beaumont also sent some gastric juice to Charles F. Jackson, one of the co-discoverers of ether anesthesia.

The experiments were concluded by November 1833, and in December of that year his book was published at Plattsburg in an edition of 1,000 copies. The work is an octavo volume of 280 pages entitled *Experiments and Observations on the Gastric Juice and the Physiology of Digestion.* The book is divided into two parts, a general discussion of the physiology of digestion and a detailed description of the experiments. The presentation concludes with fifty-one inferences drawn by the author from his researches. The material is presented in an unpretentious, matter-of-fact style. Beaumont restricted himself to a relation of his experiments and observations, and was very cautious, avoiding all unsupported assertions.

In 1834, after the publication of his book, Beaumont was posted at St. Louis, where he remained in service until his resignation in 1839, when he went into general practice. As a general practitioner he exhibited the strong common sense that characterizes his experimental work, earning the esteem of his fellow citizens. In March 1853, he suffered a fall, resulting in a fractured hip. Several weeks later a carbuncle appeared on his neck, and on April 25, he succumbed to his illness.

Not only did Beaumont's experiments soon become known to his friends, but before long, reports of his work also spread across the Atlantic to Europe. As early as 1826 two articles dealing with the case of St. Martin appeared in Germany, and it was soon noticed in Scotland and France. The publication of Beaumont's book created considerable interest among European scientists and physicians, and in general was favorably received. A German translation was published at Leipzig in 1834, and at about the same time, the American edition was noted in the English, German, and French literature. The most significant response came from Germany, where Beaumont's experiments influenced various investigators, among them Johannes Müller, Theodor Schwann, and J. B. Purkinje. In France, Nicolas Blondlot, professor of chemistry at Nancy, impressed by the reports of St. Martin's accident, his recovery, and its consequences, hit upon the idea of imitating in animals the fistula that the Canadian had retained after his recovery. Until the 1860's, Beaumont's work was referred to by physiologists, pathologists, and clinicians. Because of a number of factors, however, interest in his investigations declined during the last third of the century. The introduction of the stomach pump by Kussmaul (1867) gave research workers a simpler instrumentality with which to carry out investigations. This circumstance, together with the rapid development of physiological chemistry during the later nineteenth century, shifted the emphasis in research to the chemical aspects of digestion. Moreover, it was found that the secretions of the salivary glands, of the liver, of the pancreas, and of the intestine played a very much greater role than had previously been assumed. Nonetheless, the value of William Beaumont's contributions to gastric physiology and pathology had been established, and it is clear that he was the first American physiologist to make a major contribution to the development of the science.

In the eighteenth century Réaumur and Spal-lanzani had shown digestion to be a chemical process. Nevertheless, a good deal of confusion prevailed concerning various aspects of the digestive process in the stomach; it is to Beaumont that we owe the clarification of this subject. The results of his investigations attracted the attention of the scientific world, and within a short time gained admission to the literature dealing with the stomach.

Beaumont contributed to the development of gastric physiology by substantiating doubtful observations of other scientists and by stimulating new investigations. He demonstrated once again, both in the stomach and outside the body, that digestion is the result of a chemical process. At the time Beaumont was carrying out his experiments, the nature of the effective agent of the gastric juice was still unknown. A number of experiments on artificial digestion with dilute acids convinced him that such an effort "to imitate the gastric juice . . . was not satisfactory. Probably the gastric juice contains some principles inappreciable to the senses, or to chemical tests, besides the alkaline substances already discovered in it." Schwann's discovery of pepsin in 1836 showed that Beaumont's surmise had been correct.

Several details of gastric physiology still to be found in modern textbooks were established by Beaumont. He observed that gastric juice was not found in the stomach in the absence of food and that water and other fluids passed very rapidly and directly from the stomach through the pylorus. He also observed a retrograde passage of the duodenal contents. Beaumont ascertained by direct observation that psychic influences are to a considerable degree able to affect gastric secretion and digestion. Some investigators saw the significance of these observations, which, however, were not pursued until Pavlov began his researches.

Beaumont studied the digestibility of various foods, as well as the action of stimulants such as coffee, tea, and alcohol on gastric digestion, thus creating a foundation for practical dietetics, which even today remains one of the most important contributions to this subject. He knew very little about the functions of the rest of the digestive system, and believed that the food was almost completely digested in the stomach. Consequently, he assumed that the time that elapsed between the entry of food into the stomach and its departure therefrom represented an index of its digestibility. Moreover, he also believed that several other conditions that might possibly influence digestion—for instance, the size of the meal—could be disregarded. Despite these limitations, however, his average determinations of the time required for digestion generally agree with those later obtained by means of the stomach tube.

On the basis of his observations *in vivo*, Beaumont was the first to attempt an exact description of the way the gastric contractions move and mix the chyme within the stomach. By fixing his glance on an easily recognizable object as soon as it passed through the cardia, he was able to follow its further movements. In the course of his experiments Beaumont frequently introduced a thermometer into the stomach and convinced himself that it was subject to the same movements. Except for slight modifications by William Brinton in 1848, Beaumont's observations on gastric mobility remained unchanged until they were superseded by Walter B. Cannon's roentgenological investigations between 1898 and 1911.

The technique of animal experimentation was also greatly influenced by Beaumont's experiments. During the seventeenth century, Regnier de Graaf had established a pancreatic fistula in a dog, but the method was not developed and soon lapsed into oblivion. St. Martin's history and Beaumont's experiments stimulated Blondlot to establish artificial gastric fistula in animals. This successful endeavor led other scientific investigators to develop and to extend the fistula method. Schwann in 1844 reported the experimental creation of a gallbladder fistula, and in 1864, Thiry introduced the intestinal fistula. Klemensiewicz, in 1875, used Thiry's approach to isolate the pyloric part of the stomach, and in 1879 R. Heidenhain employed it for the isolation of a portion of the corpus. In turn, Heidenhain, under whom Pavlov worked in 1877 and 1884, greatly influenced him in his study of gastric secretion and in the experimental development of an innervated gastric pouch. As these methods developed, it became possible to study with greater precision the activity of the digestive glands, their dependence on the nervous system, and the details of the digestive process.

Beaumont's work led to a more accurate conception of gastritis and contributed to the development of gastric pathology. He described the occurrence of acute gastritis as a consequence of different causes, most frequently the excessive ingestion of alcoholic beverages or overloading the stomach with irritating foods. He also observed a reddening of the mucous membrane and cessation of gastric secretion in febrile states. These observations in turn led to therapeutic regimens for such conditions.

BIBLIOGRAPHY

I. ORIGINAL WORKS. In 1825 the *Medical Recorder* (**8**, no. 1) published a report of the case of St. Martin; the following year a report of four experiments performed on the same subject appeared in this periodical (Jan. 1826, no. 33). Beaumont published his final results as *Experiments and Observations on the Gastric Juice and the Physiology of Digestion* (Plattsburg, 1833), which was reissued in Boston in 1834, and the same year saw the appearance of a German translation at Leipzig as *Neue Versuche und Beobachtungen über den Magensaft und die Physiologie der Verdauung,* trans. by Dr. Bernhard Luden. A Scottish edition was published at Edinburgh in 1838. A second edition with corrections by Samuel Beaumont, a cousin of Beaumont, appeared in 1847 at Burlington, Vt. Facsimiles of the original edition of 1833, together with a biographical essay, "William Beaumont. A Pioneer American Physiologist," by Sir William Osler, were issued in 1929, 1941, and 1959.

Two important collections of Beaumont papers, documents, and relics are located at the Washington University School of Medicine, St. Louis, Mo., and at the University of Chicago. A Beaumont memorial on Mackinac Island, Mich., recreates some of the circumstances under which Beaumont carried on his investigations.

II. SECONDARY LITERATURE. The chief source for Beaumont's life and work besides his own writings is Jesse S. Myer, *Life and Letters of Dr. William Beaumont Including Hitherto Unpublished Data Concerning the Case of Alexis St. Martin* (St. Louis, 1912; 2nd ed., 1939). Two of Beaumont's early notebooks that give a picture of his medical training and early medical practice have been edited by Genevieve Miller: *William Beaumont's Formative Years: Two Early Notebooks 1811–1821* (New York, 1946). William Osler's essay on Beaumont in *An Alabama Student, and Other Biographical Essays* (New York, 1909) is still useful and in addition is delightful to read. Another review of Beaumont's career that should be consulted is W. S. Miller, "William Beaumont and His Book. Elisha North and His Copy of Beaumont's Book," in *Annals of Medical History,* **1** (1929), 155–179. The extensive biographical literature dealing with Beaumont is for the most part filiopietistic, derivative, repetitive, dreary, and not worth listing.

Descriptions of the Beaumont papers and artifacts are available in Arno B. Luckhardt, "The Dr. William Beaumont Collection of the University of Chicago, Donated by Mr. and Mrs. Ethan Allen Beaumont," in *Bulletin of the History of Medicine,* **7** (1939), 535–563; Alfred M. Whittaker, "The Beaumont Memorial on Mackinac Island," *ibid.,* **28** (1954), 385–389; and Phoebe A. Cassidy and Robert S. Sokol, *Index to the William Beaumont M.D. (1785–1853) Manuscript Collection* (St. Louis, 1968).

For an evaluation of the reception of Beaumont's work by his contemporaries and successors, and its influence on physiology and medicine, see George Rosen, *Die Aufnahme der Entdeckung William Beaumont's durch die europäische Medizin. Ein Beitrag zur Geschichte der Physiologie im 19. Jahrhundert* (Berlin, 1935). An English translation of this work, with a foreword by John F. Fulton, appeared as *The Reception of William Beaumont's Discovery in Europe* (New York, 1942). For further discussion of some points in the reception of Beaumont's work, see George Rosen, "Notes on the Reception and Influence of William Beaumont's Discovery," in *Bulletin of the History of Medicine,* **13** (1943), 631–642; F. N. L. Poynter, "The Reception of William Beaumont's Discovery in England. Two Additional Early References," in *Journal of the History of Medicine and Allied Sciences,* **12** (1957), 511–512; George Rosen, "The Reception of William Beaumont's Discovery. Some Comments on Dr. Poynter's Note," *ibid.,* **13** (1958), 404–406; F. N. L. Poynter, "New Light on the Reception of William Beaumont's Discovery in England," *ibid.,* 406–409.

GEORGE ROSEN

BECCARI, NELLO (*b.* Bagno a Ripoli, near Florence, Italy, 11 January 1883; *d.* Florence, 20 March 1957), *anatomy.*

Beccari, son of Odoardo Beccari, a learned naturalist who explored the interior regions of Borneo, and of Nella Goretti-Flamini, studied in Florence. After receiving his M.D. in 1907, he dedicated himself to anatomical research at the Institute of Human Anatomy of Florence, at that time directed by Giulio Chiarugi. In 1911 he obtained a teaching diploma in human anatomy and was a substitute teacher of anatomy until 1915. He served as a major in the Italian army during World War I and was wounded at the front. In 1919 he returned to civilian life, and two years later was appointed director of the Institute of Human Anatomy at Catania University. In 1925 he agreed to transfer to the University of Florence as director of the Institute of Comparative Anatomy, a position he held until his seventieth year, the legal age limit for teaching.

Beccari was a very learned anatomist. Following the belief of his teacher Chiarugi that "comparative anatomy is the key to the comprehension of human anatomy," he developed his research essentially on the plan of comparative anatomy: his last book, *Anatomia comparata dei vertebrati* (only the first two volumes of the five projected were published, in 1951 and 1955), would have been his own definitive statement of his comparative approach. Nevertheless, he also did some work in more traditional descriptive anatomy; for instance, his precise observations on the rhinencephalon in man: on the olfactory gyri (1911), on the anterior perforated substance (1911), and on the hippocampal gyrus (1911).

Beccari was a fine cytologist, as is shown by his little-known observations on the cutaneous glands of sheep (1909), and particularly those on the suborbital glands of *Gazella dorcas* (1910): he revealed new, interesting details on sebaceous secretion and demonstrated a functional synergism between epithelial cells and melanophores. But Beccari best displayed his ability as a cytologist in his great work on the genesis of the germ cells and on the early cytological differentiation of sex cells. From 1920 to 1925 he worked systematically on the *Bufo viridis,* aiming at the discovery of the origin of the germ cells and the morphological description of the initial differentiation of sex cells. Beccari confirmed that in vertebrates the germ cells spring from entodermal elements that appear very early in the embryo's development, but he could not affirm absolutely that in the fertilized egg of vertebrates a genital blastomere exists, already differentiated, in the earlier stages of segmentation. However, the primary germ cells of *Bufo* are, in the beginning, all alike, not differentiated cytologically at all. But these primary germ cells already have a sex and, contrary to the view of Ernst Haeckel, who called them hermaphroditic, are female. From the systematic study of Bidder's organ, Beccari could demonstrate that a constant ovogenesis appears before a doubtful abortive spermiogenesis. In *Bufo* the earlier morphological appearance of cellular sexuality manifests itself as an initial evolution of primary germ cells in a female direction. In addition, the fact that in *Bufo* all the males come from hermaphrodite larvae confirmed that, in *Bufo,* the female is the fundamental sex. Sexual determination results, in *Bufo,* from later embryonic development: the persistence of the primary sex cells to the periphery of the genital crest and the formation, within this, of a cavity—the so-called ovarian pocket—are signs of female development; the migration within the genital crest of primary sex cells and their proliferation, with precocious appearance of interstitial cells, are signs of masculinity.

Beccari's principal work was done, however, in the field of neurology. Undoubtedly one of the most eminent neurologists of his generation, he based his conclusions on a thorough knowledge of comparative neurology. Beccari collected and arranged his own wide neurological work in his *Nevrologia comparata anatomo-funzionale dei vertebrati e dell'uomo* (1943). In his book *Il problema del neurone* (1945) he gives us the measure of his wide critical knowledge. He defended the fundamental principle of the neuron, underlining the fact that the recent discoveries had not invalidated its individuality, even if they modified its character. Beccari also stated (1948) that in vertebrates metamery begins only when the nerves appear; that the arrangement in the spinal cord of neurons for segmental knots is consequent upon the formation of nerves, and not at all the reason for their metameric arrangement.

But Beccari's most important contributions related to the rhombencephalon. From his first note of 1906 on the Mauthner's fibers in the *Salamandrina perspicillata* to his further works (1911, 1913, 1915, 1919),

Beccari persistently analyzed and clarified their functional significance in the structure of the rhombencephalon. In 1921 and 1922 he demonstrated the importance of the tegmental centers of the medulla oblongata and of the pons. Beccari's research also revealed the role of the rhombencephalon in the determination of static extrapyramidal motility.

Beccari was a very able technician, a precise draftsman, and an excellent teacher. He was secretary of the Italian Society of Anatomy from 1929, associate founder of the Italian Society of Experimental Biology, and a member of the National Academy of the Lincei. Because his democratic beliefs were well known, in October 1944, following Florence's liberation from German occupation, he was chosen to preside over the Faculty of Natural and Physical Sciences of the University of Florence—a position he held until his death.

BIBLIOGRAPHY

Beccari's books include *Elementi di tecnica microscopica* (Milan, 1915, 1927, 1940); *La inversione sperimentale del sesso nei vertebrati* (Pavia, 1930); *Nevrologia comparata anatamo-funzionale dei vertebrati e dell'uomo* (Florence, 1943); *Genetica* (Florence, 1945); *Il problema del neurone,* 2 vols. (Florence, 1945–1947); *I problemi biologici del sesso* (Rome, 1950); and *Anatomia comparata dei vertebrati,* 2 vols. (Florence, 1951–1955).

There is no complete list of Beccari's many articles. For his scientific production between 1906 and 1922, see the bibliographical index of anatomical publications of the Institute of Human Anatomy at Florence for the years 1891–1921, in *Archivio italiano di anatomia e di embriologia,* **18** (1922), Supp.

Among Beccari's more important articles are "Sullo sviluppo delle ghiandole sudoripare e sebacee nella pecora," in *Archivio italiano di anatomia e di embriologia,* **8** (1909), 271–295; "Ricerche intorno alle tasche ed ai corpi ghiandolari suborbitali in varie specie di ruminanti: anatomia, struttura e sviluppo," *ibid.,* **9** (1910), 660–690; "La sostanza perforata anteriore e suoi rapporti col rinencefalo nel cervello dell'uomo," *ibid.,* **10** (1911), 261–275; "Le strie olfattorie nel cervello dell'uomo," in *Monitore zoologico italiano,* **22** (1911), 255–270; "La superficie degli emisferi cerebrali dell'uomo nelle regioni prossime al rinencefalo," in *Archivio italiano di anatomia e di embriologia,* **10** (1911), 482–500; "Studi sulla prima origine delle cellule genitali nei vertebrati. I. Storia delle indagini e stato attuale della questione," *ibid.,* **18** (1920), 157–190; "II. Ricerche nella *Salamandrina perspicillata,*" *ibid.,* **18** (1921), Supp. 29; "III. e IV. Ovogenesi larvale, organo del Bidder e differenziamento dei sessi nel *Bufo viridis,*" *ibid.,* **21** (1924) and **22** (1925); and "Il problema del differenziamento del sesso negli anfibi," in *Archivio di fisiologia,* **23** (1925), 385–410. See also "Dimostrazione delle fibre di Mauthner nella *Salamandrina perspicillata,*" in *Lo sperimentale,* **60** (1906), 456–460; "Ricerche sulle cellule e fibre del Mauthner e sulle loro connessioni in pesci ed anfibi," in *Archivio italiano di anatomia e di embriologia,* **6** (1907), 660–700; "Le cellule dorsali o posteriori dei ciclostomi. Ricerche nel *Petromyzon marinus,*" in *Monitore zoologico italiano,* **20** (1909), 308–325; "Sopra alcuni rapporti del fascicolo longitudinale posteriore con i nuclei di origine dei nervi oculomotore e trochleare nei teleostei," *ibid.,* 242–255; "La costituzione, i nuclei terminali e le vie di connessione del nervo acustico nella *Lacerta muralis* Merr.," in *Archivio italiano di anatomia e di embriologia,* **10** (1911), 646–660; "Sulla spettanza delle fibre del Lenhossek al sistema del nervo accessorio. Osservazioni in *Lacerta muralis,*" *ibid.,* **11** (1912), 299–315; "Il IX, X, XI e XII paio di nervi cranici ed i nervi cervicali negli embrioni di *Lacerta muralis,*" *ibid.,* **13** (1915), 1–25; "Duplicità delle cellule e delle fibre del Mauthner in un avanotto di trota," in *Monitore zoologico italiano,* **30** (1919), 88–100; "Peculiari modalità nelle connessioni di alcuni neuroni del sistema nervoso centrale dei pesci. Ulteriori ricerche sulle collaterali delle fibre del Mauthner," in *Archivio italiano di anatomia e di embriologia,* **17** (1919), 239–360; "Lo scheletro, i miotomi e le radici nervose nella regione occipitale degli avanotti di trota," *ibid.,* **19** (1921), 1–45; "Studi comparativi sulla struttura di rombencefalo. I. Nervi spino-occipitali e nervo ipoglosso. II. Centri tegmentali," *ibid.,* 122–210; "Il centro tegmentale o insterstiziale ed altre formazioni poco note nel mesencefalo e nel diencefalo di un rettile," *ibid.,* **20** (1923), 560–573; "La costituzione del nucleo del fascio ottico basale dei rettili, e la sua probabile importanza nella produzione del riflesso pupillare," in *Atti del VI° Congresso della Società Italiana di Neurologia* (Naples, 1923); "Primo differenziamento dei nuclei motori di nervi cranici," in *Monitore zoologico italiano,* **34** (1923), 161–170; "I centri tegmentali dell'asse cerebrale dei selaci," in *Archivio zoologico italiano,* **14** (1930), 411–455; "Studi comparativi sopra i nuclei terminali del nervo acustico nei pesci," *ibid.,* **16** (1931), 732–760; "Intorno all'esistenza di uno strato sinaptico nelle connessioni di alcuni neuroni dei pesci," in *Monitore zoologico italiano,* **45** (1934), 220–235; and "Morfogenesi filetica e morfogenesi embrionale del sistema nervoso dei vertebrati," report to the Ninth Congress of the Società Italiana di Anatomia (Bologna, 24–27 October 1947), *ibid.,* Supp. **56** (1948), 22–32.

PIETRO FRANCESCHINI

BECCARIA, GIAMBATISTA (*b.* Mondovì, Italy, 3 October 1716; *d.* Turin, Italy, 27 May 1781), *electricity.*

Beccaria, who is not to be confused with his younger contemporary, the Milanese publicist Cesare Beccaria, was christened Francesco, and became Giambatista when he joined the Piarists (the Clerks Regular of the Pious Schools), a teaching order established in the seventeenth century. He entered into his novitiate in 1732, studied at Rome and at Narni, and began his own pedagogical career in 1737. During the next decade he taught in Narni, Urbino, Palermo, and Rome; in 1748 he was appointed to the chair of physics at the University of Turin, which he occupied with great distinction for over twenty years.

Beccaria's predecessor at Turin, a Minim priest and a convinced Cartesian, had many followers in the university who did not appreciate the English science the new professor fancied. A battle ensued, for which Beccaria's ability, energy, and testiness admirably suited him. This struggle, which mixed local jealousies and the rivalry between Minims and Piarists with philosophical issues, was of critical importance in shaping Beccaria's career, for out of it grew his concern with electricity. One of those who had recommended Beccaria's appointment, the marchese G. Morozzo, learning of the lightning experiment of Marly, suggested to his protégé that Franklin's ideas on electricity might make an excellent weapon against the Cartesians. Electricity was a promising field for confrontation even without the glamorous new discoveries about lightning, as the Cartesian program of reducing electrical phenomena to the vortical motion of a special matter had never been very successful.

The results of Beccaria's brief, vigorous study of electricity appeared in his first book, *Dell'elettricismo artificiale e naturale* (1753). The volume, which Franklin praised, presents the elements of the new theory clearly and logically; illustrates them with variations of Franklin's experiments, to which Beccaria primarily added observations of the different appearances of discharges from positively and negatively electrified points; modifies secondary aspects of the theory and applies it to new territory; and seeks to explain meteorological and geophysical phenomena as manifestations of "natural" electricity. Apart from its new experiments and ingenious meteorological hypotheses, the book is notable for Beccaria's love of system, which caused him occasionally to oversimplify the phenomena; for his reluctance, characteristic of the Franklinian physicist, to discuss the detailed mechanical causes of electrical motions; for his courageous assertion, against the prevailing view, that air is a better conductor than pure water; and for his skill in designing apparatus, including such measuring devices as the electrical thermometer, whose invention is usually wrongly ascribed to Franklin's colleague, Ebenezer Kinnersley. The book also contains a long letter to the Abbé J. A. Nollet, who had raised objections against Franklin's system. The Parisian *franklinistes* thought the letter successful, translated it into French, and thus temporarily made Beccaria the leading champion of the new system.

In 1758 Beccaria published a second book on electricity, in the form of sixteen letters to G. B. Beccari. F. A. Eandi, Beccaria's biographer, and Priestley thought the *Lettere al Beccari* to be Beccaria's best work, although the modern reader is apt to find it annoyingly prolix. Two-thirds of it is devoted to natural electricity, particularly that of the atmosphere, which Beccaria and his students tirelessly probed with metal poles, kites, and even rockets. Here are many valuable observations of cloud formation, thunderstorms, and the accompanying electrical states of the lower air. The first seven letters, on man-made or artificial electricity, summarize, extend, and modify Franklin's system. The most successful extensions deal with insulators other than glass, from which Beccaria constructed parallel plate condensers whose relative powers he tried to estimate. Less happily, ignoring his earlier strictures, he sought a mechanical explanation of the apparent suspension of electrical attractions in the highly conducting "vacuums" produced by eighteenth-century air pumps. His investigation led him to revive Cabeo's theory, which attributes such attractions to the action of air displaced by electrical matter issuing from charged bodies. This view, although decidedly retrograde, was not necessarily anti-Franklinist, since it did not touch the characteristic Philadelphian doctrines relating to positive and negative electricity and to the perfect insulation of glass. Franklin himself had tacitly ascribed an important task to the air, that of opposing the natural tendency toward dissipation of the "electrical atmospheres" formed about charged bodies. Beccaria concurred in this view, which he tried (not altogether successfully) to combine with the hypothesis of Cabeo.

From the *Lettere*, Beccaria turned to other subjects, particularly astronomical and geophysical ones, in connection with measuring a degree of longitude in Piedmont. His interest was reawakened by the work of a former student, G. F. Cigna, who in 1765 published an account of experiments that developed Nollet's elaborations of Symmer's famous manipulations with electrified silk stockings. Beccaria pursued these experiments with all his skill, inventiveness, and energy, largely because they seemed to favor the anti-Franklinian double-fluid theory. But the more remarkable and delicate of the phenomena he investigated, which depend upon induction in the coatings from residual charges left on the dielectric after the discharge of a condenser, required something more than Franklin's system for their explanation. Beccaria, who would not admit action-at-a-distance, supplied this deficiency with a complicated scheme of electrical atmospheres and "vindicating," or regenerating, electricity. These ideas, which found their clearest expression in Beccaria's *Electricitas vindex* (1769), subsequently led Volta, while seeking alternatives to them, to the invention of the electrophorus.

Beccaria's last major contribution to the science of electricity was *Elettricismo artificiale* (1772), a difficult, verbose compendium of Beccaria's work on the subject, explained with the help of Franklin's principles, vindicating electricities and the doctrine of atmospheres. In 1775 he brought out a short volume on atmospheric electricity in fair weather, *Dell'elettricità a cielo sereno*. Thereafter, he produced a few small pieces on electricity, intermixed with short contributions on other physical and chemical subjects. In 1778 his health began to fail, and, although his painful affliction—hemorrhoids and tumors—sometimes remitted, he was thereafter unable to do much laboratory work.

Beccaria's success derived as much from his aggressive, vigorous character as from his native intelligence. He began the study in which he was to win fame as a new front in a larger battle. His thirst for fame, and his recurrent depressions when he felt unsure of it, were prominent features of his personality and his primary source of energy. He was jealous of his discoveries and quick to claim priority; Franklin was perhaps the only person he did not consider a competitor. The connection with Franklin, with whom he corresponded intermittently, was very precious to him: letters of praise from Franklin, besides the gratification they conferred, resulted in increases in financial support for himself and his work. His personality apparently did not impair his effectiveness as a teacher. Eandi thought him inspirational, an opinion strengthened by the success of his students, Cigna, Lagrange, and G. A. Saluzzo. His chief pedagogical achievement, however, may well have been his indirect, literary influence on the early studies of Volta.

BIBLIOGRAPHY

I. Original Works. Beccaria's main works on electricity are *Dell'elettricismo artificiale e naturale libri due* (Turin, 1753); *Dell'elettricismo lettere . . . al chiarissimo Signor Giacomo Bartolommeo Beccari* (Bologna, 1758); *Experimenta atque observationes quibus electricitas vindex late constituitur atque explicatur* (Turin, 1769); *Elettricismo artificiale* (Turin, 1772), which also appeared in an English version sponsored by Franklin (London, 1776); and *Dell' elettricità terrestre atmosferica a cielo sereno* (Turin, 1775), which is included in the English version of *Elettricismo artificiale*. A bibliography of Beccaria's work, both published and in manuscript, drawn up by Prospero Balbo,

appears in F. A. Eandi, *Memorie istoriche intorno gli studi del padre Giambatista Beccaria* (Turin, 1783), and in *Biblioteca degli eruditi e dei bibliofili,* no. 69 (Florence, 1961). The present location and nature of the extant manuscripts are described in A. Pace, "The Manuscripts of Giambatista Beccaria, Correspondent of Benjamin Franklin," in *Proceedings of the American Philosophical Society,* **97** (1952), 406–416.

II. Secondary Literature. The standard biography of Beccaria is Eandi's *Memorie*. Further information and references are given in A. Pace's excellent notice of Beccaria in *Dizionario biografico degli italiani,* VII (Rome, 1965). For Beccaria's work, see Joseph Priestley, *The History and Present State of Electricity,* 3rd ed. (London, 1775), *passim;* M. Gliozzi, "Giambatista Beccaria nella storia dell'elettricità," in *Archeion,* **17** (1933), 15–47; and C. W. Oseen, *Johan Carl Wilcke experimental-fysiker* (Uppsala, 1939).

John L. Heilbron

BECHER, JOHANN JOACHIM (*b*. Speyer, Germany, 6 May 1635; *d*. London, England, October 1682), *chemistry, economics.*

Becher's father, Joachim, was a Protestant pastor who died when the boy was only eight years old. His mother, Anna Margaretha Gauss, came from a prominent Speyer family; her father also was a Protestant minister. Left with four sons at the death of her husband, she married a man who squandered the family's remaining resources. Young Becher was thus forced at an early age to help support his mother and his brothers, all of whom were younger than he. He was for the most part self-educated; in his later years he recalled only one teacher who had helped him, Debus (*Konrektor* of the Speyer Retscher-Gymnasium from 1644).

At the age of thirteen Becher began his *Wanderjahren*. Residing first in Sweden, he then traveled through Holland, Germany, and Italy. His earliest dated work (1654) deals with alchemy, but his far-flung interests also included medicine, theology, politics, economics, and even the formulation of a universal language. By 1657 Becher had settled at Mainz, where he was converted to Roman Catholicism. His first published book, *Naturkündigung der Metallen,* appeared in 1661, and he was soon well established as an iatrochemist. He received the M.D. from the University of Mainz on 16 November 1661, and married Maria Veronika, the daughter of the influential jurist and imperial councillor Ludwig von Hörnigk, on 13 June 1662. In the same year Becher published his *Parnassus medicinalis illustratis,* and in 1663 he was appointed professor of medicine at Mainz and physician to the elector.

Nevertheless, the next year Becher left for Munich,

where he was named *Hofmedicus und Mathematicus* to Ferdinand Maria, elector of Bavaria; in 1666 he accepted the post of imperial commercial counsellor to Emperor Leopold I in Vienna. Always interested in problems of law, politics, and commerce, in 1668 he published his *Politischer Discurs,* which shows him to have been the leading German mercantilist of the seventeenth century. The years at Munich and Vienna were ones of great activity. In his official position it was Becher's duty to introduce profitable businesses and new industries. With this in mind, he built and organized an imperial arts and crafts center that included a glassworks and facilities for the manufacture of textiles, as well as a chemistry laboratory. Aware also of the importance of technical education for the advancement of the domestic economy of the state, he proposed important educational reforms, such as the institution of schools that gave practical instruction in civil and military engineering and statics. At the same time, eager to increase trade, Becher organized the Eastern Trading Company and proposed colonial settlements in South America. Neither did he neglect his role as alchemical advisor to the emperor. His important *Physica subterranea* appeared in 1669, and was followed by supplements in 1671 and 1675. At this time Becher also wrote his chief philological works and treatises on theology and moral philosophy.

Becher's economic policies included, in 1677, edicts against French imports that proved to be unsuccessful in the southern German cities. This failure resulted in his dismissal, and after a short imprisonment in 1678, he made his way to Holland, where he sold the plans for a machine that would spool silk cocoons to the city of Haarlem. More important, he submitted to the Dutch Assembly a plan for the extraction of gold from sea sand through smelting. This had been proposed as early as 1673, but it had been abandoned then because of the outbreak of the war with France. In 1679 a small-scale test of his process proved successful, but Becher suddenly left for England, without his family, when the process was scheduled to be repeated on a larger scale. In London, in March 1680, he completed the third and final supplement to the *Physica subterranea* in which he described the gold extraction process. He examined mines in Scotland and Cornwall; and his prefaces give evidence that he completed books at Falmouth and the Isle of Wight (the *Laboratorium portabile* and the *Centrum mundi concatenatum seu magnorum duorum productorum nitri & salis textura & anatomia,* both parts of the *Tripus Hermeticus fatidicus,* 1689, 1690). Shortly before his death he was back in London, where on 22 March 1682 he completed his *Chymischer Glücks-*

hafen, which gives 1,500 chemical processes, including detailed recipes for making the philosophers' stone. While in England, Becher unsuccessfully sought membership in the Royal Society. He had for years cited the works of Robert Boyle, and in 1680 he dedicated a short book on clock design to the Society. It was considered to be of little value, however, and he was not elected.

Becher's views on chemistry have much in common with standard seventeenth-century Paracelsian and Helmontian treatments of the subject. His major work, the *Physica subterranea,* begins in a fashion reminiscent of most theoretical iatrochemical texts. After stating the need for observations and experiments as a guide to a true understanding of the universe, Becher turned to the Mosaic account of the Creation. Here he argued that the universe gravitated from the initial Chaos into five regions (ranging from the sidereal to the mineral). Then motion was added through the rarefaction that followed the creation of light (heat).

As with all theoretical iatrochemists, the problem of the elements was a basic one for Becher. He had little respect for the four Aristotelian elements as they were commonly taught, and he felt that the efforts of Helmont and Boyle to show the elemental nature of water through the growth of vegetable substances were little better. Becher rejected their affirmation that water could be changed into earth in this fashion, and he explained that the willow tree experiment could best be understood in terms of earth being carried by the water into the substance of the tree. Similarly, he argued that observations show that the philosophical attributes of the Paracelsian triad have little in common with ordinary salt, sulfur, and mercury, so they could not really be "principles." He felt that on practical grounds—because of their familiarity—their use might be defended. Nevertheless, in the *Oedipus chimicus* (1664) Becher suggested that sulfur was analogous to earth, and salt to water, while earth and water, in more subtle form, were mercurial in nature.

Becher believed that air, water, and earth were the true elementary principles. The last two, however, form the real basis of all material things, since air is primarily an instrument for mixing. The essential substance of subterranean bodies (metals and stones) is earthy, and there is a need for three types of earth in metals and minerals. One type is needed for substance, another for color and combustibility, and a third, more subtle, for form, odor, and weight. These are, respectively, the *terra vitrescible,* the *terra pinguis,* and the *terra fluida,* earths that have been improperly identified with the Paracelsian principles: salt, sulfur, and mercury.

The concept of *terra pinguis* as a fatty, oily, and

combustible earth occurs in the older alchemical literature and Becher also calls it sulfur φλογιστὸs. Here again, he was following an old tradition, since as an adjective meaning "inflammable" φλογιστὸs may be found in the works of Sophocles and Aristotle. More recently φλογιστὸν had been used in adjectival form by Hapelius (1609), Poppius (1618), and Helmont. In *The Sceptical Chymist* (1661), a work often referred to by Becher, Boyle cited Sennert's use of φλογιστὸν in 1619.

Although Becher insisted that each combustible body must contain the cause of its combustibility within itself, he had no clearly defined position on the role to be played by this substance in the burning process. Generally he spoke of the rarefaction of the burning substance through the dissolving power of flame, and he gave relatively little attention to any part that air might play in combustion. He was aware that metals grew heavier when calcined, and, like Boyle, he credited this to the addition of ponderable fire particles.

Becher wrote in support of spontaneous generation, and he believed firmly in metallic transmutation. He wrote at length on fermentation, which, in typical alchemical fashion, he considered to be a basic natural process of great value for the chemist. For Becher, fermentation was a rarefaction leading to perfection, and it could not continue in closed vessels without a fresh supply of air. As such, fermentation may be clearly distinguished from putrefaction, in which a mixed body is completely broken down and destroyed.

Becher was a thoroughgoing vitalist who accepted the common belief that metals grow in the earth. Similarly, he compared the flow of subterranean waters in the living earth to the flow of blood in man. He believed in a perpetual circularity in nature, and he felt that earthly reactions may properly be compared to the laboratory manipulations of the chemists. He rejected the widely held hypothesis of an internal fire in the earth and sought another explanation of the origin of mountain streams and hot springs. Arguing that it is known that surface waters fall by gravity toward the center of the earth, he noted that laboratory experience gives us the further information that vapors arise when liquids are transferred from hot containers to cold ones. Becher reasoned, therefore, that hot waters from the surface are rapidly cooled at the center of the earth, where they vaporize and return to the surface. There mountains act as alembics, and condense the waters as mountain springs; in other places, separate vapors from the interior reach higher temperatures through mixing before they erupt as hot springs or medicinal spas.

Becher's importance for the history of science rests less in major innovations than in his influence on Georg Ernst Stahl. Stahl republished the *Physica subterranea* in 1703, along with his own lengthy *Specimen Beccherianum*. In this work and in others he lauded his predecessor while developing the concept of the *terra pinguis* into the phlogiston theory with the aid of experimental evidence, which was largely lacking in the writings of Becher.

BIBLIOGRAPHY

I. Original Works. Becher's complex bibliography is discussed in considerable detail by Herbert Hassinger, in his *Johann Joachim Becher 1635–1682. Ein Beitrag zur Geschichte des Merkantilismus,* Veröffentlichungen der Kommission für Neuere Geschichte Österreichs, no. 38 (Vienna, 1951), pp. 254–272. J. R. Partington gives bibliographic details of Becher's more important chemical works in his *A History of Chemistry,* II (London, 1961), 640–643.

The *Physica subterranea* appeared first as *Actorum laboratorii chymici Monacensis, seu Physicae subterraneae libri duo* (Frankfurt, 1669)—Partington states that an earlier ed. appeared in 1667. There is only one volume. The three supplements were published separately in 1671, 1675, and 1680, and are included in the 2nd ed. (Frankfurt, 1681). Becher's own German translation exists as *Chymisches laboratorium Oder Unter-erdische Naturkündigung . . .* (Frankfurt, 1680), which includes the first two supplements and the *Oedipus chimicus.* Stahl's Latin edition was published with his *Specimen Beccherianum* (Leipzig, 1703), and a final composite edition (containing original text, supps., and Stahl's *Specimen*) was printed at Leipzig in 1738. It should be noted that Becher's *Theoria & experientia de nova temporis dimetiendi ratione, & accurata horologiorum constructione, ad Societatem Regiam Anglicanum in Collegio Greshamensi* (London, 1680) forms part of the third supplement to the *Physica subterranea.*

Institutiones chimicae prodromae i.e. . . . . Oedipus chimicus obscuriorum terminorum & principiorum mysteria aperiens et resolvens (Frankfurt, 1664) rapidly became a standard text on elements, principles, and chemical processes. Besides going through numerous separate Latin editions, it was included in J. J. Manget's *Bibliotheca chemica curiosa,* I (Geneva, 1702), 306–336. It appeared in German with Becher's translation of the *Physica subterranea,* and also as part of Friedrich Roth-Scholtz's *Deutsches theatrum chemicum,* II (Nuremberg, 1728), 620 ff.

Among Becher's many other works on chemistry are *Naturkündigung der Metallen,* or *Metallurgia Becheri* (Frankfurt, 1661), which discusses metallurgical problems on the basis of the four elements; *Tripus Hermeticus fatidicus, pandens oracula chymica* (Frankfurt, 1689), which was completed at Truro, Cornwall, in 1682 and includes an account of Becher's visit to the Cornish mines in 1680; *Psychosophia oder Seelen-Weisheit* (Güstrow, 1673), which gives details of Becher's life; *Parnassus medicinalis illustratis,* 4 pts. (Ulm, 1662–1663), which contains reworked cuts from the earlier herbal by Mathiolus; *Chymischer Glücks-hafen* (Frankfurt, 1682), which contains 1,500 chemical and alchemical processes; and *Magnalia naturäe, or the Philosophers-Stone Lately Expos'd to Publick Sight and Sale . . . Published at the Request . . . Especially of Mr. Boyl, &c.* (London, 1680), which describes a transmutation at Vienna by Wenzel Seiler.

Notable among Becher's other works are *Character pro notitia linguarum universali. Inventum steganographicum* (Frankfurt, 1661); *Politischer Discurs von den eigentlichen Ursachen, des Auf- und Abnehmens der Städt, Länder und Republicken* (Frankfurt, 1668); and *Moral Discurs von den eigentlichen Ursachen des Glücks und Unglücks* (Frankfurt, 1669).

The Rostock University Library has three volumes of Becher's papers. These are briefly described in Hassinger, p. 271.

II. SECONDARY LITERATURE. Recent research on Becher has emphasized his economic and administrative policies; see F. A. Steinhüser, *Johann Joachim Becher und die Einzelwirtschaft* (Nuremberg, 1931). Although Hassinger does not ignore Becher's scientific and medical contributions, there is no question that he considers these to be distinctly less important than his administrative accomplishments. He discusses the secondary literature on this topic in his introduction, pp. 1–9.

Becher's scientific work has received far less attention. Interest in the phlogiston theory has for the most part centered on the mid-eighteenth century rather than on its origins—see especially the four papers by J. R. Partington and Douglas McKie entitled "Historical Studies on the Phlogiston Theory," which appeared in *Annals of Science,* **2** (1937), 361–404; **3** (1938), 1–58, 337–371; **4** (1939), 113–149—and although Partington's chapter on Becher—*A History of Chemistry,* II (London, 1961), 637–652—is based on extensive reading in the sources, it is somewhat less than satisfactory because it does not clearly show the close connection of Becher's views with their alchemical–Paracelsian background. Other accounts, generally with far less detail, are in most histories of chemistry and alchemy. The best of these are those of Hermann Kopp, who points out Becher's often inconsistent views on the elements: *Beiträge zur Geschichte der Chemie,* 3 vols. (Brunswick, 1869–1875), III, 201–210; *Geschichte der Chemie,* 4 vols. (Brunswick, 1843–1847; repr. 1966), I, 178–180; II, 277–278; and *Die Alchemie in älterer und neurer Zeit. Ein Beitrag zur Culturgeschichte,* 2 vols. (Heidelberg, 1886), I, 65–68.

ALLEN G. DEBUS

BECKE, FRIEDRICH JOHANN KARL (*b.* Prague, Czechoslovakia, 31 December 1855; *d.* Vienna, Austria, 18 June 1931), *mineralogy, petrography.*

Becke's father, Friedrich, originally a bookseller in Prague, became a railway employee at Pilsen in 1866 and later at Vienna. After attending several schools, Becke enrolled in 1874 at the University of Vienna, where he studied under the geologist Gustav Tscher-

mak, who also published the journal *Mineralogische und petrographische Mitteilungen.* Becke soon devoted himself to mineralogy, and in 1878 he became Tschermak's assistant. He had already gained notice in 1877 with his studies on Greek rock formations and his inaugural dissertation, *Krystalline Schiefer des niederösterreichischen Waldviertels* (1882), the first modern petrographical study of the metamorphic rocks of Austria. In 1882, at the age of twenty-seven, Becke was appointed associate professor (and later full professor) of mineralogy at the university of the Polish town of Czernowitz (now Chernovtsy, Ukrainian S.S.R.). While there, he discovered the differential solubility of dextrose crystals (1889).

In 1890 Becke was called to the University of Prague. Three years later he developed the method for the relative determination of the refraction of light by means of what since 1896 has been known as the Becke line. The procedure for measuring the angle of optical axes, which had been developed by François E. Mallard, was extended by Becke in 1895 for application to microscopic preparations. The following year he presented the Becke volume rule, which states that—assuming isothermal conditions—with increased pressure, the formation of minerals with the smallest molecular volume (the greatest density) will be favored.

In 1898 Becke went to the University of Vienna, where he attempted to classify the solidified rocks (plutonic rocks and lava). In 1903 he put forth the differentiation—based on their chemical composition and still used today—between the Atlantic group (of alkalic origin, mainly sodium and potassium) and the Pacific group (of calc-alkalic origin, characterized by high calcium and aluminum content). The mineral composition and the chemistry of both groups were correlated by Becke with E. Suess's geotectonic concepts of an Atlantic Coast type (stratum) and a Pacific Coast type (mountain chain).

Becke's work on crystalline schists was especially extensive. For the elucidation of the crystallization stratification he used Riecke's rule, according to which mineral grains are relatively soluble in the direction of the applied pressure, whereas crystallization will proceed more rapidly perpendicular to the direction of applied pressure; thus the parallel planar texture of many rocks ("foliation") develops independent of their original layering, and is characteristic for many metamorphic rocks. Becke's explanation for the process in general considers only pressure as the cause, i.e., the process is static. According to more recent research, this is controversial.

For transformations in the solid state Becke introduced the terms *crystalloblastic, granoblastic, por-*

phyroblastic, blastophytic, blastogranitic, and *blastoporphyric.* With the aid of the graphic representation of rock components that he developed, it was possible, by utilizing the Si-U-L (Si$=$Si$+$Ti, U$=$Al$+$Fe$+$Mg, L$=$Ca$+$Na$+$K) triangle, to differentiate between orthorocks (solidified rocks transformed by metamorphosis) and pararocks (transformed sedimentary rocks). In 1909 Becke originated the term *diaphthoresis* for the adjustment of highly metamorphosed rocks to the conditions prevailing at lesser depths; the process is also known as regressive metamorphism. In later works he also dealt with the classification of the facies of metamorphic rocks, the mass movement during metamorphosis, and the graphic representation of rock analyses. His last publications dealt with the crystal systems and the nomenclature of the thirty-two symmetry point groups.

From 1899 on, Becke was the editor of Tschermak's *Mineralogische und petrographische Mitteilungen,* Volume 38 of which was dedicated to him in honor of his seventieth birthday. He was director of the Mineralogical Institute of the University of Vienna from 1906 until 1927, and in 1911 he was appointed secretary-general of the Viennese Academy of Sciences. Immediately after World War I, Becke was rector of the University of Vienna, and in 1929 he received the Wollaston Medal of the Geological Society of London.

Becke did fundamental work in the elucidation of metamorphism, combining exact observations with bold and sophisticated theoretical considerations. Many students came to his institute to learn the methods of the "Vienna School." His most important findings, especially those on metamorphic rocks, are still included in textbooks of mineralogy and geology.

BIBLIOGRAPHY

I. Original Works. Becke published many articles. Among the most important are "Beziehungen zwischen Dynamometamorphose und Molekularvolumen," in *Neues Jahrbuch für Mineralogie,* II (1896), 182–183; "Fortschritte auf dem Gebiete der Metamorphose," in *Fortschritte der Mineralogie,* no. 2 (1911), 221–256, and no. 5 (1916), 210–264; *Das Wachstum und der Bau der Kristalle,* his inaugural lecture as rector of the University of Vienna (1918); "Struktur and Klüftung," in *Fortschritte der Mineralogie,* no. 9 (1924), 185–220; and "Vorschläge zur Systematik und Nomenklatur der 32 Symmetrie-klassen," *ibid.,* nos. 11 (1927), 289–292, and 12 (1927), 97–103. He also published many works in *Mineralogische und petrographische Mitteilungen* between 1883 and 1928.

II. Secondary Literature. Of most value are A. Himmelbauer's obituary of Becke in *Mineralogische und petrographische Mitteilungen,* **42** (1932), i-viii; and the obituary in *Verhandlungen der Geologischen Bundesanstalt Wien* (1931), 239-241. A short but comprehensive article is by Walther Fischer, in *Neue deutsche Biographie,* I (1953), 708–709.

Hans Baumgärtel

BECKER, GEORGE FERDINAND (*b.* New York, N.Y., 5 January 1847; *d.* Washington, D.C., 20 April 1919), *geology.*

The son of Alexander Christian and Sarah Tuckerman Becker, George Becker grew up in a home where serious intellectual endeavor was rewarded. His mother encouraged his early inclination toward science, introducing him to her friends in the Boston and Cambridge academic communities: Asa Gray, Louis Agassiz, Benjamin Peirce, Jeffries Wyman, and Benjamin Gould. It was only natural that he studied at Harvard. He earned advanced degrees in chemistry and mathematics at the University of Heidelberg and the Royal Academy of Mines, Berlin.

His formal education completed, Becker worked in the German Royal Iron Works for a year before returning to the United States. From 1874 to 1879 he was employed at the University of California at Berkeley as an instructor of mining and metallurgy; there he met Clarence King, first director of the U.S. Geological Survey. Becker joined the Survey and contributed detailed studies of mining districts—the monograph *Geology of the Comstock Lode and Washoe District* (1882) and the article "Reconnaissance of San Francisco, Eureka and Bodie Districts" (1880)—as well as broader accounts of the Pacific Coast ranges and the Sierra Nevada.

Becker's great concern for mathematical, geophysical, and geochemical approaches to mining geology are evident in his field research. Several of his more general theoretical papers are devoted to geophysical problems, including the structure of the globe: "An Elementary Proof of the Earth's Rigidity" (1890), "The Finite Elastic Stress-Strain Function" (1893), and "Finite Homogeneous Strain, Flow and Rupture of Rocks" (1893). Becker maintained that subsidence phenomena followed from the theory that the earth is solid throughout.

Becker's interest in geophysics was manifested in deed as well as in published word. He was instrumental in establishing the Carnegie Geophysical Laboratory and was its first director. He also left a sizable portion of his estate to the Smithsonian Institution to promote the advancement of geophysics.

BIBLIOGRAPHY

Becker's writings include "Reconnaissance of San Francisco, Eureka and Bodie Districts Nevada," in U.S. Geological Survey, *First Annual Report* (Washington, D.C., 1880), pp. 34–37; "A Summary of the Geology of the Comstock Lode and Washoe District," in U.S. Geological Survey, *Second Annual Report* (1880–1881); *Geology of the Comstock Lode and Washoe District. Monographs of the U.S. Geological Survey,* III (Washington, 1882), 1–422; "The Relation of Mineral Belts of the Pacific Slope to the Great Upheavals," in *American Journal of Science,* 3rd ser., **28** (1884), 209–212; "An Elementary Proof of the Earth's Rigidity," *ibid.,* **39** (1890), 336–352; "The Finite Elastic Stress-Strain Function," *ibid.,* **46** (1893), 337–356; "Finite Homogeneous Strain, Flow and Rupture of Rocks," in *Bulletin of the Geological Society of America,* **4** (1893), 13–90; and "The Witwatersrand and the Revolt of the Uitlanders," in *National Geographic Magazine,* **7** (1896), 349–367. A five-page bibliography, compiled by Isabel P. Evans, may be found in *Memoirs of the National Academy of Sciences,* **21** (1926), 15–19.

An article on Becker is George P. Merrill, "Biographical Memoir of George Ferdinand Becker," in *Memoirs of the National Academy of Sciences,* **21** (1926), 1–13.

MARTHA B. KENDALL

BECKMANN, ERNEST OTTO (*b.* Solingen, Germany, 4 July 1853; *d.* Berlin, Germany, 12 July 1923), *chemistry.*

Beckmann's ancestors were originally from Hannover and settled as farmers near Solingen. His father, Johannes Friedrich Wilhelm, established a small dye and emery works in Solingen and in 1814 independently discovered Paris green. His mother, Julie, was the daughter of a tanner. After five years of laboratory activity, including a year with Remigius Fresenius in Wiesbaden, Beckmann entered the University of Leipzig in 1875 and completed his degree in 1878 under Hermann Kolbe and Ernest S. C. Meyer. He then became an assistant to the toxicologist Robert Otto at the Technische Hochschule in Brunswick. In 1883 he returned to Leipzig, where he studied briefly with Kolbe and Johannes Wislicenus, and, after 1887, with Wilhelm Ostwald. In 1891 he became an extraordinary professor at Giessen, and from 1892 to 1897 was ordinary professor at Erlangen. In 1897, as ordinary professor, he organized the applied chemistry laboratory at Leipzig. After refusing offers from Munich and Berlin, in 1912 he became director of the newly founded Kaiser Wilhelm Institute of Applied and Pharmaceutical Chemistry. Here, except for the war years, when the institute was concerned with military work, he continued his research.

By gentle oxidation methods Beckmann was able to produce menthone and thymol and from early investigations on the oximes of menthone he was led to consider the nature of isonitroso compounds. In 1886 during this study he obtained a rapid reaction now known as the Beckmann transformation, in which ketoximes are converted into amides by the action of acids, acid chlorides, or phosphorous pentachloride. It was believed that this reaction could establish the *syn*-isomeric form of the original ketoxime until Meisenheimer showed in 1921 that it was not the *syn* but the *anti* form which underwent intermolecular arrangement. The exact mechanism of this reaction has had considerable theoretical interest for chemists and drew attention to isomerism in nitrogen bonding. Beckmann's work on isomerism of benzoldoxime contributed to an understanding of the valence properties of nitrogen. Interest in the physical properties of oximes led Beckmann to develop a thermometer in which it is possible to vary the amount of mercury in the bulb and thereby change the range of the thermometer. The Beckmann thermometer is a practical device for determining molecular weight based on the theoretical work of Raoult on the freezing point depression and boiling point elevation of solutions. Beckmann also identified SCl_4, and investigated the properties of furfurol.

BIBLIOGRAPHY

I. ORIGINAL WORKS. Beckmann's writings include "Zur Kenntniss der Isonitrosoverbindungen," in *Berichte der Deutschen chemischen Gesellschaft,* **19** (1886), 988–993; **20** (1887), 1507–1510, 2580–2585, 2766–2768; **21** (1888), 766–769; "Ueber die Methode der Molekulargewichtsbestimmung durch Gefrierpunktserniedrigung," in *Zeitschrift für physikalische Chemie,* **2** (1888), 638–645, 715–743; "Ueber die Bestimmung von Molekulargewichten aus Siedepunktserhöhungen," *ibid.,* **3** (1889), 603–604; "Zur Isomerie der Oximidoverbindungen. Isomere monosubstitutirte Hydroxylamine," in *Berichte der Deutschen chemischen Gesellschaft,* **22** (1889), 429–440, 514–517; "Untersuchungen in der Campherreihe. Erste Abhandlung," in *Annalen der Chemie,* no. 250 (1889), 322–375; *Das Laboratorium für angewandte Chemie der Universität Leipzig* (Leipzig, 1908); and "Ueber die Verbindung des Schwefels mit Chlor," in *Zeitschrift für physikalische Chemie,* **55** (1923), 81–82; **61** (1928), 87–130, written with T. Klopfer and F. Junker.

II. SECONDARY LITERATURE. Works on Beckmann are G. Lockemann, "Ernst Beckmann, zum siebzigsten Geburtstage am 4. Juli 1923," in *Zeitschrift für angewandte Chemie,* **26** (1923), 341–344, and *Ernst Beckmann, sein Leben und Werken* (Berlin, 1927); O. Ostwald, "Ernst Beckmann's Anfange als Physico-Chemiker," in *Zeitschrift* *für angewandte Chemie,* **26** (1923), 344; C. Paal, "Nachruf auf Ernest Otto Beckmann," in *Bericht über die Verhandlungen der Sächsischen Akademie der Wissenschaften zu Leipzig,* **76** (1924), 83–94; W. Schenk, "Gedachtnisrede," in *Sitzungsberichte der Deutschen Akademie der Wissenschaften zu Berlin,* Kl. Phil.-hist., **104** (1924); and Alfred Stock, "Forschungsinstitut," in *Zeitschrift für angewandte Chemie,* **26** (1923), 344–345.

RUTH ANNE GIENAPP

BECKMANN, JOHANN (*b.* Hoya, Germany, 4 June 1739; *d.* Göttingen, Germany, 3 February 1811), *economy, technology.*

Beckmann was the oldest son of the director of taxation and custodian of postal services, Nicolaus Beckmann, who died in 1745. His mother, the daughter of a Protestant parson, devoted herself to the education of the children. In 1754, at the age of fifteen, Beckmann enrolled in the Gymnasium at Stade, and in 1759 he entered the University of Göttingen, where he studied theology. He soon turned, however, to mathematics, the natural sciences, public finance and administration, and philology. He fancied languages just as much as scientific subjects.

In 1762, after completing his studies, Beckmann traveled to Brunswick and Holland, where he visited factories, mines, and natural history museums. In 1763 he accepted a teaching position at St. Peter's Gymnasium, a Lutheran school in St. Petersburg, which had been founded by Anton Friedrich Büsching. He taught there for two years. Aside from his teaching, Beckmann occupied himself with projects in the natural sciences, such as meteorological observations, and with the history of the natural sciences. In St. Petersburg he became friendly with August Ludwig Schloezer, who was later active in Göttingen as a historian and a political scientist; this friendship greatly influenced Beckmann's later historical researches. After his sojourn in St. Petersburg, he took an educational trip, which lasted most of the year 1765–1766, through Sweden and Denmark. Again he inspected factories, mines, and foundries, as well as collections of art and of natural objects. His love for natural history led him to Linnaeus, with whom he studied. In the fall of 1766 Beckmann was appointed extraordinary professor of philosophy in Göttingen. At this time he published his first larger work, *De historia naturali veterum libellus I,* which admirably combines aspects of natural science with philology.

In 1767 Beckmann married the daughter of a parson. Since his labors turned more and more to applied botany, agriculture, and public economy, an ordinary professorship of economic sciences was estab-

lished in 1770 for him, and he occupied this post until his death. He lectured on mineralogy, agriculture, technology, materials science, commerce, and general public administration. Aside from his teaching duties, he devoted himself to writing.

Beckmann's scientific importance lies especially in the agricultural sciences, technology, and the history of technology and invention. He can be called the most important representative of German agricultural economy in the second half of the eighteenth century. He founded the independent science of agriculture with his textbook *Grundsätze der teutschen Landwirthschaft* (1769), and he stressed that practical agriculture needed a scientific foundation: natural history, mineralogy, chemistry, physics, and mathematics were recognized as necessary auxiliary sciences of agriculture. Beckmann's agricultural science followed the empirical treatment of agriculture practiced by the so-called *Hausväter* and the older economists. In his general economic treatment of agriculture, however, their special treatments of vegetable raising and of animal husbandry received short shrift. Yet his textbook remained prominent in the field for nearly half a century, until superseded by the work of Albrecht Thaer.

Since agriculture concerns the production of natural products and mining technology leads one into the production of metals, Beckmann became interested in the processing of raw materials by the individual trades. By 1769 he was calling this science of trades "technology," and in 1777 his *Anleitung zur Technologie* appeared, the first advanced textbook in this field. It is noteworthy for its systematic approach to the various vocations and for its descriptions of a number of trades. The book was addressed primarily to governmental economic officials, in order to make them cognizant of the problems of trade and manufacture within the framework of public affairs. Beckmann was not without precursors in his attempts to spread technological knowledge, but he was the only one to succeed in introducing technology as a separate subject into the high school curriculum. He enlivened his lectures by using models and by demonstrations, as well as by conducting inspections of manufacturing establishments. His attempt in 1806 (*Entwurf der algemeinen Technologie*) to compare the processes that are utilized in the various areas of technology and that are based on the same objectives also deserves special attention. Thus, for example, the various methods of crushing or grinding were examined with a view toward profiting from the transfer of an especially efficient procedure from one field to another.

Beckmann should also be credited with being the

first reliable historian of inventions, with his *Beyträge zur Geschichte der Erfindungen* (1782 *et seq.*), which is not a complete history of technology but, rather, an admirable collection of historical descriptions of individual inventions. For sources he used primarily literary material, and his excellent philological and good technological knowledge served him well.

BIBLIOGRAPHY

I. ORIGINAL WORKS. The Staatsbibliothek of the Stiftung Preussischer Kulturbesitz in Berlin has forty-two letters written by Beckmann, among them thirty-eight to F. Nicolai; the Library of the Deutsches Museum in Munich has nine letters. Six letters written by Beckmann to Linnaeus between 1765 and 1770 are in *Carl von Linné, Bref och skrifvelser,* II, pt. 1 (Uppsala, 1916), 254–268. Handwritten material used by W. Exner for his biography of Beckmann cannot be traced.

The most important published works by Beckmann are *De historia naturali veterum libellus I* (St. Petersburg–Göttingen, 1766); *Anfangsgründe der Naturhistorie* (Göttingen, 1767); *Grundsätze der teutschen Landwirthschaft* (Göttingen, 1769; 6th ed., 1806); *Physikalisch-ökonomische Bibliothek,* 23 vols. (Göttingen, 1770–1806); *Anleitung zur Technologie* (Göttingen, 1777; 7th ed., 1823); *Grundriss zu Vorlesungen über die Naturlehre* (Göttingen, 1779, 1785); *Beyträge zur Oekonomie, Technologie, Polizey und Cameralwissenschaft,* 12 pts. (Göttingen, 1779–1791), of which Beckmann is primarily the editor; *Beyträge zur Geschichte der Erfindungen,* 5 vols. (Leipzig, 1782–1805; 2nd ed. of Vol. I, 1786; English trans., London, 1797; 4th ed., 1846); *Sammlung auserlesener Landesgesetze, welche das Policey- und Cameralwesen zum Gegenstande haben,* 10 pts. (Frankfurt, 1783–1793); *Vorbereitung zur Waarenkunde,* 2 pts. (Göttingen, 1794–1800); *Vorrath kleiner Anmerkungen über mancherley gelehrte Gegenstände,* 3 pts. (Göttingen, 1795–1806), of which the third part is *Entwurf der algemeinen Technologie* (also pub. separately); *Lexicon botanicum* (Göttingen, 1801); *Litteratur der älteren Reisebeschreibungen,* 2 vols. (Göttingen, 1808–1810); and *Schwedische Reise in den Jahren 1765–1766* (Uppsala, 1911), a diary.

II. SECONDARY LITERATURE. Works on Beckmann are W. Exner, *Johann Beckmann, Begründer der technologischen Wissenschaft* (Vienna, 1878); G. Grundke, "Johann Beckmann als Begründer der Technologie in Deutschland," in *Wissenschaftliche Zeitschrift der Karl-Marx-Universität, Leipzig,* Mathematical-Natural Sciences Section, no. 3/4 (1954/1955), 343–352; H. J. Herpel, *Entwicklung des landwirtschaftlichen Studiums an der Universität Göttingen* (Göttingen, 1932); C. G. Heyne, "Memoria Jo. Beckmann," in *Commentationes Societatis Regiae Scientiarum Gottingensis recentiores,* 1 (1808–1811), appendix, 1–15; *Ideengeschichte der Agrarwirtschaft und Agrarpolitik im deutschen Sprachgebiet* (Munich, 1957);

Carl, Count of Klinckowstroem, "Johann Beckmann," in *Neue deutsche Biographie,* I (Berlin, 1953), 725–726; G. Schmid, "Linné im Urteil Johann Beckmanns," in *Svenska Linné-sällskapets årsskrift,* **20** (1937), 47–70; and U. Troitzsch, *Ansätze technologischen Denkens bei den Kameralisten des 17. and 18. Jahrhunderts* (Berlin, 1966), pp. 150–165.

FRIEDRICH KLEMM

BECQUEREL, ALEXANDRE-EDMOND (*b.* Paris, France, 24 March 1820; *d.* Paris, 11 May 1891), *experimental physics.*

Becquerel was the second son of Antoine-César Becquerel, experimental physicist and professor at the Muséum d'Histoire Naturelle. At the age of eighteen, Edmond was admitted to both the École Polytechnique and the École Normale Supérieure. He decided, however, to refuse both these opportunities in order to assist his father at the museum. After having served as assistant at the University of Paris and then as professor of physics at the short-lived Institut Agronomique de Versailles, Becquerel was appointed, in December 1852, to the chair of physics at the Conservatoire des Arts et Métiers. From 1860 to 1863, he taught chemistry at the Société Chimique de Paris; and after having served a term as *aide-naturaliste* at the museum, he succeeded his father as director of that institution in 1878. Becquerel received a Doctor of Science degree from the University of Paris in 1840 and was elected to the Académie des Sciences in 1863.

Becquerel's most important achievements in science were in electricity, magnetism, and optics. In electricity he measured the properties of currents and investigated the conditions under which they arose. In 1843 he showed that Joule's law governing the production of heat in the passage of an electrical current applied to liquids as well as to solids. In 1844 he rectified Faraday's law of electrochemical decomposition to include several phenomena that had not been taken into account, and in 1855 he discovered that the mere displacement of a metallic conductor in a liquid was sufficient to produce a current of electricity. Becquerel's measurement of the electromotive force of the voltaic pile was achieved through the use of his father's ingeniously devised electrostatic balance, an instrument that, in effect, allowed him to weigh the relative force of an electric current. He also studied the separate effects of the liquid, the metal, the temperature, and the polarization of the electrodes on the functioning of voltaic piles.

From 1845 to 1855, Becquerel devoted most of his attention to the investigation of diamagnetism. Anxious to preserve the simplicity of Ampère's electrical theory of magnetic action, he was unwilling to accept Faraday's contention that diamagnetic phenomena were fundamentally different from those of ordinary magnetism. To explain the repulsion of certain substances by the poles of a magnet, he conceived an "Archimedean law" of magnetic action, so called because of its resemblance to Archimedes' hydrostatic principle: "A body placed away from a magnetic center is attracted toward that center with a force equal to the difference which exists between the specific magnetism of the body and that of the milieu in which it is immersed" (*Traité d'électricité* . . . , III, 52). Just as specifically heavier bodies sink and lighter bodies rise in a liquid, so substances less magnetic than their surroundings are pushed away from a magnet, whereas the more magnetic ones are attracted to it.

Becquerel set out to measure the magnetic properties of oxygen, one of the substances composing the milieu in which magnetic action most often took place. He condensed a large volume of the gas in a glass tube filled with highly absorbent charcoal. When placed in a magnetic field, the tube containing oxygen was found to be much more magnetic than one containing only charcoal. This discovery might have provided conclusive proof of the validity of Becquerel's theory had it not been for the highly embarrassing fact that diamagnetic action took place in the vacuum as well as in the air. Becquerel attempted in vain to overcome this objection by assigning magnetic (and thus electrical) properties to the ether.

Becquerel's early investigations of light phenomena were closely related to his interest in electricity. In 1840 he demonstrated that electrical currents arose from certain light-induced chemical reactions. On the basis of this discovery, he constructed an instrument, called an "actinometer," that measured the intensity of light by measuring the intensity of the electrical currents produced in photochemical reactions. Later, he showed that by relating light intensity to heat intensity one could use this device to determine optically the temperatures of extremely hot bodies.

In spectroscopy Becquerel revealed in 1843 the presence of Fraunhofer lines in photographs of the ultraviolet portion of the spectrum. Earlier he had shown that rays at the red end of the spectrum reinforced or "continued" the chemical action initiated by rays at the violet end.

Becquerel did his most important work in optics on the phenomena of luminescence. In the middle years of the nineteenth century, he virtually monopolized the significant discoveries made in this field. His researches began in 1839, when he published a paper dealing primarily with the effects of temperature on the duration of phosphorescent light emission. In 1843 he demonstrated that phosphorescence was stimulated in different substances by specific frequencies of light and that at some frequencies the phosphorescent glow seemed to stop immediately after the cutting off of incident light rays. Between 1857 and 1859, Becquerel produced three pioneering studies on luminescent phenomena; these were collected and published in 1859 under the title *Recherches sur les divers effets lumineux qui resultent de l'action de la lumière sur les corps*. It was in these studies that Becquerel first described the phosphoroscope, an instrument of his own invention consisting of a box sealed with two disks mounted on the same axis and pierced with holes arranged in such a way that light could not at any one time pass through the entire apparatus. By rapidly revolving these perforated disks, an observer could continuously view substances in the dark only fractions of a second after they had been exposed to brilliant light; and by regulating the speed of revolution of the disks, one could measure the length of time that substances continued to glow after exposure to light. Using this device, Becquerel was able to identify many new phosphorescent substances and to show that the phenomenon G. G. Stokes had named fluorescence in 1852 was in reality only phosphorescence of an extremely short duration. By attaching a prism to his phosphoroscope, Becquerel was able to examine the spectra of light emitted from luminescent bodies. In this manner substances could be analyzed without physical or chemical alteration.

BIBLIOGRAPHY

I. ORIGINAL WORKS. Becquerel's *Traité d'électricité et de magnétisme, leurs applications aux sciences physiques, aux arts et à l'industrie*, 3 vols. (Paris, 1855–1856), was written in collaboration with his father. Besides the *Recherches sur les divers effets lumineux* . . . (Paris, 1859), Becquerel wrote *La lumière, ses causes et ses effets*, 2 vols. (Paris, 1867–1868). The first volume of this work is devoted to the study of luminescent phenomena.

II. SECONDARY LITERATURE. Works on Becquerel are Henri Becquerel, "La chaire de physique du Muséum," in *Revue scientifique*, **49**, No. 22 (28 May 1892), 673–678; and Jules Violle, "L'oeuvre scientifique de M. Edmond Becquerel," *ibid.*, No. 12 (19 March 1892), 353–360. See also E. N. Harvey, *A History of Luminescence From the Earliest Times Until 1900* (Philadelphia, 1957), 207–219, 351–360.

J. B. GOUGH

BECQUEREL, ANTOINE-CÉSAR (*b.* Châtillon-sur-Loing, Loiret, France, 7 March 1788; *d.* Paris, France, 18 January 1878), *electrochemistry.*

Becquerel's father was the royal lieutenant at Châtillon-sur-Loing. Becquerel himself entered the École Polytechnique in 1806, and on graduation embarked on a military career in the Corps of Engineers, being promoted to captain in 1812. The following year he was appointed *sous inspecteur* of the École Polytechnique; he returned to active service in 1814, but after the fall of Napoleon in 1815 devoted himself entirely to science. Becquerel was elected to the Académie des Sciences in 1829; was awarded the Copley Medal of the Royal Society of London in 1837; and, when the chair of physics at the Muséum d'Histoire Naturelle was founded in 1838, became its first occupant. In 1813 he married Aimée-Cécile Darlui, a relative of the duc de Feltre, and became the founder of a dynasty of distinguished scientists. His son Alexandre Edmond succeeded him at the Museum, and his grandson Antoine Henri was the discoverer of radioactivity. Becquerel lived to a ripe old age, and his vivacity amazed his younger colleagues in the Academy, in the proceedings of which he took a lively and regular part to the end of his life.

Becquerel's first studies were in mineralogy, and in association with Alexandre Brongniart, whose disciple he was, he discovered in 1819 a collection of important recent deposits at Auteuil that contained previously unknown crystalline forms of calcium phosphate. The study of minerals led easily to electrical experiments. Following up Haüy's observation that Iceland spar became electrified when compressed, Becquerel showed that this phenomenon was general, provided that the crystals under investigation were insulated; his studies on tourmaline became classics. This effect is called the piezoelectric effect, and obtains only in crystals which possess no center of symmetry. From studying the electrical effects of compression, Becquerel moved on to thermoelectricity, investigating the electrical effects of heating minerals. He discovered various definite transition temperatures, at which the electrical state of a substance changes discontinuously. These researches led to experiments on the electrical measurement of temperature.

Of perhaps greater interest was Becquerel's work on the voltaic cell. In the early decades of the nineteenth century, it was not clear whether the production of electricity in the cell was due to the mere contact of dissimilar bodies, or whether it depended upon a chemical reaction. The principle of conserva-

tion of energy had not yet been clearly enunciated; but Becquerel believed that there was a close relationship between electricity on the one hand, and heat, light, and chemical forces on the other. In a series of careful experiments, he put it beyond doubt that electricity could be generated only by the contact of dissimilar bodies when they reacted together chemically, or differed in temperature, or were rubbed together. Conversely, he established that all chemical reactions can generate electricity. This was related to earlier work, notably by Humphry Davy, and in 1829 Becquerel employed Davy's discovery that a battery could be made of two liquids separated by a solid barrier in the construction of the first battery that, not being polarized, could supply current at a reasonably constant EMF.

Using these cells, Becquerel performed elegant small-scale experiments on the synthesis of mineral substances. Since he was able to control his EMF's, through secondary electrolysis he succeeded in obtaining crystals of various substances—notably sulfides—that had previously been produced only in an amorphous condition. He suggested that the presence of crystalline substances in mineral veins might be accounted for by their having been deposited by electric currents operating over a very long period of time. Becquerel remarked that chemical synthesis had lagged behind analysis, and hoped that through his techniques many naturally occurring crystals would be synthesized and the balance thus redressed. It was for this work that he received the Copley Medal. These researches found industrial applications in the treatment of silver-bearing ores and the extraction of potassium chloride from the sea.

Becquerel wrote a great number of papers; of his joint papers, the majority were written in collaboration with his son, but his co-workers also included Ampère and Biot. He corresponded with Michael Faraday over diamagnetism; he had noticed examples of it before Faraday but had failed to generalize from them. He also invented an electromagnetic balance and a differential galvanometer.

BIBLIOGRAPHY

I. ORIGINAL WORKS. Becquerel's papers are listed in the *Royal Society Catalogue of Scientific Papers,* I (1867), 233–239; VII (1877), 118–121; IX (1891), 164–166. See also *Analyse succint des travaux de M. Becquerel* (Paris, 1829), published by the Académie des Sciences. His most important books are *Traité expérimental de l'électricité et du magnétisme, et de leur rapports avec les phénomènes naturels,* 7 vols. (Paris,

1834–1840); *Traité de physique considérée dans ses rapports avec la chimie et les sciences naturelles*, 2 vols. (Paris, 1842–1844); *Élements d'électro-chimie appliquée aux sciences naturelles et aux arts* (Paris, 1843; 1864), also translated into German (Erfurt, 1845; 1848; 1857); and *Résumé de l'histoire de l'électricité et du magnétisme, et des applications de ces sciences à la chimie, aux sciences naturelles et aux arts* (Paris, 1858), written with Alexandre Edmond Becquerel. There is an extensive collection of MSS of A. C. Becquerel at the Académie des Sciences in Paris.

II. SECONDARY LITERATURE. Obituaries of Becquerel are in *Comptes rendus de l'Académie des sciences*, **86** (1878), 125–131. See also *Abstracts of the Philosophical Transactions*, **4** (1843), 22–23; and T. Cooper, ed., *Men of the Time*, 9th ed. (London, 1875), p. 87.

DAVID M. KNIGHT

BECQUEREL, [ANTOINE-] HENRI (*b.* Paris, France, 15 December 1852; *d.* Le Croisic, Brittany, France, 25 August 1908), *physics*.

Becquerel is known for his discovery of radioactivity, for which he received the Nobel Prize for physics jointly with the Curies in 1903, and for other contributions to that field which he made during the half-dozen years when he was most active in it. He was a member of the Academy of Sciences, became its president, and was elected to the far more influential post of permanent secretary. He held three chairs of physics in Paris—at the Museum of Natural History, at the École Polytechnique, and at the Conservatoire National des Arts et Métiers—and attained high rank as an engineer in the National Administration of Bridges and Highways (Ponts et Chaussées).

Henri's father, Alexandre-Edmond Becquerel, and his grandfather, Antoine-César Becquerel, were renowned and prolific physicists, both members of the Academy of Sciences and each in his turn professor of physics at the Museum of Natural History. When Henri was born in the professor's house at the Museum, he was born almost literally into the inner circles of French science. He was educated at the Lycée Louis-le-Grand, from which he went to the École Polytechnique (1872–1874) and then to the École des Ponts et Chaussées (1874–1877), where he received his engineering training and from which he entered the Administration of Bridges and Highways with the rank of *ingénieur*. On leaving the Polytechnique, he married Lucie-Zoé-Marie Jamin, daughter of J.-C. Jamin, academician and professor of physics in the Faculty of Sciences of Paris. Before the end of his schooling he had begun both his private research (1875) and his teaching career (1876) as *répétiteur* at the Polytechnique. In January 1878 his grandfather died; his wife died the following March,

a few weeks after the birth of their son Jean. At this time Becquerel succeeded to the post of *aide-naturaliste*, which his father had hitherto held at the Museum, and from then on, his professional life was shared among the Museum, the Polytechnique, and the Ponts et Chaussées.

Becquerel's early research was almost exclusively optical. His first extensive investigations (1875–1882) dealt with the rotation of plane-polarized light by magnetic fields. He turned next to infrared spectra (1883), making visual observations by means of the light released from certain phosphorescent crystals under infrared illumination. He then studied the absorption of light in crystals (1886–1888), particularly its dependence on the plane of polarization of the incident light and the direction of its propagation through the crystal. With these researches Becquerel obtained his doctorate from the Faculty of Sciences of Paris (1888) and election to the Academy of Sciences (1889), after two preparatory nominations (1884, 1886), in the second of which he polled twenty of the fifty-one votes. He had in the meantime been promoted to *ingénieur de première classe* in the Ponts et Chaussées.

With his doctorate achieved, Becquerel became substantially inactive in research. In 1890 he married his second wife, the daughter of E. Lorieux, an inspector general of mines. Following the death of Edmond Becquerel in 1891, he succeeded in the following year to his father's two chairs of physics, at the Conservatoire National des Arts et Métiers and at the Museum. In the same year Alfred Potier withdrew from active teaching because of illness, and Becquerel took over his lectures in physics at the École Polytechnique. Two years later (1894) he became *ingénieur en chef* with the Ponts et Chaussées and the next year (1895) was named to succeed Potier at the Polytechnique.

Thus the beginning of 1896 found Becquerel, at the age of forty-three, established in rank and responsibility, his years of active research behind him and everything for which he is now remembered still undone. In the very opening days of the year, Roentgen had announced his discovery of X rays by a mailing of preprints and photographs, but Becquerel's personal knowledge of the discovery dates to 20 January, when two physicians, Paul Oudin and Toussaint Barthélemy, submitted an X-ray photograph of the bones of a living hand to the Academy. From Henri Poincaré, who had received a preprint, Becquerel learned that in Roentgen's tubes the X rays arose from the fluorescent spot where a beam of cathode rays played on the glass wall. Thus a natural, if perhaps not plausible, inference arose that the visible light and invisible X rays might be produced by the same mechanism, and that X rays might accompany all luminescence.

Becquerel's researches had been essentially descriptive, with a primary commitment to observation and a careful avoidance of theorizing. Nevertheless, this X-ray hypothesis caught his fancy. He had some personal acquaintance with luminescent crystals, he was familiar with his father's researches on them, and he began to hunt for a crystalline emitter of penetrating radiation. On 24 February 1896 he reported to the Academy that fluorescent crystals of potassium uranyl sulfate had exposed a photographic plate wrapped in black paper while they both lay for several hours in direct sunlight. On 2 March he reported comparable exposures when both crystals and plate lay in total darkness. By his working hypothesis, that would have been impossible because the luminescence of potassium uranyl sulfate ceases immediately when the ultraviolet radiation that excites it is withdrawn. One might speculate, nevertheless, that the penetrating rays persisted longer than the visible fluorescence when their common excitation was cut off. Becquerel did so, conscientiously condemned the speculation as unjustified, and then proceeded to act upon it.

He did not neglect his general studies. He showed that, like X rays, the penetrating rays from his crystals could discharge electrified bodies (in modern terms, could ionize the air they passed through). He found evidence to suggest that the rays were refracted and reflected like visible light, although later he attributed these effects to secondary electrons ejected from his glass plates and mirrors. Nevertheless, he devoted a substantial effort to searching out the radiation that had first excited his penetrating rays. He kept some of his crystals in darkness, hoping that their pent-up energy might dissipate itself and make them ready for reexcitation. He tried other luminescent crystals and found that only those containing uranium emitted the penetrating radiation. He tried ingeniously but unsuccessfully to release the energy of uranyl nitrate by warming its crystals in darkness until they dissolved in their own water of crystallization. He tested nonluminescent compounds of uranium and found that they emitted his penetrating rays. Finally, he tried a disk of pure uranium metal and found that it produced penetrating radiation three to four times as intense as that he had first seen with potassium uranyl sulfate.

With this last announcement, on 18 May, Becquerel's discovery of radioactivity was complete, although he continued with ionization studies of his penetrating radiation until the following spring. What he had accomplished at the most general level was to establish the occurrence and the properties of that radiation, so that it could be identified unambiguously. Of more importance, he had shown that the power of emitting penetrating rays was a particular property of uranium. However, the implications of this second conclusion were by no means clear at the time. Becquerel characterized his own achievement as the first observation of phosphorescence in a metal. His immediate successors, G. C. Schmidt and Marie Curie, started with quite conventional views about the rays and came only gradually to realize that such radiation might also be emitted by other elements. Both then searched among the known elements, finding that only thorium was also a ray-emitter. Marie Curie and her husband, Pierre, pushed on to search for unknown elements with the same property, however, and so discovered polonium and radium. With these discoveries, the field of radioactivity (a term that the Curies coined) was fully established.

Nothing that Becquerel subsequently accomplished was as important as this discovery, by which he opened the way to nuclear physics. Nevertheless, there were two other occasions on which he stood directly on the path of history: when he identified electrons in the radiations of radium (1899–1900) and when he published the first evidence of a radioactive transformation (1901).

Marie Curie's work, which attracted Becquerel's attention, brought the Curies within the circle of his acquaintance and turned him back to radioactive studies. He became the intermediary through whom their papers reached the Academy, and they lent him radium preparations from time to time. Toward the end of 1899 (his first report is dated 11 December), he began to investigate the effects on the radiation from radium of magnetic fields in various orientations to the direction of its propagation (in modern terms, the magnetic deflection of the beta rays from short-term decay products in equilibrium with the radium). In this work he united two descriptive traditions, the magneto optics of his own experience and a line of qualitative studies of the discharge of electricity through gases. He soon moved from these to J. J. Thomson's more radical program of quantitative observations on collimated beams, in which Thomson had shown (1897) that the cathode rays were corpuscular and consisted of streams of swiftly moving, negatively charged particles whose masses were probably subatomic. By 26 March 1900, Becquerel had duplicated those experiments for the radium radiation and had shown that it too consisted of negatively charged ions, moving at 1.6×10^{10} cm./sec. with a ratio of $m/e = 10^{-7}$ gm./abcoul. Thus Thomson's "corpuscles" (electrons) constituted a part of the radiations of radioactivity.

At this period an idea was current, although seldom formally expressed, that radioactivity should be a property only of rare substances like radium, and not of ordinary chemical elements. Perhaps under the impulse of such a notion, Becquerel undertook to remove from uranium a magnetically deviable (or beta) radiation he had recently identified. His method was borrowed from André Debierne, who had found it effective with actinium. To a solution of uranium chloride, he added barium chloride and precipitated the barium as the sulfate. The precipitate entrained something, for the deviable radiation of the uranium was diminished; by a long repetition of such operations he succeeded in July 1900 in reducing that radiation, in one specimen, to one-sixth of its original value. In confirmation of this result, he found that earlier that spring, Crookes had succeeded, by more effective chemical procedures, in separating from uranium the photographically active radiation, which he now attributed to a substance provisionally named uranium X. Something over a year later, Becquerel realized the logical incongruity of these two successes. It had been relatively easy to remove the apparent radioactivity from uranium by chemical purification, yet no one who had investigated uranium over the last five years had ever observed a nonradioactive specimen. It followed, then, that whatever radioactivity was lost in purification must always regenerate itself; and he verified this logical conclusion on his own earlier specimens. The uranium had regained its lost radioactivity, and the barium sulfate precipitates had lost all that they had carried down. The explanations he attempted were thoroughly confusing, but the facts remained.

These facts were brought squarely to the attention of Ernest Rutherford and Frederick Soddy, who had just succeeded in separating a thorium X analogous to Crookes's uranium X. Their subsequent tests showed a similar regeneration of the lost radioactivity of the thorium. From this they inferred, and immediately verified, a regeneration of the thorium X in those specimens and then came to realize that this chemically distinct thorium X could have been formed there only by a transformation of the thorium. On the basis of these and similar experiments, in a few months they formulated the transformation theory, which became the basic theory of radioactivity.

In 1903 the Nobel Prize for physics was divided between Henri Becquerel and Pierre and Marie Curie. It was an appropriate division. Becquerel's pioneer investigations had opened the way to the Curies'

discoveries, and their discoveries had validated and shown the importance of his. On 31 December 1906, Becquerel was elected vice-president of the Academy of Sciences, serving in that capacity during 1907 and succeeding to the presidency in 1908. On 29 June 1908 he was elected as one of the two permanent secretaries of the Academy, following the death of Lapparent. On confirmation by the president of the republic, he was installed in that office on 6 July, taking his seat beside Darboux, who had taught him mathematics nearly four decades before at the Lycée Louis-le-Grand. He died soon after at Le Croisic in Brittany, the ancestral home of his wife's family, the Lorieux.

In an assessment of Becquerel's scientific powers, it should be noted that he had little taste for physical theories, either his own or those of others, and much of his research effort was dissipated on observations of no great significance. Against this, he displayed an admirable versatility in experiment in unfamiliar as well as familiar fields. His greatest asset, however, was a strong, persistent power of critical afterthought. On those rare occasions when Becquerel did pursue a hypothesis, this critical power continually corrected his enthusiasms and redirected his line of investigation; so that, for example, while he persistently searched for X rays in phosphorescence, he managed to discover the inherent radioactivity of uranium.

BIBLIOGRAPHY

I. ORIGINAL WORKS. Becquerel wrote an account of his radioactive investigations in an extended *mémoire*, "Recherches sur une propriété nouvelle de la matière. Activité radiante spontanée ou radioactivité de la matière," in *Mémoires de l'Académie des sciences, Paris,* **46** (1903). Aside from this, his scientific work is to be found in some 150 papers and notes in various journals. No single list of them exists, but those published up to 1900 may be found in the Royal Society's *Catalogue of Scientific Papers,* IX, 166–167, and XIII, 395–396. His papers on radioactivity are listed in the bibliography of 214 items included with his *mémoire.* Among these papers on radioactivity, all of them in the *Comptes rendus de l'Académie des sciences, Paris,* are "Émission de radiations nouvelles par l'uranium métallique," **122** (1896), 1086–1088; "Sur quelques propriétés nouvelles des radiations invisibles émises par divers corps phosphorescents," *ibid.,* 559–564; "Sur les radiations émises par phosphorescence," *ibid.,* 420–421; "Sur les radiations invisibles émises par les corps phosphorescents," *ibid.,* 501–503; "Sur les radiations invisibles émises par les sels d'uranium," *ibid.,* 689–694; "Sur diverses propriétés des rayons uraniques," **123** (1896), 855–858; "Sur la loi de décharge dans l'air de l'uranium électrisé," **124** (1897), 800–803; "Recherches sur les rayons uraniques," *ibid.,* 444; "Influence d'un champ magnétique sur le rayonnement des corps radio-actifs," **129** (1899), 996–1001; "Sur le rayonnement des corps radio-actifs," *ibid.*, 1205–1207; "Contribution à l'étude du rayonnement du radium," **130** (1900), 206–211; "Déviation du rayonnement du radium dans un champ électrique," *ibid.*, 809–815; "Sur la dispersion du rayonnement du radium dans un champ magnétique," *ibid.*, 372–376; "Note sur le rayonnement de l'uranium," *ibid.*, 1583–1585, and **131** (1900), 137–138; and "Sur la radioactivité de l'uranium," **133** (1901), 977–980.

II. SECONDARY LITERATURE. There is a somewhat padded biography by Albert Ranc, *Henri Becquerel et la découverte de la radioactivité,* Sciences et Savants, no. 3 (Paris, 1946). Important material is in G. Darboux, E. Perrier, M. Vieille, and L. Passy, "Discours prononcés aux funerailles de M. Henri Becquerel," in *Comptes rendus de l'Académie des sciences, Paris,* **147** (1908), 443–451; and in the sketch included in *Les Prix Nobel en 1903* (Stockholm, 1906), pp. 62–63.

Critical studies include Sir O. Lodge, "Becquerel Memorial Lecture," in *Journal of the Chemical Society,* **101** (1912), 2005–2042, for a contemporary assessment; and L. Badash, " 'Chance Favors the Prepared Mind': Henri Becquerel and the Discovery of Radioactivity," in *Archives internationales d'histoire des sciences,* **18** (1965), 55–66, for a modern one.

ALFRED ROMER

BECQUEREL, PAUL (*b.* Paris, France, 14 April 1879; *d.* Évian, France, 22 June 1955), *biology.*

Through his researches Paul Becquerel did much to explain the physiological nature of the plant seed and the reactions of protoplasm to freezing and dehydration. Becquerel, grandson of Edmond Becquerel and nephew of Henri Becquerel, received his licentiate in natural sciences at the Faculty of Sciences at Paris in 1903 and his doctorate in 1907. In that same year he was named an assistant at the Faculty of Sciences. For a period of time after World War I, Becquerel was a member of the Faculty of Sciences at Nancy, following which, in 1927, he was appointed professor of general botany at the University of Poitiers. He remained at Poitiers until his retirement.

Becquerel began his career with researches on the nature of the life of seeds. Were they, as some physiologists from Spallanzani through Claude Bernard had suggested, actually nonliving, in a state of suspended or latent life? Or were they merely in a state in which the life processes were greatly slowed?—an idea suggested by, among others, Leeuwenhoek and Gaston Bonnier, one of Becquerel's teachers in Paris. After studying the structure and function of the various parts of seeds, Becquerel concluded that a portion of the seed always lived, protected from hostile external environments by an impermeable protective layer. Shorn of this layer, seeds could easily be killed by toxic liquids and gases. However, Becquerel went on to show that plant and animal tissue could in fact attain a state of suspended or latent life. He produced this condition in seeds; in fern, moss, bacteria, and mushroom spores; and in algae, rotifers, and infusoria by dehydrating them as much as possible in a vacuum. Living objects so treated could withstand exposure to liquid hydrogen (*ca.* −253°C.) and liquid helium (*ca.* −269°C.) and still be revived by warming and rehydration.

Becquerel then turned his attention to naturally occurring cases of "suspended life." Working with seeds of known ages—from 25 to 135 years old—he was able to produce a small percentage of germinations; and, in later experiments (1933), he was able to bring about the germination of two 158-year-old seeds of *Cassia multijuga.* He found in these results confirmation of his ideas, maintaining that these seeds had retained their germinative ability because they had undergone a strong dehydration and their seed coats were quite thick.

In 1937 Becquerel began a study of the effects of freezing on vegetable protoplasm, showing in 1939 that plant cells are not killed by plasmolysis upon freezing; rather, the lowered temperature induces synaeresis. This was elaborated upon in a 1949 paper.

BIBLIOGRAPHY

Becquerel's work appeared in a large number of short papers, most of them published in the *Comptes rendus de l'Académie des sciences, Paris.* Among his most important papers were the following: "Action de l'air liquide sur les graines décortiquées," in *Comptes rendus de l'Académie des sciences, Paris,* **140** (1905), 1652–1654; "Recherches expérimentales sur la vie latente des spores des *Mucorinées* et des *Ascomycétes* aux basses températures de l'hydrogène liquide," *ibid.*, **150** (1910), 1437–1439; "Action abiotique des rayons ultraviolets sur les spores sèches aux basses températures et l'origine cosmique de la vie," *ibid.*, **151** (1910), 86–88; "La suspension de la vie des graines dans le vide à −271°C.," *ibid.*, **181** (1925), 805–807; "La vie latente des graines de pollen dans le vide à 271°C. au-dessous de zéro," *ibid.*, **188** (1929), 1308–1310; "La vie latente des spores des Fougères dans le vide aux basses températures de l'hélium liquide," *ibid.*, **190** (1930), 1134–1136; "La vie latente des spores des bactéries et des moisissures," in *Travaux cryptogamiques, dédiés à Louis Mangin* (Paris, 1931), pp. 303–307; "La vie latente des spores des Mousses aux basses températures," in *Comptes rendus de l'Académie des sciences, Paris,* **194** (1932), 1378–1380; "L'anhydrobiose des tubercules des Renoncules dans l'azote liquide," *ibid.*, **194** (1932), 1974–1976; "La reviviscence des plantules desséchées soumises aux actions du vide et des très basses températures," *ibid.*, 2158–2159; "Sur la résistance de certains organismes végétaux aux actions des basses températures de l'azote et de l'hélium liquides, réalisées au laboratoire cryogène de Leiden," in *Actes du VIème Congrès International du Froid* (1932), IV, 23–27; "Role de la synérèse dans le mécanisme de la congélation cellulaire," in *Chronica botanica,* **5** (1939), 10–11, a brief summary article; "Reviviscence du *Xanthoria parietina* desséché avec sa faune, six ans dans le vide et deux semaines à −189°C. Ses conséquences biologiques," in *Comptes rendus de l'Académie des sciences, Paris,* **226** (1948), 1413–1415; and "L'action du froid sur la cellule végétale," in *Botaniste,* **34** (1949), 57–74.

A short biographical obituary of Becquerel, without bibliographical material, appeared in *Comptes rendus de l'Académie des sciences, Paris,* **241** (1955), 137–140.

ALAN S. KAY

BEDDOE, JOHN (*b.* Bewdley, Worcestershire, England, 21 September 1826; *d.* Bradford-on-Avon, England, 19 July 1911), *physical anthropology.*

Beddoe suffered from ill health in his youth. Although he was intended for a career in the law, he studied medicine at University College, London, and the University of Edinburgh; in 1853 he received the M.D. from the latter institution, with a thesis entitled "On the Geography of Phthisis." Beddoe next served as a house physician in the Royal Edinburgh Infirmary. During the Crimean War he was on the medical staff of a civilian hospital at Renkioi in the Dardanelles. After the war he went to Vienna to complete his medical training, then made an extensive tour of Austria, Hungary, Italy, and France, studying medicine and physical anthropology. Upon his return to England in 1857 he set up a medical practice in Clifton, a suburb of Bristol, where he remained until his retirement in 1891.

Beddoe was elected a fellow of the Royal Society in 1873. He was a founding member, in 1857, of the Ethnological Society; was president of the Anthropological Society in 1869–1870; and was president of the Royal Anthropological Institute in 1889–1891. In 1905 he gave the Huxley lecture, "Colour and Race," and received the Huxley Medal. Beddoe received an honorary LL.D at Edinburgh in 1891 and there delivered the Rhind lectures. The University of Bristol elected him honorary professor of anthropology in 1908.

From the age of twenty Beddoe was a keen observer of the physical variations in man, beginning with observations on hair and eye color in the west of England, then extending his work to the Orkneys, which resulted in his *Contributions to Scottish Ethnology* (1853). In 1864 A. Johnes, of Garthmyl, Wales, contributed a prize of 100 guineas, to be awarded at the Welsh National Eisteddfod, for the best essay on the origin of the English nation. For four years, although there were contenders, the prize was not awarded. In 1868 it was won by Beddoe, and the essay was published as *The Races of Britain: A Contribution to the Anthropology of Western Europe* (1885). In the preface Beddoe says: "The successful work, however, though composed expressly for the occasion, was really the outcome of a great part of the leisure of fifteen years devoted to the application of the numerical and inductive method to the ethnology of Britain and of Western Europe."

Beddoe's Rhind lectures extended the theme of his Eisteddfod essay to cover all Europe. The year after his death, they appeared in a revised form: *The Anthropological History of Europe, Being the Rhind Lectures for 1912* (1912).

Beddoe loved traveling, and set down some of the incidents of his widespread journeys in *Memories of Eighty Years* (1910). This book also describes his friendship and correspondence with all the major figures of the time who were interested in the physical and cultural history of early man in Europe: Broca, Davis, Topinard, Virchow, Darwin, Retzius, Rhys, Boyd-Dawkins, Cartailhac, Deniker, John Evans, Pitt-Rivers, and Ridgeway. His *Races of Britain* is dedicated "to Rudolf Virchow and Paul Topinard, and to the memory of Paul Broca and Joseph Barnard Davis."

Beddoe was first of all a descriptive physical anthropologist, noting and measuring the varieties of man's hair color, skin color, height, cephalic index, and so forth, throughout the British Isles and Europe. But he was not content with description; he wanted to explain the observed physical variations in terms of the spread of language and culture, and against the picture produced by prehistorians in the nineteenth century and the known movements of people in historical times. He continually sought to produce a coherent story in which the movements of, for example, speakers of the Celtic languages, or the people of the great migration period of post-Roman times, or the Jews and the Gypsies were integrated into the anthropological history of Europe.

The following passage, taken from the end of chapter 3 of *The Races of Britain,* shows the quality of Beddoe's thinking:

> The natives of South Britain, at the time of the Roman conquest, probably consisted mainly of several strata, unequally distributed, of Celtic-speaking people, who in race and physical type, however, partook more of the tall blond stock of Northern Europe than of the thick-set, broad-headed, dark stock which Broca has called Celtic, and which those who object to this attribution of that much-contested name may, if they like,

denominate Arvernian. Some of these layers were Gaelic in speech, some Cymric; they were both superposed on a foundation principally composed of the long-headed dark races of the Mediterranean stock, possibly mingled with the fragments of still more ancient races, Mongoliform or Allophylian. This foundation-layer was still very strong and coherent in Ireland and the north of Scotland, where the subsequent deposits were thinner, and in some parts wholly or partially absent. The most recent layers were Belgic, and may have contained some portion or colouring of Germanic blood: but no Germans, recognisable as such by speech as well as person, had as yet entered Britain.

Beddoe was a pioneer in this sort of synthetic writing about the physical, linguistic, and cultural history of Europe. His works were widely read, and greatly influenced the thinking of a wide range of people in the late nineteenth and early twentieth centuries, from pure physical anthropologists to historians like Rice Holmes, archaeologists like Ridgeway, and linguistic scholars like Sir John Rhys.

Even though today, over half a century after Beddoe's death, it is no longer considered possible to lump together in any meaningful way the facts and hypotheses about the physical, linguistic, and cultural history of Britain and Europe, we should not forget that Beddoe's work was instrumental in the development of anthropology. Prior thereto much speculation about the origins of the physical varieties of man in Europe had been largely guesswork. Beddoe put this matter on a firm basis of observed fact, of which his interpretations were in keeping with the evidence.

BIBLIOGRAPHY

I. Original Works. Among Beddoe's writings are *Contributions to Scottish Ethnology* (Edinburgh, 1853); *The Races of Britain: A Contribution to the Anthropology of Western Europe* (Bristol–London, 1885); "Colour and Race," in *Journal of the Royal Anthropological Institute,* **35** (1905), 98–140; *Memories of Eighty Years* (Bristol–London, 1910); and *The Anthropological History of Europe, Being the Rhind Lectures for 1912* (Paisley, 1912).

Glyn Daniel

BEDDOES, THOMAS (*b.* Shifnal, Shropshire, England, 13 April 1760; *d.* Clifton, England, 24 December, 1808), *medicine, chemistry.*

Beddoes' father was a tanner and wished his son to follow the same trade, but the boy proved bookish. His grandfather, a man of parts, recognized his abilities and insisted that he be trained for a profession. Beddoes therefore attended Bridgnorth Grammar School, Shropshire, and in 1776 went to Pembroke College, Oxford. There, while reading medicine, he became interested in chemistry and in modern languages. On going down from Oxford, he translated, or edited translations of, works by Bergman, Scheele, and Spallanzani. In 1784 he went to Edinburgh for three years and then paid a visit to France, where he met Lavoisier, to whose antiphlogistic chemistry he adhered. In 1788 Beddoes was appointed reader in chemistry at Oxford and attracted audiences larger than any lecturer since the thirteenth century. He supported the French Revolution, and his strong political views partly explain his resignation from Oxford in 1792. In 1794 he married Anna Edgeworth, sister of the novelist Maria Edgeworth; their eldest son, Thomas Lovell Beddoes, became a famous poet.

Beddoes' name is not perpetuated in any important discovery in chemistry or in medicine: while perhaps his most important contribution to science was his discovery of Humphry Davy, he was well known in his own day for his popular works on preventive medicine and his investigations of the use of gases in treating diseases. Among his publications are *Isaac Jenkins,* a moral tale (1792); *Essay on Consumption* (1799); and *Hygëia,* a series of essays describing the regimen necessary for avoiding disease (1802–1803). Beddoes considered it deplorable that although about one person in a million died annually of hydrophobia, and one in a hundred of tuberculosis, everybody dreaded hydrophobia and took tuberculosis for granted. He observed that some occupations carried great risks of consumption and declared that in civilized societies victims were thus sacrificed to alcohol, to fashion, and to commerce. Beddoes agreed that it was foolish to encourage people to doctor themselves; but to persuade them to adopt a healthy way of life, and to learn some biology, seemed eminently reasonable.

He called on doctors to produce more case studies and censured hospitals particularly for their failure to develop adequate statistics; when an adequate supply of genuine facts was available, medicine could be brought to the level of chemistry or astronomy, where charlatans stood no chance of success. Chemistry interested Beddoes primarily because he believed that true medical science must have a chemical basis. With this in mind, in 1798 he set up his Pneumatic Institution at Clifton for treating diseases by the administration of gases. He appointed Davy, then age nineteen, superintendent, and published his first essays on heat and light; like Davy, Beddoes adhered to the kinetic theory of heat. After Davy's departure in 1801, the Pneumatic Institution became a clinic where advice was given on preventive medicine.

Beddoes was associated with the Lunar Society of

Birmingham during its last years. His mind was restless, and he died unhappy at his lack of solid achievement.

BIBLIOGRAPHY

I. ORIGINAL WORKS. *The History of Isaac Jenkins, and of the Sickness of Sarah his wife, and their three children* (Madeley, Shropshire, 1792); *An Essay on the Causes, Early Signs, and Prevention of Pulmonary Consumption* (Bristol, 1799); *Hygëia; or Essays Moral and Medical on the Causes Affecting the Personal State of Our Middling and Affluent Classes,* 3 vols. (Bristol, 1802–1803). The following works were written by Beddoes and James Watt: *Considerations on the Medicinal Use of Factitious Airs, and on the Manner of Obtaining Them in Large Quantities* (Bristol, 1794; 2nd ed., 1795; 3rd ed., 1796); *Medical Cases and Speculations; Including Parts IV and V of Considerations on the Medicinal Powers, and the Production of Factitious Airs* (Bristol, 1796). With Beddoes as editor: *Chemical Experiments and Opinions, Extracted from a Work Published in the Last Century* [Mayow's experiments] (Oxford, 1790); *Contributions to Physical and Medical Knowledge, Principally From the West of England* (Bristol, 1799).

II. SECONDARY LITERATURE. Works on Beddoes are J. E. Stock, *Memoirs of the Life of Thomas Beddoes, M.D.* (London, 1811), which contains a bibliography of Beddoes' writings; F. F. Cartwright, *The English Pioneers of Anaesthesia* (Bristol, 1952), pp. 49–164; E. Robinson, "Thomas Beddoes, M.D., and the Reform of Science Teaching in Oxford," in *Annals of Science,* **11** (1955), 137–141; Editorial, in *Endeavour,* **19** (1960), 123–124; and R. E. Schofield, *The Lunar Society of Birmingham* (Oxford, 1963), pp. 373–377.

DAVID M. KNIGHT

BEDE, THE VENERABLE (*b.* Northumbria, England, A.D. 672/673; *d.* Jarrow-on-Tyne, England, A.D. 735), *philosophy.*

At the canonical age of seven Bede was entrusted to the care of Benedict Biscop, founding abbot of the monasteries of Wearmouth and Jarrow (near Newcastle). In Bede's words, written in 731, "From that time, spending all the days of my life in residence at that monastery, I devoted myself wholly to Scriptural meditation. And while observing the regular discipline and the daily round of singing in the church, I have always taken delight in learning, or teaching, or writing."[1] A disciple, Cuthbert, described his death in loving but not hagiographical terms.[2] There are no other biographical events of record, but from the twelve octavo volumes of his extant Latin writings emerges a consistent picture of a dedicated scholar and scientist.

Apparently Bede never traveled farther than fifty miles from his monastery, but he had unusual resources there. The English settlement of Britain in the fifth to the seventh centuries suggests the European settlement of North America in the seventeenth to the nineteenth centuries. Benedict Biscop, who founded his monastery two centuries after the first English settlement, had studied at Lérins (the most famous Western school of the period) and at Rome. He brought Archbishop Theodore and Abbot Hadrian from Rome to England. Hadrian came from culturally rich North Africa, via Naples. Theodore, whose home had been the "university city" of Tarsus in Cilicia, was schooled in Greek, law, and philosophy. Later, Benedict brought John, the archchanter of St. Peter's in Rome, to teach and to compose musical texts. In Northumbria, Benedict was surrounded by students from Ireland and Frankland, including, for example, the famous Abbess Hilda of Whitby, an English princess who had been educated in Ireland and Paris. In all, he made five trips to the Continent, importing examples of all the arts and crafts and "a very rich library." His successor Ceolfrid, Bede's master and abbot, was an author and the creator of the famous *Codex Amiatinus.* Bede himself was the primary voice of this flowering English culture.

Half of Bede's volumes are scriptural exegesis, an art in which he excelled. Five of the remaining six volumes contain homilies, hagiography, history, a guide to holy places (derived from the pilgrim Arculf), religious and occasional verses, and letters. They include his renowned work, *Historia ecclesiastica gentis Anglorum.* Cuthbert reports that he composed Anglo-Saxon verse and prose, but none has survived.

The remaining volume contains Bede's several *opera didascalica,* textbooks designed for such courses in the emerging vocational curriculum of monastic schools as *notae* (scribal work), *grammar* (literary science), and *computus* (the art and science of telling time). For the study of *notae* Bede composed *De orthographia* (dealing with spelling, word formation, and so forth), in the tradition of Caper, Agroecius, and Cassiodorus. For *grammar* he composed *De arte metrica* (on versification) and *De schematibus et tropis* (on figurative language). The first contains the first known treatment of isosyllabic rhythm (*De rhythmo*), which was then supplanting quantity as the formative principle of Western verse, while the second is unique in maintaining, with evidence, that every Greco-Roman figure of speech had been anticipated in the Hebrew Scriptures.

The study of *computus* had arisen pragmatically to meet the needs of Christian monastic communities, in which time was of the essence. The migrations of different peoples, each of whom had a different mode of reckoning time in both short and long units, and the establishment among them of convents as models for living in which the residents emphasized cycles of psalms and prayers through ordained days and years, made the study of *computus* second only to that of the grammar necessary for studying the Scriptures. Eventually *computus* attracted, as part of its discipline, most of the content (although not in those categories) of what might later be deceptively called the *quadrivium* (arithmetic, geometry, astronomy, and music). As time passed, the science necessary to physicians (largely dietary regimens and periodic phlebotomy), to agriculturists, to mariners, to historians (chronology), to geographers and cosmologists, and to musicians and versifiers was incorporated. The basic pattern for Bede's primary texts was a theoretical section (rules and formulas with explanations) and a practical section (a chronicle of world history emphasizing such "timely" events as eclipses, earthquakes, human and natural calamities), to which were appended a wide variety of calendars, tables, and formularies.

This pattern had begun to develop with Julius Africanus about A.D. 200. The Eusebius-Jerome Chronicle, which largely determined the medieval view of history, probably originated as part of such a text. Bede's earlier text of this kind, *De temporibus,* was published in 703. At about the same time, he wrote *De natura rerum,* an ancillary text on the model of Isidore's *Liber rotarum,* using sections of Pliny's *Natural History* together with patristic lore. Cosmology and natural history were traditionally (after Origen, Basil, Ambrose) linked to hexamera, that is, to commentaries on the six days of creation as described in Genesis. Bede wrote such a commentary, in which he refined some earlier statements of his own and of the Fathers. In 725 he rewrote his earlier text *On Times (De temporum ratione)*, lengthening it tenfold because, he said, "When I tried to present and explain it to some brothers, they said it was far more condensed than they wanted, especially respecting the calculation of Easter, which seemed most useful; and so they persuaded me to write somewhat more at length about the nature, course, and end of time."[3] Bede reproduced or created tables of calculation, Easter tables, calendars, formularies, mnemonic verses, and the like. A letter to Plegwin defended his chronology; another, to Wicthede, explained contradictions in a document later proved a forgery.[4]

In this area three particular contributions are noteworthy. He is the first to have created, or at least to have recorded, on the basis of the Metonic nineteen-year lunar cycle, a perpetual (532-year) cycle of Easters and to have tabulated it. True, Victorius of Aquitaine (fifth century) had created a 532-year table, and even earlier Christians had created an eighty-four-year cycle, but Bede practically reconciled the two. Bede built upon the work of Dionysius Exiguus (*ca.* 525) and took his anchor date, the *annus Domini.* Because annals were added in the margins of these tables and because Bede incorporated such annals with their anchor dates in his historical writing, he became the first historian to use the Christian era. His popular *Historia ecclesiastica* helped to spread the practice. Finally, he first stated the tidal principle of "establishment of port," which has been described (e.g., by Duhem) as the only original formulation of nature to be made in the West for some eight centuries. Pseudo-Isidore's *De ordine creaturarum,* almost certainly written in Bede's time and region, uses Bede's technical diction for tides, but not his principle. It is not surprising that scholars living by the North Sea, in or near Lindisfarne, an island at high tide and a peninsula at low tide, should have been concerned with observed tidal action.

In the eighth century, Boniface (Winfrid), apostle to the Germans, and innumerable other insular missionaries and wandering scholars (e.g., Alcuin), in cooperation with Carolingian rulers, developed Continental schools based on English Scholasticism. Bede's writings were the staple texts. Among Carolingian epithets for Bede were "Doctor Modernus" and "Venerabilis." From the eleventh century on, these texts were supplanted in diocesan schools by Boethian texts. Judging by extant manuscripts, the ninth century was clearly the Age of Bede on the Continent, whereas his works had virtually disappeared from England, a fact which may be explained in part by the raids of the Danes and the decline of English ecclesiastical vigor. An unknown author of the eleventh century thought Bede first a geographer, "Living in the very corner of the world, after death he lived renowned in every other corner through his books. In them he discriminatingly described at length the locations, resources, qualities of the different lands and provinces."[5] Bede's manuscripts were more in demand in the twelfth century, but only in line with the increase for all standard authors. Another peak in the fifteenth century may reflect the reformers' search for pristine purity. Bede's greatest practical effect was on the Western calendar. His decisions (beginning the year, calculation of Easter, names of days and months, calculations of eras, and so forth) in most instances finally determined usage that was only refined, not changed, by Gregorian reform.

NOTES

1. *Historia ecclesiastica,* V, 24.
2. *De obitu Bedae,* trans. Plummer, I, lxxii–lxxviii.
3. *Praefatio,* ed. Jones, p. 175.
4. The *Liber Anatholi de ratione paschali,* ed. Bruno Krusch, in *Studien zur christlich-mittelalterlichen Chronologie* (Leipzig, 1880), pp. 311–327. See E. Dekkers and A. Gaar, *Clavis patrum Latinorum,* Sacris Eruditi III, editio altera (Bruges, 1961), no. 2303, p. 514.
5. *Patrologia Latina,* XC, 37C.

BIBLIOGRAPHY

I. Original Works. Collected editions of Bede's work include J. Hervagius, ed., *Opera Bedae Venerabilis omnia* . . ., 8 vols. (Basel, 1563), the first collected edition; J. P. Migne, ed., *Patrologia cursus completus* . . . *series Latina,* XC–XCIV (Paris, 1850), useful reprints of earlier editions; C. Plummer, ed., *Bedae opera historica,* 2 vols. (Oxford, 1896), containing editions of Bede's historical works and Cuthbert's *De obitu Bedae* (I, clx–clxiv; translated I, lxxii–lxxviii), with valuable information about all works; and Fratres Abbatiae Sancti Petri, O.S.B., Steenbrugis, Belgiae, eds., *Corpus Christianorum series Latina: Bedae opera omnia* (Turnholt, Belgium, 1955–   ).

Individual works include J. Sichardus, ed., *Bedae* . . . *de natura rerum et temporum ratione* (Basel, 1529); K. F. Halm, ed., *Rhetores Latini minores* (Leipzig, 1863), pp. 607–618 (*De schematibus*); H. Kiel, ed., *Grammatici Latini,* VII (Leipzig, 1880), 227–294 (includes *De orthographia* and *De arte metrica*); P. Geyer, ed., *Itinera Hierosolymitana saeculi IV-VIII,* Vol. XXXIX in the series Corpus Scriptorum Ecclesiasticorum Latinorum (Vienna, 1898), which contains *De locis sanctis;* Theodore Mommsen, ed., *Bedae chronica maiora, chronica minora,* XIII, 3 in the series Monumenta Germaniae Historica, Auctores Antiquissimi (Berlin, 1898), which contains *Chronica;* C. W. Jones, ed., *Bedae opera de temporibus* (Cambridge, Mass., 1943), pp. 175–303, 307–315, 317–325 (includes *De temporibus, De temporum ratione, Ep. ad Plegwin,* and *Ep. ad Wichtede*); and B. Colgrave and R. A. B. Mynors, *The Ecclesiastical History of the English People,* in the series Oxford Medieval Texts (Oxford, 1968).

II. Secondary Literature. Studies are the following: W. F. Bolton, *A History of Anglo-Latin Literature, 597–1066,* I (Princeton, 1967), 101–185 and an excellent bibliography, 264–287; C. W. Jones, "The 'Lost' Sirmond MS. of Bede's *Computus,*" in *English Historical Review,* **52** (1937), 209–219, and "Manuscripts of Bede's *De natura rerum,*" in *Isis,* **27** (1937), 430–440; M. L. W. Laistner, *A Hand-list of Bede MSS.* (Ithaca, N.Y., 1943); W. Levison, *England and the Continent in the Eighth Century* (Oxford, 1946); R. B. Palmer, "Bede as a Textbook Writer: A Study of his *De arte metrica,*" in *Speculum,* **34** (1959), 573–584; F. Strunz, "Beda in der Geschichte der Naturbetrachtung und Naturforschung," in *Zeitschrift für deutsche Geschichte,* **1** (1935), 311–321; A. H. Thompson, ed., *Bede: His Life, Times, and Writings* (Oxford, 1935); and Beda Thum,

"Beda Venerabilis in der Geschichte der Naturwissenschaften," in *Studia Anselmiana,* **6** (1936), 51–71.

Charles W. Jones

BEECKMAN, ISAAC (*b.* Middelburg, Zeeland, Netherlands, 10 December 1588; *d.* Dordrecht, Netherlands, 19 May 1637), *physics, mechanics.*

In preparation for a career in the Reformed Church, Beeckman studied letters, philosophy, and theology. As a student at Leiden from 1607 to 1610 he came into contact with the Ramist philosopher Rudolph Snell and his son Willebrord. He continued his ministerial studies at Saumur in 1612; in the interim he had privately studied mathematics and nautical science and had learned Hebrew, in Amsterdam, from the Brownist Ainsworth. After he had completed his studies, Beeckman entered his father's factory, which made candles and water conduits for various purposes, as an apprentice. When his apprenticeship was over, he pursued the same trade in Zierikzee, on the isle of Schouwen, Zeeland, which provided him easy access to the equipment required for experiments in combustion, pumping, and hydrodynamics. In addition to all this, Beeckman found time to study medicine—he received the M.D. from Caen in 1618—although he never practiced it.

In 1618–1619 Beeckman was conrector (assistant headmaster) of the Latin school in Veere, on the island of Walcheren, his brother Jacob being headmaster. While there, he made astronomical observations with Philip van Lansbergen, a well-known Copernican astronomer. In 1619–1620 Beeckman was conrector in Utrecht; he later filled the same position in Rotterdam, once again under his brother's rectorship. In Rotterdam he founded a Collegium Mechanicum, a society of craftsmen and scholars who occupied themselves with scientific problems, especially those that had technological applications.

In 1627 Beeckman was appointed rector of the Latin school at Dordrecht, which under his direction grew to 600 students and became the best school in the Netherlands. There, in 1628, with the help of the magistrate he established the first meteorological station in Europe, recording wind velocity and direction, rainfall, and temperature, and making astronomical observations with his former pupil Martinus Hortensius and the Reformed minister Andreas Colvius. Among his students were Frederick Stevin, the son of Simon Stevin; Jan de Witt, who became Grand Pensionary of Holland; and George Ent, who was one of the first adherents of Harvey and one of the first members of the Royal Society. Beeckman also planned a series of lectures on physics and mathematics, to be given in the vernacular, "for the benefit of carpenters, bricklayers, skippers, and other burghers."[1] He made experiments in physics and was the unsalaried adviser to the burgomasters on water regulation. Some of the greatest French philosophers went to Dordrecht to see him—Descartes made the trip in 1628 and 1629, Gassendi (who called Beeckman "the best philosopher I have met up to now") in 1629, and Mersenne in 1630. (Beeckman had first met Descartes at Breda in 1618; Descartes wrote his *Compendium musicae* for him and recognized that he had never before met one who so closely connected physics with mathematics.) He was an early proponent of the application of a mathematical method in physics; in his inaugural address at Dordrecht (1627) he said that he would introduce his pupils into "the true, that is the mathematical-physical, philosophy." Nevertheless, he emphasized the necessity of using experiments to check deductions.

Beeckman was a progressive thinker. He accepted the Copernican hypothesis, although with due reservations, and also the conceptions of the infinity of the universe and of atoms and the void. He became an early adherent of the doctrine of circulation of the blood, of which he learned from Ent. His work in astronomy, mechanics, and engineering was strongly influenced by that of Simon Stevin and Willebrord Snell. His early espousal of the corpuscular theory of matter was inspired mainly by the ancient engineers Hero of Alexandria and Vitruvius, by the physician Asclepiades, and, to a lesser extent, by Lucretius—in keeping with these diverse models, Beeckman's approach to this subject was undogmatic.

As early as 1613, Beeckman, rejecting any internal cause of motion, put forward a principle of inertia for both circular and rectilinear movement: When there is no impediment, there is no reason why velocity and curvature of movement should be altered. He stated that in collision the total quantity of movement remains the same, and deduced different laws for elastic and nonelastic bodies. In 1618 he worked out the law of uniformly accelerated movement of bodies falling *in vacuo* by combining his law of inertia with the hypothesis that the earth discontinuously attracts falling bodies by tiny impulses. On this basis he found the correct relation between time and space traversed: the distances are as the squares of the times. ("It was Beeckman who went beyond Oresme and Galileo by introducing sound infinitesimal considerations into Oresme's 'triangular' proof" [Clagett, 1961].) When the first impulse imparts the velocity v, the space traversed in the first moment t will be vt; in the second mo-

ment the effect of another impulse will be added to the continuing motion acquired in the first moment, so that double the space, i.e., $2vt$, will be traversed. Consequently, in n moments the total space traversed will be (in algebraic notation)

$$vt(1 + 2 + \cdots + n) = \frac{n(n + 1)}{2} vt.$$

In a time twice as long, the space will be $2n(2n + 1)/2vt$. That is, the distances traversed will be as $n(n + 1)/2$ is to $2n(2n + 1)/2$, that is, as $(n + 1)$ is to $(4n + 2)$. If the moments are supposed to be infinitely small, and n is supposed to be infinitely great, the proportion will be as $1:4$.

Beeckman was a professional scholar as well as a craftsman; consequently his experimental work was as concerned with purely scientific inquiry as with practical applications. Many of the procedures he describes are thought experiments; in other instances, however, he carried out the actual manipulations and made the measurements requisite to formulating the phenomenal law. In 1615, for example, Beeckman determined experimentally the law of the velocity of the outflow of water (usually attributed to Torricelli): The quantity of water passing through a hole in the bottom of a vessel varies as the square root of the height of the water column. He also gave experimental proof that water cannot be changed into air (as was then generally believed) and added a discussion of the errors possible in the procedure that he used. In 1626 he determined the relation between pressure and volume in a measured quantity of air, and discovered that pressure increases in a degree slightly greater than the diminution of the volume. Beeckman attributed the ascent of water in a pump tube not to the "horror of a vacuum," nor yet to the "weight" of the atmosphere, but rather to the pressure of the air.

Francis Bacon's works were known to Beeckman as early as 1623. He made both appreciative and devastating comments on the experiments contained in the *Historia experimentalis:* he agreed that heat is a kind of motion, but thought that Bacon "talks nonsense when saying that water can be transformed into air" and that he "wrongly" believed that refrigeration was always followed by contraction, even when water is turned to ice.[2] *Sylva sylvarum* gave, in Beeckman's opinion, "dubious arguments" of the experiments described.[3] He stated the weakness of Bacon's natural philosophy, saying that Bacon did not know how to relate mathematics to physics.[4]

In 1627 Beeckman learned of Gilbert's work; he deemed much of it conformable to his own findings but rejected "internal magnetical force" as the motive power of the earth, holding that the earth is subject to inertial motion in empty space. Beeckman himself offered a purely mechanistic explanation of magnetism; believing only in action by contact, he rejected the notion of any attractive force. He deemed arguments based on simplicity or beauty (as those of Copernicus and Kepler) to be of "no value," and condemned the idea that the earth should possess intelligence and a soul (as set forth by Gilbert and Kepler) as "unworthy of a philosopher."[5] Beeckman found only mechanistic explanations satisfactory, since only they "put things as it were sensible before the imagination." When Colvius informed him of Galileo's theory of tides, Beeckman considered it a strong argument for the rotation of the earth, but suggested first making a mechanical model to test it.[6]

Beeckman was no more uncritical of his own atomistic philosophy than he was of the theories of others. He confessed to having an irrefutable "argument against all atomists, and accordingly against myself": while the absolute solidity and incompressibility of true atoms exclude their resilience after collision, their deflection is indeed observable in a multitude of phenomena, so that "it seems that the doctrine of atoms is fundamentally overthrown by these phenomena." It was therefore necessary to accept the idea of flexible primary particles—even though their properties might be unintelligible—since the scholastic explanations of elasticity were even more incomprehensible.[7]

Beeckman's approach to scientific theorizing therefore clearly demonstrates the difference between his method and the more rationalistic one of Descartes. Beeckman's conceptions were formalized before his meeting with Descartes, and the two were to differ on many questions (for instance, Beeckman held that light is propagated with a finite velocity). Descartes and Mersenne certainly read Beeckman's diary, however, and Gassendi knew his ideas. Beeckman may thus be considered "a link of the highest importance in the history of the evolution of scientific ideas."[8]

NOTES

1. *Journal,* II, 455.
2. *Ibid.,* 476.
3. *Ibid.,* III, 57.
4. *Ibid.,* 51.
5. *Ibid.,* 17.
6. *Ibid.,* 171, 206.
7. *Ibid.,* II, 100–101, 157.
8. Koyré, p. 101.

BIBLIOGRAPHY

I. ORIGINAL WORKS. Beeckman's dissertation for his M.D. is *Theses de febre tertiana intermittente . . .* (Caen, 1618). *D. Isaaci Beeckmanni medici et rectoris apud Dordracenos mathematico-physicarum meditationum, quaestionum, solutionum centuria* (Utrecht, 1644) is a selection of Beeckman's notes, which was published by his younger brother Abraham. Of major importance is *Journal tenu par Isaac Beeckman de 1604 à 1634,* with notes and introduction by C. de Waard, 4 vols. (The Hague, 1939–1953). This work (in Latin and Dutch) is valuable because de Waard's notes are based largely on sources destroyed in World War II. Vol. IV contains some of Beeckman's discourses and documents relating to his life and work.

II. SECONDARY LITERATURE. Beeckman's work is dealt with in E. J. Dijksterhuis, *Val en Worp* (Groningen, 1924), pp. 304–321; R. Hooykaas, "Science and Religion in the 17th Century; Isaac Beeckman (1588–1637)," in *Free University Quarterly,* **1** (1951), 169–183; A. Koyré, *Études galiléennes,* II (Paris, 1939), 25–40; and C. de Waard, *L'expérience barométrique* (Thouars, 1936), pp. 75–91, 145–168.

R. HOOYKAAS

BEER, WILHELM (*b.* Berlin, Germany, 4 January 1797; *d.* Berlin, 27 March 1850), *astronomy.*

A scion of a cultivated Jewish family (his brother was the poet Michael Beer; and his half-brother was the composer Jacob Meyer Beer, better known under the name of Meyerbeer), Beer was a banker by profession; by avocation, however, he was an amateur astronomer and the owner of a private observatory made famous by the work of Johann Mädler.

Beer's place in the history of astronomy is inseparably connected with the contributions that he and Mädler made between 1830 and 1840 to selenography and solar-system studies in general. Their first joint work was *Physikalische Beobachtungen des Mars in der Erdnähe* (1830), and their chef d'oeuvre was *Mappa selenographica totam lunae hemisphaeram visibilem complectens* (1836). This map, based on its author's observations made at Beer's private observatory with a Fraunhofer refractor of only 9.4-centimeter free aperture, constitutes a milestone in the development of selenographical literature. It was the first map to be divided into four quadrants (corresponding to a diameter of 97.5 centimeters for the apparent lunar disk) and contained a remarkably faithful representation of the moon's face as it is visible through a 4-inch refractor. Its topographic structure was based on the positions of 105 fundamental points measured micrometrically by Beer and Mädler (and related to the previous measurements by Wilhelm Lohrmann).

Moreover, an accompanying volume, *Der Mond nach seinen kosmischen und individuellen Verhältnissen, oder allgemeine vergleichende Selenographie* (1837), contains the results of micrometric measurements of the diameters of 148 lunar craters and of the relative altitudes of 830 lunar mountains, determined by the shadow method. This book also contains a reduced version (to 32 centimeters) of the original map of 1836.

One more book appeared under the joint authorship of Beer and Mädler—*Beiträge zur physischen Kenntniss der himmlichen Körper im Sonnensystem* (1839)—before Mädler left Berlin to accept the professorship of astronomy and directorship of the astronomical observatory in Dorpat (now Tartu), Estonia. His departure ended the ten-year partnership with Beer. For the remainder of his life Beer was unimportant in the history of astronomy, and one may suspect that, in his selenographical work with Mädler, he largely played the role of a Maecenas. His name remains inseparably connected, however, with the best map of the moon produced in the first half of the nineteenth century, a map that remained unsurpassed until the publication of the famous *Charte der Gebirge des Mondes* by J. F. J. Schmidt in 1878.

ZDENĚK KOPAL

BEEVOR, CHARLES EDWARD (*b.* London, England, 12 June 1854; *d.* London, 5 December 1908), *neurology, neurophysiology.*

Beevor was the eldest son of Charles Beevor, a fellow of the Royal College of Surgeons, and Elizabeth Burrell. He was educated at Blackheath Proprietary School, London, and University College, London. He qualified as a member of the Royal College of Surgeons in 1878, M.B. in 1879, L.S.A. in 1880, received the M.D. in 1881, was elected a member of the Royal College of Physicians in 1882, and became a fellow of the Royal College of Physicians of London in 1888. From 1882 to 1883 he studied in Austria, Germany, and France with Carl Weigert, Julius Cohnheim, Wilhelm Heinrich Erb, and others. Beevor was appointed assistant physician to the National Hospital, Queen Square, London, in 1883 and to the Great (later Royal) Northern Central Hospital in 1885. He became full physician at each of these hospitals, but was able to carry out neurophysiological investigations in addition to practicing clinical neurology. On 5 December 1882 he married Blanche Adine Leadam, who bore him a son and a daughter.

Beevor was a man of pleasant yet simple personality and graceful courtesy, with a keen sense of humor and considerable musical talent. His powers of observation, his industry, and his precision as a recorder were unsurpassed, and he was intensely self-critical. He possessed such marked scientific caution that occasionally he would not publish the results of his investigations if they seemed to refute established opinion. He was retiring, modest, and quite unselfish.

Essentially, Beevor was an excellent clinical neurologist whose main ambition was to make possible more accurate diagnosis of diseases of the nervous system. He was also, however, a general physician and practiced internal medicine as well as neurology for many years. His *Diseases of the Nervous System: A Handbook for Students and Practitioners* (1898) revealed his clinical ability as well as his literary skill, and his work on the diagnosis and localization of cerebral tumors was outstanding.

Beevor's researches in neurophysiology encompassed three areas.

(1) Cerebral cortical function. From 1883 to 1887 Beevor collaborated with Victor Horsley at the Brown Institution in London. They extended the work of Gustav Theodor Fritsch, Eduard Hitzig, and David Ferrier on the representation of function in the cerebral cortex. In particular they studied the motor region in monkeys by means of electrical stimulation and then carried out similar investigations on the internal capsule. Minute representation of movement could be mapped at each site. This work was an important landmark in the development of the concept of cerebral localization, and Beevor became widely known after it was published (1887–1891).

(2) Muscle movements. Beevor meticulously observed the function of muscles and muscle groups both in health and in disease. His Croonian lectures given before the Royal College of Physicians of London in 1903 and published in 1904 embodied his findings, which he linked to the earlier studies he had made on the motor cortex of the cerebral hemisphere.

(3) Cerebral circulation. Stimulated by the work of Otto Heubner (1872) and Henri Duret (1874), Beevor carried out experiments on the human brain in order to discover the areas of distribution of the five main arteries. He injected colored gelatin into all five vessels simultaneously, under a constant pressure. His findings, which appeared in 1908 and were of outstanding importance, were the first accurate ones to be published. Unfortunately, Beevor agreed with Duret that the brain arteries were end-arteries, each with its own territory. This view dominated anatomical and pathological considerations of cerebral circulation for two decades and was finally disproved by

R. A. Pfeifer in 1928. It is now known that Beevor's experiments and the deductions derived from them were incorrect and that all parts of the cerebral cortex are linked by an anastomosing vascular network.

BIBLIOGRAPHY

I. ORIGINAL WORKS. With Victor Horsley, Beevor wrote "A Minute Analysis (Experimental) of the Various Movements Produced by Stimulating in the Monkey Different Regions of the Cortical Centre for the Upper Limb, as Defined by Professor Ferrier," in *Philosophical Transactions of the Royal Society, Part B,* **178** (1887), 153–167; "A Further Minute Analysis by Electrico Stimulation of the So-called Motor Region of the Cortex Cerebri in the Monkey (*Macacus sinicus*)," *ibid.,* **179** (1888), 205–256; and "An Experimental Investigation Into the Arrangement of the Excitable Fibres of the Internal Capsule of the Bonnet Monkey (*Macacus sinicus*)," *ibid.,* **181** (1890), 49–88. Also see *Diseases of the Nervous System: A Handbook for Students and Practitioners* (London, 1898); *The Croonian Lectures on Muscular Movements and Their Representation in the Central Nervous System* (London, 1904); and "On the Distribution of the Different Arteries Supplying the Human Brain," in *Philosophical Transactions of the Royal Society, Part B,* **200** (1908), 1–55.

II. SECONDARY LITERATURE. Obituaries of Beevor are in *The Lancet,* **2** (1908), 1854–1855; and *British Medical Journal,* **2** (1908), 1785–1786. A short account of his life can be found in *Dictionary of National Biography,* 2nd supp., (London, 1912). For Beevor and his contribution to our knowledge of cerebral blood supply, see E. Clarke and C. D. O'Malley, *The Human Brain and Spinal Cord* (Berkeley-Los Angeles, 1968), pp. 779–783.

EDWIN CLARKE

BÉGHIN, HENRI (*b.* Lille, France, 16 September 1876; *d.* Paris, France, 22 February 1969), *mechanics.*

Béghin studied at the École Normale Supérieure from 1894 to 1897 and placed first in the mathematics *agrégation* in 1897. For over twenty years he lived in Brest, where his inclination toward mechanics was strengthened. At the *lycée* there he gave courses that would prepare students for the École Navale (1899–1908) and later taught mechanics at the École Navale itself (1908–1921). Béghin organized the training of radio electricians during World War I. He began his university career in Montpellier (1921–1924) and later occupied the chair of mechanics at Lille (1924–1929). He lectured in fluid mechanics at Paris from 1929 to 1932 and was made professor of physical and experimental mechanics and director of the mechanics laboratory. Béghin also taught at the École des Beaux-Arts (1924–1930), the École Supérieure d'Aéronautique (1930–1939), and the

École Polytechnique (from 1936). He was elected to the Académie des Sciences on 25 February 1946.

A remarkable teacher and inspirer of applied research, Béghin had a long and fruitful career. His accomplishments stem from his ability to rephrase classical mechanics and to enlarge its scope. Béghin is associated with the most general treatment of systems of nonholonomic linkage, through which he demonstrated, in his first works (1902–1903), how to use Lagrange's equations in percussion problems. He also provided an elegant extension of Carnot's theorem that leads to an exhaustive formulation. He extended the solution of Painlevé's paradox by increasing the examples of dynamic interference due to friction. Béghin also showed the significance of indeterminates, which sometimes appear in very simple cases, for theoretical solutions in a branch of mechanics whose principles do not involve any consideration of microscopic deformations. In elastic impact, he showed that the main characteristic of the end of the impact is that the loss of kinetic energy equals the work absorbed by friction during the impact, and that the reversal of the normal component of the relative speed, until then believed to occur in all such impacts, is realized only under specific conditions of symmetry.

The theory of the gyrostatic compass, which Béghin published in 1921 and later perfected, is significant for his fusion of the extensions of rational mechanics with technical and experimental data. He thus became a specialist in servomechanisms. In this field he studied and experimented with the elimination of vibrations and developed numerous applications, notably for automatic piloting of ships and planes.

Béghin, whose training was classical, was ahead of his time because of his new method of scientific work. He always worked with others, which at times makes it difficult to assess his contribution.

BIBLIOGRAPHY

Among Béghin's writings are "Sur les percussions dans les systèmes non holonomes," in *Journal de mathématiques pures et appliquées,* **9** (1903), 21–26, written with T. Rousseau; "Extension du théorème de Carnot au cas où certaines liaisons dépendent du temps," *ibid.; Étude théorique des compas gyrostatiques Anschütz et Sperry* (Paris, 1921); *Statique et dynamique,* 2 vols. (Paris, 1921; 7th ed., 1957); "Sur un nouveau compas gyrostatique," in *Comptes rendus de l'Académie des sciences,* **176** (1923), written with P. Monfraix; "Étude d'une machine locomotive à l'aide du théorème des travaux virtuels," in *Bulletin de l'élève ingénieur* (1924); "Étude théorique d'un compas zénithal gyrostatique à amortisseur tournant," in *Annales hydro-*

graphiques (1924), written with P. Monfraix; "Sur certains problèmes de frottement," in *Nouvelles annales de mathématiques*, **2** (1924) and **3** (1925); "Sur les transmissions par adhérence," in *Bulletin de l'élève ingénieur* (1925); *Leçons sur la mécanique des fils* (Tourcoing, 1927–1929), a course given at the École Technique Supérieure de Textile; "Sur les conditions d'application des équations de Lagrange à un système non holonome," in *Bulletin de la Société mathématique de France*, no. 57 (1929); "Sur le choc de deux solides en tenant compte du frottement," *ibid.*; *Exercices de mécanique*, 2 vols. (Paris, 1930; 2nd ed., 1946, 1951), written with G. Julia; *Cours de mécanique de l'École Polytechnique*, privately mimeographed (1942–1943), Vol. I later pub. (Paris, 1947); *Cours de mécanique théorique et appliquée à l'usage des ingénieurs et des étudiants de facultés*, 2 vols. (Paris, 1952); and "Les preuves de la rotation de la terre," in *Conférences du Palais de la Découverte*, ser. A, no. 207 (23 Apr. 1955).

A more complete bibliography and a lengthy list of studies and theses done under Béghin's supervision at the Laboratory of Physical Mechanics of the Faculty of Sciences, Paris, may be found in Béghin's *Notice sur les travaux scientifiques de M. Henri Béghin* (1943, 1945), at the secretariat of the Academy of Sciences, Paris.

PIERRE COSTABEL

BEGUIN, JEAN (*b.* Lorraine, France, *ca.* 1550; *d.* Paris, France, *ca.* 1620), *chemistry.*

Little is known of Beguin's family and early life, but he seems to have received a good classical education. When he arrived in Paris, possibly from Sedan, the influence of the royal physician, Jean Ribit, and of Turquet de Mayerne enabled him to obtain permission to set up a laboratory and give public lectures on the preparation of the new chemical medicaments of Quercetanus and others. His clear and lucid exposition and demonstration of chemical techniques won him large audiences. He complained that his unveiling of the mysteries of iatrochemistry so angered other "spagyrists" that they twice broke into his laboratory, plundering drugs and valuable manuscripts.

Beguin's first publication was an edition of Michael Sendivogius' *Novum lumen chymicum* with a preface (1608). The signature to the dedication shows that he was then almoner to Henry IV. Jeremias Barth, a Silesian who had studied medicine at Sedan, became Beguin's pupil at some time and encouraged him to publish a "little book," so that he would not have to dictate his lectures to his pupils. As a result, Beguin published the *Tyrocinium chymicum* (1610), a slim volume of seventy pages. The book was immediately pirated at Cologne, and Beguin published a revised edition with a long defense of chemical remedies (1612).

According to information in various editions of the *Tyrocinium*, Beguin had visited the mines of Hungary and Slovenia in 1604, and visited the Hungarian mines again in 1642. In a letter to Barth in 1613, he said he had earned 700 crowns by his skill, and could hardly earn more by teaching. The preface to the 1615 French edition says he was about to depart for Germany in search of the repose he had once found there, but yielded to the wishes of his friends and remained in France. In the same edition he acknowledged the authority and censorship of the Paris Faculty of Medicine, which may be the reason for his omission of a Paracelsian quotation.

For Beguin, chemistry was the art of separating and recombining natural mixed bodies to produce agreeable and safe medicines. The book opened with a Paracelsian quotation, followed by an exposition of the *tria prima* in a short theoretical section. The three elements were spiritual rather than corporeal, since they were impregnated by seeds emanating from the celestial bodies. Most of the work is concerned with chemical operations rather than with theory, and Beguin emphasized that the most effective therapy combined Galenic and Paracelsian remedies. The "quintessences" brought into prominence by the *Archidoxes* of Paracelsus occupy only a short third book. Beguin is credited with the first mention of acetone, which he called "the burning spirit of Saturn." Long sections on techniques and processes in Beguin parallel Libavius' *Alchymia* (1597), and both may have depended on a common source. Beguin cited Hermes Trismegistus, Lull, and the *Turba philosophorum* as authorities, and was a firm believer in transmutation.

Tyrocinium chymicum was immensely popular through the seventeenth century, and had swollen to nearly 500 pages in some later editions. It was translated into the major European languages and issued in many editions; it set the pattern for the notable series of French chemical textbooks in the later part of the century and was not really superseded until the appearance of Nicolas Lémery's *Cours de chymie* (1675).

BIBLIOGRAPHY

I. ORIGINAL WORKS. Beguin's writings include the dedication and preface to an edition of Michael Sendivogius' *Novum lumen chymicum* (Paris, 1608); *Tyrocinium chymicum* (Paris, 1610; rev. ed., 1612, the *editio princeps*); and *Les élémens de chymie* (Paris, 1615), English trans. by Richard Russell (London, 1669).

II. SECONDARY LITERATURE. Beguin and *Tyrocinium chymicum* are comprehensively discussed in T. S. Patterson, "Jean Beguin and His *Tyrocinium chymicum*," in *Annals of Science*, **2** (1937), 243–298; the editions are conveniently listed in J. R. Partington, *A History of Chemistry,* III (London, 1962), 2–3. Various aspects are discussed in A. Kent and O. Hannaway, "Some New Considerations on Beguin and Libavius," in *Annals of Science,* **16** (1960), 241–250; Hélène Metzger, *Les doctrines chimiques en France, du début du XVIIIe siècle à la fin du XVIIIe siècle* (Paris, 1923), pp. 36–44; R. P. Multhauf, "Libavius and Beguin," in E. Farber, ed., *Great Chemists* (New York-London, 1961), pp. 65–74; John Read, *Humour and Humanism in Chemistry* (London, 1947), pp. 81–88; and Lynn Thorndike, *A History of Magic and Experimental Science,* VIII (New York, 1958), 106–113.

P. M. RATTANSI

BÉGUYER DE CHANCOURTOIS, ALEXANDRE-ÉMILE (*b.* Paris, France, 20 January 1820; *d.* Paris, 14 November 1886), *geology.*

A grandson of René-Louis-Maurice Béguyer de Chancourtois, a noted artist and architect, Alexandre-Émile entered the École Polytechnique in 1838 and the École des Mines in 1840. At the age of twenty-three he left the latter to travel through Armenia, Turkestan, the Banat, and Hungary, and became involved in the exploration and study of their mountainous regions.

He returned to the École des Mines in 1848 as professor of descriptive geometry and subsurface topology, and retained his affiliation with this institution until his death. Here he met Élie de Beaumont, whose geological theories greatly influenced him. Béguyer became *professeur suppléant* to Élie in 1852, succeeding him as professor of geology in 1875. Élie, who headed the French Geological Survey, had his protégé named assistant director, and together they undertook an exploration of the Haute-Marne regions. This venture resulted in Béguyer's publication in 1860 of a geological map of that region (drawn by M. Duhamel) as well as his collaboration with Élie on *Études stratigraphiques sur le départ de la Haute-Marne* (1862). The latter work contained a detailed study of the geological distribution of certain mineral deposits (sulfur, sodium, chlorine, the hydrocarbons); according to Élie's theories, they should have been found in particular mineralogical, petrographic, and geological association.

Generalizing further from Élie's ideas, Béguyer formulated a method for classifying chemical elements based "in the last analysis upon the distribution of these elements in the crust of the globe." His scheme, a precursor of the periodic table, was put forth in "Vis tellurique, classement des corps simples ou radicaux au moyen d'une système de classification helicoïdal et numérique" (1862). The model for his theory was the "telluric screw," a helical graph wound about a cylinder. The base of the cylinder was divided by sixteen equally spaced points, and the screw thread was similarly divided on each of its turns; the seventeenth point was on the second turn directly above the first, the eighteenth above the second, and so forth. Each point was supposed to represent the "characteristic number" of some element that could be deduced from its physical properties or chemical characteristics. Actually, Béguyer used unit equivalent weights as characteristic numbers, following Prout, who made hydrogen the unit. These weights were derived by measuring the specific heat of each element in a manner suggested by Regnault.

When placed on the telluric screw, elements whose equivalent weights differed by sixteen units were aligned in vertical columns. Sodium, for example, with a weight of 23, appeared one thread above lithium, with a weight of 7; potassium was above sodium, manganese above potassium. To the right of these columns was the group containing magnesium (24), calcium (40), iron (56), strontium (88), uranium (120), and barium (152). Directly opposite this group on the screw, oxygen (16) was aligned with sulfur (32), tellurium (128), and bismuth (224). One could, Béguyer believed, draw helices of any pitch through any two characteristic numbers of elements in different columns and find relationships among the elements so connected. Contrasts and analogies in mineralogical associations of the elements would become apparent through the sequences of their characteristic numbers along these helices. He showed that a line passed through magnesium and potassium (associated in the micas) would unite them, just as a line through sodium and calcium would show an association confirmed in the feldspars. If such lines were extended through or near the characteristic numbers of other elements, one would also be able to relate them to these mineral groups.

The name "telluric screw" was suggested to Béguyer by several circumstances, "especially the position of tellurium in the middle of the table and at the end of a characteristic series" and by the geognostic origin of his ideas, "since *tellus* refers to globe in the most positive and familiar sense, in the sense of Mother Earth."

Despite an unfortunate lapse into numerology and several errors in determining equivalent weights, "Vis tellurique" may be said to have anticipated Mendeleev's periodic table. When describing the theoretical origins of his work, Mendeleev mentioned that he was aware of Béguyer's ideas among others; he further acknowledged that his own periodic classification was influenced to some extent by his knowledge of previous systems.

Béguyer made still other contributions to geology. He worked with Le Play in organizing the Universal Exposition of 1855. Prince Napoleon, who had been interested in the exposition and was pleased by its success, invited Béguyer to participate in the voyage of the *Reine Hortense* to the polar regions the following year. In 1875 Béguyer was appointed director general of mines in France and initiated programs for the safety of miners and engineers. He also advocated the use of stereographic and gnomonic projections and campaigned for the adoption of a uniform system of cartographic gradation based on the metric system.

Béguyer served as secretary of Prince Napoleon's Imperial Commission for the 1867 Universal Exposition. He also organized the French geological exhibits at the expositions in Venice (1881) and Madrid (1883), and was *chef de cabinet* during Prince Napoleon's administration of Algeria and the African colonies.

A man of diverse interests, Béguyer attempted to develop a universal alphabet. He also studied human geography, trying to see if there was any consistent relationship between the geology of a country and the life style of its people. He devoted a great deal of time and effort to the improvement of the geological collections of the École des Mines and, finally, he toyed with ideas for using imaginary numbers in physics.

BIBLIOGRAPHY

I. ORIGINAL WORKS. Béguyer contributed nearly 75 memoirs and notes, which may be found in *Comptes rendus de l'Académie des sciences* (1844–1864); *Annales des mines* (1846); and *Bulletin de la Société géologique* (1874–1884). Among his works are "Sur la distribution des minéraux de fer," in *Comptes rendus de l'Académie des sciences,* **51** (1860), 414–417, the text accompanying Duhamel's map; *Études stratigraphiques sur le départ de la Haute-Marne* (Paris, 1862); and, most important, "Vis tellurique," in *Comptes rendus de l'Académie des sciences,* **54** (1862), 757–761, 840–843, 967–971.

II. SECONDARY LITERATURE. Works on Béguyer are Roman D'Amat, "Béguyer de Chancourtois," in *Dictionnaire de biographie française,* V (1951), 1279; and Léon Sagnet, "Chancourtois," in *La grande encyclopédie,* X (1890), 495.

MARTHA B. KENDALL

BEHAIM, MARTIN, also known as **Martin of Bohemia** (*b.* Nuremberg, Germany, 1459; *d.* Lisbon, Portugal, 29 July 1507), *geography.*

The mercantile interests of Behaim's family extended from Venice to Flanders. It is traditionally acknowledged that he was a disciple of Regiomontanus, from whom he may have learned how to use astronomical instruments. He quite certainly was influenced by the *Ephemerides* published by the latter between 1475 and 1506. As a youth he began in the textile business in Flanders. He was in business in Lisbon in 1480.

There has been much speculation about Behaim's role in Portugal. We know that he became a member of the Council of Mathematicians created by John II and that he became friendly with José Vicinho. Nevertheless, we can no longer defend the thesis that celestial navigation was possible only because of Behaim's teaching the Portuguese how to use the cross staff (Jacob's staff, or *ballestilla*) and the astronomical tables of Regiomontanus. The cross staff, invented by Levi ben Gerson, was already well known on the Iberian Peninsula; and the declination of the sun given in the *Tabula directionum* of Regiomontanus is different from that found in the *Regimento do astrolabio . . . Tractado da spera do mundo* prepared by the Council of Mathematicians for use by navigators. Joaquín Bensaúde has demonstrated that the numerical values in the *Regimento* are copies of those in the four-year-cycle sun table in the *Almanach perpetuum* (1473) of Abraham Zacuto, a Jew from Salamanca (*d. ca.* 1515), who had been a teacher of Vicinho. The latter was also involved in the scientific movement at the University of Salamanca (with Diego Ortiz and Juan de Salaya), and thus one must believe that the scientific elements that made celestial navigation possible were already present on the peninsula before the arrival of Behaim.

Behaim took part in the expedition of Diogo Cão (1485–1486) that followed the coast of Africa to Cape Cross. It is difficult to determine whether he carried out an observation of the latitude of the North Star while on this trip, or whether this should be attributed to Diogo Gomes (who dictated his memoirs to Behaim) and thus be dated a few years earlier. The text in question, which constitutes the birth certificate of celestial navigation in the Atlantic Ocean (although not in the East Indian), says: "When I went to these places, I took a quadrant. I marked the latitude of the North Pole on the table of the quadrant, and I noticed that the quadrant is more useful than the chart. It is true that on the latter one can see the sea route, but if it is incorrect [i.e., if one has committed an error in determining the course] one never arrives at the point previously designated."

During a landfall at Fayal, Azores, on the return voyage in 1486, Behaim married the daughter of Job Huerter de Moerbeke (in Portuguese, Joz Dutra or Jorge de Utra), the leader of a large Flemish colony there. From 1491 to 1493 he was in Nuremberg, where with the assistance of the painter Glockenthon he built his famous globe. Upon his return to Portugal, Behaim was entrusted with a number of official missions and was taken prisoner by the English while on a journey to Flanders. After he was released, he took up residence in Fayal. He died in the Hospice of Saint Bartholomew while on one of his trips to Lisbon.

A nautical chart, since lost, that showed the strait discovered years later by Magellan was attributed to Behaim. His most important work, which places him among the greatest geographers of the Renaissance, is the globe that has been preserved in Nuremberg. It is a sphere fifty-one centimeters in diameter, covered with parchment luxuriously adorned with many types of figures (111 miniatures, forty-eight banners, and fifteen coats of arms). Many inscriptions clarify and explain, from the most diverse points of view, the geography of 1,100 localities in many parts of the world. Actually, this globe constitutes an adaptation of a nautical chart onto a sphere. It lacks coordinates, but it does represent the equator and the tropics. The space between the western coast of Europe and the eastern coast of Asia is full of fanciful islands from medieval tradition, such as Antilia, which has no relation to the Antilles.

BIBLIOGRAPHY

Behaim's globe has been reproduced in almost every book on the history of geography.

For information on Behaim and his work, see G. Beaujouan, "Les aspects internationaux de la découverte océanique aux XVe et XVIe siècles," in *Actes du Cinquième Colloque International d'Histoire Maritime* (Paris, 1960–1966), pp. 69–73; J. Bensaúde, *Histoire de la science nautique portugaise à l'époque des grandes découvertes. Collection de documents . . .,* I, *Regimento do astrolabio e do quadrante. Tractado da spera do mundo,* facs. (Munich, 1914); S. Gunther, *Martin Behaim,* Bayerische Bibliothek, XIII (Bamberg, 1890); R. Henning, *Terrae incognitae,* IV (Leiden, 1939), 342–376, and indexes; E. G. Ravenstein, *Martin Behaim, His Life and His Globe* (London, 1908); A. Reichenbach, *Martin Behaim, ein deutscher Seefahrer aus den 15 Jahrhundert* (Wurzen–Leipzig, 1889); and R. Uhden, "Die Behaimsche Erdkugel und die Nürnberger Globen technik am Ende des 15 Jahrhunderts," in *Minutes of the Amsterdam Geography Congress, Works of Section IV: Géographie historique et histoire de la géographie,* IV (1938), 196–198.

JUAN VERNET

BEHRING, EMIL VON (*b*. Hansdorf, Germany, 15 March 1854; *d*. Marburg, Germany, 31 March 1917), *medicine, serology.*

Behring, one of twelve children of August Georg Behring, a teacher, and his second wife, Augustine Zech, grew up in simple circumstances in Hansdorf, a small town that is now under Polish administration. His father intended him to be a teacher or a minister, both traditional family professions, and in 1866 enrolled him in the Gymnasium of Hohenstein, in East Prussia. During his school years Behring discovered his interest in medicine, but he saw no hope of pursuing it. Accordingly, he planned to enter the University of Königsberg as a theology student.

Fortunately, one of Behring's teachers arranged for his acceptance at the Friedrich Wilhelms Institute in Berlin, where future military surgeons received a free medical education in return for promising to serve in the Prussian Army for ten years after passing their university examinations. Thus, in 1874 Behring became a cadet at the institute. In 1878 he received the M.D. and in 1880 passed his state board examinations. In the same year he was appointed intern at the Charité, a Berlin hospital, and in 1881 was attached to a cavalry regiment in Posen (now Poznan, Poland) as assistant surgeon. In between, he served for a short time as physician to a battalion stationed in Wohlau.

Behring, who had shown remarkable dedication at the Friedrich Wilhelms Institute, began to ponder scientific questions during his service in Wohlau and Posen. He was particularly interested in the possibility of combating infectious diseases through the use of disinfectants.

In 1881 Behring wrote his first paper on sepsis and antisepsis in theory and practice. In it he raised the question whether, in addition to external disinfection, the entire living organism could not be disinfected internally. He started investigations on iodoform (discovered as early as 1822 but introduced into wound treatment only in 1880) and the disinfecting effect of its derivatives. In 1882 he published his first treatise, "Experimentelle Arbeiten über desinficierende Mittel," which had been written in Posen. He had to admit that in many cases the disinfectant's toxic effect upon the organism was obviously much stronger than its disinfecting effect upon the bacteria. He concluded that the favorable results observed after the application of iodoform to infected wounds were not due to its being a parasiticide, but to its antitoxic effects. On the basis of later research, however, he came to reject its general use. In 1898 he wrote:

The fact that living animal and human body cells show much more sensitivity to disinfecting agents than any hitherto known bacteria may almost be considered a law of nature. As a result, before bacteria are killed by a disinfectant or their growth in the organs can be stunted, the infected animal body itself is killed by this same agent ["Über Heilprinzipien, insbesondere über das ätiologische und das isopathische Heilprinzip," in *Deutsche medizinische Wochenschrift,* **24,** no. 5 (1898), 67].

According to Behring's own statements, these iodoform experiments were the beginning of his preoccupation with antitoxic blood-serum therapy.

In 1883, at his own request, Behring was transferred from remote West Prussia to Winzig, Silesia. There he published another paper on iodoform poisonings and their treatment. At this time he prepared for the civil service medical examinations, since he planned to enter the Prussian Public Health Service after completing his service as a military surgeon. In 1887 he was promoted to captain and sent to the Pharmacological Institute in Bonn for further training. The director of this institute, Carl Binz, was especially interested in all problems concerning disinfectants. In the same year Behring published a report on new investigations concerning iodoform and acetylene. At the institute he acquired the knowledge and working habits necessary for accurate animal experiments and research in toxicology. In 1888 Behring was sent to Berlin, and after a brief service at the Academy for Military Medicine, in 1889 he joined the Institute for Hygiene of the University of Berlin, then presided over by Robert Koch. Here, between 1889 and 1895, Behring developed his pioneering ideas on serum therapy and his theory of antitoxins. Also in 1889, Behring finished his army service and became Koch's full-time assistant.

As early as 1887, in Bonn, Behring had ascertained that the serum of tetanus-immune white rats contained a substance that neutralized anthrax bacilli. This he saw as the cause of "resistance." Beginning in 1889, he worked in Berlin with Shibasaburo Kitasato on the isolation and definition of this agent. One of their goals was still the discovery of suitable systemic disinfecting agents, especially against anthrax, for which iodine, gold, and zinc compounds were tested. But of greater promise were experiments aimed at inhibiting the causative agents by using certain sera similar in effect to disinfectants, since the organism showed far greater tolerance to the sera. On 4 December 1890 Behring and Kitasato jointly published their first paper on blood-serum therapy, followed on 11 December by another report, signed by Behring alone, which discussed the blood-serum therapy not only in the treatment of tetanus but also of diphtheria. In it he stressed four points:

(1) The blood of tetanus-immune rabbits possesses tetanus toxin-destroying properties.

(2) These properties are also present in extravascular blood and in the cell-free serum obtained from the latter.

(3) These properties are so lasting that they remain effective when injected into other animals, thus making it possible to achieve excellent therapeutic effects with blood or serum transfusions.

(4) Tetanus toxin-destroying properties are not present in the blood of animals not immune to tetanus.

Behring immediately recognized that evidently a new principle of defense by the organism against infection had been discovered, one that clearly clashed with the then-prevalent cellular pathology of Virchow. Subsequently, Behring clashed with Virchow over the importance of his discoveries. One day before the publication of Behring's discovery, Ludwig Brieger and Carl Fränkel published a paper in the *Berliner klinische Wochenschrift* on the isolation of a protein substance—in their opinion a toxic substance—from bacteria; they called it "toxalbumine" and ascribed to it the severity of various infectious diseases. In the following years, however, Behring was able to show that the therapeutic principle in the serum, which he called "antitoxin," was ineffective against "toxalbumine" but acted against a specific toxin secreted by the bacteria. Incidentally, he succeeded in obtaining his new antitoxin-containing blood serum from guinea pigs treated not only with live diphtheria bacilli but also with diphtheria toxin alone in increasing dosages. Thus, in contrast with the hitherto prevailing phagocytosis theory of Élie Metchnikoff, he demonstrated the humoral defense capacities of the organism. Accordingly, he terminated his first work with the famous passage from Goethe's *Faust*: "Blood is a very special liquid."

When Paul Ehrlich demonstrated in 1891 that even vegetable poisons led to the formation of antitoxins in the organism, Behring's theory was confirmed and a lifelong friendship was formed. Both Behring and Ehrlich were then serving as assistants at the Koch Institute in Berlin. Behring immediately recognized the unusual importance of his discovery, and wrote:

For hundreds and thousands of years the wisest physicians and scientists have studied the properties of blood and its relation to health and illness, without ever suspecting the specific antibodies appearing in the blood as a result of an infectious disease, which are capable of rendering infectious toxins harmless [Kleinschmidt, p. 347].

In 1891, at the Seventh International Hygiene Congress in London, Behring appeared for the first time before the public and delivered a lecture entitled

"Desinfektion am lebenden Organismus." He stressed that his method resulted above all in a natural increase of natural healing powers, leading in turn to increased resistance to nerve and cell toxins produced by pathogens. In 1892 he published his investigations in *Die praktischen Ziele der Blutserumtherapie und der Immunisierungsmethoden zum Zwecke der Gewinnung von Heilserum* and *Das Tetanusheilserum und seine Anwendung auf tetanuskranke Menschen.* Behring had to defend himself incessantly against all kinds of attacks. Failures due to the low antitoxin content of his first sera made his enthusiastic statements less credible. Furthermore, Behring—who at times used sharp language in his polemics—was forced to take issue with priority claims by other authors.

The legendary account of the first use of diphtheria serum on a patient on Christmas Eve 1891 has not been fully verified. A critical case of diphtheria is said to have been successfully treated with the serum by Behring's colleagues Geissler and Wernicke, in the infectious-disease ward of the surgical clinic of Berlin University. It is doubtful that sufficient serum was available at that time, since it was obtained exclusively from guinea pigs and then from sheep. When, in 1894, Roux and André Martin introduced the immunization of horses, Behring immediately adopted and extended this procedure. From 1892 on, he was backed by Farbwerke Meister, Lucius und Brüning, a dye works in Höchst, a suburb of Frankfurt. Until then Behring had put his own money in his research.

From 1893 on, serum therapy experimentation was conducted on a more extensive scale. In that year Behring became professor. Soon afterward there appeared the first publications by Hermann Kossel and Otto Heubner on results obtained with the new serum therapy, which reduced the mortality rate from 52 percent to 25 percent. In 1894 the first serum therapy experiments were carried out in France, England, and the United States. In the meantime, in 1893 Behring had written two important works on problems of great interest to him, *Die ätiologische Behandlung der Infektionskrankheiten* and *Geschichte der Diphtherie,* to which he added two books on the treatment of infectious diseases (1894, 1898).

Behring was quick to see that in order to obtain results in man, methods for standardizing the serum must be found. These methods were developed in 1897 by Ehrlich. Since 1895, however, standardization of the serum had been under state control. In 1896 the control authority became the Institute for Serum Research and Testing; today it is known as the Paul Ehrlich Institute and performs the same tasks on a more extensive scale.

In the fall of 1894 Behring, whose relationship with Koch had perceptibly cooled, was appointed associate professor of hygiene in Halle. He taught there for only a short time and with moderate success. The following year he was appointed professor of hygiene in Marburg—against the wishes of the Medical Faculty and thanks to determined efforts on his behalf by Friedrich Althoff, a powerful figure in the Prussian Ministry for Education. In Marburg, Behring carried on intensive research and organized what is now known as the Behring Institute. In the meantime, he had acquired great renown, especially in France, where Roux and Metchnikoff had become his close friends. He was made an officer of the Legion of Honor in 1895 and with Roux shared the 50,000-franc prize of the Académie de Médecine as well as the 50,000-franc prize of the Académie des Sciences. Also in 1895 he received the Prussian title of *Geheimrat* (privy councillor), and in 1901 his lifework was crowned with the first Nobel Prize in physiology and medicine, followed by his elevation to the hereditary nobility.

Beginning in 1889, Behring dedicated himself to a new task, the fight against tuberculosis. In competition with Koch he also attempted to find a substance suitable for tuberculosis vaccination. Finally, he felt he had succeeded with "tulase," an extract from tuberculosis bacilli treated with chloral hydrate, but his vaccination attempts failed. Nevertheless, we are indebted to Behring for his important findings on the spread of tuberculosis, which he ascribed mainly to the consumption by infants of milk containing tuberculosis bacilli. In contrast with Koch, he was convinced bovine and human tuberculosis were identical, a belief based on an understandable error. Nevertheless, his suggestions for combating bovine tuberculosis were of extreme importance and brought about vital changes in public health policy. In 1900, however, he realized that he was not achieving his objective and concluded one of his papers as follows: "Here I should like to say simply that I have definitely abandoned my hope for obtaining antitoxin for humans from cured and immunized tubercular cattle. Consequently, I have stopped searching for an antitoxin against tuberculosis."

Nevertheless, Behring's preoccupation with tuberculosis continued, and in 1903 and 1904 he devoted two monographs to this subject. Finally, in 1905 he suggested disinfection of milk for infants by adding Formalin and hydrogen peroxide, a process that proved impractical.

In 1913, in dogged pursuit of his theory of the origin of antitoxins as a result of insufficient toxin in the organism, Behring introduced active preventive vaccination against diphtheria. Its basis was a balanced toxin-antitoxin mixture, rendered stable by formaldehyde.

World War I, which separated Behring from his friends outside Germany, helped to substantiate his theories. The preventive, although still passive, tetanus vaccination saved the lives of millions of German soldiers. For his contributions Behring was awarded the Iron Cross, an unusual decoration for a noncombatant.

In 1896 Behring had married Else Spinola, daughter of one of the directors of the Charité Hospital in Berlin, who bore him six sons. The Villa Behring in Marburg, still standing today, was the gathering place of society. Behring also owned a house on Capri, where he was fond of vacationing. He liked to seclude himself in Switzerland, especially when suffering from the serious depressions that occasionally required sanatorium treatment. A fractured thigh, which initially seemed harmless, led to a pseudarthrosis that resulted in increasingly limited mobility. When Behring contracted pneumonia, his already weakened constitution was unable to withstand the multiple strain, and he died in Marburg on 31 March 1917.

For the discovery of antitoxins and the development of passive and active preventive vaccinations against diphtheria and tetanus, Behring was honored with the epithet "Children's Savior." By the same token, he could be called the "Soldier's Savior." His modern concepts raised humoral pathology to renewed importance, and he was certainly the equal of the other two pioneers in bacteriology, Pasteur and Koch. In his antitoxin theory Behring discovered a new principle in the fight against infections. He was able to realize his plan for an important and worthwhile lifework only by single-mindedly pursuing his original ideas. He thereby became involved in disputes with certain experts. Also, since he embraced the principle of "authority, not majority," he was not particularly adept at making friends or founding a school. He remained one of the great solitary figures in the history of medicine.

BIBLIOGRAPHY

I. Original Works. Most of Behring's scientific papers may be found in two editions of collected works, the first covering the period 1882–1893 and the second the later period up to 1915: *Gesammelte Abhandlungen zur ätiologischen Therapie von ansteckenden Krankheiten* (Leipzig, 1893); and *Gesammelte Abhandlungen. Neue Folge* (Bonn, 1915). The most important papers and monographs are "Über Iodoform und Iodoformwirkung" in *Deutsche medizinische Wochenschrift,* **8** (1882), 146–148; "Die Bedeutung des Iodoforms in der antiseptischen Wundbehandlung," *ibid.,* 323–329; "Über das Zustandekommen der Diphtherie-Immunität und der Tetanus-Immunität bei Thieren," *ibid.,* **16** (1890), 113–114, written with S. Kitasato; "Untersuchungen über das Zustandekommen der Diphtherie-Immunität bei Thieren," *ibid.,* 1145–1148; "Über Immunisierung und Heilung von Versuchsthieren bei der Diphtherie," in *Zeitschrift für Hygiene und Infektionskrankheiten,* **12** (1892), 10–44, written with E. Wernicke; *Die praktischen Ziele der Blutserumtherapie und die Immunisierungsmethoden zum Zwecke der Gewinnung von Heilserum* (Leipzig, 1892); "Die Behandlung der Diphtherie mit Diphtherieheilserum," in *Deutsche medizinische Wochenschrift,* **19** (1893), 543–547, and **20** (1894), 645–646; *Die Geschichte der Diphtherie* (Leipzig, 1893); *Die Bekämpfung der Infektionskrankheiten* (Leipzig, 1894); *Allgemeine Therapie der Infektionskrankheiten* (Berlin–Vienna, 1898); *Diphtherie, Begriffsbestimmung, Zustandekommen, Erkennung und Verhütung* (Berlin, 1901); *Tuberkulosebekämpfung* (Marburg, 1903); "Tuberkuloseentstehung, Tuberkulosebekämpfung und Säuglingsernährung," in *Beiträge zur experimentellen Therapie,* **8** (1904); *Einführung in die Lehre von der Bekämpfung der Infektionskrankheiten* (Berlin, 1912); and "Über ein neues Diphtherieschutzmittel," in *Deutsche medizinische Wochenschrift,* **39** (1913), 873–876, and **40** (1914), 1139.

II. Secondary Literature. The best biography, with many illustrations and references, is H. Zeiss and R. Bieling, *Behring. Gestalt und Werk* (Berlin, 1940). An exhaustive bibliography may be found in H. Dold, *In memoriam Paul Ehrlich und Emil von Behring zur 70. Wiederkehr ihrer Geburtstage* (Berlin, 1924). A biographical novel is H. Unger, *Emil von Behring* (Hamburg, 1948). Additional biographical articles are E. Bauereisen, "Emil von Behring," in *Neue deutsche Biographie,* II (Berlin, 1955), 14–15; H. von Behring, "Emil v. Behring," in *Lebensbilder aus Kurhessen und Waldeck,* **1** (1935), 10–14; and "Emil v. Behring zum 100. Geburtstag," in *Deutsches medizinisches Journal,* **5** (1954), 172–173; A. Beyer, "Zum 100. Geburtstag von Paul Ehrlich und Emil v. Behring," in *Deutsches Gesundheitswesen,* **9** (1954), 293–296; C. H. Browning, "Emil von Behring and Paul Ehrlich; Their Contributions to Science," in *Nature,* **175** (1955), 616–619; K. W. Clauberg, "Das immunologische Vermächtnis Emil von Behrings und Paul Ehrlichs," in *Deutsches medizinisches Journal,* **5** (1954), 138–146; C. Hallauer, "Emil von Behring und sein Werk," in *Schweizerische Zeitschrift für allgemeine Pathologie und Bakteriologie,* **17** (1954), 392–399; M. Jantsch, "Gemeinsames im wissenschaftlichen Werk Ehrlichs und Behrings," in *Wiener klinische Wochenschrift,* **66** (1954), 181–182; H. Kleinschmidt, "Zum 100. Geburtstag von Emil v. Behring," in *Medizinische* (1954), 347–348; A. S. Macnalty, "Emil von Behring," in *British Medical Journal* (1954), **1**, 668–670; and P. Schaaf, *Emil von Behring zum Gedächtnis. Herausgegeben von der Universität Marburg* (Marburg, 1944); *Robert Koch und Emil von Behring. Ursprung und Geist einer Forschung* (Berlin, 1944); and obituary notices in *British Medical Journal* (1917), **1**, 498; and *Lancet* (1917), **1**, 890.

H. SCHADEWALDT

BEILSTEIN, KONRAD FRIEDRICH (*b.* St. Petersburg, Russia, 17 February 1838; *d.* St. Petersburg, 18 October 1906), *chemistry.*

Beilstein's parents, Friedrich Beilstein and Catharine Margaret Rutsch, were German. His father, a salesman and tailor from Lichtenberg near Darmstadt, was related to Justus Liebig. His mother came from a farming and weaving family, and her uncle, Johannes Conrad Rutsch, was court tailor to the czar. Rutsch took an interest in Beilstein and sent him, at the age of fifteen, to Germany for study. Beilstein studied with leading figures in Germany—Bunsen and Kekulé at Heidelberg, Liebig at Munich, and Wöhler at Göttingen. In 1858 he received the doctorate at Göttingen, then continued his studies with Wurtz and Charles Friedel in Paris, and with Löwig in Breslau. In 1860 he began to teach at Göttingen, and in 1865 was appointed extraordinary professor. As a result of family difficulties following his father's death, Beilstein moved to the Technical Institute of St. Petersburg in 1866 and remained there the rest of his life. From 1865 to 1871 he, Hübner, and Fittig edited the *Zeitschrift für Chemie.* He belonged to the Deutsche Chemische Gesellschaft, and in 1881 was elected to the St. Petersburg Academy of Sciences.

Beilstein's work with many of the leading chemists of the day impressed him with the differences and difficulties in organic chemistry. Some chemists were guided by dualistic electrochemical notions and the older radical theory, while others viewed compounds as substitution products of several basic types of molecules. In addition, ideas about valence and the geometrical arrangement of bonds in structural formulas were being put forth. Beilstein was aware of all these views. He was attracted by Kekulé's ideas, for they seemed to provide a possible solution to the difficulties and to permit the writing of specific formulas for compounds. His own work heightened his awareness of the need for specific formulas. In 1860, for example, he showed that ethylidene chloride, obtained by Wurtz in 1858, was identical with the *éther hydrochlorique monochloridée* of Regnault. With F. Reichenbach he showed in 1864 that Kolbe and Lautemann's salicylic acid was only impure benzoic, and with J. Wilbrand he showed in 1863 that dracylic acid from nitrodracylic acid (i.e., p-nitro-benzoic acid) was also identical with benzoic acid. He himself had prepared pure hydracrylic acid in 1862, only to see the formula he had assigned to this compound over-

turned two years later by the work of Moldenhauer. In 1866, through his work with P. Geitner on the chlorination of benzene compounds, he became more convinced of the importance of Kekulé's ideas. They had investigated when chlorination would occur on a side chain and when in the nucleus. He also worked on aromatic compounds in various petroleum fractions.

At Göttingen, Beilstein had attempted to bring order into organic chemistry and had started his *Handbuch der organische Chemie,* which superseded Gmelin's textbook. In Beilstein's handbook, material that had previously been included in textbooks in an abbreviated form was now expanded into a new form of chemical literature. The first edition (1880–1882) described 15,000 compounds. The rapid growth of organic chemistry made new editions imperative. By the end of the century the magnitude of the task was too great for one man. The Deutsche Chemische Gesellschaft agreed to prepare a supplement to the third edition. After Beilstein's death they began to prepare a fourth edition, which would survey the literature to 1910. This edition appeared in 1937. The following year a supplement of equal length appeared, covering the decade 1910–1919. Work continued on a second supplement.

BIBLIOGRAPHY

I. ORIGINAL WORKS. Among Beilstein's writings are "Ueber die Einwirkung verschiedener Aetherarten auf Aether-Natron und über die Aethylkohlensäure," in *Justus Liebigs Annalen der Chemie,* **112** (1859), 121–125; "Ueber die Umwandlung des Acetals zu Alderhyd," *ibid.,* 239–240; "Ueber die Identität des Aethylidenchlorürs und des Chlorürs des gechlorten Aethyls," *ibid.,* **113** (1860), 110–112; "Ueber die Umwandlung der Glycerinsäure in Acrylsäure," *ibid.,* **122** (1862), 366–374; "Ueber die Zersetzung der Aldehyde und Acetone durch Zinkäthyl," *ibid.,* **126** (1863), 241–247, written with K. F. Rieth and R. Rieth; "Ueber eine neue Reihe isomerer Verbindungen der Benzoegruppe—Nitrodracylsäure und deren Derivate," *ibid.,* **128** (1863), 257–273, written with J. Wilbrand; "Ueber die Natur der sogenannten Salylsäure," in *Annalen der Chemie und Pharmacie,* **132** (1864), 309–321, written with E. Reichenbach; "Untersuchung über Isomerie in der Benzoëreihe: Ueber das Verhalten der Homologen des Benzols gegen Chlor," *ibid.,* **139** (1866), 331–342, written with P. Geitner; "Ueber die Scheidung des Zinks von Nickel," in *Berichte der Deutschen chemischen Gesellschaft,* **11** (1878), 1715–1718; "Ueber die Natur des Kaukasischen Petroleums," *ibid.,* **13** (1880), 1818–1821, written with K. F. Kurbatov and A. Kurbatov; and *Handbuch der organischen Chemie,* 2 vols. (1880–1883; 2nd ed., 1886–1889; 3rd ed., 1892–1899; 4th ed., 1916–1937).

Letters to Zincke and others are in the Kekulé Archiv and in the Preussische Staatsbibliothek. Letters to R. Anschutz are in the possession of Prof. L. Anschutz.

II. SECONDARY LITERATURE. Works on Beilstein are F. Hjelt, "Verzeichnis in der deutschen and franzoischen Zeitschriften erscheinen Abhandlungen Beilstein," in *Berichte der Deutschen chemischen Gesellschaft,* **40** (1907), 5074–5078; F. Richter, "Konrad Friedrich Beilstein, sein Werk und seine Zeit," *ibid.,* **71** (1938), Abt. A, 35–55; and F. Richter, "Zum 100. Geburtstag von Konrad Friedrich Beilstein," in *Forschungen und Fortschritte,* **14** (1938), 59–60.

RUTH ANNE GIENAPP

BEKETOV, NIKOLAI NIKOLAEVICH (*b.* Alferevka village, Penzensky district, Russia, 13 January 1827; *d.* St. Petersburg [now Leningrad], Russia, 13 December 1911), *chemistry.*

Beketov graduated from Kazan University in 1849 and then worked in Zinin's laboratory at the Academy of Medicine and Surgery in St. Petersburg. In 1855 he became a junior scientific assistant at Kharkov University, and from 1859 to 1886 he was professor of chemistry. In 1864 Beketov organized the department of chemistry and physics at Kharkov, with laboratory work in physical chemistry, and taught a course in physical chemistry. He was elected a member of the Petersburg Academy of Sciences in 1886.

Under Zinin's influence Beketov began his scientific activity with work in organic chemistry, studying esterification reactions. In his master's thesis (1853) he further developed the concepts of basicity and affinity, which had been worked out by C. F. Gerhardt and his followers. In Beketov's work one can find the sources of the study of "chemical value," which was later developed by the Butlerov school.

Beketov's later interests were physical and inorganic chemistry. As a result of his studies of the liberation of certain metals by hydrogen and by other metals, Beketov established an activity series of metals, demonstrating that the process of reduction is associated with the formation of galvanic pairs. In order to promote concentration of the reagent, Beketov subjected the hydrogen to pressures of 100 atmospheres and higher. "This action of hydrogen," he wrote, "depends on the gas pressure and the concentration of the metal [in acids], or in other words, depends on the chemical mass of the reducing body." In this work he closely approached the law of mass action and also studied the reversibility of the reaction:

$$(CH_3COO)_2Ca + CO_2 + H_2O \rightleftharpoons 2CH_3COOH + CaCO_3$$

The results of all these investigations were stated in his doctoral dissertation (1865).

Beketov later discovered and substantiated the theoretical possibility that metals could be reduced from their oxides by using aluminum, thus opening the way to the creation of the method of aluminothermal reduction. His constant interest in the theory of chemical affinity led to a large series of thermochemical researches, begun in Kharkov and continued in St. Petersburg. Specifically, Beketov determined the heats of formation and hydration of the oxides of the alkali metals. Beketov established that the heats of formation of chlorides, bromides, iodides, and oxides are in parallel with the compression taking place during the reactions.

BIBLIOGRAPHY

I. ORIGINAL WORKS. Beketov's writings include *O nekotorykh novykh sluchayakh khimicheskogo sochetania i obshchie zamechania ob etikh yavleniakh* ("On Several New Cases of Chemical Combination and General Remarks About These Occurrences"; St. Petersburg, 1853); *Issledovania nad yavleniami vytesnenia odnikh elementov drugimi* ("Researches Into the Occurrences of Liberation of Certain Elements by Other Elements"; Kharkov, 1865); "Recherches sur la formation et les propriétés de l'oxyde de sodium anhydre," in *Mémoires de l'Académie des sciences de St. Pétersbourg,* 7th ser., **30**, no. 2 (1881), 1–16; *Dinamicheskaya storona khimicheskikh yavleny* ("Dynamic Site of Chemical Phenomena"; Kharkov, 1886); "De quelques propriétés physico-chimiques de sels haloïdes du césium," in *Bulletin de l'Académie des sciences de St. Pétersbourg,* n.s., **4** (1894), 197–199; *Rechi khimika 1862–1903* ("Speeches of a Chemist 1862–1903"; St. Petersburg, 1908); and N. A. Izmailov, ed., *Izbrannie proizvedenia po fizicheskoy khimy* ("Selected Works on Physical Chemistry"; Kharkov, 1955), with a bibliography of his scientific works.

II. SECONDARY LITERATURE. Works on Beketov are A. I. Belyaev, *Nikolai Nikolaevich Beketov—vydayushchiysya russky fiziko-khimik i metallurg, 1827–1911* ("Nikolai Nikolaevich Beketov—Prominent Russian Physical Chemist and Metallurgist"; Moscow, 1953), with a bibliography of Beketov's works, and Y. I. Turchenko, *Nikolai Nikolaevich Beketov* (Moscow, 1954), which includes a list of Beketov's works and literature on him.

G. V. BYKOV

BEKHTEREV, VLADIMIR MIKHAILOVICH (*b.* Sorali, Vyatskaya oblast, Russia, 20 January 1857; *d.* Leningrad, U.S.S.R., 24 December 1927), *neurology, psychology.*

After graduating from the Vyatskaya Gymnasium, Bekhterev enrolled at the Medical and Surgical

Academy of St. Petersburg in 1873. He graduated in 1878, then prepared for a teaching career in the clinic of I. P. Merzheevsky. In 1881 Bekhterev defended his dissertation for the M.D., which dealt with the possible relation between body temperature and some forms of mental illness, then began work with Flechsig and Meinert, Westfall and Charcot, Du Bois-Reymond, and Wundt. In 1885 he was made a professor of psychiatry at Kazan University, where he organized the first laboratory for research on the anatomy and physiology of the nervous system. While in Kazan, Bekhterev completed investigations of the role of the cortex in the regulation of the functions of internal organs and prepared the first edition of the classic monograph *Provodyashchie puti spinnogo i golovnogo mozga* ("Passages of the Spinal Cord and Cerebrum") and the two-volume *Nervnye bolezni v otdelnykh nablyudeniakh* ("Nervous Diseases in Separate Observations").

From 1893 to 1913, Bekhterev headed the department of nervous and psychic diseases of the Military Medical Academy in St. Petersburg. During this period he published *Osnovy uchenia o funktsiakh mozga* ("Foundations of Knowledge About the Functions of the Brain"; 1903–1907). The last ten years of Bekhterev's life were devoted to the study of "reflexology" (objective psychology) and other areas of psychology.

In the anatomy and physiology of the central nervous system, Bekhterev defined more precisely the path and separation of the posterior rootlets of the spinal cord and described a group of cells on the surface of the shaft of the posterior horn (Bekhterev cells) and the internal bundle of the lateral column. He also described the large bundles of the brain stem and the pia mater nodes of the base of the brain; studied in detail and described the reticular formation (*formatio reticularis*) in 1885; and established the precise location of the taste center within the brain cortex in 1900.

In nervous diseases, Bekhterev isolated a number of reflexes and symptoms that have important diagnostic significance and described new illnesses: numbness of the spine (Bekhterev's disease), apoplectic hemitonia (*hemitonia postapopletica*), syphilitic dissipating sclerosis, a special form of facial tic, severe motor ataxia (*tabes dorsalistrans*), acroerythrosis, chorenic epilepsy (*epilepsia choreica*), and new phobias and obsessive states.

Bekhterev was a great organizer who created centers for the study of the neurological sciences and psychic illnesses—the Psychoneurological Institute, in 1908, and the State Institute for the Study of the Brain in St. Petersburg, which today bears his name. He also was the founder of the first Russian journals on nervous and psychic diseases: *Nevrologicheskii vestnik* and *Obozrenie psikhiatrii, nevrologii i eksperimentalnoy psikhologii.*

BIBLIOGRAPHY

I. ORIGINAL WORKS. Among Bekhterev's 800 or so publications are "O prodolnykh voloknakh setevidnoy formatsy na osnovany issledovania ikh razvitia i o soedineniakh setchatogo yadra pokryshki" ("About the Longitudinal Fibers of the Reticular Formation, on the Basis of an Investigation of Their Development, and About the Junctions of the Retinal Nucleus of the Cover"), in *Vrach,* no. 6 (1885); *Provodyashchie puti spinnogo i golovnogo mozga. Rukovodstvo k izucheniyu vnutrennikh svyazey mozga* ("Passages of the Spinal Cord and Cerebrum. Handbook Toward the Study of the Internal Connections of the Brain"), 2nd ed., rev. and enl., 2 vols. (St. Petersburg, 1896–1898); *Osnovy uchenia o funktsiakh mozga* ("Foundations of Knowledge About the Functions of the Brain"), 7 vols. (St. Petersburg, 1903–1907); *Zadachi i metod obektivnoy psikhology* ("The Tasks and Method of Objective Psychology"; St. Petersburg, 1909); *Obshchaya diagnostika bolezney nervnoy sistemy* ("General Diagnostics of Diseases of the Nervous System"), 2 vols. (Petrograd, 1911–1915); *Obshchie osnovy refleksology cheloveka (rukovodstvo k obektivnomu izucheniyu lichnosti)* ("General Foundations of the Reflexology of Man [Handbook Toward the Objective Study of Personality]"), 3rd ed. (Petrograd, 1926); *Avtobiografia (posmertnaya)* ("Autobiography [Posthumous]"; Moscow, 1928); *Mozg i ego deyatelnost* ("The Brain and Its Activity"), L. V. Gerver, ed. (Moscow–Leningrad, 1928); and *Izbrannye proizvedenia (stati i doklady)* ("Selected Works [Articles and Reports]"), ed. with introductory articles by V. N. Myasishchev (Moscow, 1951).

II. SECONDARY LITERATURE. Works on Bekhterev are V. D. Dmitriev, *Vydayushchysya russky ucheny V. M. Bekhterev* ("The Outstanding Russian Scientist V. M. Bekhterev"; Cheboskary, Chuvash Autonomous SSR, 1960); N. I. Grashchenkov, *Rol V. M. Bekhtereva v razvity otechestvennoy nevrology* ("The Role of V. M. Bekhterev in the Development of National Neurology"; Moscow, 1959); V. N. Myasishchev and T. Y. Khvilivitsky, eds., *"V. M. Bekhterev i sovremennye problemy stroenia i funktsy mozga v norme i patology. Trudy vsesoyuznoy konferentsy, posvyashchennoy stoletiyu so dnya rozhdenia V. M. Bekhtereva* ("V. M. Bekhterev and Modern Problems of the Structure and Functions of the Brain in Norm and in Pathology. Works of the All-Union Conference on the One Hundredth Anniversary of the Birthday of V. M. Bekhterev"; Leningrad, 1959); V. P. Osipov, *Bekhterev* (Moscow, 1947); and *Sbornik, posvyashchenny Vladimiru Mikhailovichu Bekhterevu. K 40-letiyu professorskoy deyatelnosti (1885–1925)* ("A Collection Dedicated to Vladimir

Mikhailovich Bekhterev. On the 40th Anniversary of His Professorial Career [1885–1925]"; Leningrad, 1926).

N. GRIGORYAN

BELAIEW, NICHOLAS TIMOTHY, in Russian **Nikolai Timofeevich Beliaev** (*b.* St. Petersburg, Russia, 26 June 1878; *d.* Paris, France, 5 November 1955), *metallurgy.*

Belaiew was the son of Gen. T. M. Beliaev. From 1902 to 1905 he studied at the Mikhailovskoi Artilleriiskoi Akademii, a graduate school of military engineering in St. Petersburg. He remained at this academy until 1914, first as a tutor and later (from 1909) as professor of metallurgical chemistry. Wounded early in World War I, in 1915 Belaiew was sent to England in connection with munitions supply; he remained there after the Revolution, working as an industrial consultant. In 1934 he moved to Paris.

Belaiew's papers have a strong historical bent. He claimed inspiration from his famed teacher, D. K. Chernoff, and from P. P. Anosov, who had established the manufacture of Damascus steel swords in Russia in 1841. Belaiew himself wrote a classic paper on the history and metallurgy of Damascus steel (1918). In 1944 he studied, in engineering steels, the coalescence of iron carbide that the Oriental swordmakers had unknowingly achieved through their methods of forging. His scientific contributions are mainly in his first book, *Kristallizatsia, struktura i svoystva stali pri medlennom okhlazhdenii* (1909), which provided the basis for several later papers in French, German, and English as well as for a small book in English (1922).

He showed that the geometric Widmanstätten structure, which had been discovered in 1804 in meteorites, could also be produced in steel under certain conditions of cooling. (He achieved the right structure by accident, because a foreman, anxious to get on with production, disregarded instructions and removed the steel ingot from the furnace before it was fully transformed.) Belaiew's emphasis on the crystallographic basis of the change and his detailed analysis of the geometry in this one case strongly influenced an important decade of metallurgical thinking.

BIBLIOGRAPHY

Belaiew's principal works are *Kristallizatsia, struktura i svoystva stali pri medlennom okhlazhdenii* (St. Petersburg, 1909); "Damascene Steel," in *Journal of the Iron and Steel Institute,* **97** (1918), 417–437, and **104** (1921), 181–184; *The Crystallization of Metals* (London, 1922); "Swords and Meteors," in *Mining and Metallurgy,* **20** (1939), 69–70; ". . .

la coalescence dans les aciers eutectoïdes et hyper-eutectoïdes," in *Revue de métallurgie,* **41** (1944), 65 ff. (in 8 parts).

Also see Robert F. Mehl, "On the Widmanstätten Structure," in *The Sorby Centennial Symposium on the History of Metallurgy* (New York, 1965), pp. 245–269.

C. S. SMITH

BÉLIDOR, BERNARD FOREST DE (*b.* Catalonia, Spain, 1697/1698; *d.* Paris, France, 1761), *mechanics, ballistics, military and civil architecture.*

Bélidor's career belongs to the early stages of engineering mechanics.

When Bélidor was born, his father, Jean-Baptiste Forest de Bélidor, a French officer of dragoons, was on duty in Spain. Both his father and his mother, Marie Hébert, died within five months of his birth, and he was brought up by the family of the widow of his godfather, an artillery officer named de Fossiébourg. Grateful for the family's protection during his childhood, Bélidor married Fossiébourg's daughter (or possibly his granddaughter) two years before his own death.

His life mingled the scientific with the military. A flair for practical mathematics secured him a post in the field under Jacques Cassini and Philippe de La Hire in the survey of the meridian from Paris to the English Channel, which they completed in 1718 and published in Cassini's *De la grandeur et de la figure de la terre* (1720). Bélidor's talents came to the attention of the regent, the Duc d'Orléans, who discouraged him from taking holy orders and arranged his appointment as professor of mathematics at the new artillery school at La Fère. In this post he made himself known as an author of textbooks and technical manuals in the 1720's and 1730's. After an interval of active duty in Bavaria, Italy, and Belgium during the War of the Austrian Succession, Bélidor settled in Paris with the rank of brigadier, was named chevalier of the Order of Saint Louis, and was elected an *associé libre* of the Academy of Sciences in 1756.

The book that made his reputation was *Nouveau cours de mathématique,* a text for artillery cadets and engineers. A second, *Le bombardier françois,* was for use in combat and contained systematic firing tables. It was with two fuller works, however—*La science des ingénieurs* (1729) and *Architecture hydraulique* (1737–1739)—that Bélidor entered into the science of mechanics proper with a summons to builders to base design and practice on its principles. The first of these treatises was concerned primarily with fortifications, their erection and reduction (the term *génie* then referred mainly to military and naval enterprises). The second, *Architecture hydraulique,* embraced civil constructions. The choice of title was a reflection of the actual prominence of problems involving transport, shipbuilding, waterways, water supply, and ornamental fountains. Both books opened with formulations of the principles of mechanics in mathematical terms, in which there was nothing original. The discussion was elementary, for the putative marriage of mathematics to mechanics was a rite more often celebrated than consummated in the early eighteenth century.

Nevertheless, the practical contents of both works proved to be invaluable to architects, builders, and engineers. They amount to rationalized engineering handbooks in which the man in charge of a construction might look up model specifications for a foundation or a cornice, a pediment or an arch; find diagrams he could follow or adapt; and consult job analyses and work plans for dividing and directing the labor. Both works were reprinted so often that the copper plates wore out and had to be reengraved for the final editions, in 1813 and 1819 respectively. Those editions were republished with notes by Navier, who in order to conserve the practical value, found it wiser to correct Bélidor's theoretical faults by up-to-date annotation than to revise or rewrite. He chose this course despite the immense development, amounting almost to creation of analytical mechanics as a science, that had occurred since Bélidor's first edition.

In that interval, Bélidor's writings had instructed innumerable practitioners as well as the first two generations of engineers who were also intrinsically scientists: for example, Lazare Carnot, Coulomb, and Meusnier, followed by Coriolis, Navier, and Poncelet, all of whom, under the designation "science of machines," inaugurated engineering mechanics. Bélidor's influence, therefore, was the reciprocal of what he intended: rather than introducing mathematics into practical construction, he brought the problems of engineering to mechanics.

BIBLIOGRAPHY

I. ORIGINAL WORKS. Bélidor's important writings were *Nouveau cours de mathématique à l'usage de l'artillerie et du génie* (Paris, 1725); *La science des ingénieurs dans la conduite des travaux de fortification et d'architecture civile* (Paris, 1729), also ed. with notes by Louis Navier (Paris, 1813; repub. 1830); *Le bombardier françois, ou nouvelle méthode de jetter les bombes avec précision* (Paris, 1731); and *Architecture hydraulique, ou l'art de conduire, d'élever et de ménager les eaux pour les différens besoins de la vie,* 2 vols. (Paris, 1737–1739), also ed. by Navier (Paris, 1819)—the most successful eighteenth-century edition was that published in 5 vols. (Paris, 1739–1790). Bélidor also published two memoirs in the *Mémoires de l'Académie Royale des Sciences:* "Théorie sur la science des mines propres à la guerre, fondée sur un grand nombre d'expériences" (1756), pp. 1–25; and "Seconde mémoire sur les mines, servant de suite au précédent" (1756), pp. 184–202.

II. SECONDARY LITERATURE. Bélidor's *éloge* by Grandjean de Fouchy is in *Histoire de l'Académie Royale des Sciences, année 1761* (Paris, 1763), pp. 167–181. Further biographical tradition is recalled in the introduction to the Navier edition of *Architecture hydraulique*.

CHARLES C. GILLISPIE

BELL, ALEXANDER GRAHAM (*b.* Edinburgh, Scotland, 3 March 1847; *d.* Baddeck, Nova Scotia, 2 August 1922), *technology*.

Both Bell's grandfather, Alexander, and his father, Alexander Melville, were teachers of elocution; his father was well known as the inventor of Visible Speech (a written code indicating the position and action of throat, tongue, and lips in forming sounds). Bell had a lifelong interest in teaching the deaf to speak, an interest intensified because his mother and his wife were deaf. In 1870, after the second of Bell's two brothers died of tuberculosis, the family moved to Canada. Bell did his early telephone work in Boston and subsequently moved to Washington. He became a citizen of the United States in 1882.

Bell achieved fame as inventor of the telephone and fortune under a broad interpretation given to the patent granted him 10 March 1876. His early experimental work was spurred on by a persistent belief in its ultimate commercial value, an enthusiasm unshared by his predecessor Philip Reis and his contemporary Elisha Gray. Although the telephone is not properly called a scientific invention (Bell's knowledge of electricity at the time was extremely limited), a fair proportion of the wealth he received from it was used by Bell to pursue scientific researches of his own and to support those of others.

His interest in the deaf led Bell to publish several articles on hereditary deafness. This in turn led to studies on longevity and a long-term series of experiments in which he attempted to develop a breed of sheep with more than the usual two nipples. In 1909, after twenty years of selection, he had a flock consisting solely of six-nippled sheep. He found, as he had suspected, that twin production increased with the number of nipples. Bell made a number of suggestions on the medical use of electricity but performed few experiments himself. His approach to these areas was as an amateur, although one with an active, inquiring mind.

Bell's financial support of science took several

forms. In 1880 he used the 50,000 francs of the Volta Prize to establish the Volta Laboratory Association (later the Volta Bureau), largely devoted to work for the deaf, in Washington. In 1882 he conceived the idea of the journal *Science,* which began publication in 1883. In the first eight years of its existence, Bell and his father-in-law, G. G. Hubbard, subsidized this journal to the amount of about $100,000. To allay S. P. Langley's concern that his post as secretary of the Smithsonian Institution would be merely administrative, Bell and J. H. Kidder each gave $5,000 for Langley's personal research; this money was used in the establishment of the Smithsonian's astrophysical observatory. In 1891 Bell gave $5,000 to support Langley's flight experiments. He himself experimented with kites, and in 1907 he organized the Aerial Experimental Association, which lasted for a year and a half and was financed by his wife. Bell also helped to organize and finance the National Geographic Society, serving as its president from 1898 to 1903.

Bell was elected to membership in the National Academy of Sciences in 1883 and was appointed a regent of the Smithsonian Institution in 1898.

BIBLIOGRAPHY

I. ORIGINAL WORKS. A complete list of Bell's publications is given in Osborne's article (see below). His notebooks, letters, and other documentary material are nicely housed by the Bell family at the National Geographic Society; some of these have been reproduced on microfilm and are available at the Library of Congress and the Bell Telephone Company of Canada, Montreal. Bell's court testimony dealing with the telephone appears in *The Bell Telephone* (Boston, 1908). Most of the surviving pieces of apparatus are preserved at the Smithsonian Institution.

II. SECONDARY LITERATURE. No satisfactory biography of Bell exists. Basic details can be found in W. C. Langdon's article on Bell, in *Dictionary of American Biography,* II, 148–152; C. D. Mackenzie, *Alexander Graham Bell, the Man Who Contracted Space* (New York, 1928); and H. S. Osborne, "Alexander Graham Bell," in *National Academy of Sciences, Biographical Memoirs,* **23** (1945), 1–30. Part of the experimental telephone work is analyzed in B. S. Finn, "Alexander Graham Bell's Experiments With the Variable-Resistance Transmitter," in *Smithsonian Journal of History,* **1**, no. 4 (1966), 1–16.

BERNARD S. FINN

BELL, CHARLES (*b.* Edinburgh, Scotland, November 1774; *d.* Hallow, Worcestershire, England, 28 April 1842), *anatomy.*

Bell introduced new methods of determining the functional anatomy of the nervous system. For the spinal and cranial nerves he correlated anatomical division with functional differentiation by cutting or stimulating the anatomical divisions and observing the changes produced in the experimental animals' behavior. Bell's techniques and observations led to Johannes Müller's generalizations on the sensory functions of the nervous system.

Bell was the son of a minister of the Church of England. His father died when he was five, and he received his basic education from his mother. He was also tutored in art and attended Edinburgh High School for three years. Bell's older brother John was a surgeon who gave private classes in anatomy. Charles assisted him in his classes, learning medicine from him and from lectures at Edinburgh University. He was admitted to the Royal College of Surgeons in 1799. The success of John Bell's anatomy classes aroused the jealousy of the medical faculty of the university, who succeeded in barring him and Charles from practice in the Royal Hospital of Edinburgh.

Since his career in Edinburgh was blocked, in 1804 Bell moved to London, where he opened his own school of anatomy and gradually built up a surgical practice. He combined his skill in painting with his scientific interests in *Essays on the Anatomy of Expression in Painting* (1806). Besides being an exposition of the anatomical and physiological basis of facial expression for artists, the book included much philosophy and critical history of art. The book gained Bell some reputation and remained popular, going through several editions up to 1893. He was co-owner of and principal lecturer at the Great Windmill Street School of Anatomy, founded by William Hunter, from 1812 to 1825 and was instrumental in the founding of the Middlesex Hospital Medical School in 1828. He returned to Edinburgh University as professor of surgery in 1836. Bell was knighted in 1831, in recognition of his scientific achievement. Further recognition came when he was selected to write the fourth Bridgewater Treatise, in which series he published *The Hand* in 1833.

Bell developed his experimental techniques involving the peripheral nerves in order to discover how the brain functions. In 1811 he published *Idea of a New Anatomy of the Brain,* a book giving his views on the brain. He circulated one hundred copies to his acquaintances, then published nothing more on the subject for ten years. Bell's first concern in *Idea* was to establish that the different parts of the brain serve different functions, rather than that the entire organ was involved in all functions. His statement that the peripheral nerves are composed of divisions "united for convenience of distribution" but "distinct in office" was a concomitant of this view of the brain.

Each division of a peripheral nerve received its functional specificity from the part of the brain with which it was connected. This was the crucial element in what were to be Müller's laws of sensation, and in *Idea* Bell incidentally stated the central law, that of specific nerve energies. It was Bell's techniques, however, not his generalizations, that influenced Müller.

Idea included a description of an experiment that demonstrated the differing functions of each root of a spinal nerve. Bell cut the posterior roots and observed no convulsions of the muscles of the back; touching the anterior roots convulsed them. Bell did not deduce the Bell-Magendie law—that the anterior roots are motor, the posterior sensory—from the experiment. Rather, it supported his opinion that the cerebellum, which he thought was the origin of the posterior root filaments, was the locus of the involuntary nervous functions. The cerebrum, the origin of the anterior root filaments, was the locus of the voluntary nervous functions. Bell reasoned that filaments of involuntary nerves did not elicit convulsions because there was no conscious sensation of pain.

Magendie did his own experimental work, formulating and publishing the Bell-Magendie law (1822) after hearing of Bell's work from John Shaw, Bell's assistant at the Great Windmill School. The law was a special case of the general principle of nervous function that Bell had worked out, but it was the special case that was noted and became the subject of a bitter priority dispute between Bell and Magendie.

Bell's later experimental studies, which he correlated with clinical observations, involved the functions of the cranial nerves.

BIBLIOGRAPHY

I. ORIGINAL WORKS. Bell's major works are *Essays on the Anatomy of Expression in Painting* (London, 1806); *Idea of a New Anatomy of the Brain* (London, 1811), a rare work that is reprinted in Gordon-Taylor and Walls; *An Exposition of the Natural System of Nerves of the Human Body* (London, 1824), which includes revisions of papers first published in *Philosophical Transactions of the Royal Society; The Nervous System of the Human Body* (London, 1830); and *The Hand, Its Mechanism and Vital Endowments, as Evincing Design* (London, 1833).

II. SECONDARY LITERATURE. Gordon Gordon-Taylor and E. W. Walls, *Sir Charles Bell, His Life and Times* (London, 1958), the important work on Bell, is an accurate but discursive biography and includes a bibliography of Bell's writings and the literature on him. J. M. D. Olmsted, *François Magendie* (New York, 1944), pp. 93–122, details the Bell-Magendie priority dispute.

PETER AMACHER

BELL, ERIC TEMPLE (*b.* Aberdeen, Scotland, 7 February 1883; *d.* Watsonville, California, 21 December 1960), *mathematics.*

The younger son of James Bell, of a London commercial family, and Helen Lyndsay Lyall, whose family were classical scholars, he was tutored before entering the Bedford Modern School, where a remarkable teacher, E. M. Langley, inspired his lifelong interest in elliptic functions and number theory. Bell migrated to the United States in 1902 "to escape being shoved into Woolwich or the India Civil Service" (as he later explained) and was able to "cover all the mathematics offered" at Stanford and graduate Phi Beta Kappa in two years. A single year at the University of Washington netted an M.A. in 1908; another at Columbia sufficed for the Ph.D. in 1912. The years between he spent as a ranch hand, mule skinner, surveyor, school teacher, and partner in an unsuccessful telephone company. In 1910 he married Jessie L. Brown, who died in 1940. They had one son, Taine Temple Bell, who became a physician in Watsonville. Bell produced about 250 mathematical research papers, four learned books, eleven popularizations, and, as "John Taine," seventeen science fiction novels, many short stories, and some poetry. He was active in organizations of research mathematicians, teachers, and authors. In religion and politics he was an individualist and uncompromising iconoclast. He remained active in retirement and was writing his last book in the hospital when overtaken by a fatal heart attack.

At the University of Washington from 1912, Bell published a number of significant contributions on numerical functions, analytic number theory, multiply periodic functions, and Diophantine analysis. His "Arithmetical Paraphrases" (1921) won a Bôcher Prize. Other honors (e.g., the presidency of the Mathematical Association of America [1931–1933]), editorial duties, and invitations multiplied, but they did not reduce his output. After lecturing at Chicago and Harvard, he went, in 1926, to the California Institute of Technology, where he remained (emeritus after 1953) until hospitalized a year before his death. Bell will be longest known for his *Men of Mathematics* and other widely read books "on the less inhuman aspects of mathematics," and for *The Development of Mathematics,* whose insights and provocative style continue to influence and intrigue professional mathematicians—in spite of their historical inaccuracies and sometimes fanciful interpretations.

BIBLIOGRAPHY

I. ORIGINAL WORKS. Typical are his first publication, "An Arithmetical Theory of Certain Numerical Functions,"

University of Washington Publication, no. 1 (1915); "Arithmetical Paraphrases, Part I," in *Transactions of the American Mathematical Society*, **22**, no. 1 (Jan. 1921), 1–30, and no. 3 (Oct. 1921), 273–275, which won a Bôcher Prize; *Algebraic Arithmetic,* American Mathematical Society Colloquium Publication, no. 7 (1927), which was based on his invited lectures at the Eleventh Colloquium of the American Mathematical Society in 1927; *Before the Dawn* (Baltimore, Md., 1934), which was his favorite science fiction novel, the only one published under his own name and inspired, he said, by boyhood views of models of dinosaurs in Croydon Park near London; *Men of Mathematics* (New York, 1937), awarded the gold medal of the Commonwealth Club of California; *The Development of Mathematics* (New York, 1940; 2nd ed., 1945); *Mathematics, Queen and Servant of Science* (New York, 1951), his most ambitious popularization based on two previous books, *Queen of the Sciences* and *The Handmaiden of the Sciences;* and *The Last Problem* (New York, 1961), a study of Fermat's conjecture, which was unfinished at the time of Bell's death.

II. SECONDARY LITERATURE. There is no detailed biography. Only the following give more information than appears in *American Men of Science, Who's Who in America,* and *Who Was Who:* an autobiography in *Twentieth Century Authors,* supp. 1 (New York, 1955), 70–71, from which we have taken the quotations in the article; T. A. A. Broadbent, obituary in *Nature,* no. 4763 (11 Feb. 1961), 443; and a news release from the California Institute of Technology News Bureau (21 Dec. 1960).

KENNETH O. MAY

BELL, ROBERT (*b.* Toronto, Ontario, 3 June 1841; *d.* Rathwell, Manitoba, 19 June 1917), *geology.*

The son of Rev. Andrew Bell, at fifteen Robert was appointed junior assistant on a Canadian Geological Survey party on the Gaspé Peninsula and continued to work for the Survey during the summers of his high school and college years. When he received a civil engineering degree from McGill University in 1861, he also won the Governor General's Gold Medal. Following a year at Edinburgh, Bell was appointed professor of chemistry and natural history at Queen's University in 1863. He resigned four years later, in order to devote full time to the Survey, and served as its chief geologist and acting director from 1901 until his retirement in 1906. By adroit use of his spare time he gained the M.D.,C.M. degree in 1878. His knowledge of medicine and surgery proved useful in his travels and resulted in his being appointed medical officer on government ships visiting Hudson Bay.

Among Bell's honors were honorary D.Sc. degrees from Queen's and Cambridge universities; fellowship of the Geological Society of London (1862), the Royal Society of Canada (1882), the Geological Society of America (1889), the Royal Society of London (1897)

and the Royal Astronomical Society (Canada); the Imperial Science Order (1903); the King's Gold Medal, from the Royal Geographic Society (1906); and the Cullum Gold Medal, from the American Geographic Society (1906).

After preliminary surveying projects on the Gaspé Peninsula and the north shores of the Great Lakes, in 1870 Bell commenced the work for which he is justly famous—thirty continuous years of exploration of the territory from Lake Superior northward to the Arctic and from Saskatchewan to the east shore of Hudson Bay—work that today would be classified as reconnaissance mapping. He traveled mainly by canoe, and his only instruments were the compass, sextant, boat log, and Rochon micrometer. His most important contribution was the mapping of both shores of Hudson Bay and parts of the Nottaway, Churchill, and Nelson rivers, which flow into it, as a result of which he became a strong advocate of the Hudson Bay route to the Atlantic. Bell also explored other parts of Canada: he was the first to survey Great Slave, Nipigon, and Amadjuak lakes, the latter in the interior of Baffin Island. He produced more than thirty reports on the geology of the areas he surveyed, the balance of his more than 200 titles dealing with the geography, zoology and botany, resources, and Indian lore along his routes.

No man has accomplished so much pioneer exploration in territory where previously only Indians had been. He used Indian names to a very great extent, and he has been called the "place-name father of Canada."

BIBLIOGRAPHY

A complete list of Bell's writings on North American geology is in *Bulletin of the United States Geological Survey,* no. 746 (1923), 89–91.

Articles on Bell are F. J. Alcock, "Bell and Exploration," in *A Century in the History of the Geological Survey of Canada,* National Museum of Canada, Special Contribution no. 47.1 (Ottawa, 1947), 48–54; H. M. Ami, "Memorial of Robert Bell," in *Bulletin of the Geological Society of America,* **38** (1927), 18–34; Charles Hallock, "One of Canada's Explorers," in *Forest and Stream,* **53,** no. 41 (1901), 9–15; and "Robert Bell," in *Proceedings and Transactions of the Royal Society of Canada* (1918), x–xiv.

T. H. CLARK

BELLANI, ANGELO (*b.* Monza, Italy, 31 October 1776; *d.* Milan, Italy, 28 August 1852), *physics, chemistry.*

Bellani received his education in religious institutions, as was common. He studied rhetoric at the school of the Merate dei Somaschi; philosophy at the school of Monza, run by former Jesuits; and theology at the seminary of Milan, where he was ordained a priest. He was appointed honorary canon of the basilica of Monza, and was a member of the Istituto Lombardo Accademia di Scienze e Lettere and of the Società Italiana delle Scienze di Verona.

Bellani began his scientific activity with the construction and study of thermometers. He designed the "thermometergraph." He made an instrument with a double scale that served as an inspiration to the English physicist Six and was to prove helpful in the automatic registering of maximum and minimum temperatures. In 1808 Bellani demonstrated how "zero" on the thermometer's scale is subject to variations caused by deformations of the glass over the years. In that year he also established a factory in Milan for the manufacture of thermometers, a business that flourished from the outset.

Bellani was also interested in chemistry, especially as it related to the construction of physical instruments. In fact, in his research on combustion, on the temperature of liquefaction and of ebullition of phosphorus, his idea was to construct a phosphorus eudiometer that would not present the limitations of the one invented by the Piedmontese chemist Giovanni Antonio Giobert and used by Lazzaro Spallanzani in his biological experiments; it would permit an exact quantitative determination of the gas produced. In 1824 Bellani also distinguished the catalytic function of a platinum sponge saturated with hydrogen. After 1815 he widened the scope of his scientific studies to include meteorology and agriculture, and during the later years of his life he turned his attention to natural history.

In meteorology Bellani continued his interest in instrumentation. He made a hygrometer from a fish bladder (1836) and perfected Landriani's *atmidomètre*. In 1834 he defined his theory on the formation of hail, resuming the criticism, which dated back to 1817, of the ideas that Alessandro Volta had expressed on this subject. Basing his arguments on laboratory data and on direct meteorological observations, he demonstrated that Volta's theory was founded on the false and contradictory principle of the extreme cold produced by the warming action of the sun.

BIBLIOGRAPHY

I. ORIGINAL WORKS. Most of Bellani's works were published in scientific journals and reviews. In the *Nuova scelta d'opuscoli interessanti sulle scienze e sulle arti* are "Descrizione di un termometro ad indice" (1804); "Osser-

vazioni sull'uso dell'aerometro di Farenheit e di Baumé" (1804); "Sulla divisione decimale del pesa-licori" (1804); and "Osservazioni d'esperienze fatte colla pila di Volta sulla produzione dell'acido muriatico ossigenato" (1806).

In the *Giornale di fisica, chimica e storia naturale* are "Sopra la spiegazione di un fenomeno idrostatico dato dal Sign. Robinet" (1808); "Esame dell'ebollizione dei liquidi" (1809–1810); "Dell'ascensione del mercurio ne' tubi capillari" (1810); "Sopra un nuovo termografo" (1811); "Sulla deliquescenza de' corpi" (1812); "Sull'antichità dei telegrafi" (1812); "Sul fosforo come mezzo eudiometrico" (1813–1814); "Se la fosforescenza di alcune piante sia analoga alla lenta combustione del fosforo" (1814); "Riflessione intorno all'evaporizzazione" (1816–1817); "Nuova ipotesi sulla coda di comete" (1820); "Descrizione di un nuovo atmidometro" (1820); "Storia di un aerolito" (1822); "Sull'origine e la natura delle stelle cadenti" (1822); "Dell'incertezza nel determinare il punto del ghiaccio" (1822); "Di alcune proprietà del mercurio e del vetro" (1823); "Sulla proprietà che posseggono alcune sostanze di facilitare la combinazione del gas idrogeno con l'ossigenio" (1824); "Sopra la cristallizzazione e congelazione" (1827); "Sul termobarometro" (1827); and "Sulla salsedine dell'acqua del mare" (1823).

In the *Memorie dell'Istituto lombardo* are "Sopra la teoria della combustione del fosforo" (1813); "Esposizione di alcune esperienze relative alla dilatazione dei corpi" (1814); "Sul freddo prodotto dall'evaporazione" (1815); and "Intorno alla corona ferrea esistente nella basilica di Monza" (1818).

In the *Giornale e biblioteca dell'Istituto lombardo* are "Sull'arte di filare il vetro" (1840); "Sopra diversi argomenti fisico-chimici" (1842); "Sopra una supposta causa principale dell'utilità degli avvicendamenti agrari" (1842); "Sulle funzioni delle radici nei vegetali" (1843); "Sopra un fenomeno di sospesa evaporazione" (1844); "Sulla filatura dei bozzoli a freddo" (1844); and "Osservazioni di fisiologia vegetale" (1846–1847).

In the *Giornale dell'Istituto lombardo* are "Conseguenze della vigente teoria dei vapori applicabile alla ispirazione di quelli sviluppatisi dall'etere solforico" (1847); and "Del gelso in agricoltura" (1850).

In the *Memorie di matematica e fisica della Società italiana delle scienze* are "Sullo spostamento del mercurio osservato al punto del ghiaccio nella scala dei termometri" (1841); and "Della malaria vicino ai fontanini d'irrigazione" (1844).

His books include *Tentativi per determinare l'aumento di volume che acquista l'acqua prima e dopo la congelazione* (Pavia, 1808); *Riflessioni intorno ad alcune recenti opinioni riguardanti il fosforo* (Pavia, 1814); *Delle rotazioni agrarie* (Pesaro, 1833); *Sulla grandine* (Milan, 1834); *Della indefinibile durabilità della vita delle bestie* (Milan, 1836); *Revisione di alcuni supposti assioma fisiologici intorno l'assorbimento o la evaporazione delle foglie nelle piante* (Milan, 1837); and *Osservazioni sulla bacologia,* 3 vols. (Milan, 1852).

II. SECONDARY LITERATURE. The only works that deal in depth with Bellani's work are the obituary by G. Veladini, in *Giornale dell'Istituto lombardo,* **9** (1856), 485–489; and G. Cantoni, "Sopra due strumenti metereologici ideati da Angelo Bellani," in *Rendiconti dell'Istituto lombardo,* **10** (1877), 17–23; **11** (1878), 873–880.

The transactions of the congresses of Italian scientists, in which Bellani participated actively, contain extensive extracts of his remarks.

In agriculture he collaborated on the *Giornale agrario lombardo-veneto,* contributing articles on the cultivation of the silkworm, wood, malaria, and the function of the roots of plants.

GIORGIO PEDROCCO

BELLARDI, LUIGI (*b.* Genoa, Italy, 18 May 1818; *d.* Turin, Italy, 17 September 1889), *paleontology, entomology.*

Although a native of Genoa, Bellardi spent most of his life in Turin, where, following the wishes of his family, he studied law. Since his early youth, however, the natural sciences had attracted him; and in his leisure time he collected the Cenozoic Mollusca abundant in the hills around Turin, Superga, Asti, and Tortona. At the age of twenty he published his first paper on the gastropod genus *Borsonia,* and from that time on, his major scientific activity concentrated on the Cenozoic Mollusca of the Piedmont and of Liguria. He also visited the Middle East, particularly Egypt, bringing back extensive collections for comparative study.

Between 1854 and 1874 a variety of circumstances prevented Bellardi from dedicating himself entirely to paleontology, and he therefore undertook entomological research, mostly on the diptera of the Piedmont. He also took some interest in botany and agriculture, being the first in Italy to discuss the phylloxera and its relationship to viticulture.

Upon the introduction of evolutionary ideas into paleontology, Bellardi immediately understood their fundamental importance, and his last works show the relationships between the different forms of Mollusca, and their probable filiation through geological time. During the last twenty years of his life he returned entirely to paleontology, but never completed his extensive and important *I molluschi,* which is characterized by perfectionism in presentation and content. With a similar attitude, he taught natural history for thirty years at the Liceo Gioberti and was curator of the paleontological collection of the Royal Geological Museum of Turin, to which he made many contributions. His desire to increase interest in natural history led him to write several elementary textbooks, also characterized by clarity of expression and precision of data.

Bellardi was elected an honorary member of many academies and scientific societies, and King Victor Emmanuel requested him to teach the natural sciences to his sons, an assignment that Bellardi particularly enjoyed.

BIBLIOGRAPHY

Among Bellardi's works are "Saggio orittografico sulla classe dei gasteropodi fossili dei terreni Terziarii del Piemonte," in *Memorie della Reggia Accademia delle scienze di Torino,* 2nd ser., **3** (1841), 93–174, written with G. Michelotti; "Description des cancellaires fossiles des terrains Tertiaires du Piémont," *ibid.,* 225–264; "Monografia delle pleurotome fossili del Piemonte," *ibid.,* **9** (1848), 531–650; "Monografia delle columbelle fossili del Piemonte," *ibid.,* **10** (1849), 225–247; "Monografia delle mitre fossili del Piemonte," *ibid.,* **11** (1851), 357–390; and *I molluschi dei terreni Terziarii del Piemonte e della Liguria,* 30 vols. (Turin, 1873–1904), I–V by Bellardi and VI–XXX by F. Sacco—I–VIII, XI, and XIII also in *Memorie della Reggia Accademia delle scienze di Torino,* 2nd ser., **27–44** (1873–1894).

ALBERT V. CAROZZI

BELLARMINE, ROBERT (*b.* Montepulciano, Italy, 4 October 1542; *d.* Rome, Italy, 17 September 1621), *theology, philosophy.*

Third of the twelve children of Vincenzo Bellarmino and Cynthia Cervini, half-sister of Pope Marcellus II, Robert joined the newly founded Jesuit order in 1560 and took a master's degree in philosophy at the Spanish-staffed Roman College in 1563. Natural philosophy formed an important part of his studies there, but it appears to have been wholly and routinely Aristotelian in character. Ordained priest in 1570, he completed his theological studies in Louvain.

The struggle between the Catholic and Protestant wings of Christendom had by then attained an extraordinary ferocity all over Europe. One of the major theoretical issues separating the two groups concerned the norms for the proper interpretation of Scripture. Because of his profound scriptural scholarship and his thorough grasp of the major Protestant writers (both of these achievements very rare in the Catholic church of the day), Bellarmine soon became the leading theologian on the Catholic side of the debate. His three-volume *Disputationes de controversiis* was by far the most effective piece of Catholic polemic scholarship of the century. After its appearance in 1588, he was recognized as the leading defender of the papacy; successive popes forced on a man whose natural temperament was at once gentle and gay the uncongenial role of controversialist and apologist.

Made rector of the Roman College in 1592, cardinal in 1599, and archbishop of Capua in 1602, Bellarmine was never far from Rome, and in his last years lived at the Vatican as the pope's major theological adviser.

Bellarmine's relevance to the history of science comes only from his role in the Galileo story. In 1611 he was among the Roman dignitaries whom Galileo invited to see the new-found wonders in the sky. The old man was disturbed at the implications of what he saw, and asked the astronomers of his old college (among them Clavius) to test the accuracy of Galileo's claims. This they soon did. Galileo sent him a copy of his important and effectively anti-Aristotelian work on hydrostatics (1612), to which Bellarmine replied that "the affection you have thus shown me is fully reciprocated on my part; you will see that this is so, if ever I get an opportunity of doing you a service." The opportunity was not long in coming.

The Aristotelian cosmology was crumbling in the face of the new astronomical evidence, notably that of the phases of Venus and the sunspots. The Aristotelians of the universities fell back on the authority of Scripture as a last desperate expedient to save their case. Galileo answered them in his brilliant *Letter to the Grand Duchess Cristina of Lorraine* (1615). Two rather different, and ultimately incompatible, positions were argued by him. On the one hand, he argued with great cogency that the language in which the scriptural writers described physical phenomena could not possibly have been intended to carry any probative weight in questions of natural science. On the other hand, he also appeared to concede the traditional Augustinian maxim: So great is the weight of authority behind the words of revelation that the literal sense ought to be taken as the correct one in every case, except where such an interpretation could be strictly shown, on commonsense or philosophical grounds, to lead to falsity.

In a letter written at this time to Foscarini, a Carmelite who had defended similar views on the nonrelevance of scriptural phrases to problems of physical science, Bellarmine accepted the Augustinian maxim, but went on to emphasize that since the heliocentric theory of Copernicus could in no way be "strictly demonstrated," the troublesome scriptural phrases about the motion of the sun could not be regarded as metaphorical. If, of course, a "strict proof" of heliocentrism were to be found (a contingency he regarded as in the highest degree unlikely but, significantly, did not wholly exclude), the scriptural texts would have to be reexamined. To argue that the celestial appearances are "saved" by supposing the earth to go around the sun does not constitute a strict proof that this is what really happens. When a vessel recedes from the shore, the illusion that the shore is moving is corrected by *seeing* the ship to be in motion. Likewise, the experience of the wise man "tells him plainly that the earth is standing still."

This is the sort of unshakable trust in the ultimacy of observation that had made Aristotle (who had once seemed so dangerous an intellectual threat to Christian beliefs) a congenial cosmologist for those who regarded the Hebrew turn of phrase about sun or stars as somehow carrying a special authority. In Bellarmine's view, Solomon's phrase about the sun "returning to its place" carried far more weight than did the Copernican theory. The latter was no more than a "hypothesis," whereas Solomon had his wisdom from God.

A year later, a specially appointed tribunal of eleven theologians went much further than Bellarmine had, and advised the Congregation of the Holy Office that the heliostatic view was formally heretical, because it called into question the inspiration of Scripture. No account of the tribunal's deliberations survives, but presumably its arguments were the standard ones summarized in Bellarmine's letter.

The consequences, both for science and for the church, of the ensuing decree (1616) suspending the work of Copernicus "until it be corrected" can scarcely be overestimated. Once this decree was put into effect, the die was cast; and although later incidents (notably Galileo's trial) would come to have a greater symbolic and dramatic significance, it was with the decree of 1616 that the parting of the ways really came. The disastrous potentialities for conflict that were latent in Augustine's theory of scriptural interpretation were now for the first time realized. If the literal sense of Scripture is to be retained unless and until its untenability be *strictly* demonstrated, an impossible burden is laid on theologian and scientist alike. Each will be called on to evaluate the arguments of the other. And the argument of the scientist will not be allowed *any* weight until it is conclusive, when all of a sudden it will be conceded. The notions of evidence and probability underlying this approach (which originally derived from Augustine's theory of divine illumination as a basis for all human knowledge) are ultimately inconsistent.

In his criticisms of this approach, Galileo showed himself a better theologian than Bellarmine and the consultors. He had a far keener appreciation of what language is, and what the conditions for communication are. That his opponents did not accept his arguments, cogent as they seem to us today, was due mainly to the fact that the norms for the proper interpretation of Scripture were one of the two main issues then dividing Protestants and Catholics. Any liberalizing suggestion in this quarter was hardly likely to meet with favor on either side. It was a far cry from the calmer days of Oresme and Cusa, two centuries before, when similar suggestions about the interpretation of Scripture scarcely caused a ripple.

In his *Système du monde,* Duhem suggests that in one respect, at least, Bellarmine had shown himself a better scientist than Galileo by disallowing the possibility of a "strict proof" of the earth's motion, on the grounds that an astronomical theory merely "saves the appearances" without necessarily revealing what "really happens." This claim has often been repeated, most recently by Karl Popper, who makes Bellarmine seem a pioneer of the nineteenth-century positivist theory of science. In point of fact, nothing could be further from the case. Bellarmine by no means denied that strict demonstrations of what is "really" the case could be given in astronomical matters. In his view, however, such demonstrations had to rest on "physical" considerations of the type used by Aristotle, not on the mathematical models of positional astronomy.

This distinction between two epistemologically different types of astronomy was a time-honored one, taking its origin in the medieval debates over the relative merits of the Aristotelian and Ptolemaic astronomies. The former clearly gave a good causal account of *why* the planets moved, but was quite unable to provide any practical aids for the compiling of calendars and the like. On the other hand, it appeared impossible to account for the complex and eccentric epicyclic motions of Ptolemaic astronomy in causal terms, even though they did provide a good descriptive and predictive account of apparent planetary positions. The orthodox Aristotelian reading of this situation, such as one will find in writers like Aquinas, was that *real* motion could be asserted only on the basis of demonstrations of a properly "physical" sort; the models of the mathematical astronomer did not lend themselves to dynamic explanation because their purpose was merely that of computation.

Although the phrase "saving the appearances" was often used in reference to mathematical astronomy, it is important in this context to distinguish between the Aristotelian and Platonic views of what physics in general could accomplish. Aristotle argued that a strict science of physics can be achieved, one that tells us how the world really is. Plato, on the other hand, held that physical inquiry could at best only "save the appearances." Admittedly, such a "saving" provided some sort of insight into the physical world because of the relation of image between it and the

domain of Form, but the insight is a limited and defective one because the imaging is such a flickering and uncertain affair.

Bellarmine's comments in his letter to Foscarini cannot be construed as a protopositivist declaration. He was, indeed, just as much of an "essentialist" in his theory of science (to use Popper's term) as either Aristotle or Galileo. Even if he had been a Platonist, and extended the notion of "saving the appearances" to all of physics and not just to mathematical astronomy, it still would not be correct to take this in the positivist sense favored by Duhem.

To refute the Aristotelian separation between the two types of astronomy, it would be necessary to construct a dynamical substructure for Copernican kinematics, something Galileo could not do. It was not until Newton that the new mathematical astronomy was given an adequate causal interpretation in terms of central forces. In his *Dialogo,* Galileo attempted to meet Bellarmine's challenge to provide a dynamical proof of the earth's motion, but the tidal arguments he used carried little conviction. Galileo's opponents could, therefore, claim that the Copernican theory was still no more than a "hypothesis," in the traditional sense of a fictional account, because it lacked the "physics" (i.e., the dynamics) that, in their view, it would need to transform it into a claim about the nature of the real.

When the decree outlawing Copernicanism was promulgated in 1616, Galileo was in Rome. He was not mentioned in the decree, probably because of the respect in which he was held and the support of his many friends in Rome. But since he was the main protagonist both of Copernicanism and of the views on the interpretation of Scripture that were disapproved, he obviously was the person most affected by it. Wishing to make sure that Galileo appreciated the gravity of the matter, the pope asked Bellarmine to call him in and notify him officially of the contents of the decree before it was made public. If he showed himself unwilling to accept it, he was to be enjoined personally not to support or even discuss Copernicanism in any fashion.

What happened at this famous interview has been the subject of endless controversy in the past century, since the documents of the "Galileo case" have been made public. According to a document introduced in evidence at Galileo's trial nearly twenty years later, the personal injunction apparently *was* given to him, and the prosecution made much of the fact that its existence had not been made known to the censors in charge of licensing the *Dialogo.* Galileo protested that he could recall no such formal injunction, although he remembered the interview with Bellarmine well enough. In addition, he produced an attestation drawn up by Bellarmine before Galileo left Rome in 1616, in which the aged cardinal affirmed that Galileo had not been forced to abjure Copernicanism, as rumor had claimed. Bellarmine's note, whose existence obviously had not been suspected by the prosecution, forced an alteration in the strategy of the trial; in its later stages, the personal injunction was not mentioned.

Had it actually been delivered? The record in the Holy Office file is not signed in the usual form, and Bellarmine's attestation strongly suggests that it could not be valid. Some have claimed that it was forged by enemies of Galileo, either in 1616 or in 1633, with a view to trapping him. Others have suggested that it *was* delivered in 1616, but that there were no legal grounds for doing so. Still others argue that a genuine injunction was given, and that Bellarmine's attestation was the action of a friend protecting Galileo's reputation. We shall never know for sure. And in any event, it makes little difference, since the trial verdict would very likely have been the same whether or not a special injunction had been given to Galileo in 1616. Once the decree of 1616 implied that the heliocentric view is formally heretical, the writing of a book like the *Dialogo* automatically gave grounds for the suspicion of heresy, if the pope or the Holy Office cared to press the charge. This was where Bellarmine and the theologians of 1616 failed. Beset by the polemics of Reformation and Counter-Reformation, they did not grasp the limits of scriptural inspiration that were already becoming evident to the pioneers of the new sciences. One can account for their failure easily enough, but it was to have disastrous consequences for their church and for religion in general.

BIBLIOGRAPHY

The relationship between Bellarmine and Galileo is fully covered in James Brodrick, *Robert Bellarmine* (Westminster, Md., 1961). Brodrick's earlier *Life and Work of Robert Francis Bellarmine* (London, 1928) is quite defective in its treatment of the Galileo case. The most colorful recent account of the Bellarmine–Galileo dispute is Giorgio de Santillana, *The Crime of Galileo* (Chicago, 1955); a quite different reconstruction of the circumstances under which the disputed injunction came to be entered into the file is given by Stillman Drake in the appendix to his trans. of Ludovico Geymonat, *Galileo Galilei* (New York, 1965). Popper's view of Bellarmine as an "instrumentalist," in contrast with Galileo, the "essentialist," is worked out in his "Three Views Concerning Human Knowledge," in H. D. Lewis, ed., *Contemporary British Philosophy* (New York, 1956), pp. 355–388.

ERNAN MCMULLIN

BELLAVITIS, GIUSTO (*b.* Bassano, Vicenza, Italy, 22 November 1803; *d.* Tezze, near Bassano, 6 November 1880), *mathematics.*

Bellavitis was the son of Ernesto Bellavitis, an accountant with the municipal government of Bassano, and Giovanna Navarini; the family belonged to the nobility but was in modest circumstances. He did not pursue regular studies but was tutored under the guidance of his father, who directed his interest toward mathematics. Soon he surpassed his tutor and diligently pursued his studies on his own, occupying himself with the latest mathematical problems.

From 1822 to 1843 Bellavitis worked for the municipal government of Bassano—without pay for the first ten years—and conscientiously discharged his duties, occupying his free time with mathematical studies and research. During this period he published his first major works, including papers (1835, 1837) on the method of equipollencies, which were hailed as one of his major contributions. On 26 September 1840 Bellavitis became a fellow of the Istituto Veneto, and in 1843 he was appointed professor of mathematics and mechanics at the *liceo* of Vicenza. He then married Maria Tavelli, the woman who for fourteen years had comforted and encouraged him in his difficult career.

On 4 January 1845, through a competitive examination, Bellavitis was appointed full professor of descriptive geometry at the University of Padua. On 4 July 1846, the university awarded him an honorary doctorate in philosophy and mathematics. He transferred in 1867 to the professorship of complementary algebra and analytic geometry. On 15 March 1850, Bellavitis became a fellow of the Società Italiana dei Quaranta, and in 1879 a member of the Accademia dei Lincei. In 1866 he was named a senator of the Kingdom of Italy.

Bellavitis' method of equipollencies belongs to a special point of view in mathematical thought: geometric calculus. According to Peano, geometric calculus consists of a system of operations to be carried out on geometric entities; these operations are analogous to those executed on numbers in classical algebra. Such a calculus "enables us to express by means of formulae the results of geometric constructions, to represent geometric propositions by means of equations, and to replace a logical argument with the transformation of equations." This approach had been developed by Leibniz, who intended to go beyond the Cartesian analytic geometry, by performing calculations directly on the geometric elements, rather than on the coordinates (numbers). Moebius' barycentric calculus finds its expression within this context, but Bellavitis made special reference to

Carnot's suggestion of 1803, when he wrote in 1854:

> This method complies with one of Carnot's wishes, i.e., he wanted to find an algorithm that could simultaneously represent both the magnitude and the position of the various components of a figure; with the immediate result of obtaining elegant and simple graphic solutions to geometrical problems ["Sposizione del metodo delle equipollenze," p. 226].

In order to indicate that two segments, AB and DC, are equipollent—i.e., equal, parallel, and pointing in the same direction—Bellavitis used the formula

$$AB \simeq DC.$$

Thus we are given a kind of algebra analogous to that of complex numbers with two units; it found its application in various problems of plane geometry and mechanics, and paved the way for W. R. Hamilton's theory of quaternions (1853), through which geometric calculus can be applied to space; it also led to Grassmann's "Ausdehnungslehre" (1844), and finally to the vector theory. With his barycentric calculus, Bellavitis created a calculus more general than Moebius' "baricentrische Calcul."

In 1834, in his formula expressing the area of polygons and the volume of polyhedra as a function of the distances between their vertexes, Bellavitis anticipated results that were later newly discovered by Staudt and published in 1842.

In algebraic geometry, Bellavitis introduced new criteria for the classification of curves, and then completed Newton's findings on plane cubic curves, adding six curves to the seventy-two already known; these six had not been mentioned by Euler and Cramer. He also began the classification of curves of class three. He offered a graphical solution of spherical triangles, based on the transformation—through reciprocal vector radia—of a spherical surface into a plane. This method finds application in the solution of crystallographic problems.

Bellavitis furthered the progress of descriptive geometry with his textbook on the subject. Considering mathematics to be based essentially upon physical facts and proved by sensible experience, Bellavitis looked down on geometry of more than three dimensions and on non-Euclidean geometry. He did, however, like Beltrami's research on the interpretation of Lobachevski's geometry of the pseudosphere, for he felt that this research would help to diminish the prestige of the new geometry, reducing it to geometry of the pseudosphere. He continued to pursue his research on geodetic triangles on such surfaces as the pseudosphere.

In algebra, Bellavitis thoroughly investigated and continued Paolo Ruffini's research on the numerical solution of an algebraic equation of any degree; he also studied the theory of numbers and of congruences. He furnished a geometric base for the theory of complex numbers. Several of Bellavitis' contributions deal with infinitesimal analysis. In this connection we should mention his papers on the Eulerian integrals and on elliptic integrals.

Bellavitis solved various mechanical problems by original methods, among them Hamilton's quaternions. He developed very personal critical observations about the calculus of probabilities and the theory of errors. He also explored physics, especially optics and electrology, and chemistry. As a young man, Bellavitis weighed the problem of a universal scientific language and published a paper on this subject in 1863. He also devoted time to the history of mathematics and, among other things, he vindicated Cataldi by attributing the invention of continuous fractions to him.

BIBLIOGRAPHY

I. Original Works. Bibliographies of Bellavitis' works are in A. Favaro, in *Zeitschrift für Mathematik und Physik,* Historisch-literarische Abteilung, **26** (1881); and E. Nestore Legnazzi, *Commemorazione del Conte Giusto Bellavitis* (Padua, 1881), pp. 74–88, which gives the titles of 181 published works, together with numerous "Riviste di giornali," in which Bellavitis examines the results of other authors and uses his problem-solving methods, published in the *Atti dell'Istituto veneto* between 1859 and 1880.

Among his works are "Sopra alcune formule e serie infinite relative ai fattoriali ed agli integrali euleriani," in *Annali delle scienze del Regno Lombardo Veneto,* **4** (1834), 10–19; "Teoremi generali per determinare le aree dei poligoni ed i volumi dei poliedri col mezzo delle distanze dei loro vertici," in *Annali Fusinieri* (1834); "Saggio di applicazioni di un nuovo metodo di geometria analitica-calcolo delle equipollenze," *ibid.,* **5** (1835); "Memoria sul metodo delle equipollenze," in *Annali delle scienze del Regno Lombardo Veneto,* **7** (1837), 243–261; **8** (1838), 17–37, 85–121; "Sul movimento di un liquido che discende in modo perfettamente simmetrico rispetto a un asse verticale," in *Atti dell'Istituto veneto,* **3** (1844), 206–210, and *Memorie dell'Istituto veneto,* **2** (1845), 339–360; "Sul più facile modo di trovare le radici reali delle equazioni algebriche e sopra un nuovo metodo per la determinazione delle radici immaginarie," *ibid.,* **3** (1847), 109–220; "Considerazioni sulle nomenclature chimiche, sugli equivalenti chimici e su alcune proprietà, che con questi si collegano," *ibid.,* 221–267; *Lezioni di geometria descrittiva* (Padua, 1851, 1858); "Sulla classificazioni delle curve del terzo ordine," in *Memorie della Società italiana delle scienze (dei Quaranta),* ser. 1, **25** (1851), 1–50; "Classificazione delle curve della terza classe," in *Atti dell'Istituto veneto,* ser. 3, **4** (1853),

234–240; "Teoria delle lenti," in *Annali Tortolini,* **4** (1853), 26–269, and *Atti dell'Istituto veneto,* ser. 4, **2** (1872), 392–406; "Sposizione del metodo delle equipollenze," in *Memorie della Società italiana delle scienze,* ser. 1, **25** (1854), 225–309, trans. into French by C. A. Laisant, in *Nouvelles annales de mathématiques* (1874); "Calcolo dei quaternioni di W. R. Hamilton e sue relazioni col metodo delle equipollenze," in *Memorie della Società italiana delle scienze,* ser. 2, **1** (1858), 126–184, and *Atti dell'Istituto veneto,* ser. 3, **3** (1856–1857), 334–342; "Sulla misura delle azioni elettriche," *ibid.,* **9** (1863), 773–786, 807–818; "Pensieri sopra una lingua universale e sopra alcuni argomenti analoghi," in *Memorie dell'Istituto veneto,* **11** (1863), 33–74; and "Sopra alcuni processi di geometria analitica" in *Rivista periodica della R. Accademia di scienze lettere e arti di Padova,* **30** (1880), p. 73.

II. SECONDARY LITERATURE. Works on Bellavitis are G. Loria, *Storia delle matematiche,* III (Turin, 1933), 500–501; E. Nestore Legnazzi (see above); G. Peano, *Calcolo geometrico secondo l'Ausdehnungslehre di H. Grassmann* (Turin, 1888), p. v; D. Turazza, "Commemorazione di G. Bellavitis," in *Atti dell'Istituto veneto,* ser. 5., **8** (1881–1882), 395–422; and N. Virgopia, "Bellavitis, Giusto," in *Dizionario biografico degli italiani* (Rome, 1965), VII.

ETTORE CARRUCCIO

BELLEVAL, PIERRE RICHER DE (Châlons-sur-Marne, France, *ca.* 1564; *d.* Montpellier, France, 17 November 1632), *medicine.*

Nothing is known about Belleval's origins. He came to Montpellier to study medicine on 22 October 1584, but it was in Avignon that he received his physician's degree on 4 June 1587. He practiced medicine in Avignon and then in Pézenas, where he met Henri de Montmorency, the governor of Languedoc, who became his lifelong protector.

When Henri IV created a chair of anatomy and botanical studies at the medical college of Montpellier, Belleval was named to it in December 1593. On 10 July 1595 he received his doctorate from Montpellier.

Also in December 1593 the first botanical garden in France was established at Montpellier, and Belleval devoted all of his time and money to it. The garden comprised the King's Garden (medicinal plants), the Queen's Garden (mountain plants from many foreign countries), and the King's Square (plants of purely botanical interest). During the Wars of Religion all these gardens were destroyed; Belleval set to work once again, but the King's Garden was never restored.

Belleval was planning to publish a general herbarium of the Languedoc when he died. We possess a great number of the plates that were to illustrate

it; the work was to utilize a binary nomenclature in Latin or Greek.

BIBLIOGRAPHY

Works on Belleval are P. J. Amoreux, *Notice sur la vie et les ouvrages de Pierre Richer de Belleval, pour servir à l'histoire de cette faculté et à celle de la botanique* (Avignon, 1786); J. A. Dorthès, *Éloge historique de Pierre Richer de Belleval, instituteur du Jardin royal de botanique de Montpellier sous Henri IV* (Montpellier, 1854); L. Guiraud, *Le premier jardin des plantes de Montpellier. Essai historique et descriptif* (Montpellier, 1854); and J. E. Planchon, *Pierre Richer de Belleval, fondateur du Jardin des plantes de Montpellier et Appendice contenant les pièces justificatives* (Montpellier, 1869).

LOUIS DULIEU

BELLINGSHAUSEN, FABIAN VON. See **Bellinsgauzen, Faddei.**

BELLINI, LORENZO (*b.* Florence, Italy, 3 September 1643; *d.* Florence, 8 January 1704), *physiology, medical theory.*

Bellini, born to a family of small businessmen, benefited from the patronage of Duke Ferdinand II of Tuscany from his early youth. Under the duke's protection, he attended the University of Pisa, where he studied philosophy and mathematics with some of Italy's leading scientists, most notably Giovanni Alfonso Borelli. At the precocious age of twenty, Bellini was appointed professor of theoretical medicine at Pisa, and with Duke Ferdinand's assistance he acquired a chair of anatomy five years later. He resigned the chair when he was about fifty, to become first physician to Duke Cosimo III of Tuscany.

Considered a founder of Italian iatromechanism, Bellini was a pioneer in applying mechanical philosophy to the explanation of the functions of the human body. His earliest interests were anatomy and physiology. The first essay he published, *Exercitatio anatomica de usu renum* (1662), was an important study of the structure and function of the kidneys. Until Bellini's time, the kidneys were widely understood in terms laid down by Galen. Said to be composed of a dense, undifferentiated "parenchymatous" material, they were thought to form urine through the exercise of a special "faculty" that controlled the selective secretion of urine from the mass of the incurrent blood. But under the influence of the mechanical philosophy he learned from Borelli, Bellini rejected this Galenic theory as absurd. He sought a less verbal and more mechanical explanation, and when he reexamined renal anatomy in this frame of mind, he discovered in the supposedly unorganized parenchyma a complicated structure composed of fibers, open spaces, and densely packed tubules opening into the pelvis of the kidney. This unsuspected structure provided the key to true renal function.

Bellini posited that arterial blood brought into the kidneys is separated into urinous and sanguineous portions by a sievelike arrangement in the renal vessels and fibers; the urinous portion collected in the urinary tubules and the blood returned to the circulatory stream through the venules. He meant this mechanical explanation of urinary secretion, achieved by the "configuration alone" of the renal vessels, as a general substitute for Galen's incomprehensible "faculties."

Bellini's mechanical manner of physiological explanation won the admiration of contemporary scientists in Italy and abroad, and his anatomical discoveries were considered worthy enough in themselves to merit careful scrutiny by, among others, Marcello Malpighi. Nevertheless, after his initial triumph Bellini's direct interest in anatomy and physiology slackened. In 1665 he published an essay on taste, *Gustus organum,* which included sections on the functional anatomy of the tongue. The intention of this work, however, was mainly to account for the general phenomena of gustatory sensation according to corpuscular principles. For years afterward, Bellini published no other serious anatomical work, although he did maintain active friendships with Francesco Redi and, after 1676, with Malpighi. He kept abreast of scientific developments through his contacts and correspondence, and in 1683 he returned to print with *De urinis et pulsibus et missione sanguinis,* the first important attempt by an Italian systematically to apply the mechanical philosophy to medical theory.

In *De urinis,* Bellini seems to have been inspired by two earlier authors: the English physician and corpuscular philosopher Thomas Willis, whose medical works were published on the Continent in the early 1680's, and Bellini's old mentor Borelli, whose *De motu animalium* appeared posthumously in 1680. Both Willis and Borelli had tried, to some extent, to apply the mechanical philosophy to medical theory. Willis in particular had attempted to formulate corpuscular hypotheses, both to account for disease phenomena and to justify such traditional therapeutic methods as bleeding, purging, and vomiting. Bellini sympathized with Willis' intentions but felt that he had introduced too many unnecessary and *ad hoc* assumptions. Willis supposed, for example, that a "fermentation" of the blood's constituent particles was required to explain such diseases as fevers. By contrast, Bellini, under Borelli's influence, preferred to think of the blood as a physical fluid with such simple mechanical and mathematicizable attributes as density, viscosity, and momentum. He postulated that health consisted in a well-ordered circulation and that disease implied some sort of circulatory imbalance or inefficiency. Thus, to arrive at the proper theory for a particular disease, one needed merely to set out the pathological phenomena and then to deduce them as consequences of an increased or diminished velocity of the blood. In this manner, Bellini thought, one could get beyond Willis' tentative hypotheses to the real and "necessary" mechanical causes of fevers. He therefore substituted a hydraulic iatromechanism for a corpuscular one.

First reactions to Bellini's hydraulic iatromechanism were uncertain. A few scattered admirers, such as Bohn in Germany and Baglivi in Italy, communicated their enthusiasm, but otherwise the *De urinis* seems to have made little real impact. Bellini turned seriously to medical practice, and in his letters he consoled Malpighi with the news that he too had many enemies and critics. But in 1692 Bellini's affairs took a dramatic turn for the better. The Scots mathematician and physician Archibald Pitcairne, then lecturer on theoretical medicine at Leiden, wrote to express his admiration. Pitcairne was then trying to construct a mathematical and "Newtonian" medical theory, and he saw in Bellini's work an example of the "methods of the Geometers" applied to medical problems. Pitcairne praised Bellini's general theory of disease and urged him to develop further some of the ideas contained only in compressed form in the *De urinis.*

Bellini reacted favorably to Pitcairne's encouragement; and he devoted the next few years to his last set of essays, which he dedicated to Pitcairne and published in 1695 as *Opuscula aliquot.* The *Opuscula* developed Bellini's earlier iatromechanical themes most fully. Organized into postulates, theorems, and corollaries, it treats problems ranging from the hydraulics of intrauterine and extrauterine circulation to the mechanics of the "contractile villi." For example, he considered the blood to be a fluid flowing through conical vessels, according to Borelli's laws of hydraulics, and he imagined that the "contractile villi" (which explain the body's reaction to stimuli) expand, contract, and vibrate like ordinary musical strings. In these carefully stated propositions Bellini hoped to explain all important physiological phenomena according to the laws of mechanics.

By the time the *Opuscula* was published, Bellini had already begun to enjoy an international reputation, largely through the influence of Pitcairne. During the early decades of the eighteenth century that reputation spread. Hermann Boerhaave, the most influential medical teacher of the time, studied with Pitcairne at Leiden and absorbed his enthusiasm for Bellini's medical science. In England, too, Bellini's theories enjoyed a considerable vogue from 1710 to 1730, when such physicians as George Cheyne and Richard Mead tried to build a "Newtonian" theory of the "animal oeconomy" and turned appreciatively to Bellini's writings. His influence was somewhat tempered in Italy by the Hippocratic revival encouraged by Giorgio Baglivi, who had once been Bellini's ardent admirer. Nevertheless, Bellini remained a major scientific authority until the mid-eighteenth century, when a general reaction to iatromechanism, in all its forms, set in.

BIBLIOGRAPHY

I. ORIGINAL WORKS. Bellini's total scientific production was collected in a handsome posthumous edition, 2 vols. (Venice, 1732). Correspondence between Bellini and Malpighi has been edited by Gaetano Atti as *Notizie edite ed inedite della vita e della opere di Marcello Malpighi e di Lorenzo Bellini* (Bologna, 1847).

His individual works include *Exercitatio anatomica de usu renum* (Florence, 1662); *De urinis et pulsibus et missione sanguinis* (Bologna, 1683); and *Opuscula aliquot* (Leiden, 1695).

II. SECONDARY LITERATURE. There is no full-length study of Bellini. A useful short biography can be found in *Dizionario biografico degli italiani,* VII (Rome, 1965), 713–716. Augusto Botto-Micco's account in *Rivista di storia delle scienze mediche e naturale,* **12** (1930), 38–49, is also helpful. Charles Daremberg presents a summary of some of Bellini's theories, along with a general account of the medical environment of the late seventeenth and early eighteenth centuries, in *Histoire des sciences médicales,* II (Paris, 1870), esp. 765–783. Useful information on Bellini's career, particularly on his connections with Malpighi, can be found throughout Howard Adelmann's mammoth *Marcello Malpighi and the Evolution of Embryology,* 5 vols. (Ithaca, N.Y., 1966).

THEODORE M. BROWN

BELLINSGAUZEN, FADDEI F. (*b.* Arensburg, on the island of Oesel, Russia [now Kingissepp, Sarema, Estonian Soviet Socialist Republic], 30 August 1779; *d.* Kronstadt, Russia, 25 January 1852), *navigation, oceanography.*

Bellinsgauzen began his naval career in 1789 as a cadet in Kronstadt. From 1803 to 1806 he participated in the first round-the-world voyage by a Russian ship, the *Nadezhda,* under the command of Ivan F. Kruzenstern. Following this trip, and until July 1819, Bellinsgauzen commanded various ships on the Baltic and Black seas. From 1819 to 1821 he headed a Russian Antarctic expedition, then commanded various naval units in the Mediterranean, Black, and Baltic seas. From 1839 until the end of his life Bellinsgauzen was the military governor of Kronstadt. He married in 1826 and had four daughters. Bellinsgauzen was also one of the founders of the Russian Geographic Society in 1845.

Bellinsgauzen's fame is a result of the discoveries made on the expedition he led to the Antarctic. When the Russian government decided to send an expedition to study the Antarctic, he was designated commander because of his solid knowledge of physics, astronomy, hydrography, and cartography, and because of his wide naval experience. He also was responsible for practically all the maps of the Kruzenstern expedition. During his Black Sea service he had determined the coordinates of the main points of the eastern shore and had corrected several inaccuracies on the map of the shoreline.

Two three-masted vessels, the *Vostok* and the *Mirny,* were outfitted for the trip to the Antarctic. Bellinsgauzen commanded the *Vostok;* the commander of the *Mirny* was Mikhail P. Lazarev. The expedition was to survey South Georgia Island, sail to the east of the Sandwich Islands, go as close to the pole as possible, and not turn back unless it met impassable obstacles.

The *Vostok* and the *Mirny* left Kronstadt on 15 July 1819. In December the expedition sighted the south shore of South Georgia Island, and at the beginning of January 1820 it came upon the Traverse Islands. Reaching the Sandwich Islands seven days later, the expedition found not a single island, as Cook had proposed, but several islands. Naming them the South Sandwich Islands, the expedition headed south and, in spite of ice barriers, on 27 January 1820, near the coast of Princess Martha's Land at a latitude of 69°25′ (according to Bellinsgauzen's report of 20 April 1820 to the Russian minister) came within twenty miles of the Antarctic mainland, the shoreline of which was plotted. Bellinsgauzen wrote on this day that ice, which appeared "like white clouds in the snow that was then falling," was sighted. This was the first view of the earth's sixth continent, and on the navigational map he noted, "Sighted solid ice." Lazarev, who arrived at approximately the same place several hours later, wrote:

> . . . we reached latitude 69°23′, there to meet continuous ice of an immense height; watched from the crosstrees on that beautiful evening . . . ice ranged as far as the eye could see; but we could not enjoy that wonderful sight for very long because the sky soon went dull again and it started to snow as usual. From this place we

proceeded to the east, venturing at every opportunity to the south, but meeting each time an ice-covered continent before we could reach 70° [*Dokumenty,* I, 150].

On 1 February, Bellinsgauzen's expedition was about thirty miles from the icy continent, at latitude 69°25' south and longitude 1°11' west. The third leaf of the navigational map shows the ice, which the expedition again approached on 17–18 February. In a report from Port Jackson [Sydney], Australia, to the war minister on 20 April 1820, Bellinsgauzen wrote of these approaches:

Here behind ice fields of smaller ice and islands, a continent of ice is seen, the borders of which are broken off perpendicularly and which ranges as far as we could see. The flat ice islands are situated close to that continent rising toward the south . . . and show clearly that they are wreckage of that continent, for their borders and surface are like the continent [*Dvukratnye izyskania* ("Twofold Investigations"), 3rd ed., p. 37].

The expedition later discovered a series of islands in the Pacific. In January 1821 the southernmost point of the trip was reached (latitude 69°53' south, longitude 92°19' west) and an island (which was named Peter the Great) and a coastline (which was named Alexander I Coast) were sighted.

Bellinsgauzen expressed his firm conviction that there was an ice continent at the South Pole: "I call the great ice rising to form sloping mountains as one proceeds to the South Pole the inveterate ice, provided it is 4° cold in the midst of the most perfect summer day. I suppose it is no less cold farther to the south, and thus I conclude that the ice ranges over the Pole and must be stationary . . ." (*ibid.,* p. 420).

In 751 sailing days, of which 122 were spent below the sixtieth parallel, the *Vostok* and the *Mirny* covered over 55,000 miles. Besides discovering Antarctica and sailing around it, one of the great achievements of the Bellinsgauzen-Lazarev expedition was the first description of large oceanic regions adjoining the ice continent. It discovered twenty-nine islands and one coral reef and conducted valuable oceanographic and other scientific observations. A test of the water at a depth of 402 meters, using a bathometer with a thermometer placed inside, showed higher specific weight and lower temperature proportional to depth. The climatic peculiarities of the Antarctic as recorded by Bellinsgauzen are generally in agreement with modern observations. The generalization concerning the temperatures of the equatorial and tropic zones of the Pacific is also important: "Here I ought to note that the greatest heat is not to be expected directly at the equator, where the passing southern trade wind refreshes the air. The greatest heat is in a zone of calm between the southern and the northern trade winds" (*ibid.,* p. 110).

Bellinsgauzen made the first attempt to describe and classify the Antarctic ice and determined that the Kanarsky flow is a branch of the Floridsky. He explained the origin of coral islands and on the basis of 203 observations of compass variations determined with great precision the position of the South Magnetic Pole at that time—latitude 76° south, longitude 142° 30' west. He wrote of this in a letter to Kruzenstern, asking him to pass on to Gauss, at the latter's request, his table of compass variations. This table was published in Leipzig by Gauss (1840).

A sea in the Antarctic was named for Bellinsgauzen, as well as a cape in the southern part of Sakhalin Island and an island in the Tuamotus.

BIBLIOGRAPHY

Bellinsgauzen's account of the Antarctic expedition is *Dvukratnye izyskania v Yuzhnom Ledovitom okeane i plavanie vokrug sveta v prodolzhenie 1819, 20 i 21 godov, sovershennoe na shlyupakh "Vostoke" i "Mirnom"* ("Twofold Investigations in the Antarctic Ocean and a Voyage Around the World During 1819, 1820 and 1821, Completed on the Sloops *Vostok* and *Mirny*"; St. Petersburg, 1821; 3rd ed., Moscow, 1961).

Works on Bellinsgauzen are M. I. Belov, ed., *Pervaya russkaya antarkticheskaya ekspeditsia 1819–1821 gg. i ee otchetnaya navigatsionnaya karta* ("The First Russian Antarctic Expedition 1819–1821 and Its Navigational Map"; Leningrad, 1963), and "Slavu pervogo tochnogo vychislenia mestopolozhenia yuzhnogo magnitnogo polyusa Ross dolzhen razdelit c Bellinsgauzenom" ("Ross Must Share With Bellinsgauzen the Fame for the First Precise Calculation of the Location of the South Magnetic Pole"), in *Nauka i zhizn* ("Science and Life," 1966), no. 8, 21–23; "Geograficheskie nablyudenia v Antarktike ekspeditsy Kuka 1772–1775 gg. i Bellinsgauzena-Lazareva 1819–1820–1821 gg." ("Geographic Observations in the Antarctic of the Cook Expedition, 1772–1775, and the Bellinsgauzen-Lazarev Expedition, 1819–1821"), in *Doklady Mezhduvedomstvennoy Komissy po izucheniyu Antarktiki za 1960 g.* ("Reports of the Joint Commission for the Study of Antarctica, 1960"; Moscow, 1961), pp. 7–23; and M. P. Lazarev, *Dokumenty,* I (Moscow, 1952), 150.

IVAN A. FEDOSEYEV

BELON, PIERRE (*b.* Soultière, near Cerans, France, 1517; *d.* Paris, France, 1564), *zoology, botany.*

Belon's birthplace—or the house traditionally considered as such—still stands at Soultière. Practically nothing is known of his ancestry, and his biographer, Paul Delaunay, has been unable to pierce the mystery surrounding his origins. We know that he came from an obscure family and that as a boy he was apprenticed to an apothecary at Foulletourte. About 1535 he became apothecary to Guillaume Duprat, bishop of Clermont. In the course of subsequent wanderings (in Flanders and England) and zoological research he came back to the Auvergne. About that time he became the protégé of René du Bellay, bishop of Le Mans, a situation that enabled him to go to the University of Wittenberg and study under the botanist Valerius Cordus. In 1542 he went to Paris, where Duprat recommended him as an apothecary to François Cardinal de Tournon. Belon never acquired the doctorate, but in 1560, when Brigard was dean, he obtained the licentiate in medicine from the Paris Faculty of Medicine.

In his *Histoire naturelle des estranges poissons marins* (1551), Belon presented an orderly classification of fish that included the sturgeon, the tuna, the *malarmat* (peristedion), the dolphin, and the hippopotamus. The last, incidentally, was drawn from an Egyptian sculpture. Nevertheless, Belon can be considered the originator of comparative anatomy. By the same token, he depicted a porpoise embryo and set forth the first notions of embryology. Belon enriched the biological sciences by new observations and contributed greatly to the progress of the natural sciences in the sixteenth century. His learning was not derived solely from books. He was one of the first explorer-naturalists; and between 1546 and 1550 he undertook long voyages through Greece, Asia, Judaea, Egypt, Arabia, and other foreign countries. He passed through Constantinople, and in Rome he met the zoologists Rondelet and Salviani.

Belon discarded the bases of the comparative method and was not at all afraid of drawing parallels between human and bird skeletons. He was the first to bring order into the world of feathered animals, distinguishing between raptorial birds, diurnal birds of prey, web-footed birds, river birds, field birds, etc.

Belon was also a talented botanist and recorded the results of his observations in a beautiful work adorned with woodcuts showing, for the first time, several plants of the Near East, including *Platanus orientalis, Umbilicus pendulinus, Acacia vera,* and *Caucalis orientalis.* He was more interested in the practical uses of plants than in their scientific description. He also advocated the acclimatization of exotic plants in France.

Belon dwelt at great length on the applications of medicinal substances. He clarified the use of bitumen, which the ancient Egyptians had used for mummifying corpses. Its agglutinative and antiputrefactive properties had induced physicians to use it therapeutically.

Belon's observations were generally correct. He looked at the world as an analyst devoted to detail. He succeeded in winning the confidence of the great and was famous during his lifetime. His works were translated by Charles de l'Escluse and Ulisse Aldrovandi, both of whom recognized his authority. Charles IX installed him at the Château de Madrid and granted him a pension. Belon was murdered in the Bois de Boulogne under mysterious circumstances. He was only forty-seven.

Charles Plumier dedicated the species *Bellonia* (Rubiaceae) to Belon. Charles Alexandre Filleul, a sculptor from Le Mans, erected a statue to him in Le Mans in 1887. Pavlov called him the "prophet of comparative anatomy."

BIBLIOGRAPHY

I. ORIGINAL WORKS. Belon's writings are *L'histoire naturelle des estranges poissons marins, avec la vraie peincture et description du daulphin, et de plusieurs autres de son espèce, observée par Pierre Belon . . .* (Paris, 1551); *De admirabili operum antiquorum et rerum suspiciendarum praestantia liber primus. De medicato funere seu cadavere condito et lugubri defunctorum ejulatione liber secundus. De medicamentis non-nullis servandi cadaveris vim obtinentibus liber tertius* (Paris, 1553); *De aquatilibus libri duo . . .* (Paris, 1553); *De arboribus coniferis resiniferis, aliis quoque non-nullis sempiterna fronde virentibus . . .* (Paris, 1553); *Les observations de plusieurs singularitez et choses mémorables trouvées en Grèce, Asie, Judée, Égypte, Arabie et autres pays estranges, rédigées en trois livres . . .* (Paris, 1553); *L'histoire de la nature des oyseaux, avec leurs descriptions et naïfs portraicts retirez du naturel, escrite en sept livres . . .* (Paris, 1555); *La nature et diversité des poissons, avec leurs pourtraicts représentez au plus près du naturel, par Pierre Belon . . .* (Paris, 1555); *Portraits d'oyseaux, animaux, serpens, herbes, arbres, hommes et femmes d'Arabie et d'Égypte, observez par P. Belon, . . . le tout enrichy de quatrains, pour plus facile cognoissance des oyseaux et autres portraits . . .* (Paris, 1557); and *Les remonstrances sur le défault du labour et culture des plantes et de la cognoissance d'icelles . . .* (Paris, 1558).

II. SECONDARY LITERATURE. Works on Belon are "La cronique de Pierre Belon, du Mans, médecin," Paris, Bibliothèque de l'Arsenal, MS 4561, fols. 88–141; Paul Delaunay, *Les voyages en Angleterre du médecin naturaliste Pierre Belon* (Anvers, 1923); and *L'aventureuse existence de Pierre Belon du Mans* (Paris, 1926), with a bibliography; and R. J. Forbes, *Pierre Belon and Petroleum* (Brussels, 1958).

M. WONG

BELOPOLSKY, ARISTARKH APOLLONOVICH
(*b.* Moscow, Russia, 13 July 1854; *d.* Pulkovo, U.S.S.R., 16 May 1934), *astrophysics.*

Belopolsky was born into an intellectual but poor family; his father, Apollon Grigorievich, a teacher in a Gymnasium, had not graduated from the Faculty of Medicine at the University of Moscow because of a lack of funds. His mother, the daughter of a doctor, taught music in Moscow. Upon graduating from the Gymnasium in 1873, Belopolsky entered Moscow University, graduating from its Faculty of Physics and Mathematics in 1877.

F. A. Bredikhin, director of the Moscow Observatory, enlisted Belopolsky to work there on photographing the sun. Belopolsky thus became seriously interested in and decided to devote himself to astronomy. In 1879 he was named a supernumerary assistant at the observatory.

An investigation of the photographs that he had taken of the sun served as the topic of Belopolsky's master's thesis, "Pyatna na solntse i ikh dvizhenie" ("Spots on the Sun and Their Movements," 1886). In 1888 Belopolsky was appointed a junior assistant in astronomy at the Pulkovo Observatory, and in 1891 a staff astrophysicist. He was elected an extraordinary academician in 1903 and ordinary academician in 1906. From 1908 to 1916 he was the vice-director of Pulkovo Observatory, from 1917 to 1919 its director, and from 1933 its honorary director.

During his eleven years at Moscow Observatory, in addition to his photographic work, Belopolsky measured on the meridional circle the precise positions of a selected group of stars, planets, and asteroids, and the positions of comets. Besides systematically photographing the sun and studying the law of its rotation, Belopolsky was the first in Russia to attempt to photograph stars; he achieved notable success with low-sensitivity bromide plates, photographing stars up to magnitude 8.5. He photographed the total solar eclipse of 1887, at which time he obtained on one negative a photograph of the internal solar corona, taken simultaneously by four separate objectives.

The main area of astrophysics in which Belopolsky worked was the determination of the radial velocity of celestial bodies. The application of photography to the study of their spectra had much significance for the development of astrophysics at the end of the nineteenth century. Belopolsky built spectrographs and was a tireless observer who used these devices in conjunction with all the powerful refractors at the Pulkovo Observatory.

The first two years of Belopolsky's stay at Pulkovo were devoted not to astrophysics, however, but to astrometrical observation, using a transit instrument, and to the working up of prior observations by August Wagner, from which he obtained reliable parallaxes for a number of bright stars (1889). Only in 1891, after Bredikhin became director at Pulkovo, did Belopolsky's active and fruitful career in astrophysics begin. Belopolsky reestablished the abandoned astrophysics laboratory and ordered from the observatory's workshops several spectrographs, which he himself helped to build. He was the first to use dry photographic plates, instead of the previously used colloidal plates. Belopolsky quickly became, with Scheiner and Fogel of Potsdam, a leading specialist in solar and laboratory spectroscopy. In 1902 he was invited to join the editorial board of the American *Astrophysical Journal.*

Belopolsky began his spectrographic work in 1895 with a study of the large planets, his goal being to explain the peculiarities of their axial rotation. It turned out that the angular rate of rotation of Jupiter's equatorial zones is 4–5 percent greater than that at other jovicentric latitudes. This confirmed a conclusion drawn by Belopolsky while he was still in Moscow; in analyzing observations of Jupiter taken over a period of 200 years, he had established that the period of rotation of the planet's equatorial region ($9^h\ 50^m$) differs from the period of rotation of the remainder of the surface ($9^h\ 55^m$), which is separated from the equatorial region by two dark bands.

In 1895, using a spectrograph attached to a 30-inch refractor to study the radial velocities of various points on Saturn's rings, Belopolsky brilliantly confirmed the theoretical conclusion of James Clerk Maxwell and Sofia V. Kovalevskaya that Saturn's rings are not solid, but consist of a multitude of small satellites. In addition, he found that the spectrum of the ring was rich in ultraviolet rays, which he explained as the influence of the planet's atmosphere on the spectrum of the planet itself.

At Pulkovo he continued his study of the sun's surface, but he shifted from a study of the sun's rotation by observing its faculae—the method he himself had proposed—to systematic observations of its protuberances and eruptions and, later, to a study of the movements of matter within the sun, a problem that is still important. Belopolsky also studied the fine structure of spectral lines and their changes in shape over time.

In 1904 Belopolsky joined the International Union for Cooperation in Solar Research, organized by G. E. Hale. In Russia there was a branch of the Union, the Commission for the Investigation of the Sun, to which many eminent physicists and astronomers belonged. The Union decided to undertake an eleven-and-a-half-year study of the sun, and for this work Belopolsky ordered a special three-prism spectrograph. In 1915 he published Russia's first study in spectrophotometry, "O temperature solnechnykh pyaten" ("On the Temperature of Sunspots"), in which he obtained a temperature of 3,500° C. for these spots. This has been confirmed by the latest investigations.

Belopolsky participated in two more expeditions to observe solar eclipses. In 1896 he succeeded in determining from the inclination of the spectral lines in the spectrum of the solar corona that the corona does not rotate like a solid body. The second expedition, in 1907, was not successful because of bad weather.

The study of star spectra on the basis of the Doppler principle was begun with the effective determination of the rate of expansion of the shell of Nova Aurigae, which appeared in 1892; Belopolsky conducted investigations of the spectra of Nova Persei (1901), which manifested semiperiodic fluctuations and changes in its spectrum, as well as of Nova Geminorum (1912), Nova Aquilae (1918), Nova Cygni (1920), and several others.

Belopolsky began studying the spectra of common (i.e., not new) stars in 1890, primarily to measure their radial velocities, and gave special attention to spectroscopic binary stars. He discovered the spectral duality of many stars, especially the star α Lyrae, which, until then had been considered a standard star in all catalogs of radial velocities. For the majority of spectroscopic binary stars he studied, Belopolsky determined the elements of their orbits and, in a number of cases, their changes. These changes of the elements attested to the presence of a third component in these systems (for example, Algol's third component and the polestar's third component).

Belopolsky discovered the variability of the spectrum of α_2 Canum Venaticorum, which bespoke strong and irregular changes in the atmosphere of this star, the prototype of a special class of stars with strong perturbations in their atmospheres.

A study of the spectra of stars of the δ Cephei type—Cepheid variables—led Belopolsky to the discovery of the noncoincidence of the phases of changes in brightness and changes of radial velocities, as well as the discovery of periodic changes in the intensity of absorption lines. Belopolsky's determination of the parallaxes and linear dimensions of several visual binary stars is also of interest. It is worth noting that in 1896, at Belopolsky's defense of his doctoral dissertation, *Issledovanie spektra peremennoy zvezdy δ Cephei* ("An Investigation of the Spectrum of the Variable Star δ Cephei"), the physicist N. A. Umov

first explained the periodic changes of radial velocity (observed by Belopolsky) by the hypothesis of an individual star's pulsation. The pulsation theory of Cepheids was not completely developed until the work of the Soviet astrophysicist S. A. Zhevakin.

Belopolsky's laboratory investigations occupy a special place in the history of science. In his master's thesis, as a supplement to the theoretical analysis of the laws of motion of solar matter, Belopolsky conducted an original experiment using a glass flask filled with water, in which were suspended minute particles of stearin. A coordinate grid plotted on the surface of the flask facilitated registration of the behavior of the stearin particles, which revealed the particularities of the liquid's rotation. The angular velocity of the rotation declined monotonically from the equator to the latitude of 55°, while the meridional velocity increased up to this same latitude, recalling the corresponding particularities of the rotation of elements of the sun's surface.

His verification of the validity of Doppler's principle in optics is considered a classic. For this experiment Belopolsky constructed an exceedingly original device in which, by means of the multiple reflections of a beam of light between two oppositely rotating "water wheels" whose blades were strips of plane mirrors, he succeeded in obtaining a speed of the image's motion on the order of 1 km./sec., which was capable of being measured with the sufficient certainty to verify the Doppler principle convincingly.

BIBLIOGRAPHY

I. ORIGINAL WORKS. Belopolsky's major writings are "Pyatna na solntse i ikh dvizhenie" ("Spots on the Sun and Their Movements"), master's thesis (University of Moscow, 1886); "Issledovanie smeshchenia liniy v spektre Saturna i ego koltsa" ("An Investigation of the Shift of Lines in the Spectrum of Saturn and of Its Ring"), in *Izvestiya Imperatorskoi akademii nauk,* **3** (1895); *Issledovanie spektra peremennoy zvezdy δ Cephei* ("An Investigation of the Spectrum of the Variable Star δ Cephei"; St. Petersburg, 1895); "O zvezde α′ Bliznetsov kak spektralno-dvoynoy" ("On the Star α′ Geminorum as a Spectral-Binary Star"), in *Izvestiya Imperatorskoi akademii nauk,* **7**, no. 1 (1897); "Opyt issledovania printsipa Doplera-Fizo, ne pribegaya k kosmicheskim skorostyam" ("An Attempt to Investigate the Doppler-Fizo Principle, Without Resorting to Cosmic Velocities"), *ibid.,* **13**, no. 5 (1900), 461–474; "O vrashcheny Yupitera" ("On the Rotation of Jupiter"), *ibid.,* 6th ser., **3** (1909); "Avtobiografia" ("Autobiography"), in *Materialy dlya biograficheskogo slovarya deystvitelnykh chlenov Akademii nauk. 1889–1914, chast pervaya,* I (Petrograd, 1915), pp. 121–122; "O spektre Novoy 1918 g. (predvaritelnoe soobshchenie)" ("On the

Spectrum of the Nova of 1918 [Preliminary Report]"), in *Izvestiya Imperatorskoi akademii nauk; Astrospektroskopia* ("Astrospectroscopy"; Petrograd, 1921); "Comets and Ionization," in *Observatory,* **46** (1923), 124–125; "Über die Intensitätsveränderlichtkeit der Spektrallinien einiger Cepheiden," in *Izvestiya Pulkovo Obs.,* 2nd ser., **2,** no. 101 (1927), 79–88; "Ob izmeny intensivnosti liny v spektrakh nekotorykh tsefeid," ("On Changes in the Intensity of Lines in the Spectra of Certain Cepheids"), in *Izvestiya Akademii nauk,* 7th ser., no. 1 (1928); and "Bestimmung der Sonnenrotation auf spektroskopischen Wege in den Jahren 1931, 1932 und 1933 in Pulkovo," in *Zeitschrift für Astrophysik,* **7** (1933), 357–363.

II. SECONDARY LITERATURE. Works on Belopolsky are S. N. Blazhko, "A. A. Belopolsky," in *Bolshaya sovetskaya entsiklopedia,* IV (1950), 462–464; V. G. Fesenkov, "Aristarkh Apollonovich Belopolsky," in *Lyudi russkoy nauki* ("People of Russian Science"; Moscow, 1961), pp. 185–192; B. P. Gerasimovich, "A. A. Belopolsky. 1854–1934," in *Astronomicheskii zhurnal (SSSR),* **2,** pt. 3 (1934), 251–254; O. A. Melnikov, "Aristarkh Apollonovich Belopolsky (1854–1934). Nauchno-biografichesky ocherk" ("Aristarkh Apollonovich Belopolsky [1854–1934]. A Scientific-biographical Essay"), in *A. A. Belopolsky. Astronomicheskie trudy* ("A. A. Belopolsky. Astronomical Works"; Moscow, 1954), pp. 7–58; Y. G. Perel, *Vydayushchiesya russkie astronomy* ("Outstanding Russian Astronomers"; Moscow, 1951), pp. 85–107; K. D. Pokrovsky, "A. A. Belopolsky (k 50-letiyu ego nauchnoy deyatelnosti 1877–1927)" ("A. A. Belopolsky [on the 50th Anniversary of His Scientific Career 1877–1927]"), in *Astronomicheskii kalendar na 1928 god* ("Astronomical Calendar for 1928"; Nizhni Novgorod, 1927), pp. 123–125, with illustrations; and D. A. Zhukov, "Spisok nauchnykh rabot akademika A. A. Belopolskogo 1877–1934" ("A List of the Scientific Papers of Academician A. A. Belopolsky 1877–1934"), in *Byulleten' Komissii po issledovaniyu solntsa akademii nauk SSSR,* nos. 10–11 (1934), 7–20.

P. G. KULIKOVSKY

BELTRAMI, EUGENIO (*b.* Cremona, Italy, 16 November 1835; *d.* Rome, Italy, 4 June 1899), *mathematics.*

Beltrami was born into an artistic family: his grandfather, Giovanni, was an engraver of precious stones, especially cameos; his father, Eugenio, painted miniatures. Young Eugenio studied mathematics from 1853 to 1856 at the University of Pavia, where Francesco Brioschi was his teacher. Financial difficulties forced Beltrami to become secretary to a railroad engineer, first in Verona and then in Milan. In Milan he continued his mathematical studies and in 1862 published his first mathematical papers, which deal with the differential geometry of curves.

After the establishment of the kingdom of Italy in 1861, Beltrami was offered the chair of complementary algebra and analytic geometry at Bologna, which he held from 1862 to 1864; from 1864 to 1866 he held the chair of geodesy in Pisa, where Enrico Betti was his friend and colleague. From 1866 to 1873 he was back in Bologna, where he occupied the chair of rational mechanics. After Rome had become the capital of Italy in 1870, Beltrami became professor of rational mechanics at the new University of Rome, but served there only from 1873 to 1876, after which he held the chair of mathematical physics at Pavia, where he also taught higher mechanics. In 1891 he returned to Rome, where he taught until his death. He became the president of the Accademia dei Lincei in 1898 and, the following year, a senator of the kingdom. A lover of music, Beltrami was interested in the relationship between mathematics and music.

Beltrami's works can be divided into two main groups: those before *ca.* 1872, which deal with differential geometry of curves and surfaces and were influenced by Gauss, Lamé, and Riemann, and the later ones, which are concerned with topics in applied mathematics that range from elasticity to electromagnetics. His most lasting work belongs to this first period, and the paper "Saggio di interpretazione della geometria non-euclidea" (1868) stands out. In a paper of 1865 Beltrami had shown that on surfaces of constant curvature, and only on them, the line element $ds^2 = E du^2 + 2F du dv + G dv^2$ can be written in such a form that the geodesics, and only these, are represented by linear expressions in u and v. For positive curvature R^{-2} this form is

$$ds^2 = R^2[(v^2 + a^2)du^2 - 2uv du dv + (u^2 + a^2)dv^2]$$
$$\times (u^2 + v^2 + a^2)^{-2}.$$

The geodesics in this case behave, locally speaking, like the great circles on a sphere. It now occurred to Beltrami that, by changing R to iR and a to ia ($i = \sqrt{-1}$), the line element thus obtained,

$$ds^2 = R^2[(a^2 - v^2)du^2 + 2uv du dv + (u^2 + a^2)dv^2]$$
$$\times (a^2 - u^2 - v^2)^{-2},$$

which defines surfaces of constant curvature $-R^{-2}$, offers a new type of geometry for its geodesics inside the region $u^2 + v^2 < a^2$. This geometry is exactly that of the so-called non-Euclidean geometry of Lobachevski, if geodesics on such a surface are identified with the "straight lines" of non-Euclidean geometry.

This geometry, developed between 1826 and 1832, was known to Beltrami through some of Gauss's letters and some translations of the work of Lobachevski. Few mathematicians, however, had paid attention to it. Beltrami now offered a representation of this geometry in terms of the acceptable Euclidean geometry: "We have tried to find a real foundation [*sub-*

strato] to this doctrine, instead of having to admit for it the necessity of a new order of entities and concepts." He showed that all the concepts and formulas of Lobachevski's geometry are realized for geodesics on surfaces of constant negative curvature and, in particular, that there are rotation surfaces of this kind. The simplest of this kind of "pseudospherical" surface (Beltrami's term) is the surface of rotation of the tractrix about its asymptote, now usually called the pseudosphere, which Beltrami analyzed more closely in a paper of 1872.

Thus Beltrami showed how possible contradictions in non-Euclidean geometry would reveal themselves in the Euclidean geometry of surfaces; and this removed for most, or probably all, mathematicians the feeling that non-Euclidean geometry might be wrong. Beltrami, by "mapping" one geometry upon another, made non-Euclidean geometry "respectable." His method was soon followed by others, including Felix Klein, a development that opened entirely new fields of mathematical thinking.

Beltrami pointed out that his representation of non-Euclidean geometry was valid for two dimensions only. In his "Saggio" he was hesitant to claim the possibility of a similar treatment of non-Euclidean geometry of space. After he had studied Riemann's *Über die Hypothesen welche der Geometrie zu Grunde liegen,* just published by Dedekind, he had no scruples about extending his representation of non-Euclidean geometry to manifolds of $n > 2$ dimensions in "Teoria fondamentale degli spazi di curvatura costante."

In a contribution to the history of non-Euclidean geometry, Beltrami rescued from oblivion the Jesuit mathematician and logician Giovanni Saccheri (1667–1733), author of *Euclides ab omni naevo vindicatus,* which foreshadowed non-Euclidean geometry but did not achieve it.

In his "Ricerche di analisi applicata alla geometria," Beltrami, following an idea of Lamé's, showed the power of using so-called differential parameters in surface theory. This can be considered the beginning of the use of invariant methods in differential geometry.

Much of Beltrami's work in applied mathematics shows his fundamental geometrical approach, even in his analytical investigations. This trait characterizes the extensive "Richerche sulle cinematica dei fluidi" (1871–1874) and his papers on elasticity. In these he recognized how Lamé's fundamental formulas depend on the Euclidean character of space, and he sketched a non-Euclidean approach (1880–1882). He studied potential theory, particularly that of ellipsoids and cylindrical discs; wave theory in connection with Huygens' principle; and further problems in thermo-

dynamics, optics, and conduction of heat that led to linear partial differential equations. Some papers deal with Maxwell's theory and its mechanistic interpretation, suggesting a start from d'Alembert's principle rather than from that of Hamilton (1889).

BIBLIOGRAPHY

I. ORIGINAL WORKS. Beltrami's works are collected in *Opere matematiche,* 4 vols. (Milan, 1902–1920). Important individual works are "Saggio di interpretazione della geometria non-euclidea," in *Giornale di matematiche,* **6** (1868), 284–312, and *Opere,* I, 374–405, also translated into French in *Annales scientifiques de l'École Normale Supérieure,* **6** (1869), 251–288; "Richerche di analisi applicata alla geometria," in *Giornale di matematiche,* **2** (1864) and **3** (1865), also in *Opere,* I, 107–206; a paper on surfaces of constant curvature, in *Opere,* I, 262–280; "Teoria fondamentale degli spazi di curvatura costante," in *Annali di matematica,* ser. 2 (1868–1869), 232–255, and *Opere,* I 406–429; "Richerche sulle cinematica dei fluidi," in *Opere,* II, 202–379; a paper on the pseudosphere, in *Opere,* II, 394–409; a non-Euclidean approach to space, in *Opere,* III, 383–407; "Sulla teoria della scala diatonica," in *Opere,* III, 408–412; an article on Saccheri, in *Rendiconti della Reale Accademia dei Lincei,* ser. 4, **5** (1889), 441–448, and *Opere,* IV, 348–355; and papers on Maxwell's theory, in *Opere,* IV, 356–361.

II. SECONDARY LITERATURE. There is a biographical sketch by L. Cremona in *Opere,* I, ix–xxii. See also L. Bianchi, "Eugenio Beltrami," in *Enciclopedia italiana,* VI (1930), 581; G. H. Bryan, "Eugenio Beltrami," in *Proceedings of the London Mathematical Society,* **32** (1900), 436–439; and G. Loria, "Eugenio Beltrami e le sue opere matematiche," in *Bibliotheca mathematica,* ser. 3, **2** (1901), 392–440. On Beltrami's contribution to non-Euclidean geometry, consult, among others, R. Bonola, *Non-Euclidean Geometry* (Chicago, 1912; New York, 1955), pp. 130–139, 234–236.

D. J. STRUIK

BENEDEN, EDOUARD VAN (*b.* Louvain, Belgium, 5 March 1846; *d.* Liège, Belgium, 28 April 1910), *zoology, embryology.*

Van Beneden's father, the zoologist P. J. Van Beneden, was professor at the Catholic University in Louvain. Edouard was appointed professor at the University of Liège in 1870 with the qualification of *chargé de cours* and was promoted to *ordinarius* in 1874.

His scientific work is characterized by a great unity resulting from the character of the problems to which he devoted his attention. In 1872 Van Beneden went to Brazil, and from there he brought back a number of specimens, particularly *Annelida,* which were studied by Armauer Hansen. P. J. Van Beneden had organized a modest laboratory on the Belgian sea-coast at Ostend, and there Edouard had the opportunity to collect and study many specimens of fauna, particularly from Thornton Bank, near Ostend. His main interests at that time were directed toward the animal groups his father had studied: protozoa, hydraria, cestodes, nematodes, and tunicates. He soon extended these studies to dicyemida, and later to vertebrates, particularly mammals.

In a paper on the origin of the sexual cells of hydroids (1874), Van Beneden showed, besides great care in observation, his tendency to sometimes bold generalization. At that time, the gastrula theory of metazoan development was presented by Huxley, Lankester, and Haeckel; Van Beneden suggested that ectoderm and endoderm have opposed sexual significance, the ectoderm being the male layer and the endoderm the female layer. He thereafter recognized the hermaphrodite nature of the egg, an idea he later developed in his studies on cestodes.

Van Beneden's first publication on dicyemida dates from 1876. He made a thorough and careful study of their structure and observed that they derive from an epibolic gastrula, the hypoblast of which is formed by a long, central single cell. In 1877 he proposed the creation of the phylum Mesozoa, considering it an ideal transition between monocellular and multicellular animal forms. This idea, after a temporary eclipse, has regained popularity.

In 1864, by the application of the embryogenetic method and the biogenetic law, Kovalevski had shown, to everyone's surprise, that tunicates were chordates. They therefore were excellent material for studies in comparative morphology, with a view to establishing their phylogenetic relations with other animals. In collaboration with his colleague Charles Julin, Van Beneden showed, in a contribution to ascidian embryology that represents one of the first and best works on the segmentation of the egg, that the germ in formation shows a bilateral symmetry and a clear polarity. In 1884 Van Beneden and Julin were the first to follow, in a strictly bilateral egg, what is now called cell lineage.

In 1887, Van Beneden and Julin published an important paper on tunicate morphology in which they stated that the mesoblast derives from the enterocele. They also accepted that the cardiopericardic vesicle and the epicardia derive from common forms, the procardia, which they considered to be pharyngeal diverticula.

Van Beneden pursued these studies until his death and left notes that have been published by his disciple Marc de Selys-Longchamps, who, from drawings left by his master, concluded that the endoblast is not derived from the enterocele and showed that

the pericardium of tunicates is the ultimate remainder of the chordate celom.

Van Beneden's most famous contributions to science are his papers on the maturation and fertilization of the egg of *Ascaris megalocephala,* the first of which was published in 1883. In this paper he revealed the essential nature of fertilization: the union of two half-nuclei, one female and the other male. He showed that in *Ascaris,* it is not until the male and female pronuclei have formed what we now call chromosomes (which are accurately represented in his plates) that the respective nuclear membranes break down. He described how each set of chromosomes moves to the equatorial plate. Van Beneden saw that in the variety of *Ascaris* he called *univalens,* which had only two chromosomes, each parent contributes one chromosome to the pair found in the zygote. Through this discovery, the individuality of the single chromosome was first demonstrated.

In *bivalens* (the variety with four chromosomes in the fertilized egg) Van Beneden showed the presence of two chromosomes in each of the pronuclei, and of four in the zygote. He also discovered that in giving off the polar bodies, the number of chromosomes within the egg nucleus is reduced from four to two.

Van Beneden's opinion on the mechanism of karyogamic reduction, which he had discovered, was that of the four chromosomes of *bivalens,* two entered the first polar body and two remained to form the female pronucleus. It was shown independently, by Theodor Boveri in 1887–1888, and by Oscar Hertwig in 1890, that the real nature of the "maturation" division leading to the formation of ripe gametes in both sexes is that each chromosome in the mother cell divides once, while the cell itself divides twice. In 1892 Boveri showed, in *Ascaris megalocephala bivalens,* that two of the eight daughter chromosomes of the egg's mother cell go into each of four cells: into each of the three polar bodies (if the first polar body divides after being given off) and into the ovum.

In a paper published in collaboration with the photographer Neyt (1887), Van Beneden described the centrosome and showed that it was a permanent cell organ which remained in the cell during the resting period and divided into two parts before the beginning of the next mitosis.

From the beginning of his scientific work, Van Beneden had been preoccupied with the problem of the origin of vertebrates. His first interpretation of the didermic mammalian embryo was immediately accepted, but in 1888 he concluded a study of the gastrulation of mammals that became a classic only after his death.

BIBLIOGRAPHY

I. ORIGINAL WORKS. A complete list of Van Beneden's publications is in A. Brachet, "Notice sur Edouard Van Beneden," in *Annuaire de l'Académie royale de Belgique,* **89** (1923), 167–242. The most important of his works are "De la distinction originelle du testicule et de l'ovaire. Caractère sexuel des deux feuillets primordiaux de l'embryon. Hermaphrodisme morphologique de toute individualité animale. Essai d'une théorie de la fécondation," in *Bulletin de l'Académie royale de Belgique. Classe des sciences,* 2nd ser., **37** (1874), 530–595; "Recherches sur les dicyémides, survivants actuels d'un embranchement des mésozoaires," *ibid.,* **41** (1876), 1160–1205; **42** (1876), 35–97; "L'appareil sexuel femelle de l'ascaride mégalocéphale," in *Archives de biologie,* **4** (1883), 95–142; "La segmentation chez les ascidiens dans ses rapports avec l'organisation de la larve," in *Bulletin de l'Académie royale de Belgique. Classe des sciences,* 3rd ser., **7** (1884), 431–447, written with C. Julin; "La segmentation chez les ascidiens et ses rapports avec l'organisation de la larve," in *Archives de biologie,* **5** (1884), 111–126, written with C. Julin; "Nouvelles recherches sur la fécondation et la division mitosique chez l'ascaride mégalocéphale. Communication préliminaire," in *Bulletin de l'Académie royale de Belgique. Classe des sciences,* 3rd ser., **14** (1887), 215–295, written with A. Neyt; and "Recherches sur la morphologie des tuniciers," in *Archives de biologie,* **6** (1887), 237–476, written with C. Julin.

II. SECONDARY LITERATURE. The best biography of Van Beneden is the one by Brachet (see above). Van Beneden had asked in his will that his biography be written by Walter Flemming and Karl Rabl, published by them in a German periodical, and translated into French in *Archives de biologie.* Flemming was dead by 1910, so Rabl wrote the biography alone: "Edouard Van Beneden und der gegenwärtige Stand der Wichtigsten von ihm behandelten Probleme," in *Archiv für mikroskopische Anatomie,* **88** (1915), 1–470. This extensive biography, in spite of all its good points, was considered by Van Beneden's disciples as too polemic and too replete in allusions to Rabl's own work. Its French translation was replaced, in the *Archives de biologie,* by a reproduction of Brachet's notice.

MARCEL FLORKIN

BENEDEN, PIERRE-JOSEPH VAN (*b.* Mechelen [French, Malines], Belgium, 19 December 1809; *d.* Louvain, Belgium, 8 January 1894), *zoology.*

After studying the humanities, Van Beneden was apprenticed to the pharmacist Louis Stoffels, a great collector of natural history specimens, whose house was a veritable museum that inspired Van Beneden to become a zoologist. At that time in the kingdom of the Low Countries, it was not necessary to attend a university in order to become a pharmacist, but

Stoffels recognized in Van Beneden the talents of a scientist and persuaded the boy's parents to send him to the University of Louvain (then still a state university), where he studied medicine. After obtaining the M.D., Van Beneden went to Paris to study zoology, intending to become a professor of zoology at one of the state universities of the new kingdom of Belgium. Since other professors had already been appointed to these chairs, he accepted the post of professor of zoology at the newly created Catholic University of Louvain on 10 April 1835.

Van Beneden's contributions to zoology concern most animal phyla and are characterized by the importance given to embryology in the recognition of systematic affinities. He was a naturalist whose curiosity extended to the broadest spectrum of animal species. His main contribution, however, was the discovery of the life cycle of the cestodes (1849). When he started this work in 1845, the cycle was entirely unknown. It was known that the digestive tract of certain animals contains certain taenias, and the presence of cysticerci in other forms was also known, but no relation had been established between these forms, which were considered to be distinct and autonomous organisms, the products of a spontaneous generation in the tissues of their hosts. Taenias were considered to be hypertrophied intestinal villi.

Dujardin had already noticed a similarity between the heads of certain cysticerci of the liver of bony fishes and the head of Tetrarhynchus living in the gut of cartilaginous fishes that fed on bony fishes. From an extensive study of the contents of the digestive tracts of a large number of fishes, Van Beneden concluded, in January 1849, that a cysticercus is an incomplete taenioid. Siebold adopted this view in 1850, and the following year Küchenmeister demonstrated experimentally that *Cysticercus cellulosae* from a rabbit's peritoneum, fed to a dog, becomes *Taenia serrata.*

Since the Parisian zoologist Valenciennes refused to accept his theory, Van Beneden left for Paris on 22 April 1858 with four dogs, one of which had been fed thirty-two cysticercus; another, seventy; and the other two, none. In Paris he met Milne-Edwards and Quatrefages in Valenciennes's laboratory; he predicted which dogs would contain the taenias and confirmed his predictions by autopsy.

In 1853 the Institut de France gave an important prize to a paper by Van Beneden on the mode of development and transmission of intestinal worms. This report, published in 1858, covers a wide range of data on parasites, concerning not only cestodes and trematodes, but also nematodes, *Gordiacea,* and Acanthocephala. The paper ends with a masterly treatment of the systematics of worms that is based on embryology.

After 1859 Van Beneden devoted himself to the study of Cetacea, both living and fossil. In 1878 he determined that the first fossil skeleton discovered in the coal mine of Bernissart belonged to the genus *Iguanodon*. During the last years of his life Van Beneden devoted his efforts to new studies on parasites. In 1898 his native town raised a statue to honor his memory.

BIBLIOGRAPHY

I. ORIGINAL WORKS. A complete list of Van Beneden's publications is in *Notices biographiques et bibliographiques de l'Académie royale de Belgique* (1886, 1896). The most important are "Les Helminthes cestoïdes, considérés sous le rapport de leurs métamorphoses, de leur composition anatomique et de leur classification, et mention de quelques espèces nouvelles de nos poissons Plagiostomes," in *Bulletin de l'Académie royale des sciences de Belgique,* **16** (1849), 269; "Notice sur un nouveau genre d'Helminthe cestoïde," *ibid.,* 182; "Faune littorale de Belgique. Les vers cestoïdes, considérés sous le rapport physiologique, embryogénique et zooclassique," *ibid.,* **17** (1850), 102; "Notice sur l'éclosion du *Tenia dispar* et la manière dont les embryons de cestoïdes pénétrent à travers les tissus, se logent dans les organes creux, et peuvent même passer de la mère au foetus," *ibid.,* **20** (1853), 287; *Mémoire sur les vers intestinaux, Comptes rendus de l'Académie des sciences* (Paris), supp. 2 (1858); "Sur la découverte de reptiles fossiles gigantesques dans le charbonnage de Bernissart près de Péruwelz," in *Bulletin de l'Académie royale des sciences de Belgique,* 2nd ser., **45** (1878), 578–579.

II. SECONDARY LITERATURE. The most detailed biography of Van Beneden is A. Kemna, *P. J. Van Beneden, la vie et l'oeuvre d'un zoologiste* (Antwerp, 1897). Other publications concerning his life and work are J. B. Abeloos, *Discours prononcé à la Salle des Promotions . . . après le service funèbre . . . de M. Pierre-Joseph Van Beneden* (Louvain, 1894); Charles Van Bambeke, "P. J. Van Beneden, 1809–1894," in *Annales de la Société belge de microscopie,* **20** (1896); Paul Brien, "Pierre-Joseph Van Beneden," in *Florilège des sciences en Belgique* (Brussels, 1967), pp. 825–851; P. Debaisieux, "Un siècle de biologie à l'Université de Louvain," in *Revue des questions scientifiques* (1937); H. Filhol, "Inauguration de la statue de Van Beneden à Malines le 24 juillet 1898," in *Comptes rendus de l'Académie des sciences de Paris,* **127** (1898), 91; A. Gaudry, "Statue de Van Beneden et les fêtes de Malines," in *La nature,* **26** (1898); Auguste Lameere, "Notice sur Pierre-Joseph Van Beneden," in *Annuaire de l'Académie royale de Belgique,* **107** (1941), 1–13, with portrait; and "Pierre-Joseph Van Beneden," in *Biographie nationale,* XXVI, col. 184; Dr. F. Lefebvre, "Discours prononcé aux funérailles de P. J. Van Beneden," in *Bulletin de l'Académie de médecine de Belgique* (1894); *Manifestation en l'honneur de M. le professeur P. J. Van Beneden, Louvain* (Ghent, 1877); *Manifestation en l'honneur de M. le professeur P. J. Van Beneden, à l'occasion de son cinquantenaire de professorat, Louvain* (Louvain, 1886); "Manifestation en l'honneur de Pierre-Joseph Van Beneden à l'occasion du cinquantième anniversaire de sa nomination comme membre titulaire de la Classe des Sciences (1842–1892)," in *Bulletin de l'Académie royale de Belgique,* 3rd ser., **23** (1892), 702–709; M. Mourlon, "Discours prononcé aux funérailles de P. J. Van Beneden," *ibid.,* **27** (1894), 201–208; P. Pelseneer, "P. J. Van Beneden malacologiste," in *Mémoires de la Société royale malacologique de Belgique,* **29** (1894); J. Van Raemdonck, "Souvenirs du professeur Van Beneden," in *Annales du Cercle Archéologique du Pays de Waes,* **14** (1894); and *Souvenir de l'inauguration de la statue de P. J. Van Beneden . . .* (Malines, 1898).

MARCEL FLORKIN

BENEDETTI, ALESSANDRO (*b.* province of Verona, Italy, *ca.* 1450; *d.* Venice, Italy, 30 October 1512), *anatomy, medicine.*

Alessandro, the son of Lorenzo Benedetti, came from a medical family (a maternal uncle was also a physician), and his works attest to an excellent education in both letters and medicine. One of his teachers was the historian and humanist Giorgio Merula. He lived in a transitional period of Venetian and Italian history, and his career was very much influenced by the military and political events of the time. From his works, from the portion of his correspondence that has been published, and from documents we know that he transferred early to Padua, where he studied and taught. He practiced medicine in Venice and was a physician in the war against Charles VIII of France in 1495. For many years he also served Venice abroad—Greece, Crete, Melos, and the Dalmatian coast are mentioned. Among his friends were not only families high in the Venetian nobility and government but also the humanist and physician Giorgio Valla, the poet Quinzio Emiliano Cimbriaco, the historian Marino Sanudo, and the writer Jacopo Antiquari. In his will his wife, Lucia, is mentioned along with a daughter, Giulia.

Benedetti's services to his patients, his thirty-book codification of diseases, his painstaking labors to improve the text of the thirty-seven books of Pliny's *Natural History,* and his contributions to medical and general knowledge of the Caroline War in his diary of that event have assured him a position of importance in both medical history and historiography. His place in natural science rests upon his contributions to the study of anatomy. His importance consisted not in startling discoveries on the nature of the human body but in dissection before his students and in his treatise *Historia corporis humani sive anatomice.* He had been assembling material for this treatise at least since 1483, and parts of it were probably circulated in the closing years of the fifteenth century; it appeared complete in Venice (1502), with a letter of dedication dated 1 August 1497, and appeared in later editions at Paris (1514), Cologne (1527), Strasbourg (1528), and in the collected editions of his medical and anatomical works that were published at Basel (1539, 1549). The *Historia* was known to Leonardo da Vinci; Leonhart Fuchs called attention to a number of errors in it; and Giovanni Battista Morgagni accorded importance in anatomy to its author. It therefore had, we may believe, something of the authority of a textbook in a period when anatomists in Italy were becoming increasingly concerned with observation of the human rather than the animal body. The work comprises five books, which describe the body roughly *a calce ad caput*. It concludes with a paragraph praising dissection, in which the author urges all students, together with established physicians and surgeons, to seek truth in the anatomical theater and not rely solely upon the written word. This paragraph is a natural extension of the introductions to the several books in which Benedetti describes an anatomical theater inspired in form by the Colosseum at Rome and the Roman arena at Verona, and invites various political and literary figures to dissections. This encouragement of dissection was probably Benedetti's greatest contribution to natural science.

Benedetti, while profiting from earlier writers, followed the same firsthand methods in practicing medicine and in his encyclopedic *Omnium a vertice ad calcem morborum signa, causae, indicationes et remediorum compositiones utendique rationes,* in which a number of his cases are cited. He was the author also of aphorisms, of a tract on the pest (1493), and of a work on Paul of Aegina, which was not published.

BIBLIOGRAPHY

I. ORIGINAL WORKS. Benedetti's works include *Collectiones medicinae* (Venice, *ca.* 1493); *De observatione in pestilentia* (Venice, 1493); *Diaria de bello Carolino* (Venice, after 26 August 1496), the modern edition and translation of which by Dorothy M. Schullian (New York, 1967) provides an extensive bibliography of original works of Benedetti as well as secondary works on him, and makes unnecessary any lengthy listing here; *Historia corporis humani sive anatomice* (Venice, 1502); his edition of C. Plinius Secundus, *Historia naturalis libri XXXVII* (Venice, 1513); and *Omnium a vertice ad calcem morborum signa, causae, indicationes et remediorum compositiones utendique rationes* . . . (Basel, 1539). The correspondence of Giorgio Valla with Benedetti and others was edited by Johan Ludvig Heiberg in *Centralblatt für Bibliothekswesen,* Beiheft XVI (Leipzig, 1896).

II. SECONDARY LITERATURE. References to Benedetti are contained in Nicolaus Comnenus Papadopoli, *Historia gymnasii Patavini* (Venice, 1726); and in Marino Sanudo, *La spedizione di Carlo VIII in Italia* (Venice, 1873), and *I diarii,* XV (Venice, 1886), col. 283. Also see Roberto Massalongo, "Alessandro Benedetti e la medicina veneta nel quattrocento," in *Atti del Reale Istituto Veneto di Scienze Lettere ed Arti,* **76,** pt. 2 (1916–1917), 197–259; Curt F. Bühler, "Stoppress and Manuscript Corrections in the Aldine Edition of Benedetti's *Diaria de bello Carolino,*" in *Papers of the Bibliographical Society of America,* **43** (1949), 365–373; Glauco De Bertolis, "Alessandro Benedetti; Il primo teatro anatomico padovano," in *Acta medicae historiae Patavina,* **3** (1956–1957), 1–13; Hans Dieter Kickartz, *Die Anatomie des Zahn-, Mund- und Kieferbereiches in dem Werk "HISTORIA CORPORIS HUMANI SIVE ANATOMICE" von Alessandro Benedetti,* doctoral dissertation (Düsseldorf, 1964); Wolfgang Matschke, *Die Zahnheilkunde in Alessandro Benedettis posthumen Werk "Omnium a vertice ad calcem morborum signa, causae, indicationes et remediorum compositiones utendique rationes, generatim libris XXX conscripta,"* doctoral dissertation (Freiburg, 1965); and Mario Crespi, "Benedetti, Alessandro," in *Dizionario biografico degli italiani,* VIII (Rome, 1966), 244–247.

For additional references see the 1967 edition of Benedetti's *Diaria* cited above.

DOROTHY M. SCHULLIAN

BENEDETTI, GIOVANNI BATTISTA (*b.* Venice, Italy, 14 August 1530; *d.* Turin, Italy, 20 January 1590), *mathematics, physics.*

Benedetti is of special significance in the history of science as the most important immediate forerunner of Galileo. He was of patrician status, but has not been definitely connected with any of the older known families of that name resident at Venice. His father was described by Luca Guarico as a Spaniard, philosopher, and *physicus,* probably in the sense of "student of nature" but possibly meaning "doctor of medicine." It was to his father that Benedetti owed most of his education, which Guarico says made him a philosopher, musician, and mathematician by the age of eighteen. One of the few autobiographical records left by Benedetti asserts that he had no formal education beyond the age of seven, except that he studied the first four books of Euclid's *Elements* under Niccolò Tartaglia, probably about 1546–1548. Their relations appear to have been poor, for Tartaglia nowhere mentions Benedetti as a pupil; Benedetti named Tartaglia in 1553 only "to give him his due" and severely criticized his writings in later years.

Benedetti's originality of thought and mathematical skill are evident in his first book, the *Resolutio,* published at Venice when he was only twenty-two. The

Resolutio concerns the general solution of all the problems in Euclid's *Elements* (and of some others) using only a compass of fixed opening. Benedetti's treatment was more comprehensive and elegant than that of Tartaglia or Ludovico Ferrara in the published polemics of 1546–1547, and was more systematic than Tartaglia's later attack on the same problem in his final work, the *Trattato generale di numeri e misure* of 1560, in which he ignored the work of his former pupil.

Benedetti had one daughter, who was born at Venice in 1554 and died at Turin in 1580, but there is no record of his marriage. In 1558 he went to Parma as court mathematician to Duke Ottavio Farnese, in whose service he remained about eight years. In the winter of 1559/60 he lectured at Rome on the science of Aristotle; Girolamo Mei, who heard him there, praised his acumen, independence of mind, fluency, and memory. At Parma, Benedetti gave instruction at the court, served as astrologer, and advised on the engineering of public works. He also carried out some astronomical observations and constructed sundials mentioned in a later book on that subject. It appears that his private means were considerable, so that he was not inconvenienced by long delays in the payment of his salary.

In 1567 he was invited to Turin by the duke of Savoy and remained there until his death. The duke, Emanuele Filiberto, had great plans for the rehabilitation of Piedmont through public works, military engineering, and the general elevation of culture. Benedetti's duties included the teaching of mathematics and science at court. Tradition places him successively at the universities of Mondovì and Turin, although supporting official records are lacking and Benedetti never styled himself a professor. He appears, however, to have served as the duke's adviser on university affairs; for instance, he secured the appointment of Antonio Berga to the chair of philosophy at the University of Turin in 1569. Benedetti later engaged in a polemic with Berga, and on the title page of his *Consideratione* (1579) he referred to Berga as professor at Turin, but to himself only as philosopher to the duke of Savoy.

While at Turin, Benedetti designed and constructed various public and private works, such as sundials and fountains. His learning and mathematical talents were frequently praised by the duke and were mentioned by the Venetian ambassador in 1570, when Benedetti was granted a patent of nobility. In 1585 he appears to have been married a second time or rejoined by the mother of his daughter. In the same year he published his chief work, the *Speculationum,* a collection of treatises and of letters written to various correspondents on mathematical and scientific topics.

Benedetti died early in 1590. He had forecast his death for 1592 in the final lines of his last published book. On his deathbed he recomputed his horoscope and declared that an error of four minutes must have been made in the original data (published in 1552 by Luca Guarico), thus evincing his lifelong faith in the doctrines of judiciary astrology.

Benedetti's first important contribution to the birth of modern physics was set forth in the letter of dedication to his *Resolutio.* The letter was addressed to Gabriel de Guzman, a Spanish Dominican priest with whom he had conversed at Venice in 1552. It appears that Guzman had shown interest in Benedetti's theory of the free fall of bodies, and had asked him to publish a demonstration in which the speeds of fall would be treated mathematically. In order to forestall the possible theft of his ideas, Benedetti published his demonstration in this letter despite its irrelevance to the purely geometrical content of the book. Benedetti held that bodies of the same material, regardless of weight, would fall through a given medium at the same speed, and not at speeds proportional to their weights, as maintained by Aristotle. His demonstration was based on the principle of Archimedes, which probably came to his attention through Tartaglia's publication at Venice in 1551 of a vernacular translation of the first book of the Archimedean treatise on the behavior of bodies in water. Benedetti's "buoyancy theory of fall" is in many respects identical with that which Galileo set forth in his first treatise *De motu,* composed at Pisa about 1590 but not published during his lifetime.

Although no mention of Benedetti's theory has been found in books or correspondence of the period, lively discussions appear to have taken place concerning it, some persons denying the conclusion and others asserting that it did not contradict Aristotle. In answer to those contentions, Benedetti promptly published a second book, the *Demonstratio* (1554), restating the argument and citing the particular texts of Aristotle that it contradicted. In the new preface, also addressed to Guzman, Benedetti mentioned opponents as far away as Rome who had declared that since Aristotle could not err, his own theory must be false. Such discussions may explain the otherwise remarkable coincidence that another book published in 1553 also contains a statement related to free fall. This was *Il vero modo di scrivere in cifra,* by Giovanni Battista Bellaso of Brescia, in which it was asked why a ball of iron and one of wood will fall to the ground at the same time.

Two editions of Benedetti's *Demonstratio,* which

was by no means a mere republication of the *Resolutio,* appeared in rapid succession. The first edition maintained, as did the *Resolutio,* that unequal bodies of the same material would fall at equal speed through a given medium. The second edition stated that resistance of the medium is proportional to the surface rather than the volume of the falling body, implying that precise equality of speed for homogeneous bodies of the same material and different weight would be found only in a vacuum. This correction of the original statement was repeated in Benedetti's later treatment of the question in *Speculationum* (1585).

Benedetti's original publication of his thesis in 1553 was designed to prevent its theft; perhaps he had in mind the fate of Tartaglia's solution of the cubic equation a few years earlier. But even repeated publication failed to protect it, and indeed became the occasion of its theft. Jean Taisnier, who pirated the work of Petrus Peregrinus de Maricourt in his *Opusculum . . . de natura magnetis* (1562), included with it—as his own—Benedetti's *Demonstratio.* Taisnier's impudent plagiarism enjoyed wider circulation than Benedetti's original, and was translated into English by Richard Eden about 1578. Simon Stevin cited the proposition as Taisnier's when he published his own experimental verification of it in 1586. But since Taisnier had stolen the *Demonstratio* in its earlier form, he was criticized by Stevin for the very fault which Benedetti had long since corrected in the second *Demonstratio* of 1554. Taisnier's appropriation of his book ultimately became known to Benedetti, who complained of it in the preface to his *De gnomonum* (1573). The relatively small circulation of Benedetti's works is evidenced by the fact that it was not until 1741 that general attention was first called to the theft, by Pierre Bayle.

Benedetti's ultimate expansion of his discussion of falling bodies in the *Speculationum* is of particular interest because it includes an explanation of their acceleration in terms of increments of impetus successively impressed *ad infinitum.* That conception is found later in the writings of Beeckman and Gassendi, but it appears never to have occurred to Galileo. Despite this insight, however, Benedetti failed to arrive at (or to attempt) a mathematical formulation of the rate of acceleration. The difference between Galileo's treatment and Benedetti's is perhaps related to the fact that Benedetti neglected the medieval writers who had attempted a mathematical analysis of motion and did not adopt their terminology, which is conspicuous in Galileo's early writings. Benedetti was deeply imbued with the notion of impetus as a self-exhausting force, a concept that may have prevented his further progress toward the inertial idea implicit in the accretion of impetus.

Benedetti's next contribution to physics was made about 1563, the most probable date of two letters on music written to Cipriano da Rore and preserved in the *Speculationum.* Those letters, in the opinion of Claude Palisca, entitle Benedetti to be considered the true pioneer in the investigation of the mechanics of the production of musical consonances. Da Rore was choirmaster at the court of Parma in 1561–1562, when he returned to Venice. Benedetti's letters probably supplemented his discussions with da Rore at Parma. Departing from the prevailing numerical theories of harmony, Benedetti inquired into the relation of pitch, consonance, and rates of vibration. He attributed the generation of musical consonances to the concurrence or cotermination of waves of air. Such waves, resulting from the striking of air by vibrating strings, should either agree with or break in upon one another. Proceeding thus, and asserting that the frequencies of vibration of two strings under equal tension vary inversely with the string lengths, Benedetti proposed an index of agreement obtained by multiplication of the terms of the ratio of a given consonance; by this means he could express the degree of concordance in a mathematical scale. Benedetti's empirical approach to musical theory, as applied to the tuning of instruments, anticipated the later method of equal temperament and contrasted sharply with the rational numerical rules offered by Gioseffo Zarlino. It is of interest that Zarlino was the teacher of Galileo's father, who in 1578 attacked Zarlino's musical theories on somewhat similar empirical grounds. But since Benedetti's letters were not published until 1585, they were probably not known to Vincenzio Galilei when he launched his attack.

Benedetti's first publication after his move to Turin was a book on the theory and construction of sundials, *De gnomonum* (1573), the most comprehensive treatise on the subject to that time. It dealt with the construction of dials at various inclinations and also with dials on cylindrical and conical surfaces. This book was followed by *De temporum emendatione,* on the correction of the calendar (1578). In 1579 he published *Consideratione,* a polemic work in reply to Antonio Berga, concerning a dispute over the relative volumes of the elements earth and water. As with Galileo's polemic on floating bodies, the dispute had arisen at court as a result of the duke's custom of inviting learned men to debate topics of philosophical or scientific interest before him. Of all Benedetti's books, this appears to be the only one to have received notice in a contemporary publication, Agostino Michele's *Trattato della grandezza dell'acqua et della terra* (1583).

Benedetti's final work, containing the most important Italian contribution to physical thought prior to Galileo, was the *Diversarum speculationum* (1585). Its opening section includes a number of arithmetical propositions demonstrated geometrically. Other mathematical sections include a treatise on perspective, a commentary on the fifth book of Euclid's *Elements,* and many geometrical demonstrations—including a general solution of the problem of circumscribing a quadrilateral of given sides; the development of various properties of spherical triangles, circles, and conic sections; discussion of the angle of contact between circular arcs; and theorems on isoperimetric figures, regular polygons, and regular solids.

The section on mechanics is largely a critique of certain parts of the pseudo-Aristotelian *Questions of Mechanics* and of propositions in Tartaglia's *Quesiti, et inventioni diverse.* Benedetti disputed Tartaglia's assertion that no body may be simultaneously moved by natural and violent motions, although he did not enter into a discussion of projectile motion giving effect to composition. He did, however, assert clearly and for the first time that the impetus of a body freed from rapid circular motion is rectilinear and tangential in character, a conception of fundamental importance to his criticisms of Aristotle and to his attempted explanation of the slowing down of wheels and of spinning tops.

Following the section on mechanics is an attack on many of Aristotle's basic physical conceptions. This section restates the "buoyancy theory of fall" as it was set forth in the second edition of the *Demonstratio.* For equality of speed of different weights falling *in vacuo,* Benedetti proposed a thought experiment that is often said to be identical with Galileo's, although the difference is considerable. Benedetti supposes two bodies of the same weight connected by a line and falling *in vacuo* at the same speed as a single body having their combined weight; he appeals to intuition to show that whether connected or not, the two smaller bodies will continue to fall at the same speed. In Galileo's argument, two bodies of different weight—and therefore of different speeds, according to Aristotle—are tied together; by the Aristotelian assumption, the slower would impede the faster, resulting in an intermediate speed for the pair. But the pair being heavier than either of its parts, it should fall faster than either, under the Aristotelian rule. Thus Galileo's argument, unlike Benedetti's, imputes self-contradiction to Aristotle's view. Bene-

detti's discussion of the ratios of speeds of descent in different media is also essentially different from Galileo's in *De motu,* for it includes both buoyancy and the effect of resistance proportional to the surface; the latter effect was neglected by Galileo in his earlier writings.

Again, Benedetti correctly holds that natural rectilinear motion continually increases in speed because of the continual impression of downward impetus, whereas Galileo wrongly believed that acceleration was an accidental and temporary effect at the beginning of fall only, an error which vitiated much of the reasoning in *De motu* and was corrected only in his later works. These differences create historical perplexities described below.

Another of Benedetti's contributions to mechanics is the description of hydrostatic pressure and the idea of a hydraulic lift, prior to Stevin's discussion of the hydrostatic paradox (1586). Benedetti also attributed winds to changes in density of air, caused by alterations of heat. In opposition to the view that clouds are held in suspension by the sun, he applied the Archimedean principle and stated that clouds seek air of density equal to their own; he also observed that bodies are heated by the sun in relation to their degree of opacity.

Benedetti published no separate work on astronomy, but his letters in the *Speculationum* show that he was an admirer of Copernicus and that he was much concerned with accuracy of tables and precise observation. His astronomical interests appear to have been astrological rather than physical and systematic, as were those of Kepler, Galileo, and Stevin. Benedetti offered a correct explanation of the ruddy color of the moon under total eclipse, however, based on refraction of sunlight in the earth's atmosphere.

Benedetti's scientific originality and versatility leave little doubt that his work afforded a basis for the overthrow of Aristotelian physics. The extent of its actual influence on others, however, presents very difficult questions. Stevin was certainly unaware of Benedetti when he published his basic contributions to mechanics and hydrostatics. He had seen Benedetti's *Speculationum* before 1605, when he published on perspective, but in that work he built more on Guido Ubaldo del Monte than on any other writer. Kepler mentioned Benedetti but once, and only in the most general terms. Willebrord Snell's attention was called to Benedetti by Stevin. The case of Galileo is the most perplexing. It is widely held that he was directly indebted to Benedetti for the ideas underlying *De motu,* but the resemblances of those ideas are easily accounted for by the Archimedean principle and the medieval impetus theory, easily accessible to both men independently, while the differences, particularly with respect to acceleration and the accumulation of impressed motion, are hard to explain if the young Galileo had the work of Benedetti before him. The absence of Benedetti's name in Galileo's books and notes, where other kindred spirits such as Gilbert and Guido Ubaldo are praised, is suggestive; much more so is the fact that Benedetti is not mentioned to or by Galileo in the vast surviving correspondence of his time. Jacopo Mazzoni has been proposed as a positive link—he was a colleague and friend of Galileo's at Pisa about 1590, and certainly knew Benedetti's work by 1597; but since Galileo left Pisa for Padua in 1592, the connection is uncertain. Benedetti appears to have remained unknown to Galileo's teacher at Pisa, Francesco Buonamico, who in 1591 published a treatise, *De motu,* of over a thousand pages. On the whole, it appears that Benedetti's *Speculationum* was not widely read by his contemporaries, despite its outstanding achievements in extending the horizons of mathematics, physics, and astronomy beyond the Peripatetic boundaries.

BIBLIOGRAPHY

I. ORIGINAL WORKS. No collection of Benedetti's work has been published. Because the original editions are very scarce, locations of known copies not listed in the Union Catalogue are indicated by the following abbreviations: BM—British Museum; BN—Bibliothèque Nationale; BNT—Biblioteca Nazionale di Torino; ULT—University of Toronto Library.

Resolutio omnium Euclidis problematum aliorumque ad hoc necessario inventorum una tantummodo circini data apertura, per Ioannem Baptistam de Benedictis inventa (Venice, 1553), BM, BN, BNT, ULT.

Demonstratio proportionum motuum localium contra Aristotelem et omnes philosophes (Venice, 1554), first ed. in Vatican Library, 2nd ed. in Biblioteca Universitaria, Padua. First edition pirated by Jean Taisnier, *Opusculum perpetua memoria dignissimum de natura magnetis... Item de motu continuo, demonstratio proportionum motuum localium contra Aristotelem etc.* (Cologne, 1562; facs. repr., London, 1966). English translation by Richard Eden is in *A very necessarie and profitable Booke concerning Navigation, compiled in Latin by Joannes Taisnierus...* (London, 1578?), BM, Brown University Library. Both eds. repr. in C. Maccagni, *Le speculazioni giovanili "de motu" di G. B. Benedetti* (Pisa, 1967).

De gnomonum umbrarumque solarium usu liber... nunc primum publicae utilitati, studiosorumque commoditati in lucem aeditus (Turin, 1573), BM, BN, BNT, ULT.

De temporum emendatione opinio... (Turin, 1578), BM,
MSS copies in BNT and Archivio di Stato, Turin. Repr. in *Speculationum,* pp. 205–210.

Consideratione di Gio. Battista Benedetti... d'intorno al discorso della grandezza della terra, et dell'acqua, del Eccelent. Sig. Antonio Berga... (Turin, 1579), BN, BNT, ULT; a Latin trans. by F. M. Vialardi is reported to be contained in Antonio Berga, *Disputatio de magnitudine terrae et aquae* (Turin, 1580).

Lettera per modo di discorso all'Ill. Sig. Bernardo Trotto intorno ad alcune nuove riprensioni et emendationi contra alli calculatori delle effemeridi... (Turin, 1581), BNT, Latin trans. in *Speculationum,* pp. 228–248.

Diversarum speculationum mathematicarum, et physicarum, liber (Turin, 1585), BM, BN, BNT, ULT. Reissued as *Speculationum mathematicarum, et physicarum, fertilissimus, pariterque utilissimus tractatus...* (Venice, 1586) and as *Speculationum liber: in quo mira subtilitate haec tractata continentur...* (Venice, 1599), BM, Biblioteca Marciana, Venice.

De coelo et elementis... (Ferrara, 1591), sometimes reported as Benedetti's, was in fact written by Giovanni Benedetto of Tirna (Orsova).

Two volumes of manuscript letters and astronomical observations by Benedetti, formerly in the Biblioteca Nazionale, Turin, were lost in 1904 in a fire that also destroyed the only known portrait of Benedetti.

Manuscript volumes reported to be privately owned in Italy are "Descrittione, uso et ragioni del triconolometro. Al serenissimo Prencipe di Piemonte. Trattato di Giovan Battista Benedetti. MDLXXVII," 94 unnumbered pages including 21 blanks; "La generale et necessaria instruttione per l'intelligentia et compositione d'ogni sorte horologij solari," 46 folio pages, unnumbered, without the name of the author but in the hand of same scribe as the above MS; and "Dechiaratione delle parti et use dell'instromento chiamato isogonio," 24 folio pages in the same hand as the foregoing.

II. SECONDARY LITERATURE. The principal monograph is Giovanni Bordiga, "Giovanni Battista Benedetti, filosofo e matematico veneziano del secolo XVI," in *Atti del Reale Istituto veneto di scienze, lettere ed arti,* **85,** pt. 2 (1925–1926), 585–754.

Apart from histories of mathematics or physics, such as those of Guillaume Libri, Kurt Lasswitz, Moritz Cantor, Rafaello Caverni, and Ernst Mach, discussions of Benedetti's work (listed chronologically) are in Emil Wohlwill, "Die Entdeckung des Beharrungsgesetzes," in *Zeitschrift für Völkerpsychologie und Sprachwissenschaft,* **14** (1885), 391–401, and *Galileo Galilei und sein Kampf...* (Hamburg-Leipzig, 1909), I, 111 ff.; Giovanni Vailati, "Le speculazione di Giovanni Battista Benedetti sul moto dei gravi," in *Atti dell'Accademia delle scienze di Torino,* **33** (1897–1898), 559 ff., reprinted in *Scritti di G. Vailati* (Leipzig-Florence, 1911), pp. 161–178; Pierre Duhem, *Les origines de la statique* (Paris, 1905), I, 226–235; "De l'accélération produite par une force constante," Congrès International d'Histoire des Sciences, IIIe Session (Geneva, 1906), pp. 885 ff; and *Études sur Léonard de Vinci* (Paris, 1913), III, 214 ff.

See also E. J. Dijksterhuis, *Val en Worp* (Groningen, 1924), pp. 179–190, and *The Mechanization of the World Picture* (Oxford, 1961), pp. 269–271; Alexandre Koyré, *Études galiléennes* (Paris, 1939), I, 41–54, and "Jean-Baptiste Benedetti critique d'Aristote," in *Mélanges offerts à Étienne Gilson* (Toronto–Paris, 1959), pp. 351–372, reprinted in *Études d'histoire de la pensée scientifique* (Paris, 1966), pp. 122–146, an English trans. in *Galileo, Man of Science,* ed. E. McMullin (New York, 1967); Claude Palisca, "Scientific Empiricism in Musical Thought," in *Seventeenth Century Science and the Arts* (Princeton, 1961), pp. 104 ff.; I. E. Drabkin, "Two Versions of G. B. Benedetti's *Demonstratio,*" in *Isis,* **54** (June 1963), 259–262, and "G. B. Benedetti and Galileo's *De motu,*" in *Proceedings of the Tenth International Congress of the History of Science* (Paris, 1964), I, 627–630; and C. Maccagni, "G. B. Benedetti: *De motu,*" in *Atti del Symposium Internazionale di Storia, Metodologia, Logica e Filosofia della Scienza* (Florence, 1966), pp. 53–54; "Contributi alla biobibliografia di G. B. Benedetti," in *Physis,* **9** (1967), 337–364; and *Le speculazioni "de motu" di G. B. Benedetti* (Pisa, 1967). English translations of Benedetti's most important scientific writings by I. E. Drabkin are included in *Mechanics in Sixteenth-Century Italy* (Madison, Wis., 1968).

STILLMAN DRAKE

BENEDICKS, CARL AXEL FREDRIK (*b.* Stockholm, Sweden, 27 May 1875; *d.* Stockholm, 16 July 1958), *metallography.*

Benedicks' father, Edvard Otto Benedicks, and his mother, Sofia Elisabeth Tholander, came from families that had been involved in the Swedish steel industry for generations. Interested from boyhood in the theoretical study of minerals and metals, Benedicks concentrated on the natural sciences at the University of Uppsala and received the Ph.D. in 1904 with the dissertation *Recherches physiques et physico-chimiques sur l'acier au carbone.*

In 1910 Benedicks was appointed professor of physics at the University of Stockholm. He is regarded as the father of Swedish metallography because he pleaded for the establishment of a special research laboratory for metals and metallography. Sponsored by the iron and steel industry and the government, the Swedish Institute of Metallography in Stockholm became a reality in 1920, and Benedicks served as its director for fifteen years. He continued his scientific work for twenty years more at the Laboratorium Benedicks.

Benedicks personally performed many experiments, usually employing apparatus designed and constructed by himself or in collaboration with his assistants. One of the fields in which he pioneered was metal microscopy.

In 1908 Benedicks was awarded the Iron & Steel Institute's gold medal for his investigations that were published as "Experimental Researches on the Cooling Power of Liquids on Queendring Velocities and on Constituents Troostite and Austenite."

In the light of modern physics, some of Benedicks' theories and interpretations of thermoelectrical phenomena and some of his solutions to problems concerning physical properties of steel seem to be outdated and are subject to criticism. Nevertheless, during his lifetime they aroused great interest in international circles.

Benedicks donated his private library of rare books on alchemy, natural science, metallurgy, and iron and steel manufacturing, totaling about 1,500 volumes, to the Institute of Metallography, now reorganized and named the Swedish Metal Research Institute.

BIBLIOGRAPHY

I. ORIGINAL WORKS. Benedicks' scholarly writings, often published simultaneously in various European journals, reflect a wide range of interests and considerable originality. Among them are "Thalénit, ein neues Mineral aus Österby in Dalekarlien," in *Bulletin of the Geological Institute of Uppsala,* **4** (1898–1899), 1–15; "On Fragments of Cast Iron, Designated as Crystals," in *The Iron and Steel Metallurgist and Metallographist,* **7** (1904), 252–257; "Sur les fers météoriques naturels et synthétiques et leur conductibilité électrique," in *Arkiv för matematik, astronomi och fysik,* **12,** no. 17 (1917), 1–11; "Le nouvel effet thermo-électrique et le principe d'étranglement," in *Revue de métallurgie,* **15** (1918), 296–332; *Non-metallic Inclusions in Iron and Steel* (London, 1930), written with H. Löfquist; "Über den Mechanismen der Supraleitung," in *Annalen der Physik,* **17** (1933), 184–196; "Effect of Gas Ions on the Benedicks Effects in Mercury," in *Nature,* **141** (1938), 1097, written with P. Sederholm; "Experiments Regarding the Influence of an Adsorbed Layer in Cohesion," in *Arkiv för matematik, astronomi och fysik,* **30A,** no. 6 (1944), 1–34, written with P. Sederholm; and "Theory of the Lightning-balls and Its Application to the Atmospheric Phenomenon Called 'Flying Saucers,'" in *Arkiv för geofysik,* **2,** no. 1 (1954), 1–11. A MS by Benedicks on his 483 articles and books is at the Swedish Metal Research Institute, Stockholm.

II. SECONDARY LITERATURE. Biographies are in *Journal of the Iron & Steel Institute, London,* **160,** no. 3 (1948), and The Svedberg, in *Svenskt biografiskt lexikon,* III (Stockholm, 1922), 163–170, which lists Benedicks' published works up to 1920. Erik Rudberg, in *Jernkontorets annaler,* **142** (1958), 733–738, is an elaborate obituary.

TORSTEN ALTHIN

BENEDICT, FRANCIS GANO (*b.* Milwaukee, Wisconsin, 3 October 1870; *d.* Machiasport, Maine, 14 May 1957), *chemistry, physiology.*

Washington Gano Benedict, a businessman, and Harriet Emily Barrett were average middle-class parents with secondary-school backgrounds. They moved in 1881 to Boston, where Francis attended public high school. He studied the piano and his parents planned a musical career for him. Meanwhile, he dabbled in his basement chemical laboratory.

Upon graduation (1888), Benedict devoted a year to the study of chemistry at the Massachusetts College of Pharmacy. He continued at Harvard University and received a B.A. (1893) and M.A. (1894) in chemistry. An additional year at Heidelberg under Professor Victor Meyer led to the Ph.D., *magna cum laude*. On his return Benedict assisted W. O. Atwater at Wesleyan University, where he became lecturer in chemistry in 1905 and professor in 1907. He supplemented his income through research as a chemist at the Storrs Agricultural Experimental Station (1896–1900) and as physiological chemist for the Department of Agriculture (1895–1907).

Atwater transformed Benedict from a chemist into the world's foremost expert on animal calorimetry and respiratory gas analysis. Benedict applied his mechanical skill to improvement of the apparatus used in these studies and the establishment of rigorous experimental controls.[1] William Welch and John Shaw Billings were impressed with Benedict's early publications on animal heat and metabolism, and they convinced the Carnegie Foundation trustees to establish a nutrition laboratory under Benedict's direction.[2] The result was the Boston Nutrition Laboratory, where Benedict remained until his retirement (1907–1937).

Benedict the man was straightforward and eminently Victorian. His marriage in 1897 to a third cousin, Cornelia Golay, provided Benedict with a research assistant and eventually a daughter. He was against alcohol, trade unions, and the "decline" of culture. His friendships and professional associations were largely European. Magic tricks and the piano were his hobbies. He equated science with progress and "the spirit of service" to humanity.[3]

Benedict's European affiliations were the result of his chosen field of research. The study of metabolism through calorimetry and the analysis of body intake and output was developed in the nineteenth century and was still current in Europe. In 1897, when Benedict joined him, Atwater prepared an exhaustive compilation of European contributions to the technique.[4] Atwater and Benedict confirmed the validity of energy conservation in animal metabolism.

The concept "metabolism" was radically changing in the early decades of the twentieth century.[5] The keys to energy transformation clearly lay within the emerging theories of hormonal control, catalysis, enzyme chemistry, and the vitamins. Yet Benedict continued in the classic methods, perhaps because of his chemical rather than biological training. His acknowledgment of the newer methods shows neither enthusiasm nor personal conviction.[6]

Benedict took care to distinguish between an organism's loss of heat and production of heat. He began with the basic assumption that all animal tissue produces heat to the same degree (calories per kilogram body weight per unit time). He tested the assumption through extensive comparisons of various cold- and warm-blooded animals and searched for extremes to prove his point. The newborn, the young, the elderly, the obese, the thin, the dieter, the vegetarian, patients with overactive thyroids or one lung, diabetics, the tiniest mouse, even the elephant, came under his scrutiny. By 1910 he realized that organisms do not produce heat in any simple, mechanical fashion. Large animals produced greater amounts of heat but small animals yielded more heat per unit of body weight. He remained steadfast, however, in the belief that homeostasis was maintained by heat loss, not heat production.[7] Accurate data were his driving passion, and comparative physiology provided the basis for his judgments.

He established criteria of comparison for the variable rates of metabolism that he found: sex, age, condition, water content, and the idea that "active protoplasmic mass" differed from total body weight. Two standards of judging metabolic rates were available to him: the relation to body surface area and to body weight. Benedict unequivocally favored the latter.

His most important contribution was the invention of an apparatus to measure simultaneously, directly, and accurately oxygen consumption, expired air, and heat (1924). His respirator provided the foundation for the basal metabolic-rate test, which has only recently given ground to less involved methods. His standards for the basal metabolic rates of humans are still valuable (1919). Insensible perspiration was found proportional to basal metabolism and body weight (1926), variations in the temperature of anatomical structures were mapped out (1911), lipogenesis investigated, and the caloric values of foods established. Diabetics were thought to have a low metabolic rate. Benedict revised clinical treatment of these patients by demonstrating that their metabolic rate was higher than normal (1910).

He was a member of the National Academy of Sciences (1914), American Philosophical Society (1910), American Academy of Arts and Sciences (1930), Society of American Magicians (1930), and honorary member of medical and scientific societies across Europe. He received the National Institute of Social Sciences medal in 1917 (for his work on the alcohol problem), the gold honor medal of the University of Hamburg in 1929 (physiology), and was given an honorary M.D. by the University of Würzburg in 1932.

NOTES

1. The best descriptions of his methods and apparatus are found in Benedict and Carpenter (1910), Benedict and Talbot (1914), and Benedict and Burger, Abderhalden's *Handbuch,* Abt. 4 (1924).
2. DuBois and Riddle, p. 69.
3. Commencement address given at the University of Maine, 9 June 1924; repr. in *Science,* n.s., **60** (1924), 209, 212–213.
4. W. O. Atwater and C. F. Langworthy, *A Digest of Metabolism Experiments in which the Balance of Income and Outgo was Determined,* bull. no. 45, U.S.D.A. Office of Experimental Stations (Washington, 1897).
5. See O. Folin, "A Theory of Protein Metabolism," in *American Journal of Physiology,* **13** (1905), 117–133; Russell Chittenden, *The Nutrition of Man* (New York, 1907). Benedict was aware of the changes: Atwater and Benedict (1899), p. 6, and the latter's work on creatinine (1907).
6. Benedict and Talbot (1921), p. 1; Benedict, *Lectures on Nutrition* (1925), pp. 17, 20; Benedict (1938), p. 200; DuBois and Riddle, pp. 73–74.
7. Benedict (1938), pp. 203, 212.

BIBLIOGRAPHY

I. ORIGINAL WORKS. Benedict published extensively. A list drawn up by E. DuBois and O. Riddle (see below) should be consulted. W. O. Atwater and Benedict joint publications are not included. They are as follows: *Experiments on the Metabolism of Matter and Energy in the Human Body,* bull. no. 69, U.S.D.A. Office of Experimental Stations (Washington, 1899); *Experiments on the Metabolism of Matter and Energy in the Human Body, 1898–1900,* bull. no. 109 (Washington, 1902); *Experiments on the Metabolism of Matter and Energy in the Human Body, 1900–1902,* bull. no. 136 (Washington, 1903).

II. SECONDARY WORKS. O. Riddle, "Francis Gano Benedict (1870–1957)," in *The American Philosophical Society Yearbook, 1957* (Philadelphia, 1958), pp. 109–113; E. F. DuBois and O. Riddle, "Francis Gano Benedict," in *Biographical Memoirs. National Academy of Sciences,* **32** (1958), 66–98.

CHARLES A. CULOTTA

BENIVIENI, ANTONIO (*b.* Florence, Italy, 3 November 1443; *d.* Florence, 11 November 1502), *pathological anatomy.*

A contemporary and friend of Angelo Poliziano, Marsilio Ficino, and Lorenzo the Magnificent, Benivieni was a famous physician, yet we have little infor-

mation about him as a person. His father, Paolo, a nobleman, was a notary; he himself was the eldest of five brothers, of whom two others achieved distinction—Domenico as a theologian at the University of Pisa, and Girolamo as a philosopher and poet in Florence. Benivieni studied medicine at Pisa and practiced in Florence; his house stood where modern Ricasoli Street is, near the present-day Academy of Fine Arts. He had as patients the most important families of the city—the Bardi, Brunelleschi, Guicciardini, Pazzi, Strozzi, and the Medici themselves. He was on excellent terms with his medical colleagues Bernardo Torni (1452–1497) and Lorenzo Lorenzi (known as Laurentianus, who died in 1502), who were teachers in the University of Pisa, and he was well regarded by both Ficino and Savonarola. He was buried in the chapel of St. Michael in the Church of the SS. Annunziata, Florence. No reliable portrait of him exists.

Antonio Benivieni left a number of works in manuscript—*De pestilentia ad Laurentium Medicem; Consilium contra pestem Magistri Antonii Benivieni; De virtutibus,* an essay on Galenic physiology; notes on *De opinionibus antiquorum;* the title of a chapter of a *Liber de cometa ad Julianum Medicem;* separate notes on fossils and minerals; and a treatise, *De chirurgia.* A learned humanist, Benivieni occupies a place in the history of science for his *De abditis nonnullis ac mirandis morborum et sanationum causis,* an early essay on pathological anatomy published posthumously by Filippo Giunti at Florence in 1507. Originally conceived of by the author as a treatise of 300 selected observations or chapters, the book was put forth by his brother Girolamo with the aid of a physician (Giovanni Rosati) in an incomplete form containing only 111 chapters; a copy of this first edition is to be found in the Bibliotheca Marucelliana, Florence. Later issues of this incomplete version appeared at Paris (1528), Basel (1529), Cologne (1581), Leiden (1585), and Antwerp (1585). Alfonso Corradi in 1885 recorded an edition printed at Naples in 1519.

Although Benivieni's book was noted by Morgagni and Haller, it was virtually forgotten until Carlo Burci (1813–1875), the first ordinary professor (Florence, 1840) of pathological anatomy in Italy, translated it into Italian; it has been translated into English by Charles Singer and Esmond Long under the title *The Hidden Causes of Diseases* (1954). Both translations are based on the edition of 1507, and a complete knowledge of the work requires study of the author's manuscript, which was discovered by Francesco Puccinotti in 1855. Puccinotti noted in his researches that Benivieni had performed at least twenty autopsies and had observed gallstones, urinary calculi, scirrhous cancer of the stomach, fibrous tumor of the heart, peritonitis arising from intestinal perforation, and transmission of syphilis to the fetus. Benivieni was also a competent surgeon, as Burci pointed out.

The autograph manuscript of the *De abditis* was given by Puccinotti to Cesare Guasti, a paleographer, in order that a transcription of the unpublished parts might be made. This was most provident, for the original autograph again disappeared; fortunately, Guasti's transcription survives in the National Library of Florence and is believed to represent the text of the previously unpublished parts, unmodified and unedited.

Benivieni possessed among his books a copy of *De medicina libri octo* of Celsus, and Antonio Costa and his pupil Weber clearly documented the Celsian humanism of the *De abditis;* indeed, the title of Benivieni's work would appear to have been suggested by Celsus' "abditae morborum causae" (cf. Celsus, *De medicina*, Bk. I, *Proemium*). The critical work on the *De abditis* published by Costa and Weber is without doubt the best study of Benivieni's accomplishment and establishes his importance on a firm basis. As Ralph Major noted in 1935, "Benivieni's *De abditis* marks the beginning of a new method of thinking in medical science. . . . He was unquestionably a pathfinder in medicine who blazed a new path which physicians waited for more than two centuries and a half to follow."

BIBLIOGRAPHY

Benivieni's works are cited in the text.

Literature on Benivieni is Luigi Belloni, "Antonii Benivieni, De regimine sanitatis ad Laurentium Medicem," in *Atti del Congresso di Torino: 8–10 Giugno 1951, della Società italiana di patologia* (Milan, 1951); C. Burci, *Di alcune ammirabili ed occulte cause di morbi e loro guarigioni. Libro di Antonio Benivieni con un elogio storico intorno alla vita e alle opere dell'autore* (Florence, 1843); A. Corradi, "Un libro raro di sifilografia, e un'edizione ignota del Benivieni," in *Annali universali di medicina e chirurgia,* **271** (1885), 228–240; A. Costa and G. Weber, "L'inizio dell'anatomia patologica nel quattrocento fiorentino," in *Archivio De Vecchi,* **39** (1963), 429–878, 939–993, which includes a rich bibliography on the subject; B. De Vecchi, "La vita e l'opera di Maestro Antonio Benivieni," in *Atti della Società Colombaria di Firenze,* **30** (1930–1931), 103–122; and "Les livres d'un médecin humaniste," in *Janus,* **37** (1933), 97–108; L. Landucci, *Diario fiorentino dal 1450 al 1516* (Florence, 1883); Ralph Major, "Antonio di Pagolo Benivieni," in *Bulletin of the History of Medicine,* **3** (1935), 739–755; M. G. Nardi, "Antonio Benivieni e un suo scritto inedito sulla peste," in *Atti e memorie dell'Accademia di storia dell'arte sanitaria,* **4** (1938), 124–133; F. Puccinotti, *Storia della medicina* (Leghorn, 1855), II, pt. 1, 232–255; and Lynn Thorndike, "A Physician of Florence: Antonio Benivieni," in *A History of Magic and Experimental Science,* IV, 586–592.

PIETRO FRANCESCHINI

BENOIT, JUSTIN-MIRANDE RENÉ (*b.* Montpellier, France, 28 November 1844; *d.* Dijon, France, 5 May 1922), *physics.*

As director of the Bureau International des Poids et Mesures from 1889 to 1915, René Benoit played a large role in standardizing units of length, temperature, and electrical resistance for the scientific world.

Benoit's early training was in medicine, in compliance with the wishes of his father, Justin Benoit, a distinguished surgeon and dean of the faculty at the medical school of Montpellier. No sooner had René received his medical doctorate (1869), however, than he turned to his first interest, physics, and entered the laboratory of the École des Hautes Études. Here he conducted a series of experiments on the temperature dependence of electrical resistance in metals and received his *doctorat ès sciences* in 1873. Four years of work in the electrical industry followed, after which the Bureau International des Poids et Mesures offered him an assistant directorship.

The bureau was hardly three years old when Benoit arrived, and its main concern was the preparation of prototype standard units for its member nations. The new appointee was charged with determining the best method of measuring lengths. This involved a detailed study of thermal expansion, the various devices for measuring dilation, and the relative merits of different thermometers. Once the standard lengths were set up, Benoit played a large role in their verification and in establishing their relation to other standard units, such as the English yard.

The distribution of the first set of prototype lengths in 1889 coincided with Benoit's appointment as director of the bureau. In this capacity he became deeply involved in research to determine the relationship between the standard meter and various wavelengths of light, work that was carried out primarily by A. A. Michelson in 1891 and by C. Fabry and A. Perot in 1906. He was also associated with the standardization of twenty-four-meter Jaderin surveying wires and with the determination of the standard ohm.

Along with the directorship of the bureau, Benoit held the honorary position of president of the Société Française de Physique, correspondent of the Académie des Sciences, honorary fellow of the Physical Society of London, and officer of the Legion of

Honor. On his retirement in 1915, due to failing health and eyesight, his colleagues at the bureau made him honorary director as a token of their esteem.

BIBLIOGRAPHY

I. ORIGINAL WORKS. Benoit's published works are cataloged in Poggendorff, III, 107; IV, 98; V, 93; VI, 278; and in the *Royal Society Catalogue of Scientific Papers,* VII, 139; IX, 191; XIII, 449.

His thesis for his *doctorat ès sciences* is *Études expérimentales sur la résistance électrique des métaux et sa variation sous l'influence de la température* (Paris, 1873). Devices for measuring dilation are discussed in "Mesures de dilation et comparaison des règles métriques," in *Mémoires et travaux du Bureau international des poids et mesures,* 2 (1883), C.1–C.174, C.i–C.clxvii; and 3 (1884), C.1–C.44, C.1–C.xlvi. Benoit's work in determining the standard ohm is presented in *Détermination de l'ohm* (Paris, 1884), written with E. E. N. Mascart and F. G. Nerville; and *Construction d'étalons prototypes de résistance électrique* (Paris, 1885). An account of the relative merits of different thermometers is "Études préliminaires sur les thermomètres . . .," in *Mémoires et travaux du Bureau international des poids et mesures,* 7 (1890), 10–13. Research on the relationship between the standard meter and various wavelengths of light is presented in "Nouvelles déterminations du mètre en longueurs d'ondes lumineuses," in *Comptes rendus de l'Académie des sciences,* 144 (1907), 1082. For an idea of his work as director of the bureau, see his "Rapports règlementaires du directeur du Bureau international des poids et mesures," *Procès-verbaux des séances du Comité international des poids et mesures,* in each volume from 1890 to 1915.

II. SECONDARY LITERATURE. The most complete biography of Benoit is Charles Édouard Guillaume, in *Procès-verbaux des séances du Comité international des poids et mesures,* 20 (1923). For shorter works, see *Nature,* 109 (1922), 820; and *Dictionnaire de biographie française,* V, 1442.

EUGENE FRANKEL

BENSLEY, ROBERT RUSSELL (*b.* Hamilton, Ontario, 13 November 1867; *d.* Chicago, Illinois, 11 June 1956), *anatomy.*

Bensley was the third of six children born to Robert Daniel Bensley, a prosperous farmer. From his mother, Caroline Vandeleur, Bensley acquired his Irish wit, his love of music and the fine arts, and his talent for languages (he mastered French, German, Italian, and Spanish).

In 1883 he graduated from the Collegiate Institute in Hamilton, a notable achievement in that he had walked the two and a half miles (each way) up and down the "mountain" (as the Niagara escarpment is called there) each day and had also managed to do his share of the farm chores. The following year, Bensley entered University College of the University of Toronto. His academic career was almost ended when, on a hunting trip, he received a shotgun wound in the left leg that severed an artery. The limb was amputated twice, first below the knee and later above the knee, when gangrene set in. After a year of convalescence, Bensley managed to return to University College, and upon his graduation he received the Governor General's Medal in both arts and sciences. During his convalescence, working in his mother's kitchen, he learned to stain tissues obtained from farm animals with dyes made from local barks and herbs. He prepared histological slides so well that he was not only excused from the histology laboratory at medical school but was also congratulated for his excellent preparations.

In 1889 Bensley entered the medical department of the University of Toronto; three years later he received the M.B. and became an assistant demonstrator in biology there upon graduation. Four years later, in a paper that won high praise from Sir William Osler, he showed clearly the replenishment of the cells of the gastric mucosa.

Bensley joined the anatomy department of the University of Chicago in 1901, becoming its acting head in the same year and its director in 1907. He differentially stained the cells of the islands of Langerhans in 1906, an achievement that led to Banting's discovery of insulin. Among his other accomplishments were confirmation of the presence of the Golgi apparatus of cells in 1910 and, with B. C. H. Harvey in 1912, the demonstration of the mechanism of the gastric secretion of hydrochloric acid.

Bensley pioneered in the study of cell organelles. I. Altman, A. Fisher, W. B. Hardy, and L. Michaelis had previously described mitochondria but, in 1934, with his student I. Gersh, Bensley modified Altman's freezing-drying technique so that mitochondria could be isolated and subjected to microchemical analysis.

During his twenty-six years at Chicago, Bensley brought to the department of anatomy C. Judson Herrick, George W. Bartelmez, Alexander Maximov, Charles Swift, and William Bloom.

Arthur Benjamin Bensley, Robert's younger brother, gained fame for his book *Practical Anatomy of the Rabbit,* as well as for his directorship of the Ontario Museum of Zoology in Toronto.

Bensley's daughter, Caroline May, was for many years technical assistant in the department of anatomy at the University of Chicago. His son, Robert (husband of Sylvia Holton Bensley), has contributed much to color photography as well as aiding his father in some of the latter's endeavors in photomicrography.

BIBLIOGRAPHY

I. ORIGINAL WORKS. A complete list of Bensley's publications follows Norman L. Hoerr's memoir (see below), pp. 15–18. Among his works are "The Cardiac Glands of Mammals," in *American Journal of Anatomy,* **2** (1902), 105–156; "Upon the Formation of Hydrochloric Acid in the Foveolae and on the Surface of the Gastric Mucous Membrane and the Non-acid Character of the Contents of Gland Cells and Lumina," in *Biological Bulletin,* **23** (1912), 225–249, written with B. C. H. Harvey; "The Formation of Hydrochloric Acid on the Free Surface and Not in the Glands of the Gastric Mucous Membrane," in *Transactions of the Chicago Pathological Society,* **19** (1913), 14–16, written with B. C. H. Harvey; "The Thyroid Gland of the Opossum," in *Anatomical Record,* **8** (1914), 431–440; "Structure and Relationship of the Islets of Langerhans: Criteria of Histological Control in Experiments on the Pancreas," in *Harvey Lectures,* **10** (1915), 250–289; "Functions of Differentiated Segments of Uriniferous Tubules," in *American Journal of Anatomy,* **41** (1928), 75–96, written with W. B. Steen; "The Gastric Glands," in *Cowdry's Special Cytology* (New York, 1928); "The Functions of the Differentiated Parts of the Uriniferous Tubule in the Mammal," in *American Journal of Anatomy,* **47** (1931), 241–275, written with S. H. Bensley; "Studies on Cell Structure by the Freezing-Drying Method. I. Introduction. II. The Nature of Mitochondria in the Hepatic Cell of Amblystoma," in *Anatomical Record,* **57** (1933), 205–235, written with I. Gersh; "Studies on Cell Structure by the Freezing-Drying Method. III. The Distribution in Cells of the Basophil Substances, in Particular the Nissl Substance of the Nerve Cell," *ibid.,* 369–385, written with I. Gersh; "Studies on Cell Structure by the Freezing-Drying Method. IV. The Structure of the Interkinetic and Resting Nuclei," *ibid.,* **58** (1933), 1–15; "Studies on Cell Structure by the Freezing-Drying Method. V. The Chemical Basis of the Organization of the Cell," *ibid.,* **60** (1934), 251–266, written with N. L. Hoerr; and "Studies on Cell Structure by the Freezing-Drying Method. VI. The Preparation and Properties of Mitochondria," *ibid.,* 449–455, written with N. L. Hoerr.

II. SECONDARY LITERATURE. Hoerr wrote on his work with Bensley in "Introduction to Cytological Studies with the Freezing-Drying Method. II. Section of HCl in the Stomach," in *Anatomical Record,* **65** (1936), 417–435. His memoir on Bensley, prepared with the help of Sylvia H. Bensley, Gordon Scott, *et al.,* is in *Anatomical Record,* **128** (1957), 1–15.

P. G. ROOFE

BENTHAM, GEORGE (*b.* Stoke, near Plymouth, England, 22 September 1800; *d.* London, England, 10 September 1884), *botany.*

George Bentham was the third child and second son of Samuel Bentham and Maria Sophia Fordyce. His father, inspector-general of naval works, was ennobled in 1809; his mother was the eldest daughter of Dr. George Fordyce, F.R.S., a noted physician. Jeremy Bentham, the well-known authority on jurisprudence and ethics, was his uncle.

Bentham's early education was rather sporadic, largely because of the peripatetic family life, and was provided mainly by private tutors. During his father's tour of duty in St. Petersburg from 1805 to 1807, his precocity was evidenced in the ease with which he acquired conversational proficiency in Russian, French, and German and a knowledge of Latin. Later, in France, Bentham attended the faculty of theology at Montauban, where he studied French and Latin literature, natural philosophy, mathematics, and Hebrew, while indulging his tastes for music and drawing. Later in life he was able to read botanical works in fourteen languages, and it is a tribute to his industry, concentration, and high powers of reception that he did so largely by his own efforts.

He first became interested in botany at the age of seventeen, during travels in France, where he and his parents lived for eleven years. It was the encouragement of his mother, who was an accomplished gardener and a knowledgeable botanist, and access to her copy of Alphonse de Candolle's *Flore française,* whose analytical keys for the identification of plants appealed to his orderly mind, that fostered a penchant for systematic botany which became his consuming interest for over fifty years and to which he made outstanding contributions.

It was at Montauban that Bentham made his first dried specimens and thus began a herbarium which through his own collecting, purchase, and gift amounted to over 100,000 specimens when he gave it to Kew in 1854. Throughout the course of his studies he consistently worked at botany during his limited leisure time. He made his debut as a botanical author in November 1826, with publication in Paris of his *Catalogue des plantes indigènes des Pyrénées et du bas Languedoc.* As further testimony to his precocity and breadth of intellectual achievement, in 1827 he published *Outlines of a New System of Logic,* of which only about sixty copies were sold. The rest, owing to a financial crisis at the publisher, were disposed of for wastepaper.

Bentham studied law at Lincoln's Inn, and in November 1831, was called to the bar. However, in 1833, possessed of adequate wealth inherited from his father and his uncle, he determined to give up the legal profession for botany.

On 11 April 1833 Bentham married Sarah, daughter of Harford Brydges, onetime British envoy to Persia. They had no children. Bentham received many honors in recognition of his scientific achievements. In 1828 he was admitted as a fellow of the Linnean Society, of which he became president in 1861; in 1863 he was elected F.R.S., having been awarded the Society's Royal Medal in 1859. He received the LL.D. from Cambridge in 1874, and five years later was admitted to the Companionship of the Order of St. Michael and St. George. From 1829 to 1840 he was an extremely energetic and conscientious honorary secretary of the Royal Horticultural Society and, with John Lindley, steered its affairs through a very critical period.

Bentham corresponded with most of the leading botanists of the day and gave unstinting help to the many who requested it. His first major work, which appeared between 1832 and 1836, was *Labiatarum genera et species,* a masterly treatment of a very important family; and in 1848, at the request of Candolle, he contributed a revision of the group for the classic *Prodromus.* Subsequently he made additional contributions to this fundamental work.

Once his collections and library were amalgamated, by a generous gift in 1854, with those of the Hookers at Kew, Bentham was given special facilities to continue his research; in the years of intense effort which followed, some of his greatest taxonomic publications were produced. The *Genera plantarum* (1862–1883), in every respect the fulfillment of complete collaboration with Joseph D. Hooker, was the culmination of his scientific career. This monumental synthesis was based on critical analysis of the material in the Kew Herbarium and Gardens and is a masterly and meticulous extension of Candolle's system.

Bentham was one of the most unassuming of men, always regarding himself as an amateur and reluctant to accept any honor, yet a man who in his lucid, concise, and accurate writing did immense service to systematic botany.

BIBLIOGRAPHY

I. Original Works. Bentham's works include *Catalogue des plantes indigènes des Pyrénées et du bas Languedoc* (Paris, 1826); *Outlines of a New System of Logic* (London, 1827); *Labiatarum genera et species* (London, 1832–1836); *Handbook of the British Flora* (London, 1858); *Flora Hongkongensis* (London, 1861); *Genera plantarum* (London, 1862–1883); *Flora Australiensis* (London, 1863–1878); "On the Recent Progress and Present State of Systematic Botany," in *Report of the British Association for the Advancement of Science* (1875), pp. 27–54.

II. Secondary Literature. Works relevant to Bentham are Leonard Huxley, *Life and Letters of Sir Joseph Dalton Hooker* (London, 1918); B. Daydon Jackson, *George Bentham* (London, 1906).

George Taylor

BENZENBERG, JOHANN FRIEDRICH (*b.* Schöller, near Düsseldorf, Germany, 5 May 1777; *d.* Bilk, near Düsseldorf, 7 June 1846), *astronomy, geodesy, physics.*

Benzenberg was the son of Heinrich Benzenberg, a Protestant clergyman and theological writer. He studied theology in Herborn and Marburg, but later, in Göttingen, became interested in the natural sciences. He received his doctorate from the University of Duisburg in 1800, with a thesis "De determinatione longitudinis per stellas transvolantes." In 1805 Benzenberg became professor of mathematics at the Lyceum in Düsseldorf; later he directed the land survey of the duchy of Berg (1805–1810), organized its land registry, established the teaching of surveying, and wrote several textbooks for surveyors. He gave up this position and lived in Switzerland during the French occupation of the Rhineland. After his return to Germany, Benzenberg devoted himself to studying science as a private citizen; he simultaneously began to gain influence as a writer on politics, particularly constitutional law and economics. Benzenberg's political views were those of an enlightened liberal who advocated a strong central monarchy and a concomitant restriction of the power of the diet.

Benzenberg had begun original scientific investigation as early as 1798, while he was still a student at Göttingen; his independent work there, in which his collaborator was H. W. Brandes, was encouraged by the physicists A. G. Kästner and Georg Lichtenberg. With Brandes, he made the first simultaneous observations of meteors that made use of terminal points on a basis of either ten or fifteen kilometers. They then used these measurements to determine for the first time the height and velocity of the meteors. These data corroborated Chladni's theory of the cosmic origin of meteorites and their relation to fireballs, which had been published in 1794 and which was still hotly disputed. Benzenberg himself used his data to formulate a theory that "the shooting-stars are stones from moon-volcanoes." As late as 1839 (by which time it was widely assumed that meteorites were small heavenly bodies that rotated around the sun or the earth), he defended this idea against Olbers and Arago, among others.

Benzenberg's experiments on falling bodies were as original as his work on meteors. In these investigations he determined the displacement toward the east of falling lead spheres—in the tower of the Michaelis Church in Hamburg in 1802, and in a mine shaft in Schlebusch, in the Earldom of Mark, in 1804. He thereby demonstrated the revolution of the earth some fifty years before Foucault did. (That such a demonstration might be possible had been suspected by Newton, to be sure, but Robert Hooke's experiments of 1679 were inconclusive and those of Domenico Guglielmini in 1791 were highly inaccurate.)

In his later years Benzenberg occupied himself with ballistic experiments and published further works on geodetical, astronomical, and physical subjects. Two years before his death he built a small observatory on his own property in Bilk. In his will, he left his observatory to the city of Düsseldorf, providing a grant to pay the salary of a resident astronomer. Johann Schmidt, F. Brünnow, and R. Luther all worked there and made important contributions to astronomy, particularly in observations of the minor planets.

BIBLIOGRAPHY

I. ORIGINAL WORKS. Among Benzenberg's works are *Versuche die Entfernung, die Geschwindigkeit und die Bahnen der Sternschnuppen zu Bestimmen* (Hamburg, 1800), written with H. W. Brandes; *Über die Bestimmung der geographischen Länge durch Sternschnuppen* (Hamburg, 1802); *Versuche über das Gesetz des Falls, über den Widerstand der Luft und über die Umdrehung der Erde* (Dortmund, 1804); *Vollständiges Handbuch der angewandten Geometrie* (1813); *Über den Cataster* (1818); *Über die Daltonsche Theorie* (Düsseldorf, 1830); and *Die Sternschnuppen* (Hamburg, 1839).

II. SECONDARY LITERATURE. More on Benzenberg and his work can be found in articles by C. Reinhertz, in *Zeitschrift für Vermessungswesen,* **32** (1903), 17–25, 52–57, 65–92; K. Ketter, in *Allgemeine Vermessungsnachrichten,* **39** (1927), 385 f; W. Lindemann, in *Sternenwelt,* **3** (1951), 163–166; Poggendorff, I, 145; and in *Allgemeine deutsche Biographie,* II, 384; and *Neue deutsche Biographie,* II, 60, with a complete list of Benzenberg's works and secondary literature.

BERNHARD STICKER

BÉRARD, JACQUES ÉTIENNE (*b.* Montpellier, France, 12 October 1789; *d.* Montpellier, 10 June 1869), *chemistry.*

Bérard was the son of Étienne Bérard, a chemical manufacturer and associate of Chaptal, by whom he was recommended to the chemist Berthollet as a laboratory assistant. About 1807 young Bérard went to live in Berthollet's house at Arcueil, near Paris, and he soon became a member of the Society of Arcueil. He took advantage of his proximity to Paris to study at the newly reestablished university and was successively *bachelier-ès-lettres* (1811) and *licencié-ès-sciences.* He returned to Montpellier in 1813 and received the M.D. on 9 July 1817. He became professor of chemistry in the faculty of pharmacy and later in the faculty of medicine. He was elected a correspondent in the chemistry section of the Paris Académie des Sciences on 20 December 1819.

Bérard's first published work (1809–1810) was on the analysis of salts and a study of solubilities, research that he undertook at the behest of Berthollet. His value for the density of nitric oxide was used by Gay-Lussac as a datum in the establishment of his law of combining volumes of gases. Bérard collaborated with Malus in a study of infrared and ultraviolet radiation, finding that both can be polarized.

Bérard's best-known research is that carried out in collaboration with François Delaroche on the specific heats of gases. This won the prize offered by the First Class of the Institute in 1811. To compare the specific heats of gases, they passed them through a spiral tube immersed in a copper calorimeter filled with water. The rise in temperature of the water when a current of hot gas under constant pressure was passed through the spiral was taken to be proportional to the specific heat. Their method was essentially that used earlier by Lavoisier. The accuracy of their results, although fair, was impaired by their failure to ensure that the gases were dry.

In 1821 the Académie des Sciences awarded Bérard a prize for his work on the ripening of fruit. This was the first scientific investigation of the effect of different atmospheres on the ripening of fruit. Bérard recognized that harvested fruits use oxygen and give off carbon dioxide. He stated that fruit does not ripen in the absence of oxygen, at least for a limited period, and therefore suggested that some fruits could be stored for a period of up to three months by placing them in a sealed jar with a paste of lime and ferrous sulfate, which was supposed to remove the oxygen.

BIBLIOGRAPHY

I. ORIGINAL WORKS. Bérard's works include "Sur les élémens de quelques combinaisons, et principalement des carbonates et souscarbonates alcalins," in *Annales de chimie,* **71** (1809), 41–69; "Sur l'eau contenu dans la soude fondue," *ibid.,* **72** (1809), 96–101; "Mémoire sur la détermination de la chaleur spécifique des différens gaz," *ibid.,* **85** (1813), 72–110, 113–182, written with François Delaroche; "Mémoire sur les propriétés physiques et chimiques des divers rayons qui composent la lumière solaire," *ibid.,* 309–325; "Observations sur les oxalates et suroxalates alcalins," *ibid.,* **73** (1810), 263–289; "Mémoire sur les propriétés des différentes espèces de rayons qu'on peut séparer au moyen du prisme de la lumière solaire," in *Mémoires de la Société d'Arcueil,* **3** (1817), 1–47; "Mémoire sur la maturation des fruits," in *Annales de chimie et de physique,* **16** (1821), 152–183, 225–252; and "Lettre à M. Gay-Lussac sur les usines de gaz inflammable de la houille," *ibid.,* **28** (1825), 113–128.

II. SECONDARY LITERATURE. Further information on Bérard is in Maurice Crosland, *The Society of Arcueil. A View of French Science at the Time of Napoleon I* (Cambridge, Mass., 1967). Bérard's work on the ripening of fruit is discussed in Dana G. Dalrymple, *The Development of Controlled Atmosphere Storage of Fruit* (Washington, D.C., 1967), pp. 3–4.

M. P. CROSLAND

BÉRARD, JOSEPH FRÉDÉRIC (*b.* Montpellier, France, 8 November 1789; *d.* Montpellier, 16 April 1828), *medicine.*

Bérard's M.D. thesis, "Plan d'une médecine naturelle" (1811), aroused interest, and he soon became a very successful private teacher. He abandoned teaching to go to Paris, where he collaborated on the *Dictionnaire des sciences médicales,* contributing articles on cranioscopy, the elements, trance, and muscle strength. Returning to Montpellier in 1816, he tried unsuccessfully to found a journal and then returned to teaching. In 1823 Bérard was appointed professor of public health at the Faculté de Médecine of his native city, and he took the chair in 1826. He died two years later, at the age of thirty-nine.

Bérard was essentially an analyst of ideas and a philosopher as well as a historian, and his books are of great interest to those who wish to learn at first hand about the fundamental ideas of the leaders of the Montpellier school of science. He wished to prove that all these scholars were eager to have experience and observation triumph, but he had to admit that most of them were snared into the very errors that they condemned. For example, he wrote about Barthez, the great theoretician of vitalism:

> The term of vital principle inserts into physiological language a genuine obscurity; it turns attention away from direct observation of phenomena and their comparative analysis . . . and directs it toward the search for causes . . . and thus destroys science. . . .
> Barthez usually proceeds by . . . the synthetic method . . . the shortest and the least sure . . . which seems to me dangerous. On the contrary, the analytic method . . . which in physiology starts with individual facts and goes on to general phenomena, is sure and easy. It permits a free examination of dogmas and allows an

opportune place for all improvements possible [*Doctrine médicale de l'École de Montpellier . . .,* pp. 110–112].

Because of his acute critical sense, his lucidity, and his remarkable gift of exposition, Bérard deserves to be rescued from oblivion.

BIBLIOGRAPHY

I. ORIGINAL WORKS. Bérard's writings are "Plan d'une médecine naturelle," thesis (Montpellier, 1811); *Essai sur les anomalies de la variole et de la varicelle* (Montpellier, 1818), written with de Lavit; *Doctrine médicale de l'École de Montpellier et comparaison de ses principes avec ceux des autres écoles de l'Europe* (Montpellier, 1819); *Mémoire sur les avantages politiques et scientifiques du concours en général* (Paris, 1820); the articles "Cranioscopie," "Éléments," "Extase," and "Forces musculaires," in *Dictionnaire des sciences médicales* (1821–1824); various writings in *Revue médicale,* **6** (1821), 341–370; **7** (1822), 185–223, 456–493; **8** (1822), 152–180, 282–299; **9** (1822), 240–262; n.s. **1** (1824), 1–32, 462–486; n.s. **3** (1824), 277–294; *Doctrines des rapports du physique et du moral . . .* (Paris, 1823); *Lettre posthume et inédite de Cabanis à Fouquet sur les causes premières* (Paris, 1824), with notes; and *Notes additionnelles à l'édition de la doctrine générale des maladies chroniques de Dumas,* 2 vols. (Paris, 1824).

Détermination expérimentale des apports du système nerveux en général . . . was announced for publication in 1823 but never appeared.

II. SECONDARY LITERATURE. Works on Bérard are E. Beaugrand, "Bérard," in *Dictionnaire Dechambre,* IX (1868), 100; and R. de Saussure, "Fr. Bérard historien de la médecine," in *Bulletin of the History of Medicine,* supp. **3** (1944), 309–317.

PIERRE HUARD

BERENGARIO DA CARPI, GIACOMO (*b.* Carpi, Italy, *ca.* 1460; *d.* Ferrara, Italy, 24 November 1530 [?]), *medicine.*

Giacomo Berengario (or correctly, Barigazzi) was one of the five children of Faustino Barigazzi, surgeon of Carpi. He received rudimentary training in anatomy and surgery from his father and possibly some classical education from Aldus Manutius, who was in Carpi between 1469 and 1477 as tutor to the children of Lionello Pio, prince of Carpi. Berengario apparently studied more systematically, perhaps in Ferrara or Bologna, before entering the medical school of the University of Bologna. He studied there under Girolamo Manfredi, Lionello dei Vittori, Gabriele Zerbi, and Alessandro Achillini, and received his degree on 4 August 1489.

Nothing definite is known of Berengario's activities

from the time he left the university until his appointment as a member of its faculty of medicine in the early sixteenth century. It is likely, however, that he returned to Carpi, at least for a time, to assist his father in his surgical practice; and he probably practiced surgery independently during the wars that plagued Italy at this time and were further aggravated by the French invasion of 1494. That Berengario had acquired considerable distinction as a surgeon, very possibly as a military surgeon, is indicated by his appointment in the latter part of 1502 as lecturer in surgery at Bologna, where he was one of the four "foreign" members of the faculty chosen for their achievements and designated the *eminenti*. In 1506 he became a Bolognese citizen through the mediation of Pope Julius II, and in 1508 the government of Bologna placed him in charge of treating victims of the plague epidemic.

Berengario enjoyed great popularity as a teacher, despite a somewhat fiery and quarrelsome nature. In 1511, for reasons not now known, he developed a bitter enmity toward one of his colleagues; armed and accompanied by his servant and sixteen other companions, he searched for the luckless colleague in order to do him bodily harm. Thwarted in this, he incited his companions with the cry "To his home, let us kill his father and mother," which the group seemed not loath to do. Happily, they could not get into the house, and had to be content with smashing its exterior. The university authorities seem to have been willing to put up with several such violent incidents, partly because of Berengario's support by powerful individuals and families, notably the Medici, and partly because of his popularity with the students. Indeed, a record in the university archives reveals Berengario's success by a comparison of the numbers in his class with the much smaller numbers in the class of the second lecturer in surgery.

At some time during the pontificate of Julius II, Berengario was called to Rome for medical consultation. In 1513, Pope Leo X, a Medici, was directly responsible for Berengario's leave of absence from his academic duties, thus enabling him to go to Florence and take over the medical care of Alessandro Soderini, who was related to the pope by marriage. On several occasions thereafter Berengario was of service to the Medici, who repaid him with their patronage and protection.

In 1514 Berengario produced an edition of Mondino da Luzzi's early fourteenth-century Galenico-medieval dissection manual, *Anothomia Mundini noviter impressa ac per Carpum castigata*. Presumably the work was prepared as an aid for his students, but its publication also suggests that Berengario had by this time begun to give greater prominence to anatomical investigation, which in his original appointment as surgical lecturer was merely an ancillary discipline.

In 1517 Berengario was one of the physicians called to attend Lorenzo de' Medici, who had received a gunshot wound and an occipital skull fracture in battle. Although he was not responsible for the immediate treatment and trepanation of Lorenzo's skull, Berengario was placed in charge of the postoperative care; this assignment led to his second book, *Tractatus de fractura calvae sive cranei* (1518). The *Tractatus* was written in little more than two months, soon after Berengario's return to Bologna, and dedicated to Lorenzo de' Medici. It opens with a short discussion of various sorts of skull fractures, followed by a grouping of the consequent lesions according to their symptoms. This is the most interesting and valuable portion of the work, for Berengario was able to cite from contemporary knowledge or from his own direct observation the relationship between the location of the lesions and the resulting neurological effects. Next, he discusses prognosis, diagnosis, treatment, the instruments to be employed, and the technique of craniotomy. Berengario's book was the most original neurosurgical treatise until then and was not surpassed until the appearance of Ambroise Paré's similar work in 1562, in which Paré expressed his appreciation of his predecessor's efforts and made use of them.

In 1520 Berengario was called to Cremona as one of the medical consultants for Marchese Galeazzo Pallavicini, who, according to Berengario, died in that same year of a renal complaint.

Although Berengario was officially lecturer in surgery, he was also responsible for instruction in anatomy, which, in the course of time, appears to have become his major interest. In his *Isagogae breves* (1522) he declares that by that time he had dissected several hundred bodies, and in the *Commentaria* (1521) he refers to a number of specific dissections he had performed on adult cadavers and on fetuses. It is not known when Berengario's interest in anatomy became predominant, although this may be marked by his edition of Mondino's *Anothomia* in 1514; and somewhere toward the close of the second decade of the sixteenth century his dissatisfaction with traditional accounts of the human body became strong enough to cause him to write his own treatise. It seems to have been produced very quickly, in approximately two years, and was published under the title *Commentaria cum amplissimis additionibus super anatomia Mundini cum textu eiusdem in pristinum &*

verum nitorem redacto, with a dedication to Cardinal Giulio de' Medici, later Pope Clement VII.

The *Commentaria,* consisting of slightly more than a thousand pages, is so arranged that each topic is introduced by the appropriate section of Mondino's *Anothomia* and followed by Berengario's critical commentary. The commentary presents the opinions of ancient and medieval writers, as well as those of Berengario's contemporaries, and finally his own judgment of the problem; sometimes these judgments are illustrated from his own cases or from other, contemporary ones known to him. As one who had an unusually great knowledge of human anatomy, as well as a considerable degree of intellectual independence and an argumentative and even pugnacious spirit, Berengario not only extended the knowledge of human anatomy but also opposed traditional, often Galenic, beliefs and sought to replace them with his own. The *Commentaria* was the first work since the time of Galen to display any considerable amount of anatomical information based upon personal investigation and observation, and although Berengario's antitraditional attitude was not the result of a consistent principle of independent investigation, his *Commentaria* nevertheless must be considered the most important forerunner of Vesalius' *Fabrica.*

After a brief discussion of the value of anatomical studies, Berengario, following the sequence of Mondino's text, systematically describes the general characteristics of the major structures and divisions of the body and the properties of fat, membrane, flesh, fiber, ligament, sinew and tendon, nerve, and muscle. This description, more extensive than any until then, is followed by a fairly extensive account of the abdominal muscles. In accordance with Mondino's arrangement, the abdominal organs, the most susceptible to putrefaction, are next considered. The account begins with mention of the peritoneum, but only the visceral portion is described; and Berengario erroneously criticizes Gentile da Foligno for referring to a muscular portion as well. The description of the intestines contains the first mention of the vermiform appendix; the yellow staining of the duodenum, caused by bile, is noted; and attention is called to the fact that the common biliary duct opens into the duodenum. The stomach is described as being formed of three intrinsic coats, to which a fourth, arising from the peritoneum, is added, although Berengario mentions only two intrinsic coats in the *Isagogae breves* of 1522. In his description of the kidneys Berengario denies that they contain a filter or sieve for straining off the urine, and is especially critical of his former teacher Gabriele Zerbi, who had claimed actual observation of such

a filter. During a public dissection in 1521, but too late for mention in the *Commentaria,* Berengario observed a fused kidney with horseshoe configuration, which he described in the *Isagogae breves.*

The description of the male and female reproductive organs, of reproduction itself, and of the fetus is much more extensive than any earlier account. In the course of this description Berengario for the first time called attention to the greater proportional capacity of the female pelvis than the male pelvis, and elsewhere he noted the proportionately larger size of the male chest. He also denied the medieval belief in the seven-celled uterus, and in direct opposition to Galen he declared that the umbilical cord carried a single vein rather than two.

Turning his attention to the neck and thorax, Berengario recognized five cartilages in the larynx, describing the two arytenoid cartilages for the first time, and provided the first good account of the thymus. He declared that the lungs were a single organ, although he admitted that some said they were plural. He did, however, note the existence of three right lobes, in contrast with two on the left. He remarked upon the oblique position of the heart, described the pericardium in some detail, and declared that it contained pericardial fluid at all times. In his description of the ventricles of the heart he sought a compromise between the Aristotelian description of a three-chambered heart and the Galenic description of a two-chambered one by declaring that the third ventricle posited by Aristotle was in the traditionally accepted Galenic pores of the cardiac septum. Although erroneous, this assertion was of some significance, for Niccolo Massa answered it in 1536 with the declaration that the heart's midwall was solid. Although Massa seems not to have realized the implication of his statement, he and Berengario unwittingly preluded the dispute that developed later in the century over the correct course of the blood from the right to the left side of the heart. In addition, although Berengario correctly described the aorta as arising from the left ventricle, he displayed some confusion regarding the position and structure of the pulmonary artery (which he called *vena arterialis*) and pulmonary vein (which he called *arteria venalis*).

In his description of the skull and its contents, Berengario was the first to describe the sphenoidal sinus, which he considered to be the source of catarrh, but he declared that the ethmoid plate was impervious to the passage of cerebral fluids. He also called attention to two of the ossicles of the ear, the malleus and incus, although he did not provide them with these names or claim the discovery. In his description of the brain, the account of the ventricles is relatively clear and extensive. Contrary to the then common practice of locating the mental faculties in the four ventricles, however, he placed them all in the first two, or lateral, ventricles and thereby reduced the significance of the remainder. He considered the third ventricle as being merely a passage through which excess cerebral fluids were transported to the infundibulum for ultimate excretion; it also served as a route for the transmission of a portion of the animal spirit into the fourth ventricle. The fourth ventricle served only as the receptacle for that portion of the animal spirit which served to operate the spinal nerves.

Of the other cerebral structures, Berengario noted the corpus striatum, declared that the choroid plexus was formed of veins and arteries, and described the pituitary and pineal glands. His most noteworthy anti-Galenic heresy was denial of the existence of the *rete mirabile* in the human brain, for the excellent reason that he had never been able to find it. However, since the accepted theory of the day would not permit him to deny the existence of animal spirit, the motive force of the nervous system until then asserted to be manufactured in the *rete mirabile,* Berengario declared that the spirit was manufactured in the very small branches of the arteries dispersed throughout the *pia mater.* Consequently, it was Berengario who began the movement to give greater importance to the entire brain substance.

Despite the significance of Berengario's anatomical findings and his correction of traditional errors, as well as his citations, which reflect wide reading in classical and contemporary literature, his literary style was more medieval than Renaissance. Whatever his merits or deficiencies as a stylist, he was greatly hindered by the absence of any standard anatomical vocabulary. Numerous medieval Latin translations from the Arabic by a number of different translators, often not really familiar with the subject matter of their translations, had produced a confusion of terminology; an anatomical structure might have several names or a single term might apply to several different structures. Berengario was well aware of this problem, and on one occasion described it in respect to the graphic illustration of a vein:

> In these figures can be seen the course of the salvatella of Mondino and Rhazes, the sceylen of Avicenna, the salubris of Haly, and that branch of the basilica which ends between the little and ring finger which Rhazes [also] calls salvatella. It can furthermore be seen how the vein called funis brachii by Avicenna ends around the middle finger in a branch called sceylen by Avicenna and salubris by Haly and how also the funis brachii

is a branch of the cephalic and terminates between the index finger and thumb [*Isagogae breves,* 1522, fol. 65 *r*].

Such conditions recommend visual assistance, and Berengario appears to have been the first anatomist to recognize the significance of anatomical illustrations properly related to the text. The *Commentaria* contains twenty-one pages of illustrations, some of them with the names of the significant structures written on the figures, with a brief explanation of the meaning of the particular illustration printed along its border. The figures are rather crude woodcuts, but the crudity does not greatly impede the explanation of anatomical terminology. Infrequently there is reference from the main text to the illustration. The illustrations are less successful when, as in those of the uterus, the purpose is to reveal details of structure rather than to explain terminology. It is particularly apparent in these figures that Berengario had not completely broken away from the older idea that illustrations must serve a decorative purpose, an idea that interfered with the presentation of anatomical detail. One figure, presumably displaying the abdominal muscles (actually plagiarized from Pietro d'Abano's *Conciliator* of 1496), is utterly worthless because the muscles are wholly imaginary. However, the remaining sequence of figures in which the successive muscle layers of the abdomen are displayed, dimly suggests, despite anatomical errors, the later Vesalian "muscle men." Berengario's results, however, were more important for the direction they took than for their achievement.

In 1521 there also appeared an edition of Ulrich von Hutten's small treatise of 1519 on the use of guaiac wood in the treatment of syphilis, *Ulrichi de Hutten Eq. de guaiaci medicina et morbo gallico liber unus.* It is uncertain whether the publication was primarily a publisher's speculation, since guaiac wood had gained sudden and very considerable popularity as a specific, or occurred at the urging of Berengario, whose name, however, appears only on the final page in the colophon. Berengario himself preferred to treat syphilis with mercury. In 1522 he was responsible for publishing an edition of Galen's work on medical prognostication, *Habes in hoc volumine candide lector magni Galeni Pergamensis medicorum principis libros tres de crisi. i. de judicationibus interprete Laurentiano medico Florentino,* and dedicated it to one of his students, Ochoa Gonzáles. Despite his intermittent criticisms of Galenic anatomy, Berengario remained a supporter of the "prince of physicians," who was not opposed for basing human anatomy on that of animals until 1543.

A much more important publication, in 1522, was the compendium of the *Commentaria,* entitled *Isagogae breves perlucide ac uberrime in anatomia humani corporis a communi medicorum academia usitatam a Carpo in almo Bononiensi Gymnasio ordinariam chirurgiae publice docente ad suorum scholasticorum preces in lucem datae* and dedicated to Alberto Pio, prince of Carpi. As a condensed version of the more extensive *Commentaria,* but with the same arrangement of contents, the *Isagogae breves* was intended by Berengario as a manual for his students and a replacement of his edition of Mondino's *Anothomia,* which he had made obsolete. If we may believe the title, it was prepared at his students' request. Its success is indicated by the fact that a second edition was published in 1523, with some alteration and increase in the number of illustrations, emphasizing the anatomy of the heart and brain.

In 1525, at the command of Pope Clement VII, Berengario went to Piacenza to assist in the care of Giovanni dalle Bande Nere, a member of the Medici family, who had suffered a wound of the right leg in battle. During 1526 Berengario spent several months in Rome as physician to the ailing Cardinal Pompeo Colonna, and, according to Vasari, in lieu of his fee accepted a "St. John in the Desert" painted by Raphael. It was also at this time that he met the sculptor and goldsmith Benvenuto Cellini, who described Berengario as a clever surgeon and a man of much learning whose services were sought on a permanent basis by Clement VII. Cellini also referred to Berengario's lucrative but ultimately disastrous practice of venerology, declaring that "he was a person of great sagacity and did wisely to get out of Rome," since through the excessive use of mercurial fumigations in the treatment of syphilis, "all the patients . . . grew so ill . . . that he would certainly have been murdered if he had remained."

Berengario's return to Bologna was brief, however, since he was dismissed from his position in the medical faculty. According to Gabriele Falloppia, he was charged with human vivisection, of which, however, there is no documentary evidence. Whatever the reason, Berengario retired to Ferrara, where he edited a collection of Latin translations of Galen: *Libri anatomici, horum indicem versa pagina indicabit. De motu musculorum liber primus, Nicolao Leoniceno vicentino interprete. Anatomicarum aggressionum interprete Demetrio Chalcondylo. De arteriarum et venarum dissectione, interprete Antonio Fortolo Ioseriensi. De hirudinibus, revulsione etc., interprete Ferdinando Balamio Siculo* (1529). The date of Berengario's death is uncertain and the place of his burial is unknown, although possibly it is the church of San Francesco in Ferrara.

BIBLIOGRAPHY

Berengario's writings include his edition of Mondino da Luzzi's *Anothomia Mundini noviter impressa ac per Carpum castigata* (Bologna, 1514; Venice, 1529, *ca.* 1530, 1538, *ca.* 1575); *Tractatus de fractura calvae sive cranei* (Bologna, 1518; Venice, 1535; Leiden, 1629, 1651, 1715, 1728); *Commentaria cum amplissimis additionibus super anatomia Mundini cum textu eiusdem in pristinum & verum nitorem redacto* (Bologna, 1521); his edition of Galen's *Habes in hoc volumine candide lector magni Galeni Pergamensis medicorum principis libros tres de crisi. i. de judicationibus interprete Laurentiano medico Florentino* (Bologna, 1522); *Isagogae breves perlucide ac uberrime in anatomia humani corporis a communi medicorum academia usitatam a Carpo in almo Bononiensi Gymnasio ordinariam chirurgiae publice docente ad suorum scholasticorum preces in lucem datae* (Bologna, 1522, 1523; Strasbourg, 1530; Venice, 1535); and his edition of a collection of Latin translations of Galen, *Libri anatomici, horum indicem versa pagina indicabit. De motu musculorum liber primus, Nicolao Leoniceno vicentino interprete. Anatomicarum aggressionum interprete Demetrio Chalcondylo. De arteriarum et venarum dissectione, interprete Antonio Fortolo Ioseriensi. De hirudinibus, revulsione etc., interprete Ferdinando Balamio Siculo* (Bologna, 1529).

All editions of the above works are very rare, and none has been published since the last date given for each. There is, however, an Italian translation of *De fractura calvae* in Vittorio Putti, *Berengario da Carpi saggio biografico e bibliografico* (Bologna, 1937). There is also an English translation of the *Isagogae breves* (London, 1660, 1664) and in *Jacopo Berengario da Carpi. A Short Introduction to Anatomy* (*Isagogae breves*), translated with introduction and historical notes by L. R. Lind and with anatomical notes by Paul G. Roofe (Chicago, 1959), pp. 3–29; it suffers, however, from some misunderstanding of Berengario's original text.

The best biographical account, including the pertinent documents and records, is in Putti's work cited above. The introduction to Lind's translation contains a brief biographical account drawn from Putti.

C. D. O'MALLEY

BERG, LEV SIMONOVICH (*b.* Bendery, Bessarabia, Russia, 14 February 1876; *d.* Leningrad, U.S.S.R., 24 December 1950), *geography, ichthyology.*

The son of Simon Grigor'evich Berg, a notary, and Klara L'vovna Bernstein-Kogan, Berg was awarded the gold medal when he graduated from the Second Kishinev Gymnasium in 1894. He then enrolled in the natural science section of the Faculty of Physics and Mathematics at Moscow University. In 1898 he received the gold medal and a first-degree diploma in zoology for his paper "Droblenie yaitsa i obrazovanie parablasta u shchuki" ("The Breakdown of the Egg and the Formation of the Parablast in Pike").

Striving to broaden his theoretical knowledge through practical work, Berg rejected an offer to remain at Moscow University and, having obtained the position of inspector of fisheries in the Aral Sea and on the Syr-Dar'ya River, he studied the lakes and rivers of central Asia and Kazakhstan for four years.

In 1902–1903 he was sent by the Russian Department of Agriculture to study oceanography in Bergen, Norway. Upon his return in 1904, Berg obtained the position of zoologist and director of the ichthyology section of the Zoological Museum of the Academy of Sciences in St. Petersburg, where he remained for ten years. In 1909 the degree of doctor of geography was conferred on Berg for his dissertation *Aral'skoe more* ("The Aral Sea"), for which he was also awarded the P. P. Semenov Gold Medal by the Russian Geographical Society. The following year Berg married Polina Abramovna Kotlovker, the daughter of a teacher, who bore him a son and a daughter. They were divorced in 1913, and in 1922 Berg married Maria Mikhailovna Ivanova, the daughter of a ship's commander.

In 1913 the Moscow Agricultural Institute made Berg professor of ichthyology, and the following year he moved to Moscow. In 1917 Petrograd University appointed him professor of geography, and he spent the rest of his life there. In addition, Berg was simultaneously head of the applied ichthyology section of the State Institute of Experimental Agronomy, which was later renamed the Institute of the Fish Industry (1922–1934), and ichthyologist and head of the fossil fish section of the Zoological Institute of the Academy of Sciences of the U.S.S.R. (1934–1950). He also taught for several years at the Pedagogical Institute and the Geographical Institute.

In 1934 Berg was awarded the degree of doctor of zoology for his many important ichthyological investigations. In recognition of his outstanding scientific services, the Academy of Sciences elected him an associate member in 1928 and an academician in 1946. He was also awarded the titles Honored Scientist of the R.S.F.S.R. (1934) and Laureate of the State, first degree (1951). From 1940 to 1950 he was president of the All-Union Geographical Society. Among his awards were the Konstantinovsky Medal of the Russian Geographical Society (1915) and the Medal of the Asiatic Society of India (1936).

Berg's works deal with a wide range of topics in geography and zoology. His early investigations were concentrated on the study of the lakes of northern Kazakhstan: the salinity of the water, the temperature regimen, the peculiarities of the shores, the fauna inhabiting them, and the origin of the lakes and all their components. Studying the changes in the mineralization of lakes, he put forth the notion (subsequently confirmed) that such changes occur because salts are carried away by the wind when the lakes temporarily decrease in size.

These detailed investigations, the beginning of limnology in Russia, gave Berg the basis for opposing the hypothesis popular at the end of the last century concerning the drying up of the lakes of central Asia. He convincingly demonstrated that these lakes do not dry up, but experience periodic fluctuations in their level and size that correspond to secular changes in climate and hydrological regimen.

Berg's limnological investigations are recognized as classics. He considered a lake to be a geographical complex, taking into account the history of its formation, its connections with the surrounding territory, the peculiarities of climatic and hydrobiological regimens, and an evaluation of its economic importance as a reservoir. These works were intimately connected with observations of climate, for study of the history of lakes demonstrated the existence of a clear link between the hydrobiological regimen of a lake and paleoclimatic changes. Berg's diversified works played an important role in the development of climatology as a science.

Berg's contributions to ichthyology are extremely significant. His works contain valuable information on the anatomy, embryology, and paleontology, as well as on the systematics and geographical distribution, of all the fishes in the U.S.S.R. Of great scientific value are his studies of summer and winter spawning runs of migratory fish, the periodicity of fish reproduction and distribution, and the influence of climatic changes on fish migration. He also established the symbiotic relationship between the lamprey and salmon families, which arose as a result of similar conditions of existence.

Most significant of all Berg's works are those on geography. Classifying the earth's surface according to climatic, soil, biological, and other natural factors, he distinguished ten different geographical zones, several of which he divided into subzones. This system of zones followed a latitudinal sequence in lowland areas and a longitudinal one in mountainous areas.

It contributed to the explanation of the surface characteristics of each area, ensuring detailed geographic study and the full exploitation of natural resources.

Berg opposed the opinion of some scientists that the earth's climate was becoming drier, and, having analyzed a mass of geological, geographical, and historical material, he demonstrated that in the modern epoch the earth's arid zones are contracting and that a displacement of zones is observable in the direction of the equator: the tundra is encroaching upon forest land, the forest is encroaching upon the steppe. On the other hand, equatorial forests are moving apart in the direction of the poles. This process was brought about, in Berg's opinion, by general climatic fluctuations, determined by cosmic causes.

Berg distinguished geographical zones according to the principle of the uniformity of landscape: the relief, climate, plants, and soil combine into a unified, harmonious whole that typically is duplicated over an entire geographical zone. He examined landscapes as they developed and continually changed. By reconstructing the paleogeographic conditions, he sought to trace their transformation into the modern landscape zones.

During his study of landscape, Berg devoted much attention to a thorough study of soils, especially of loess. He concluded that loess originated as a result of the weathering of fine-grained calcareous rocks in a dry climate. This set of conditions, which arose in the southern part of European Russia after the Ice Age, led, in his opinion, to the rise of loess there. Analyzing the climatic peculiarities of the more remote geological past, Berg concluded that even before the Ice Age a geographical zonality had existed, and that there were seasonal rhythms and the alternation of dry and moist epochs. In any case, loess-type rocks had appeared in the Upper Paleozoic.

Berg coordinated his paleoclimatologic and paleogeographic reconstructions with the origin of various sedimentary rocks, the history of relief development, the formation of various soils, and the displacement of landscape zones. These investigations contributed to the intimate coordination of modern geography with historical geology. His works included separate statements about, and penetrating investigations of, the physicogeographical conditions on Precambrian continents, the origin of land and sea organisms, the development of floras and faunas, the influence of the Ice Age on the present distribution of plants, the origin of iron and bauxite ores, and some general laws of sediment formation.

Berg believed that with a change of geographical landscape there also occurred a change in the character of the sedimentary rocks; thus, no periodicity or cyclical recurrence in the formation of sedimentary rocks exists, inasmuch as landscapes are unique. He stressed the significance of living organisms in the migration of chemical elements and in the formation of sedimentary rocks. Since the organic world has been continuously transformed throughout the history of the earth, the sedimentary rocks associated with it can neither remain unchanged nor be cyclically repeated.

Berg took exception to the concept of a fiery liquid stage in the earth's origin and supported the idea that the earth was initially solid. He also proposed that the position of the poles has changed little throughout geological history. On the basis of a biogeographic analysis, he determinedly spoke against Wegener's theory and thought there are better data in favor of comparatively minor vertical movements of the earth's surface than of its horizontal shifts for thousands of kilometers.

In his early papers Berg stated that great uplifts of the earth's crust caused continental glaciations, but he later concluded that a change in solar activity or more remote cosmic processes were decisive factors in the origin of glacial epochs. In this way, regions of low temperature arose not only in mountainous or high-latitude regions but also in low-lying areas and in subtropic zones. This explains the bipolar distribution of many marine organisms.

The zoogeographical analyses completed by Berg, particularly that on the distribution of fish in the carp family, permitted him to determine with reasonable precision the time of the appearance of glacial epochs and the periods in which the climate grew warmer. Discussing the problem of the development of the organic world, Berg spoke about distinct boundaries between separate species and about a saltatory transition from some species to others.

In some of his papers Berg dealt with the origin of life on earth. He believed that the first organisms were autotrophic and needed neither oxygen nor light. They developed near the earth's surface or in marshland. Subsequently, through their life processes, soils and atmospheric oxygen appeared and conditions were created for the transfer of life to the earth's surface and the ocean. He believed that there were epochs when the formation of new species proceeded very intensively in all groups of living organisms.

In the last years of his life Berg devoted serious attention to the study of the history of geography and geographic discoveries, especially in Asia and the Antarctic.

Berg published about 700 works, including a number of monographs and textbooks. His name is perpetuated by a peak and a glacier in the southwestern Pamir, a glacier in the Dzhungarskiy Alatau Mountains, a volcano in the Kuril Islands, and a promontory in the Arctic.

BIBLIOGRAPHY

I. Original Works. Among Berg's writings are *Aral'skoe more. Opyt fiziko-geograficheskoj monografii* ("The Aral Sea. A Physicogeographical Monograph"; St. Petersburg, 1908); *Osnovy klimatologii* ("Fundamentals of Climatology"), 2nd ed., rev. and enl. (Leningrad, 1938); *Geograficheskie zony Sovetskogo Sojuza* ("Geographical Zones of the Soviet Union"), 3rd ed., 2 vols. (Moscow, 1947–1952); *Ryby presnykh vod SSSR i sopredel'nykh stran* ("Freshwater Fish of the U.S.S.R. and Neighboring Countries"), 4th ed., rev. and enl., 3 vols. (Moscow–Leningrad, 1948–1949); and *Izbrannye trudy* ("Collected Works"), 5 vols. (Moscow–Leningrad, 1956–1962).

II. Secondary Literature. Works on Berg are *Lev Semenovich Berg (1876–1950)*, Academy of Sciences of the U.S.S.R., Materials and Bibliography of Scientists of the U.S.S.R., Geographical Series, no. 2 (Moscow–Leningrad, 1952); and E. Pavlovsky, ed., *Pamjati akademika L. S. Berga. Sbornik rabot po geografii i biologii* ("In Memory of L. S. Berg. A Collection of Papers on Geography and Biology"; Moscow–Leningrad, 1955).

V. V. Tikhomirov

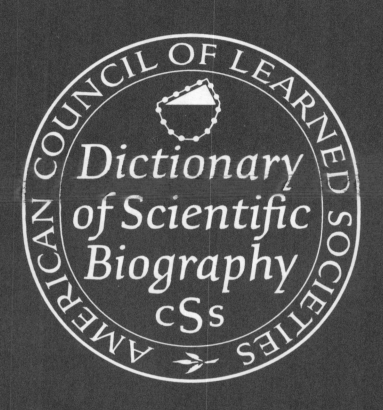

AMERICAN COUNCIL OF LEARNED SOCIETIES

Dictionary
of Scientific
Biography

cSs